The

Radio Amateur's

Handbook

By the HEADQUARTERS STAFF

of the

AMERICAN RADIO RELAY LEAGUE

NEWINGTON, CONN., U.S.A.   06111

Doug DeMaw, W1CER
Editor

1969

Forty-sixth Edition

FOREWORD

For more than forty years, *The Radio Amateur's Handbook* has been a mainstay of the American Radio Relay League's program to provide its member-amateurs with up-to-date, practical training and reference material. In that period it has built up an international reputation as *the* basic reference book for the radio amateur.

The *Handbook* had its rather modest beginnings in 1925 when F. E. Handy, W1BDI, for many years the League's communications manager, commenced work on a small manual of amateur operating procedure in which it was deemed desirable to include a certain amount of "technical" information. It was published in 1926 and enjoyed instant success. Increasing in size and scope with the growth of amateur radio itself, the *Handbook* soon required participation of numerous of the skilled amateurs at ARRL Hq., and became a family affair, the joint product of the staff. The need for coordinating the results of this collaboration, as well as independently generating new material, eventually led to placing the primary responsibility for the Handbook on the shoulders of a full-time editor. The present book was produced under the editorship of Doug DeMaw, W1CER.

Virtually continuous modification is a feature of the *Handbook*, but always with the objective of presenting the soundest aspects of current practice rather than the merely new and novel. Written with the needs of the practical amateur constantly in mind, it has earned universal acceptance not only among amateurs but by all segments of the technical radio world. This wide dependence on the *Handbook* is founded on its practical utility, its treatment of radio communications problems in terms of how-to-do-it rather than by abstract discussion.

The *Handbook* has long been considered an indispensable part of the amateur's equipment. We earnestly hope that the present edition will succeed in bringing as much inspiration and assistance to amateurs and would-be amateurs as have its predecessors.

JOHN HUNTOON
General Manager, ARRL

Newington, Conn.
January, 1969

SCHEMATIC SYMBOLS USED IN CIRCUIT DIAGRAMS

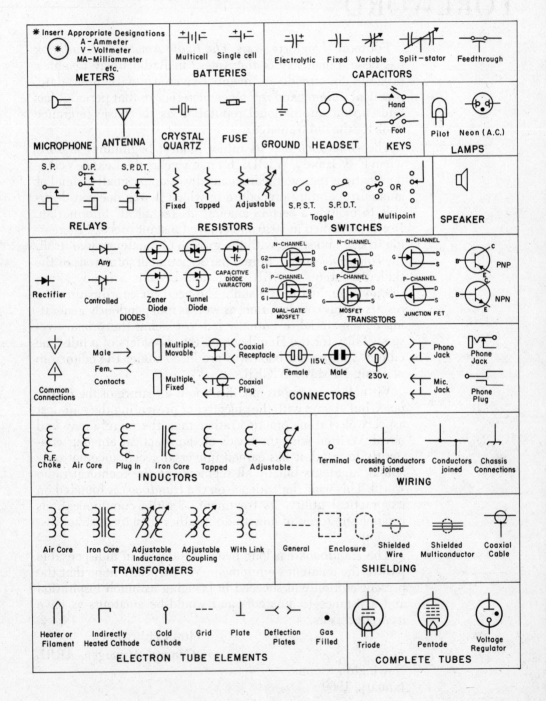

CONTENTS

The Amateur's Code

ONE

The Amateur is Gentlemanly . . . He never knowingly uses the air for his own amusement in such a way as to lessen the pleasure of others. He abides by the pledges given by the ARRL in his behalf to the public and the Government.

TWO

The Amateur is Loyal . . . He owes his amateur radio to the American Radio Relay League, and he offers it his unswerving loyalty.

THREE

The Amateur is Progressive . . . He keeps his station abreast of science. It is built well and efficiently. His operating practice is clean and regular.

FOUR

The Amateur is Friendly . . . Slow and patient sending when requested, friendly advice and counsel to the beginner, kindly assistance and cooperation for the broadcast listener; these are marks of the amateur spirit.

FIVE

The Amateur is Balanced . . . Radio is his hobby. He never allows it to interfere with any of the duties he owes to his home, his job, his school, or his community.

SIX

The Amateur is Patriotic . . . His knowledge and his station are always ready for the service of his country and his community.

—PAUL M. SEGAL

Chapter 1

Amateur Radio

Amateur radio is a scientific hobby, a means of gaining personal skill in the fascinating art of electronics and an opportunity to communicate with fellow citizens by private short-wave radio. Scattered over the globe are over 350,000 amateur radio operators who perform a service defined in international law as one of "self-training, intercommunication and technical investigations carried on by . . . duly authorized persons interested in radio technique solely with a personal aim and without pecuniary interest."

From a humble beginning at the turn of the century, amateur radio has grown to become an established institution. Today the American followers of amateur radio number over 250,000, trained communicators from whose ranks will come the professional communications specialists and executives of tomorrow—just as many of today's radio leaders were first attracted to radio by their early interest in amateur radio communication. A powerful and prosperous organization now provides a bond between amateurs and protects their interests; an internationally respected magazine is published solely for their benefit. The military services seek the cooperation of the amateur in developing communications reserves. Amateur radio supports a manufacturing industry which, by the very demands of amateurs for the latest and best equipment, is always up-to-date in its designs and production techniques—in itself a national asset. Amateurs have won the gratitude of the nation for their heroic performances in times of natural disaster; traditional amateur skills in emergency communication are also the stand-by system for the nation's civil defense. Amateur radio is, indeed, a magnificently useful institution.

Although as old as the art of radio itself, amateur radio did not always enjoy such prestige. Its first enthusiasts were private citizens of an experimental turn of mind whose imaginations went wild when Marconi first proved that messages actually could be sent by wireless. They set about learning enough about the new scientific marvel to build homemade spark transmitters. By 1912 there were numerous Government and commercial stations, and hundreds of amateurs; regulation was needed, so laws, licenses and wavelength specifications appeared. There was then no amateur organization nor spokesman. The official viewpoint toward amateurs was something like this:

"Amateurs? . . . Oh, yes. . . . Well, stick 'em on 200 meters and below; they'll never get out of their backyards with that."

But as the years rolled on, amateurs found out how, and DX (distance) jumped from local to 500-mile and even occasional 1000-mile two-way contacts. Because all long-distance messages had to be relayed, relaying developed into a fine art— an ability that was to prove invaluable when the Government suddenly called hundreds of skilled amateurs into war service in 1917. Meanwhile U.S. amateurs began to wonder if there were amateurs in other countries across the seas and if, some day, we might not span the Atlantic on 200 meters.

Most important of all, this period witnessed the birth of the American Radio Relay League, the amateur radio organization whose name was to be virtually synonymous with subsequent amateur progress and short-wave development. Conceived and formed by the famous inventor, the late Hiram Percy Maxim, ARRL was formally launched in early 1914. It had just begun to exert its full force in amateur activities when the United States declared war in 1917, and by that act sounded the knell for amateur radio for the next two and a half years. There were then over 6000 amateurs. Over 4000 of them served in the armed forces during that war.

Today, few amateurs realize that World War I not only marked the close of the first phase of amateur development but came very near marking its end for all time. The fate of amateur radio was in the balance in the days immediately following the signing of the Armistice. The

HIRAM PERCY MAXIM
President ARRL, 1914–1936

Government, having had a taste of supreme authority over communications in wartime, was more than half inclined to keep it. The war had not been ended a month before Congress was considering legislation that would have made it impossible for the amateur radio of old ever to be resumed. ARRL's President Maxim rushed to Washington, pleaded, argued, and the bill was defeated. But there was still no amateur radio; the war ban continued. Repeated representations to Washington met only with silence. The League's offices had been closed for a year and a half, its records stored away. Most of the former amateurs had gone into service; many of them would never come back. Would those returning be interested in such things as amateur radio? Mr. Maxim, determined to find out, called a meeting of the old Board of Directors. The situation was discouraging: amateur radio still banned by law, former members scattered, no organization, no membership, no funds. But those few determined men financed the publication of a notice to all the former amateurs that could be located, hired Kenneth B. Warner as the League's first paid secretary, floated a bond issue among old League members to obtain money for immediate running expenses, bought the magazine *QST* to be the League's official organ, started activities, and dunned officialdom until the wartime ban was lifted and amateur radio resumed again, on October 1, 1919. There was a headlong rush by amateurs to get back on the air. Gangway for King Spark! Manufacturers were hard put to supply radio apparatus fast enough. Each night saw additional dozens of stations crashing out over the air. Interference? It was bedlam!

But it was an era of progress. Wartime needs had stimulated technical development. Vacuum tubes were being used both for receiving and transmitting. Amateurs immediately adapted the new gear to 200-meter work. Ranges promptly increased and it became possible to bridge the continent with but one intermediate relay.

TRANSATLANTICS

As DX became 1000, then 1500 and then 2000 miles, amateurs began to dream of transatlantic work. Could they get across? In December, 1921, ARRL sent abroad an expert amateur, Paul F. Godley, 2ZE, with the best receiving equipment available. Tests were run, and *thirty* American stations were heard in Europe. In 1922 another transatlantic test was carried out and 315 American calls were logged by European amateurs and one French and two British stations were heard on this side.

Everything now was centered on one objective: two-way amateur communication across the Atlantic! It must be possible—but somehow it couldn't quite be done. More power? Many already were using the legal maximum. Better receivers? They had superheterodynes. Another wavelength? What about those undisturbed wavelengths *below* 200 meters? The engineering world thought they were worthless—but they had

said that about 200 meters. So, in 1922, tests between Hartford and Boston were made on 130 meters with encouraging results. Early in 1923, ARRL-sponsored tests on wavelengths down to 90 meters were successful. Reports indicated that *as the wavelength dropped the results were better*. Excitement began to spread through amateur ranks.

Finally, in November, 1923, after some months of careful preparation, two-way amateur transatlantic communication was accomplished, when Fred Schnell, 1MO (now W4CF) and the late John Reinartz, 1XAM (later K6BJ) worked for several hours with Deloy, 8AB, in France, with all three stations on 110 meters! Additional stations dropped down to 100 meters and found that they, too, could easily work two-way across the Atlantic. The exodus from the 200-meter region had started. The "short-wave" era had begun!

By 1924 dozens of commercial companies had rushed stations into the 100-meter region. Chaos threatened, until the first of a series of national and international radio conferences partitioned off various bands of frequencies for the different services. Although thought still centered around 100 meters, League officials at the first of these frequency-determining conferences, in 1924, wisely obtained amateur bands not only at 80 meters but at 40, 20, and even 5 meters.

Eighty meters proved so successful that "forty" was given a try, and QSOs with Australia, New Zealand and South Africa soon became commonplace. Then how about 20 meters? This new band revealed entirely unexpected possibilities when 1XAM worked 6TS on the West Coast, direct, at high noon. The dream of amateur radio—daylight DX!—was finally true.

PUBLIC SERVICE

Amateur radio is a grand and glorious hobby but this fact alone would hardly merit such wholehearted support as is given it by our Government at international conferences. There are other reasons. One of these is a thorough appreciation by the military and civil defense authorities of the value of the amateur as a source of skilled radio personnel in time of war. Another asset is best described as "public service."

About 4000 amateurs had contributed their skill and ability in '17–'18. After the war it was only natural that cordial relations should prevail between the Army and Navy and the amateur. These relations strengthened in the next few years and, in gradual steps, grew into cooperative activities which resulted, in 1925, in the establishment of the Naval Communications Reserve and the Army-Amateur Radio System (now the Military Affiliate Radio System). In World War II thousands of amateurs in the Naval Reserve were called to active duty, where they served with distinction, while many other thousands served in the Army, Air Forces, Coast Guard and Marine Corps. Altogether, more than 25,000 radio amateurs served in the armed forces of the United States. Other thousands were engaged in vital civilian electronic research, development and manufacturing. They also organized and manned the War Emergency Radio Service, the communications section of OCD.

The "public-service" record of the amateur is a brilliant tribute to his work. These activities can be roughly divided into two classes, expeditions and emergencies. Amateur cooperation with expeditions began in 1923 when a League member, Don Mix, 1TS, of Bristol, Conn. (now assistant technical editor of *QST*), accompanied MacMillan to the Arctic on the schooner *Bowdoin* with an amateur station. Amateurs in Canada and the U.S. provided the home contacts. The success of this venture was so outstanding that other explorers followed suit. During subsequent years a total of perhaps two hundred voyages and expeditions were assisted by amateur radio, the several explorations of the Antarctic being perhaps the best known.

Since 1913 amateur radio has been the principal, and in many cases the only, means of outside communication in several hundred storm, flood and earthquake emergencies in this country. The 1955 northeastern and west coast floods, the great Alaskan earthquake of early 1964 and the 1967 floods there, and the southeast and Gulf of Mexico hurricanes in the fall of 1967 called for the amateur's greatest emergency effort. In these disasters and many others— tornadoes, sleet storms, forest fires, blizzards —amateurs played a major role in the relief work and earned wide commendation for their resourcefulness in effecting communication where all other means had failed. During 1938 ARRL inaugurated a new emergency-preparedness program, registering personnel and equipment in its Emergency Corps and putting into effect a comprehensive program of cooperation with the Red Cross, and in 1947 a National Emergency Coordinator was appointed to full-time duty at League headquarters.

The amateur's outstanding record of organized preparation for emergency communications and performance under fire has been largely responsible for the decision of the Federal Government to set up special regulations and set aside special frequencies for use by amateurs in providing auxiliary communications for civil defense purposes in the event of war. Under the banner, "Radio Amateur Civil Emergency Service," amateurs are setting up and manning community and area networks integrated with civil defense functions of the municipal governments. Should a war cause the shut-down of routine amateur activities, the RACES will be immediately available in the national defense, manned by amateurs highly skilled in emergency communication.

TECHNICAL DEVELOPMENTS

The amateur is constantly in the forefront of technical progress. His incessant curiosity, his eagerness to try anything new, are two reasons. Another is that ever-growing amateur radio continually overcrowds its frequency assignments, spurring amateurs to the development and adoption of new techniques to permit the accommoda-

A view of the ARRL laboratory.

tion of more stations.

During World War II, thousands of skilled amateurs contributed their knowledge to the development of secret radio devices, both in Government and private laboratories. Equally as important, the prewar technical progress by amateurs provided the keystone for the development of modern military communications equipment.

From this work, amateurs have moved on to satellites of their own, launched piggyback on regular space shots at no cost to the taxpayer. The Project Oscar Association, an ARRL affiliate with headquarters in Sunnyvale, California, has designed and constructed the first two non-government satellites ever placed in orbit, Oscar I on December 12, 1961, and Oscar II on June 2, 1962. Oscar III, a more sophisticated satellite which received and retransmitted signals from the ground, went into orbit on March 9, 1965. Oscar IV, also a translator with input in the 144 Mc. band and output near 432 Mc., was launched on December 21, 1965. The name Oscar is taken from the initials of the phrase, "Orbital Satellite Carrying Amateur Radio."

Another space-age field in which amateurs are currently working is that of long-range communication using the moon as a passive reflector. The amateur bands from 144 to 1296 Mc. are being used for this work. . . . Moonbounce communications have been carried out between Finland and California on 144 Mc. and between Massachusetts and Hawaii on both 432 and 1296 Mc.

THE AMERICAN RADIO RELAY LEAGUE

The ARRL is today not only the spokesman for amateur radio in the U.S. and Canada but it is the largest amateur organization in the world. It is strictly of , by and for amateurs, is noncommercial and has no stockholders. The members of the League are the owners of the ARRL and *QST*.

The League is pledged to promote interest in two-way amateur communication and experimentation. It is interested in the relaying of messages by amateur radio. It is concerned with the advancement of the radio art. It stands for the maintenance of fraternalism and a high standard of conduct. It represents the amateur in legislative matters.

One of the League's principal purposes is to keep amateur activities so well conducted that the amateur will continue to justify his existence. Amateur radio offers its followers countless pleasures and unending satisfaction. It also calls for the shouldering of responsibilities—the maintenance of high standards, a cooperative loyalty to the traditions of amateur radio, a dedication to its ideals and principles, so that the institution of amateur radio may continue to operate "in the public interest, convenience and necessity."

The operating territory of ARRL is divided into one Canadian and fifteen U. S. divisions. The affairs of the League are managed by a Board of Directors. One director is elected every two years by the membership of each U.S. division, and one by the Canadian membership. These directors then choose the president and three vice-presidents, who are also members of the Board. The secretary and treasurer are also appointed by the Board. The directors, as representatives of the amateurs in their divisions, meet annually to examine current amateur problems and formulate ARRL policies thereon. The directors appoint a general manager to supervise the operations of the League and its headquarters, and to carry out the policies and instructions of the Board.

ARRL owns and publishes the monthly magazine, *QST*. Acting as a bulletin of the League's organized activities, *QST* also serves as a medium for the exchange of ideas and fosters amateur spirit. Its technical articles are renowned. It has grown to be the "amateur's bible," as well as one of the foremost radio magazines in the world. Membership dues include a subscription to *QST*.

ARRL maintains a model headquarters amateur station, known as the Hiram Percy Maxim Memorial Station, in Newington, Conn. Its call is W1AW, the call held by Mr. Maxim until his death and later transferred to the League station by a special government action. Separate transmitters of maximum legal power on each amateur band have permitted the station to be heard regularly all over the world. More important, W1AW transmits on regular schedules bulletins of general interest to amateurs, conducts code practice as a training feature, and engages in two-way work on all popular bands with as many amateurs as time permits.

At the headquarters of the League in Newington, Conn., is a well-equipped laboratory to assist staff members in preparation of technical material for *QST* and the *Radio Amateur's Handbook*. Among its other activities, the League maintains a Communications Department concerned with the operating activities of League members. A large field organization is headed by a Section Communications Manager in each of the League's seventy-four sections. There are appointments for qualified members in various fields, as outlined in Chapter 24. Special activities and contests promote operating skill. A special place is reserved each month in *QST* for amateur news from every section.

AMATEUR LICENSING IN THE UNITED STATES

Pursuant to the law, the Federal Communications Commission (FCC) has issued detailed regulations for the amateur service.

A radio amateur is a duly authorized person interested in radio technique solely with a personal aim and without pecuniary interest. Amateur operator licenses are given to U. S. citizens who pass an examination on operation and apparatus and on the provisions of law and regulations affecting amateurs, and who demonstrate ability to send and receive code. There are five available classes of amateur license—Novice, Technician, General ("Conditional" if taken by mail), Advanced, and Amateur Extra Class. Each has different requirements, the first two being the simplest and consequently conveying limited privileges as to frequencies available. Effective November 22, 1968, Extra Class licensees have exclusive use of the frequencies 3.5-3.525, 3.8-3.825, 7.0-7.025, 14.0-14.025, 21.0-21.025 and 21.25-21.275 Mc. Advanced and Extra Class licensees have exclusive use of 3.825-3.85, 7.2-7.25, 14.2-14.235, 21.275-21.3 and 50.0-50.1 Mc. Effective November 22, 1969, Extra Class licensees have exclusive use of the frequencies 3.5-3.55, 3.8-3.825, 7.0-7.05, 14.0-14.05, 21.0-21.05 and 21.25-21.275 Mc. Advanced and Extra have exclusive use of the frequencies 3.825-3.9, 7.2-7.25, 14.2-14.275, 21.275-21.35 and 50.0-50.25 Mc. Exams for Novice, Technician and Conditional classes are taken by mail under the supervision of a volunteer examiner. Station licenses are granted only to licensed operators. An amateur station may not be used for material compensation of any sort nor for broadcasting. Narrow bands of frequencies are allocated exclusively for use by amateur stations. Transmissions may be on any frequency within the assigned bands. All the frequencies may be used for c.w. telegraphy; some are available for radiotelephone, others for special forms of transmission such as teletype, facsimile, amateur television or radio control. The input to the final stage of amateur stations is limited to 1000 watts (with lower limits in some cases; see the table on page 13) and on frequencies below 144 Mc. must be adequately filtered direct current. Emissions must be free from spurious radiations. The licensee must provide for measurement of the transmitter frequency and establish a procedure for checking it regularly. A complete log of station operation must be maintained, with specified data. The station license also authorizes the holder to operate portable and mobile stations subject to further regulations. All radio licensees are subject to penalties for violation of regulations.

In the U.S., amateur licenses are issued only to citizens, without regard to age or physical condition. A fee of $4.00 (payable to the Federal Communications Commission) must accompany applications for new and renewed licenses (except Novices: no fee). The fee for license modification is $2.00. When you are able to copy code at the required speed, have studied basic transmitter theory and are familiar with the law and amateur regulations, you are ready to give serious thought to securing the Government amateur licenses which are issued you, after examination by an FCC engineer (or by a volunteer, depending on the license class), through the FCC Licensing Unit, Gettysburg, Pa., 17325. A complete up-to-the-minute discussion of license requirements, the FCC regulations for the amateur service, and study guides for those preparing for the examinations, are to be found in *The Radio Amateur's License Manual,* available from the American Radio Relay League, Newington, Conn. 06111, for 50¢, postpaid.

AMATEUR LICENSING IN CANADA

The agency responsible for amateur radio in Canada is the Department of Transport, with its principal offices in Ottawa. Prospective amateurs, who must be at least 15 years old, may take the examination for an Amateur Radio Operator Certificate at one of the regional offices of the DOT. The test is in three parts: a Morse code test at ten words per minute, a written technical exam and an oral examination. Upon passing the examination, the amateur may apply for a station license, the fee for which is $10 per year. At this point, the amateur is permitted to use c.w. on all authorized amateur bands (see table on page 13) and phone on those bands above 50 Mc.

After six months, during which the station has been operated on c.w. on frequencies below 29.7 Mc., the Canadian amateur may have his certificate endorsed for phone operation on the 26.96-27.0 Mc. and 28.0-29.7 Mc. bands. The amateur may take a 15 w.p.m. code test and more-difficult oral and written examinations, for the Advanced Amateur Radio Operator Certificate, which permits phone operations on portions of all authorized amateur bands. Holders of First or Second Class or Special Radio Operator's Certificates may enjoy the privileges of Advanced class without further examination. The maximum input power to the final stage of an amateur transmitter is limited to 1,000 watts.

Prospective amateurs living in remote areas may obtain a provisional station license after signing a statement that they can meet the technical and operating requirements. A provisional license is valid for a maximum of twelve consecutive months only; by then, a provisional licensee should have taken the regular examination.

Licenses are available to citizens of Canada, to citizens of other countries in the British Commonwealth, and to non-citizens who qualify as "landed immigrants" within the meaning of Canadian immigration law. The latter status may be enjoyed for only six years, incidentally. A U.S. citizen who obtained a Canadian license as a "landed immigrant" would have to become a Canadian citizen at the end of six years or lose his Canadian license.

Copies of the Radio Act and of the General Radio Regulations may be obtained for a nominal fee from the Queen's Printer, Ottawa, and in other places where publications of the Queen's Printer are available. An extract of the amateur rules, Form AR-5-80, is available at DOT offices. A wealth of additional information on amateur radio in Canada can be found in the *Radio Amateur Licensing Handbook,* by Jim Kitchin, VE7KN, published by R. Mack & Co. Ltd., 1485 S.W. Marine Dr., Vancouver 14, B.C., for $2.50.

RECIPROCAL OPERATING

U.S. amateurs may operate their amateur stations while visiting in Argentina, Australia, Austria, Barbados, Belgium, Bolivia, Canada, Chile, Colombia, Costa Rica, Dominican Republic, Ecuador, El Salvador, Finland, France, Germany, Guyana, Honduras, India, Israel, Kuwait, Luxembourg, Netherlands, New Zealand, Nicaragua, Norway, Panama, Paraguay, Peru, Portugal, Sierre Leone, Switzerland, Trinidad & Tobago, the United Kingdom and Venezuela and vice versa. For the latest information, write to ARRL headquarters.

LEARNING THE CODE

In starting to learn the code, you should consider it simply another means of conveying information. The spoken word is one method, the printed page another, and typewriting and shorthand are additional examples. Learning the code is as easy—or as difficult—as learning to type.

The important thing in beginning to study code is to think of it as a language of *sound,* never as combinations of dots and dashes. It is easy to "speak" code equivalents by using "dit" and *"dah,"* so that A would be *"didah"* (the "t" is dropped in such combinations). The sound "di" should be staccato; a code character such as "5" should sound like a machinegun burst: didididi-dit! Stress each *"dah"* equally; they are underlined or italicized in this text because they should be slightly accented and drawn out.

Take a few characters at a time. Learn them thoroughly in di*dah* language before going on to new ones. If someone who is familiar with code can be found to "send" to you, either by whistling or by means of a buzzer or code oscillator, enlist his cooperation. Learn the code by *listening* to it. Don't think about speed to start; the first requirement is to learn the characters to the point where you can recognize each of them without hesitation. Concentrate on any difficult letters. Learning the code is not at all hard; a simple booklet treating the subject in detail is another of the beginner publications available from the League, and is entitled, *Learning the Radiotelegraph Code,* 50¢ postpaid.

Code-practice transmissions are sent by W1AW every evening at 0030 and 0230 GMT (0130 and 2330 May through October). See Chapter 24, "Code Proficiency."

A	didah	N	dahit
B	dahdididit	O	dahdahdah
C	dahdidahdit	P	didahdahdit
D	dahdidit	Q	dahdahdidah
E	dit	R	didahdit
F	dididahdit	S	dididit
G	dahdahdit	T	dah
H	dmidididit	U	dididah
I	didit	V	didididah
J	didahdahdah	W	didahdah
K	dahdidah	X	dahdididah
L	didahdidit	Y	dahdidahdah
M	dahdah	Z	dahdahdidit

1	didahdahdahdah	6	dahdidididit
2	dididahdahdah	7	dahdahdididit
3	didididahdah	8	dahdahdahdidit
4	didididah	9	dahdahdahdahdit
5	dididididit	0	dahdahdahdahdah

Period : didahdidahdidah. Comma : dahdahdididahdah. Question mark : dididahdahdidit. Error : dididididididit. Double dash : dahdidididah. Colon : dahdahdahdidit. Semicolon : dahdidahdidahdit. Parenthesis : dahdidahdahdidah. Fraction bar : dahdididahdit. Wait : didahdididit. End of message : didahdidahdit. Invitation to transmit : dahdidah. End of work : dididididahdidah.

Fig. 1-1—The Continental (International Morse) code.

A Code-Practice Set

The simple circuit shown in Fig. 1-2 is easy to build and is not costly. The entire unit, including home-made key, can be built for less than $5.00. The tone from the speaker is loud enough to provide room volume, making the oscillator useful for group code-practice sessions.

The circuit can be built on a 2½ x 2½-inch piece of circuit board, Formica, linoleum tile, or Masonite as shown in Fig. 1-2. The main chassis can be a home-made aluminum, brass, or galvanized-iron channel which is 6 inches long, 2¾ inches wide, and 1 inch high. The tiny 2-inch diameter speaker shown here was removed from a junk 6-transistor pocket radio. Any small speaker whose voice-coil impedance is between 3.2 and 10 ohms will work satisfactorily. Although a battery holder is used at BT_1, the battery could be taped to the chassis, or used outboard, reducing the total cost. The circuit connections are made with short lengths of insulated hookup wire. A phono jack is used at J_1, but isn't necessary. A few more cents could be saved by wiring the key directly into the circuit.

The Key

A home-made key is shown in the photo. The base is a piece of plywood which is ¾ inch thick, 6 inches long, and is 4 inches wide. The key lever is a piece of ⅜-inch wide brass strip, No. 16

View of the code-practice set. The speaker mounts under the chassis and is protected by a piece of aluminum screening. Ordinary window screen will work here. The circuit board is mounted over a cut-out area in the chassis. Allow a ¼-inch overlap on all sides of the circuit board for mounting purposes. Four 4-40 bolts hold the board in place. The battery holder is a Keystone No. 175.

gauge. It is 5 inches long and is bent slightly near the center to raise the operating end approximately ¼ inch above the base board. A piece of circuit board is glued to the operating end of the lever, serving as a finger plate for the key. A poker chip or large garment button can be used in place of the item shown. Epoxy glue holds the chip firmly in place.

The brass lever is attached to the base board by means of two 6-32 bolts, each one inch in length. One of the keying leads (the one going to the chassis *ground* terminal) connects to one of the bolts, under the board. Another 6-32 x 1-inch screw is placed under the finger end of the lever (about ¼ inch in from the end of the lever) and serves as the contact element when the key is depressed. The remaining key lead connects to this screw, again under the base board. The spacing

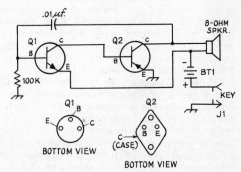

Fig. 1—2—Schematic diagram of the code oscillator. Resistance is in ohms. K = 1000. The 0.01-uf. capacitor is disk ceramic. BT_1 is a 1.5-volt size-D flashlight cell. J_1 is a phono connector. Q_1 is an RCA 40309 (a 2N2102 is suitable also). Q_2 is an RCA 2N2869/2N301. (An RCA 40022 is suitable, also). The cases of Q_1 and Q_2 should be insulated from the chassis.

between the lever and the contact element can be adjusted by bending the brass lever with a pair of pliers. It should be set to suit the operator. Commercially-made keys can be used if the operator prefers. There are many bargain-priced units of this type on the market.

INTRODUCTION TO RADIO THEORY

As you start your studies for an amateur license, you may wish to have the additional help available in *How to Become a Radio Amateur* ($1.00). It features an elementary description of radio theory and constructional details on a simple receiver and transmitter.

Another aid is *A Course in Radio Fundamentals* ($1.00), a study guide using this *Handbook* as its text. There are experiments, discussions, and quizzes to help you learn radio fundamentals.

A new League publication, *Understanding Amateur Radio,* explains radio theory and practice in greater detail than is found in *How to Become a Radio Amateur,* but is at a more basic level than this *Handbook. Understanding Amateur Radio* contains 320 pages, and is priced at $2.00.

These booklets are available postpaid from ARRL, Newington, Connecticut 06111.

THE AMATEUR BANDS

Amateurs are assigned bands of frequencies at approximate harmonic intervals throughout the spectrum. Like assignments to all services, they are subject to modification to fit the changing picture of world communications needs. Modifications of rules to provide for domestic needs are also occasionally issued by FCC and DOT, and in that respect each amateur should keep himself informed by W1AW bulletins, *QST* reports, or by communication with ARRL Hq. concerning a specific point.

On this page and page 14 are summaries of the Canadian and U.S. amateur bands on which operation is permitted as of our press date. Figures are megacycles. AØ and FØ mean unmodulated carriers. A1 means c.w. telegraphy, A2 is tone-modulated c.w. telegraphy, A3 is amplitude-modulated phone (n.f.m. may also be used in such bands, except on 1.8-2.0 Mc.), A4 is facsimile, A5 is television, n.f.m. designates narrow-band frequency- or phase-modulated radiotelephony, F1 is frequency-shift keying, F2 is frequency-modulated tone keying (Morse or teletype), F3 is f.m. phone, F4 is f.m. facsimile and F5 is f.m. television.

CANADIAN AMATEUR BANDS

80 meters	3.500–	3.725 Mc.	A1, F1,
	3.725–	4.000 Mc.	A1, A3[1], F3[1],
40 m.	7.000–	7.150 Mc.	A1, F1,
	7.150–	7.300 Mc.	A1, A3[1], F3[1],
20 m.	14.000–	14.100 Mc.	A1, F1,
	14.100–	14.350 Mc.	A1, A3[1], F3[1],
15 m.	21.000–	21.100 Mc.	A1, F1,
	21.100–	21.450 Mc.	A1, A3[1], F3[1],
11 m.	26.960–	27.000 Mc.	A1, A2, A3[2], F3[2],
10 m.	28.000–	28.100 Mc.	A1, F1,
	28.100–	29.700 Mc.	A1, A3[2], F3[2],
6 m.	50.000–	50.050 Mc.	A1
	50.050–	51.000 Mc.	A1, A2, A3, F1, F2, F3
	51.000–	54.000 Mc.	AØ, A1, A2, A3, F1, F2, F3,
2 m.	144.000–	144.100 Mc.	A1

144.100– 148.000 Mc.	AØ, A1, A2, A3, F1, F2, F3,
220.000– 225.000 Mc.	
420.000– 450.000 Mc.	
1215.000– 1300.000 Mc.	AØ, A1, A2, A3, A5[3], F1, F2, F3,
2300.000– 2450.000 Mc.	
3300.000– 3500.000 Mc.	
5650.000– 5925.000 Mc.	
10000.000–10500.000 Mc.	
21000.000–22000.000 Mc.	

[1] Phone privileges are restricted to holders of Advanced Amateur Radio Operator Certificates, and of Commercial Certificates.

[2] Phone privileges are restricted as in footnote 1, and to holders of Amateur Radio Operators Certificates whose certificates have been endorsed for operation on phone in these bands; see text.

[3] Special endorsement required for amateur television transmission.

Operation in the frequency bands 1.800-2.000 Mc. shall be limited to the areas as indicated in the following table and shall be limited to the indicated maximum d.c. power input to the anode circuit of the final radio frequency stage of the transmitter during day and night hours respectively; for the purpose of the subsection, "day" means the hours between sunrise and sunset, and "night" means the hours between sunset and sunrise: A1, A3, and F3 emission are permitted.

	A	B	C	D	E	F	G	H
B.C. North of 54° N. Lat.	1	0	0	1	0	0	0	0
B.C. South of 54° N. Lat.	0	0	0	0	0	0	0	1
Alberta	1	0	0	1	1	0	0	1
Saskatchewan	2	0	0	2	2	1	1	3
Manitoba	3	1	1	2	2	1	1	3
Ontario North of 50° N. Lat.	3	1	0	0	0	0	0	2
Ontario South of 50° N. Lat.	3	2	1	0	0	0	0	1
P.Q. North of 52° N. Lat.	1	0	0	1	1	0	0	1
P.Q. South of 52° N. Lat.	3	1	0	0	0	0	0	0
N.B., N.S., P.E.I.	3	2	1	0	0	0	0	0
Newfoundland	3	1	1	0	0	0	0	0
Labrador	2	0	0	0	0	0	0	0
Yukon Territory	2	0	0	1	0	0	0	0
District of MacKenzie	2	0	0	2	1	0	0	1
District of Keewatin	1	0	0	1	2	1	1	3
District of Franklin	0	0	0	0	1	0	0	1

Frequency Band

A	1800—1825 kc.	E	1900—1925 kc.
B	1825—1850 kc.	F	1925—1950 kc.
C	1850—1875 kc.	G	1950—1975 kc.
D	1875—1900 kc.	H	1975—2000 kc.

Power Level—Watts

0—Operation not permitted.

1—25 night	100 day
2—50 night	200 day
3—100 night	400 day

Except as otherwise specified, the maximum amateur power input is 1,000 watts.

U.S. AND POSSESSIONS AMATEUR BANDS

	Kc.	
80 m.*	3500–4000	A1
	3500–3800	F1
	3800–3850	A5, F5[1]
	3850–3900	A5, F5[2]
	3800–4000	A3, F3[3]
40 m.*	7000–7300	A1
	7000–7200	F1
	7200–7225	A5, F5[1]
	7225–7250	A5, F5[2]
	7200–7300	A3, F3[3]
20 m.*	14000–14350	A1
	14000–14200	F1
	14200–14235	A5, F5[1]
	14235–14275	A5, F5[2]
	14200–14350	A3, F3[3]

	Mc/s	
15 m.*	21.00–21.45	A1
	21.00–21.25	F1
	21.25–21.30	A5, F5[1]
	21.30–21.35	A5, F5[2]
	21.25–21.45	A3, F3[3]
10 m.	28.0–29.7	A1
	28.5–29.7	A3, A5,[1] F3,[3] F5[1]
	29.0–29.7	F1
6 m.*	50.0–54.0	A1
	50.1–54.0	A2, A3, A4, A5,[4] F1, F2, F3, F5[4]
	51.0–54.0	A0
2 m.	144–148	A1
	144–147.9	A0, A2, A3, A4, A5,[4] F0, F1, F2, F3, F5[4]

Mc.	
220–225	—A0, A1, A2, A3, A4, A5[4] F0, F1, F2, F3, F4, F5[4]
420–450[5]	A0, A1, A2, A3, A4, A5, F0, F1, F2, F3, F4, F5
1,215–1,300	
2,300–2,450	
3,300–3,500	A0, A1, A2, A3, A4, A5. F0, F1, F2, F3, F4, F5, pulse
5,650–5,925	
10,000–10,500[6]	
21,000–22,000	
All above 40,000	

[1] Slow-scan television no wider than a single-sideband voice signal may be used; if voice is simultaneously used, the total signal can be no wider than a standard a.m. signal.

[2] Additional frequencies for slow-scan television after November 22, 1969.

[3] Narrow-band frequency- or phase-modulation no wider than standard a.m. voice signal.

[4] Slow-scan television no wider than a standard a.m. voice signal.

[5] Input power must not exceed 50 watts in Fla., Ariz., and parts of Ga., Ala., Miss., N. Mex., Tex., Nev., and Calif. See the *License Manual* or write ARRL for further details.

[6] No pulse permitted in this band.

NOTE: Frequencies from 3.9 to 4.0 Mc. are not available to amateurs on Baker, Canton, Enderbury, Guam, Howland, Jarvis, Palmyra, American Samoa, and Wake islands.

The bands 220 through 10,500 Mc. are shared with the Government Radio Positioning Service, which has priority.

In addition, A1 and A3 on portions of 1.800–2.000 Mc., as follows. Figures in the right columns are maximum d.c. plate power input.

Area	1800–1825 kc. Day/Night	1825–1850 kc. Day/Night	1850–1875 kc. Day/Night	1875–1900 kc. Day/Night	1900–1925 kc. Day/Night	1925–1950 kc. Day/Night	1950–1975 kc. Day/Night	1975–2000 kc. Day/Night
Ala., La., Miss.	500/100	100/25	0	0	0	0	100/25	500/100
Alaska	200/50	0	0	200/50	0	0	0	0
Arizona	0	0	0	0	0	200/50	500/100	1000/200
Ark., Mo.	1000/200	200/50	100/25	0	0	100/25	100/25	500/100
California	0	0	0	0	100/25	200/50	200/50	500/100
Colorado	200/50	0	0	0	0	200/50	200/50	1000/200
Conn., Me., Mass., N.H., N.J., N.Y., Penn., R.I., Vt.	500/100	100/25	0	0	0	0	0	0
Del., D.C., Md., N.C., Va.	500/100	100/25	0	0	0	0	0	100/25
Florida	500/100	100/25	0	0	0	0	100/25	500/100
Ga., S.C., P.R., Virgin Is., Navassa	500/100	100/25	0	0	0	0	0	200/50
Hawaii, Oregon	0	0	0	0	200/50	100/25	100/25	500/100
Idaho, Montana	100/25	0	0	100/25	100/25	100/25	100/25	500/100
Illinois	1000/200	200/50	100/25	0	0	0	0	200/50
Ind., Ken., Tenn.	1000/200	500/100	100/25	0	0	0	0	200/50
Iowa	1000/200	200/50	200/50	0	0	100/25	100/25	500/100
Kansas, Okla.	500/100	100/25	0	0	0	100/25	200/50	500/100
Mich., Ohio, W.Va.	1000/200	500/100	100/25	0	0	0	0	100/25
Minnesota	500/100	100/25	100/25	100/25	100/25	100/25	100/25	500/100
Nebraska	500/100	100/25	100/25	0	0	200/50	200/50	1000/200
Nevada	0	0	0	0	100/25	200/50	200/50	1000/200
New Mexico	100/25	0	0	0	0	100/25	500/100	1000/200
No. Dak., So. Dak.	500/100	100/25	100/25	100/25	100/25	200/50	200/50	1000/200
Texas	200/50	0	0	0	0	0	100/25	500/100
Utah	100/25	0	0	100/25	100/25	200/50	200/50	1000/200
Washington	0	0	0	0	200/50	0	0	500/100
Wisconsin	1000/200	200/50	200/50	0	0	0	0	200/50
Wyoming	200/50	0	0	100/25	100/25	200/50	200/50	1000/200
Roncador Key, Swan Is., Serrana Bank	500/100	100/25	0	0	0	0	100/25	500/100
Baker, Canton, Enderbury, Howland Is.	100/25	0	0	100/25	100/25	0	0	100/25
Guam, Johnson, Midway Is.	0	0	0	0	100/25	0	0	100/25
American Samoa	200/50	0	0	200/50	200/50	0	0	200/50
Wake Island	100/25	0	0	100/25	0	0	0	0
Palmyra, Jarvis Is.	0	0	0	0	0	200/50	0	200/50

Novice licensees may use the following frequencies, transmitters to be crystal-controlled and have a maximum power input of 75 watts.

3.700–3.750 Mc. A1   21.100–21.250 Mc. A1
7.150–7.200 Mc. A1   145–147 Mc. A1, A2, F1, F2

Technician licensees are permitted all amateur privileges in 50 Mc.,* 145–147 Mc. and in the bands 220 Mc. and above.

Except as otherwise specified, the maximum amateur power input is 1000 watts.

* See page 11 for restrictions on usage of parts of these bands after November 22, 1968

Chapter 2

Electrical Laws and Circuits

ELECTRIC AND MAGNETIC FIELDS

When something occurs at one point in space because something else happened at another point, with no visible means by which the "cause" can be related to the "effect," we say the two events are connected by a **field**. In radio work, the fields with which we are concerned are the **electric** and **magnetic**, and the combination of the two called the **electromagnetic** field.

A field has two important properties, intensity (magnitude) and direction. The field exerts a *force* on an object immersed in it; this force represents potential (ready-to-be-used) energy, so the **potential** of the field is a measure of the **field intensity**. The **direction** of the field is the direction in which the object on which the force is exerted will tend to move.

An electrically charged object in an electric field will be acted on by a force that will tend to move it in a direction determined by the direction of the field. Similarly, a magnet in a magnetic field will be subject to a force. Everyone has seen demonstrations of magnetic fields with pocket magnets, so intensity and direction are not hard to grasp.

A "static" field is one that neither moves nor changes in intensity. Such a field can be set up by a stationary electric charge (**electrostatic field**) or by a stationary magnet (**magnetostatic field**). But if either an electric or magnetic field is moving in space or changing in intensity, the motion or change sets up the other kind of field. That is, a changing electric field sets up a magnetic field, and a changing magnetic field generates an electric field. This interrelationship between magnetic and electric fields makes possible such things as the electromagnet and the electric motor. It also makes possible the **electromagnetic waves** by which radio communication is carried on, for such waves are simply traveling fields in which the energy is alternately handed back and forth between the electric and magnetic fields.

Lines of Force

Although no one knows what it is that composes the field itself, it is useful to invent a picture of it that will help in visualizing the forces and the way in which they act.

A field can be pictured as being made up of **lines of force**, or **flux lines**. These are purely imaginary threads that show, by the direction in which they lie, the direction the object on which the force is exerted will move. The *number* of lines in a chosen cross section of the field is a measure of the *intensity* of the force. The number of lines per unit of area (square inch or square centimeter) is called the **flux density**.

ELECTRICITY AND THE ELECTRIC CURRENT

Everything physical is built up of atoms, particles so small that they cannot be seen even through the most powerful microscope. But the atom in turn consists of several different kinds of still smaller particles. One is the **electron**, essentially a small particle of electricity. The quantity or **charge** of electricity represented by the electron is, in fact, the smallest quantity of electricity that can exist. The kind of electricity associated with the electron is called **negative**.

An ordinary atom consists of a central core called the **nucleus**, around which one or more electrons circulate somewhat as the earth and other planets circulate around the sun. The nucleus has an electric charge of the kind of electricity called **positive**, the amount of its charge being just exactly equal to the sum of the negative charges on all the electrons associated with that nucleus.

The important fact about these two "opposite" kinds of electricity is that they are strongly attracted to each other. Also, there is a strong force of repulsion between two charges of the *same* kind. The positive nucleus and the negative electrons are attracted to each other, but two electrons will be repelled from each other and so will two nuclei.

In a normal atom the positive charge on the nucleus is exactly balanced by the negative charges on the electrons. However, it is possible for an atom to lose one of its electrons. When that happens the atom has a little less negative charge than it should — that is, it has a net positive charge. Such an atom is said to be **ionized**, and in this case the atom is a **positive ion**. If an atom picks up an extra electron, as it sometimes does, it has a net negative charge and is called a **negative ion**. A positive ion will attract any stray electron in the vicinity, including the extra one that may be attached to a nearby negative ion. In this way it is possible for electrons to travel from atom to atom. The movement of ions or electrons constitutes the **electric current**.

The **amplitude** of the current (its intensity or magnitude) is determined by the rate at which electric charge — an accumulation of electrons or ions of the same kind — moves past a point in a circuit. Since the charge on a single electron or ion is extremely small, the number that must move as a group to form even a tiny current is almost inconceivably large.

Conductors and Insulators

Atoms of some materials, notably metals and acids, will give up an electron readily, but atoms of other materials will not part with any of their electrons even when the electric force is extremely strong. Materials in which electrons or ions can be moved with relative ease are called **conductors**, while those that refuse to permit such movement are called **nonconductors** or **insulators**. The following list shows how some common materials are classified:

Conductors	Insulators	
Metals	Dry Air	Glass
Carbon	Wood	Rubber
Acids	Porcelain	Resins
	Textiles	

Electromotive Force

The electric force or potential (called **electromotive force**, and abbreviated **e.m.f.**) that causes current flow may be developed in several ways. The action of certain chemical solutions on dissimilar metals sets up an e.m.f.; such a combination is called a **cell**, and a group of cells forms an electric **battery**. The amount of current that such cells can carry is limited, and in the course of current flow one of the metals is eaten away. The amount of electrical energy that can be taken from a battery consequently is rather small. Where a large amount of energy is needed it is usually furnished by an electric **generator**, which develops its e.m.f. by a combination of magnetic and mechanical means.

Direct and Alternating Currents

In picturing current flow it is natural to think of a single, constant force causing the electrons to move. When this is so, the electrons always move in the same direction through a path or **circuit** made up of conductors connected together in a continuous chain. Such a current is called a **direct current**, abbreviated **d.c.** It is the type of current furnished by batteries and by certain types of generators.

It is also possible to have an e.m.f. that periodically reverses. With this kind of e.m.f. the current flows first in one direction through the circuit and then in the other. Such an e.m.f. is called an alternating e.m.f., and the current is called an **alternating current** (abbreviated **a.c.**). The reversals (alternations) may occur at any rate from a few per second up to several billion per second. Two reversals make a **cycle**; in one cycle the force acts first in one direction, then in the other, and then returns to the first direction to begin the next cycle. The number of cycles in one second is called the **frequency** of the alternating current.

The difference between direct current and alternating current is shown in Fig. 2-1. In these graphs the horizontal axis measures time, increasing toward the right away from the vertical axis. The vertical axis represents the amplitude or strength of the current, increasing in either the up or down direction away from the horizontal axis. If the graph is *above* the horizontal axis the current is flowing in one direction through the circuit (indicated by the + sign) and if it is *below* the horizontal axis the current is flowing in the reverse direction through the circuit (indicated by the − sign). Fig. 2-1A shows that, if we close the circuit — that is, make the path for the current complete — at the time indicated by X, the current instantly takes the amplitude indicated by the height A. After that, the current continues at the same amplitude as time goes on. This is an ordinary *direct* current.

In Fig. 2-1B, the current starts flowing with the amplitude A at time X, continues at that amplitude until time Y and then instantly ceases. After an interval YZ the current again begins to flow and the same sort of start-and-stop performance is repeated. This is an *intermittent* direct current. We could get it by alternately closing and opening a switch in the circuit. It is a *direct* current because the *direction* of current flow does not change; the graph is always on the + side of the horizontal axis.

In Fig. 2-1C the current starts at zero, increases in amplitude as time goes on until it reaches the amplitude A_1 while flowing in the + direction, then decreases until it drops to zero amplitude once more. At that time (X) the *direction* of the current flow reverses; this is indicated by the fact that the next part of the graph is below the axis. As time goes on the amplitude increases, with the current now flowing in the − direction, until it reaches amplitude A_2. Then

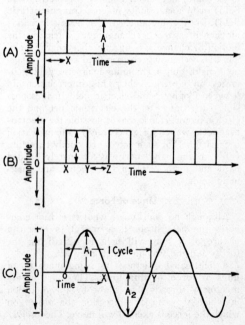

Fig. 2-1—Three types of current flow. A—direct current; B—intermittent direct current; C—alternating current.

the amplitude decreases until finally it drops to zero (Y) and the direction reverses once more. This is an *alternating* current.

Waveforms

The type of alternating current shown in Fig. 2-1C is known as a **sine wave.** The variations in many a.c. waves are not so smooth, nor is one half-cycle necessarily just like the preceding one in shape. However, these **complex waves** can be shown to be the sum of two or more sine waves of frequencies that are exact integral (whole-number) multiples of some lower frequency. The lowest frequency is called the **fundamental,** and the higher frequencies are called **harmonics.**

Fig. 2-2 shows how a fundamental and a second harmonic (twice the fundamental) might add to form a complex wave. Simply by changing the relative amplitudes of the two waves, as well as the times at which they pass through zero amplitude, an infinite number of waveshapes can be constructed from just a fundamental and second harmonic. More complex waveforms can be constructed if more harmonics are used.

Frequency multiplication, the generation of second, third and higher-order harmonics, takes place whenever a fundamental sine wave is passed through a nonlinear device. The distorted output is made up of the fundamental frequency plus harmonics; a desired harmonic can be selected through the use of tuned circuits. Typical nonlinear devices used for frequency multiplication include rectifiers of any kind and amplifiers that distort an applied signal.

Electrical Units

The unit of electromotive force is called the **volt.** An ordinary flashlight cell generates an e.m.f. of about 1.5 volts. The e.m.f. commonly supplied for domestic lighting and power is 115 volts a.c. at a frequency of 60 cycles per second.

The flow of electric current is measured in **amperes.** One ampere is equivalent to the movement of many billions of electrons past a point in the circuit in one second. The *direct* currents used in amateur radio equipment usually are not large, and it is customary to measure such currents in **milliamperes.** One milliampere is equal to one one-thousandth of an ampere.

A "d.c. ampere" is a measure of a *steady* current, but the "a.c. ampere" must measure a current that is continually varying in amplitude and periodically reversing direction. To put the two on the same basis, an a.c. ampere is defined as the current that will cause the same heating effect as one ampere of steady direct current. For sine-wave a.c., this **effective** (or **r.m.s.,** for *root mean square,* the mathematical derivation) **value** is equal to the *maximum* (or **peak**) amplitude (A_1 or A_2 in Fig. 2-1C) multiplied by 0.707. The **instantaneous value** is the value that the current (or voltage) has at any selected instant in the cycle. If all the instantaneous values in a sine wave are averaged over a *half*-cycle, the resulting figure is the **average** value. It is equal to 0.636 times the maximum amplitude.

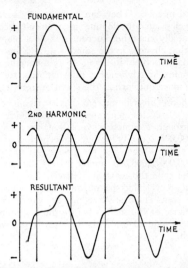

Fig. 2-2—A complex waveform. A fundamental (top) and second harmonic (center) added together, point by point at each instant, result in the waveform shown at the bottom. When the two components have the same polarity at a selected instant, the resultant is the simple sum of the two. When they have opposite polarities, the resultant is the *difference;* if the negative-polarity component is larger, the resultant is negative at that instant.

FREQUENCY AND WAVELENGTH

Frequency Spectrum

Frequencies ranging from about 15 to 15,000 cycles per second (c.p.s. Hertz, or Hz.) are called **audio** frequencies, because the vibrations of air particles that our ears recognize as sounds occur at a similar rate. Audio frequencies (abbreviated **a.f.**) are used to actuate loudspeakers and thus create sound waves.

Frequencies above about 15,000 c.p.s. are called **radio** frequencies (**r.f.**) because they are useful in radio transmission. Frequencies all the way up to and beyond 10,000,000,000 c.p.s. have been used for radio purposes. At radio frequencies it becomes convenient to use a larger unit than the cycle. Two such units are the **kilocycle,** which is equal to 1000 cycles and is abbreviated **kc.,** or **kHz.,** and the **megacycle,** which is equal to 1,000,000 cycles or 1000 kilocycles and is abbreviated **Mc.,** or **MHz.**

The various radio frequencies are divided off into classifications. These classifications, listed below, constitute the **frequency spectrum** so far as it extends for radio purposes at the present time.

Frequency	Classification	Abbreviation
10 to 30 kc.	Very-low frequencies	v.l.f.
30 to 300 kc.	Low frequencies	l.f.
300 to 3000 kc.	Medium frequencies	m.f.
3 to 30 Mc.	High frequencies	h.f.
30 to 300 Mc.	Very-high frequencies	v.h.f.
300 to 3000 Mc.	Ultrahigh frequencies	u.h.f.
3000 to 30,000 Mc.	Superhigh frequencies	s.h.f.

Wavelength

Radio waves travel at the same speed as light —300,000,000 meters or about 186,000 miles a second in space. They can be set up by a radio-frequency current flowing in a circuit, because the rapidly changing current sets up a magnetic field that changes in the same way, and the varying magnetic field in turn sets up a varying electric field. And whenever this happens, the two fields move outward at the speed of light.

Suppose an r.f. current has a frequency of 3,000,000 cycles per second. The fields will go through complete reversals (one cycle) in 1/3,000,000 second. In that same period of time the fields — that is, the wave — will move 300,000,000/3,000,000 meters, or 100 meters. By the time the wave has moved that distance the next cycle has begun and a new wave has started out. The first wave, in other words, covers a distance of 100 meters before the beginning of the next, and so on. This distance is the **wavelength**.

The longer the time of one cycle—that is, the lower the frequency—the greater the distance occupied by each wave and hence the longer the wavelength. The relationship between wavelength and frequency is shown by the formula

$$\lambda = \frac{300,000}{f}$$

where λ = Wavelength in meters
f = Frequency in kilocycles

or
$$\lambda = \frac{300}{f}$$

where λ = Wavelength in meters
f = Frequency in megacycles

Example: The wavelength corresponding to a frequency of 3650 kilocycles is

$$\lambda = \frac{300,000}{3650} = 82.2 \text{ meters}$$

RESISTANCE

Given two conductors of the same size and shape, but of different materials, the amount of current that will flow when a given e.m.f. is applied will be found to vary with what is called the **resistance** of the material. The lower the resistance, the greater the current for a given value of e.m.f.

Resistance is measured in **ohms**. A circuit has a resistance of one ohm when an applied e.m.f. of one volt causes a current of one ampere to flow. The **resistivity** of a material is the resistance, in ohms, of a cube of the material measuring one centimeter on each edge. One of the best conductors is copper, and it is frequently convenient, in making resistance calculations, to compare the resistance of the material under consideration with that of a copper conductor of the same size and shape. Table 2-I gives the ratio of the resistivity of various conductors to that of copper.

The longer the path through which the current flows the higher the resistance of that conductor. For direct current and low-frequency alternating

currents (up to a few thousand cycles per second) the resistance is *inversely* proportional to the cross-sectional area of the path the current must travel; that is, given two conductors of the same material and having the same length, but differing in cross-sectional area, the one with the larger area will have the lower resistance.

Resistance of Wires

The problem of determining the resistance of a round wire of given diameter and length—or its opposite, finding a suitable size and length of wire to supply a desired amount of resistance—can be easily solved with the help of the copper-wire table given in a later chapter. This table gives the resistance, in ohms per thousand feet, of each standard wire size.

Example: Suppose a resistance of 3.5 ohms is needed and some No. 28 wire is on hand. The wire table in Chapter 20 shows that No. 28 has a resistance of 66.17 ohms per thousand feet. Since the desired resistance is 3.5 ohms, the length of wire required will be

$$\frac{3.5}{66.17} \times 1000 = 52.89 \text{ feet.}$$

Or, suppose that the resistance of the wire in the circuit must not exceed 0.05 ohm and that the length of wire required for making the connections totals 14 feet. Then

$$\frac{14}{1000} \times R = 0.05 \text{ ohm}$$

where R is the maximum allowable resistance in ohms per thousand feet. Rearranging the formula gives

$$R = \frac{0.05 \times 1000}{14} = 3.57 \text{ ohms/1000 ft.}$$

Reference to the wire table shows that No. 15 is the smallest size having a resistance less than this value.

When the wire is not copper, the resistance values given in the wire table should be multiplied by the ratios given in Table 2-I to obtain the resistance.

TABLE 2-I	
Relative Resistivity of Metals	
Material	*Resistivity Compared to Copper*
Aluminum (pure)	1.6
Brass	3.7–4.9
Cadmium	4.4
Chromium	1.8
Copper (hard-drawn)	1.03
Copper (annealed)	1.00
Gold	1.4
Iron (pure)	5.68
Lead	12.8
Nickel	5.1
Phosphor Bronze	2.8–5.4
Silver	0.94
Steel	7.6–12.7
Tin	6.7
Zinc	3.4

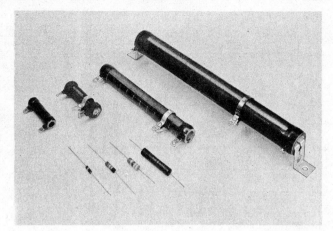

Types of resistors used in radio equipment. Those in the foreground with wire leads are carbon types, ranging in size from ½ watt at the left to 2 watts at the right. The larger resistors use resistance wire wound on ceramic tubes; sizes shown range from 5 watts to 100 watts. Three are of the adjustable type, having a sliding contact on an exposed section of the resistance winding.

Example: If the wire in the first example were nickel instead of copper the length required for 3.5 ohms would be

$$\frac{3.5}{66.17 \times 5.1} \times 1000 = 10.37 \text{ feet.}$$

Temperature Effects

The resistance of a conductor changes with its temperature. Although it is seldom necessary to consider temperature in making resistance calculations for amateur work, it is well to know that the resistance of practically all metallic conductors increases with increasing temperature. Carbon, however, acts in the opposite way; its resistance *decreases* when its temperature rises. The temperature effect is important when it is necessary to maintain a constant resistance under all conditions. Special materials that have little or no change in resistance over a wide temperature range are used in that case.

Resistors

A "package" of resistance made up into a single unit is called a **resistor.** Resistors having the same resistance value may be considerably different in size and construction. The flow of current through resistance causes the conductor to become heated; the higher the resistance and the larger the current, the greater the amount of heat developed. Resistors intended for carrying large currents must be physically large so the heat can be radiated quickly to the surrounding air. If the resistor does not get rid of the heat quickly it may reach a temperature that will cause it to melt or burn.

Skin Effect

The resistance of a conductor is not the same for alternating current as it is for direct current. When the current is alternating there are internal effects that tend to force the current to flow mostly in the outer parts of the conductor. This decreases the effective cross-sectional area of the conductor, with the result that the resistance increases.

For low audio frequencies the increase in resistance is unimportant, but at radio frequencies this **skin effect** is so great that practically all the current flow is confined within a few thousandths of an inch of the conductor surface. The r.f. resistance is consequently many times the d.c. resistance, and increases with increasing frequency. In the r.f. range a conductor of thin tubing will have just as low resistance as a solid conductor of the same diameter, because material not close to the surface carries practically no current.

Conductance

The reciprocal of resistance (that is, $1/R$) is called **conductance.** It is usually represented by the symbol G. A circuit having large conductance has low resistance, and vice versa. In radio work the term is used chiefly in connection with vacuum-tube characteristics. The unit of conductance is the **mho.** A resistance of one ohm has a conductance of one mho, a resistance of 1000 ohms has a conductance of 0.001 mho, and so on. A unit frequently used in connection with vacuum tubes is the **micromho,** or one-millionth of a mho. It is the conductance of a resistance of one megohm.

OHM'S LAW

The simplest form of electric circuit is a battery with a resistance connected to its terminals, as shown by the symbols in Fig. 2-3. A complete circuit must have an unbroken path so current

Fig. 2-3—A simple circuit consisting of a battery and resistor.

Batt.   R

can flow out of the battery, through the apparatus connected to it, and back into the battery. The circuit is **broken,** or **open,** if a connection is removed at any point. A **switch** is a device for making and breaking connections and thereby closing or opening the circuit, either allowing current to flow or preventing it from flowing.

The values of current, voltage and resistance in a circuit are by no means independent of each other. The relationship between them is known as **Ohm's Law.** It can be stated as follows: The

TABLE 2-II
Conversion Factors for Fractional and Multiple Units

To change from	To	Divide by	Multiply by
Units	Micro-units		1,000,000
	Milli-units		1000
	Kilo-units	1000	
	Mega-units	1,000,000	
Micro-units	Milli-units	1000	
	Units	1,000,000	
Milli-units	Micro-units		1000
	Units	1000	
Kilo-units	Units		1000
	Mega-units	1000	
Mega-units	Units		1,000,000
	Kilo-units		1000

current flowing in a circuit is directly proportional to the applied e.m.f. and inversely proportional to the resistance. Expressed as an equation, it is

$$I \text{ (amperes)} = \frac{E \text{ (volts)}}{R \text{ (ohms)}}$$

The equation above gives the value of current when the voltage and resistance are known. It may be transposed so that each of the three quantities may be found when the other two are known:

$$E = IR$$

(that is, the voltage acting is equal to the current in amperes multiplied by the resistance in ohms) and

$$R = \frac{E}{I}$$

(or, the resistance of the circuit is equal to the applied voltage divided by the current).

All three forms of the equation are used almost constantly in radio work. It must be remembered that the quantities are in *volts, ohms* and *amperes;* other units cannot be used in the equations without first being converted. For example, if the current is in milliamperes it must be changed to the equivalent fraction of an ampere before the value can be substituted in the equations.

Table 2-II shows how to convert between the various units in common use. The prefixes attached to the basic-unit name indicate the nature of the unit. These prefixes are:

micro — one-millionth (abbreviated μ)
milli — one-thousandth (abbreviated m)
kilo — one thousand (abbreviated k)
mega — one million (abbreviated M)

For example, one microvolt is one-millionth of a volt, and one megohm is 1,000,000 ohms. There are therefore 1,000,000 microvolts in one volt, and 0.000001 megohm in one ohm.

The following examples illustrate the use of Ohm's Law:

The current flowing in a resistance of 20,000 ohms is 150 milliamperes. What is the voltage? Since the voltage is to be found, the equation to use is $E = IR$. The current must first be converted from milliamperes to amperes, and reference to the table shows that to do so it is necessary to divide by 1000. Therefore,

$$E = \frac{150}{1000} \times 20,000 = 3000 \text{ volts}$$

When a voltage of 150 is applied to a circuit the current is measured at 2.5 amperes. What is the resistance of the circuit? In this case R is the unknown, so

$$R = \frac{E}{I} = \frac{150}{2.5} = 60 \text{ ohms}$$

No conversion was necessary because the voltage and current were given in volts and amperes.

How much current will flow if 250 volts is applied to a 5000-ohm resistor? Since I is unknown

$$I = \frac{E}{R} = \frac{250}{5000} = 0.05 \text{ ampere}$$

Milliampere units would be more convenient for the current, and 0.05 amp. $\times$ 1000 = 50 milliamperes.

SERIES AND PARALLEL RESISTANCES

Very few actual electric circuits are as simple as the illustration in the preceding section. Commonly, resistances are found connected in a

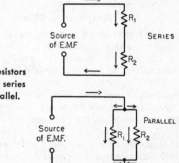

Fig. 2-4—Resistors connected in series and in parallel.

variety of ways. The two fundamental methods of connecting resistances are shown in Fig. 2-4. In the upper drawing, the current flows from the source of e.m.f. (in the direction shown by the arrow, let us say) down through the first resistance, R_1, then through the second, R_2, and then back to the source. These resistors are connected in **series**. The current everywhere in the circuit has the same value.

In the lower drawing the current flows to the common connection point at the top of the two resistors and then divides, one part of it flowing through R_1 and the other through R_2. At the lower connection point these two currents again combine; the total is the same as the current that flowed into the upper common connection. In this case the two resistors are connected in **parallel**.

Resistors in Series

When a circuit has a number of resistances connected in series, the total resistance of the circuit is the sum of the individual resistances. If these are numbered R_1, R_2, R_3, etc., then

$$R \text{ (total)} = R_1 + R_2 + R_3 + R_4 + \ldots \ldots$$

where the dots indicate that as many resistors as necessary may be added.

Example: Suppose that three resistors are connected to a source of e.m.f. as shown in Fig. 2-5. The e.m.f. is 250 volts, R_1 is 5000 ohms, R_2 is 20,000 ohms, and R_3 is 8000 ohms. The total resistance is then

$$R = R_1 + R_2 + R_3 = 5000 + 20,000 + 8000$$
$$= 33,000 \text{ ohms}$$

The current flowing in the circuit is then

$$I = \frac{E}{R} = \frac{250}{33,000} = 0.00757 \text{ amp.} = 7.57 \text{ ma.}$$

(We need not carry calculations beyond three significant figures, and often two will suffice because the accuracy of measurements is seldom better than a few per cent.)

Voltage Drop

Ohm's Law applies to *any part* of a circuit as well as to the whole circuit. Although the current is the same in all three of the resistances in the example, the total voltage divides among them. The voltage appearing across each resistor (the **voltage drop**) can be found from Ohm's Law.

Example: If the voltage across R_1 (Fig. 2-5) is called E_1, that across R_2 is called E_2, and that across R_3 is called E_3, then

$$E_1 = IR_1 = 0.00757 \times 5000 = 37.9 \text{ volts}$$
$$E_2 = IR_2 = 0.00757 \times 20,000 = 151.4 \text{ volts}$$
$$E_3 = IR_3 = 0.00757 \times 8000 = 60.6 \text{ volts}$$

The applied voltage must equal the sum of the individual voltage drops:

$$E = E_1 + E_2 + E_3 = 37.9 + 151.4 + 60.6$$
$$= 249.9 \text{ volts}$$

The answer would have been more nearly exact if the current had been calculated to more decimal places, but as explained above a very high order of accuracy is not necessary.

In problems such as this considerable time and trouble can be saved, when the current is small enough to be expressed in milliamperes, if the

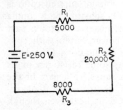

Fig. 2-5—An example of resistors in series. The solution of the circuit is worked out in the text.

resistance is expressed in kilohms rather than ohms. When resistance in kilohms is substituted directly in Ohm's Law the current will be in milliamperes if the e.m.f. is in volts.

Resistors in Parallel

In a circuit with resistances in parallel, the total resistance is *less* than that of the *lowest* value of resistance present. This is because the total current is always greater than the current in any individual resistor. The formula for finding the total resistance of resistances in parallel is

$$R = \frac{1}{\dfrac{1}{R_1} + \dfrac{1}{R_2} + \dfrac{1}{R_3} + \dfrac{1}{R_4} + \ldots \ldots}$$

where the dots again indicate that any number

of resistors can be combined by the same method. For only two resistances in parallel (a very common case) the formula becomes

$$R = \frac{R_1 R_2}{R_1 + R_2}$$

Example: If a 500-ohm resistor is paralleled with one of 1200 ohms, the total resistance is

$$R = \frac{R_1 R_2}{R_1 + R_2} = \frac{500 \times 1200}{500 + 1200} = \frac{600,000}{1700}$$
$$= 353 \text{ ohms}$$

It is probably easier to solve practical problems by a different method than the "reciprocal of reciprocals" formula. Suppose the three re-

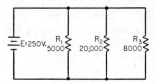

Fig. 2-6—An example of resistors in parallel. The solution is worked out in the text.

sistors of the previous example are connected in parallel as shown in Fig. 2-6. The same e.m.f., 250 volts, is applied to all three of the resistors. The current in each can be found from Ohm's Law as shown below, I_1 being the current through R_1, I_2 the current through R_2 and I_3 the current through R_3.

For convenience, the resistance will be expressed in kilohms so the current will be in milliamperes.

$$I_1 = \frac{E}{R_1} = \frac{250}{5} = 50 \text{ ma.}$$

$$I_2 = \frac{E}{R_2} = \frac{250}{20} = 12.5 \text{ ma.}$$

$$I_3 = \frac{E}{R_3} = \frac{250}{8} = 31.25 \text{ ma.}$$

The total current is

$$I = I_1 + I_2 + I_3 = 50 + 12.5 + 31.25$$
$$= 93.75 \text{ ma.}$$

The total resistance of the circuit is therefore

$$R = \frac{E}{I} = \frac{250}{93.75} = 2.66 \text{ kilohms (= 2660 ohms)}$$

Resistors in Series-Parallel

An actual circuit may have resistances both in parallel and in series. To illustrate, we use the same three resistances again, but now connected as in Fig. 2-7. The method of solving a circuit such as Fig. 2-7 is as follows: Consider R_2 and R_3 in parallel as though they formed a single resistor. Find their equivalent resistance. Then this resistance in series with R_1 forms a simple series circuit, as shown at the right in Fig. 2-7. An example of the arithmetic is given under the illustration.

Using the same principles, and staying within the practical limits, a value for R_2 can be computed that will provide a given voltage drop across R_3 or a given current through R_1. Simple algebra is required.

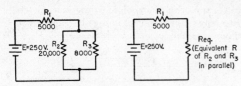

Fig. 2-7—An example of resistors in series-parallel. The equivalent circuit is at the right. The solution is worked out in the text.

Example: The first step is to find the equivalent resistance of R_2 and R_3. From the formula for two resistances in parallel,

$$R_{eq.} = \frac{R_2 R_3}{R_2 + R_3} = \frac{20 \times 8}{20 + 8} = \frac{160}{28}$$
$$= 5.71 \text{ kilohms}$$

The total resistance in the circuit is then

$$R = R_1 + R_{eq.} = 5 + 5.71 \text{ kilohms}$$
$$= 10.71 \text{ kilohms}$$

The current is

$$I = \frac{E}{R} = \frac{250}{10.71} = 23.3 \text{ ma.}$$

The voltage drops across R_1 and $R_{eq.}$ are

$$E_1 = IR_1 = 23.3 \times 5 = 117 \text{ volts}$$
$$E_2 = IR_{eq.} = 23.3 \times 5.71 = 133 \text{ volts}$$

with sufficient accuracy. These total 250 volts, thus checking the calculations so far, because the sum of the voltage drops must equal the applied voltage. Since E_2 appears across both R_2 and R_3,

$$I_2 = \frac{E_2}{R_2} = \frac{133}{20} = 6.65 \text{ ma.}$$

$$I_3 = \frac{E_2}{R_3} = \frac{133}{8} = 16.6 \text{ ma.}$$

where I_2 = Current through R_2
       I_3 = Current through R_3

The total is 23.25 ma., which checks closely enough with 23.3 ma., the current through the whole circuit.

POWER AND ENERGY

Power—the rate of doing work—is equal to voltage multiplied by current. The unit of electrical power, called the **watt,** is equal to one volt multiplied by one ampere. The equation for power therefore is

$$P = EI$$

where P = Power in watts
      E = E.m.f. in volts
      I = Current in amperes

Common fractional and multiple units for power are the **milliwatt,** one one-thousandth of a watt, and the **kilowatt,** or one thousand watts.

Example: The plate voltage on a transmitting vacuum tube is 2000 volts and the plate current is 350 milliamperes. (The current must be changed to amperes before substitution in the formula, and so is 0.35 amp.) Then

$$P = EI = 2000 \times 0.35 = 700 \text{ watts}$$

By substituting the Ohm's Law equivalents for E and I, the following formulas are obtained for power:

$$P = \frac{E^2}{R}$$

$$P = I^2 R$$

These formulas are useful in power calculations when the resistance and either the current or voltage (but not both) are known.

Example: How much power will be used up in a 4000-ohm resistor if the voltage applied to it is 200 volts? From the equation

$$P = \frac{E^2}{R} = \frac{(200)^2}{4000} = \frac{40,000}{4000} = 10 \text{ watts}$$

Or, suppose a current of 20 milliamperes flows through a 300-ohm resistor. Then

$$P = I^2 R = (0.02)^2 \times 300 = 0.0004 \times 300$$
$$= 0.12 \text{ watt}$$

Note that the current was changed from milliamperes to amperes before substitution in the formula.

Electrical power in a resistance is turned into heat. The greater the power the more rapidly the heat is generated. Resistors for radio work are made in many sizes, the smallest being rated to "dissipate" (or carry safely) about ¼ watt. The largest resistors used in amateur equipment will dissipate about 100 watts.

Generalized Definition of Resistance

Electrical power is not always turned into heat. The power used in running a motor, for example, is converted to mechanical motion. The power supplied to a radio transmitter is largely converted into radio waves. Power applied to a loudspeaker is changed into sound waves. But in every case of this kind the power is completely "used up"—it cannot be recovered. Also, for proper operation of the device the power must be supplied at a definite ratio of voltage to current. Both these features are characteristics of resistance, so it can be said that any device that dissipates power has a definite value of "resistance." This concept of resistance as something that absorbs power at a definite voltage/current ratio is very useful, since it permits substituting a simple resistance for the **load** or power-consuming part of the device receiving power, often with considerable simplification of calculations. Of course, every electrical device has some resistance of its own in the more narrow sense, so a part of the power supplied to it is dissipated in that resistance and hence appears as heat even though the major part of the power may be converted to another form.

Efficiency

In devices such as motors and vacuum tubes, the object is to obtain power in some other form than heat. Therefore power used in heating is considered to be a loss, because it is not the *useful* power. The **efficiency** of a device is the useful power output (in its converted form) divided by the power input to the device. In a vacuum-tube transmitter, for example, the object is to convert power from a d.c. source into a.c. power at some radio frequency. The ratio of the r.f. power output to the d.c. input is the efficiency of the tube. That is,

$$Eff. = \frac{P_o}{P_i}$$

where $Eff.$ = Efficiency (as a decimal)
  P_o = Power output (watts)
  P_1 = Power input (watts)

Example: If the d.c. input to the tube is 100 watts and the r.f. power output is 60 watts, the efficiency is

$$Eff. = \frac{P_o}{P_1} = \frac{60}{100} = 0.6$$

Efficiency is usually expressed as a percentage; that is, it tells what per cent of the input power will be available as useful output. The efficiency in the above example is 60 per cent.

Energy

In residences, the power company's bill is for electric **energy**, not for power. What you pay for is the *work* that electricity does for you, not the *rate* at which that work is done. Electrical work is equal to power multiplied by time; the common unit is the **watt-hour**, which means that a power of one watt has been used for one hour. That is,

$$W = PT$$

where W = Energy in watt-hours
  P = Power in watts
  T = Time in hours

Other energy units are the **kilowatt-hour** and the **watt-second.** These units should be self-explanatory.

Energy units are seldom used in amateur practice, but it is obvious that a small amount of power used for a long time can eventually result in a "power" bill that is just as large as though a large amount of power had been used for a very short time.

CAPACITANCE

Suppose two flat metal plates are placed close to each other (but not touching) and are connected to a battery through a switch, as shown in Fig. 2-8. At the instant the switch is closed, electrons will be attracted from the upper plate to the positive terminal of the battery, and the same number will be repelled into the lower plate from

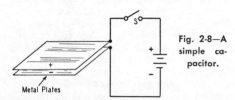

Metal Plates

Fig. 2-8—A simple capacitor.

the negative battery terminal. Enough electrons move into one plate and out of the other to make the e.m.f. between them the same as the e.m.f. of the battery.

If the switch is opened after the plates have been **charged** in this way, the top plate is left with a deficiency of electrons and the bottom plate with an excess. The plates remain charged despite the fact that the battery no longer is connected. However, if a wire is touched between the two plates (**short-circuiting** them) the excess electrons on the bottom plate will flow through the wire to the upper plate, thus restoring electrical neutrality. The plates have then been **discharged.**

The two plates constitute an electrical **capacitor**; a capacitor possesses the property of storing electricity. (The energy actually is stored in the electric field between the plates.) During the time the electrons are moving—that is, while the capacitor is being charged or discharged—a current is flowing in the circuit even though the circuit is "broken" by the gap between the capacitor plates. However, the current flows only during the time of charge and discharge, and this time is usually very short. There can be no continuous flow of direct current "through" a capacitor, but an alternating current can pass through easily if the frequency is high enough.

The **charge** or quantity of electricity that can be placed on a capacitor is proportional to the applied voltage and to the **capacitance** of the capacitor. The larger the plate area and the smaller the spacing between the plate the greater the capacitance. The capacitance also depends upon the kind of insulating material between the plates; it is smallest with air insulation, but substitution of other insulating materials for air may increase the capacitance many times. The ratio of the capacitance with some material other than air between the plates, to the capacitance of the same capacitor with air insulation, is called the **dielectric constant** of that particular insulating material. The material itself is called a **dielectric.** The dielectric constants of a number of materials commonly used as dielectrics in capacitors are

Table 2-III

Dielectric Constants and Breakdown Voltages

Material	Dielectric Constant *	Puncture Voltage **
Air	1.0	
Alsimag 196	5.7	240
Bakelite	4.4–5.4	300
Bakelite, mica-filled	4.7	325–375
Cellulose acetate	3.3–3.9	250–600
Fiber	5–7.5	150–180
Formica	4.6–4.9	450
Glass, window	7.6–8	200–250
Glass, Pyrex	4.8	335
Mica, ruby	5.4	3800–5600
Mycalex	7.4	250
Paper, Royalgrey	3.0	200
Plexiglass	2.8	990
Polyethylene	2.3	1200
Polystyrene	2.6	500–700
Porcelain	5.1–5.9	40–100
Quartz, fused	3.8	1000
Steatite, low-loss	5.8	150–315
Teflon	2.1	1000–2000

* At 1 Mc. ** In volts per mil (0.001 inch)

given in Table 2-III. If a sheet of polystyrene is substituted for air between the plates of a capacitor, for example, the capacitance will be increased 2.6 times.

Units

The fundamental unit of capacitance is the **farad**, but this unit is much too large for practical work. Capacitance is usually measured in **microfarads** (abbreviated μf.) or **picofarads** (pf.). The microfarad is one-millionth of a farad,

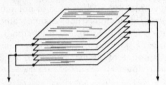

Fig. 2-9—A multiple-plate capacitor. Alternate plates are connected together.

and the picofarad (formerly micromicrofarad) is one-millionth of a microfarad. Capacitors nearly always have more than two plates, the alternate plates being connected together to form two sets as shown in Fig. 2-9. This makes it possible to attain a fairly large capacitance in a small space, since several plates of smaller individual area can be stacked to form the equivalent of a single large plate of the same total area. Also, all plates, except the two on the ends, are exposed to plates of the other group on *both sides,* and so are twice as effective in increasing the capacitance.

The formula for calculating capacitance is:

$$C = 0.224 \frac{KA}{d} (n - 1)$$

where C = Capacitance in pf.
    K = Dielectric constant of material between plates
    A = Area of one side of *one* plate in square inches
    d = Separation of plate surfaces in inches
    n = Number of plates

If the plates in one group do not have the same area as the plates in the other, use the area of the *smaller* plates.

Capacitors in Radio

The types of capacitors used in radio work differ considerably in physical size, construction, and capacitance. Some representative types are shown in the photograph. In **variable** capacitors (almost always constructed with air for the dielectric) one set of plates is made movable with respect to the other set so that the capacitance can be varied. **Fixed** capacitors—that is, assemblies having a single, non-adjustable value of capacitance—also can be made with metal plates and with air as the dielectric, but usually are constructed from plates of metal foil with a thin solid or liquid dielectric sandwiched in between, so that a relatively large capacitance can be secured in a small unit. The solid dielectrics commonly used are mica, paper and special ceramics. An example of a liquid dielectric is mineral oil. The **electrolytic** capacitor uses aluminum-foil plates with a semiliquid conducting chemical compound between them; the actual dielectric is a very thin film of insulating material that forms on one set of plates through electrochemical action when a d.c. voltage is applied to the capacitor. The capacitance obtained with a given plate area in an electrolytic capacitor is very large, compared with capacitors having other dielectrics, because the film is so thin—much less than any thickness that is practicable with a solid dielectric.

The use of electrolytic and oil-filled capacitors is confined to power-supply filtering and audio bypass applications. Mica and ceramic capacitors are used throughout the frequency range from audio to several hundred megacycles.

Voltage Breakdown

When a high voltage is applied to the plates of a capacitor, a considerable force is exerted on the electrons and nuclei of the dielectric. Because the dielectric is an insulator the electrons do not become detached from atoms the way they do in conductors. However, if the force is great enough the dielectric will "break down"; usually it will puncture and may char (if it is solid) and permit current to flow. The **breakdown voltage** depends upon the kind and thickness of the dielectric, as shown in Table 2-III. It is not directly proportional to the thickness; that is, doubling

Fixed and variable capacitors. The large unit at the left is a transmitting-type variable capacitor for r.f. tank circuits. To its right are other air-dielectric variables of different sizes ranging from the midget "air padder" to the medium-power tank capacitor at the top center. The cased capacitors in the top row are for power-supply filters, the cylindrical-can unit being an electrolytic and the rectangular one a paper-dielectric capacitor. Various types of mica, ceramic, and paper-dielectric capacitors are in the foreground.

the thickness does not quite double the breakdown voltage. If the dielectric is air or any other gas, breakdown is evidenced by a spark or arc between the plates, but if the voltage is removed the arc ceases and the capacitor is ready for use again. Breakdown will occur at a lower voltage between pointed or sharp-edged surfaces than between rounded and polished surfaces; consequently, the breakdown voltage between metal plates of given spacing in air can be increased by buffing the edges of the plates.

Since the dielectric must be thick to withstand high voltages, and since the thicker the dielectric the smaller the capacitance for a given plate area, a high-voltage capacitor must have more plate area than a low-voltage one of the same capacitance. High-voltage high-capacitance capacitors are physically large.

CAPACITORS IN SERIES AND PARALLEL

The terms "parallel" and "series" when used with reference to capacitors have the same circuit meaning as with resistances. When a number of capacitors are connected in parallel, as in Fig. 2-10, the total capacitance of the group is equal to the sum of the individual capacitances, so

$$C \text{ (total)} = C_1 + C_2 + C_3 + C_4 + \cdots\cdots\cdots$$

However, if two or more capacitors are connected in series, as in the second drawing, the total capacitance is less than that of the smallest capacitor in the group. The rule for finding the capacitance of a number of series-connected capacitors is the same as that for finding the resistance of a number of *parallel*-connected resistors. That is,

$$C \text{ (total)} = \frac{1}{\frac{1}{C_1} + \frac{1}{C_2} + \frac{1}{C_3} + \frac{1}{C_4} + \cdots\cdots\cdots}$$

and, for only two capacitors in series,

$$C \text{ (total)} = \frac{C_1 C_2}{C_1 + C_2}$$

The same units must be used throughout; that is, all capacitances must be expressed in either $\mu f.$ or pf.; both kinds of units cannot be used in the same equation.

Capacitors are connected in parallel to obtain a larger total capacitance than is available in one unit. The largest voltage that can be applied safely to a group of capacitors in parallel is the voltage that can be applied safely to the one having the *lowest* voltage rating.

When capacitors are connected in series, the applied voltage is divided up among them; the situation is much the same as when resistors are in series and there is a voltage drop across each. However, the voltage that appears across each capacitor of a group connected in series is in

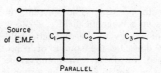

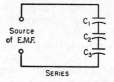

Fig. 2-10—Capacitors in parallel and in series.

inverse proportion to its capacitance, as compared with the capacitance of the whole group.

Example: Three capacitors having capacitances of 1, 2, and 4 $\mu f.$, respectively, are connected in series as shown in Fig. 2-11. The total capacitance is

$$C = \frac{1}{\frac{1}{C_1} + \frac{1}{C_2} + \frac{1}{C_3}} = \frac{1}{\frac{1}{1} + \frac{1}{2} + \frac{1}{4}} = \frac{1}{\frac{7}{4}} = \frac{4}{7}$$
$$= 0.571 \ \mu f.$$

The voltage across each capacitor is proportional to the *total* capacitance divided by the capacitance of the capacitor in question, so the voltage across C_1 is

$$E_1 = \frac{0.571}{1} \times 2000 = 1142 \text{ volts}$$

Similarly, the voltages across C_2 and C_3 are

$$E_2 = \frac{0.571}{2} \times 2000 = 571 \text{ volts}$$
$$E_3 = \frac{0.571}{4} \times 2000 = 286 \text{ volts}$$

totaling approximately 2000 volts, the applied voltage.

Capacitors are frequently connected in series to enable the group to withstand a larger voltage (at the expense of decreased total capacitance) than any individual capacitor is rated to stand. However, as shown by the previous example, the applied voltage does not divide equally among the capacitors (except when all the capacitances are the same) so care must be taken to see that the voltage rating of no capacitor in the group is exceeded.

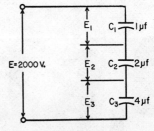

Fig. 2-11—An example of capacitors connected in series. The solution to this arrangement is worked out in the text.

INDUCTANCE

It is possible to show that the flow of current through a conductor is accompanied by magnetic effects; a compass needle brought near the conductor, for example, will be deflected from its normal north-south position. The current, in other words, sets up a magnetic field.

The transfer of energy to the magnetic field represents work done by the source of e.m.f. Power is required for doing work, and since power is equal to current multiplied by voltage, there must be a voltage drop in the circuit during the time in which energy is being stored in the field. This voltage "drop" (which has nothing to do with the voltage drop in any resistance in the circuit) is the result of an opposing voltage "induced" in the circuit while the field is building up to its final value. When the field becomes constant the **induced e.m.f.** or **back e.m.f.** disappears, since no further energy is being stored.

Since the induced e.m.f. opposes the e.m.f. of the source, it tends to prevent the current from rising rapidly when the circuit is closed. The amplitude of the induced e.m.f. is proportional to the rate at which the current is changing and to a constant associated with the circuit itself, called the **inductance** of the circuit.

Inductance depends on the physical characteristics of the conductor. If the conductor is formed into a coil, for example, its inductance is increased. A coil of many turns will have more inductance than one of few turns, if both coils are otherwise physically similar. Also, if a coil is placed on an iron core its inductance will be greater than it was without the magnetic core.

The polarity of an induced e.m.f. is always such as to oppose any change in the current in the circuit. This means that when the current in the circuit is increasing, work is being done against the induced e.m.f. by storing energy in the magnetic field. If the current in the circuit tends to decrease, the stored energy of the field returns to the circuit, and thus adds to the energy being supplied by the source of e.m.f. This tends to keep the current flowing even though the applied e.m.f. may be decreasing or be removed entirely.

The unit of inductance is the **henry.** Values of inductance used in radio equipment vary over a wide range. Inductance of several henrys is required in power-supply circuits (see chapter on Power Supplies) and to obtain such values of inductance it is necessary to use coils of many turns wound on iron cores. In radio-frequency circuits, the inductance values used will be measured in **millihenrys** (a **mh.**, one one-thousandth of a henry) at low frequencies, and in **microhenrys** (**µh.**, one one-millionth of a henry) at medium frequencies and higher. Although coils for radio frequencies may be wound on special iron cores (ordinary iron is not suitable) most r.f. coils made and used by amateurs are of the "air-core" type; that is, wound on an insulating support consisting of nonmagnetic material.

Every conductor has inductance, even though the conductor is not formed into a coil. The inductance of a short length of straight wire is small, but it may not be negligible because if the current through it changes its intensity rapidly enough the induced voltage may be appreciable. This will be the case in even a few inches of wire when an alternating current having a frequency of the order of 100 Mc. or higher is flowing. However, at much lower frequencies the inductance of the same wire could be ignored because the induced voltage would be negligibly small.

Calculating Inductance

The approximate inductance of single-layer air-core coils may be calculated from the simplified formula

$$L \ (\mu h.) = \frac{a^2 n^2}{9a + 10b}$$

where $L =$ Inductance in microhenrys
    $a =$ Coil radius in inches
    $b =$ Coil length in inches
    $n =$ Number of turns

The notation is explained in Fig. 2-12. This

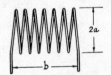

Fig. 2-12—Coil dimensions used in the inductance formula. The wire diameter does not enter into the formula.

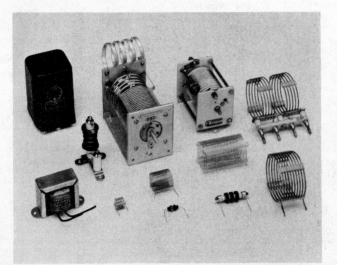

Inductors for power and radio frequencies. The two iron-core coils at the left are "chokes" for power-supply filters. The mounted air-core coils at the top center are adjustable inductors for transmitting tank circuits. The "pie-wound" coils at the left and in the foreground are radio-frequency choke coils. The remaining coils are typical of inductors used in r.f. tuned circuits, the larger sizes being used principally for transmitters.

formula is a close approximation for coils having a length equal to or greater than 0.8a.

> Example: Assume a coil having 48 turns wound 32 turns per inch and a diameter of ¾ inch. Thus $a = 0.75 \div 2 = 0.375$, $b = 48 \div 32 = 1.5$, and $n = 48$. Substituting,
>
> $$L = \frac{.375 \times .375 \times 48 \times 48}{(9 \times .375) + (10 \times 1.5)} = 17.6 \ \mu h.$$

To calculate the number of turns of a single-layer coil for a required value of inductance,

$$n = \sqrt{\frac{L \ (9a + 10b)}{a^2}}$$

> Example: Suppose an inductance of 10μh. is required. The form on which the coil is to be wound has a diameter of one inch and is long enough to accommodate a coil of 1¼ inches. Then $a = 0.5$, $b = 1.25$, and $L = 10$. Substituting,
>
> $$n = \sqrt{\frac{10 \ (4.5 + 12.5)}{.5 \times .5}} = \sqrt{680} = 26.1 \text{ turns}$$
>
> A 26-turn coil would be close enough in practical work. Since the coil will be 1.25 inches long, the number of turns per inch will be $26.1 \div 1.25 = 20.8$. Consulting the wire table, we find that No. 17 enameled wire (or anything smaller) can be used. The proper inductance is obtained by winding the required number of turns on the form and then adjusting the spacing between the turns to make a uniformly-spaced coil 1.25 inches long.

Inductance Charts

Most inductance formulas lose accuracy when applied to small coils (such as are used in v.h.f. work and in low-pass filters built for reducing harmonic interference to television) because the conductor thickness is no longer negligible in comparison with the size of the coil. Fig. 2-13 shows the measured inductance of v.h.f. coils, and may be used as a basis for circuit design. Two curves are given: curve A is for coils wound to an inside diameter of ½ inch; curve B is for coils of ¾-inch inside diameter. In both curves the wire size is No. 12, winding pitch 8 turns to the inch (⅛ inch center-to-center turn spacing). The inductance values given include leads ½ inch long.

The charts of Figs. 2-14 and 2-15 are useful for rapid determination of the inductance of coils of the type commonly used in radio-frequency circuits in the range 3-30 Mc. They are of sufficient accuracy for most practical work. Given the coil length in inches, the curves show the multiplying factor to be applied to the inductance value given in the table below the curve for a coil of the same diameter and number of turns per inch.

> Example: A coil 1 inch in diameter is 1¼ inches long and has 20 turns. Therefore it has 16 turns per inch, and from the table under Fig. 2-15 it is found that the reference inductance for a coil of this diameter and number of turns per inch is 16.8 μh. From curve B in the figure the multiplying factor is 0.35, so the inductance is
>
> $$16.8 \times 0.35 = 5.9 \ \mu h.$$

The charts also can be used for finding suitable dimensions for a coil having a required value of inductance.

> Example: A coil having an inductance of 12 μh. is required. It is to be wound on a form having a diameter of 1 inch, the length available for the winding being not more than 1¼ inches. From Fig. 2-15, the multiplying factor for a 1-inch diameter coil (curve B) having the maximum possible length of 1¼ inches is 0.35. Hence the number of turns per inch must be chosen for a reference inductance of at least 12/0.35, or 34 μh. From the Table under Fig. 2-15 it is seen that 16 turns per inch (reference inductance 16.8 μh.) is too small. Using 32 turns per inch, the multiplying factor is 12/68, or 0.177, and from curve B this corresponds to a coil length of ¾ inch. There will be 24 turns in this length, since the winding "pitch" is 32 turns per inch.

Machine-wound coils with the diameters and turns per inch given in the tables are available in many radio stores, under the trade names of "B&W Miniductor" and "Illumitronic Air Dux."

IRON-CORE COILS

Permeability

Suppose that the coil in Fig. 2-16 is wound on an iron core having a cross-sectional area of 2 square inches. When a certain current is sent through the coil it is found that there are 80,000 lines of force in the core. Since the area is 2 square inches, the flux density is 40,000 lines per square inch. Now suppose that the iron core is removed and the same current is maintained in the coil, and that the flux density without the iron core is found to be 50 lines per square inch. The ratio of the flux density with the given core material to the flux density (with the same coil and same current) with an air core is called the **permeability** of the material. In this case the permeability of the iron is $40,000/50 = 800$. The inductance of the coil is increased 800 times by inserting the iron core since, other things being equal, the inductance will be proportional to the magnetic flux through the coil.

The permeability of a magnetic material varies with the flux density. At low flux densities (or with an air core) increasing the current through

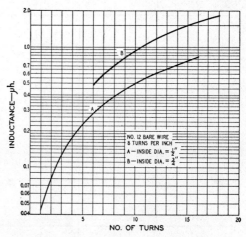

Fig. 2-13—Measured inductance of coils wound with No. 12 bare wire, 8 turns to the inch. The values include half-inch leads.

the coil will cause a proportionate increase in flux, but at very high flux densities, increasing the current may cause no appreciable change in the flux. When this is so, the iron is said to be **saturated**. Saturation causes a rapid decrease in permeability, because it decreases the ratio of flux lines to those obtainable with the same current and an air core. Obviously, the inductance of an iron-core inductor is highly dependent upon the current flowing in the coil. In an air-core coil, the inductance is independent of current because air does not saturate.

Iron core coils such as the one sketched in Fig. 2-16 are used chiefly in power-supply equipment. They usually have direct current flowing through the winding, and the variation in inductance with current is usually undesirable. It may be overcome by keeping the flux density below the saturation point of the iron. This is done by opening the core so that there is a small "air gap," as indicated by the dashed lines. The magnetic "resistance" introduced by such a gap is so large—even though the gap is only a small fraction of an inch—compared with that of the iron that the gap, rather than the iron, controls the

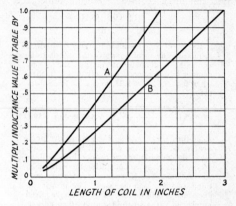

Fig. 2-15—Factor to be applied to the inductance of coils listed in the table below, as a function of coil length. Use curve A for coils marked A, curve B for coils marked **B**.

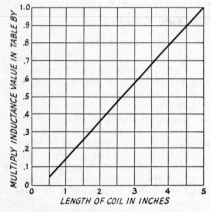

Fig. 2-14—Factor to be applied to the inductance of coils listed in the table below, for coil lengths up to 5 inches.

Coil diameter, Inches	No. of turns per inch	Inductance in µh.
1¼	4	2.75
	6	6.3
	8	11.2
	10	17.5
	16	42.5
1½	4	3.9
	6	8.8
	8	15.6
	10	24.5
	16	63
1¾	4	5.2
	6	11.8
	8	21
	10	33
	16	85
2	4	6.6
	6	15
	8	26.5
	10	42
	16	108
2½	4	10.2
	6	23
	8	41
	10	64
3	4	14
	6	31.5
	8	56
	10	89

Coil diameter, Inches	No. of turns per inch	Inductance in µh.
½ (A)	4	0.18
	6	0.40
	8	0.72
	10	1.12
	16	2.9
	32	12
⅝ (A)	4	0.28
	6	0.62
	8	1.1
	10	1.7
	16	4.4
	32	18
¾ (B)	4	0.6
	6	1.35
	8	2.4
	10	3.8
	16	9.9
	32	40
1 (B)	4	1.0
	6	2.3
	8	4.2
	10	6.6
	16	16.8
	32	68

flux density. This reduces the inductance, but makes it practically constant regardless of the value of the current.

Eddy Currents and Hysteresis

When alternating current flows through a coil wound on an iron core an e.m.f. will be induced, as previously explained, and since iron is a conductor a current will flow in the core. Such currents (called **eddy currents**) represent a waste

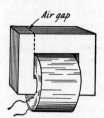

Fig. 2-16—Typical construction of an iron-core inductor. The small air gap prevents magnetic saturation of the iron and thus maintains the inductance at high currents.

of power because they flow through the resistance of the iron and thus cause heating. Eddy-current losses can be reduced by **laminating** the core; that is, by cutting it into thin strips. These strips or **laminations** must be insulated from each other by painting them with some insulating material such as varnish or shellac.

There is also another type of energy loss: the iron tends to resist any change in its magnetic state, so a rapidly-changing current such as a.c. is forced continually to supply energy to the iron to overcome this "inertia." Losses of this sort are called **hysteresis** losses.

Eddy-current and hysteresis losses in iron increase rapidly as the frequency of the alternating current is increased. For this reason, ordinary iron cores can be used only at power and audio frequencies—up to, say, 15,000 cycles. Even so, a very good grade of iron or steel is necessary if the core is to perform well at the higher audio frequencies. Iron cores of this type are completely useless at radio frequencies.

For radio-frequency work, the losses in iron cores can be reduced to a satisfactory figure by grinding the iron into a powder and then mixing it with a "binder" of insulating material in such a way that the individual iron particles are insulated from each other. By this means cores can be made that will function satisfactorily even through the v.h.f. range—that is, at frequencies up to perhaps 100 Mc. Because a large part of the magnetic path is through a nonmagnetic material, the permeability of the iron is low compared with the values obtained at power-supply frequencies. The core is usually in the form of a "slug" or cylinder which fits inside the insulating form on which the coil is wound. Despite the fact that, with this construction, the major portion of the magnetic path for the flux is in air, the slug is quite effective in increasing the coil inductance. By pushing the slug in and out of the coil the inductance can be varied over a considerable range.

INDUCTANCES IN SERIES AND PARALLEL

When two or more inductors are connected in series (Fig. 2-17, left) the total inductance is equal to the sum of the individual inductances, *provided the coils are sufficiently separated so that no coil is in the magnetic field of another.* That is,

$$L_{total} = L_1 + L_2 + L_3 + L_4 + \ldots\ldots$$

If inductors are connected in parallel (Fig. 2-17, right)—and the coils are separated sufficiently,

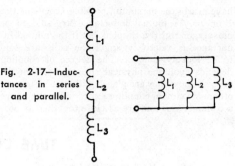

Fig. 2-17—Inductances in series and parallel.

the total inductance is given by

$$L_{total} = \cfrac{1}{\dfrac{1}{L_1} + \dfrac{1}{L_2} + \dfrac{1}{L_3} + \dfrac{1}{L_4} + \ldots\ldots}$$

and for two inductances in parallel,

$$L = \frac{L_1 L_2}{L_1 + L_2}$$

Thus the rules for combining inductances in series and parallel are the same as for resistances, *if* the coils are far enough apart so that each is unaffected by another's magnetic field. When this is not so the formulas given above cannot be used.

MUTUAL INDUCTANCE

If two coils are arranged with their axes on the same line, as shown in Fig. 2-18, a current sent through Coil 1 will cause a magnetic field which "cuts" Coil 2. Consequently, an e.m.f. will be induced in Coil 2 whenever the field strength is changing. This induced e.m.f. is similar to the e.m.f. of self-induction, but since it appears in the *second* coil because of current flowing in the *first*, it is a "mutual" effect and results from the **mutual inductance** between the two coils.

If all the flux set up by one coil cuts all the turns of the other coil the mutual inductance has its maximum possible value. If only a small part of the flux set up by one coil cuts the turns of the other the mutual inductance is relatively small. Two coils having mutual inductance are said to be **coupled.**

The ratio of actual mutual inductance to the maximum possible value that could theoretically be obtained with two given coils is called the **coefficient of coupling** between the coils. It is frequently expressed as a percentage. Coils that

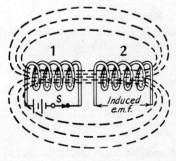

Fig. 2-18—Mutual inductance. When the switch, S, is closed current flows through coil No. 1, setting up a magnetic field that induces an e.m.f. in the turns of coil No. 2.

have nearly the maximum possible (coefficient = 1 or 100%) mutual inductance are said to be **closely,** or **tightly,** coupled, but if the mutual inductance is relatively small the coils are said to be **loosely** coupled. The degree of coupling depends upon the physical spacing between the coils and how they are placed with respect to each other. Maximum coupling exists when they have a common axis and are as close together as pos-

sible (one wound over the other). The coupling is least when the coils are far apart or are placed so their axes are at right angles.

The maximum possible coefficient of coupling is closely approached only when the two coils are wound on a closed iron core. The coefficient with air-core coils may run as high as 0.6 or 0.7 if one coil is wound over the other, but will be much less if the two coils are separated.

TIME CONSTANT

Capacitance and Resistance

Connecting a source of e.m.f. to a capacitor causes the capacitor to become charged to the full e.m.f. practically instantaneously, if there is no resistance in the circuit. However, if the circuit contains resistance, as in Fig. 2-19A, the resistance limits the current flow and an appreciable length of time is required for the e.m.f. between the capacitor plates to build up to the same value as the e.m.f. of the source. During this "building-up" period the current gradually decreases from its initial value, because the increasing e.m.f. stored on the capacitor offers increasing opposition to the steady e.m.f. of the source.

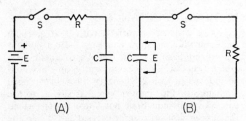

Fig. 2-19—Illustrating the time constant of an RC circuit.

Theoretically, the charging process is never really finished, but eventually the charging current drops to a value that is smaller than anything that can be measured. The **time constant** of such a circuit is the length of time, in seconds, required for the voltage across the capacitor to reach 63 per cent of the applied e.m.f. (this figure is chosen for mathematical reasons). The voltage across the capacitor rises with time as shown by Fig. 2-20.

The formula for time constant is
$$T = RC$$
where T = Time constant in seconds
C = Capacitance in farads
R = Resistance in ohms

If C is in microfarads and R in megohms, the time constant also is in seconds. These units usually are more convenient.

> Example: The time constant of a 2-μf. capacitor and a 250,000-ohm (0.25 megohm) resistor is
> $$T = RC = 0.25 \times 2 = 0.5 \text{ second}$$
> If the applied e.m.f. is 1000 volts, the voltage between the capacitor plates will be 630 volts at the end of ½ second.

If a charged capacitor is *discharged* through a

resistor, as indicated in Fig. 2-19B, the same time constant applies. If there were no resistance, the capacitor would discharge instantly when S was closed. However, since R limits the current flow the capacitor voltage cannot instantly go to zero, but it will decrease just as rapidly as the capacitor can rid itself of its charge through R. When the capacitor is discharging through a resistance, the time constant (calculated in the same way as above) is the time, in seconds, that it takes for the capacitor to *lose* 63 per cent of its voltage; that is, for the voltage to drop to 37 per cent of its initial value.

> Example: If the capacitor of the example above is charged to 1000 volts, it will discharge to 370 volts in ½ second through the 250,000-ohm resistor.

Inductance and Resistance

A comparable situation exists when resistance and inductance are in series. In Fig. 2-21, first consider L to have no resistance and also assume that R is zero. Then closing S would tend to

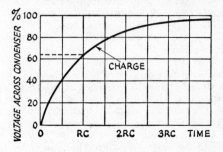

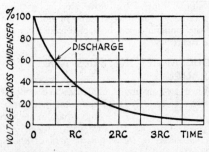

Fig. 2-20—How the voltage across a capacitor rises, with time, when charged through a resistor. The lower curve shows the way in which the voltage decreases across the capacitor terminals on discharging through the same resistor.

send a current through the circuit. However, the instantaneous transition from no current to a finite value, however small, represents a very rapid *change* in current, and a *back e.m.f.* is developed by the self-inductance of L that is practically equal and opposite to the applied e.m.f. The result is that the initial current is very small.

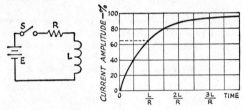

Fig. 2-21—Time constant of an LR circuit.

The back e.m.f. depends upon the *change* in current and would cease to offer opposition if the current did not continue to increase. With no resistance in the circuit (which would lead to an infinitely large current, by Ohm's Law) the current would increase forever, always growing just fast enough to keep the e.m.f. of self-induction equal to the applied e.m.f.

When resistance is in series, Ohm's Law sets a limit to the value that the current can reach. The back e.m.f. generated in L has only to equal the *difference* between E and the drop across R, because that difference is the voltage actually applied to L. This difference becomes smaller as the current approaches the final Ohm's Law value. Theoretically, the back e.m.f. never quite disappears and so the current never quite reaches the Ohm's Law value, but practically the difference becomes unmeasurable after a time. The time constant of an inductive circuit is the time in seconds required for the current to reach 63 per cent of its final value. The formula is

$$T = \frac{L}{R}$$

where T = Time constant in seconds

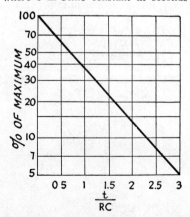

Fig. 2-22—Voltage across capacitor terminals in a discharging RC circuit, in terms of the initial charged voltage. To obtain time in seconds, multiply the factor t/RC by the time constant of the circuit.

L = Inductance in henrys
R = Resistance in ohms

The resistance of the wire in a coil acts as if it were in series with the inductance.

> Example: A coil having an inductance of 20 henrys and a resistance of 100 ohms has a time constant of
>
> $$T = \frac{L}{R} = \frac{20}{100} = 0.2 \text{ second}$$
>
> if there is no other resistance in the circuit. If a d.c. e.m.f. of 10 volts is applied to such a coil, the final current, by Ohm's Law, is
>
> $$I = \frac{E}{R} = \frac{10}{100} = 0.1 \text{ amp. or 100 ma.}$$
>
> The current would rise from zero to 63 milliamperes in 0.2 second after closing the switch.

An inductor cannot be "discharged" in the same way as a capacitor, because the magnetic field disappears as soon as current flow ceases. Opening S does not leave the inductor "charged." The energy stored in the magnetic field instantly returns to the circuit when S is opened. The rapid disappearance of the field causes a very large voltage to be induced in the coil—ordinarily many times larger than the voltage applied, because the induced voltage is proportional to the *speed* with which the field changes. The common result of opening the switch in a circuit such as the one shown is that a spark or arc forms at the switch contacts at the instant of opening. If the inductance is large and the current in the circuit is high, a great deal of energy is released in a very short period of time. It is not at all unusual for the switch contacts to burn or melt under such circumstances. The spark or arc at the opened switch can be reduced or suppressed by connecting a suitable capacitor and resistor in series across the contacts.

Time constants play an important part in numerous devices, such as electronic keys, timing and control circuits, and shaping of keying characteristics by vacuum tubes. The time constants of circuits are also important in such applications as automatic gain control and noise limiters. In nearly all such applications a resistance-capacitance (RC) time constant is involved, and it is usually necessary to know the voltage across the capacitor at some time interval larger or smaller than the actual time constant of the circuit as given by the formula above. Fig. 2-22 can be used for the solution of such problems, since the curve gives the voltage across the capacitor, in terms of percentage of the initial charge, for percentages between 5 and 100, at any time after discharge begins.

> Example: A 0.01-μf. capacitor is charged to 150 volts and then allowed to discharge through a 0.1-megohm resistor. How long will it take the voltage to fall to 10 volts? In percentage, $10/150 = 6.7\%$. From the chart, the factor corresponding to 6.7% is 2.7. The time constant of the circuit is equal to $RC = 0.1 \times 0.01 = 0.001$. The time is therefore $2.7 \times 0.001 = 0.0027$ second, or 2.7 milliseconds.

ALTERNATING CURRENTS

PHASE

The term **phase** essentially means "time," or the *time interval* between the instant when one thing occurs and the instant when a second related thing takes place. The later event is said to **lag** the earlier, while the one that occurs first is said to **lead**. In a.c. circuits the current amplitude changes continuously, so the concept of phase or time becomes important. Phase can be measured in the ordinary time units, such as the second, but there is a more convenient method: Since each a.c. cycle occupies exactly the same amount of time as every other cycle of the same frequency, we can use the cycle itself as the time unit. Using the cycle as the time unit makes the specification or measurement of phase independent of the frequency of the current, so long as only one frequency is under consideration at a time. When two or more frequencies are to be considered, as in the case where harmonics are present, the phase measurements are made with respect to the lowest, or fundamental, frequency.

The time interval or "phase difference" under consideration usually will be less than one cycle. Phase difference could be measured in decimal parts of a cycle, but it is more convenient to divide the cycle into 360 parts or **degrees**. A phase degree is therefore 1/360 of a cycle. The reason for this choice is that with sine-wave alternating current the value of the current at any instant is proportional to the sine of the angle that corresponds to the number of degrees—that is, length of time—from the instant the cycle began. There is no actual "angle" associated with an alternating current. Fig. 2-23 should help make this method of measurement clear.

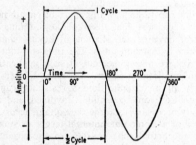

Fig. 2-23—An a.c. cycle is divided off into 360 degrees that are used as a measure of time or phase.

Measuring Phase

The phase difference between two currents of the same frequency is the time or angle difference between corresponding parts of cycles of the two currents. This is shown in Fig. 2-24. The current labeled *A* leads the one marked *B* by 45 degrees, since *A*'s cycles begin 45 degrees earlier in time. It is equally correct to say that *B lags A* by 45 degrees.

Two important special cases are shown in

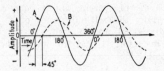

Fig. 2-24—When two waves of the same frequency start their cycles at slightly different times, the time difference or phase difference is measured in degrees. In this drawing wave B starts 45 degrees (one-eighth cycle) later than wave A, and so lags 45 degrees behind A.

Fig. 2-25. In the upper drawing *B* lags 90 degrees behind *A;* that is, its cycle begins just one-quarter cycle later than that of *A*. When one wave is passing through zero, the other is just at its maximum point.

In the lower drawing *A* and *B* are 180 degrees out of phase. In this case it does not matter which one is considered to lead or lag. *B* is always positive while *A* is negative, and vice versa. The two waves are thus *completely* out of phase.

The waves shown in Figs. 2-24 and 2-25 could represent current, voltage, or both. *A* and *B* might be two currents in separate circuits, or *A* might represent voltage and *B* current in the same circuit. If *A* and *B* represent two currents in the *same* circuit (or two voltages in the same circuit) the total or **resultant** current (or voltage) also is a sine wave, because adding any number of sine waves of the same frequency always gives a sine wave also of the same frequency.

Phase in Resistive Circuits

When an alternating voltage is applied to a resistance, the current flows exactly in step with the voltage. In other words, the voltage and current are **in phase**. This is true at any frequency if the resistance is "pure"—that is, is free from the reactive effects discussed in the next section. Practically, it is often difficult to obtain a purely

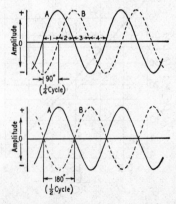

Fig. 2-25—Two important special cases of phase difference. In the upper drawing, the phase difference between A and B is 90 degrees; in the lower drawing the phase difference is 180 degrees.

resistive circuit at radio frequencies, because the reactive effects become more pronounced as the frequency is increased.

In a purely resistive circuit, or for purely resistive parts of circuits, Ohm's Law is just as valid for a.c. of any frequency as it is for d.c.

REACTANCE

Alternating Current in Capacitance

In Fig. 2-26 a sine-wave a.c. voltage having a maximum value of 100 volts is applied to a capacitor. In the period OA, the applied voltage increases from zero to 38 volts; at the end of this period the capacitor is charged to that voltage. In interval AB the voltage increases to 71 volts; that is, 33 volts additional. In this interval a *smaller* quantity of charge has been added than in OA, because the voltage rise during interval AB is smaller. Consequently the average current during AB is smaller than during OA. In the third interval, BC, the voltage rises from 71 to 92 volts, an increase of 21 volts. This is less than the voltage increase during AB, so the quantity of electricity added is less; in other words, the average current during interval BC is still smaller. In the fourth interval, CD, the voltage increases only 8 volts; the charge added is smaller than in any preceding interval and therefore the current also is smaller.

By dividing the first quarter cycle into a very large number of intervals it could be shown that the current charging the capacitor has the shape of a sine wave, just as the applied voltage does. The current is largest at the beginning of the cycle and becomes zero at the maximum value of the voltage, so there is a phase difference of 90 degrees between the voltage and current. During the first quarter cycle the current is flowing in the normal direction through the circuit, since the capacitor is being charged. Hence the current is positive, as indicated by the dashed line in Fig. 2-26.

In the second quarter cycle—that is, in the time from D to H, the voltage applied to the capacitor decreases. During this time the capacitor *loses* its charge. Applying the same reasoning, it is plain that the current is small in interval DE and continues to increase during each succeeding interval. However, the current is flowing *against* the applied voltage because the capacitor is discharging into the circuit. The current flows in

the *negative* direction during this quarter cycle.

The third and fourth quarter cycles repeat the events of the first and second, respectively, with this difference—the polarity of the applied voltage has reversed, and the current changes to correspond. In other words, an alternating current flows in the circuit because of the alternate charging and discharging of the capacitance. As shown by Fig. 2-26, the current starts its cycle 90 degrees before the voltage, so the current in a capacitor leads the applied voltage by 90 degrees.

Capacitive Reactance

The quantity of electric charge that can be placed on a capacitor is proportional to the applied e.m.f. and the capacitance. This amount of charge moves back and forth in the circuit once each cycle, and so the *rate* of movement of charge —that is, the current—is proportional to voltage, capacitance and frequency. If the effects of capacitance and frequency are lumped together, they form a quantity that plays a part similar to that of resistance in Ohm's Law. This quantity is called **reactance**, and the unit for it is the ohm, just as in the case of resistance. The formula for it is

$$X_C = \frac{1}{2\pi f C}$$

where X_C = Capacitive reactance in ohms
  f = Frequency in cycles per second
  C = Capacitance in farads
  π = 3.14

Although the unit of reactance is the ohm, there is no power dissipation in reactance. The energy stored in the capacitor in one quarter of the cycle is simply returned to the circuit in the next.

The fundamental units (cycles per second, farads) are too large for practical use in radio circuits. However, if the capacitance is in microfarads and the frequency is in megacycles, the reactance will come out in ohms in the formula.

> Example: The reactance of a capacitor of 470 pf. (0.00047 μf.) at a frequency of 7150 kc. (7.15 Mc.) is
>
> $$X = \frac{1}{2\pi f C} = \frac{1}{6.28 \times 7.15 \times 0.00047} = 47.4 \text{ ohms}$$

Inductive Reactance

When an alternating voltage is applied to a *pure* inductance (one with no resistance—all *practical* inductors have resistance) the current is again 90 degrees out of phase with the applied voltage. However, in this case the current *lags* 90 degrees behind the voltage—the opposite of the capacitor current-voltage relationship.

The primary cause for this is the *back e.m.f.* generated in the inductance, and since the amplitude of the back e.m.f. is proportional to the rate at which the current changes, and this in turn is proportional to the frequency, the amplitude of the current is inversely proportional to the applied frequency. Also, since the back e.m.f. is proportional to inductance for a given rate of current change, the current flow is inversely propor-

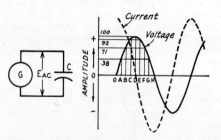

Fig. 2-26—Voltage and current phase relationships when an alternating voltage is applied to a capacitor.

tional to inductance for a given applied voltage and frequency. (Another way of saying this is that just enough current flows to generate an induced e.m.f. that equals and opposes the applied voltage.)

The combined effect of inductance and frequency is called **inductive reactance**, also expressed in ohms, and the formula for it is

$$X_\text{L} = 2\pi fL$$

where $X_\text{L} =$ Inductive reactance in ohms
$f =$ Frequency in cycles per second
$L =$ Inductance in henrys
$\pi = 3.14$

> Example: The reactance of a coil having an inductance of 8 henrys, at a frequency of 120 cycles, is
>
> $X_\text{L} = 2\pi fL = 6.28 \times 120 \times 8 = 6029$ ohms

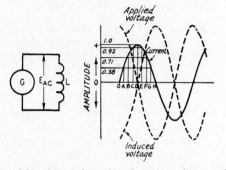

Fig. 2-27—Phase relationships between voltage and current when an alternating voltage is applied to an inductance.

In radio-frequency circuits the inductance values usually are small and the frequencies are large. If the inductance is expressed in millihenrys and the frequency in kilocycles, the conversion factors for the two units cancel, and the formula for reactance may be used without first converting to fundamental units. Similarly, no conversion is necessary if the inductance is in microhenrys and the frequency is in megacycles.

> Example: The reactance of a 15-microhenry coil at a frequency of 14 Mc. is
>
> $X_\text{L} = 2\pi fL = 6.28 \times 14 \times 15 = 1319$ ohms

The resistance of the wire of which the coil is wound has no effect on the reactance, but simply acts as though it were a separate resistor connected in series with the coil.

Ohm's Law for Reactance

Ohn's Law for an a.c. circuit containing *only* reactance is

$$I = \frac{E}{X}$$

$$E = IX$$

$$X = \frac{E}{I}$$

where $E =$ E.m.f. in volts
$I =$ Current in amperes
$X =$ Reactance in ohms

The reactance in the circuit may, of course, be

either inductive or capacitive.

> Example: If a current of 2 amperes is flowing through the capacitor of the earlier example (reactance = 47.4 ohms) at 7150 kc., the voltage drop across the capacitor is
>
> $E = IX = 2 \times 47.4 = 94.8$ volts
>
> If 400 volts at 120 cycles is applied to the 8-henry inductor of the earlier example, the current through the coil will be
>
> $I = \dfrac{E}{X} = \dfrac{400}{6029} = 0.0663$ amp. (66.3 ma.)

Reactance Chart

The accompanying chart, Fig. 2-28, shows the reactance of capacitances from 1 pf. to 100 μf., and the reactance of inductances from 0.1 μh. to 10 henrys, for frequencies between 100 c.p.s. and 100 megacycles per second. The approximate value of reactance can be read from the chart or, where more exact values are needed, the chart will serve as a check on the order of magnitude of reactances calculated from the formulas given above, and thus avoid "decimal-point errors".

Reactances in Series and Parallel

When reactances of the same kind are connected in series or parallel the resultant reactance is that of the resultant inductance or capacitance. This leads to the same rules that are used when determining the resultant resistance when resistors are combined. That is, for series reactances of the same kind the resultant reactance is

$$X = X_1 + X_2 + X_3 + X_4$$

and for reactances of the same kind in parallel the resultant is

$$X = \frac{1}{\dfrac{1}{X_1} + \dfrac{1}{X_2} + \dfrac{1}{X_3} + \dfrac{1}{X_4}}$$

or for two in parallel,

$$X = \frac{X_1 X_2}{X_1 + X_2}$$

The situation is different when reactances of opposite kinds are combined. Since the current in a capacitance leads the applied voltage by 90 degrees and the current in an inductance lags the applied voltage by 90 degrees, the voltages at the terminals of opposite types of reactance are 180 degrees out of phase in a series circuit (in which the current has to be the same through all elements), and the currents in reactances of opposite types are 180 degrees out of phase in a parallel circuit (in which the same voltage is applied to all elements). The 180-degree phase relationship means that the currents or voltages are of opposite polarity, so in the series circuit of Fig. 2-29A the voltage E_L across the inductive reactance X_L is of opposite polarity to the voltage E_C across the capacitive reactance X_C. Thus if we call X_L "positive" and X_C "negative" (a common convention) the applied voltage E_AC is $E_\text{L} - E_\text{C}$. In the parallel circuit at B the total current, I, is equal to $I_\text{L} - I_\text{C}$, since the currents are 180 degrees out of phase.

In the series case, therefore, the resultant re-

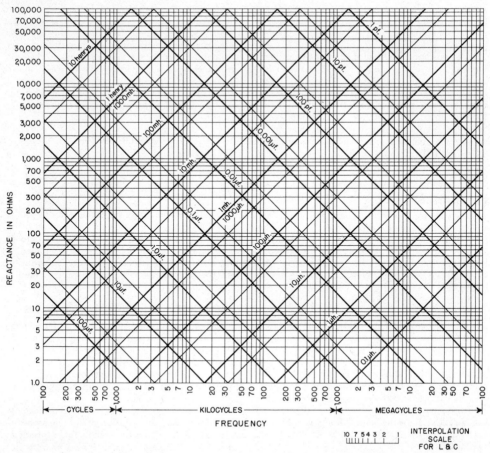

Fig. 2-28—Inductive and capacitive reactance vs. frequency. Heavy lines represent multiples of 10, intermediate light lines multiples of 5; e.g., the light line between 10 μh. and 100 μh. represents 50 μh., the light line between 0.1 μf. and 1 μf. represents 0.5 μf., etc. Intermediate values can be estimated with the help of the interpolation scale.

Reactances outside the range of the chart may be found by applying appropriate factors to values within the chart range. For example, the reactance of 10 henrys at 60 cycles can be found by taking the reactance to 10 henrys at 600 cycles and dividing by 10 for the 10-times decrease in frequency.

actance of X_L and X_C is

$$X = X_L - X_C$$

and in the parallel case

$$X = \frac{-X_L X_C}{X_L - X_C}$$

Note that in the series circuit the total reactance is negative if X_C is larger than X_L; this indicates that the total reactance is capacitive in such a case. The resultant reactance in a series circuit is always smaller than the larger of the two individual reactances.

In the parallel circuit, the resultant reactance is negative (i.e., capacitive) if X_L is larger than X_C, and positive (inductive) if X_L is smaller than X_C, but in every case is always larger than the smaller of the two individual reactances.

In the special case where $X_L = X_C$ the total reactance is zero in the series circuit and infinitely large in the parallel circuit.

Reactive Power

In Fig. 2-29A the voltage drop across the inductor is larger than the voltage applied to the circuit. This might seem to be an impossible condition, but it is not; the explanation is that while energy is being stored in the inductor's

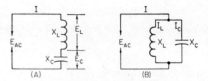

Fig. 2-29—Series and parallel circuits containing opposite kinds of reactance.

magnetic field, energy is being returned to the circuit from the capacitor's electric field, and vice versa. This stored energy is responsible for the fact that the voltages across reactances in series can be larger than the voltage applied to them.

In a resistance the flow of current causes heating and a power loss equal to I^2R. The power in a reactance is equal to I^2X, but is not a "loss"; it is simply power that is transferred back and forth between the field and the circuit but not used up in heating anything. To distinguish this "nondissipated" power from the power which is actually consumed, the unit of reactive power is called the **volt-ampere-reactive**, or **var**, instead of the watt. Reactive power is sometimes called "wattless" power.

IMPEDANCE

When a circuit contains both resistance and reactance the combined effect of the two is called **impedance,** symbolized by the letter Z. (Impedance is thus a more general term than either resistance or reactance, and is frequently used even for circuits that have only resistance or reactance, although usually with a qualification —such as "resistive impedance" to indicate that the circuit has only resistance, for example.)

The reactance and resistance comprising an impedance may be connected either in series or in parallel, as shown in Fig. 2-30. In these circuits the reactance is shown as a box to indicate that it may be either inductive or capacitive. In the series circuit the current is the same in both elements, with (generally) different voltages appearing across the resistance and reactance. In the parallel circuit the same voltage is applied to both elements, but different currents flow in the two branches.

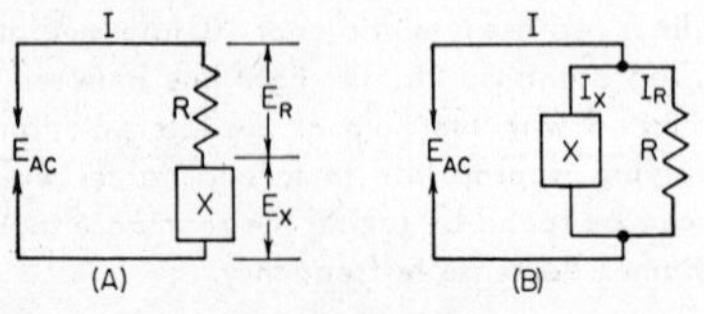

(A)   (B)

Fig. 2-30—Series and parallel circuits containing resistance and reactance.

Since in a resistance the current is in phase with the applied voltage while in a reactance it is 90 degrees out of phase with the voltage, the phase relationship between current and voltage in the circuit as a whole may be anything between zero and 90 degrees, depending on the relative amounts of resistance and reactance.

Series Circuits

When resistance and reactance are in series, the impedance of the circuit is

$$Z = \sqrt{R^2 + X^2}$$

where Z = impedance in ohms
R = resistance in ohms
X = reactance in ohms.

The reactance may be either capacitive or inductive. If there are two or more reactances in the circuit they may be combined into a resultant

by the rules previously given, before substitution into the formula above; similarly for resistances.

The "square root of the sum of the squares" rule for finding impedance in a series circuit arises from the fact that the voltage drops across the resistance and reactance are 90 degrees out of phase, and so combine by the same rule that applies in finding the hypothenuse of a right-angled triangle when the base and altitude are known.

Parallel Circuits

With resistance and reactance in parallel, as in Fig. 2-30B, the impedance is

$$Z = \frac{RX}{\sqrt{R^2 + X^2}}$$

where the symbols have the same meaning as for series circuits.

Just as in the case of series circuits, a number of reactances in parallel should be combined to find the resultant reactance before substitution into the formula above; similarly for a number of resistances in parallel.

Equivalent Series and Parallel Circuits

The two circuits shown in Fig. 2-30 are equivalent if the same current flows when a given voltage of the same frequency is applied, and if the phase angle between voltage and current is the same in both cases. It is in fact possible to "transform" any given series circuit into an equivalent parallel circuit, and vice versa.

Transformations of this type often lead to simplification in the solution of complicated circuits. However, from the standpoint of practical work the usefulness of such transformations lies in the fact that the impedance of a circuit may be modified by the addition of *either* series or parallel elements, depending on which happens to be most convenient in the particular case. Typical applications are considered later in connection with tuned circuits and transmission lines.

Ohm's Law for Impedance

Ohm's Law can be applied to circuits containing impedance just as readily as to circuits having resistance or reactance only. The formulas are

$$I = \frac{E}{Z}$$

$$E = IZ$$

$$Z = \frac{E}{I}$$

where E = E.m.f. in volts
I = Current in amperes
Z = Impedance in ohms

Fig. 2-31 shows a simple circuit consisting of a resistance of 75 ohms and a reactance of 100 ohms in series. From the formula previously given, the impedance is

$$Z = \sqrt{R^2 + X_L^2} = \sqrt{(75)^2 + (100)^2} = 125$$
ohms.

If the applied voltage is 250 volts, then

$$I = \frac{E}{Z} = \frac{250}{125} = 2 \text{ amperes.}$$

This current flows though both the resistance and reactance, so the voltage drops are

$$E_R = IR = 2 \times 75 = 150 \text{ volts}$$
$$E_{XL} = IX_L = 2 \times 100 = 200 \text{ volts}$$

The simple arithmetical sum of these two drops, 350 volts, is greater than the applied voltage because the two voltages are 90 degrees out of phase. Their actual resultant, when phase is taken into account, is

$$\sqrt{(150)^2 + (200)^2} = 250 \text{ volts}.$$

Power Factor

In the circuit of Fig. 2-31 an applied e.m.f. of 250 volts results in a current of 2 amperes, giving an apparent power of $250 \times 2 = 500$ watts. However, only the resistance actually consumes power. The power in the resistance is

$$P = I^2R = (2)^2 \times 75 = 300 \text{ watts}$$

The ratio of the power consumed to the apparent power is called the **power factor** of the circuit, and in this example the power factor would be $300/500 = 0.6$. Power factor is frequently expressed as a percentage; in this case, it would be 60 per cent.

"Real" or dissipated power is measured in watts; apparent power, to distinguish it from real power, is measured in volt-amperes. It is simply the product of volts and amperes and has no direct relationship to the power actually used up or dissipated unless the power factor of the circuit is known. The power factor of a purely resistive circuit is 100 per cent or 1, while the power factor of a pure reactance is zero. In this

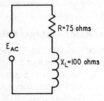

Fig. 2-31—Circuit used as an example for impedance calculations.

illustration, the reactive power is $VAR = I^2X = (2)^2 \times 100 = 400$ volt-amperes.

Reactance and Complex Waves

It was pointed out earlier in this chapter that a complex wave (a "nonsinusoidal" wave) can be resolved into a fundamental frequency and a series of harmonic frequencies. When such a complex voltage wave is applied to a circuit containing reactance, the current through the circuit will not have the same wave shape as the applied voltage. This is because the reactance of an inductor and capacitor depend upon the applied frequency. For the second-harmonic component of a complex wave, the reactance of the inductor is twice and the reactance of the capacitor one-half their respective values at the fundamental frequency; for the third harmonic the inductor reactance is three times and the capacitor reactance one-third, and so on. Thus the circuit impedance is different for each harmonic component.

Just what happens to the current wave shape depends upon the values of resistance and reactance involved and how the circuit is arranged. In a simple circuit with resistance and inductive reactance in series, the amplitudes of the harmonic currents will be reduced because the inductive reactance increases in proportion to frequency. When capacitance and resistance are in series, the harmonic current is likely to be accentuated because the capacitive reactance becomes lower as the frequency is raised. When both inductive and capacitive reactance are present the shape of the current wave can be altered in a variety of ways, depending upon the circuit and the "constants," or the relative values of L, C, and R, selected.

This property of nonuniform behavior with respect to fundamental and harmonics is an extremely useful one. It is the basis of "filtering," or the suppression of undesired frequencies in favor of a single desired frequency or group of such frequencies.

TRANSFORMERS FOR AUDIO FREQUENCIES

Two coils having mutual inductance constitute a **transformer.** The coil connected to the source of energy is called the **primary** coil, and the other is called the **secondary** coil.

The usefulness of the transformer lies in the fact that electrical energy can be transferred from one circuit to another without direct connection, and in the process can be readily changed from one voltage level to another. Thus, if a device to be operated requires, for example, 115 volts a.c. and only a 440-volt source is available, a transformer can be used to change the source voltage to that required. A transformer can be used only with a.c., since no voltage will be induced in the secondary if the magnetic field is not changing. If d.c. is applied to the primary of a transformer, a voltage will be induced in the secondary only at the instant of closing or open-

ing the primary circuit, since it is only at these times that the field is changing.

THE IRON-CORE TRANSFORMER

As shown in Fig. 2-32, the primary and secondary coils of a transformer may be wound on a core of magnetic material. This increases the inductance of the coils so that a relatively small number of turns may be used to induce a given value of voltage with a small current. A **closed core** (one having a continuous magnetic path) such as that shown in Fig. 2-32 also tends to insure that practically all of the field set up by the current in the primary coil will cut the turns of the secondary coil. However, the core introduces a power loss because of hysteresis and eddy currents so this type of construction is normally practicable only at power and audio frequencies.

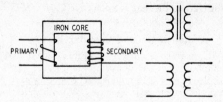

Fig. 2-32—The transformer. Power is transferred from the primary coil to the secondary by means of the magnetic field. The upper symbol at right indicates an iron-core transformer, the lower one an air-core transformer.

The discussion in this section is confined to transformers operating at such frequencies.

Voltage and Turns Ratio

For a given varying magnetic field, the voltage induced in a coil in the field will be proportional to the number of turns in the coil. If the two coils of a transformer are in the same field (which is the case when both are wound on the same closed core) it follows that the induced voltages will be proportional to the number of turns in each coil. In the primary the induced voltage is practically equal to, and opposes, the applied voltage, as described earlier. Hence,

$$E_s = \frac{n_s}{n_p} E_p$$

where E_s = Secondary voltage
E_p = Primary applied voltage
n_s = Number of turns on secondary
n_p = Number of turns on primary

The ratio n_s/n_p is called the secondary-to-primary **turns ratio** of the transformer.

> Example: A transformer has a primary of 400 turns and a secondary of 2800 turns, and an e.m.f. of 115 volts is applied to the primary. The secondary voltage will be
>
> $$E_s = \frac{n_s}{n_p} E_p = \frac{2800}{400} \times 115 = 7 \times 115$$
> $$= 805 \text{ volts}$$
>
> Also, if an e.m.f. of 805 volts is applied to the 2800-turn winding (which then becomes the primary) the output voltage from the 400-turn winding will be 115 volts. Either winding of a transformer can be used as the primary, providing the winding has enough turns (enough inductance) to induce a voltage equal to the applied voltage without requiring an excessive current flow.

Effect of Secondary Current

The current that flows in the primary when no current is taken from the secondary is called the **magnetizing current** of the transformer. In any properly-designed transformer the primary inductance will be so large that the magnetizing current will be quite small. The power consumed by the transformer when the secondary is "open" —that is, not delivering power—is only the amount necessary to supply the losses in the iron core and in the resistance of the wire with which the primary is wound.

When power is taken from the secondary winding, the secondary current sets up a magnetic field that opposes the field set up by the primary current. But if the induced voltage in the primary is to equal the applied voltage, the original field must be maintained. Consequently, the primary must draw enough additional current to set up a field exactly equal and opposite to the field set up by the secondary current.

In practical calculations on transformers it may be assumed that the entire primary current is caused by the secondary "load." This is justifiable because the magnetizing current should be very small in comparison with the primary "load" current at rated power output.

If the magnetic fields set up by the primary and secondary currents are to be equal, the primary current multiplied by the primary turns must equal the secondary current multiplied by the secondary turns. From this it follows that

$$I_p = \frac{n_s}{n_p} I_s$$

where I_p = Primary current
I_s = Secondary current
n_p = Number of turns on primary
n_s = Number of turns on secondary

> Example: Suppose that the secondary of the transformer in the previous example is delivering a current of 0.2 ampere to a load. Then the primary current will be
>
> $$I_p = \frac{n_s}{n_p} I_s = \frac{2800}{400} \times 0.2 = 7 \times 0.2 = 1.4 \text{ amp.}$$
>
> Although the secondary voltage is higher than the primary voltage, the secondary *current* is *lower* than the primary current, and by the same ratio.

Power Relationships; Efficiency

A transformer cannot create power; it can only transfer it and change the e.m.f. Hence, the power taken from the secondary cannot exceed that taken by the primary from the source of applied e.m.f. There is always some power loss in the resistance of the coils and in the iron core, so in all practical cases the power taken from the source will exceed that taken from the secondary. Thus,

$$P_o = nP_1$$

where P_o = Power output from secondary
P_1 = Power input to primary
n = Efficiency factor

The efficiency, n, always is less than 1. It is usually expressed as a percentage; if n is 0.65, for instance, the efficiency is 65 per cent.

> Example: A transformer has an efficiency of 85% at its full-load output of 150 watts. The power input to the primary at full secondary load will be
>
> $$P_1 = \frac{P_o}{n} = \frac{150}{0.85} = 176.5 \text{ watts}$$

A transformer is usually designed to have its highest efficiency at the power output for which it is rated. The efficiency decreases with either lower or higher outputs. On the other hand, the *losses* in the transformer are relatively small at low output but increase as more power is taken.

The amount of power that the transformer can handle is determined by its own losses, because these heat the wire and core. There is a limit to the temperature rise that can be tolerated, because too-high temperature either will melt the wire or cause the insulation to break down. A transformer can be operated at reduced output, even though the efficiency is low, because the actual loss also will be low under such conditions.

The full-load efficiency of small power transformers such as are used in radio receivers and transmitters usually lies between about 60 and 90 per cent, depending upon the size and design.

Leakage Reactance

In a practical transformer not all of the magnetic flux is common to both windings, although in well-designed transformers the amount of flux that "cuts" one coil and not the other is only a small percentage of the total flux. This **leakage flux** causes an e.m.f. of self-induction; consequently, there are small amounts of **leakage inductance** associated with both windings of the transformer. Leakage inductance acts in exactly the same way as an equivalent amount of ordinary inductance inserted in series with the circuit.

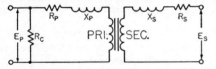

Fig. 2-33—The equivalent circuit of a transformer includes the effects of leakage inductance and resistance of both primary and secondary windings. The resistance R_C is an equivalent resistance representing the core losses, which are essentially constant for any given applied voltage and frequency. Since these are comparatively small, their effect may be neglected in many approximate calculations.

It has, therefore, a certain reactance, depending upon the amount of leakage inductance and the frequency. This reactance is called **leakage reactance.**

Current flowing through the leakage reactance causes a voltage drop. This voltage drop increases with increasing current, hence it increases as more power is taken from the secondary. Thus, the greater the secondary current, the smaller the secondary terminal voltage becomes. The resistances of the transformer windings also cause voltage drops when current is flowing; although these voltage drops are not in phase with those caused by leakage reactance, together they result in a lower secondary voltage under load than is indicated by the turns ratio of the transformer.

At power frequencies (60 cycles) the voltage at the secondary, with a reasonably well-designed transformer, should not drop more than about 10 per cent from open-circuit conditions to full load. The drop in voltage may be considerably more than this in a transformer operating at audio frequencies because the leakage reactance increases directly with the frequency.

Impedance Ratio

In an ideal transformer—one without losses or leakage reactance—the following relationship is true:

$$Z_p = Z_s \left(\frac{N_p}{N_s}\right)^2$$

where

Z_p = Impedance looking into primary terminals from source of power

Z_s = Impedance of load connected to secondary

N_p/N_s = Turns ratio, primary to secondary

That is, a load of any given impedance connected to the secondary of the transformer will be transformed to a different value "looking into" the primary from the source of power. The impedance transformation is proportional to the square of the primary-to-secondary turns ratio.

Example: A transformer has a primary-to-secondary turns ratio of 0.6 (primary has 6/10 as many turns as the secondary) and a load of 3000 ohms is connected to the secondary. The impedance looking into the primary then will be

$$Z_p = Z_s \left(\frac{N_p}{N_s}\right)^2 = 3000 \times (0.6)^2 = 3000 \times 0.36 = 1080 \text{ ohms}$$

By choosing the proper turns ratio, the impedance of a fixed load can be transformed to any desired value, within practical limits. If transformer losses can be neglected, the transformed or "reflected" impedance has the same phase angle as the actual load impedance; thus if the load is a pure resistance the load presented by the primary to the source of power also will be a pure resistance.

The above relationship may be used in practical work even though it is based on an "ideal" transformer. Aside from the normal design requirements of reasonably low internal losses and low leakage reactance, the only requirement is that the primary have enough inductance to operate with low magnetizing current at the voltage applied to the primary.

The primary impedance of a transformer—*as it appears to the source of power*—is determined wholly by the load connected to the secondary and by the turns ratio. If the characteristics of the transformer have an appreciable effect on the impedance presented to the power source, the transformer is either poorly designed or is not suited to the voltage and frequency at which it is being used. Most transformers will operate quite well at voltages from slightly above to well below the design figure.

Impedance Matching

Many devices require a specific value of load resistance (or impedance) for optimum operation. The impedance of the actual load that is to dissipate the power may differ widely from this value, so a transformer is used to change the actual load into an impedance of the desired value. This is called **impedance matching.** From the preceding,

$$\frac{N_p}{N_s} = \sqrt{\frac{Z_p}{Z_s}}$$

where $N_p/N_s =$ Required turns ratio, primary to
              secondary
     $Z_p =$ Primary impedance required
     $Z_s =$ Impedance of load connected to
             secondary

Example: A vacuum-tube a.f. amplifier requires a load of 5000 ohms for optimum performance, and is to be connected to a loudspeaker having an impedance of 10 ohms. The turns ratio, primary to secondary, required in the coupling transformer is

$$\frac{N_p}{N_s} = \sqrt{\frac{Z_p}{Z_s}} = \sqrt{\frac{5000}{10}} = \sqrt{500} = 22.4$$

The primary therefore must have 22.4 times as many turns as the secondary.

Impedance matching means, in general, adjusting the load impedance—by means of a transformer or otherwise—to a desired value. However, there is also another meaning. It is possible to show that any source of power will deliver its maximum possible output when the impedance of the load is equal to the internal impedance of the source. The impedance of the source is said to be "matched" under this condition. The efficiency is only 50 per cent in such a case; just as much power is used up in the source as is delivered to the load. Because of the poor efficiency, this type of impedance matching is limited to cases where only a small amount of power is available and heating from power loss in the source is not important.

Transformer Construction

Transformers usually are designed so that the magnetic path around the core is as short as possible. A short magnetic path means that the transformer will operate with fewer turns, for a given applied voltage, than if the path were long.

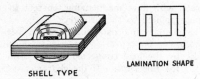

SHELL TYPE   LAMINATION SHAPE

CORE TYPE

Fig. 2-34—Two common types of transformer construction. Core pieces are interleaved to provide a continuous magnetic path.

A short path also helps to reduce flux leakage and therefore minimizes leakage reactance.

Two core shapes are in common use, as shown in Fig. 2-34. In the shell type both windings are placed on the inner leg, while in the core type the primary and secondary windings may be placed on separate legs, if desired. This is some-

times done when it is necessary to minimize capacitive effects between the primary and secondary, or when one of the windings must operate at very high voltage.

Core material for small transformers is usually silicon steel, called "transformer iron." The core is built up of laminations, insulated from each other (by a thin coating of shellac, for example) to prevent the flow of eddy currents. The laminations are interleaved at the ends to make the magnetic path as continuous as possible and thus reduce flux leakage.

The number of turns required in the primary for a given applied e.m.f. is determined by the size, shape and type of core material used, and the frequency. The number of turns required is inversely proportional to the cross-sectional area of the core. As a rough indication, windings of small power transformers frequently have about six to eight turns per volt on a core of 1-square-inch cross section and have a magnetic path 10 or 12 inches in length. A longer path or smaller cross section requires more turns per volt, and vice versa.

In most transformers the coils are wound in layers, with a thin sheet of treated-paper insulation between each layer. Thicker insulation is used between coils and between coils and core.

Autotransformers

The transformer principle can be utilized with only one winding instead of two, as shown in Fig. 2-35; the principles just discussed apply

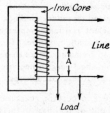

Fig. 2-35—The autotransformer is based on the transformer principle, but uses only one winding. The line and load currents in the common winding (A) flow in opposite directions, so that the resultant current is the difference between them. The voltage across A is proportional to the turns ratio.

equally well. A one-winding transformer is called an **autotransformer**. The current in the common section (A) of the winding is the difference between the line (primary) and the load (secondary) currents, since these currents are out of phase. Hence if the line and load currents are nearly equal the common section of the winding may be wound with comparatively small wire. This will be the case only when the primary (line) and secondary (load) voltages are not very different. The autotransformer is used chiefly for boosting or reducing the power-line voltage by relatively small amounts. Continuously-variable autotransformers are commercially available under a variety of trade names; "Variac" and "Powerstat" are typical examples.

THE DECIBEL

In most radio communication the received signal is converted into sound. This being the case, it is useful to appraise signal strengths in terms of relative loudness as registered by the ear. A peculiarity of the ear is that an increase or decrease in loudness is responsive to the *ratio* of the amounts of power involved, and is practically independent of absolute value of the power. For example, if a person estimates that the signal is "twice as loud" when the transmitter power is increased from 10 watts to 40 watts, he will also estimate that a 400-watt signal is twice as loud as a 100-watt signal. In other words, the human ear has a *logarithmic* response.

This fact is the basis for the use of the relative-power unit called the **decibel** (abbreviated **db.**) A change of one decibel in the power level is just detectable as a change in loudness under ideal conditions. The number of decibels corresponding to a given power ratio is given by the following formula:

$$Db. = 10 \log \frac{P_2}{P_1}$$

Common logarithms (base 10) are used.

Voltage and Current Ratios

Note that the decibel is based on *power* ratios. Voltage or current ratios can be used, but only when the impedance is the same for both values of voltage, or current. The gain of an amplifier cannot be expressed correctly in db. if it is based on the ratio of the output voltage to the input voltage unless both voltages are measured across the same value of impedance. When the impedance at both points of measurement is the same, the following formula may be used for voltage or current ratios:

$$Db. = 20 \log \frac{V_2}{V_1}$$

$$\text{or } 20 \log \frac{I_2}{I_1}$$

Decibel Chart

The two formulas are shown graphically in Fig. 2-36 for ratios from 1 to 10. Gains (increases) expressed in decibels may be added arithmetically; losses (decreases) may be subtracted. A power decrease is indicated by prefixing the decibel figure with a minus sign. Thus +6 db. means that the power has been multiplied by 4, while —6 db. means that the power has been divided by 4.

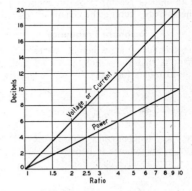

Fig. 2-36—Decibel chart for power, voltage and current ratios for power ratios of 1:1 to 10:1. In determining decibels for current or voltage ratios the currents (or voltages) being compared must be referred to the same value of impedance.

The chart may be used for other ratios by adding (or subtracting, if a loss) 10 db. each time the ratio scale is multiplied by 10, for power ratios; or by adding (or subtracting) 20 db. each time the scale is multiplied by 10 for voltage or current ratios. For example, a power ratio of 2.5 is 4 db. (from the chart). A power ratio of 10 times 2.5, or 25, is 14 db. (10 + 4), and a power ratio of 100 times 2.5, or 250, is 24 db. (20 + 4). A voltage or current ratio of 4 is 12 db., a voltage or current ratio of 40 is 32 db. (20 + 12), and one of 400 is 52 db. (40 + 12).

RADIO-FREQUENCY CIRCUITS

RESONANCE IN SERIES CIRCUITS

Fig. 2-37 shows a resistor, capacitor and inductor connected in series with a source of alternating current, the frequency of which can be varied over a wide range. At some *low* frequency the capacitive reactance will be much larger than the resistance of R, and the inductive reactance will be small compared with either the reactance of C or the resistance of R. (R is assumed to be the same at all frequencies.) On the other hand, at some very *high* frequency the reactance of C will be very small and the reactance of L will be very large. In either case the current will be small, because the net reactance is large.

At some intermediate frequency, the reactances of C and L will be equal and the voltage drops across the coil and capacitor will be equal and

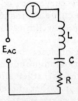

Fig. 2-37.—A series circuit containing L, C and R is "resonant" at the applied frequency when the reactance of C is equal to the reactance of L.

180 degrees out of phase. Therefore they cancel each other completely and the current flow is determined wholly by the resistance, R. At that frequency the current has its largest possible value, assuming the source voltage to be constant regardless of frequency. A series circuit in which the inductive and capacitive reactances are equal is said to be **resonant**.

The principle of resonance finds its most extensive application in radio-frequency circuits. The reactive effects associated with even small inductances and capacitances would place drastic limitations on r.f. circuit operation if it were not possible to "cancel them out" by supplying the right amount of reactance of the opposite kind—in other words, "tuning the circuit to resonance."

Resonant Frequency

The frequency at which a series circuit is resonant is that for which $X_L = X_C$. Substituting the formulas for inductive and capacitive reactance gives

$$f = \frac{1}{2\pi\sqrt{LC}}$$

where f = Frequency in cycles per second
L = Inductance in henrys
C = Capacitance in farads
π = 3.14

These units are inconveniently large for radio-frequency circuits. A formula using more appropriate units is

$$f = \frac{10^6}{2\pi\sqrt{LC}}$$

where f = Frequency in kilocycles (kc.)
L = Inductance in microhenrys (μh.)
C = Capacitance in picofarads (pf.)
π = 3.14

> Example: The resonant frequency of a series circuit containing a 5-μh. inductor and a 35-pf. capacitor is
>
> $$f = \frac{10^6}{2\pi\sqrt{LC}} = \frac{10^6}{6.28 \times \sqrt{5 \times 35}}$$
> $$= \frac{10^6}{6.28 \times 13.2} = \frac{10^6}{83} = 12{,}050 \text{ kc.}$$

The formula for resonant frequency is not affected by resistance in the circuit.

Resonance Curves

If a plot is drawn of the current flowing in the circuit of Fig. 2-37 as the frequency is varied (the applied voltage being constant) it would look like one of the curves in Fig. 2-38. The shape of the **resonance curve** at frequencies near resonance is determined by the ratio of reactance to resistance.

If the reactance of either the coil or capacitor is of the same order of magnitude as the resistance, the current decreases rather slowly as the frequency is moved in either direction away from resonance. Such a curve is said to be **broad**. On the other hand, if the reactance is considerably larger than the resistance the current decreases

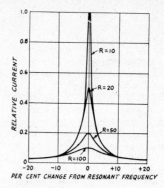

Fig. 2-38—Current in a series-resonant circuit with various values of series resistance. The values are arbitrary and would not apply to all circuits, but represent a typical case. It is assumed that the reactances (at the resonant frequency) are 1000 ohms. Note that at frequencies more than plus or minus ten per cent away from the resonant frequency the current is substantially unaffected by the resistance in the circuit.

rapidly as the frequency moves away from resonance and the circuit is said to be **sharp**. A sharp circuit will respond a great deal more readily to the resonant frequency than to frequencies quite close to resonance; a broad circuit will respond almost equally well to a group or band of frequencies centering around the resonant frequency.

Both types of resonance curves are useful. A sharp circuit gives good **selectivity**—the ability to respond strongly (in terms of current amplitude) at one desired frequency and discriminate against others. A broad circuit is used when the apparatus must give about the same response over a band of frequencies rather than to a single frequency alone.

Q

Most diagrams of resonant circuits show only inductance and capacitance; no resistance is indicated. Nevertheless, resistance is always present. At frequencies up to perhaps 30 Mc. this resist-

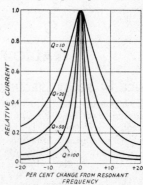

Fig. 2-39—Current in series-resonant circuits having different Qs. In this graph the current at resonance is assumed to be the same in all cases. The lower the Q, the more slowly the current decreases as the applied frequency is moved away from resonance.

ance is mostly in the wire of the coil. Above this frequency energy loss in the capacitor (principally in the solid dielectric which must be used to form an insulating support for the capacitor plates) also becomes a factor. This energy loss is equivalent to resistance. When maximum sharpness or selectivity is needed the object of design is to reduce the inherent resistance to the lowest possible value.

The value of the reactance of either the inductor or capacitor at the resonant frequency of a series-resonant circuit, divided by the *series* resistance in the circuit, is called the **Q** (quality factor) of the circuit, or

$$Q = \frac{X}{r}$$

where Q = Quality factor
X = Reactance of either coil or capacitor in ohms
r = Series resistance in ohms

Example: The inductor and capacitor in a series circuit each have a reactance of 350 ohms at the resonant frequency. The resistance is 5 ohms. Then the Q is

$$Q = \frac{X}{r} = \frac{350}{5} = 70$$

The effect of Q on the sharpness of resonance of a circuit is shown by the curves of Fig. 2-39. In these curves the frequency change is shown in percentage above and below the resonant frequency. Qs of 10, 20, 50 and 100 are shown; these values cover much of the range commonly used in radio work. The **unloaded Q** of a circuit is determined by the inherent resistances associated with the components.

Voltage Rise at Resonance

When a voltage of the resonant frequency is inserted in series in a resonant circuit, the voltage that appears across either the inductor or capacitor is considerably higher than the applied voltage. The current in the circuit is limited only by the resistance and may have a relatively high value; however, the same current flows through the high reactances of the inductor and capacitor and causes large voltage drops. The ratio of the reactive voltage to the applied voltage is equal to the ratio of reactance to resistance. This ratio is also the Q of the circuit. Therefore, the voltage across either the inductor or capacitor is equal to QE, where E is the voltage inserted in series. This fact accounts for the high voltages developed across the components of series-tuned antenna couplers (see chapter on "Transmission Lines").

RESONANCE IN PARALLEL CIRCUITS

When a variable-frequency source of constant voltage is applied to a parallel circuit of the type shown in Fig. 2-40 there is a resonance effect similar to that in a series circuit. However, in this case the "line" current (measured at the point indicated) is *smallest* at the frequency for which the inductive and capacitive reactances are equal. At that frequency the current through L is ex-

actly canceled by the out-of-phase current through C, so that only the current taken by R flows in the line. At frequencies *below* resonance the current through L is larger than that through C, because the reactance of L is smaller and that of C higher at low frequencies; there is only partial cancellation of the two reactive currents and the line current therefore is larger than the current taken by R alone. At frequencies *above* resonance the situation is reversed and more current flows through C than through L, so the line current again increases. The current at resonance, being determined wholly by R, will be small if R is large and large if R is small.

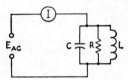

Fig. 2-40—Circuit illustrating parallel resonance.

The resistance R shown in Fig. 2-40 is not necessarily an actual resistor. In many cases it will be the series resistance of the coil "transformed" to an equivalent parallel resistance (see later). It may be antenna or other load resistance coupled into the tuned circuit. In all cases it represents the total effective resistance in the circuit.

Parallel and series resonant circuits are quite alike in some respects. For instance, the circuits given at A and B in Fig. 2-41 will behave identically, when an external voltage is applied, if (1) L and C are the same in both cases; and (2) R multiplied by r equals the square of the reactance (at resonance) of either L or C. When these conditions are met the two circuits will have the same Q. (These statements are approximate, but are quite accurate if the Q is 10 or more.) The circuit at A is a *series* circuit if it is viewed from the "inside"—that is, going around the loop formed by L, C and r—so its Q can be found from the ratio of X to r.

Thus a circuit like that of Fig. 2-41A has an equivalent **parallel impedance** (at resonance) of $R = \dfrac{X^2}{r}$; X is the reactance of either the inductor or the capacitor. Although R is not an actual resistor, to the source of voltage the

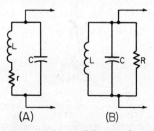

(A)   (B)

Fig. 2-41—Series and parallel equivalents when the two circuits are resonant. The series resistance, r, in A is replaced in B by the equivalent parallel resistance $(R = X_C^2/r = X_L^2/r)$ and vice versa.

parallel-resonant circuit "looks like" a pure resistance of that value. It is "pure" resistance because the inductive and capacitive currents are 180 degrees out of phase and are equal; thus there is no reactive current in the line. In a practical circuit with a high-Q capacitor, at the resonant frequency the parallel impedance is

$$Z_r = QX$$

where Z_r = Resistive impedance at resonance
Q = Quality factor of inductor
X = Reactance (in ohms) of either the inductor or capacitor

Example: The parallel impedance of a circuit with a coil Q of 50 and having inductive and capacitive reactances of 300 ohms will be
$$Z_r = QX = 50 \times 300 = 15,000 \text{ ohms.}$$

At frequencies off resonance the impedance is no longer purely resistive because the inductive and capacitive currents are not equal. The off-resonant impedance therefore is complex, and is lower than the resonant impedance for the reasons previously outlined.

The higher the Q of the circuit, the higher the parallel impedance. Curves showing the variation of impedance (with frequency) of a parallel circuit have just the same shape as the curves showing the variation of current with frequency in a series circuit. Fig. 2-42 is a set of such curves. A set of curves showing the relative response as a function of the departure from the resonant frequency would be similar to Fig. 2-39. The −3 db. bandwidth (bandwidth at 0.707 relative response) is given by

$$Bandwidth \; -3 \text{ db.} = f_o/Q$$

where f_o is the resonant frequency and Q the circuit Q. It is also called the "half-power" bandwidth, for ease of recollection.

Parallel Resonance in Low-Q Circuits

The preceding discussion is accurate only for Qs of 10 or more. When the Q is below 10, resonance in a parallel circuit having resistance in series with the coil, as in Fig. 2-41A, is not so

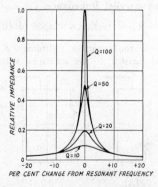

Fig. 2-42.—Relative impedance of parallel-resonant circuits with different Qs. These curves are similar to those in Fig. 2-39 for current in a series-resonant circuit. The effect of Q on impedance is most marked near the resonant frequency.

easily defined. There is a set of values for L and C that will make the parallel impedance a pure resistance, but with these values the impedance does not have its maximum possible value. Another set of values for L and C will make the parallel impedance a maximum, but this maximum value is not a pure resistance. Either condition could be called "resonance," so with low-Q circuits it is necessary to distinguish between **maximum impedance** and **resistive impedance** parallel resonance. The difference between these L and C values and the equal reactances of a series-resonant circuit is appreciable when the Q is in the vicinity of 5, and becomes more marked with still lower Q values.

Q of Loaded Circuits

In many applications of resonant circuits the only power lost is that dissipated in the resistance of the circuit itself. At frequencies below 30 Mc. most of this resistance is in the coil. Within limits, increasing the number of turns in the coil increases the reactance faster than it raises the resistance, so coils for circuits in which the Q must be high are made with relatively large inductance for the frequency.

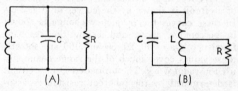

(A)   (B)

Fig. 2-43—The equivalent circuit of a resonant circuit delivering power to a load. The resistor R represents the load resistance. At B the load is tapped across part of L, which by transformer action is equivalent to using a higher load resistance across the whole circuit.

However, when the circuit delivers energy to a load (as in the case of the resonant circuits used in transmitters) the energy consumed in the circuit itself is usually negligible compared with that consumed by the load. The equivalent of such a circuit is shown in Fig. 2-43A, where the parallel resistor represents the load to which power is delivered. If the power dissipated in the load is at least ten times as great as the power lost in the inductor and capacitor, the parallel impedance of the resonant circuit itself will be so high compared with the resistance of the load that for all practical purposes the impedance of the combined circuit is equal to the load resistance. Under these conditions the Q of a parallel-resonant circuit loaded by a resistive impedance is

$$Q = \frac{R}{X}$$

where R = Parallel load resistance (ohms)
X = Reactance (ohms)

Example: A resistive load of 3000 ohms is connected across a resonant circuit in which the inductive and capacitive reactances are each 250 ohms. The circuit Q is then
$$Q = \frac{R}{X} = \frac{3000}{250} = 12$$

Radio-Frequency Circuits

The "effective" Q of a circuit loaded by a parallel resistance becomes higher when the reactances are decreased. A circuit loaded with a relatively low resistance (a few thousand ohms) must have low-reactance elements (large capacitance and small inductance) to have reasonably high Q.

Impedance Transformation

An important application of the parallel-resonant circuit is as an impedance-matching device in the output circuit of a vacuum-tube r.f. power amplifier. As described in the chapter on vacuum tubes, there is an optimum value of load resistance for each type of tube and set of operating conditions. However, the resistance of the load to which the tube is to deliver power usually is considerably lower than the value required for proper tube operation. To transform the actual load resistance to the desired value the load may be tapped across part of the coil, as shown in Fig. 2-43B. This is equivalent to connecting a higher value of load resistance across the whole circuit, and is similar in principle to impedance transformation with an iron-core transformer. In high-frequency resonant circuits the impedance ratio does not vary exactly as the square of the turns ratio, because all the magnetic flux lines do not cut every turn of the coil. A desired reflected impedance usually must be obtained by experimental adjustment.

When the load resistance has a very low value (say below 100 ohms) it may be connected in series in the resonant circuit (as in Fig. 2-41A, for example), in which case it is transformed to an equivalent parallel impedance as previously described. If the Q is at least 10, the equivalent parallel impedance is

$$Z_r = \frac{X^2}{r}$$

where Z_r = Resistive parallel impedance at resonance
X = Reactance (in ohms) of either the coil or capacitor
r = Load resistance inserted in series

If the Q is lower than 10 the reactance will have to be adjusted somewhat, for the reasons given in the discussion of low-Q circuits, to obtain a resistive impedance of the desired value.

Reactance Values

The charts of Figs. 2-44 and 2-45 show reactance values of inductances and capacitances in the range commonly used in r.f. tuned circuits for the amateur bands. With the exception of the 3.5-4 Mc. band, limiting values for which are shown on the charts, the change in reactance over a band, for either inductors or capacitors, is small enough so that a single curve gives the reactance with sufficient accuracy for most practical purposes.

L/C Ratio

The formula for resonant frequency of a circuit shows that the same frequency always will be obtained so long as the *product* of L and C is con-

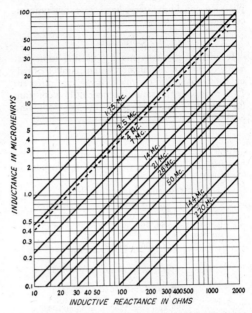

Fig. 2-44—Reactance chart for inductance values commonly used in amateur bands from 1.75 to 220 Mc.

stant. Within this limitation, it is evident that L can be large and C small, L small and C large, etc. The relation between the two for a fixed frequency is called the **L/C ratio**. A **high-C** circuit is one that has more capacitance than "normal" for the frequency; a **low-C** circuit one that has less than normal capacitance. These terms depend to a considerable extent upon the particular ap-

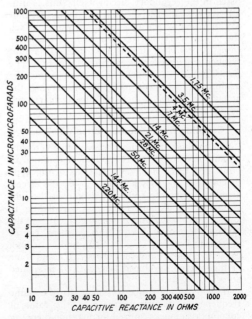

Fig. 2-45—Reactance chart for capacitance values commonly used in amateur bands from 1.75 to 220 Mc.

plication considered, and have no exact numerical meaning.

LC Constants

It is frequently convenient to use the numerical value of the **LC constant** when a number of calculations have to be made involving different L/C ratios for the same frequency. The constant for any frequency is given by the following equation:

$$LC = \frac{25,330}{f^2}$$

where L = Inductance in microhenrys (μh.)
C = Capacitance in micromicrofarads ($\mu\mu$f.)
f = Frequency in megacycles

Example: Find the inductance required to resonate at 3650 kc. (3.65 Mc.) with capacitances of 25, 50, 100, and 500 $\mu\mu$f. The LC constant is

$$LC = \frac{25,330}{(3.65)^2} = \frac{25,330}{13.35} = 1900$$

With   25 $\mu\mu$f. $L = 1900/C = 1900/25$
                $= 76$ μh.
      50 $\mu\mu$f. $L = 1900/C = 1900/50$
                $= 38$ μh.
    100 $\mu\mu$f. $L = 1900/C = 1900/100$
                $= 19$ μh.
    500 $\mu\mu$f. $L = 1900/C = 1900/500$
                $= 3.8$ μh.

COUPLED CIRCUITS

Energy Transfer and Loading

Two circuits are **coupled** when energy can be transferred from one to the other. The circuit delivering power is called the **primary** circuit; the one receiving power is called the **secondary** circuit. The power may be practically all dissipated in the secondary circuit itself (this is usually the case in receiver circuits) or the secondary may simply act as a medium through which the power is transferred to a load. In the latter case, the coupled circuits may act as a radio-frequency impedance-matching device. The matching can be accomplished by adjusting the loading on the secondary and by varying the amount of coupling between the primary and secondary.

Coupling by a Common Circuit Element

One method of coupling between two resonant circuits is through a circuit element common to both. The three common variations of this type of coupling are shown in Fig. 2-46; the circuit element common to both circuits carries the subscript M. At A and B current circulating in $L_1 C_1$ flows through the common element, and the voltage developed across this element causes current to flow in $L_2 C_2$. At C, C_M and C_2 form a capacitive voltage divider across $L_1 C_1$, and some of the voltage developed across $L_1 C_1$ is applied across $L_2 C_2$.

If both circuits are resonant to the same frequency, as is usually the case, the value of coupling reactance required for maximum energy transfer can be approximated by the following, based on $L_1 = L_2$, $C_1 = C_2$ and $Q_1 = Q_2$:

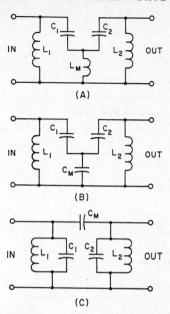

(A)

(B)

(C)

Fig. 2-46—Three methods of circuit coupling.

(A) $L_M \approx L_1/Q_1$;   (B) $C_M \approx Q_1 C_1$;   (C) $C_M \approx C_1/Q_1$.

The coupling can be increased by increasing the above coupling elements in A and C and decreasing the value in B. When the coupling is increased, the resultant bandwidth of the combination is increased, and this principle is sometimes applied to "broad-band" the circuits in a transmitter or receiver. When the coupling elements in A and C are decreased, or when the coupling element in B is increased, the coupling between the circuits is decreased below the *critical coupling* value on which the above approximations are based. Less than critical coupling will decrease the bandwidth and the energy transfer; the principle is often used in receivers to improve the selectivity.

Inductive Coupling

Figs. 2-47 and 2-48 show inductive coupling, or coupling by means of the mutual inductance between two coils. Circuits of this type resemble the iron-core transformer, but because only a part of

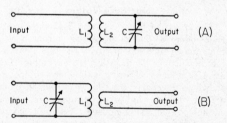

Fig. 2-47—Single-tuned inductively coupled circuits.

the magnetic flux lines set up by one coil cut the turns of the other coil, the simple relationships between turns ratio, voltage ratio and impedance ratio in the iron-core transformer do not hold.

Two types of inductively-coupled circuits are shown in Fig. 2-47. Only one circuit is resonant. The circuit at A is frequently used in receivers for coupling between amplifier tubes when the tuning of the circuit must be varied to respond to signals of different frequencies. Circuit B is used principally in transmitters, for coupling a radio-frequency amplifier to a resistive load.

In these circuits the coupling between the primary and secondary coils usually is "tight"— that is, the coefficient of coupling between the coils is large. With very tight coupling either circuit operates nearly as though the device to which the untuned coil is connected were simply tapped across a corresponding number of turns on the tuned-circuit coil, thus either circuit is approximately equivalent to Fig. 2-43B.

By proper choice of the number of turns on the untuned coil, and by adjustment of the coupling, the parallel impedance of the tuned circuit may be adjusted to the value required for the proper operation of the device to which it is connected. In any case, the maximum energy transfer possible for a given coefficient of coupling is obtained when the reactance of the untuned coil is equal to the resistance of its load.

The Q and parallel impedance of the tuned circuit are reduced by coupling through an untuned coil in much the same way as by the tapping arrangement shown in Fig. 2-43B.

Coupled Resonant Circuits

When the primary and secondary circuits are both tuned, as in Fig. 2-48, the resonance effects

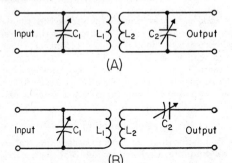

(A)

(B)

Fig. 2-48—Inductively-coupled resonant circuits. Circuit A is used for high-resistance loads (load resistance much higher than the reactance of either L_2 or C_2 at the resonant frequency). Circuit B is suitable for low resistance loads (load resistance much lower than the reactance of either L_2 or C_2 at the resonant frequency).

in both circuits make the operation somewhat more complicated than in the simpler circuits just considered. Imagine first that the two circuits are not coupled and that each is independently tuned to the resonant frequency. The impedance of each will be purely resistive. If the primary circuit is connected to a source of r.f. energy of the resonant frequency and the secondary is then loosely coupled to the primary, a current will flow in the secondary circuit. In flowing through the resistance of the secondary circuit and any load that may be connected to it, the current causes a power loss. This power must come from the energy source through the primary circuit, and manifests itself in the primary as an increase in the equivalent resistance in series with the primary coil. Hence the Q and parallel impedance of the primary circuit are decreased by the coupled secondary. As the coupling is made greater (without changing the tuning of either circuit) the coupled resistance becomes larger and the parallel impedance of the primary continues to decrease. Also, as the coupling is made tighter the amount of power transferred from the primary to the secondary will increase to a maximum at one value of coupling, called **critical coupling**, but then decreases if the coupling is tightened still more (still without changing the tuning).

Critical coupling is a function of the Qs of the two circuits. A higher coefficient of coupling is required to reach critical coupling when the Qs are low; if the Qs are high, as in receiving applications, a coupling coefficient of a few per cent may give critical coupling.

With loaded circuits such as are used in transmitters the Q may be too low to give the desired power transfer even when the coils are coupled as tightly as the physical construction permits. In such case, increasing the Q of either circuit will be helpful, although it is generally better to increase the Q of the lower-Q circuit rather than the reverse. The Q of the parallel-tuned primary (input) circuit can be increased by decreasing the L/C ratio because, as shown in connection with Fig. 2-43, this circuit is in effect loaded by a parallel resistance (effect of coupled-in resistance). In the parallel-tuned secondary circuit, Fig. 2-48A, the Q can be increased, for a fixed value of load resistance, either by decreasing the L/C ratio or by tapping the load down (see Fig. 2-43). In the series-tuned secondary circuit, Fig. 2-48B, the Q may be increased by *increasing* the L/C ratio. There will generally be no difficulty in securing sufficient coupling, with practicable coils, if the product of the Qs of the two tuned circuits is 10 or more. A smaller product will suffice if the coil construction permits tight coupling.

Selectivity

In Fig. 2-47 only one circuit is tuned and the selectivity curve will be essentially that of a single resonant circuit. As stated, the effective Q depends upon the resistance connected to the untuned coil.

In Fig. 2-48, the selectivity is increased. It approaches that of a single tuned circuit having a Q equalling the sum of the individual circuit Qs—*if* the coupling is well below critical (this is not the condition for optimum power transfer discussed immediately above) and both circuits are tuned to resonance. The Qs of the individual circuits are affected by the degree of coupling, because each couples resistance into the other; the

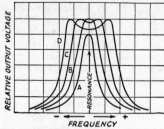

Fig. 2-49—Showing the effect on the output voltage from the secondary circuit of changing the coefficient of coupling between two resonant circuits independently tuned to the same frequency. The voltage applied to the primary is held constant in amplitude while the frequency is varied, and the output voltage is measured across the secondary.

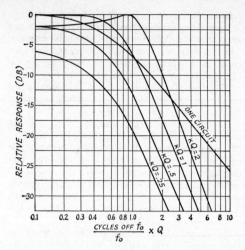

Fig. 2-50—Relative response for a single tuned circuit and for coupled circuits. For inductively-coupled circuits

(Figs. 2-46A and 2-48A), $k = \dfrac{M}{\sqrt{L_1 L_2}}$ where M is the mutual inductance. For capacitance-coupled circuits (Figs. 2-46B and 2-46C), $k \cong \dfrac{\sqrt{C_1 C_2}}{C_M}$ and $k \cong \dfrac{C_M}{\sqrt{C_1 C_2}}$ respectively.

tighter the coupling, the lower the individual Qs and therefore the lower the over-all selectivity.

If both circuits are independently tuned to resonance, the over-all selectivity will vary about as shown in Fig. 2-49 as the coupling is varied. With loose coupling, *A*, the output voltage (across the secondary circuit) is small and the selectivity is high. As the coupling is increased the secondary voltage also increases until critical coupling, *B*, is reached. At this point the output voltage at the resonant frequency is maximum but the selectivity is lower than with looser coupling. At still tighter coupling, *C*, the output voltage at the resonant frequency decreases, but as the frequency is varied either side of resonance it is found that there are two "humps" to the curve, one on either side of resonance. With very tight coupling, *D*, there is a further decrease in the output voltage at resonance and the "humps" are farther away from the resonant frequency. Curves such as those at *C* and *D* are called **flat-topped** because the output voltage does not change much over an appreciable band of frequencies.

Note that the off-resonance humps have the same maximum value as the resonant output voltage at critical coupling. These humps are caused by the fact that at frequencies off resonance the secondary circuit is reactive and couples reactance as well as resistance into the primary. The coupled resistance decreases off resonance, and each hump represents a new condition of critical coupling at a frequency to which the primary is tuned by the additional coupled-in reactance from the secondary.

Fig. 2-50 shows the response curves for various degrees of coupling between two circuits tuned to a frequency f_0. Equals Qs are assumed in both circuits, although the curves are representative if the Qs differ by ratios up to 1.5 or even 2 to 1. In these cases, a value of $Q = \sqrt{Q_1 Q_2}$ should be used.

Band-Pass Coupling

Over-coupled resonant circuits are useful where substantially uniform output is desired over a continuous band of frequencies, without read-

justment of tuning. The width of the flat top of the resonance curve depends on the Qs of the two circuits as well as the tightness of coupling; the frequency separation between the humps will increase, and the curve become more flat-topped, as the Qs are lowered.

Band-pass operation also is secured by tuning the two circuits to slightly different frequencies, which gives a double-humped resonance curve even with loose coupling. This is called **stagger tuning**. To secure adequate power transfer over the frequency band it is usually necessary to use tight coupling and experimentally adjust the circuits for the desired performance.

Link Coupling

A modification of inductive coupling, called **link coupling**, is shown in Fig. 2-51. This gives the effect of inductive coupling between two coils that have no mutual inductance; the link is simply a means for providing the mutual inductance. The total mutual inductance between two coils coupled by a link cannot be made as great as if the coils themselves were coupled. This is because the coefficient of coupling between air-

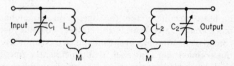

Fig. 2-51—Link coupling. The mutual inductances at both ends of the link are equivalent to mutual inductance between the tuned circuits, and serve the same purpose.

core coils is considerably less than 1, and since there are two coupling points the over-all coupling coefficient is less than for any *pair* of coils. In practice this need not be disadvantageous because the power transfer can be made great enough by making the tuned circuits sufficiently high-Q. Link coupling is convenient when ordinary inductive coupling would be impracticable for constructional reasons.

The link coils usually have a small number of turns compared with the resonant-circuit coils. The number of turns is not greatly important, because the coefficient of coupling is relatively independent of the number of turns on either coil; it is more important that both link coils should have about the *same* inductance. The length of the link between the coils is not critical if it is very small compared with the wavelength, but if the length is more than about one-twentieth of a wavelength the link operates more as a transmission line than as a means for providing mutual inductance. In such case it should be treated by the methods described in the chapter on Transmission Lines.

IMPEDANCE-MATCHING CIRCUITS

The coupling circuits discussed in the preceding section have been based either on inductive coupling or on coupling through a common circuit element between two resonant circuits. These are not the only circuits that may be used for transferring power from one device to another.

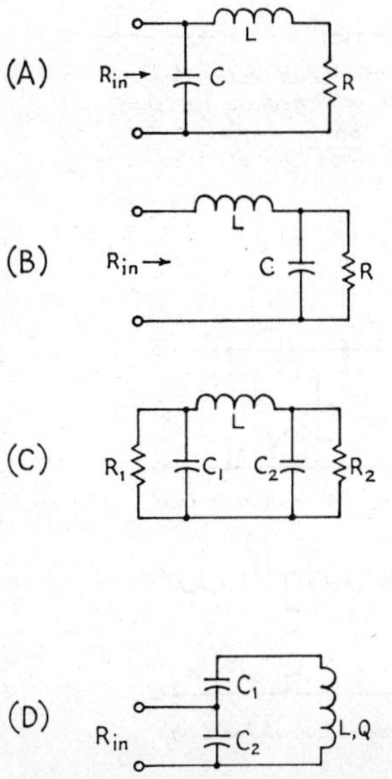

$R_{in} > R$

$X_L = \sqrt{RR_{in} - R^2}$

$X_C = \dfrac{R \, R_{in}}{X_L}$

$R_{in} < R$

$X_C = R\sqrt{\dfrac{R_{in}}{R - R_{in}}}$

$X_L = \dfrac{R \, R_{in}}{X_C}$

$R_1 > R_2$

$X_{C_1} = \dfrac{R_1}{Q}$

$X_{C_2} = R_2\sqrt{\dfrac{R_1/R_2}{Q^2 + 1 - (R_1/R_2)}}$

$X_L = \dfrac{QR_1 + (R_1 R_2 / X_{C_2})}{Q^2 + 1}$

$R_{in} = \dfrac{QX_L}{\left(\frac{C_2}{C_1} + 1\right)^2}$

Fig. 2-52—Impedance-matching networks adaptable to amateur work. (A) L network for transforming to a lower value of resistance. (B) L network for transforming to a higher resistance value. (C) Pi network. R_1 is the larger of the two resistors; Q is defined as R_1/X_{C1}. (D) Tapped tuned circuit used in some receiver applications. The impedance of the tuned circuit is transformed to a lower value, R_{1n}, by the capacitive divider.

There is, in fact, a wide variety of such circuits available, all of them being classified generally as **impedance-matching networks.** Several networks frequently used in amateur equipment are shown in Fig. 2-52.

The L Network

The L network is the simplest possible impedance-matching circuit. It closely resembles an ordinary resonant circuit with the load resistance, R, Fig. 2-52, either in series or parallel. The arrangement shown in Fig. 2-52A is used when the desired impedance, R_{IN}, is larger than the actual load resistance, R, while Fig. 2-52B is used in the opposite case. The design equations for each case are given in the figure, in terms of the circuit reactances. The reactances may be converted to inductance and capacitance by means of the formulas previously given or taken directly from the charts of Figs. 2-44 and 2-45.

When the impedance transformation ratio is large—that is, one of the two impedances is of the order of 100 times (or more) larger than the other—the operation of the circuit is exactly the same as previously discussed in connection with impedance transformation with a simple LC resonant circuit.

The Q of an L network is found in the same way as for simple resonant circuits. That is, it is equal to X_L/R or R_{IN}/X_C in Fig. 2-52A, and to X_L/R_{IN} or R/X_C in Fig. 2-52B. The value of Q is determined by the ratio of the impedances to be matched, and cannot be selected independently. In the equations of Fig. 2-52 it is assumed that both R and R_{IN} are pure resistances.

The Pi Network

The pi network, shown in Fig. 2-52C, offers more flexibility than the L since the operating Q may be chosen practically at will. The only limitation on the circuit values that may be used is that the reactance of the series arm, the inductor L in the figure, must not be greater than the square root of the product of the two values of resistive impedance to be matched. As the circuit is applied in amateur equipment, this limiting value of reactance would represent a network with an undesirably low operating Q, and the circuit values ordinarily used are well on the safe side of the limiting values.

In its principal application as a "tank" circuit matching a transmission line to a power amplifier tube, the load R_2 will generally have a fairly low value of resistance (up to a few hundred ohms) while R_1, the required load for the tube, will be of the order of a few thousand ohms. In such a case the Q of the circuit is defined as R_1/X_{C1}, so the choice of a value for the operating Q immediately sets the value of X_{C1} and hence of C_1. The values of X_{C2} and X_L are then found from the equations given in the figure.

Graphical solutions for practical cases are given in the chapter on transmitter design in the discussion of plate tank circuits. The L and C values may be calculated from the reactances or read from the charts of Figs. 2-44 and 2-45.

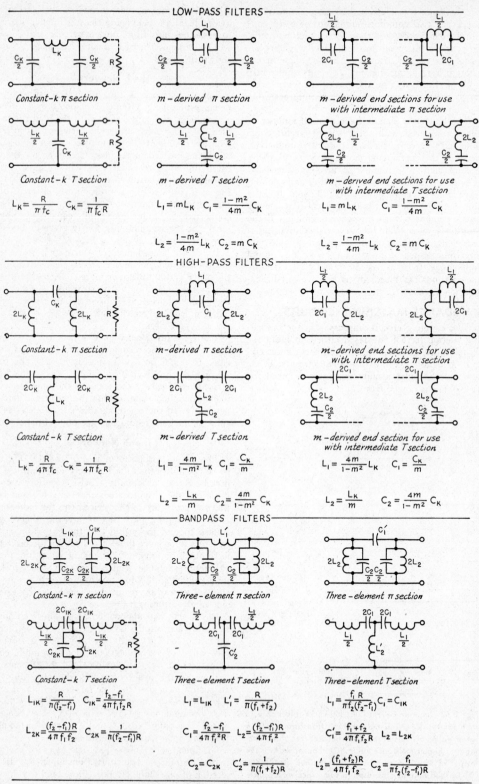

Fig. 2-53—Basic filter sections and design formulas. In the above formulas R is in ohms, C in farads, L in henrys, and f in cycles per second.

Tapped Tuned Circuit

The tapped tuned circuit of Fig. 2-52D is useful in some receiver applications, where it is desirable to use a high-impedance tuned circuit as a lower-impedance load. When the Q of the inductor has been determined, the capacitors can be selected to give the desired impedance transformation and the necessary resultant capacitance to tune the circuit to resonance.

FILTERS

A **filter** is an electrical circuit configuration (**network**) designed to have specific characteristics with respect to the transmission or attenuation of various frequencies that may be applied to it. There are three general types of filters: **low-pass, high-pass,** and **band-pass.**

A low-pass filter is one that will permit all frequencies below a specified one called the **cut-off frequency** to be transmitted with little or no loss, but that will attenuate all frequencies above the cut-off frequency.

A high-pass filter similarly has a cut-off frequency, above which there is little or no loss in transmission, but below which there is considerable attenuation. Its behavior is the opposite of that of the low-pass filter.

A band-pass filter is one that will transmit a selected band of frequencies with substantially no loss, but that will attenuate all frequencies either higher or lower than the desired band.

The **pass band** of a filter is the frequency spectrum that is transmitted with little or no loss. The transmission characteristic is not necessarily perfectly uniform in the pass band, but the variations usually are small.

The **stop band** is the frequency region in which attenuation is desired. The attenuation may vary in the stop band, and in a simple filter usually is least near the cut-off frequency, rising to high values at frequencies considerably removed from the cut-off frequency.

Filters are designed for a specific value of purely resistive impedance (the **terminating impedance** of the filter). When such an impedance is connected to the output terminals of the filter, the impedance looking into the input terminals has essentially the same value, throughout most of the pass band. Simple filters do not give perfectly uniform performance in this respect, but the input impedance of a properly-terminated filter can be made fairly constant, as well as closer to the design value, over the pass band by using **m-derived** filter sections.

A discussion of filter design principles is beyond the scope of this *Handbook,* but it is not difficult to build satisfactory filters from the circuits and formulas given in Fig. 2-53. Filter circuits are built up from elementary sections as shown in the figure. These sections can be used alone or, if greater attenuation and sharper cut-off (that is, a more rapid rate of rise of attenuation with frequency beyond the cut-off frequency) are required, several sections can be connected in series. In the low- and high-pass filters, f_c repre-

sents the cut-off frequency, the highest (for the low-pass) or the lowest (for the high-pass) frequency transmitted without attenuation. In the band-pass filter designs, f_1 is the low-frequency cut-off and f_2 the high-frequency cut-off. The units for L, C, R and f are henrys, farads, ohms and cycles per second, respectively.

All of the types shown are "unbalanced" (one side grounded). For use in balanced circuits (e.g., 300-ohm transmission line, or push-pull audio circuits), the series reactances should be equally divided between the two legs. Thus the balanced constant-k π-section low-pass filter would use two inductors of a value equal to $L_k/2$, while the balanced constant-k π-section high-pass filter would use two capacitors each equal to $2C_k$.

If several low- (or high-) pass sections are to be used, it is advisable to use m-derived end sections on either side of a constant-k center section, although an m-derived center section can be used. The factor m determines the ratio of the cut-off frequency, f_c, to a frequency of high attenuation, f_∞. Where only one m-derived section is used, a value of 0.6 is generally used for m, although a deviation of 10 or 15 per cent from this value is not too serious in amateur work. For a value of $m = 0.6$, f_∞ will be $1.25f_c$ for the low-pass filter and $0.8f_c$ for the high-pass filter. Other values can be found from

$$ m = \sqrt{1 - \left(\frac{f_c}{f_\infty} \right)^2} \text{ for the low-pass filter and} $$

$$ m = \sqrt{1 - \left(\frac{f_\infty}{f_c} \right)^2} \text{ for the high-pass filter.} $$

The output sides of the filters shown should be terminated in a resistance equal to R, and there should be little or no reactive component in the termination.

PIEZOELECTRIC CRYSTALS

A number of crystalline substances found in nature have the ability to transform mechanical strain into an electrical charge, and *vice versa.* This property is known as the **piezoelectric effect.** A small plate or bar cut in the proper way from a quartz crystal and placed between two conducting electrodes will be mechanically strained when the electrodes are connected to a source of voltage. Conversely, if the crystal is squeezed between two electrodes a voltage will be developed between the electrodes.

Piezoelectric crystals can be used to transform mechanical energy into electrical energy, and vice versa. They are used in microphones and phonograph pick-ups, where mechanical vibrations are transformed into alternating voltages of corresponding frequency. They are also used in headsets and loudspeakers, transforming electrical energy into mechanical vibration. Crystals of Rochelle salts are used for these purposes.

Crystal Resonators

Crystalline plates also are mechanical resonators that have natural frequencies of vibration ranging from a few thousand cycles to tens of megacycles per second. The vibration frequency depends on the kind of crystal, the way the plate is cut from the natural crystal, and on the dimensions of the plate. The thing that makes the **crystal resonator** valuable is that it has extremely high Q, ranging from a minimum of about 20,000 to as high as 1,000,000.

Analogies can be drawn between various mechanical properties of the crystal and the electrical characteristics of a tuned circuit. This leads to an "equivalent circuit" for the crystal. The electrical coupling to the crystal is through the holder plates between which it is sandwiched; these plates form, with the crystal as the dielectric, a small capacitator like any other capacitor constructed of two plates with a dielectric between. The crystal itself is equivalent to a series-resonant circuit, and together with the capacitance of the holder forms the equivalent circuit shown in Fig. 2-54. At frequencies of the order of

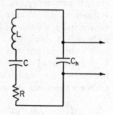

Fig. 2-54—Equivalent circuit of a crystal resonator. L, C and R are the electrical equivalents of mechanical properties of the crystal; C_h is the capacitance of the holder plates with the crystal plate between them.

450 kc., where crystals are widely used as resonators, the equivalent L may be several henrys and the equivalent C only a few hundredths of a micromicrofarad. Although the equivalent R is of the order of a few thousand ohms, the reactance at resonance is so high that the Q of the crystal likewise is high.

A circuit of the type shown in Fig. 2-54 has a series-resonant frequency, when viewed from the circuit terminals indicated by the arrowheads, determined by L and C only. At this frequency the circuit impedance is simply equal to R, providing the reactance of C_h is large compared with R (this is generally the case). The circuit also

has a parallel-resonant frequency determined by L and the equivalent capacitance of C and C_h in series. Since this equivalent capacitance is smaller than C alone, the parallel-resonant frequency is higher than the series-resonant frequency. The separation between the two resonant frequencies depends on the ratio of C_h to C, and when this ratio is large (as in the case of a crystal resonator, where C_h will be a few $\mu\mu f.$ in the average case) the two frequencies will be quite close together. A separation of a kilocycle or less at 455 kc. is typical of a quartz crystal.

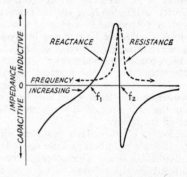

Fig. 2-55—Reactance and resistance vs. frequency of a circuit of the type shown in Fig. 2-54. Actual values of reactance, resistance and the separation between the series- and parallel-resonant frequencies, f_1, and f_2, respectively, depend on the circuit constants.

Fig. 2-55 shows how the resistance and reactance of such a circuit vary as the applied frequency is varied. The reactance passes through zero at both resonant frequencies, but the resistance rises to a large value at parallel resonance, just as in any tuned circuit.

Quartz crystals may be used either as simple resonators for their selective properties or as the frequency-controlling elements in oscillators as described in later chapters. The series-resonant frequency is the one principally used in the former case, while the more common forms of oscillator circuit use the parallel-resonant frequency.

PRACTICAL CIRCUIT DETAILS

COMBINED A.C. AND D.C.

Most radio circuits are built around vacuum tubes, and it is the nature of these tubes to require direct current (usually at a fairly high voltage) for their operation. They convert the direct current into an alternating current (and sometimes the reverse) at frequencies varying from well down in the audio range to well up in the super-high range. The conversion process almost invariably requires that the direct and alternating currents meet somewhere in the circuit.

In this meeting, the a.c. and d.c. are actually combined into a single current that "pulsates" (at the a.c. frequency) about an average value equal to the direct current. This is shown in Fig. 2-56. It is convenient to consider that the alter-

Fig. 2-56—Pulsating d.c., composed of an alternating current or voltage superimposed on a steady direct current or voltage.

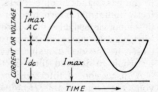

nating current is **superimposed** on the direct current, so we may look upon the actual current as having two components, one d.c. and the other a.c.

In an alternating current the positive and negative alternations have the same average amplitude, so when the wave is superimposed on a direct current the latter is alternately increased and decreased by the same amount. There is thus no *average* change in the direct current. If a d.c. instrument is being used to read the current, the reading will be exactly the same whether or not the a.c. is superimposed.

However, there is actually more power in such a combination current than there is in the direct current alone. This is because power varies as the square of the instantaneous value of the current, and when all the instantaneous squared values are averaged over a cycle the total power is greater than the d.c. power alone. If the a.c. is a sine wave having a peak value just equal to the d.c., the power in the circuit is 1.5 times the d.c. power. An instrument whose readings are proportional to power will show such an increase.

Series and Parallel Feed

Fig. 2-57 shows in simplified form how d.c. and a.c. may be combined in a vacuum-tube circuit. In this case, it is assumed that the a.c. is at radio frequency, as suggested by the coil-and-capacitor tuned circuit. It is also assumed that r.f. current can easily flow through the d.c. supply; that is, the impedance of the supply at radio frequencies is so small as to be negligible.

In the circuit at the left, the tube, tuned circuit, and d.c. supply all are connected in series. The direct current flows through the r.f. coil to get to the tube; the r.f. current generated by the tube

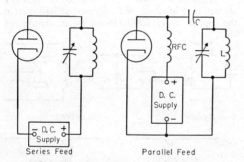

| Series Feed | Parallel Feed |

Fig. 2-57—Illustrating series and parallel feed.

flows through the d.c. supply to get to the tuned circuit. This is **series feed**. It works because the impedance of the d.c. supply at radio frequencies is so low that it does not affect the flow of *r.f.* current, and because the d.c. resistance of the coil is so low that it does not affect the flow of *direct* current.

In the circuit at the right the direct current does not flow through the r.f. tuned circuit, but instead goes to the tube through a second coil, *RFC* **(radio-frequency choke)**. Direct current cannot flow through *L* because a **blocking capacitance,** *C,* is placed in the circuit to prevent it. (Without *C,* the d.c. supply would be short-circuited by the low resistance of *L.*) On the other hand, the r.f. current generated by the tube can easily flow through *C* to the tuned circuit because the capacitance of *C* is intentionally chosen to have low reactance (compared with the impedance of the tuned circuit) at the radio frequency. The r.f. current cannot flow through the

d.c. supply because the inductance of *RFC* is intentionally made so large that it has a very high reactance at the radio frequency. The resistance of *RFC,* however, is too low to have an appreciable effect on the flow of direct current. The two currents are thus in *parallel,* hence the name **parallel feed.**

Either type of feed may be used for both a.f. and r.f. circuits. In parallel feed there is no d.c. voltage on the a.c. circuit, a desirable feature from the viewpoint of safety to the operator, because the voltages applied to tubes—particularly transmitting tubes—are dangerous. On the other hand, it is somewhat difficult to make an r.f. choke work well over a wide range of frequencies. Series feed is often preferred, therefore, because it is relatively easy to keep the impedance between the a.c. circuit and the tube low.

Bypassing

In the series-feed circuit just discussed, it was assumed that the d.c. supply had very low impedance at radio frequencies. This is not likely to be true in a practical power supply, partly because the normal physical separation between the supply and the r.f. circuit would make it necessary to use rather long connecting wires or leads. At radio frequencies, even a few feet of wire can have fairly large reactance—too large to be considered a really "low-impedance" connection.

An actual circuit would be provided with a **bypass capacitor,** as shown in Fig. 2-58. Capacitor *C* is chosen to have low reactance at the operating frequency, and is installed right in the circuit where it can be wired to the other parts with quite short connecting wires. Hence the r.f. current will tend to flow through it rather than through the d.c. supply.

To be effective, the reactance of the bypass

Fig. 2-58—Typical use of a bypass capacitor and r.f. choke in a series-feed circuit.

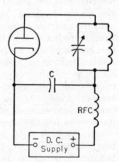

capacitor should not be more than one-tenth of the impedance of the bypassed part of the circuit. Very often the latter impedance is not known, in which case it is desirable to use the largest capacitance in the bypass that circumstances permit. To make doubly sure that r.f. current will not flow through a non-r.f. circuit such as a power supply, an r.f. choke may be connected in the lead to the latter, as shown in Fig. 2-58.

The same type of bypassing is used when audio frequencies are present in addition to r.f. Because the reactance of a capacitor changes with frequency, it is readily possible to choose a capacitance that will represent a very low reactance at radio frequencies but that will have such high reactance at audio frequencies that it is practically an open circuit. A capacitance of 0.001 μf. is practically a short circuit for r.f., for example, but is almost an open circuit at audio frequencies. (The actual value of capacitance that is usable will be modified by the impedances concerned.) Capacitors also are used in audio circuits to carry the audio frequencies around a d.c. supply.

Distributed Capacitance and Inductance

In the discussions earlier in this chapter it was assumed that a capacitor has only capacitance and that an inductor has only inductance. Unfortunately, this is not strictly true. There is always a certain amount of inductance in a conductor of any length, and a capacitor is bound to have a little inductance in addition to its intended capacitance. Also, there is always capacitance between two conductors or between parts of the same conductor, and thus there is appreciable capacitance between the turns of an inductance coil.

This **distributed inductance** in a capacitor and the **distributed capacitance** in an inductor have important practical effects. Actually, every capacitor is in effect a series-tuned circuit, resonant at the frequency where its capacitance and inductance have the same reactance. Similarly, every inductor is in effect a parallel-tuned circuit, resonant at the frequency where its inductance and distributed capacitance have the same reactance. At frequencies well below these **natural resonances,** the capacitor will act like a capacitance and the coil will act like an inductor. Near the natural resonance points, the inductor will have its highest impedance and the capacitor will have its lowest impedance. At frequencies above resonance, the capacitor acts like an inductor and the inductor acts like a capacitor. Thus there is a limit to the amount of capacitance that can be used at a given frequency. There is a similar limit to the inductance that can be used. At audio frequencies, capacitances measured in microfarads and inductances measured in henrys are practicable. At low and medium radio frequencies, inductances of a few mh. and capacitances of a few thousand pf. are the largest practicable. At high radio frequencies, usable inductance values drop to a few μh. and capacitances to a few hundred pf.

Distributed capacitance and inductance are important not only in r.f. tuned circuits, but in bypassing and choking as well. It will be appreciated that a bypass capacitor that actually acts like an inductance, or an r.f. choke that acts like a low-reactance capacitor, cannot work as it is intended they should.

Grounds

Throughout this book there are frequent references to **ground** and **ground potential**. When a connection is said to be "grounded" it does not necessarily mean that it actually goes to earth. What it means is that an actual earth connection to that point in the circuit should not disturb the operation of the circuit in any way. The term also is used to indicate a "common" point in the circuit where power supplies and metallic supports (such as a metal chassis) are electrically tied together. It is general practice, for example, to "ground" the negative terminal of a d.c. power supply, and to "ground" the filament or heater power supplies for vacuum tubes. Since the cathode of a vacuum tube is a junction point for grid and plate voltage supplies, and since the various circuits connected to the tube elements have at least one point connected to cathode, these points also are "returned to ground." Ground is therefore a common reference point in the radio circuit. "Ground potential" means that there is no "difference of potential"—no voltage—between the circuit point and the earth.

Single-Ended and Balanced Circuits

With reference to ground, a circuit may be either **single-ended** (unbalanced) or **balanced.** In a single-ended circuit, one side of the circuit (the **cold** side) is connected to ground. In a balanced circuit, the electrical midpoint is connected to ground, so that the circuit has two "hot" ends each at the same voltage "above" ground.

Typical single-ended and balanced circuits are shown in Fig. 2-59. R.f. circuits are shown in the upper row, while iron-core transformers

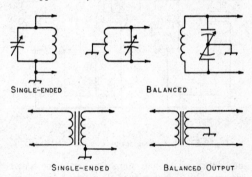

SINGLE-ENDED   BALANCED

SINGLE-ENDED   BALANCED OUTPUT

Fig. 2-59—Single-ended and balanced circuits.

(such as are used in power-supply and audio circuits) are shown in the lower row. The r.f. circuits may be balanced either by connecting the center of the coil to ground or by using a "balanced" or "split-stator" capacitor and connecting its rotor to r.f. ground. In the iron-core transformer, one or both windings may be tapped at the center of the winding to provide the ground connection.

Shielding

Two circuits that are physically near each other usually will be coupled to each other in some degree even though no coupling is intended. The metallic parts of the two circuits form a small capacitance through which energy can be transferred by means of the electric field. Also, the magnetic field about the coil or wiring of one circuit can couple that circuit to a second through the latter's coil and wiring. In many cases these unwanted couplings must be prevented if the circuits are to work properly.

Capacitive coupling may readily be prevented by enclosing one or both of the circuits in grounded low-resistance metallic containers, called **shields.** The electric field from the circuit components does not penetrate the shield. A metallic plate, called a **baffle shield,** inserted between two components also may suffice to prevent electrostatic coupling between them. It should be large enough to make the components invisible to each other.

Similar metallic shielding is used at radio frequencies to prevent magnetic coupling. The shielding effect for magnetic fields increases with frequency and with the conductivity and thickness of the shielding material.

A closed shield is required for good magnetic shielding; in some cases separate shields, one about each coil, may be required. The baffle shield is rather ineffective for magnetic shielding, al-

though it will give partial shielding if placed at right angles to the axes of, and between, the coils to be shielded from each other.

Shielding a coil reduces its inductance, because part of its field is canceled by the shield. Also, there is always a small amount of resistance in the shield, and there is therefore an energy loss. This loss raises the effective resistance of the coil. The decrease in inductance and increase in resistance lower the Q of the coil, but the reduction in inductance and Q will be small if the spacing between the sides of the coil and the shield is at least half the coil diameter, and if the spacing at the ends of the coil is at least equal to the coil diameter. The higher the conductivity of the shield material, the less the effect on the inductance and Q. Copper is the best material, but aluminum is quite satisfactory.

For good magnetic shielding at audio frequencies it is necessary to enclose the coil in a container of high-permeability iron or steel. In this case the shield can be quite close to the coil without harming its performance.

U.H.F. CIRCUITS

RESONANT LINES

In resonant circuits as employed at the lower frequencies it is possible to consider each of the reactance components as a separate entity. The fact that an inductor has a certain amount of self-capacitance, as well as some resistance, while a capacitor also possesses a small self-inductance, can usually be disregarded.

At the very-high and ultrahigh frequencies it is not readily possible to separate these components. Also, the connecting leads, which at lower frequencies would serve merely to join the capacitor and coil, now may have more inductance than the coil itself. The required inductance coil may be no more than a single turn of wire, yet even this single turn may have dimensions comparable to a wavelength at the operating frequency. Thus the energy in the field surrounding the "coil" may in part be radiated. At a sufficiently high frequency the loss by radiation may represent a major portion of the total energy in the circuit.

For these reasons it is common practice to utilize resonant sections of transmission line as tuned circuits at frequencies above 100 Mc. or so. A quarter-wavelength line, or any odd multiple thereof, shorted at one end and open at the other exhibits large standing waves, as described in the section on transmission lines. When a voltage of the frequency at which such a line is resonant is applied to the open end, the response is very similar to that of a parallel resonant circuit. The equivalent relationships are shown in Fig. 2-60. At frequencies off resonance the line displays qualities comparable with the inductive and capacitive reactances of a conventional tuned circuit, so sections of transmission line can be used in much the same manner as inductors and capacitors.

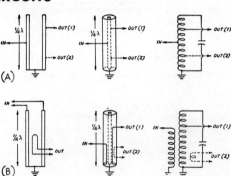

Fig. 2-60—Equivalent coupling circuits for parallel-line, coaxial-line and conventional resonant circuits.

To minimize radiation loss the two conductors of a parallel-conductor line should not be more than about one-tenth wavelength apart, the spacing being measured between the conductor axes. On the other hand, the spacing should not be less than about twice the conductor diameter because of "proximity effect," which causes eddy currents and an increase in loss. Above 300 Mc. it is difficult to satisfy both these requirements simultaneously, and the radiation from an open line tends to become excessive, reducing the Q. In such case the coaxial type of line is to be preferred, since it is inherently shielded.

Representative methods for adjusting coaxial lines to resonance are shown in Fig. 2-61. At the left, a sliding shorting disk is used to reduce the effective length of the line by altering the position of the short-circuit. In the center, the same effect is accomplished by using a telescoping tube in the end of the inner conductor to vary its length and thereby the effective length of the line. At the right, two possible methods of using

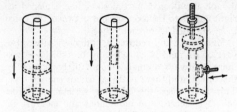

Fig. 2-61—Methods of tuning coaxial resonant lines.

parallel-plate capacitors are illustrated. The arrangement with the loading capacitor at the open end of the line has the greatest tuning effect per unit of capacitance; the alternative method, which is equivalent to tapping the capacitor down on the line, has less effect on the Q of the circuit. Lines with capacitive "loading" of the sort illustrated will be shorter, physically, than unloaded lines resonant at the same frequency.

Two methods of tuning parallel-conductor lines are shown in Fig. 2-62. The sliding short-

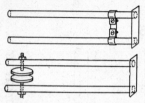

Fig. 2-62—Methods of tuning parallel-type resonant lines.

circuiting strap can be tightened by means of screws and nuts to make good electrical contact. The parallel-plate capacitor in the second drawing may be placed anywhere along the line, the tuning effect becoming less as the capacitor is located nearer the shorted end of the line. Although a low-capacitance variable capacitor of ordinary construction can be used, the circular-plate type shown is symmetrical and thus does not unbalance the line. It also has the further advantage that no insulating material is required.

WAVEGUIDES

A waveguide is a conducting tube through which energy is transmitted in the form of electromagnetic waves. The tube is not considered as carrying a current in the same sense that the wires of a two-conductor line do, but rather as a *boundary* which confines the waves to the enclosed space. Skin effect prevents any electromagnetic effects from being evident outside the guide. The energy is injected at one end, either through capacitive or inductive coupling or by radiation, and is received at the other end. The waveguide then merely confines the energy of the fields, which are propagated through it to the receiving end by means of reflections against its inner walls.

Analysis of waveguide operation is based on the assumption that the guide material is a perfect conductor of electricity. Typical distributions

of electric and magnetic fields in a rectangular guide are shown in Fig. 2-63. It will be observed that the intensity of the electric field is greatest (as indicated by closer spacing of the lines of force) at the center along the x dimension, Fig. 2-63(B), diminishing to zero at the end walls. The latter is a necessary condition, since the existence of any electric field parallel to the walls at the surface would cause an infinite current to flow in a perfect conductor. This represents an impossible situation.

Modes of Propagation

Fig. 2-63 represents a relatively simple distribution of the electric and magnetic fields.

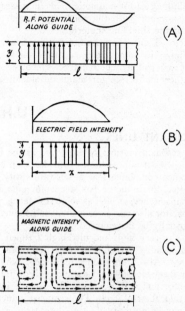

Fig. 2-63—Field distribution in a rectangular waveguide. The $TE_{1,0}$ mode of propagation is depicted.

There is in general an infinite number of ways in which the fields can arrange themselves in a guide so long as there is no upper limit to the frequency to be transmitted. Each field configuration is called a **mode**. All modes may be separated into two general groups. One group, designated TM (**transverse magnetic**), has the magnetic field entirely transverse to the direction of propagation, but has a component of electric field in that direction. The other type, designated TE (**transverse electric**) has the electric field entirely transverse, but has a component of magnetic field in the direction of propagation. TM waves are sometimes called E waves, and TE waves are sometimes called H waves, but the TM and TE designations are preferred.

The particular mode of transmission is identified by the group letters followed by two subscript numerals; for example, $TE_{1.0}$, $TM_{1.1}$, etc. The number of possible modes increases with frequency for a given size of guide. There is only one possible mode (called the **dominant mode**) for the lowest frequency that can be transmitted. The dominant mode is the one generally used in practical work.

Waveguide Dimensions

In the rectangular guide the critical dimension is x in Fig. 2-63; this dimension must be more than one-half wavelength at the lowest frequency to be transmitted. In practice, the y dimension usually is made about equal to $\frac{1}{2}x$ to avoid the possibility of operation at other than the dominant mode.

Other cross-sectional shapes than the rectangle can be used, the most important being the circular pipe. Much the same considerations apply as in the rectangular case.

Wavelength formulas for rectangular and circular guides are given in the following table, where x is the width of a rectangular guide and r is the radius of a circular guide. All figures are in terms of the dominant mode.

	Rectangular	Circular
Cut-off wavelength	$2x$	$3.41r$
Longest wavelength transmitted with little attenuation	$1.6x$	$3.2r$
Shortest wavelength before next mode becomes possible	$1.1x$	$2.8r$

Cavity Resonators

Another kind of circuit particularly applicable at wavelengths of the order of centimeters is the **cavity resonator**, which may be looked upon as a section of a waveguide with the dimensions chosen so that waves of a given length can be maintained inside.

Typical shapes used for resonators are the cylinder, the rectangular box and the sphere, as shown in Fig. 2-64. The resonant frequency depends upon the dimensions of the cavity and the mode of oscillation of the waves (comparable to

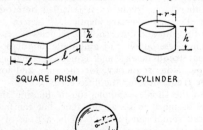

SQUARE PRISM   CYLINDER

SPHERE

Fig. 2-64—Forms of cavity resonators.

the transmission modes in a waveguide). For the lowest modes the resonant wavelengths are as follows:

Cylinder	$2.61r$
Square box	$1.41l$
Sphere	$2.28r$

The resonant wavelengths of the cylinder and square box are independent of the height when the height is less than a half wavelength. In other modes of oscillation the height must be a multiple of a half wavelength as measured inside the cavity. A cylindrical cavity can be tuned by a sliding shorting disk when operating in such a mode. Other tuning methods include placing adjustable tuning paddles or "slugs" inside the cavity so that the standing-wave pattern of the electric and magnetic fields can be varied.

A form of cavity resonator in practical use is the re-entrant cylindrical type shown in Fig. 2-65. In construction it resembles a concentric line closed at both ends with capacitive loading at the top, but the actual mode of oscillation may

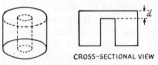

CROSS-SECTIONAL VIEW

Fig. 2-65—Re-entrant cylindrical cavity resonator.

differ considerably from that occurring in coaxial lines. The resonant frequency of such a cavity depends upon the diameters of the two cylinders and the distance d between the cylinder ends.

Compared with ordinary resonant circuits, cavity resonators have extremely high Q. A value of Q of the order of 1000 or more is readily obtainable, and Q values of several thousand can be secured with good design and construction.

Coupling to Waveguides and Cavity Resonators

Energy may be introduced into or abstracted from a waveguide or resonator by means of either the electric or magnetic field. The energy transfer frequently is through a coaxial line, two methods for coupling to which are shown in Fig. 2-66. The probe shown at A is simply a short extension of the inner conductor of the coaxial line, so oriented that it is parallel to the electric lines of force. The loop shown at B is arranged so that it encloses some of the magnetic lines of force. The point at which maximum coupling will be secured depends upon the particular mode of propagation in the guide or cavity; the coupling will be maximum when the coupling device is in the most intense field.

Coupling can be varied by turning the probe or loop through a 90-degree angle. When the probe is perpendicular to the electric lines the coupling will be minimum; similarly, when the plane of the loop is parallel to the magnetic lines the coupling will have its minimum value.

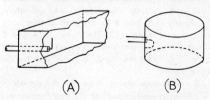

(A)   (B)

Fig. 2-66—Coupling to waveguides and resonators.

MODULATION, HETERODYNING AND BEATS

Since one of the most widespread uses of radio frequencies is the transmission of speech and music, it would be very convenient if the audio spectrum to be transmitted could simply be shifted up to some radio frequency, transmitted as radio waves, and shifted back down to audio at the receiving point. Suppose the audio signal to be transmitted by radio is a pure 1000-cycle tone, and we wish to transmit it at 1 Mc. (1,000,000 cycles per second). One possible way might be to add 1.000 Mc. and 1 kc. together, thereby obtaining a radio frequency of 1.001 Mc. No simple method for doing this directly has been devised, although the *effect* is obtained and used in "single-sideband transmission."

When two different frequencies are present simultaneously in an ordinary circuit (specifically, one in which Ohm's Law holds) each be-

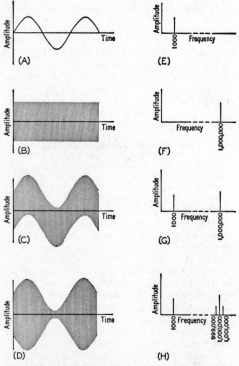

Fig. 2-67—Amplitude-vs.-time and amplitude-vs.-frequency plots of various signals. (A) 1½ cycles of an audio signal, assumed to be 1000 c.p.s. in this example. (B) A radio-frequency signal, assumed to be 1 Mc.; 1500 cycles are completed during the same time as the 1½ cycles in A, so they cannot be shown accurately. (C) The signals of A and B in the same circuit; each maintains its own identity. (D) The signals of A and B in a circuit where the amplitude of A can control the amplitude of B. The 1-Mc. signal is modulated by the 1000-cycle signal.

E, F, G and H show the spectrums for the signals in A, B, C and D, respectively. Note the new frequencies in H, resulting from the modulation process.

haves as though the other were not there. The total or resultant voltage (or current) in the circuit will be the sum of the instantaneous values of the two at every instant. This is because there can be only one value of current or voltage at any single point in a circuit at any instant. Figs. 2-67A and B show two such frequencies, and C shows the resultant. The amplitude of the 1-Mc. current is not affected by the presence of the 1-kc. current, but the axis is shifted back and forth at the 1-kc. rate. An attempt to transmit such a combination as a radio wave would result in only the radiation of the 1-Mc. frequency, since the 1-kc. frequency retains its identity as an audio frequency and will not radiate.

There are devices, however, which make it possible for one frequency to control the amplitude of the other. If, for example, a 1-kc. tone is used to control a 1-Mc. signal, the maximum r.f. output will be obtained when the 1-kc. signal is at the peak of one alternation and the minimum will occur at the peak of the next alternation. The process is called **amplitude modulation,** and the effect is shown in Fig. 2-67D. The resultant signal is now entirely at radio frequency, but with its amplitude varying at the modulation rate (1 kc.). Receiving equipment adjusted to receive the 1-Mc. r.f. signal can reproduce these changes in amplitude, and reveal what the audio signal is, through a process called **detection.**

It might be assumed that the only radio frequency present in such a signal is the original 1.000 Mc., but such is not the case. Two new frequencies have appeared. These are the sum (1.000 + .001) and the difference (1.000 − .001) of the two, and thus the radio frequencies appearing after modulation are 1.001, 1.000 and .999 Mc.

When an audio frequency is used to control the amplitude of a radio frequency, the process is generally called "amplitude modulation," as mentioned, but when a radio frequency modulates another radio frequency it is called **heterodyning.** The processes are identical. A general term for the sum and difference frequencies generated during heterodyning or amplitude modulation is "beat frequencies," and a more specific one is **upper side frequency,** for the sum, and **lower side frequency** for the difference.

In the simple example, the modulating signal was assumed to be a pure tone, but the modulating signal can just as well be a *band* of frequencies making up speech or music. In this case, the side frequencies are grouped into the **upper sideband** and the **lower sideband.** Fig. 2-67H shows the side frequencies appearing as a result of the modulation process.

Amplitude modulation (**a.m.**) is not the only possible type nor is it the only one in use. Such signal properties as phase and frequency can also be modulated. In every case the modulation process leads to the generation of a new set (or sets) of radio frequencies symmetrically disposed about the original radio (**carrier**) frequency.

Chapter 3

Vacuum-Tube Principles

CURRENT IN A VACUUM

The outstanding difference between the vacuum tube and most other electrical devices is that the electric current does not flow through a conductor but through empty space—a vacuum. This is only possible when "free" electrons—that is, electrons that are not attached to atoms—are somehow introduced into the vacuum. Free electrons in an evacuated space will be attracted to a positively charged object within the same space, or will be repelled by a negatively charged object. The movement of the electrons under the attraction or repulsion of such charged objects constitutes the current in the vacuum.

The most practical way to introduce a sufficiently large number of electrons into the evacuated space is by **thermionic emission.**

Thermionic Emission

If a piece of metal is heated to incandescence in a vacuum, electrons near the surface are given enough energy of motion to fly off into the surrounding space. The higher the temperature, the greater the number of electrons emitted. The name for the emitting metal is **cathode.**

If the cathode is the only thing in the vacuum, most of the emitted electrons stay in its immediate vicinity, forming a "cloud" about the cath-

ode. The reason for this is that the electrons in the space, being negative electricity, form a negative charge **(space charge)** in the region of the cathode. The space charge repels those electrons nearest the cathode, tending to make them fall back on it.

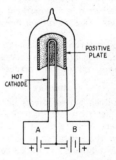

Fig. 3-1—Conduction by thermionic emission in a vacuum tube. The A battery is used to heat the cathode to a temperature that will cause it to emit electrons. The B battery makes the plate positive with respect to the cathode, thereby causing the emitted electrons to be attracted to the plate. Electrons captured by the plate flow back through the B battery to the cathode.

Now suppose a second conductor is introduced into the vacuum, but not connected to anything else inside the tube. If this second conductor is given a positive charge by connecting a voltage source between it and the cathode, as indicated in Fig. 3-1, electrons emitted by the cathode are attracted to the positively charged conductor. An electric current then flows through the circuit formed by the cathode, the charged conductor, and the voltage source. In Fig. 3-1 this voltage source is a battery ("B" battery); a second battery ("A" battery) is also indicated for heating the cathode to the proper operating temperature.

The positively charged conductor is usually a metal plate or cylinder (surrounding the cathode) and is called an **anode** or **plate.** Like the other working parts of a tube, it is a **tube element** or **electrode.** The tube shown in Fig. 3-1 is a **two-element** or **two-electrode** tube, one element being the cathode and the other the anode or plate.

Since electrons are negative electricity, they will be attracted to the plate *only* when the plate is positive with respect to the cathode. If the plate is given a negative charge, the

Transmitting tubes are in the back and center rows. Receiving tubes are in the front row (l. to r.): miniature, pencil, planar triode (two), Nuvistor and 1-inch diameter cathode-ray tube.

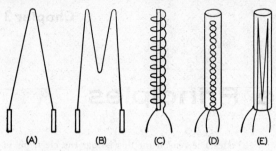

Fig. 3-2—Types of cathode construction. Directly heated cathodes or "filaments" are shown at A, B, and C. The inverted V filament is used in small receiving tubes, the M in both receiving and transmitting tubes. The spiral filament is a transmitting-tube type. The indirectly-heated cathodes at D and E show two types of heater construction, one a twisted loop and the other bunched heater wires. Both types tend to cancel the magnetic fields set up by the current through the heater.

electrons will be repelled back to the cathode and no current will flow. The vacuum tube therefore can conduct *only in one direction.*

Cathodes

Before electron emission can occur, the cathode must be heated to a high temperature. However, it is not essential that the heating current flow through the actual material that does the emitting; the filament or heater can be electrically separate from the emitting cathode. Such a cathode is called **indirectly heated,** while an emitting filament is called a **directly heated** cathode. Fig. 3-2 shows both types in the forms which they commonly take.

Much greater electron emission can be obtained, at relatively low temperatures, by using special cathode materials rather than pure metals. One of these is **thoriated tungsten,** or tungsten in which thorium is dissolved. Still greater efficiency is achieved in the **oxide-coated** cathode, a cathode in which rare-earth oxides form a coating over a metal base.

Although the oxide-coated cathode has much the highest efficiency, it can be used successfully only in tubes that operate at rather low plate voltages. Its use is therefore confined to receiving-type tubes and to the smaller varieties of transmitting tubes. The thoriated filament, on the other hand, will operate well in high-voltage tubes.

Plate Current

If there is only a small positive voltage on the plate, the number of electrons reaching it will be small because the space charge (which is negative) prevents those electrons nearest the cathode from being attracted to the plate. As the plate voltage is increased, the effect of the space charge is increasingly overcome and the number of electrons attracted to the plate becomes larger. That is, the **plate current** increases with increasing plate voltage.

Fig. 3-3 shows a typical plot of plate current *vs.* plate voltage for a two-element tube or **diode.** A curve of this type can be obtained with the circuit shown, if the plate voltage is increased in small steps and a current reading taken (by means of the current-indicating instrument—a milliammeter) at each voltage. The plate current is zero with no plate voltage and the curve rises until a **saturation point** is reached. This is where the positive charge on the plate has substantially overcome the space charge and almost all the electrons are going to the plate. At higher voltages the plate current stays at practically the same value.

The plate voltage multiplied by the plate current is the **power input** to the tube. In a circuit like that of Fig. 3-3 this power is all used in heating the plate. If the power input is large, the plate temperature may rise to a very high value (the plate may become red or even white hot). The heat developed in the plate is radiated to the bulb of the tube, and in turn radiated by the bulb to the surrounding air.

RECTIFICATION

Since current can flow through a tube in only one direction, a diode can be used to change alternating current into direct current. It does this by permitting current to flow only when the anode is positive with respect to the cathode. There is no current flow when the plate is negative.

Fig. 3-4 shows a representative circuit. Alternating voltage from the secondary of the transformer, T, is applied to the diode tube in series with a **load resistor,** R. The voltage varies as is usual with a.c., but current flows through the tube and R only when the plate is positive with respect to the cathode—that is, during the half-cycle when the upper end of the transformer winding is positive. During the negative half-cycle there is simply a gap in the current flow. This **rectified** alternating current therefore is an *intermittent* direct current.

The load resistor, R, represents the actual circuit in which the rectified alternating current does work. All tubes work with a load of one type or another; in this respect a tube is much like a generator or transformer. A circuit that did not

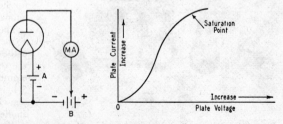

Fig. 3-3—The diode, or two-element tube, and a typical curve showing how the plate current depends upon the voltage applied to the plate.

provide a load for the tube would be like a short-circuit across a transformer; no useful purpose would be accomplished and the only result would be the generation of heat in the transformer. So it is with vacuum tubes; they must cause power to be developed in a load in order to serve a useful purpose. Also, to be *efficient* most of the power must do useful work in the load and not be used in heating the plate of the tube. Thus the voltage drop across the load should be much higher than the drop across the diode.

With the diode connected as shown in Fig. 3-4,

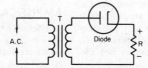
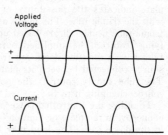

Fig. 3-4—Rectification in a diode. Current flows only when the plate is positive with respect to the cathode, so that only half-cycles of current flow through the load resistor, R.

the polarity of the current through the load is as indicated. If the diode were reversed, the polarity of the voltage developed across the load R would be reversed.

VACUUM-TUBE AMPLIFIERS

TRIODES

Grid Control

If a third element—called the **control grid**, or simply **grid**—is inserted between the cathode and plate as in Fig. 3-5, it can be used to control the effect of the space charge. If the grid is given a positive voltage with respect to the cathode, the positive charge will tend to neutralize the negative space charge. The result is that, at any

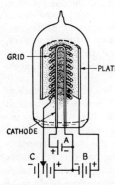

Fig. 3-5—Construction of an elementary triode vacuum tube, showing the directly-heated cathode (filament), grid (with an end view of the grid wires) and plate. The relative density of the space charge is indicated roughly by the dot density.

selected plate voltage, more electrons will flow to the plate than if the grid were not present. On the other hand, if the grid is made negative with respect to the cathode the negative charge on the grid will add to the space charge. This will reduce the number of electrons that can reach the plate at any selected plate voltage.

The grid is inserted in the tube to control the space charge and not to attract electrons to itself, so it is made in the form of a wire mesh or spiral. Electrons then can go through the open spaces in the grid to reach the plate.

Characteristic Curves

For any particular tube, the effect

of the grid voltage on the plate current can be shown by a set of **characteristic curves**. A typical set of curves is shown in Fig. 3-6, together with the circuit that is used for getting them. For each value of plate voltage, there is a value of negative grid voltage that will reduce the plate current to zero; that is, there is a value of negative grid voltage that will cut off the plate current.

The curves could be extended by making the grid voltage positive as well as negative. When the grid is negative, it repels electrons and therefore none of them reaches it; in other words, no current flows in the grid circuit. However, when the grid is positive, it attracts electrons and a current **(grid current)** flows, just as current flows to the positive plate. Whenever there is grid current there is an accompanying power loss in the grid circuit, but so long as the grid is negative no power is used.

It is obvious that the grid can act as a valve to control the flow of plate current. Actually, the grid has a much greater effect on plate current flow than does the plate voltage. A small change in grid voltage is just as effective in bringing about a given change in plate current as is a large change in plate voltage.

The fact that a small voltage acting on the grid

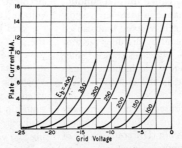
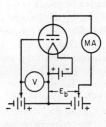

Fig. 3-6—Grid-voltage-vs.-plate-current curves at various fixed values of plate voltage (E_b) for a typical small triode. Characteristic curves of this type can be taken by varying the battery voltages in the circuit at the right.

is equivalent to a large voltage acting on the plate indicates the possibility of **amplification** with the triode tube. The many uses of the electronic tube nearly all are based upon this amplifying feature. The amplified output is not obtained from the tube itself, but from the voltage source connected between its plate and cathode. The tube simply controls the power from this source, changing it to the desired form.

To utilize the controlled power, a load must be connected in the plate or "output" circuit, just as in the diode case. The load may be either a resistance or an impedance. The term "impedance" is frequently used even when the load is purely resistive.

Tube Characteristics

The physical construction of a triode determines the relative effectiveness of the grid and plate in controlling the plate current. The control of the grid is increased by moving it closer to the cathode or by making the grid mesh finer.

The **plate resistance** of a vacuum tube is the a.c. resistance of the path from cathode to plate. For a given grid voltage, it is the quotient of a small change in plate voltage divided by the resultant change in plate current. Thus if a 1-volt change in plate voltage caused a plate-current change of 0.01 ma. (0.00001 ampere), the plate resistance would be 100,000 ohms.

The **amplification factor** (usually designated by the Greek letter μ) of a vacuum tube is defined as the ratio of the change in plate voltage to the change in grid voltage to effect equal changes in plate current. If, for example, an increase of 10 plate volts raised the plate current 1.0 ma., and an increase in (negative) grid voltage of 0.1 volt were required to return the plate current to its original value, the amplification factor would be 100. The amplification factors of triode tubes range from 3 to 100 or so. A **high-μ** tube is one with an amplification of perhaps 30 or more; **medium-μ** tubes have amplification factors in the approximate range 8 to 30, and **low-μ** tubes in the range below 7 or 8. The μ of a triode is useful in computing stage gains.

The best all-around indication of the effectiveness of a tube as an amplifier is its gridplate **transconductance**—also called **mutual conductance** or g_m. It is the change in plate current divided by the change in grid voltage that caused the change; it can be found by dividing the amplification factor by the plate resistance. Since current divided by voltage is conductance, transconductance is measured in the unit of conductance, the mho.

Practical values of transconductance are very small, so the micromho (one millionth of a mho) is the commonly-used unit. Different types of tubes have transconductances ranging from a few hundred to several thousand. The higher the transconductance the greater the possible amplification.

AMPLIFICATION

The way in which a tube amplifies is best shown by a type of graph called the **dynamic characteristic**. Such a graph, together with the circuit used for obtaining it, is shown in Fig. 3-7.

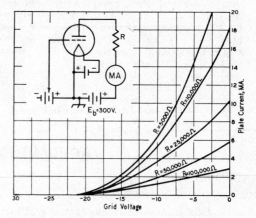

Fig. 3-7—Dynamic characteristics of a small triode with various load resistances from 5000 to 100,000 ohms.

The curves are taken with the plate-supply voltage fixed at the desired operating value. The difference between this circuit and the one shown in Fig. 3-6 is that in Fig. 3-7 a load resistance is connected in series with the plate of the tube. Fig. 3-7 thus shows how the plate current will vary, with different grid voltages, when the plate current is made to flow through a load and thus do useful work.

The several curves in Fig. 3-7 are for various values of load resistance. When the resistance is small (as in the case of the 5000-ohm load) the plate current changes rather rapidly with a given change in grid voltage. If the load resistance is high (as in the 100,000-ohm curve), the change in plate current for the same grid-voltage change is relatively small; also, the curve tends to be straighter.

Fig. 3-8 is the same type of curve, but with the circuit arranged so that a source of alternating voltage **(signal)** is inserted between the grid and the grid battery **("C" battery)**. The voltage of the grid battery is fixed at -5 volts, and from the curve it is seen that the plate current at this grid voltage is 2 milliamperes. This current flows when the load resistance is 50,000 ohms, as indicated in the circuit diagram. If there is no a.c. signal in the grid circuit, the voltage drop in the load resistor is $50,000 \times 0.002 = 100$ volts, leaving 200 volts between the plate and cathode.

When a sine-wave signal having a peak value of 2 volts is applied in series with the bias voltage in the grid circuit, the instantaneous voltage at the grid will swing to -3 volts at the instant the

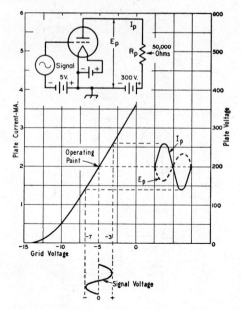

Fig. 3-8—Amplifier operation. When the plate current various in response to the signal applied to the grid, a varying voltage drop appears across the load, R_p, as shown by the dashed curve, E_p. I_p is the plate current.

signal reaches its positive peak, and to -7 volts at the instant the signal reaches its negative peak. The maximum plate current will occur at the instant the grid voltage is -3 volts. As shown by the graph, it will have a value of 2.65 milliamperes. The minimum plate current occurs at the instant the grid voltage is -7 volts, and has a value of 1.35 ma. At intermediate values of grid voltage, intermediate plate-current values will occur.

The instantaneous voltage between the plate and cathode of the tube also is shown on the graph. When the plate current is maximum, the instantaneous voltage drop in R_p is 50,000 $\times$ 0.00265 $= 132.5$ volts; when the plate current is minimum the instantaneous voltage drop in R_p is 50,000 $\times$ 0.00135 $= 67.5$ volts. The actual voltage between plate and cathode is the difference between the plate-supply potential, 300 volts, and the voltage drop in the load resistance. The plate-to-cathode voltage is therefore 167.5 volts at maximum plate current and 232.5 volts at minimum plate current.

This varying plate voltage is an a.c. voltage superimposed on the steady plate-cathode potential of 200 volts (as previously determined for no-signal conditions). The peak value of this a.c. **output voltage** is the difference between either the maximum or minimum plate-cathode voltage and the no-signal value of 200 volts. In the illustration this difference is 232.5 $-$ 200 or 200 $-$ 167.5; that is, 32.5 volts in either case. Since the grid signal voltage has a peak value of 2 volts, the **voltage-amplification ratio** of the amplifier is 32.5/2 or 16.25. That is, approximately 16 times as much voltage is obtained from

the plate circuit as is applied to the grid circuit.

As shown by the drawings in Fig. 3-8, the alternating component of the plate voltage swings in the *negative* direction (with reference to the no-signal value of plate-cathode voltage) when the grid voltage swings in the *positive* direction, and vice versa. This means that the alternating component of plate voltage (that is, the amplified signal) is 180 degrees out of phase with the signal voltage on the grid.

Bias

The fixed negative grid voltage (called **grid bias**) in Fig. 3-8 serves a very useful purpose. One object of the type of amplification shown in this drawing is to obtain, from the plate circuit, an alternating voltage that has the same wave-shape as the signal voltage applied to the grid. To do so, an **operating point** on the straight part of the curve must be selected. The curve must be straight in both directions from the operating point at least far enough to accommodate the maximum value of the signal applied to the grid. If the grid signal swings the plate current back and forth over a part of the curve that is not straight, as in Fig. 3-9, the shape of the a.c. wave in the plate circuit will not be the same as the shape of the grid-signal wave. In such a case the output wave shape will be **distorted.**

A second reason for using negative grid bias is that any signal whose peak positive voltage does not exceed the fixed negative voltage on the grid cannot cause grid current to flow. With no current flow there is no power consumption, so the tube will amplify without taking any power from the signal source. (However, if the positive peak of the signal does exceed the negative bias, current will flow in the grid circuit during the time the grid is positive.)

Distortion of the output wave shape that results

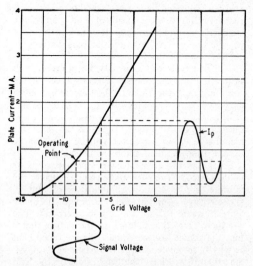

Fig. 3-9—Harmonic distortion resulting from choice of an operating point on the curved part of the tube characteristic. The lower half-cycle of plate current does not have the same shape as the upper half-cycle.

from working over a part of the curve that is not straight (that is, a **nonlinear** part of the curve) has the effect of transforming a sine-wave grid signal into a more complex waveform. As explained in an earlier chapter, a complex wave can be resolved into a fundamental and a series of harmonics. In other words, distortion from nonlinearity causes the generation of harmonic frequencies—frequencies that are not present in the signal applied to the grid. Harmonic distortion is undesirable in most amplifiers, although there are occasions when harmonics are deliberately generated and used.

Audio Amplifier Output Circuits

The useful output of a vacuum-tube amplifier is the *alternating* component of plate current or plate voltage. The d.c. voltage on the plate of the tube is essential for the tube's operation, but it almost invariably would cause difficulties if it were applied, along with the a.c. output voltage, to the load. The output circuits of vacumm tubes are therefore arranged so that the a.c. is transferred to the load but the d.c. is not.

Three types of coupling are in common use at audio frequencies. These are **resistance coupling, impedance coupling,** and **transformer coupling.** They are shown in Fig. 3-10. In all three cases the output is shown coupled to the grid circuit of a subsequent amplifier tube, but the same types of circuits can be used to couple to other devices than tubes.

In the resistance-coupled circuit, the a.c. voltage developed across the **plate resistor** R_p (that is, the a.c. voltage between the plate and cathode of the tube) is applied to a second resistor, R_g, through a **coupling capacitor,** C_c. The capacitor "blocks off" the d.c. voltage on the plate of the first tube and prevents it from being applied to the grid of tube B. The latter tube has negative grid bias supplied by the battery shown. No current flows on the grid circuit of tube B and there is therefore no d.c. voltage drop in R_g; in other words, the full voltage of the bias battery is applied to the grid of tube B.

The **grid resistor,** R_g, usually has a rather high value (0.5 to 2 megohms). The reactance of the coupling capacitor, C_c, must be low enough compared with the resistance of R_g so that the a.c. voltage drop in C_c is negligible at the lowest frequency to be amplified. If R_g is at least 0.5 megohm, a 0.1-μf. capacitor will be amply large for the usual range of audio frequencies.

So far as the alternating component of plate voltage is concerned, it will be realized that if the voltage drop in C_c is negligible then R_p and R_g are effectively in parallel (although they are quite separate as far as d.c. is concerned). The resultant parallel resistance of the two is therefore the actual load resistance for the tube. That is why R_g is made as high in resistance as possible; then it will have the least effect on the load represented by R_p.

The impedance-coupled circuit differs from that using resistance coupling only in the substitution of a high inductance (as high as several

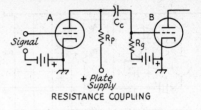

RESISTANCE COUPLING

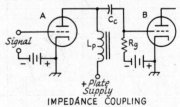

IMPEDANCE COUPLING

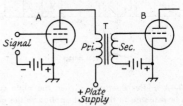

TRANSFORMER COUPLING

Fig. 3-10—Three types of coupling are in common use at audio frequencies. These are resistance coupling, impedance coupling, and transformer coupling. In all three cases the output is shown coupled to the grid circuit of a subsequent amplifier tube, but the same types of circuits can be used to couple to other devices then tubes.

hundred henrys) for the plate resistor. The advantage of using an inductor rather than a resistor at this point is that the impedance of the inductor is high for audio frequencies, but its resistance is relatively low. Thus it provides a high value of load impedance for a.c. without an excessive d.c. voltage drop, and consequently the power-supply voltage does not have to be high for effective operation.

The transformer-coupled amplifier uses a transformer with its primary connected in the plate circuit of the tube and its secondary connected to the load (in the circuit shown, a following amplifier). There is no direct connection between the two windings, so the plate voltage on tube A is isolated from the grid of tube B. The transformer-coupled amplifier has the same advantage as the impedance-coupled circuit with respect to loss of d.c. voltage from the plate supply. Also, if the secondary has more turns than the primary, the output voltage will be "stepped up" in proportion to the turns ratio.

Resistance coupling is simple, inexpensive, and will give the same amount of amplification—or **voltage gain**—over a wide range of frequencies; it will give substantially the same amplification at any frequency in the audio range, for example. Impedance coupling will give somewhat more gain, with the same tube and same plate-supply voltage, than resistance coupling. However, it is not quite so good over a wide frequency range; it tends to "peak," or give maximum gain, over a comparatively narrow band of frequencies. With a good transformer the gain of a transformer-coupled amplifier can be kept fairly constant over the audio-frequency range. On the other hand, transformer coupling in voltage amplifiers (see below) is best suited to triodes having amplification factors of about 20 or less, for the reason that the primary inductance of a practicable transformer cannot be made large enough to work well with a tube having high plate resistance.

Class A Amplifiers

An amplifier in which voltage gain is the primary consideration is called a **voltage amplifier.** Maximum voltage gain is secured when the load resistance or impedance is made as high as possible in comparison with the plate resistance of the tube. In such a case, the major portion of the voltage generated will appear across the load.

Voltage amplifiers belong to a group called **Class A amplifiers.** A Class A amplifier is one operated so that the wave shape of the output voltage is the same as that of the signal voltage applied to the grid. If a Class A amplifier is biased so that the grid is always negative, even with the largest signal to be handled by the grid, it is called a **Class A_1 amplifier.** Voltage amplifiers are always Class A_1 amplifiers, and their primary use is in driving a following Class A_1 amplifier.

Power Amplifiers

The end result of any amplification is that the amplified signal does some work. For example, an audio-frequency amplifier usually drives a loudspeaker that in turn produces sound waves. The greater the amount of a.f. power supplied to the speaker the louder the sound it will produce.

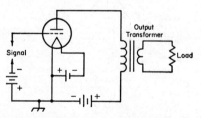

Fig. 3-11—An elementary power-amplifier circuit in which the power-consuming load is coupled to the plate circuit through an impedance-matching transformer.

Fig. 3-11 shows an elementary **power-amplifier** circuit. It is simply a transformer-coupled amplifier with the load connected to the secondary. Although the load is shown as a resistor, it actually would be some device, such as a loudspeaker, that employs the power usefully. Every power tube requires a specific value of load resistance from plate to cathode, usually some thousands of ohms, for optimum operation. The resistance of the actual load is rarely the right value for "matching" this optimum load resistance, so the transformer turns ratio is chosen to reflect the proper value of resistance into the primary. The turns ration may be either step-up or step-down, depending on whether the actual load resistance is higher or lower than the load the tube wants.

The **power-amplification ratio** of an amplifier is the ratio of the power output obtained from the plate circuit to the power required from the a.c. signal in the grid circuit. There is no power lost in the grid circuit of a Class A_1 amplifier, so such an amplifier has an infinitely large power-amplification ratio. However, it is quite possible to operate a Class A amplifier in such a way that current flows in its grid circuit during at least part of the cycle. In such a case power is used up in the grid circuit and the power amplification ratio is not infinite. A tube operated in this fashion is known as a **Class A_2 amplifier.** It is necessary to use a power amplifier to drive a Class A_2 amplifier, because a voltage amplifier cannot deliver power without serious distortion of the wave shape.

Another term used in connection with power amplifiers is **power sensitivity.** In the case of a Class A_1 amplifier, it means the ratio of power output to the grid signal voltage that causes it. If grid current flows, the term usually means the ratio of plate power output to grid power input.

The a.c. power that is delivered to a load by an amplifier tube has to be paid for in power taken from the source of plate voltage and current. In fact, there is always more power going into the plate circuit of the tube than is coming out as useful output. The difference between the input and output power is used up in heating the plate of the tube, as explained previously. The ratio of useful power output to d.c. plate input is called the **plate efficiency.** The higher the plate efficiency, the greater the amount of power that can be taken from a tube having a given plate-dissipation rating.

Parallel and Push-Pull

When it is necessary to obtain more power output than one tube is capable of giving, two or more similar tubes may be connected in **parallel.** In this case the similar elements in all tubes are connected together. This method is shown in Fig. 3-12 for a transformer-coupled amplifier. The power output is in proportion to the number of tubes used; the grid signal or **exciting voltage** required, however, is the same as for one tube.

If the amplifier operates in such a way as to consume power in the grid circuit, the grid power required is in proportion to the number of tubes used.

An increase in power output also can be secured by connecting two tubes in **push-pull.** In this case the grids and plates of the two tubes are connected to opposite ends of a balanced circuit as shown in Fig. 3-12. At any instant the

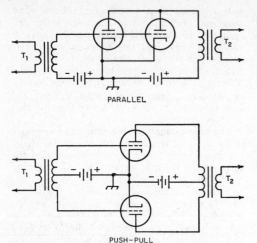

PARALLEL

PUSH-PULL

Fig. 3-12—Parallel and push-pull a.f. amplifier circuits.

ends of the secondary winding of the input transformer, T_1, will be at opposite polarity with respect to the cathode connection, so the grid of one tube is swung positive at the same instant that the grid of the other is swung negative. Hence, in any push-pull-connected amplifier the voltages and currents of one tube are out of phase with those of the other tube.

In push-pull operation the even-harmonic (second, fourth, etc.) distortion is balanced out in the plate circuit. This means that for the same power output the distortion will be less than with parallel operation.

The exciting voltage measured between the two grids must be twice that required for one tube. If the grids consume power, the driving power for the push-pull amplifier is twice that taken by either tube alone.

Cascade Amplifiers

It is readily possible to take the output of one amplifier and apply it as a signal on the grid of a second amplifier, then take the second amplifier's output and apply it to a third, and so on. Each amplifier is called a **stage**, and stages used successively are said to be in **cascade**.

Class B Amplifiers

Fig 3-13 shows two tubes connected in a push-pull circuit. If the grid bias is set at the point where (when no signal is applied) the plate current is just cut off, then a signal can cause plate current to flow in either tube only when the signal voltage applied to that particular tube is positive with respect to the cathode. Since in the balanced grid circuit the signal voltages on the grids of the two tubes always have opposite polarities, plate current flows only in one tube at a time.

The graphs show the operation of such an amplifier. The plate current of tube B is drawn inverted to show that it flows in the opposite direction, through the primary of the output transformer, to the plate current of tube A. Thus each

half of the output-transformer primary works alternately to induce a half-cycle of voltage in the secondary. In the secondary of T_2, the original waveform is restored. This type of operation is called **Class B amplification**.

The Class B amplifier has considerably higher plate efficiency than the Class A amplifier. Furthermore, the d.c. plate current of a Class B amplifier is proportional to the signal voltage on the grids, so the power input is small with small signals. The d.c. plate power input to a Class A amplifier is the same whether the signal is large, small, or absent altogether; therefore the maximum d.c. plate input that can be applied to a Class A amplifier is equal to the rated plate dissipation of the tube or tubes. Two tubes in a Class B amplifier can deliver approximately twelve times as much audio power as the same two tubes in a Class A amplifier.

A Class B amplifier usually is operated in such a way as to secure the maximum possible power output. This requires rather large values of plate current, and to obtain them the signal voltage must completely overcome the grid bias during at least part of the cycle, so grid current flows and the grid circuit consumes power. While the power requirements are fairly low (as compared with the power output), the fact that the grids are positive during only part of the cycle means that the load on the preceding amplifier or **driver stage** varies in magnitude during the cycle; the effective load resistance is high when the grids are not drawing current and relatively low when they do take current. This must be allowed for when designing the driver.

Certain types of tubes have been designed specifically for Class B service and can be operated without fixed or other form of grid bias (**zero-bias tubes**). The amplification factor is so high that the plate current is small without signal. Because there is no fixed bias, the grids start drawing current immediately whenever a

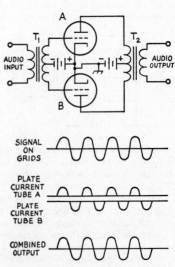

SIGNAL ON GRIDS

PLATE CURRENT TUBE A

PLATE CURRENT TUBE B

COMBINED OUTPUT

Fig. 3-13—Class B amplifier operation.

signal is applied, so the grid-current flow is countinuous throughout the cycle. This makes the load on the driver much more constant than is the case with tubes of lower μ biased to plate-current cut-off.

Class B amplifiers used at radio frequencies are known as **linear amplifiers** because they are adjusted to operate in such a way that the power output is proportional to the square of the r.f. exciting voltage. This permits amplification of a modulated r.f. signal without distortion. Push-pull is not required in this type of operation; a single tube can be used equally well.

Class AB Amplifiers

A **Class AB audio amplifier** is a push-pull amplifier with higher bias than would be normal for pure Class A operation, but less than the cut-off bias required for Class B. At low signal levels the tubes operate as Class A amplifiers, and the plate current is the same with or without signal. At higher signal levels, the plate current of one tube is cut off during part of the negative cycle of the signal applied to its grid, and the plate current of the other tube rises with the signal. The total plate current for the amplifier also rises above the no-signal level when a large signal is applied.

In a properly designed Class AB amplifier the distortion is as low as with a Class A stage, but the efficiency and power output are considerably higher than with pure Class A operation. A Class AB amplifier can be operated either with or without driving the grids into the positive region. A **Class AB₁ amplifier** is one in which the grids are never positive with respect to the cathode; therefore, no driving power is required—only voltage. A **Class AB₂ amplifier** is one that has grid-current flow during part of the cycle if the applied signal is large; it takes a small amount of driving power. The Class AB₂ amplifier will deliver somewhat more power (using the same tubes) but the Class AB₁ amplifier avoids the problem of designing a driver that will deliver power, without distortion, into a load of highly variable resistance.

Operating Angle

Inspection of Fig. 3-13 shows that either of the two tubes actually is working for only half the a.c. cycle and idling during the other half. It is convenient to describe the amount of time during which plate current flows in terms of electrical degrees. In Fig. 3-13 each tube has "180-degree" excitation, a half-cycle being equal to 180 degrees. The number of degrees during which plate current flows is called the **operating angle** of the amplifier. From the descriptions given above, it should be clear that a Class A amplifier has 360-degree excitation, because plate current flows during the whole cycle. In a Class AB amplifier the operating angle is between 180 and 360 degrees (in each tube) depending on the particular operating conditions chosen. The greater the amount of negative grid bias, the smaller the operating angle becomes.

An operating angle of less than 180 degrees leads to a considerable amount of distortion, because there is no way for the tube to reproduce even a half-cycle of the signal on its grid. Using two tubes in push-pull, as in Fig 3-13, would merely put together two distorted half-cycles. An operating angle of less than 180 degrees therefore cannot be used if distortionless output is wanted.

Class C Amplifiers

In power amplifiers operating at radio frequencies distortion of the r.f. wave form is relatively unimportant. For reasons described later in this chapter, an r.f. amplifier must be operated with tuned circuits, and the selectivity of such circuits "filters out" the r.f. harmonics resulting from distortion.

A radio-frequency power amplifier therefore can be used with an operating angle of less than 180 degrees. This is call **Class C** operation. The advantage is the that plate efficiency is increased, because the loss in the plate is proportional, among other things, to the amount of time during which the plate current flows, and this time is reduced by decreasing the operating angle.

Depending on the type of tube, the optimum load resistance for a Class C amplifier ranges from about 1500 to 5000 ohms. It is usually secured by using tuned-circuit arrangements, of the type described in the chapter on circuit fundamentals, to transform the resistance of the actual load to the value required by the tube. The grid is driven well into the positive region, so that grid current flows and power is consumed in the grid circuit. The smaller the operating angle, the greater the driving voltage and the larger the grid driving power required to develop full output in the load resistance. The best compromise between driving power, plate efficiency, and power output usually results when the minimum plate voltage (at the peak of the driving cycle, when the plate current reaches its highest value) is just equal to the peak positive grid voltage. Under these conditions the operating angle is usually between 120 and 150 degrees and the plate efficiency lies in the range of 60 to 80 per cent. While higher plate efficiencies are possible, attaining them requires excessive driving power and grid bias, together with higher plate voltage than is "normal" for the particular tube type.

With proper design and adjustment, a Class C amplifier can be made to operate in such a way that the power input and output are proportional to the square of the applied plate voltage. This is an important consideration when the amplifier is to be plate-modulated for radiotelephony, as described in the chapter on amplitude modulation.

FEEDBACK

It is possible to take a part of the amplified energy in the plate circuit of an amplifier and insert it into the grid circuit. When this is done the amplifier is said to have **feedback**.

If the voltage that is inserted in the grid circuit is 180 degrees out of phase with the signal voltage acting on the grid, the feedback is called **negative,** or **degenerative.** On the other hand, if the voltage is fed back in phase with the grid signal, the feedback is called **positive,** or **regenerative.**

Negative Feedback

With negative feedback the voltage that is fed back opposes the signal voltage. This decreases the amplitude of the voltage acting between the grid and cathode and thus has the effect of reducing the voltage amplification. That is, a larger exciting voltage is required for obtaining the same output voltage from the plate circuit.

The greater the amount of negative feedback (when properly applied) the more independent the amplification becomes of tube characteristics and circuit conditions. This tends to make the frequency-response characteristic of the amplifier **flat**—that is, the amplification tends to be the same at all frequencies within the range for which the amplifier is designed. Also, any distortion generated in the plate circuit of the tube tends to "buck itself out." Amplifiers with negative feedback are therefore comparatively free from harmonic distortion. These advantages are worth while if the amplifier otherwise has enough voltage gain for its intended use.

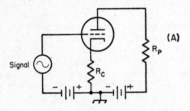

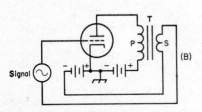

Fig. 3-14—Simple circuits for producing feedback.

In the circuit shown at A in Fig. 3-14 resistor R_c is in series with the regular plate resistor, R_p and thus is a part of the load for the tube. Therefore, part of the output voltage will appear across R_c. However, R_c also is connected in series with the grid circuit, and so the output voltage that appears across R_c is in series with the signal voltage. The output voltage across R_c opposes the signal voltage, so the actual a.c. voltage between the grid and cathode is equal to the *difference* between the two voltages.

The circuit shown at B in Fig. 3-14 can be used to give either negative or positive feedback. The secondary of a transformer is connected back into the grid circuit to insert a desired amount of

feedback voltage. Reversing the terminals of either transformer winding (but not both simultaneously) will reverse the phase.

Positive Feedback

Positive feedback increases the amplification because the feedback voltage adds to the original signal voltage and the resulting larger voltage on the grid causes a larger output voltage. The amplification tends to be greatest at one frequency (which depends upon the particular circuit arrangement) and harmonic distortion is increased. If enough energy is fed back, a self-sustaining **oscillation**—in which energy at essentially one frequency is generated by the tube itself—will be set up. In such case all the signal voltage on the grid can be supplied from the plate circuit; no external signal is needed because any small irregularity in the plate current—and there are always some such irregularities—will be amplified and thus give the oscillation an opportunity to build up. Positive feedback finds a major application in such "oscillators," and in addition is used for selective amplification at both audio and radio frequencies, the feedback being kept below the value that causs self-oscillation.

INTERELECTRODE CAPACITANCES

Each pair of elements in a tube forms a small capacitor, with each element acting as a capacitor "plate." There are three such capacitances in a triode—that between the grid and cathode, that between the grid and plate, and that between the plate and cathode. The capacitances are very small—only a few micromicrofarads at most—but they frequently have a very pronounced effect on the operation of an amplifier circuit.

Input Capacitance

It was explained perviously that the a.c. grid voltage and a.c. plate voltage of an amplifier having a resistive load are 180 degrees out of phase, using the cathode of the tube as a reference point. However, these two voltages are *in* phase going around the circuit from plate to grid as shown in Fig. 3-15. This means that their sum is acting between the grid and plate; that is, across the grid-plate capacitance of the tube.

As a result, a capacitive current flows around the circuit, its amplitude being directly proportional to the sum of the a.c. grid and plate

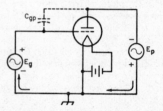

Fig. 3-15—The a.c. voltage appearing between the grid and plate of the amplifier is the sum of the signal voltage and the output voltage, as shown by this simplified circuit. Instantaneous polarities are indicated.

voltages and to the grid-plate capacitance. The source of grid signal must furnish this amount of current, in addition to the capacitive current that flows in the grid-cathode capacitance. Hence the signal source "sees" an effective capacitance that is larger than the grid-cathode capacitance. This is known as the **Miller Effect.**

The greater the voltage amplification the greater the effective input capacitance. The input capacitance of a resistance-coupled amplifier is given by the formula

$$C_{\text{input}} = C_{\text{gk}} + C_{\text{gp}}(A + 1)$$

where C_{gk} is the grid-to-cathode capacitance, C_{gp} is the grid-to-plate capacitance, and A is the voltage amplification. The input capacitance may be as much as several hundred micromicrofarads when the voltage amplification is large, even though the interelectrode capacitances are quite small.

Output Capacitance

The principal component of the output capacitance of an amplifier is the actual plate-to-cathode capacitance of the tube. The output capacitance usually need not be considered in audio amplifiers, but becomes of importance at radio frequencies.

Tube Capacitance at R.F.

At radio frequencies the reactances of even very small interelectrode capacitances drop to very low values. A resistance-coupled amplifier gives very little amplification at r.f., for example, because the reactances of the interlectrode "capacitors" are so low that they practically short-circuit the input and output circuits and thus the tube is unable to amplify. This is overcome at radio frequencies by using tuned circuits for the grid and plate, making the tube capacitances part of the tuning capacitances. In this way the circuits can have the high resistive impedances necessary for satisfactory amplification.

The grid-plate capacitance is important at radio frequencies because its reactance, relatively low at r.f., offers a path over which energy can be fed back from the plate to the grid. In practically every case the feedback is in the right phase and of sufficient amplitude to cause self-oscillation, so the circuit becomes useless as an amplifier.

Special "neutralizing" circuits can be used to prevent feedback but they are, in general, not too satisfactory when used in radio receivers. They are, however, used in transmitters.

SCREEN-GRID TUBES

The grid-plate capacitance can be reduced to a negligible value by inserting a second grid between the control grid and the plate, as indicated in Fig. 3-16. The second grid, called the **screen grid,** acts as an electrostatic shield to prevent capacitive coupling between the control grid and plate. It is made in the form of a grid or coarse screen so that electrons can pass through it.

Because of the shielding action of the screen

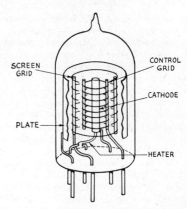

Fig. 3-16—Representative arrangement of elements in a screen-grid tetrode, with part of plate and screen cut away. This is "single-ended" construction with a button base, typical of miniature receiving tubes. To reduce capacitance between control grid and plate the leads from these elements are brought out at opposite sides; actual tubes probably would have additional shielding between these leads.

grid, the positively charged plate cannot attract electrons from the cathode as it does in a triode. In order to get electrons to the plate, it is necessary to apply a positive voltage (with respect to the cathode) to the screen. The screen then attracts electrons much as does the plate in a triode tube. In traveling toward the screen the electrons acquire such velocity that most of them shoot between the screen wires and then are attracted to the plate. A certain proportion do strike the screen, however, with the result that some current also flows in the screen-grid circuit.

To be a good shield, the screen grid must be connected to the cathode through a circuit that has low impedance at the frequency being amplified. A bypass capacitor from screen grid to cathode, having a reactance of not more than a few hundred ohms, is generally used.

A tube having a cathode, control grid, screen grid and plate (four elements) is called a **tetrode.**

Pentodes

When an electron traveling at appreciable velocity through a tube strikes the plate it dislodges other electrons which "splash" from the plate into the interelement space. This is called **secondary emission.** In a triode the negative grid repels the secondary electrons back into the plate and they cause no disturbance. In the screen-grid tube, however, the positively charged screen attracts the secondary electrons, causing a reverse current to flow between screen and plate.

To overcome the effects of secondary emission, a third grid, called the **suppressor grid,** may be inserted between the screen and plate. This grid acts as a shield between the screen grid and plate so the secondary electrons cannot be attracted by the screen grid. They are hence attracted back to the plate without appreciably obstructing the regular plate-current flow. A five-element tube of this type is called a **pentode.**

Although the screen grid in either the tetrode or pentode greatly reduces the influence of the plate upon plate-current flow, the control grid still can control the plate current in essentially the same way that it does in a triode. Consequently, the grid-plate transconductance (or mutual conductance) of a tetrode or pentode will be of the same order of value as in a triode of corresponding structure. On the other hand, since a change in plate voltage has very little effect on the plate-current flow, both the amplification factor and plate resistance of a pentode or tetrode are very high. In small receiving pentodes the amplification factor is of the order of 1000 or higher, while the plate resistance may be from 0.5 to 1 or more megohms. Because of the high plate resistance, the actual voltage amplification possible with a pentode is very much less than the large amplification factor might indicate. A voltage gain in the vicinity of 50 to 200 is typical of a pentode stage.

In practical screen-grid tubes the grid-plate capacitance is only a small fraction of a micro-microfarad. This capacitance is too small to cause an appreciable increase in input capacitance as described in the preceding section, so the input capacitance of a screen-grid tube is simply the sum of its grid-cathode capacitance and control-grid-to-screen capacitance. The output capacitance of a screen-grid tube is equal to the capacitance between the plate and screen.

In addition to their applications as radio-frequency amplifiers, pentodes or tetrodes also are used for audio-frequency power amplification. In tubes designed for this purpose the chief function of the screen is to serve as an accelerator of the electrons, so that large values of plate current can be drawn at relatively low plate voltages. Such tubes have quite high power sensitivity compared with triodes of the same power output, although harmonic distortion is somewhat greater.

Beam Tubes

A **beam tetrode** is a four-element screen-grid tube constructed in such a way that the electrons are formed into concentrated beams on their way to the plate. Additional design features overcome the effects of secondary emission so that a suppressor grid is not needed. The "beam" construction makes it possible to draw large plate currents at relatively low plate voltages, and increases the power sensitivity.

For power amplification at both audio and radio frequencies beam tetrodes have largely supplanted the non-beam types because large power outputs can be secured with very small amounts of grid driving power.

Variable-μ Tubes

The mutual conductance of a vacuum tube decreases when its grid bias is made more negative, assuming that the other electrode voltages are held constant. Since the mutual conductance controls the amount of amplification, it is possible to adjust the gain of the amplifier by adjusting the grid bias. This method of gain control is universally used in radio-frequency amplifiers designed for receivers.

The ordinary type of tube has what is known as a **sharp-cutoff** characteristic. The mutual conductance decreases at a uniform rate as the negative bias is increased. The amount of signal voltage that such a tube can handle without causing distortion is not sufficient to take care of very strong signals. To overcome this, some tubes are made with a **variable-μ** characteristic—that is, the amplification factor decreases with increasing grid bias. The variable-μ tube can handle a much larger signal than the sharp-cutoff type before the signal swings either beyond the zero grid-bias point or the plate-current cutoff point.

INPUT AND OUTPUT IMPEDANCES

The **input impedance** of a vacuum-tube amplifier is the impedance "seen" by the signal source when connected to the input terminals of the amplifier. In the types of amplifiers previously discussed, the input impedance is the impedance measured between the grid and cathode of the tube with operating voltages applied. At audio frequencies the input impedance of a Class A_1 amplifier is for all practical purposes the input capacitance of the stage. If the tube is driven into the grid-current region there is in addition a resistance component in the input impedance, the resistance having an average value equal to E^2/P, where E is the r.m.s. driving voltage and P is the power in watts consumed in the grid. The resistance usually will vary during the a.c. cycle because grid current may flow only during part of the cycle; also, the grid-voltage/grid-current characteristic is seldom linear.

The **output impedance** of amplifiers of this type consists of the plate resistance of the tube shunted by the output capacitance.

At radio frequencies, when tuned circuits are employed, the input and output impedances are usually pure resistances; any reactive components are "tuned out" in the process of adjusting the circuits to resonance at the operating frequency.

OTHER TYPES OF AMPLIFIERS

In the amplifier circuits so far discussed, the signal has been applied between the grid and cathode and the amplified output has been taken from the plate-to-cathode circuit. That is, the cathode has been the meeting point for the input and output circuits. However, it is possible to use any one of the three principal elements as the common point. This leads to two additional kinds of amplifiers, commonly called the **grounded-grid amplifier** (or **grid-separation** circuit) and the **cathode follower**.

These two circuits are shown in simplified form in Fig. 3-17. In both circuits the resistor R represents the load into which the amplifier works; the actual load may be resistance-capacitance-coupled, transformer-coupled, may be a tuned circuit if the amplifier operates at radio

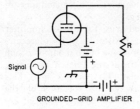

GROUNDED-GRID AMPLIFIER

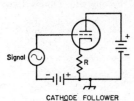

CATHODE FOLLOWER

Fig. 3-17—In the upper circuit, the grid is the junction point between the input and output circuits in the lower drawing, the plate is the junction. In either case the output is developed in the load resistor, R, and may be coupled to a following amplifier by the usual methods.

frequencies, and so on. Also, in both circuits the batteries that supply grid bias and plate power are assumed to have such negligible impedance that they do not enter into the operation of the circuits.

Grounded-Grid Amplifier

In the grounded-grid amplifier the input signal is applied between the cathode and grid, and the output is taken between the plate and grid. The grid is thus the common element. The a.c. component of the plate current has to flow through the signal source to reach the cathode. The source of signal is in series with the load through the plate-to-cathode resistance of the tube, so some of the power in the load is supplied by the signal source. In transmitting applications this fed-through power is of the order of 10 per cent of the total power output, using tubes suitable for grounded-grid service.

The input impedance of the grounded-grid amplifier consists of a capacitance in parallel with an equivalent resistance representing the power furnished by the driving source of the grid and to the load. This resistance is of the order of a few hundred ohms. The output impedance, neglecting the interelectrode capacitances, is equal to the plate resistance of the tube. This is the same as in the case of the grounded-cathode amplifier.

The grounded-grid amplifier is widely used at v.h.f. and u.h.f., where the more conventional amplifier circuit fails to work properly. With a triode tube designed for this type of operation, an r.f. amplifier can be built that is free from the type of feedback that causes oscillation. This requires that the grid act as a shield between the cathode and plate, reducing the plate-cathode capacitance to a very low value.

Cathode Follower

The cathode follower uses the plate of the tube as the common element. The input signal is applied between the grid and plate (assuming negligible impedance in the batteries) and

the output is taken between cathode and plate. This circuit is degenerative; in fact, all of the output voltage is fed back into the input circuit out of phase with the grid signal. The input signal therefore has to be larger than the output voltage; that is, the cathode follower gives a loss in voltage, although it gives the same power gain as other circuits under equivalent operating conditions.

An important feature of the cathode follower is its low output impedance, which is given by the formula (neglecting interelectrode capaci-

$$Z_{out} = \frac{r_p}{1 + \mu}$$

tances) where r_p is the tube plate resistance and μ is the amplification factor. Low output impedance is a valuable characteristic in an amplifier designed to cover a wide band of frequencies. In addition, the input capacitance is only a fraction of the grid-to-cathode capacitance of the tube, a feature of further benefit in a wide-band amplifier. The cathode follower is useful as a step-down impedance transformer, since the input impedance is high and the output impedance is low.

CATHODE CIRCUITS AND GRID BIAS

Most of the equipment used by amateurs is powered by the a.c. line. This includes the filaments or heaters of vacuum tubes. Although supplies for the plate (and sometimes the grid) are usually rectified and filtered to give **pure d.c.** — that is, direct current that is constant and without a superimposed a.c. component — the relatively large currents required by filaments and heaters usually make a rectifier-type d.c. supply impracticable.

Filament Hum

Alternating current is just as good as direct current from the heating standpoint, but some of the a.c. voltage is likely to get on the grid and cause a low-pitched "a.c. hum" to be superimposed on the output.

Hum troubles are worst with directly-heated cathodes or filaments, because with such cathodes there has to be a direct connection between the source of heating power and the rest of the circuit. The hum can be minimized by either of

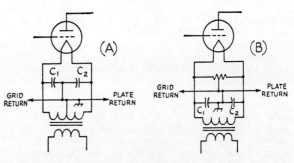

Fig. 3-18—Filament center-tapping methods for use with directly heated tubes.

the connections shown in Fig. 3-18. In both cases the grid- and plate-return circuits are connected to the electrical midpoint (center tap) of the filament supply. Thus, so far as the grid and plate are concerned, the voltage and current on one side of the filament are balanced by an equal and opposite voltage and current on the other side. The balance is never quite perfect, however, so filament-type tubes are never completely hum-free. For this reason directly-heated filaments are employed for the most part in power tubes, where the hum introduced is extremely small in comparison with the power-output level.

With indirectly heated cathodes the chief problem is the magnetic field set up by the heater. Occasionally, also, there is leakage between the heater and cathode, allowing a small a.c. voltage to get to the grid. If hum appears, grounding one side of the heater supply usually will help to reduce it, although sometimes better results are obtained if the heater supply is center-tapped and the center-tap grounded, as in Fig. 3-18.

Cathode Bias

In the simplified amplifier circuits discussed in this chapter, grid bias has been supplied by a battery. However, in equipment that operates from the power line cathode bias is almost universally used for tubes that are operated in Class A (constant d.c. input).

The cathode-bias method uses a resistor (cathode resistor) connected in series with the cathode, as shown at R in Fig. 3-19. The direction of plate-current flow is such that the end of the resistor nearest the cathode is positive. The voltage drop across R therefore places a *negative* voltage on the grid. This negative bias is obtained from the steady d.c. plate current.

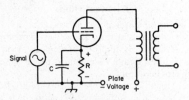

Signal
C
R
Plate
Voltage

Fig. 3-19—Cathode biasing. R is the cathode resistor and C is the cathode bypass capacitor.

If the alternating component of plate current flows through R when the tube is amplifying, the voltage drop caused by the a.c. will be degenerative (note the similarity between this circuit and that of Fig. 3-14A). To prevent this the resistor is bypassed by a capacitor, C, that has very low reactance compared with the resistance of R. Depending on the type of tube and the particular kind of operation, R may be between about 100 and 3000 ohms. For good bypassing at the low audio frequencies, C should be 10 to 50 microfarads (electrolytic capacitors are used for this purpose). At radio frequencies, capacitances of about 100 $\mu\mu$f. to 0.1 μf. are used; the small values are sufficient at very high frequencies and the largest at low and medium frequencies. In

the range 3 to 30 megacycles a capacitance of 0.01 μf. is satisfactory.

The value of cathode resistor for an amplifier having negligible d.c. resistance in its plate circuit (transformer or impedance coupled) can easily be calculated from the known operating conditions of the tube. The proper grid bias and plate current always are specified by the manufacturer. Knowing these, the required resistance can be found by applying Ohm's Law.

Example: It is found from tube tables that the tube to be used should have a negative grid bias of 8 volts and that at this bias the plate current will be 12 milliamperes (0.012 amp.). The required cathode resistance is then

$$R = \frac{E}{I} = \frac{8}{0.012} = 667 \text{ ohms.}$$

The nearest standard value, 680 ohms, would be close enough. The power used in the resistor is

$$P = EI = 8 \times 0.012 = 0.096 \text{ watt.}$$

A ¼-watt or ½-watt resistor would have ample rating.

The current that flows through R is the total cathode current. In an ordinary triode amplifier this is the same as the plate current, but in a screen-grid tube the cathode current is the sum of the plate and screen currents. Hence these two currents must be added when calculating the value of cathode resistor required for a screen-grid tube.

Example: A receiving pentode requires 3 volts negative bias. At this bias and the recommended plate and screen voltages, its plate current is 9 ma. and its screen current is 2 ma. The cathode current is therefore 11 ma. (0.011 amp.). The required resistance is

$$R = \frac{E}{I} = \frac{3}{0.011} = 272 \text{ ohms.}$$

A 270-ohm resistor would be satisfactory. The power in the resistor is

$$P = EI = 3 \times 0.011 = 0.033 \text{ watt.}$$

The cathode-resistor method of biasing is self-regulating, because if the tube characteristics vary slightly from the published values (as they do in practice) the bias will increase if the plate current is slightly high, or decrease if it is slightly low. This tends to hold the plate current at the proper value.

Calculation of the cathode resistor for a resistance-coupled amplifier is ordinarily not practicable by the method described above, because the plate current in such an amplifier is usually much smaller than the rated value given in the tube tables. However, representative data for the tubes commonly used as resistance-coupled amplifiers are given in the chapter on audio amplifiers, including cathode-resistor values.

"Contact Potential" Bias

In the absence of any negative bias voltage on the grid of a tube, some of the electrons in the space charge will have enough velocity to reach the grid. This causes a small current (of the order of microamperes) to flow in the external circuit between the grid and cathode. If the current is made to flow through a high resistance —a megohm or so — the resulting voltage drop in the resistor will give the grid a negative bias of the order of one volt. The bias so obtained is called contact-potential bias.

Contact-potential bias can be used to advantage in circuits operating at low signal levels (less than one volt peak) since it eliminates the cathode-bias resistor and bypass capacitor. It is principally used in low-level resistance-coupled audio amplifiers. The bias resistor is connected directly between grid and cathode, and must be isolated from the signal source by a blocking capacitor.

Screen Supply

In practical circuits using tetrodes and pentodes the voltage for the screen frequently is taken from the plate supply through a resistor. A typical circuit for an r.f. amplifier is shown in Fig. 3-20. Resistor R is the **screen dropping resistor,** and C is the **screen bypass capacitor.** In flowing through R, the screen current causes a voltage drop in R that reduces the plate-supply voltage to the proper value for the screen. When the plate-supply voltage and the screen current are known, the value of R can be calculated from Ohm's Law.

> Example: An r.f. receiving pentode has a rated screen current of 2 milliamperes (0.002 amp.) at normal operating conditions. The rated screen voltage is 100 volts, and the plate supply gives 250 volts. To put 100 volts on the screen, the drop across R must be equal to the difference between the plate-supply

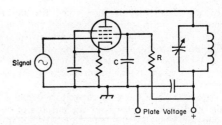

Fig. 3-20—Screen-voltage supply for a pentode tube through a dropping resistor, R. The screen bypass capacitor, C, must have low enough reactance to bring the screen to ground potential for the frequency or frequencies being amplified.

voltage and the screen voltage; that is, $250 - 100 = 150$ volts. Then

$$R = \frac{E}{I} = \frac{150}{0.002} = 75{,}000 \text{ ohms.}$$

The power to be dissipated in the resistor is

$$P = EI = 150 \times 0.002 = 0.3 \text{ watt.}$$

A $\frac{1}{2}$- or 1-watt resistor would be satisfactory.

The reactance of the screen bypass capacitor, C, should be low compared with the screen-to-cathode impedance. For radio-frequency applications a capacitance in the vicinity of 0.01 μf. is amply large.

In some vacuum-tube circuits the screen voltage is obtained from a voltage divider connected across the plate supply. The design of voltage dividers is discussed at length in Chapter 7 on Power Supplies.

OSCILLATORS

It was mentioned earlier that if there is enough positive feedback in an amplifier circuit, self-sustaining oscillations will be set up. When an amplifier is arranged so that this condition exists it is called an **oscillator.**

Oscillations normally take place at only one frequency, and a desired frequency of oscillation can be obtained by using a resonant circuit tuned to that frequency. For example, in Fig. 3-21A the circuit LC is tuned to the desired frequency of oscillation. The cathode of the tube is connected to a tap on coil L and the grid and plate are connected to opposite ends of the tuned circuit. When an r.f. current flows in the tuned circuit there is a voltage drop across L that increases progressively along the turns. Thus the point at which the tap is connected will be at an intermediate potential with respect to the two ends of the coil. The amplified current in the plate circuit, which flows through the bottom section of L, is in phase with the current already flowing in the circuit and thus in the proper relationship for positive feedback.

The amount of feedback depends on the position of the tap. If the tap is too near the grid end the voltage drop between grid and cathode is too small to give enough feedback to sustain oscillation, and if it is too near the plate end the im-

pedance between the cathode and plate is too small to permit good amplification. Maximum

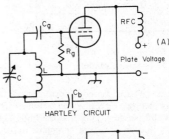

HARTLEY CIRCUIT

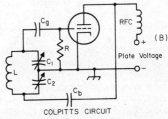

COLPITTS CIRCUIT

Fig. 3-21—Basic oscillator circuits. Feedback voltage is obtained by tapping the grid and cathode across a portion of the tuned circuit. In the Hartley circuit the tap is on the coil, but in the Colpitts circuit the voltage is obtained from the drop across a capacitor.

feedback usually is obtained when the tap is somewhere near the center of the coil.

The circuit of Fig. 3-21A is parallel-fed, C_b being the blocking capacitor. The value of C_b is not critical so long as its reactance is low (not more than a few hundred ohms) at the operating frequency.

Capacitor C_g is the **grid capacitor.** It and R_g (the **grid leak**) are used for the purpose of obtaining grid bias for the tube. In most oscillator circuits the tube generates its own bias. During the part of the cycle when the grid is positive with respect to the cathode, it attracts electrons. These electrons cannot flow through L back to the cathode because C_g "blocks" direct current. They therefore have to flow or "leak" through R_g to cathode, and in doing so cause a voltage drop in R_g that places a negative bias on the grid. The amount of bias so developed is equal to the grid current multiplied by the reistance of R_g (Ohm's Law). The value of grid-leak resistance required depends upon the kind of tube used and the purpose for which the oscillator is intended. Values range all the way from a few thousand to several hundred thousand ohms. The capacitance of C_g should be large enough to have low reactance (a few hundred ohms) at the operating frequency.

The circuit shown at B in Fig. 3-21 uses the voltage drops across two capacitors in series in the tuned circuit to supply the feedback. Other than this, the operation is the same as just described. The feedback can be varied by varying the ratio of the reactance of C_1 and C_2 (that is, by varying the ratio of their capacitances).

Another type of oscillator, called the **tuned-plate tuned-grid** circuit, is shown in Fig. 3-22.

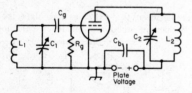

Fig. 3-22—The tuned-plate tuned-grid oscillator.

Resonant circuits tuned approximately to the same frequency are connected between grid and cathode and between plate and cathode. The two coils, L_1 and L_2, are not magnetically coupled. The feedback is through the grid-plate capacitance of the tube, and will be in the right phase to be positive when the plate circuit, C_2L_2, is tuned to a slightly higher frequency than the grid circuit, L_1C_1. The amount of feedback can be adjusted by varying the tuning of either circuit. The frequency of oscillation is determined by the tuned circuit that has the higher Q. The grid leak and grid capacitor have the same functions as in the other circuits. In this case it is convenient to use series feed for the plate circuit, so C_b is a bypass capacitor to guide the r.f. current around the plate supply.

There are many oscillator circuits (examples of others will be found in later chapters) but the basic feature of all of them is that there is positive feedback in the proper amplitude and phase to sustain oscillation.

Oscillator Operating Characteristics

When an oscillator is delivering power to a load, the adjustment for proper feedback will depend on how heavily the oscillator is loaded — that is, how much power is being taken from the circuit. If the feedback is not large enough— **grid excitation** too small — a small increase in load may tend to throw the circuit out of oscillation. On the other hand, too much feedback will make the grid current excessively high, with the result that the power loss in the grid circuit becomes larger than necessary. Since the oscillator itself supplies this grid power, excessive feedback lowers the over-all efficiency because whatever power is used in the grid circuit is not available as useful output.

One of the most important considerations in oscillator design is **frequency stability.** The principal factors that cause a change in frequency are (1) temperature, (2) plate voltage, (3) loading, (4) mechanical variations of circuit elements. Temperature changes will cause vacuum-tube elements to expand or contract slightly, thus causing variations in the interelectrode capacitances. Since these are unavoidably part of the tuned circuit, the frequency will change correspondingly. Temperature changes in the coil or the tuning capacitor will alter the inductance or capacitance slightly, again causing a shift in the resonant frequency. These effects are relatively slow in operation, and the frequency change caused by them is called **drift.**

A change in plate voltage usually will cause the frequency to change a small amount, an effect called **dynamic instability.** Dynamic instability can be reduced by using a tuned circuit of high effective Q. The energy taken from the circuit to supply grid losses, as well as energy supplied to a load, represent an increase in the effective resistance of the tuned circuit and thus lower its Q. For highest stability, therefore, the coupling between the tuned circuit and the tube and load must be kept as loose as possible. Preferably, the oscillator should not be required to deliver power to an external circuit, and a high value of grid leak resistance should be used since this helps to raise the tube grid and plate resistances as seen by the tuned circuit. Loose coupling can be effected in a variety of ways — one, for example, is by "tapping down" on the tank for the connections to the grid and plate. This is done in the "series-tuned" Colpitts circuit widely used in variable-frequency oscillators for amateur transmitters and described in a later chapter. Alternatively, the L/C ratio may be made as small as possible while sustaining stable oscillation (**high C**) with the grid and plate connected to the ends of the circuit as shown in Figs. 3-21 and 3-22. Using relatively high plate voltage and low plate current also is desirable.

In general, dynamic stability will be at maximum when the feedback is adjusted to the least value that permits reliable oscillation. The use of a tube having a high value of transconductance is desirable, since the higher the transconductance the looser the permissible coupling to the tuned circuit and the smaller the feedback required.

Load variations act in much the same way as plate-voltage variations. A temperature change in the load may also result in drift.

Mechanical variations, usually caused by vibration, cause changes in inductance and/or capacitance that in turn cause the frequency to "wobble" in step with the vibration.

Methods of minimizing frequency variations in oscillators are taken up in detail in later chapters.

Ground Point

In the oscillator circuits shown in Figs. 3-21 and 3-22 the cathode is connected to ground. It is not actually essential that the radio-frequency circuit should be grounded at the cathode; in fact, there are many times when an *r.f.* ground on some other point in the circuit is desirable. The r.f. ground can be placed at any point so long as proper provisions are made for feeding the supply voltages to the tube elements.

Fig. 3-23 shows the Hartley circuit with the plate end of the circuit grounded. The cathode

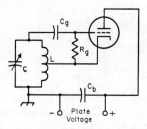

Fig. 3-23—Showing how the plate may be grounded for r.f. in a typical oscillator circuit (Hartley).

and control grid are "above ground," so far as the r.f. is concerned. An advantage of such a circuit is that the frame of the tuning capacitor can be grounded. The Colpitts circuit can also be used with the plate grounded and the cathode above ground; it is only necessary to feed the d.c. to the cathode through an r.f. choke.

A tetrode or pentode tube can be used in any of the popular oscillator circuits. A common variation is to use the screen grid of the tube as the anode for the Hartley or Colpitts oscillator circuit. It is usually used in the grounded anode circuit, and the plate circuit of the tube is tuned to the second harmonic of the oscillator frequency.

CLIPPING CIRCUITS

Vacuum tubes are readily adaptable to other types of operation than ordinary (without substantial distortion) amplification and the genera-

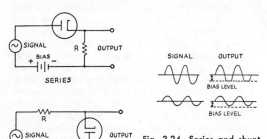

Fig. 3-24—Series and shunt diode clippers. Typical operation is shown at the right.

tion of single-frequency oscillations. Of particular interest is the clipper or limiter circuit, because of its several applications in receiving and other equipment.

Diode Clipper Circuits

Basic diode clipper circuits are shown in Fig. 3-24. In the series type a positive d.c. bias voltage is applied to the plate of the diode so it is normally conducting. When a signal is applied the current through the diode will change proportionately during the time the signal voltage is positive at the diode plate and for that part of

the negative half of the signal during which the instantaneous voltage does not exceed the bias. When the negative signal voltage exceeds the positive bias the resultant voltage at the diode plate is negative and there is no conduction. Thus part of the negative half cycle is clipped as shown in the drawing at the right. The level at which clipping occurs depends on the bias voltage, and the proportion of signal clipping depends on the signal strength in relation to the bias voltage. If the peak signal voltage is below the bias level there is no clipping and the output wave shape is the same as the input wave shape, as shown in the lower sketch. The output voltage results from the current flow through the load resistor R.

In the shunt-type diode clipper negative bias is applied to the plate so the diode is normally nonconducting. In this case the signal voltage is fed through the series resistor R to the output circuit (which must have high impedance compared with the resistance of R). When the negative half of the signal voltage exceeds the bias voltage the diode conducts, and because of the voltage drop in R when current flows the output voltage is reduced. By proper choice of R in relationship to the load on the output circuit the clipping can be made equivalent to that given by the series circuit. There is no clipping when the peak signal voltage is below the bias level.

Two diode circuits can be combined so that both negative and positive peaks are clipped.

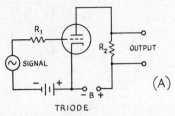

Fig. 3-25—Triode clippers. A—Single triode, using shunt-type diode clipping in the grid circuit for the positive peak and plate-current cut-off clipping for the negative peak. B—Cathode-coupled clipper, using plate-current cut-off clipping for both positive and negative peaks.

Triode Clippers

The circuit shown at A in Fig. 3-25 is capable of clipping both negative and positive signal peaks. On positive peaks its operation is similar to the shunt diode clipper, the clipping taking place when the positive peak of the signal voltage is large enough to drive the grid positive. The positive-clipped signal is amplified by the tube as a resistance-coupled amplifier. Negative peak clipping occurs when the negative peak of the signal voltage exceeds the fixed grid bias and thus cuts off the plate current in the output circuit.

In the cathode-coupled clipper shown at B in Fig. 3-25 V_1 is a cathode follower with its output circuit directly connected to the cathode of V_2, which is a grounded-grid amplifier. The tubes are biased by the voltage drop across R_1, which carries the d.c. plate currents of both tubes. When the negative peak of the signal voltage exceeds the d.c. voltage across R_1 clipping occurs in V_1, and when the positive peak exceeds the same value of voltage V_2's plate current is cut off. (The bias developed in R_1 tends to be constant because the plate current of one tube increases when the plate current of the other decreases.) Thus the circuit clips both positive and negative peaks. The clipping is symmetrical, providing the d.c. voltage drop in R_2 is small enough so that the operating conditions of the two tubes are substantially the same. For signal voltages below the clipping level the circuit operates as a normal amplifier with low distortion.

U.H.F. AND MICROWAVE TUBES

The Klystron

In the **klystron** tube the electrons emitted by the cathode pass through an electric field established by two grids in a cavity resonator called

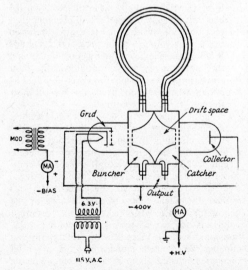

Fig. 3-26—Circuit diagram of the klystron oscillator, showing the feedback loop coupling the frequency-controlling cavities.

the **buncher.** the h.f. electric field between the grids is parallel to the electron stream. This field accelerates the electrons at one moment and retards them at another with the variations of the r.f. voltage applied. The resulting velocity-modulated beam travels through a field-free "drift space," where the slower-moving electrons are gradually overtaken by the faster ones. The electrons emerging from the pair of grids therefore are separated into groups or "bunched" along the direction of motion. The velocity-modulated electron stream then goes to a **catcher** cavity where it again passes through two parallel grids, and the r.f. current created by the bunching of the electron beam induces an r.f. voltage between the grids. The catcher cavity is made resonant at the frequency of the velocity-modulated electron beam, so that an oscillating field is set up within it by the passage of the electron bunches through the grid aperture.

If a feedback loop is provided between the two cavities, as shown in Fig. 3-26, oscillations will occur. The resonant frequncy depends on the electrode voltages and on the shape of the cavities, and may be adjusted by varying the supply voltage and altering the dimensions of the cavities. Although the bunched beam current is rich in harmonics the output wave form is remarkable pure because the high Q of the catcher cavity suppresses the unwanted harmonics.

Chapter 4

Semiconductor Devices

Materials whose conductivity falls approximately midway between that of good conductors (e.g., copper) and good insulators (e.g., quartz) are called **semi-conductors**. Some of these materials (primarily germanium and silicon) can, by careful processing, be used in **solid-state** electronic devices that perform many or all of the functions of thermionic tubes. In many applications their small size, long life and low power requirements make them superior to tubes.

The conductivity of a material is proportional to the number of free electrons in the material. Pure germanium and pure silicon crystals have relatively few free electrons. If, however, carefully controlled amounts of "impurities" (materials having a different atomic structure, such as arsenic or antimony) are added, the number of free electrons, and consequently the conductivity, is increased. When certain other impurities are introduced (such as aluminum, gallium or indium) are introduced, an electron deficiency, or **hole**, is produced. As in the case of free electrons, the presence of holes encourages the flow of electrons in the semiconductor material, and the conductivity is increased. Semiconductor material that conducts by virtue of the free electrons is

called **n-type** material; material that conducts by virtue of an electron deficiency is called **p-type**.

Electron and Hole Conduction

If a piece of p-type material is joined to a piece of n-type material as at A in Fig. 4-1 and a voltage is applied to the pair as at B, current will flow across the boundary or junction between the two (and also in the external circuit) when the battery has the polarity indicated. Electrons, indicated by the minus symbol, are attracted across the junction from the n material through the p material to the positive terminal of the battery, and holes, indicated by the plus symbol, are attracted in the opposite direction across the junction by the negative potential of the battery. Thus current flows through the circuit by means of electrons moving one way and holes the other.

If the battery polarity is reversed, as at C, the excess electrons in the n material are attracted away from the junction and the holes in the p material are attracted by the negative potential of the battery away from the junction. This leaves the junction region without any current carriers, consequently there is no conduction.

In other words, a junction of p- and n-type

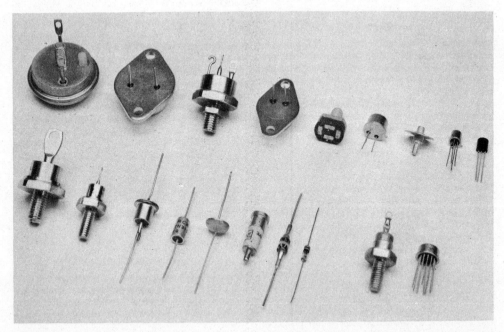

Representative semiconductor types. Various styles of transistors are shown in the back row. High-power types are at the left, medium-power types are at the center, and small-signal types are at the far right. At the extreme right in the back row is an epoxy-encapsulated field-effect transistor. The eight components at the left (in the front row) are silicon and germanium diodes in various package styles. The device at the extreme lower-right (with many leads) is an integrated-circuit assembly. Immediately to the left of it is a varactor diode.

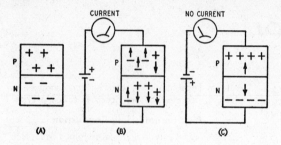

Fig. 4-1—A p-n junction (A) and its behavior when conducting (B) and non-conducting (C).

materials constitutes a rectifier. It differs from the tube diode rectifier in that there is a measurable, although comparatively very small, reverse current. The reverse current results from the presence of some carriers of the type opposite to those which principally characterize the material.

With the two plates separated by practically zero spacing, the junction forms a capacitor of relatively high capacitance. This places a limit on the upper frequency at which semiconductor devices of this construction will operate, as compared with vacuum tubes. Also, the number of excess electrons and holes in the material depends upon temperature, and since the conductivity in turn depends on the number of excess holes and electrons, the device is more temperature sensitive than is a vacuum tube.

Capacitance may be reduced by making the contact area very small. This is done by means of a **point contact**, a tiny p-type region being formed under the contact point during manufacture when n-type material is used for the main body of the device.

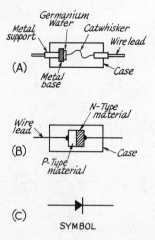

(A)

(B)

(C)   SYMBOL

Fig. 4-2—At A, a germanium point-contact diode. At B, construction of a silicon junction-type diode. The symbol at C is used for both diode types and indicates the direction of minimum resistance measured by conventional methods. At C, the arrow corresponds to the plate (anode) of a vacuum-tube diode. The bar represents the tube's cathode element.

SEMICONDUCTOR DIODES

Point-contact and junction-type diodes are used for many of the same purposes for which tube diodes are used. The construction of such diodes is shown in Fig. 4-2. Germanium and silicon are the most widely used materials; silicon finds much application as a microwave mixer diode. As compared with the tube diode for r.f. applications, the semiconductor point-contact diode has the advantages of very low interelectrode capacitance (on the order of 1 pf. or less) and not requiring any heater or filament power.

The germanium diode is characterized by relatively large current flow with small applied voltages in the "forward" direction, and small, although finite, current flow in the reverse or "back" direction for much larger applied voltages. A typical characteristic curve is shown in Fig. 4-3. The dynamic resistance in either the forward or back direction is determined by the change in current that occurs, at any given point on the curve, when the applied voltage is changed by a small amount. The forward resistance shows some variation in the region of very small applied voltages, but the curve is for the most part quite straight, indicating fairly constant dynamic resistance. For small applied voltages, the forward resistance is of the order of 200 ohms or less in most such diodes. The back resistance shows considerable variation, depending on the particular voltage chosen for the measurement. It may run from a few thousand ohms to well over a megohm. In applications such as meter rectifiers for r.f. indicating instruments (r.f. voltmeters, wavemeter indicators, and so on) where the load resistance may be small and the applied voltage of the order of several volts, the resistances vary with the value of the applied voltage and are considerably lower.

Junction Diodes

Junction-type diodes made of silicon are employed widely as rectifiers. Depending upon the design of the diode, they are capable of rectifying currents up to 40 or 50 amperes, and up to reverse peak voltages of 1000. They can be connected in series or in parallel, with suitable circuitry, to provide higher capabilities than those given above. A big advantage over thermionic rectifiers is their large surge-to-average-current ratio, which makes them suitable for use with capacitor-only filter circuits. This in turn leads to improved no-load-to-full-load voltage characteristics. Some consideration must be given to the operating temperature of silicon diodes, although many carry ratings to 150° C or so. A silicon junction diode requires a forward voltage of from 0.4 to 0.7 volts to overcome the junction potential barrier.

Ratings

Semiconductor diodes are rated primarily in terms of **maximum safe inverse voltage** and **maximum average rectified current.** Inverse voltage is a voltage applied in the direction opposite to that which would be read by a d.c. meter connected in the current path.

It is also customary with some types to specify standards of performance with respect to forward and back current. A minimum value of forward current is usually specified for one volt applied. The voltage at which the maximum tolerable back current is specified varies with the type of diode.

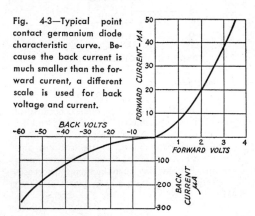

Fig. 4-3—Typical point contact germanium diode characteristic curve. Because the back current is much smaller than the forward current, a different scale is used for back voltage and current.

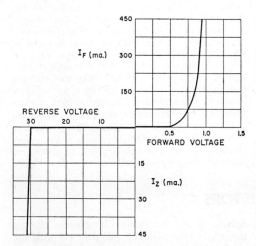

Fig. 4-4—Typical characteristic of a zener diode. In this example, the voltage drop is substantially constant at 30 volts in the (normally) reverse direction. Compare with Fig. 4-3. A diode with this characteristic would be called a "30-volt zener diode."

Zener Diodes

The "Zener diode" is a special type of silicon junction diode that has a characteristic similar to that shown in Fig. 4-4. The sharp break from non-conductance to conductance is called the Zener Knee; at applied voltages greater than this breakdown point, the voltage drop across the diode is essentially constant over a wide range of currents. The substantially constant voltage drop over a wide range of currents allows this semiconductor device to be used as a constant voltage reference or control element, in a manner somewhat similar to the gaseous voltage-regulator tube. Voltages for Zener diode action range from a few volts to several hundred and power ratings run from a fraction of a watt to 50 watts.

Zener diodes can be connected in series to advantage; the temperature coefficient is improved over that of a single diode of equivalent rating and the power-handling capability is increased.

Examples of Zener-diode applications are given in Fig. 4-5. The illustrations represent some of the more common uses to which Zeners are put. Many other applications are possible, though not shown here.

Voltage-Variable Capacitor Diodes

Voltage-variable capacitors, or **varactors,** are p-n junction diodes that behave as capacitors of reasonable Q when biased in the reverse direction. They are useful in many applications because the actual capacitance value is dependent upon the d.c. bias voltage that is applied. In a typical capacitor the capacitance can be varied over a 10-to-1 range with a bias change from 0 to — 100 volts. The current demand on the bias supply is on the order of a few microamperes.

Typical applications include remote control of tuned circuits, automatic frequency control of receiver local oscillators, and simple frequency modulators for communications and for sweep-tuning applications. Diodes used in these applications are frequently referred to as "Varicap" or "Epicap" diodes.

An important transmitter application of the varactor is as a high-efficiency frequency multiplier. The basic circuits for varactor doublers and triplers is shown in Fig. 4-6, at A and B. In these circuits the fundamental frequency flows around the input loop. Harmonics generated by the varactor are passed to the load through a filter tuned to the desired harmonic. In the case of the tripler circuit at B, an **idler** circuit, tuned to the second harmonic, is required. Tripling, efficiencies of 75 per cent are not too difficult to come by, at power levels of 10 to 20 watts.

An important receiver application of the varactor is as a **parametric** amplifier. The diode is modulated by r.f. several times higher in frequency than the signal. This **pump** r.f. adds energy to the stored signal charge. To provide the necessary phase relationship between the signal and the pump, an idler circuit is included.

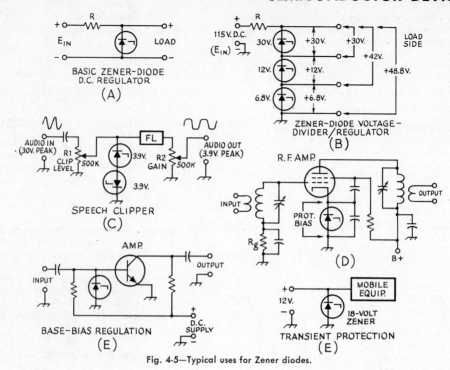

Fig. 4-5—Typical uses for Zener diodes.

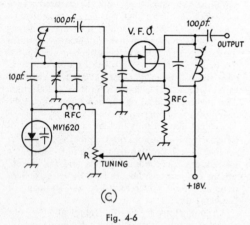

Fig. 4-6

Fig. 4-6 illustrates how a voltage-variable capacitor diode can be used to tune a v.f.o. These diodes can be used to tune other r.f. circuits also, and are particularly useful for remote tuning of r.f. circuits, such as might be encountered in vehicular installations. These diodes, because of their small size, permit tuned-circuit assemblies to be quite compact. Since the Q of the diode is a vital consideration in r.f. applications, this factor must be taken into account when designing a circuit. Present-day manufacturing processes have produced units with a Q in excess of 200 at 50 Mc.

Tunnel Diode

Much hope is held for the future use of the "tunnel diode," a junction semiconductor of special construction that has a "negative resistance" characteristic at low voltages. This characteristic (*decrease* of current with increase of voltage) permits the diode to be used as an oscillator and as an amplifier. Since electrical charges move through the diode with the speed of light, in contrast to the relatively slow motion of electrical charge carriers in other semiconductors, it has been possible to obtain oscillations at frequencies as high as 5000 Mc., making them particularly useful as amplifiers and oscillators in microwave equipment.

TRANSISTORS

Fig. 4-7 shows a "sandwich" made from two layers of p-type semiconductor material with a thin layer of n-type between. There are in effect two p-n junction diodes back to back. If a positive bias is applied to the p-type material at the left, current will flow through the left-hand junction, the holes moving to the right and the electrons from the n-type material moving to the left. Some of the holes moving into the n-type material will combine with the electrons there and be neutralized, but some of them also will travel to the region of the right-hand junction.

If the p-n combination at the right is biased negatively, as shown, there would normally be no current flow in this circuit (see Fig. 4-1C).

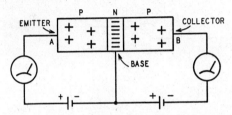

Fig. 4-7—The basic arrangement of a transistor. This represents a junction-type p-n-p unit.

However, there are now additional holes available at the junction to travel to point B and electrons can travel toward point A, so a current can flow even though this section of the sandwich is biased to prevent conduction. Most of the current is between A and B and does not flow out through the common connection to the n-type material in the sandwich.

A semiconductor combination of this type is called a **transistor**, and the three sections are known as the **emitter, base** and **collector**, respectively. The amplitude of the collector current depends principally upon the amplitude of the emitter current; that is, the collector current is controlled by the emitter current.

Power Amplification

Because the collector is biased in the back direction the collector-to-base resistance is high. On the other hand, the emitter and collector currents are substantially equal, so the power in the collector circuit is larger than the power in the emitter circuit ($P = I^2 R$, so the powers are proportional to the respective resistances, if the currents are the same). In practical transis-

tors emitter resistance is of the order of a few hundred ohms while the collector resistance is hundreds or thousands of times higher, so power gains of 20 to 40 db. or even more are possible.

Types

The transistor may be one of the types shown in Figs. 4-8 and 4-9. The assembly of p- and n-types materials may be reversed, so that p-n-p and n-p-n transistors are both possible.

The first two letters of the n-p-n and p-n-p designations indicate the respective polarities of the voltages applied to the emitter and collector in normal operation. In a p-n-p transistor, for example, the emitter is made positive with respect to both the collector and the base, and the collector is made negative with respect to both the emitter and the base.

Another type of transistor is the "overlay." **Overlay** transistors contain an emitter structure which is made up of many separate emitters, connected together by diffused and metalized regions. A precise photographic process—photolithography—is used in the manufacture of the overlay structure. This technique provides an increased emitter edge-to-area ratio over that of earlier transistor types. Because of its improved emitter geometry, the transistor's input time-constant is superior to other types of transistors, thus making it extremely useful in high-frequency applications. Overlay transistors can be used at 1000 Mc. and higher, and are capable of producing a power output of 1 watt or more in the upper u.h.f. region. Greater power-output levels are possible in the h.f., v.h.f., and lower u.h.f. regions when using overlay transistors. These transistors are also useful as frequency multipliers, especially as doublers and triplers, and are able to provide an actual power gain in the process. In this application, the collector-to-base junction performs as a varactor diode, thus helping to eliminate the need for varactor diodes at operating frequencies below approximately 432 Mc. An illustration of overlay-transistor frequency multiplication is shown in Fig. 4-9 at C and D.

Junction Transistors

The majority of transistors being manufactured are one or another version of junction transistors. These may be grown junctions, alloyed or fused junctions, diffused junctions, epitaxial junctions and electroetched and/or electroplated junctions. The diffused-junction transistor, in widespread use because the product of this type of manufacture is generally consistent, involves applying the doping agent to a semiconductor wafer by electroplating, painting, or exposing the surface to a gaseous form of the dopant. A carefully-controlled temperature cycling causes the dopant to diffuse into the surface of the solid. The diffused layer is then a different type than the base material. Epitaxial junctions refers to growth of new layers on the original base in such a manner that the new (epitaxial) layer perpetuates the crystalline structure of the original.

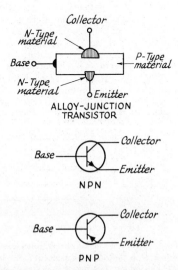

Fig. 4-8—Schematic and pictorial representations of junction-type transistors. In analogous terms the base can be thought of as a tube's grid, the collector as a plate, and the emitter as a cathode (see Fig. 4-12).

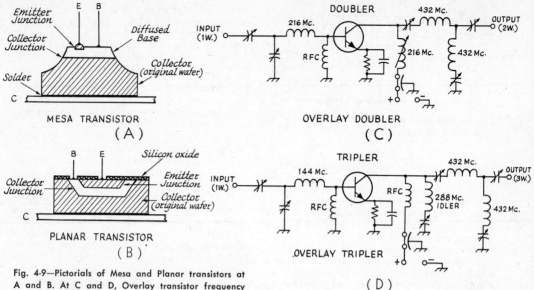

Fig. 4-9—Pictorials of Mesa and Planar transistors at A and B. At C and D, Overlay transistor frequency multipliers—a doubler and a tripler.

Transistor Structures

There are two popular terms used to describe the general physical structure of many transistors. As shown in Fig. 4-9A, the **mesa** transistor is formed by etching away the metal around the emitter and base connections, leaving the junctions exposed and with very small cross sections. This construction makes for good high-frequency response.

In the **planar** construction shown in Fig. 4-9B, the junctions are protected at the upper surface by an impervious layer of silicon oxide. This reduces leakage and increases current gain at low signal levels.

Note that in either type of construction, the collector lead also serves as a heat sink to cool the transistor.

TRANSISTOR CHARACTERISTICS

An important characteristic of a transistor is its **current amplification factor.** This is the ratio of the change in collector current to a small change in emitter current, measured in the common-base circuit described later, and is comparable with the voltage amplification factor (μ) of a vacuum tube. The current amplification factor is almost, but not quite, 1 in a junction transistor. The gain-bandwidth product (f_T) is the frequency at which the current amplification becomes unity, or 1. The f_T ratings range from 500 kc. to frequencies in the upper u.h.f. region. The f_T indicates in a general way the frequency spread over which the transistor is useful.

Each of the three elements in the transistor has a resistance associated with it. The emitter and collector resistances were discussed earlier. There is also a certain amount of resistance associated with the base, a value of a few hundred to 1000 ohms being typical of the base resistance.

The values of all three resistances vary with the type of transistor and the operating voltages. The collector resistance, in particular, is sensitive to operating conditions.

Characteristic Curves

The operating characteristics of transistors can be shown by a series of characteristic curves. One such set of curves is shown in Fig. 4-10. It shows the collector current *vs.* collector voltage for a number of fixed values of emitter current. Practically, the collector current depends almost entirely on the emitter current and is independent of the collector voltage. The separation between curves representing equal steps of emitter current is quite uniform, indicating that almost distortionless output can be obtained over the useful operating range of the transistor.

Another type of curve is shown in Fig. 4-11, together with the circuit used for obtaining it. This also shows collector current *vs.* collector voltage, but for a number of different values of base current. In this case the emitter element is

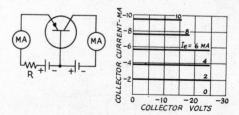

Fig. 4-10—A typical collector-current vs. collector-voltage characteristic of a junction-type transistor, for various emitter-current values. The circuit shows the setup for taking such measurements. Since the emitter resistance is low, a current-limiting resistor, R, is connected in series with the source of current. The emitter current can be set at a desired value by adjustment of this resistance.

used as the common point in the circuit. The collector current is not independent of collector voltage with this type of connection, indicating that the output resistance of the device is fairly low. The base current also is quite low, which means that the resistance of the base-emitter circuit is moderately high with this method of connection. This may be contrasted with the high values of emitter current shown in Fig. 4-10.

Ratings

The principal ratings applied to transistors are maximum collector dissipation, maximum collector voltage, maximum collector current, and maximum emitter current. The voltage and current ratings are self-explanatory.

The collector dissipation is the power, expressed in watts or milliwatts, that can safely be dissipated by the transistor as heat. With some types of transistors provision is made for transferring heat rapidly through the container, and such units usually require installation on a heat "sink," or mounting that can absorb heat.

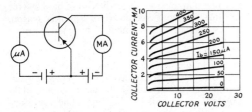

Fig. 4-11—Collector current vs. collector voltage for various values of base current, for a junction-type transistor. The values are determined by means of the circuit shown.

The amount of undistorted output power that can be obtained depends on the collector voltage, the collector current being practically independent of the voltage in a given transistor. Increasing the collector voltage extends the range of linear operation, but must not be carried beyond the point where either the voltage or dissipation ratings are exceeded.

TRANSISTOR AMPLIFIERS

Amplifier circuits used with transistors fall into one of three types, known as the **common-base**, **common-emitter**, and **common-collector** circuits. These are shown in Fig. 4-12 in elementary form. The three circuits correspond approximately to the grounded-grid, grounded-cathode and cathode-follower circuits, respectively, used with vacuum tubes.

The important transistor **parameters** in these circuits are the **short-circuit current transfer ratio**, the **cut-off frequency**, and the **input** and **output impedances**. The short-circuit current transfer ratio is the ratio of a small change in output current to the change in input current that causes it, the output circuit being short-

circuited. The cut-off frequency is the frequency at which the amplification decreases to 0.707 times its 1-kc. value. The input and output impedances are, respectively, the impedance which a signal source working into the transistor would see, and the internal output impedance of the transistor (corresponding to the plate resistance of a vacuum tube, for example).

Common-Base Circuit

The input circuit of a common-base amplifier must be designed for low impedance, since the emitter-to-base resistance is of the order of $25/I_e$ ohms, where I_e is the emitter current in milliamperes. The optimum output load impedance, R_L, may range from a few thousand ohms to 100,000, depending upon the requirements.

The current transfer ratio is alpha (α) and the cut-off frequency is defined as the frequency at which the value of alpha (for a common-base amplifier) drops to 0.707 times its 1-kc. value.

In this circuit the phase of the output (collector) current is the same as that of the input (emitter) current. The parts of these currents that flow through the base resistance are likewise in phase, so the circuit tends to be regenerative and will oscillate if the current amplification factor is greater than 1.

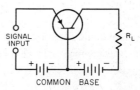

COMMON BASE

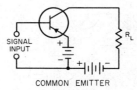

COMMON EMITTER

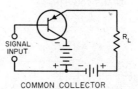

COMMON COLLECTOR

Fig. 4-12—Basic transistor amplifier circuits. R_L, the load resistance, may be an actual resistor or the primary of a transformer. The input signal may be supplied from a transformer secondary or by resistance-capacitance coupling. In any case it is to be understood that a d.c. path must exist between the base and emitter.

P-n-p transistors are shown in these circuits. If n-p-n types are used the battery polarities must be reversed.

Common-Emitter Circuit

The common-emitter circuit shown in Fig. 4-12 corresponds to the ordinary grounded-cathode vacuum-tube amplifier. As indicated by the curves of Fig. 4-11, the base current is small and the input impedance is therefore fairly high — several thousand ohms in the average case. The collector resistance is some tens of thousands of ohms, depending on the signal source impedance. The current transfer, alpha, ratio in the common-emitter circuit is equal to

$$\frac{a}{1-a}$$

Since a is close to 1 (0.98 or higher being representative), the short-circuit current gain in the grounded-emitter circuit may be 50 or more. The cut-off frequency is equal to the a cut-off frequency multiplied by $(1-a)$, and therefore is relatively low. (For example a transistor with an a cut-off of 1000 kc. and $a = 0.98$ would have a cut-off frequency of $1000 \times 0.02 = 20$ kc. in the common-emitter circuit.)

Within its frequency limitations, the common emitter circuit gives the highest power gain of the three.

In this circuit the phase of the output (collector) current is opposite to that of the input (base) current so such feedback as occurs through the small emitter resistance is negative and the amplifier is stable.

Common-Collector Circuit

Like the vacuum-tube cathode follower, the common-collector transistor amplifier has high input impedance and low output impedance. The latter is approximately equal to the impedance of the signal input source multiplied by $(1-a)$. The input resistance depends on the load resistance, being approximately equal to the load resistance divided by $(1-a)$. The fact that input resistance is directly related to the load resistance is a disadvantage of this type of amplifier if the load is one whose resistance or impedance varies with frequency.

The current transfer ratio with this circuit is

$$\frac{1}{1-a}$$

and the cut-off frequency is the same as in the grounded-emitter circuit. The output and input currents are in phase.

PRACTICAL CIRCUIT DETAILS

The bipolar transistor is no longer restricted to use in low-voltage circuits. Many modern-day transistors have collector-to-emitter ratings of 300 volts or more. Such transistors are useful in circuits that operate directly from the 115-volt a.c. line following rectification. For this reason, battery power is no longer the primary means by which to operate transistorized equipment. Many low-voltage transistor types are capable of developing a considerable amount of a.f. or r.f. power, hence draw amperes of current from the power supply. Dry batteries are seldom practical in circuits of this type. The usual approach in powering high-current, high-wattage transistorized equipment is to employ a wet-cell

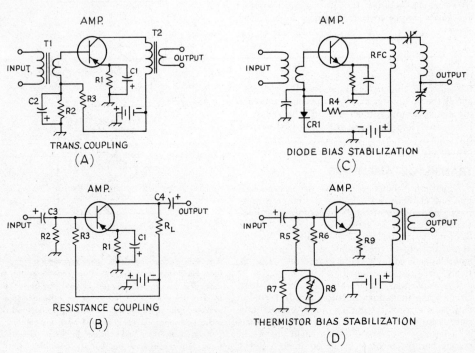

TRANS. COUPLING
(A)

RESISTANCE COUPLING
(B)

DIODE BIAS STABILIZATION
(C)

THERMISTOR BIAS STABILIZATION
(D)

Fig. 4-13—Transistor bias and bias-stabilization techniques which are commonly used.

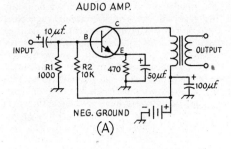

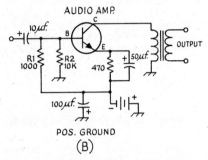

Fig. 4-14—Changing the circuit polarity.

two types of circuit. Typical impedance characteristics were discussed in the foregoing section of this chapter. It is not uncommon to encounter collector impedance levels of 10 ohms or less in high-power a.f. or r.f. amplifier stages. In circuits of this type, especially if supply voltages on the order of 28 volts or less are used, the collector current will be quite high—one ampere or more. This high d.c. current not only creates an impedance-matching problem, it complicates the problem of design because of the need for power-handling chokes, resistors, and other current-carrying components. Some typical impedance-matching techniques for r.f. amplifier circuits are shown in Fig. 4-15, illustrating how a collector impedance of less than 50 ohms can be matched to a 50-ohm termination.

In r.f. power-amplifier circuits it is common practice to operate two or more transistors in parallel to obtain a specified power level. The input and output tuned circuits become somewhat more involved because of the need for controlling the drive to each transistor, and because of the extremely low impedance levels that would be encountered were the transistors connected in parallel, using conventional methods. A typical circuit in which three high-power transistors are operated in parallel is given in Fig. 4-16. Each base has a separate input tuned circuit to permit equalization of the collector currents of each transistor. Although the collectors of the transistors could be parallel-connected, directly, the technique of Fig. 4-16 provides better efficiency because it permits parallel operation at a somewhat higher impedance level.

storage battery, or operate the equipment from a 115-volt a.c. line, stepping the primary voltage down to the desired level by means of a transformer, then rectifying the a.c. with silicon diodes.

Coupling and Impedance Matching

Coupling arrangements for introducing the signal into the circuit, and for taking it out, are similar to those used in vacuum-tube circuits. However, the actual component values will differ considerably, as will the impedance levels of the

Transistor Polarity

The manner in which a given transistor stage is wired, with regard to power supply polarity, will

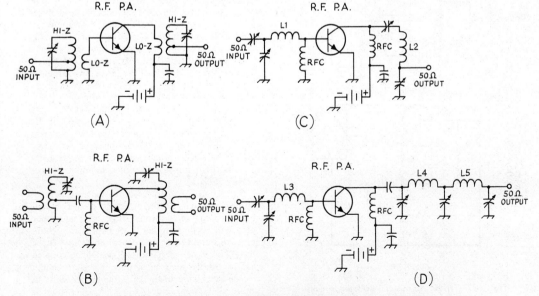

Fig. 4-15—Practical methods for matching low collector impedances to 50-ohm loads.

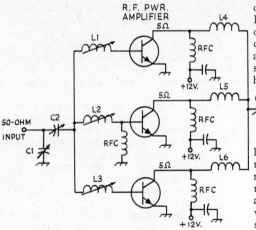

Fig. 4-16—Current-equalization method.

depend upon the transistor used, n-p-n or p-n-p. Either type will work in the circuit, regardless of the power supply polarity—negative or positive chassis ground. It is merely necessary to rearrange the circuit ground-return connections to suit the power-supply polarity. An example of how an n.p.n. transistor can be made to operate with either a negative-or positive-ground system is shown in Fig. 4-14. Similarly, a p.n.p. transistor can be used with either polarity. The circuit would not have to be rearranged were it convenient to remove the p.n.p. transistor and replace it with an n.p.n. type, or vise versa. By employing the method shown in Fig. 4-14, it is practical to have a single power-supply polarity arrangement while utilizing a mixture of n.p.n. and p.n.p. transistors in one piece of equipment.

Biasing Methods and Bias Stabilization

Typical single-battery common-emitter circuits are shown in Fig. 4-13 at A and B. R_1, in series with the emitter, is for the purpose of "swamping out" the resistance of the emitter-base diode; this swamping helps to stabilize the emitter current. The resistance of R_1 should be large compared with that of the emitter-base diode, which, as stated earlier, is approximately equal to 25 divided by the emitter current in ma.

Since the current in R_1 flows in such a direction as to bias the emitter negatively with respect to the base (a p-n-p transistor is assumed), a base-emitter bias slightly greater than the drop in R_1 must be supplied. The proper operating point is achieved through adjustment of voltage divider $R_2 R_3$, which is proportioned to give the desired value of no-signal collector current.

In the transformer-coupled circuit, input signal currents flow through R_1 and R_2, and there would be a loss of signal power at the base-emitter diode if these resistors were not bypassed by C_1 and C_2. The capacitors should have low reactance compared with the resistances across which they are connected. In the resistance-coupled circuit R_2 serves as part of the bias voltage divider and also as part of the load for the signal-input source. As seen by the signal source, R_3 is in parallel with R_2 and thus becomes part of the input load resistance. C_3 must have low reactance compared with the parallel combination of R_2, R_3 and the base-to-emitter resistance of the transistor. The load impedance will determine the reactance of C_4.

The output load resistance in the transformer-coupled case will be the actual load as reflected at the primary of the transformer, and its proper value will be determined by the transistor characteristics and the type of operation (Class A, B, etc.). The value of R_L in the resistance-coupled case is usually such as to permit the maximum a.c. voltage swing in the collector circuit without undue distortion, since Class A operation is usual with this type of amplifier.

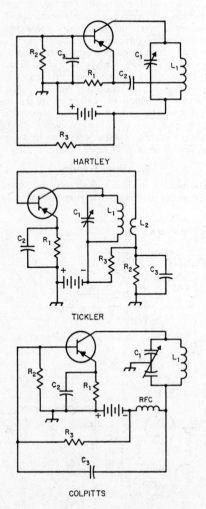

Fig. 4-17—Typical transistor oscillator circuits. Component values are discussed in the text.

Transistor currents are sensitive to temperature variations, and so the operating point tends to shift as the transistor heats. The shift in operating point is in such a direction as to increase the heating, leading to "thermal runaway" and possible destruction of the transistor. The heat developed depends on the amount of power dissipated in the transistor, so it is obviously advantageous in this respect to operate with as little internal dissipation as possible: i.e., the d.c. input should be kept to the lowest value that will permit the type of operation desired and should never exceed the rated value for the particular transistor used.

A contributing factor to the shift in operating point is the collector-to-base leakage current (usually designated I_{co}) — that is, the current that flows from collector to base with the emitter connection open. This current, which is highly temperature sensitive, has the effect of increasing the emitter current by an amount much larger than I_{co} itself, thus shifting the operating point in such a way as to increase the collector current. This effect is reduced to the extent that I_{co} can be made to flow out of the base terminal rather than through the base-emitter diode. In the circuits of Fig. 4-13, bias stabilization is improved by making the resistance of R_1 as large as possible and both R_2 and R_3 as small as possible, consistent with gain and battery economy.

It is common practice to employ certain devices in the bias networks of transistor stages that enhance the stability of the bias. **Thermistors** or diodes can be used to advantage in such circuits. Examples of both techniques are given in Fig. 4-13 at C and D. Thermistors (temperature-sensitive resistors) can be used to compensate the rapid increase in collector current which is brought about by an increase in temperature. As the temperature in that part of the circuit increases, the thermistor's resistance decreases, reducing the emitter-to-base voltage (bias). As the bias is reduced in this manner, the collector current tends to remain the same, thus providing bias stabilization.

Resistors R_5 and R_7 of Fig. 4-13D. are selected to give the most effective compensation over a particular temperature range.

A somewhat better bias-stabilization technique can be realized by using the method shown in Fig. 4-13C. In this instance, a diode is used between the base of the transistor and ground, replacing the resistor that is used in the circuits at A and B. The diode establishes a fixed value of forward bias and sets the no-signal collector current of the transistor. Also, the diode bias current varies in direct proportion with the supply voltage, tending to hold the no-signal collector current of the transistor at a steady value. If the diode is installed thermally close to the transistor with which it is used (clamped to the chassis near the transistor heat sink), it will provide protection against bias changes brought about by temperature excursions. As the diode temperature increases so will the diode bias current, thus lowering the bias voltage. Ordinarily, diode bias stabilization is applied to Class B stages. With germanium transistors, diode bias stabilization reduces collector-current variations to approximately one fifth of that obtainable with thermistor bias protection. With silicon transistors, the current variations are reduced to approximately one fifteenth the thermistor-bias value.

TRANSISTOR OSCILLATORS

Since more power is available from the output circuit than is necessary for its generation in the input circuit, it is possible to use some of the output power to supply the input circuit with a signal and thus sustain self-oscillation. Representative self-controlled oscillator circuits, based on vacuum-tube circuits of the same names, are shown in Fig. 4-17.

The upper frequency limit for oscillation is principally a function of the cut-off frequency of the transistor used, and oscillation will cease at the frequency at which there is insufficient amplification to supply the energy required to overcome circuit losses. Transistor oscillators usually will operate up to, and sometimes well beyond, the α cut-off frequency of the particular transistor used.

The approximate oscillation frequency is that of the tuned circuit, L_1C_1. R_1, R_2 and R_3 have the same functions as in the amplifier circuits given in Fig. 4-17. Bypass capacitors C_2 and C_3 should have low reactances compared with the resistances with which they are associated.

Feedback in these circuits is adjusted in the same way as with tube oscillators: position of the tap on L_1 in the Hartley, turns and coupling of L_2 in the tickler circuit, and ratio of the sections of C_1 in the Colpitts.

FIELD-EFFECT TRANSISTORS

Still another semiconductor device, the field-effect transistor, is superior to conventional transistors in many applications. Because it has a high input impedance, its characteristics more nearly approach those of a vacuum tube.

The Junction FET

Field-effect transistors are divided into two main groups: junction FETS, and insulated-gate FETS. The basic JFET is shown in Fig. 4-18.

The reason for the terminal names will become clear later. A d.c. operating condition is set up by starting a current flow between source and drain. This current flow is made up of free electrons since the semiconductor is n-type in the channel, so a positive voltage is applied at the drain. This positive voltage attracts the negatively-charged free electrons and the current flows (Fig. 4-19). The next step is to apply a gate voltage of the polarity shown in Fig. 4-19. Note that this reverse-biases the gates with respect to the source, channel, and drain. This reverse-bias gate voltage causes a depletion layer to be formed which takes up part of the channel, and since the electrons now have less volume in which to move the resistance is greater and the current between source and drain is reduced. If a large gate voltage is applied the depletion regions meet, and

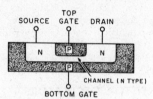

Fig. 4-18—The junction field-effect transistor.

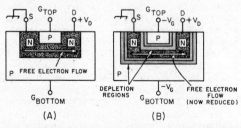

Fig. 4-19—Operation of the JFET under applied bias. A depletion region (light shading) is formed, compressing the channel and increasing its resistance to current flow.

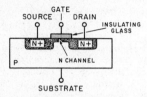

Fig. 4-20—The insulated-gate field-effect transistor.

consequently the source-drain current is reduced nearly to zero. Since the large source-drain current changed with a relatively small gate voltage, the device acts as an amplifier. In the operation of the JFET, the gate terminal is never forward biased, because if it were the source-drain current would all be diverted through the forward-biased gate junction diode.

The resistance between the gate terminal and the rest of the device is very high, since the gate terminal is always reverse biased, so the JFET has a very high input resistance. The source terminal is the *source* of current carriers, and they are *drained* out of the circuit at the drain. The gate *opens* and *closes* the amount of channel current which flows. Thus the operation of a FET closely resembles the operation of the vacuum tube with its high grid input impedance. Comparing the JFET to a vacuum tube, the source corresponds to the cathode, the gate to the grid, and the drain to the plate.

Insulated-Gate FET

The other large family which makes up field-effect transistors is the insulated-gate FET, or IGFET, which is pictured schematically in Fig. 4-20. In order to set up a d.c. operating condition, a positive polarity is applied to the drain terminal. The substrate is connected to the source, and both are at ground potential, so the channel electrons are attracted to the positive drain. In order to regulate this source-drain current, voltage is applied to the gate contact. The gate is insulated from the rest of the device by a piece of insulating glass so this is not a p-n junction between the gate and the device—thus the name insulated gate. When a negative gate polarity is applied, positive-charged holes from the p-type substrate are attracted towards the gate and the conducting channel is made more narrow; thus the source-drain current is reduced. When a positive gate voltage is connected, the holes in the substrate are repelled away, the conducting channel is made larger, and the source-drain current is increased. The IGFET is more flexible since either a positive or negative voltage can be applied to the gate. The resistance between the gate and the rest of the device is extremely high because they are separated by a layer of glass—not as clear as window glass, but it conducts just as poorly. Thus the IGFET has an extremely high input impedance. In fact, since the leakage through the insulating glass is generally much smaller than through the reverse-biased p-n gate junction in the JFET, the IGFET has a much higher input impedance. Typical values of R_{in} for the IGFET are over a million megohms, while R_{in} for the JFET ranges from megohms to over a thousand megohms.

Characteristic Curves

The characteristic curves for the FETs described above are shown in Figs. 4-21 and 4-22, where drain-source current is plotted against drain-source voltage for given gate & voltages.

The discussion of the JFET so far has left both gates separate so the device can be used as a

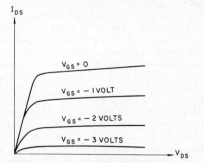

Fig. 4-21—Typical JFET characteristic curves.

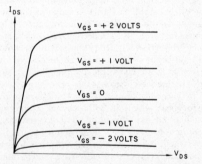

Fig. 4-22—Typical IGFET characteristic curves.

tetrode in mixer applications. However, the gates can be internally connected for triode applications. When using the IGFET the substrate is always a.c.-shorted to the source, and only the insulated gate is used to control the current flow. This is done so that both positive and negative polarities can be applied to the device, as opposed to JFET operation where only one polarity can be used, because if the gate itself becomes forward biased the unit is no longer useful.

Classifications

Field-effect transistors are classed into two main groupings for application in circuits, enhancement mode and depletion mode. The enhancement-mode devices are those specifically constructed so that they have *no* channel. They become useful only when a gate voltage is applied that causes a channel to be formed. IGFETs can be used as enhancement-mode devices since both polarities can be applied to the gate without the gate becoming forward biased and conducting.

A depletion-mode unit corresponds to Figs. 4-18 and 4-20 shown earlier, where a channel exists with no gate voltage applied. For the JFET we can apply a gate voltage and deplete the channel, causing the current to decrease. With the IGFET we can apply a gate voltage of either polarity so the device can be depleted (current decreased) or enhanced (current increased).

To sum up, a depletion-mode FET is one which has a channel constructed; thus it has a current flow for zero gate voltage. Enhancement-mode FETs are those which have no channel, so no current flows with zero gate voltage.

IGFETs are also available with two gates. The 3N159 is typical of this type. Dual-gate FETs have exceptionally good cross-modulation characteristics, a wide dynamic range, and excellent thermal stability. They are ideal as a.g.c.'d r.f. and i.f. amplifiers, as mixers, and as product detectors. A typical mixer circuit is shown in Fig. 4-24.

SILICON CONTROLLED RECTIFIERS

The silicon controlled rectifier, also known as a Thyristor, is a four-layer (p-n-p-n or n-p-n-p) three-electrode semiconductor rectifier. The three terminals are called anode, cathode and gate, Fig. 4-25B.

The SCR differs from the silicon rectifier in that it will not conduct until the voltage exceeds the *forward breakover* voltage. The value of this voltage can be controlled by the gate current. As the gate current is increased, the value of the forward breakover voltage is decreased. Once the rectifier conducts in the forward direction, the gate current no longer has any control, and the rectifier behaves as a low-forward-resistance diode. The gate regains control when the current through the rectifier is cut off, as during the other half cycle.

The SCR finds wide use in power-control applications (Chap. 20), and in time-delay circuits.

*SCR*s are available in various voltage and wattage ratings.

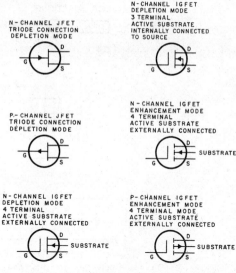

Fig. 4-23—Symbols for most-commonly available field-effect transistors.

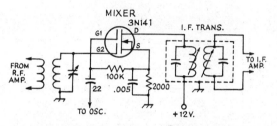

Fig. 4-24—Typical circuit for a dual-gate IGFET as a mixer.

THE UNIJUNCTION TRANSISTOR

Another useful type of semiconductor, though used infrequently in amateur radio work, is the **unijunction** (UJT) transistor. Structurally, it is built on an n-type silicon bar which has ohmic contacts—base one (B1) and base two (B2)—at opposite ends of the bar. A rectifying contact, the emitter, is attached between B1 and B2 on the bar. In normal operation, B1 is grounded and a positive bias is applied to B2. When the emitter is forward biased, emitter current will flow and the device will conduct.

The UJT finds widespread use in relaxation-oscillator circuits, in pulse- and sawtooth-generator circuits, and in timing circuits. The symbol for UJTs is given in Fig. 4-25 at C. At E, a typical UJT relaxation oscillator is used to trigger an SCR as was done with the neon lamp of Fig. 4-25D. Circuit values are only representative. Actual values depend upon the devices used and the operating voltages involved.

INTEGRATED CIRCUITS

One of the newer developments in the solid-state field is the **integrated circuit** (IC). As the term "integrated" implies, several circuit com-

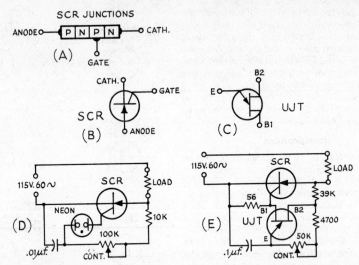

Fig. 4-25—Unijunction transistor and SCR symbols, and typical circuit applications.

ponents are contained on one semiconductor chip, and are housed in one package. It is not uncommon to see as many as 8 or more transistors contained on a single integrated-circuit chip. The same chip might contain 10 or more resistors, several capacitors, and many individual diodes. From this it can be seen that a single integrated-circuit device is capable of replacing a large number of separate, or discrete, components—aiding greatly in achieving more compact electronic packaging than might be possible with discrete components doing the same job. The advantages do not end there, however. This form of modular packaging makes possible the rapid servicing or assembling of electronics equipment, since an entire circuit section—such as audio amplifier, an i.f. amplifier, a flip-flop, or other complex circuit—can be contained on a single IC. Perhaps more significant among the advantages of their use, the various components on the IC chip receive nearly identical processing, hence are closely matched in characteristics. This close match can be maintained over a wide range of operating temperatures because all of the components are subject to the same changes in temperature. For this reason an IC of appropriate type can be used advantageously in balanced-modulator circuits, or any circuit requiring like characteristics of the transistors and diodes.

IC Structures

The basic IC is formed on a uniform chip of n-type or p-type silicon. Impurities are introduced into the chip, their depth into it being determined by the diffusion temperature and time. The geometry of the plane surface of the chip is determined by masking off certain areas, applying photochemical techniques, and applying a coating of insulating oxide. Certain areas of the oxide coating are then opened up to allow the formation of interconnecting leads between sections of the IC. When capacitors are formed on the chip, the oxide serves as the dielectric material. Fig. 4-26

shows a representative three-component IC in both pictorial and schematic form. Most integrated circuits are housed in TO-5 type cases, or in flat-pack epoxy blocks. ICs may have as many as 12 or more leads which connect to the various elements on the chip.

Types of IC Amplifiers

Some ICs are called **differential amplifiers** and others are known as **operational amplifiers.** The basic differential-amplifier IC consists of a pair of transistors that have similar input circuits. The inputs can be connected so as to enable the transistors to respond to the difference between two voltages or currents. During this function, the circuit effectively suppresses like voltages or currents. For the sake of simplicity we may think of the differential pair of transistors as a push-pull amplifier stage. Ordinarily, the differential pair of transistors are fed from a controlled, constant-current source (Q_3 in Fig. 4-27A. Q_1 and Q_2 are the differential pair in this instance). Q_3 is commonly called a **transistor current sink.** Excellent balance exists between the input terminals of differential amplifiers because the base-to-emitter voltages and current gains (beta) of the two transistors are closely matched. The match results from the fact that the transistors are formed next to one another on the same silicon chip.

Differential ICs are useful as linear amplifiers from d.c. to the v.h.f. spectrum, and can be employed in such circuits as limiters, product detectors, frequency multipliers, mixers, amplitude modulators, squelch, r.f. and i.f. amplifiers, and even in signal-generating applications. Although they are designed to be used as differential amplifiers, they can be used in other types of circuits as well, treating the various IC components as discrete units.

Operational-amplifier ICs are basically very-high-gain direct-coupled amplifiers that rely on feedback for control of their response characteristics. They contain cascaded differential amplifiers of the type shown in Fig. 4-27A. A separate output stage, Q_6-Q_7, Fig. 4-27B, is contained on the chip. Although operational ICs can be successfully operated under open-loop conditions, they are generally controlled by externally-applied negative feedback. Operational amplifiers are most often used for video amplification, as frequency-shaping (peaking, notching, or bandpass) amplifiers, or as integrator, differentiator, or comparator amplifiers. As is true of differential ICs, operational ICs can be used in circuits where their components are treated as discrete units.

Diode ICs are also being manufactured in the same manner as outlined in the foregoing section. Several diodes can be contained on a single silicon wafer to provide a near-perfect match between diode characteristics. The diode arrangement can take the form of a bridge circuit, series-connected groups, or as separate components. Diode ICs of this kind are extremely adaptable to balanced-modulator circuitry, or to any application requiring closely matched diodes.

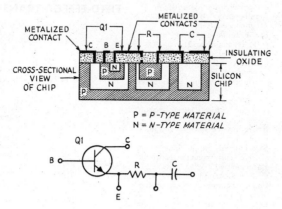

Fig. 4-26—Pictorial and schematic illustrations of a simple IC device.

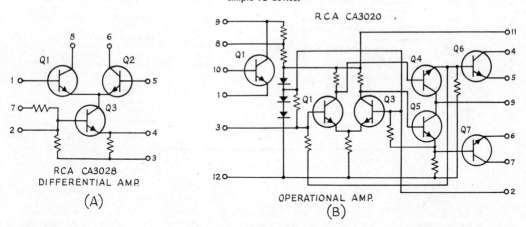

Fig. 4-27—At A, a representative circuit for a typical differential IC. An Operational Amplifier IC is illustrated at B, also in representative form.

TRANSISTOR BIBLIOGRAPHY

McGraw-Hill Publications:
Kiver, *Transistors*, 3rd edition.
Integrated Circuits, by Motorola staff.
Leonce J. Sevin, Jr., *Field-Effect Transistors*.
Transistor Circuit Design, by staff of Texas Instruments, Inc.

RCA publications:
RCA Transistor Manual
RCA Silicon Power Circuits Manual
RCA Integrated Circuit Fundamentals

Other books:
G.E. Transistor Manual, 6th edition, by General Electric.
G.E. SCR Manual, 3rd edition, by General Electric.
Motorola Data Manual, by Motorola Semiconductor Corp.
Zener Diode Handbook, by International Rectifier Corp.
Wolfendale, *The Junction Transistor And Its Applications*.
Publisher, The Macmillan Company.

ABBREVIATED SEMICONDUCTOR SYMBOL LIST

BIPOLAR TRANSISTOR SYMBOLS

C_{ibo} —Input capacitance, open circuit (common base).

C_{ieo} —Input capacitance, open circuit (common emitter).

C_{obo} —Output capacitance, open circuit (common base).

C_{oeo} —Output capacitance, open circuit (common emitter).

f_c —Cutoff frequency.

f_T —Gain-bandwidth product (frequency at which small-signal forward current-transfer ratio, common emitter, is unity, or 1).

g_{me} —Small-signal transconductance (common emitter).

h_{FB} —Static forward-current transfer ratio (common base).

h_{fb} —Small-signal forward-current transfer ratio, sort circuit (common base).

h_{FE} —Static forward-current transfer ratio (common emitter).

h_{fe} —Small-signal forward-current transfer ratio, short circuit (common emitter).

h_{IE} —Static input resistance (common emitter).

h_{ie} —Small-signal input impedance, short circuit (common emitter).

I_b —Base current.

I_c —Collector current.

I_{CBO} —Collector-cutoff current, emitter open.

I_{CEO} —Collector-cutoff current, base open.

I_E —Emitter current.

MAG —Maximum available amplifier gain.

P_{CE} —Total d.c. or average power input to collector (common emitter).

P_{OE} —Large-signal output power (common emitter).

R_L —Load resistance.

R_s —Source resistance.

V_{BB} —Base-supply voltage.

V_{BC} —Base-to-collector voltage.

V_{BE} —Base-to-emitter voltage.

V_{CB} —Collector-to-base voltage.

V_{CBO} —Collector-to-base voltage (emitter open.

V_{CC} —Collector-supply voltage.

V_{CE} —Collector-to-emitter voltage.

V_{CEO} —Collector-to-emitter voltage (base open).

$V_{CE(sat)}$ —Collector-to-emitter saturation voltage.

V_{EB} —Emitter-to-base voltage.

V_{EBO} —Emitter-to-base voltage (collector open).

V_{EE} —Emitter-supply voltage.

Y_{fe} —Forward transconductance.

Y_{ie} —Input Admittance.

Y_{oe} —Output Admittance.

FIELD-EFFECT TRANSISTOR SYMBOLS

A —Voltage amplification.

C_c —Intrinsic channel capacitance.

C_{ds} —Drain-to-source capacitance (includes approximately 1-pf. drain-to-case and interlead capacitance).

C_{gd} —Gate-to-drain capacitance (includes 0.1-pf. interlead capacitance).

C_{gs} —Gate-to-source interlead and case capacitance.

C_{iss} —Small-signal input capacitance, short circuit.

C_{rss} —Small-signal reverse transfer capacitance, short circuit.

g_{fs} —Forward transconductance.

g_{is} —input conductance

g_{os} —output conductance

I_D —dc drain current

$I_{DS}(OFF)$ —drain-to-source OFF current

I_{GSS} —gate leakage current

r_e —Effective gate series resistance.

$r_{DS}(ON)$ —Drain-to-source ON resistance.

r_{gd} —Gate-to-drain leakage resistance.

r_{gs} —Gate-to-source leakage resistance.

V_{DB} —Drain-to-substrate voltage.

V_{DS} —Drain-to-source voltage.

V_{GB} —D.c. gate-to-substrate voltage.

V_{GB} —Peak gate-to-substrate voltage.

V_{GS} —D.c. gate-to-source voltage.

V_{GS} —Peak gate-to-source voltage.

$V_{GS}(OFF)$ —Gate-to-source cutoff voltage.

Y_{fs} —forward transadmittance $\approx g_{fs}$.

Y_{os} —Output admittance.

Y_L —Load admittance.

Chapter 5

Receiving Systems

Communications **receiver's** performance can be measured by its ability to pick up weak signals and seperate them from the noise and QRM while at the same time holding them steady at the same dial settings. The difference between a good receiver and a poor one can be the difference between copying a weak signal Q5, or perhaps not copying it at all.

Whether the receiver is of home-made or commercial origin, it's performance can range from excellent to extremely poor, and high cost or circuit complexity cannot assure proper results. Some of the simplest of receivers can provide excellent results if careful attention is given to their design and proper use. Conversely, the most expensive of receivers can provide poor results if not operated in a competent manner. Therefore, the operator's success at sorting the weak signals out of the noise and QRM is dependent upon the correct use of a properly-designed, correctly-operated receiver.

Communications receivers are rated by their **sensitivity** (ability to pick up weak signals), their **selectivity** (the ability to distinguish between signals that are extremely close together in terms of frequency), and by their **stability.** The latter trait assures that once a stable signal is tuned in it will remain tuned in, and will not necessitate periodic retuning of the receiver's controls (especially the main tuning and b.f.o. controls).

A well-designed modern receiver must be able to receive all of the popular modes of emission if it is to be truly versatile. It should be capable of handling c.w., a.m., s.s.b., and RTTY signals.

The reception of f.m. and TV signals requires special techniques, and usually dictates that accessory equipment be used with the main station receiver.

The type of **detection** to be used will depend on the job the receiver is called upon to do. Simple receivers consisting of a single stage of detection (regenerative detector) followed by a one- or two-stage audio amplifier are often adequate for portable and emergency use over short distances. This type of receiver can be quite compact and light weight and can provide many hours of operation from a dry-battery pack if transistorized circuitry is used. Similarly, super-regenerative detectors can be used in the same way, but are suitable for copying only a.m. and wide-band f.m. signals. Superheterodyne receivers are the most popular and are capable of better performance than the foregoing types. *Heterodyne* detectors are used for s.s.b. and c.w. reception in the latter. If a regenerative detector is made to oscillate and provide a steady signal, it is known as an **autodyne** detector. A **beat-frequency oscillator,** or **b.f.o.,** is used to generate a steady signal in the superheterodyne receiver. This signal is applied to the detector stage to permit the reception of s.s.b. and c.w. signals.

Communications receivers should have a slow tuning rate and a smooth-operating tuning-dial mechanism if any reasonable degree of selectivity is used. Without these features c.w. and s.s.b. signals are extremely hard to tune in. In fact, one might easily tune past a weak signal without knowing it was there if a fast tuning rate were used.

RECEIVER CHARACTERISTICS

Sensitivity

In commercial circles "sensitivity" is defined as the strength of the signal (in microvolts) at the input of the receiver that is required to produce a specified audio power output at the speaker or headphones. This is a satisfactory definition for broadcast and communications receivers operating below about 20 MHz., where atmospheric and man-made electrical noises normally mask any noise generated by the receiver itself.

Another commercial measure of sensitivity defines it as the signal at the input of the receiver required to give a signal-plus-noise output some stated ratio (generally 10 db.) above the noise output of the receiver. This is a more useful sensitivity measure for the amateur, since

it indicates how well a weak signal will be heard and is not merely a measure of the over-all amplification of the receiver. However, it is not an absolute method, because the bandwidth of the receiver plays a large part in the result.

The random motion of the molecules in the antenna and receiver circuits generates small voltages called **thermal-agitation noise** voltages. Thermal-agitation noise is independent of frequency and is proportional to the (absolute) temperature, the resistance component of the impedance across which the thermal agitation is produced, and the bandwidth. Noise is generated in vacuum tubes and semiconductors by random irregularities in the current flow within them; it is convenient to express this **shot-effect noise** as an equivalent resistance in the grid circuit of a noise-free tube. This **equivalent noise resistance** is the resistance (at room temperature) that placed in the grid circuit of a noise-free tube will produce plate-circuit noise equal to that of the actual tube. The equivalent noise resistance of a vacuum tube increases with frequency.

An ideal receiver would generate no noise in its tubes or semiconductors and circuits, and the minimum detectable signal would be limited only by the thermal noise in the antenna. In a practical receiver, the limit is determined by how well the amplified antenna noise overrides the other noise of the input stage. (It is assumed that the first stage in any good receiver will be the determining factor; the noise contributions of subsequent stages should be insignificant by comparison.) At frequencies below 20 or 30 MHz. the site noise (atmospheric and man-made noise) is generally the limiting factor.

The degree to which a practical receiver approaches the quiet ideal receiver of the same bandwidth is given by the **noise figure** of the receiver. Noise figure is defined as the ratio of the signal-to-noise power ratio of the ideal receiver to the signal-to-noise power ratio of the actual receiver output. Since the noise figure is a ratio, it is usually given in decibels; it runs around 5 to 10 db. for a good communications receiver below 30 MHz. Although noise figures of 2 to 4 db. can be obtained, they are of little or no use below 30 MHz. except in extremely quiet locations or when a very small antenna is used. The noise figure of a receiver is not modified by changes in bandwidth. Measurement technique is described in Chapter 21.

Selectivity

Selectivity is the ability of a receiver to discriminate against signals of frequencies differing from that of the desired signal. The over-all selectivity will depend upon the selectivity and the number of the individual tuned circuits.

The selectivity of a receiver is shown graphically by drawing a curve that gives the ratio of signal strength required at various frequencies off resonance to the signal strength at resonance, to give constant output. A **resonance curve** of this type is shown in Fig. 5-1. The **bandwidth** is the width of the resonance curve (in Hz. or kHz.) of a receiver at a specified ratio; in the typical curve of Fig. 5-1 the bandwidths for response ratios of 2 and 1000 (described as "-6 db." and "-60 db.") are 2.4 and 12.2 kHz. respectively.

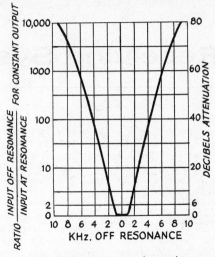

Fig. 5-1—Typical selectivity curve of a modern superheterodyne receiver. Relative response is plotted against deviations above and below the resonance frequency. The scale at the left is in terms of voltage ratios, the corresponding decibel steps are shown at the right.

The bandwidth at 6 db. down must be sufficient to pass the signal and its sidebands if faithful reproduction of the signal is desired. However, in the crowded amateur bands, it is generally advisable to sacrifice fidelity for intelligibility. The ability to reject adjacent-channel signals depends upon the **skirt selectivity** of the receiver, which is determined by the bandwidth at high attenuation. In a receiver with excellent skirt selectivity, the ratio of the 6-db. bandwidth to the 60-db. bandwidth will be about 0.25 for code and 0.5 for phone. The minimum usable bandwidth at 6 db. down is about 150 Hz. for code reception and about 2000 Hz. for phone.

Stability

The stability of a receiver is its ability to "stay put" on a signal under varying conditions of gain-control setting, temperature, supply-voltage changes and mechanical shock and distortion. The term "unstable" is also applied to a receiver that breaks into oscillation or a regenerative condition with some settings of its controls that are not specifically intended to control such a condition.

DETECTION AND DETECTORS

Detection (demodulation) is the process of extracting the signal information from a modulated carrier wave. (See "Modulation, Heterodyning and Beats," page 58.) When dialing with an a.m. signal, detection involves only the rectification of the r.f. signal. During f.m. reception, the incoming signal must be converted to an a.m. signal for detection.

Detector sensitivity is the ratio of desired detector output to the input. Detector linearity is a measure of the ability of the detector to reproduce the exact form of the modulation on the incoming signal. The resistance or impedance of the detector is the resistance or impedance it presents to the circuits it is connected to. The input resistance is important in receiver design, since if it is relatively low ·it means that the detector will consume power, and this power must be furnished by the preceding stage. The signal-handling capability means the ability to accept signals of a specified amplitude without overloading or distortion.

Diode Detectors

The simplest detector for a.m. is the diode. A germanium or silicon **crystal** is an imperfect form of diode (a small current can usually pass in the reverse direction), but the principle of detection in a semiconductor diode is similar to that in a vacuum-tube diode.

Circuits for both half-wave and full-wave diodes are given in Fig. 5-2. The simplified half-wave circuit at 5-2A includes the r.f. tuned circuit, L_2C_1, a coupling coil, L_1, from which

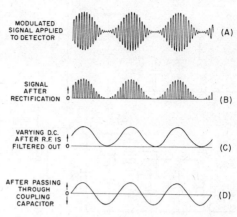

Fig. 5-3—Diagrams showing the detection process.

the r.f. energy is fed to L_2C_1, and the diode, CR_1, with its load resistance, R_1, and bypass capacitor, C_2.

The progress of the signal through the detctor or rectifier is shown in Fig. 5-3. A typical modulated signal as it exists in the tuned circuit is shown at A. When this signal is applied to the rectifier, current will flow only during the part of the r.f. cycle when the anode is positive with respect to cathode, so that the output of the rectifier consists of half-cycles of r.f. These current pulses flow in the load circuit comprised of R_1 and C_2, the resistance of R_1 and the capacity of C_2 being so proportioned that C_2 charges to the peak value of the rectified voltage on each pulse and retains enough charge between pulses so that the voltage across R_1 is smoothed out, as shown in C. C_2 thus acts as a filter for the radio-frequency component of the output of the rectifier, leaving a d.c. component that varies in the same way as the modulation on the original signal. When this varying d.c. voltage is applied to a following amplifier through a coupling capacitor (C_4 in Fig. 5-2), only the *variations* in voltage are transferred, so that the final output signal is a.c., as shown in D.

In the circuit at 5-2B, R_1 and C_2 have been divided for the purpose of providing a more effective filter for r.f. It is important to prevent the appearance of any r.f. voltage in the output of the detector, because it may cause overloading of a succeeding amplifier stage. The audio-frequency variations can be transferred to another circuit through a coupling capacitor, C_4. R_2 is usually a "potentiometer" so that the audio volume can be adjusted to a desired level.

Coupling from the potentiometer (volume control) through a capacitor also avoids any flow of d.c. through the moving contact of control. The flow of d.c. through a high-resistance volume control often tends to make the control noisy (scratchy) after a short while.

The full-wave diode circuit at 5-2C differs in operation from the half-wave circuit only in

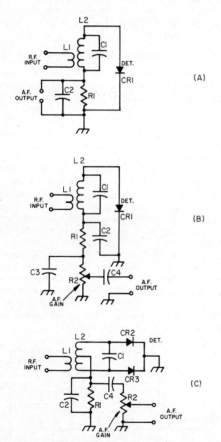

Fig. 5-2—Simplified and practical diode detector circuits. A, the elementary half-wave diode detector; B, a practical circuit, with r.f. filtering and audio output coupling; C, full-wave diode detector, with output coupling indicated. The circuit, L_2C_1, is tuned to the signal frequency; typical values for C_2 and R_1 in A and C are 250 pf. and 250,000 ohms, respectively; in B, C_2 and C_3 are 100 pf. each; R_1, 50,000 ohms; and R_2, 250,000 ohms. C_4 is 0.1 μf. and R_3 may be 0.5 to 1 megohm.

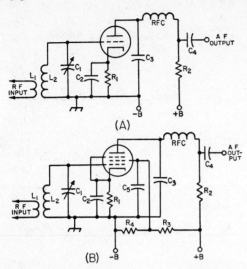

Fig. 5-4—Circuits for plate detection. A, triode; B, pentode. The input circuit, L_2C_1, is tuned to the signal frequency. Typical values for the other components are:

Component	Circuit A	Circuit B
C_2	0.5 µf. or larger.	0.5 µf. or larger.
C_3	0.001 to 0.002 µf.	250 to 500 pf.
C_4	0.1 µf.	0.1 µf.
C_5		0.5 µf. or larger.
R_1	25,000 to 150,000 ohms.	10,000 to 20,000 ohms.
R_2	50,000 to 100,000 ohms.	100,000 to 250,000 ohms.
R_3		50,000 ohms.
R_4		20,000 ohms.
RFC	2.5 mh.	2.5 mh.

Plate voltages from 100 to 250 volts may be used. Effective screen voltage in B should be about 30 volts.

that both halves of the r.f. cycle are utilized. The full-wave circuit has the advantage that r.f. filtering is easier than in the half-wave circuit. As a result, less attenuation of the higher audio frequencies will be obtained for any given degree of r.f. filtering.

The reactance of C_2 must be small compared to the resistance of R_1 at the radio frequency being rectified, but at audio frequencies must be relatively large compared to R_1. If the capacity of C_2 is too large, response at the higher audio frequencies will be lowered.

Compared with most other detectors, the gain of the diode is low, normally running around 0.8 in audio work. Since the diode consumes power, the Q of the tuned circuit is reduced, bringing about a reduction in selectivity. The loading effect of the diode is close to one-half the load resistance. The detector linearity is good, and the signal-handling capability is high.

Plate Detectors

The plate detector is arranged so that rectification of the r.f. signal takes place in the plate circuit of the tube. Sufficient negative bias is applied to the grid to bring the plate current nearly to the cut-off point, so that application of a signal to the grid circuit causes an increase in average plate current. The average plate current follows the changes in signal in a fashion similar to the rectified current in a diode detector.

In general, transformer coupling from the plate circuit of a plate detector is not satisfactory, because the plate impedance of any tube is very high when the bias is near the plate-current cut-off point. Impedance coupling may be used in place of the resistance coupling shown in Fig. 5-4. Usually 100 henrys or more inductance is required.

The plate detector is more sensitive than the diode because there is some amplifying action in the tube. It will handle large signals, but is not so tolerant in this respect as the diode. Linearity, with the self-biased circuits, shown, is good. Up to the overload point the detector takes no power from the tuned circuit, and so does not affect its Q and selectivity.

Infinite-Impedance Detector

The circuit of Fig. 5-5 combines the high signal-handling capabilities of the diode detector with low distortion and, like the plate detector, does not load the tuned circuit it connects to. The circuit resembles that of the plate detector, except that the load resistance, R_1, is connected between cathode and ground and thus is common to both grid and plate circuits, giving negative feedback for the audio frequencies. The cathode resistor is bypassed for r.f. but not for audio, while the plate circuit is bypassed to ground for both audio and radio frequencies. An r.f. filter can be connected between the cathode and C_4 to eliminate any r.f. that might otherwise appear in the output.

The plate current is very low at no signal, increasing with signal as in the case of the plate detector. The voltage drop across R_1 consequently increases with signal. Because of this and the large initial drop across R_1, the grid usually cannot be driven positive by the signal, and no grid current can be drawn.

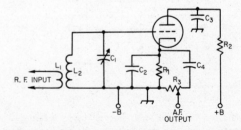

Fig. 5-5—The infinite-impedance detector. The input circuit, L_2C_1, is tuned to the signal frequency. Typical values for the other components are:

C_2—250 pf.	R_1—0.15 megohm.
C_3—0.5 µf.	R_2—25,000 ohms.
C_4—0.1 µf.	R_3—0.25-megohm volume control.

A tube having a medium amplification factor (about 20) should be used. Plate voltage should be 250 volts.

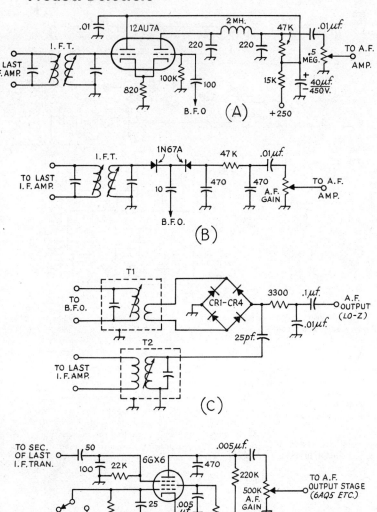

Fig. 5-6—Four versions of the product detector. A twin triode tube is used in the circuit at A. A pair of solid-state diodes perform as a product detector at B. Four diodes, CR_1-CR_4, inclusive, form a ring demodulator circuit at C. This circuit works best with approximately 1.2 volts of b.f.o. injection, providing excellent suppression of second-order IM products at that level. This type of product detector has low-impedance input and output characteristics, hence is well suited to use in transistorized equipment. The circuit at D employs a tube designed primarily for use in f.m. receivers. It combines the functions of a b.f.o., product detector, and 1st audio amplifier in one envelope.

HETERODYNE AND PRODUCT DETECTORS

Any of the foregoing a.m. detectors becomes a heterodyne detector when a local-oscillator (b.f.o.) is added to it. The b.f.o. signal amplitude should be 5 to 20 times greater than that of the strongest incoming c.w. or s.s.b. signal if distortion is to be minimized. These heterodyne detectors are frequently used in receivers that are intended for a.m. as well as c.w. and s.s.b. reception. A single detector can thus be used for all three modes, and elaborate switching techniques are not required. To receive a.m. it is merely necessary to disable the b.f.o. circuit.

The name "product detector" has been given to heterodyne detectors in which special attention has been paid to minimizing distortion and inter-

modulation (IM) products. Product detectors have been thought of by some as a type of detector whose output signal vanishes when the b.f.o. signal is removed from it. Although some product detectors function that way, such operation is not a criterion. A *product* is something that results from the combination of two or more things, hence any heterodyne detector can rightfully be regarded as a product detector. The two input signals (i.f. and b.f.o.) are fed into what is essentially a mixer stage. The difference in frequency (after filtering out and removing the i.f. and b.f.o. signals from the mixer output) is fed to the audio amplifier stages and increased to speaker or headphone level. Although product detectors are intended primarily for use with c.w. and s.s.b. signals, a.m. signals can be copied sat-

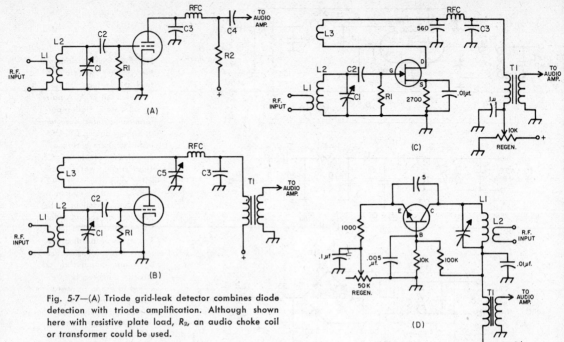

Fig. 5-7—(A) Triode grid-leak detector combines diode detection with triode amplification. Although shown here with resistive plate load, R_2, an audio choke coil or transformer could be used.

(B) Feeding some signal from the plate circuit back to the grid makes the circuit regenerative. When feedback is sufficient, the circuit will oscillate. Feedback is controlled here by varying reactance at C_5; with fixed capacitor at that point regeneration could be controlled by varying plate voltage or coupling between L_2 and L_3.

(C) An FET is used in a regenerative detector. It functions in the same manner as the circuit at B except that the regeneration is adjusted by a 10,000-ohm control which varies the drain voltage.

(D) An n-p-n bipolar transistor can be used as a regenerative detector too. Feedback occurs between collector and emitter through the 5-pf. capacitor. A 50,000-ohm control in the emitter return sets the regeneration. P-n-p transistors can also be used in this circuit, but the battery polarity must be reversed.

isfactorily on receivers which have good i.f. selectivity. The a.m. signal is tuned in as though it were a s.s.b. signal. When properly tuned in, the heterodyne from the a.m. carrier is not audible.

A double triode product-detector circuit is given in Fig. 5-6 at A. The i.f. signal is fed to the grid of the first triode and is cathode-coupled to the second half of the 12AU7A by means of a common cathode connection, above r.f. ground by virtue of the 820-ohm resistor. B.f.o. energy is supplied to the grid of the second triode where the two signals are mixed to produce audio-frequency output from the plate of the second triode, the mixer. The b.f.o. voltage should be about 2 r.m.s., and the signal should not be greater than about 0.3 r.m.s. Mixer bias is developed across the 100,-000-ohm grid resistor through rectification of the b.f.o. signal. The degree of plate filtering in the second triode will depend on the frequency of operation. At low intermediate frequencies, more elaborate filtering is needed.

In the circuit of Fig. 5-6B, two germanium diodes are used, though a 6AL5 tube could be substituted. The high back resistance of the diodes

is used as a d.c. return; if a 6AL5 is used the diodes must be shunted by 1-megohm resistors. The b.f.o. signal should be at least 10 or 20 times the amplitude of the incoming signal.

At Fig. 5-6C a four-diode product detector is shown. Matched germanium diodes can be used in this circuit, or four unmatched diodes can each be shunted by a 100,000-ohm resistor to help equalize any differences in the diode back resistances. Ideally, matched diodes should be used and this can be effected by using a diode-array integrated (IC) circuit in place of CR_1 through CR_4. An RCA CA-3019 is well suited to this circuit. Because all of the diodes are formed on the same chip in the IC, they are well matched. This circuit is similar to that of a four-diode balanced modulator and effectively works the same way. The 3300-ohm resistor isolates the i.f. and b.f.o. signals from the audio line. A 0.01-uf. bypass helps to filter the r.f. from the audio line. T_1 is tuned to the b.f.o. frequency and has a low-impedance secondary winding.

A different approach to product detection is shown in Fig. 5-6D. Here a 6GX6 performs the function of b.f.o., product detector, and 1st audio amplifier. Grid 1, Grid 2, and the cathode form a triode oscillator for the b.f.o. crystals, Y_1 (upper sideband) and Y_2 (lower sideband). Grid 2 acts as the plate of the triode. Grid 3 is coupled to the secondary winding of the last i.f. transformer and gets its d.c. return through a 22,000-ohm resistor. Grid 3, the plate, and the cathode serve as a triode mixer while also performing as an audio amplifier. In the interest of good stability, the supply voltage to grid 2 is regulated. Audio output is taken from the plate of the tube and is bypassed by a 470-pf. capacitor to help remove the i.f. and b.f.o. signals from the output line. Under normal conditions the output from this detector is of sufficient amplitude to be fed directly into the grid of the audio output stage of the receiver without the need for an intermediate amplifier section. Grids 1 and 3 are both control grids. This type of tube (6HZ6 also suitable) is specially designed for applications of this kind. Ordinary pentodes are not suitable for the circuit shown. The ratio between b.f.o. and i.f. signal levels is approximately the same as for the circuit of Fig. 5-6A.

REGENERATIVE DETECTORS

By providing controllable r.f. feedback (regeneration) in a triode, pentode, or transistorized-detector circuit, the incoming signal can be amplified many times, thereby greatly increasing the sensitivity of the detector. Regeneration also increases the effective Q of the circuit and thus the selectivity. The grid-leak type of detector is most suitable for the purpose.

The grid-leak detector is a combination diode rectifier and audio-frequency amplifier. In the circuit of Fig. 5-7A, the grid corresponds to the diode plate and the rectifying action is exactly the same as in a diode. The d.c. voltage from rectified-current flow through the grid leak, R_1, biases the grid negatively, and the audio-frequency variations in voltage across R_1 are amplified through the tube as in a normal a.f. amplifier. In the plate circuit, R_2 is the plate load resistance and C_3 and RFC a filter to eliminate r.f. in the output circuit.

A grid-leak detector has considerably greater sensitivity than a diode. The sensitivity is further increased by using a screen-grid tube instead of a triode. The operation is equivalent to that of the triode circuit. The screen bypass capacitor should have low reactance for both radio and audio frequencies.

The circuit in Fig. 5-7B is regenerative, the feedback being obtained by feeding some signal from the plate circuit back to the grid by inductive coupling. The amount of regeneration must be controllable, because maximum regenerative amplification is secured at the critical point where the circuit is just about to oscillate. The critical point in turn depends upon circuit conditions, which may vary with the frequency to which the detector is tuned. An oscillating detector can be detuned slightly from an incoming c.w. signal to give *autodyne* reception.

The circuit of Fig. 5-7B uses a variable bypass capacitor, C_5, in the plate circuit to control regeneration. When the capacitance is small the tube does not regenerate, but as it increases toward maximum its reactance becomes smaller until there is sufficient feedback to cause oscillation. If L_2 and L_3 are wound end-to-end in the same direction, the plate connection is to the outside of the plate or "tickler" coil, L_3, when the grid connection is to the outside end of L_2.

Although the regenerative grid-leak detector is more sensitive than any other type, its many disadvantages commend it for use only in the simplest receivers. The linearity is rather poor, and the signal-handling capability is limited. The signal-handling capability can be improved by reducing R_1 to 0.1 megohm, but the sensitivity will be decreased. The degree of antenna coupling is often critical.

Transistors can be used in regenerative-detector circuits too. An FET is used in the circuit of Fig. 5-7C and is similar to the vacuum-tube version shown at B. L_3 is the tickler winding and C_2R_1 form the gate leak. Regeneration is controlled by a 10,000-ohm potentiometer which varies the supply voltage to the drain of the FET. Generally, either junction FETs or insulated-gate (MOS) FETs can be used in any detector circuit that a triode tube will function in.

A bipolar transistor is used in a regenerative detector hookup at D. The emitter is returned to d.c. ground through a 1000-ohm resistor and a 50,000-ohm regeneration control. The 1000-ohm resistor keeps the emitter above ground at r.f. to permit feedback between the emitter and collector. A 5-pf. capacitor (more capacitance might be required) provides the feedback path. C_1 and L_2 comprise the tuned circuit, and the detected signal is taken from the collector return through T_1. A transistor with medium or high beta works best in circuits of this type and should have a frequency rating which is well above the desired operating frequency. The same is true of the frequency rating of any FET used in the circuit at C.

Superregenerative detectors are somewhat more sensitive than straight regenerative detectors and can employ either tubes or transistors. An in-depth discussion of superregenerative detectors is given in Chapter 16.

Tuning

For c.w. reception, the regeneration control is advanced until the detector breaks into a "hiss," which indicates that the detector is oscillating. Further advancing the regeneration control will result in a slight decrease in the hiss.

Code signals can be tuned in and will give a tone with each signal depending on the setting of the tuning control. A low-pitched beat-note cannot be obtained from a strong signal because the detector **"pulls in"** or **"blocks."**

The point just after the detector starts oscillating is the most sensitive condition for code reception. Further advancing the regeneration control makes the receiver less prone to blocking, but also less sensitive to weak signals.

If the detector is in the oscillating condition and an a.m. phone signal is tuned in, a steady audible beat-note will result. While it is possible to listen to phone if the receiver can be tuned to exact zero beat, it is more satisfactory to reduce the regeneration to the point just before the receiver goes into oscillation. This is also the most sensitive operating point.

TUNING AND BAND-CHANGING METHODS

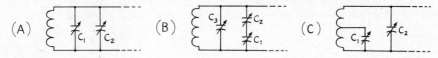

Fig. 5-8—Essentials of the three basic bandspread tuning systems.

Tuning

The resonant frequency of a circuit can be shifted by changing either the inductance or the capacitance in the circuit. Panel control of inductance (permeability-tuned oscillator, or **PTO**) is used to tune a few commercial receivers, but most receivers depend upon panel-controlled variable capacitors for tuning.

Tuning Rate

For ease in tuning a signal, it is desirable that the receiver have a tuning rate in keeping with the type of signal being received and also with the selectivity of the receiver. A tuning rate of 500 kHz. per knob revolution is normally satisfactory for a broadcast receiver, but 100 kHz. per revolution is almost too fast for easy s.s.b. reception—around 25 to 50 kHz. being more desirable.

Band Changing

The same coil and tuning capacitor cannot be used for, say, 3.5 to 14 MHz. because of the impracticable maximum-to-minimum capacitance ratio required. It is necessary, therefore, to provide a means for changing the circuit constants for various frequency bands. As a matter of convenience the same tuning capacitor usually is retained, but new coils are inserted in the circuit for each band.

One method of changing inductances is to use a switch having an appropriate number of contacts, which connects the desired coil and disconnects the others. The unused coils are sometimes short-circuited by the switch, to avoid undesirable self-resonances.

Another method is to use coils wound on forms that can be plugged into suitable sockets. These plug-in coils are advantageous when space is at a premium, and they are also very useful when considerable experimental work is involved.

Bandspreading

The tuning range of a given coil and variable capacitor will depend upon the inductance of the coil and the change in tuning capacitance. To cover a wide frequency range and still retain a suitable tuning rate over a relatively narrow frequency range requires the use of **bandspreading**. **Mechanical bandspreading** utilizes some mechanical means to reduce the tuning rate; a typical example is the two-speed planetary drive to be found in some receivers. **Electrical bandspreading** is obtained by using a suitable circuit configuration. Several of these methods are shown in Fig. 5-8.

In A, a small **bandspread capacitor,** C_1 (15- to 25-pf. maximum), is used in parallel with capacitor C_2, which is usually large enough (100 to 140 pf.) to cover a 2-to-1 frequency range. The setting of C_2 will determine the minimum capacitance of the circuit, and the maximum capacitance for bandspread tuning will be the maximum capacitance of C_1 plus the setting of C_2. The inductance of the coil can be adjusted so that the maximum-minimum ratio will give adequate bandspread. It is almost impossible, because of the non-harmonic relation of the various band limits, to get full bandspread on all bands with the same pair of capacitors. C_2 is variously called the **band-setting** or **main-tuning** capacitor. It must be reset each time the band is changed.

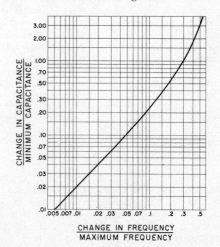

Fig. 5-9—Minimum circuit capacitance required in the circuit of Fig. 5-8A as a function of the capacitance change and the frequency change. Note that *maximum* frequency and *minimum* capacitance are used.

If the capacitance change of a tuning capacitor is known, the total fixed shunt capacitance (Fig. 5-8A) for covering a band of frequencies can be found from Fig. 5-9.

> Example:• What fixed shunt capacitance will allow a capacitor with a range of 5 to 30 pf. to tune 3.45 to 4.05 MHz.?
> $(4.05 - 3.45) \div 4.05 = 0.148$.
> From Fig. 5-10, the capacitance ratio is 0.38, and hence the minimum capacitance is $(30 - 5) \div 0.38 = 66$ pf. The 5-pf. minimum of the tuning capacitor, the tube capacitance and any stray capacitance must be included in the 66 pf.

The method shown at Fig. 5-8B makes use of capacitors in series. The tuning capacitor, C_1, may have a maximum capacitance of 100 pf. or more. The minimum capacitance is determined principally by the setting of C_3, which usually has low capacitance, and the maximum capacitance by the setting of C_2, which is of the order of 25 to 50 pf. This method is capable of close adjustment to practically any desired degree of bandspread. Either C_2 and C_3 must be adjusted for each band or separate preadjusted capacitors must be switched in.

The circuit at Fig. 5-8C also gives complete spread on each band. C_1, the bandspread capacitor, may have any convenient value; 50 pf. is satisfactory. C_2 may be used for continuous frequency coverage ("general coverage") and as a bandsetting capacitor. The effective maximum-minimum capacitance ratio depends upon C_2 and the point at which C_1 is tapped on the coil. The nearer the tap to the bottom of the coil, the greater the bandspread, and vice versa. For a given coil and tap, the bandspread will be greater if C_2 is set at higher capacitance. C_2 may be connected permanently across the individual inductor and preset, if desired. This requires a separate capacitor for each band, but eliminates the necessity for resetting C_2 each time.

Ganged Tuning

The tuning capacitors of the several r.f. circuits may be coupled together mechanically and operated by a single control. However, this operating convenience involves more complicated construction, both electrically and mechanically. It becomes necessary to make the various circuits **track**—that is, tune to the same frequency for a given setting of the tuning control.

True tracking can be obtained only when the inductance, tuning capacitors, and circuit inductances and minimum and maximum capacitances are identical in all "ganged" stages. A small **trimmer** or **padding** capacitor may be connected across the coil, so that various minimum capacitances can be compensated. The use of the trimmer necessarily increases the minimum circuit capacitance but is a necessity for satisfactory tracking. Midget capacitors having maximum capacitances of 15 to 30 pf. are commonly used.

The same methods are applied to bandspread circuits that must be tracked. The inductance can be trimmed by using a coil form with an adjustable brass (or copper) core. This core material will reduce the inductance of the coil, raising the resonant frequency of the circuit. Powdered-iron or ferrite core material can also be used, but will lower the resonant frequency of the tuned circuit because it increases the inductance of the coil. Ferrite and powdered-iron cores will raise the Q of the coil provided the core material is suitable for the frequency being used. Core material is now available for frequencies well into the v.h.f. region.

THE SUPERHETERODYNE

In a superheterodyne receiver, the frequency of the incoming signal is heterodyned to a new radio frequency, the **intermediate frequency** (abbreviated "i.f."), then amplified, and finally detected. The frequency is changed by modulating the output of a tunable oscillator (the **high-frequency**, or **local**, **oscillator**) by the incoming signal in a **mixer** or **converter** stage to produce a side frequency equal to the intermediate frequency. The other side frequency is rejected by selective circuits. The audio-frequency signal is obtained at the **detector**. Code signals are made audible by autodyne or heterodyne reception at the detector stage; this oscillator is called the "beat-frequency oscillator" or b.f.o.

As a numerical example, assume that an intermediate frequency of 455 kHz. is chosen and that the incoming signal is at 7000 kHz. Then the high-frequency oscillator frequency may be set to 7455 kHz., in order that one side frequency (7455 minus 7000) will be 455 kHz. The high-frequency oscillator could also be set to 6545 kHz. and give the same difference frequency. To produce an audible code signal at the detector of, say, 1000 Hz., the autodyning or heterodyning oscillator would be set to either 454 or 456 kHz.

The frequency-conversion process permits r.f. amplification at a relatively low frequency, the i.f. High selectivity and gain can be obtained at this frequency, and this selectivity and gain are constant. The separate oscillators can be designed for good stability and, since they are working at frequencies considerably removed from the signal frequencies, they are not normally "pulled" by the incoming signal.

Images

Each h.f. oscillator frequency will cause i.f. response at two signal frequencies, one higher and one lower than the oscillator frequency. If the oscillator is set to 7455 kHz. to tune to a 7000 kHz. signal, for example, the receiver can respond also to a signal on 7910 kHz., which likewise gives a 455 kHz. beat. The undesired signal is called the **image**. It can cause unnecessary interference if it isn't eliminated.

The radio-frequency circuits of the receiver (those used before the signal is heterodyned to the i.f.) normally are tuned to the desired signal, so that the selectivity of the circuits reduces or eliminates the response to the image signal. The ratio of the receiver voltage output from the desired signal to that from the image is called the **signal-to-image ratio**, or **image ratio**.

The image ratio depends upon the selectivity of the r.f. tuned circuits preceding the mixer tube. Also, the higher the intermediate frequency, the higher the image ratio, since raising the i.f. increases the frequency separation between the signal and the image and places the latter further away from the resonance peak of the signal-frequency input circuits.

Other Spurious Responses

In addition to images, other signals to which the receiver is not tuned may be heard. Harmonics of the high-frequency oscillator may beat with signals far removed from the desired frequency to produce output at the intermediate frequency; such spurious responses can be reduced by adequate selectivity *before* the mixer stage, and by using sufficient shielding to prevent signal pick-up by any means other than the antenna. When a strong signal is received, the harmonics generated by rectification in the detector may, by stray coupling, be introduced into the r.f. or mixer circuit and converted to the intermediate frequency, to go through the receiver in the same way as an ordinary signal. These "birdies" appear as a heterodyne beat on the desired signal, and are principally bothersome when the frequency of the incoming signal is not greatly different from the intermediate frequency. The cure is proper circuit isolation and shielding.

Harmonics of the beat oscillator also may be converted in similar fashion and amplified through the receiver; these responses can be reduced by shielding the beat oscillator and by careful mechanical design.

The Double-Conversion Superheterodyne

At high and very-high frequencies it is difficult to secure an adequate image ratio when the intermediate frequency is of the order of 455 kHz. To reduce image response the signal frequently is converted first to a rather high (1500, 5000, or even 10,000 kHz.) intermediate frequency, and then — sometimes after further amplification— reconverted to a lower i.f. where higher adjacent-channel selectivity can be obtained. Such a receiver is called a **double-conversion superheterodyne.**

FREQUENCY CONVERTERS

A circuit tuned to the intermediate frequency is placed in the plate circuit of the mixer, to offer a high impedance load for the i.f. current that is developed. The signal- and oscillator-frequency voltages appearing in the plate circuit are rejected by the selectivity of this circuit. The i.f. tuned circuit should have low impedance for

these frequencies, a condition easily met if they do not approach the intermediate frequency.

The **conversion efficiency** of the mixer is the ratio of i.f. output voltage from the plate circuit to r.f. signal voltage applied to the grid. High conversion efficiency is desirable. The mixer tube noise also should be low if a good signal-to-noise ratio is wanted, particularly if the mixer is the first tube in the receiver.

A change in oscillator frequency caused by tuning of the mixer grid circuit is called **pulling**. Pulling should be minimized, because the stability of the whole receiver depends critically upon the stability of the h.f. oscillator. Pulling decreases with separation of the signal and h.f.-oscillator frequencies, being less with high intermediate frequencies. Another type of pulling is caused by regulation in the power supply. Strong signals cause the voltage to change, which in turn shifts the oscillator frequency.

Circuits

If the mixer and high-frequency oscillator are separate tubes or transistors, the converter portion is called a "mixer." If the two are combined in one envelope (as is often done for reasons of economy or efficiency), the stage is called a "converter." In either case the function is the same.

Typical mixer circuits are shown in Fig. 5-10. The variations are chiefly in the way in which the oscillator voltage is introduced. In 5-10A, a pentode functions as a plate detector at i.f.; the oscillator voltage is capacitance-coupled to the grid of the tube through C_2. Inductive coupling may be used instead. The conversion gain and input selectivity generally are good, so long as the sum of the two voltages (signal and oscillator) impressed on the mixer grid does not exceed the grid bias. It is desirable to make the oscillator voltage as high as possible without exceeding this limitation. The oscillator power required is negligible. If the signal frequency is only 5 or 10 times the i.f., it may be difficult to develop enough oscillator voltage at the grid (because of the selectivity of the tuned input circuit). However, the circuit is a sensitive one and makes a good mixer, particularly with high-transconductance tubes like the 6CY5, 6EJ7 or 6U8A (pentode section). Triode tubes can be used as mixers in grid-injection circuits, but they are commonly used at 50 MHz. and higher, where mixer noise may become a significant factor. The triode mixer has the lowest inherent noise, the pentode is next, and the multigrid converter tubes are the noisiest.

In the circuit of Fig. 5-10A the oscillator voltage could be introduced at the cathode rather than at the control grid. If this were done, C_3 would have to be removed, and output from the oscillator would be coupled to the cathode of the mixer through a 0.0001-uf. capacitor. C_2 would also be discarded. Generally, the same rules apply as when the tube uses grid injection.

It is difficult to avoid "pulling" in a triode or pentode mixer, and a pentagrid mixer tube provides much better isolation. A typical circuit is

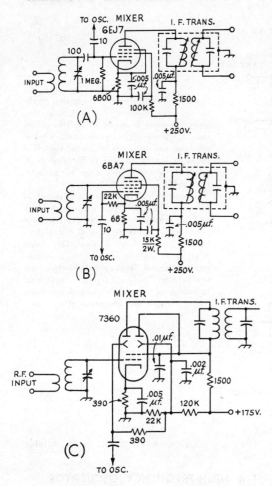

Fig. 5-10—Typical circuits for mixers. At A, a pentode such as a 6AK5 is shown with representative component values.

A pentagrid converter is used as a mixer in the circuit at B. Typical values are given for a 6BA7. Other tube types require different component values.

In the circuit at C a 7360 beam-deflection tube serves as a mixer. This circuit is capable of handling higher signal levels than the circuits of A and B.

shown in Fig. 5-10B, and tubes like the 6SA7, 6BA7 or 6BE6 are commonly used. The oscillator voltage is introduced through an "injection" grid. Measurement of the rectified current flowing in R_2 is used as a check for proper oscillator-voltage amplitude. Tuning of the signal-grid circuit can have little effect on the oscillator frequency because the injection grid is isolated from the signal grid by a screen grid that is at r.f. ground potential. The pentagrid mixer is much noisier than a triode or pentode mixer, but its isolating characteristics make it a very useful device.

Pentagrid tubes like the 6BE6 or 6BA7 are sometimes used as "converters" performing the dual function of mixer and oscillator. The usual circuit resembles Fig. 5-10-B except that the No. 1 grid connects to the top of a grounded parallel tuned circuit by means of a larger grid-blocking capacitor, and the cathode (without R_1 and C_3) connects to a tap near the grounded end of the coil. This forms a Hartley oscillator circuit. Correct location of the cathode tap is monitored by the grid current; raising the tap increases the grid current because the strength of oscillation is increased.

A more stable receiver generally results, particularly at the higher frequencies, when separate tubes are used for the mixer and oscillator.

The effectiveness of converter tubes of the type just described becomes less as the signal frequency is increased. Some oscillator voltage will be coupled to the signal grid through "space-charge" coupling, an effect that increases with frequency. If there is relatively little frequency difference between oscillator and signal, as for example a 14- or 28-MHz. signal and an i.f. of 455 kHz., this voltage can become considerable because the selectivity of the signal circuit will be unable to reject it. If the signal grid is not returned directly to ground, but instead is returned through a resistor or part of an a.g.c. system, considerable bias can be developed which will cut down the gain. For this reason, and to reduce image response, the i.f. following the first converter of a receiver should be not less than 5 or 10 percent of the signal frequency.

Another type of mixer uses a 7360 beam-deflection tube, connected as shown in Fig. 5-10C. The signal is introduced at the No. 1 grid, to modulate the electron stream running from cathode to plates. The beam is deflected from one plate to the other and back again by the b.f.o. voltage applied to one of the deflection plates. (If oscillator radiation is a problem, push-pull deflection by both deflection plates should be used.) Although the i.f. signal flows in both plates, it isn't necessary to use a push-pull output circuit unless i.f. feedthrough is a potential problem.

SOLID-STATE MIXERS

Diodes, FETS, and bipolar transistors can be used as mixers. Examples are given in Fig. 5-11. A straight diode mixer is not shown here since its application is usually limited to circuits operating in the u.h.f. region and higher. A discussion of diode mixers, plus a typical circuit, is given in Chapter 16.

Oscillator injection can be fed to the base or emitter elements of bipolar-transistor mixers, Fig. 5-11A. If emitter injection is used, the usual emitter bypass capacitor must be removed. Because the dynamic characteristics of bipolar transistors prevent them from handling high signal levels, FETs are usually preferred in mixer circuits. FETs (Fig. 5-11B and C) have greater immunity to cross-talk and overload than bipolar transistors, and offer nearly square-law performance. The circuit at B uses a junction FET, N-channel

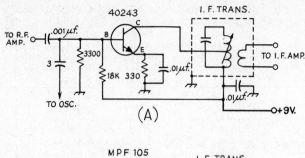

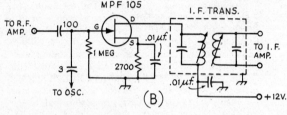

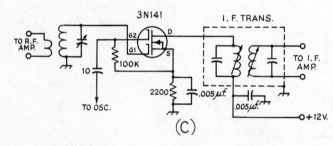

Fig. 5-11—Practical circuits for mixing applications when transistors are used. A bipolar transistor mixer is shown at A. This circuit cannot handle high signal levels without overload and cross-talk problems, therefore attention should be paid to securing good selectivity ahead of this mixer to minimize the condition.

A junction FET is used as a mixer at B. This circuit functions like a triode tube mixer and can handle high signal levels without overloading. In the circuit at C a dual-gate MOS FET performs as a mixer. This circuit offers good isolation between the oscillator and the signal frequencies, lessening the tendency for "pulling." It too is capable of handling high signal levels and is recommended over the circuit at A.

type, with oscillator injection being supplied to the gate. Source injection can also be used if desired, but the 0.01-uf. bypass would have to be removed. The value of the source resistor should be adjusted to provide a bias of approximately 0.8 volts. This value offers a good compromise between conversion gain and good intermodulation-distortion characteristics. At this bias level a local-oscillator injection of approximately 1.5 volts is desirable for good conversion gain. The lower the oscillator-injection level, the lower the gain. High Injection levels improve the mixer's immunity to cross-modulation.

A dual-gate MOS FET is used as a mixer at C. Gate 2 is used for injecting the local-oscillator signal while gate 1 is supplied with signal voltage. This type of mixer has excellent immunity to cross-modulation and overload. It offers better isolation between the oscillator and input stages than is possible with a JFET mixer. The insulated gate has extremely thin dielectric material, hence great care must be taken to prevent damage to the gates during installation. The leads should be shorted together until the device is connected in the circuit. The transistor should be handled by its case, not its leads, and it should never be plugged into (or removed from) a circuit to which operating voltages are applied. The mixers at B and C have high-Z input terminals, while the circuit at A has a relatively low-Z input impedance. The latter requires tapping the base

down on the input tuned circuit for a suitable match.

THE HIGH-FREQUENCY OSCILLATOR

Stability of the receiver is dependent chiefly upon the stability of the tunable h.f. oscillator, and particular care should be given this part of the receiver. The frequency of oscillation should be insensitive to mechanical shock and changes in voltage and loading. Thermal effects (slow change in frequency because of tube, transistor, or circuit heating) should be minimized. They can be reduced by using ceramic instead of bakelite insulation in the r.f. circuits, a large cabinet relative to the chassis (to provide for good radiation of developed heat), minimizing the number of high-wattage resistors in the receiver and putting them in the separate power supply, and not mounting the oscillator coils and tuning capacitor too close to a tube. Propping up the lid of a receiver will often reduce drift by lowering the terminal temperature of the unit.

Sensitivity to vibration and shock can be minimized by using good mechanical support for coils and tuning capacitors, a heavy chassis, and by not hanging any of the oscillator-circuit components on long leads. Tie points should be used to avoid long leads. Stiff *short* leads are excellent because they can't be made to vibrate.

Smooth tuning is a great convenience to the operator, and can be obtained by taking pains

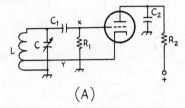

(A)

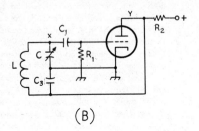

(B)

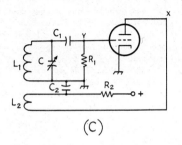

(C)

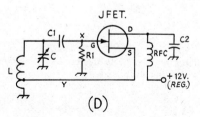

(D)

Fig. 5-12—High-frequency oscillator circuits. A, Hartley grounded-plate oscillator; B, Colpitts grounded-cathode oscillator; C, plate-tickler feedback grounded-cathode oscillator. Coupling to the mixer may be taken from points X and Y. Coupling from Y will reduce pulling effects but gives less voltage than from X. The circuit at D shows how a JFET can be used as a Hartley oscillator. The circuit is similar to that of A but uses an r.f. choke in place of R_2 to minimize the voltage drop to the drain element. Any n-channel JFET whose frequency rating is sufficiently high to match the required operating frequency is satisfactory. MOS FETS can also be used in the circuits shown here.

Typical values for components are as follows:
C_1—20 to 100 pf.
C_2—0.005 to 0.01 μf.
R_1—20,000 to 100,000 ohms.
R_2—10,000 ohms or higher, or good r.f. choke.

Oscillator output can be adjusted by changing r.f. feedback (see text) or by value of R_2.

with the mounting of the dial and tuning capacitors. They should have good alignment and no backlash. If the capacitors are mounted off the chassis on posts instead of brackets, it is almost impossible to avoid some back-lash unless the posts have extra-wide bases. The capacitors should be selected with good wiping contacts to the rotor, since with age the rotor contacts can be a source of erratic tuning. All joints in the oscillator tuning circuit should be carefully soldered, because a loose connection or "rosin joint" can develop trouble that is sometimes hard to locate. The chassis and panel materials should be heavy and rigid enough so that pressure on the tuning dial will not cause torsion and a shift in the frequency.

In addition, the oscillator must be capable of furnishing sufficient r.f. voltage and power for the particular mixer circuit chosen, at all frequencies within the range of the receiver, and its harmonic output should be as low as possible to reduce the possibility of spurious responses and "birdies."

The oscillator power should be as low as is consistent with adequate output. Low plate, collector, or drain power will reduce heating and thereby lower the frequency drift. The oscillator and mixer circuits should be well isolated, preferably by shielding, since coupling other than by the intended means may result in pulling.

If the oscillator frequency is affected by changes in operating voltage, a voltage-regulated plate or filament supply (or both) can be used.

Circuits

Several oscillator circuits are shown in Figs. 5-12 and 5-13. A Hartley circuit is shown at Fig. 5-12A and D. The latter is identical to A except that a junction FET is used, and at reduced operating voltage. JFETs and insulated-gate (MOS) FETs can be used in place of tubes in the circuits of A through C. If FETs are used, R_2 should be replaced by an r.f. choke to permit sufficient d.c. to reach the drain of the transistor. In the circuits at A and D the cathode, or source, is "above ground" (anode or drain at r.f. ground), which permits the grounding of the rotor of C. However, when the tube oscillator's cathode is above ground (a.c.-operated filaments), there is a likelihood of hum modulation of the oscillator at frequencies above 7 MHz.

The Colpitts (B) and the plate-tickler (C) circuits are shown with the cathodes grounded, although the Colpitts is often used in the grounded-anode manner.

Besides the use of a fairly high C/L ratio in the tuned circuit, it is necessary to adjust the feedback to obtain optimum results. Too much feedback may cause "squegging" of the oscillator and the generation of several frequencies simultaneously; too little feedback will cause the output to be low. In the Hartley circuit, the feedback is increased by moving the tap toward the grid end of the coil. In the Colpitts the feedback is determined by the ratio C/C_3. More feedback is obtained in the plate-tickler circuit by increasing

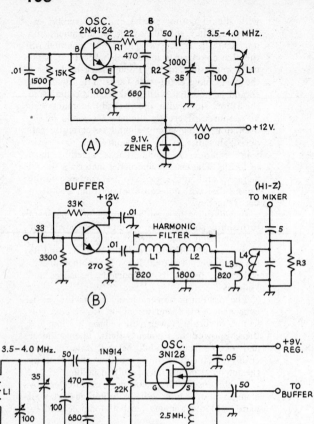

Fig. 5-13—Typical transistorized oscillators. At A, a bipolar n-p-n transistor is used in a Colpitts circuit. Output can be taken from either point A or B through a low-value coupling capacitor. The collector supply voltage is regulated by means of a Zener diode. The transistor used should have a f_T rating of at least ten times the proposed oscillator frequency. High-beta transistors should be used. R_1 discourages parasitic oscillations—a common occurrence in transistor oscillators.

The circuit at B shows a buffer stage which can be used between the circuit at A and the mixer stage. The buffer reduces interaction between the oscillator and mixer tuned circuits. A full-wave harmonic filter is shown at the output of the buffer to greatly reduce spurious responses and images caused by ocillator harmonics. Its use is recommended. Output from the low-Z filter is fed into L_3 and coupled to L_4 for an impedance step up to the mixer.

At C, an MOS FET is used as a local oscillator. A buffer stage should follow this circuit to assure good isolation between the mixer and oscillator tuned circuits.

the number of turns in L_2 or by moving L_2 closer to L_1.

A bipolar-transistor oscillator is shown at Fig. 5-13A. It is a Colpitts and operates with the base at r.f. ground. Feedback is between the collector and emitter and the actual values of capacitance used in the feedback circuit (collector to emitter, and emitter to ground) will depend upon the operating frequency and the beta of the transistor. It is wise to use the greatest amount of capacitance that will permit satisfactory oscillator operation over the entire tuning range. The 1000-ohm emitter resistor keeps that part of the circuit above r.f. ground. The 1000-ohm collector resistor R_2, serves in the same fashion. If higher collector voltage is required, an r.f. choke can be bridged across R_2. Parasitic oscillations are a common occurance with oscillators of this type, hence the 22-ohm resistor, R_1, which suppresses parasitic oscillations. A 9.1-volt Zener regulator is used to stabilize the oscillator supply voltage. Output should be fed to a buffer stage and can be taken from points A or B in drawing A. The lighter the coupling to the buffer stage, the less liklihood of oscillator "pulling."

A typical buffer stage is shown at B, Fig. 5-13. A 33-pf. capacitor offers light coupling to the oscillator and connects the oscillator output to the base of the buffer stage (low impedance). For this type of buffer arrangement, output from the circuit at A should be taken from the oscillator's emitter, point A. The buffer stage operates as an emitter-follower and its output is fed into a full-wave lo-Z filter consisting of L_1, L_2, and the associated resonating capacitors. Transistorized oscillators are particularly rich in harmonics, brought about by normal envelope distortion plus parametric frequency multiplication. The latter is caused by the nonlinear change in collector-base junction capacitance during the sine-wave cycle. Vacuum tubes are not subject to this condition, hence have cleaner output. The filter offers 25 db. or more attenuation to harmonics from the oscillator and buffer, and should be used in the interest of minimum image response and "birdies" in the receiver's output. The filter is coupled to L_3, a lo-Z winding on the ground end of L_4. L_4 is broadly tuned to the v.f.o. output frequency and is swamped by R_3 to provide near-uniform response across the oscillator tuning range. The filter values given are for operation from 3.5 to 4.0 MHz. L_1 and L_2 are 2-uh. inductors. Band-pass coupling can also be used between the oscillator chain and the mixer to reduce harmonics.

Design data for band-pass circuits and filters are given in Chapter 2. Output from a buffer of the type shown here is on the order. of 3 to 6 volts, measured at the high-Z end of L_4.

An MOS FET is used in the circuit at C. The 1N914 diode establishes a fixed value of gate bias, thus providing improved stability. Output from the oscillator should be fed to a buffer stage to provide a reasonable amount of isolation between oscillator and mixer.

IMPROVING OSCILLATOR STABILITY

In the circuit of Fig. 5-14, both the plate and filament supplies are regulated. A common fault in selective h.f. and v.h.f. receivers is that of frequency "jumping" brought about by small changes in local-oscillator filament voltage. This can happen in areas where a.c. line-voltage regulation is poor. The condition can be resolved by using a Zener-regulated d.c. filament supply as shown. By using a 12-volt filament transformer with a full-wave silicon-diode bridge rectifier, the d.c. can be dropped through R_1 to enable the Zener to regulate at 6.2 volts. If a 12-volt tube were used, a 24-volt filament transformer and a 12-volt Zener could be used in the same fashion.

By leaving the heaters turned on 24 hours a day, a marked improvement in long-term thermal stability of the oscillator can be realized. The same technique is useful even though the heater supply is not regulated, but uses straight a.c. voltage. A separate filament transformer can be used to power the local-oscillator heaters, and it can remain activated around the clock for improved stability. The use of d.c. voltage on the local-oscillator filaments will insure against hum

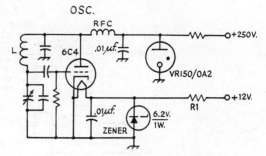

Fig. 5-14—Careful attention should be paid to the matter of oscillator stability, especially in highly-selective receivers. Here the plate supply *and* the filament voltage is regulated to offer optimum stability in the presence of line voltage fluctuations. The use of d.c. on the oscillator filaments minimizes hum modulation of the oscillator signal. For improved long-term thermal stability the filament supply can be left operating around the clock. R_1 is adjusted to provide the required Zener current for good regulation.

modulation of the oscillator signal when the circuit of Fig. 5-12A is used.

The oscillator plate voltage is regulated by a VR tube, but a 100-volt 10-watt Zener diode could also be used in that part of the circuit. Information on the use of Zener diodes is given in Chapter 4.

An in-depth treatment of oscillator stability can be found in *QST*, "V.F.O. Stability—Recap and Postscript," September 1966. Part II of the article appeared in October 1966 *QST* on page 26.

THE INTERMEDIATE-FREQUENCY AMPLIFIER

One major advantage of the superhet is that high gain and selectivity can be obtained by using a good i.f. amplifier. This can be a one-stage affair in simple receivers, or two or three stages in the more elaborate sets.

Choice of Frequency

The selection of an intermediate frequency is a compromise between conflicting factors. The lower the i.f. the higher the selectivity and gain, but a low i.f. brings the image nearer the desired signal and hence decreases the image ratio. A low i.f. also increases pulling of the oscillator frequency. On the other hand, a high i.f. is beneficial to both image ratio and pulling, but the gain is lowered and selectivity is harder to obtain by simple means.

An i.f. of the order of 455 kHz. gives good selectivity and is satisfactory from the standpoint of image ratio and oscillator pulling at frequencies up to 7 MHz. The image ratio is poor at 14 MHz. when the mixer is connected to the antenna, but adequate when there is a tuned r.f. amplifier between antenna and mixer. At 28 MHz. and on the very high frequencies, the image ratio is very poor unless several r.f. stages are used. Above 14

MHz., pulling is likely to be bad without very loose coupling between mixer and oscillator. Tuned-circuit shielding also helps.

With an i.f. of about 1600 kHz., satisfactory image ratios can be secured on 14, 21 and 28 MHz. with one r.f. stage of good design. For frequencies of 28 MHz. and higher, a common solution is to use double conversion, choosing one high i.f. for image reduction (5 and 10 MHz. are frequently used) and a lower one for gain and selectivity.

In choosing an i.f. it is wise to avoid frequencies on which there is considerable activity by the various radio services, since such signals may be picked up directly on the i.f. wiring. Shifting the i.f. or better shielding are the solutions to this interference problem.

Fidelity; Sideband Cutting

Amplitude modulation of a carrier generates sideband frequencies numerically equal to the carrier frequency plus and minus the modulation frequencies present. If the receiver is to give a faithful reproduction of modulation that contains, for instance, audio frequencies up to 5000 Hz. it must at least be capable of ampli-

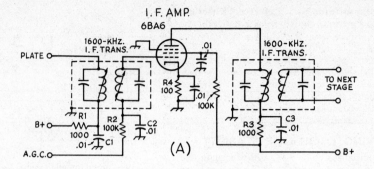

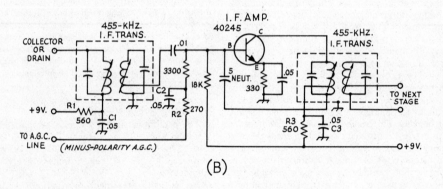

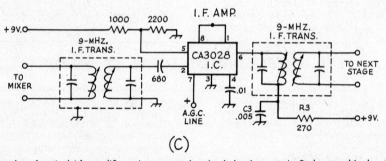

Fig. 5-15—Examples of typical i.f. amplifiers. A vacuum-tube circuit is given at A; B shows a bipolar transistor i.f. amplifier which has been neutralized; C illustrates how an integrated circuit can be used as a high-gain i.f. stage. All three circuits are shown with a.g.c. provisions. R_1 through R_3, and C_1 through C_3 in all circuits serve as r.f. decoupling networks to prevent instability from interstage power-lead coupling.

fying equally all frequencies contained in a band extending from 5000 Hz. above or below the carrier frequency. In a superheterodyne, where all carrier frequencies are changed to the fixed intermediate frequency, the i.f. amplification must be uniform over a band 5 kHz. wide, when the carrier is set at one edge. If the carrier is set in the center, a 10-kHz band is required. The signal-frequency circuits usually do not have enough over-all selectivity to affect materially the "adjacent-channel" selectivity, so that only the i.f.-amplifier selectivity need be considered.

If the selectivity is too great to permit uniform amplification over the band of frequencies occupied by the modulated signal, some of the sidebands are "cut." While sideband cutting reduces fidelity, it is frequently preferable to sacrifice naturalness of reproduction in favor of communications effectiveness.

The selectivity of an i.f.-amplifier, and hence the tendency to cut sidebands, increases with the number of tuned circuits and also is greater the lower the intermediate frequency. From the standpoint of communication, sideband cutting is never serious with two-stage amplifiers at frequencies as low as 455 kHz. A two-stage i.f. amplifier at 85 or 100 kHz. will be sharp enough to cut some of the higher-frequency sidebands, if good transformers are used. However, the cutting is not at all serious, and the gain in selectivity is worthwhile in crowded amateur bands as an aid to QRM reduction.

Circuits

I.f. amplifiers usually consist of one or more stages. The more stages employed, the greater the selectivity and overall gain of the system. In double-conversion receivers there is usually one stage at the first i.f., and sometimes as many as three or four stages at the second, or last, i.f. Most single-conversion receivers use no more than three stages of i.f. amplification.

A typical vacuum-tube i.f. stage is shown in Fig. 5-15 at A. The second or third stages would simply be duplicates of the stage shown. Remote cut-off pentodes are almost always used for i.f. amplifiers, and such tubes are operated as Class A amplifiers. For maximum selectivity, double-tuned transformers are used for interstage coupling, though single-tuned inductors and capacitive coupling can be used, but at a marked reduction in selectivity.

A.g.c. voltage can be used to reduce the gain of the stage, or stages, by applying it to the terminal marked "A.G.C.". The a.g.c. voltage should be negative. Manual control of the gain can be effected by lifting the 100-ohm cathode resistor from ground and inserting a potentiometer between it and ground. A 10,000-ohm control can be used for this purpose. A small amount of B-plus can be fed through a dropping resistor (about 56,000 ohms from a 250-volt bus) to the junction of the gain control and the 100-ohm cathode resistor to provide an increase in tube bias, in turn reducing the mutual conductance of the tube for gain reduction.

A bipolar-transistor i.f. amplifier is shown at B. Since an n-p-n transistor is used for the illustration it requires a negative a.g.c. voltage to control the gain of the stage. The a.g.c. voltage effectively reduces the fixed value of forward bias on the stage, thus reducing its ability to amplify. Were a p-n-p transistor used, a plus-polarity a.g.c. would be required. Because the input impedance of the bipolar transistor is quite low, the base is tapped down on the secondary winding of the input i.f. transformer to provide a proper match, and to reduce circuit loading which would impair the selectivity. Neutralization is usually required when this type of transistor is used. The output i.f. transformer is tapped near the "cold" end to provide a takeoff point for the neutralizing capacitor, a 5-pf. unit.

An integrated-circuit i.f. amplifier is shown at C. A positive-polarity a.g.c. voltage is required for this circuit to control the stage gain. If manual gain control provisions are desired, a potentiometer can be used to vary the plus voltage to the a.g.c. terminal of the IC. The control would be connected between the 9-volt bus and ground, its movable contact wired to the a.g.c. terminal of the IC. Other IC types are also suitable for use in i.f. amplifiers. Information on integrated circuits is given in Chapter 4.

Tubes for I.F. Amplifiers

Variable-μ (remote cut-off) pentodes are almost invariably used in i.f. amplifier stages, since grid-bias gain control is practically always applied to the i.f. amplifier. Tubes with high plate resistance will have least effect on the selectivity of the amplifier, and those with high mutual conductance will give greatest gain. The choice of i.f. tubes normally has no effect on the signal-to-noise ratio, since this is determined by the preceding mixer and r.f. amplifier.

The 6BA6, 6BJ6 and 6BZ6 are recommended for i.f. work because they have desirable remote cut-off characteristics.

When two or more stages are used the high gain may tend to cause troublesome instability and oscillation, so that good shielding, bypassing, and careful circuit arrangement to prevent stray coupling between input and output circuits are necessary.

When vacuum tubes are used, the plate and grid leads should be well separated. When transistors are used, the base and Collector circuits should be well isolated. With tubes it is advisable to mount the screen bypass capacitor directly on the bottom of the socket, crosswise between the plate and grid pins, to provide additional shielding. As a further precaution against capacitive coupling, the grid and plate leads should be "dressed" close to the chassis.

I.F. Transformers

The tuned circuits of i.f. amplifiers are built up as transformer units consisting of a metal shield container in which the coils and tuning capacitors are mounted. Both air-core and powdered iron-core universal-wound coils are used, the latter having somewhat higher Qs and hence greater selectivity and gain. In universal windings the coil is wound in layers with each turn traversing the length of the coil, back and forth, rather than being wound perpendicular to the axis as in ordinary single-layer coils. In a straight multilayer winding, a fairly large capacitance can exist between layers. Universal winding, with its "criss-crossed" turns, tends to reduce distributed-capacitance effects.

For tuning, air-dielectric tuning capacitors are preferable to mica compression types because their capacitance is practically unaffected by changes in temperature and humidity. Iron-core transformers may be tuned by varying the inductance (permeability tuning), in which case stability comparable to that of variable air-capacitor tuning can be obtained by use of high-stability fixed mica or ceramic capacitors. Such stability is of great importance, since a circuit whose frequency "drifts" with time eventually will be tuned to a different frequency than the other circuits, thereby reducing the gain and selectivity of the amplifier.

The normal **interstage** i.f. transformer is loosely coupled, to give good selectivity consistent with adequate gain. A so-called **diode transformer** is similar, but the coupling is tighter, to give sufficient transfer when working into the finite load presented by a diode detector. Using a diode transformer in place of an interstage transformer would result in loss of selectivity; using an interstage transformer to couple to the diode would result in loss of gain.

Besides the conventional i.f. transformers just mentioned, special units to give desired selectivity characteristics have been used. For higher-than-ordinary adjacent-channel selectivity, **triple-tuned** transformers, with a third tuned circuit inserted between the input and output windings, have been made. The energy is transferred from the input to the output windings via this **tertiary winding**, thus adding its selectivity to the over-all selectivity of the transformer.

A method of varying the selectivity is to vary the coupling between primary and secondary, overcoupling being used to broaden the selectivity curve. Special circuits using single tuned circuits, coupled in any of several different ways, have been used in some receivers.

Selectivity

The over-all selectivity of the i.f. amplifier will depend on the frequency and the number of stages. The following figures are indicative of the bandwidths to be expected with good-quality circuits in amplifiers so constructed as to keep regeneration at a minimum:

Tuned Circuits	Frequency	Circuit Q	Bandwidth, kHz. −6 db.	−20 db.	−60 db.
4	50kHz.	60	0.5	0.95	2.16
4	455kHz.	75	3.6	6.9	16
6	1600kHz.	90	8.2	15	34

THE BEAT OSCILLATOR AND DETECTOR

The detector in a superheterodyne receiver functions the same way as do the simple detectors described earlier in this chapter (Fig. 5-2), but usually operates at a higher input level because of the amplification ahead of it. The detectors of Fig. 5-2 are satisfactory for the reception of a.m. signals. When copying c.w. and s.s.b. signals it becomes necessary to supply a beat-oscillator (b.f.o.) signal to the detector stage as described in the earlier section on product detectors.

Any standard oscillator circuit can be employed for b.f.o. use. Special beat-oscillator transformers are available commercially for some i.f.s., and consist of tapped coils which lend themselves to use in Hartley oscillator circuits (Fig. 5-12A). A standard i.f. transformer secondary winding can be used in the circuit of Fig. 5-16A, or a slug-tuned inductor can be used for L_1. RFC constitutes but a small portion of the total inductance in the tuned circuit and is used to put the cathode above r.f. ground for obtaining feedback. Generally, the value of RFC can be approximately one tenth that of L_1. C_1 tunes the b.f.o. to the desired side of the i.f. center frequency for upper or lower sideband reception. The actual values of the components will depend upon the i.f. of the receiver.

Crystal-controlled b.f.o.s can be employed to get excellent stability. A transistorized version of such a circuit is given at B. Y_1 and Y_2 are chosen

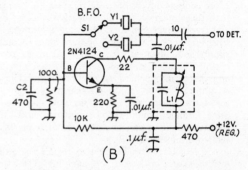

Fig. 5-16—B.f.o. circuits which are suitable for use with a.m. or product detectors of the type shown earlier. In the circuit at A, C_1 varies the oscillator frequency above or below the i.f. to permit upper- or lower-sideband reception. RFC places the cathode above r.f. ground to provide feedback. A tap near the cold end of L_1 could be used in place of the r.f. choke.

An n-p-n bipolar transistor functions as a b.f.o. at B. Y_1 and Y_2 permit upper- or lower-sideband reception and are approximately 1 kHz. above and below the center frequency of the i.f. C_2 is part of the feedback circuit and usually requires empirical derivation.

to provide upper and lower sideband reception for the i.f. used. C_2 is a feedback capacitor whose value will depend upon the operating frequency. The value shown is for operation at 455 kHz. For best stability the supply voltage to the b.f.o. stage of a receiver should be regulated.

The beat oscillator should be well shielded, to prevent coupling to any part of the receiver except the second detector and to prevent its harmonics from getting into the front end and being amplified along with desired signals. The b.f.o. power should be as low as is consistent with sufficient audio-frequency output on the strongest signals. However, if the beat-oscillator output is too low, strong signals will not give a proportionately strong audio signal. Contrary to some opinion, a weak b.f.o. is never an advantage.

AUTOMATIC GAIN CONTROL

Automatic regulation of the gain of the receiver in inverse proportion to the signal strength is an operating convenience in phone reception, since it tends to keep the output level of the receiver constant regardless of input-signal strength. The average rectified d.c. voltage, developed by the received signal across a resistance in a detector circuit, is used to vary the bias on the r.f. and i.f. amplifier tubes. Since this voltage is proportional to the average amplitude of the signal, the gain is reduced as the signal strength becomes greater. The control will be more complete and the output more constant as the number of stages to which the a.g.c. bias is applied is increased. Control of at least two stages is advisable.

Carrier-Derived Circuits

A basic diode-detector/a.g.c.-rectifier circuit is given at Fig. 5-17A. Here a single germanium diode serves both as a detector and an a.g.c. rectifier, producing a negative-polarity a.g.c. voltage. Audio is taken from the return end of the i.f. transformer secondary and is filtered by means of a 47,000-ohm resistor and two 470-pf. capacitors.

At B, CR_1 (also a germanium diode) functions as a detector while CR_2 (germanium) operates

as an a.g.c. rectifier. CR_2 furnishes a negative a.g.c. voltage to the controlled stages of the receiver. Though solid-state rectifiers are shown at A and B, vacuum-tube diodes can be used in these circuits. A 6AL5 tube is commonly used in circuits calling for two diodes (B), but a 1-megohm resistor should be shunted across the right-hand diode if a tube is used.

The circuit at C shows a typical hookup for a.g.c. feed to the controlled stages. S_1 can be used to disable the a.g.c. when this is desired. For tube and FET circuits the value of R_1 and R_2 can be 100,000 ohms, and R_3 can be 470,000 ohms. If bipolar transistors are used for the r.f. and i.f. stages being controlled, R_1 and R_2 will usually be between 1000 and 10,000 ohms, depending upon the bias network required for the transistors used. R_3 will also be determined by the bias value required in the circuit.

A two-diode tube-type delayed-a.g.c. circuit is shown at Fig. 5-18A for comparative purposes. It is somewhat similar to the circuit of Fig. 5-17B. The left-hand diode is the detector; the signal is developed across the two resistors in the return end of the i.f. transformer secondary, and is coupled to the audio amplifier by means of a 0.01-uf. capacitor. The 100,000-ohm resistor and the two associated 100-pf. capacitors serve as an r.f. filter to prevent a large r.f. component from being coupled into the audio circuits. The right-hand diode is the a.g.c. rectifier and is coupled to the last i.f. transformer through a 100-pf. capacitor. Most of the rectified voltage is developed across the 2-megohm resistor. The diode does not rectify on weak signals, however; the fixed bias at R_1 must be exceeded before rectification can take place. The values of R_1 and R_2 are selected to give 2 to 10 volts of bias at 1 to 2 ma. drain. By using the delayed-a.g.c. technique, weak-signal reception is enhanced by the fact that the a.g.c. is inoperative, thus offering optimum sensitivity. The scheme also improves the noise figure of the r.f. amplifier during weak-signal conditions—an important consideration for reception above 50 MHz. Some delayed-a.g.c. action is inherent in the circuits of Fig. 5-17A and B by virtue of the conduction point of the diode. For germanium diodes the required voltage for conduction is approximately 0.25 volt. For silicon diodes the required voltage is between 0.4 and 0.7 to overcome the junction potential barrier.

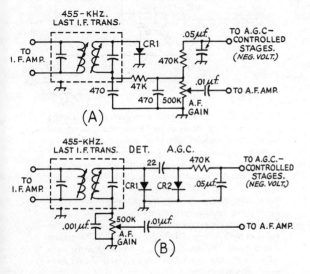

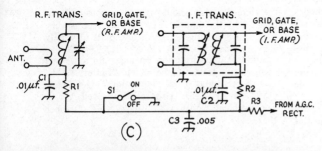

Fig. 5-17—Methods for obtaining rectified a.g.c. voltage. At A the detector furnishes a.g.c. voltage; B shows separate diodes being used for the detector and a.g.c. circuits; C illustrates how negative a.g.c. voltage is fed to the r.f. and i.f. stages of a typical receiver. S_1 is used to disable the a.g.c. when desired. R_1, R_2, and R_3, in combination with C_1, C_2, and C_3, are used for r.f. decoupling. Their values are dependent upon the device being used—tube or transistor. CR_1 and CR_2 at A and B are germanium diodes.

A.G.C. Time Constant

The time constant of the resistor-capacitor combinations in the a.g.c. circuit is an important part of the system. It must be long enough so that the modulation on the signal is completely filtered from the d.c. output, leaving only an average d.c. component which follows the relatively slow carrier variations with fading.

Audio-frequency variations in the a.g.c. voltage applied to the amplifier grids would reduce the percentage of modulation on the incoming signal. But the time constant must not be too long or the a.g.c. will be unable to follow rapid fading. The capacitance and resistance values indicated in Figs. 5-17 and 5-18A will give a time constant that is satisfactory for average reception.

C.W. and S.S.B.

A.g.c. can be used for c.w. and s.s.b. reception but the circuit is usually more complicated. The a.g.c. voltage must be derived from a rectifier that is isolated from the beat-frequency oscillator (otherwise the rectified b.f.o. voltage will reduce the receiver gain even with no signal coming through). This is done by using a separate a.g.c. channel connected to an i.f. amplifier stage ahead of the second detector (and b.f.o.) or by rectifying the audio output of the detector. If the selectivity ahead of the a.g.c. rectifier isn't good, strong adjacent-channel signals may develop a.g.c. voltages that will reduce the receiver gain while listening to weak signals. When clear channels are available, however, c.w. and s.s.b. a.g.c. will hold the receiver output constant over a wide range of signal inputs. A.g.c. systems designed to work on these signals should have fast-attack and slow-decay characteristics to work satisfactorily, and often a selection of time constants is made available.

The a.g.c. circuit shown in Fig. 5-18A is applicable to many receivers without too much modification. Audio from the receiver is amplified in V_{1A} and rectified in V_{2B}. The resultant voltage is applied to the a.g.c. line through V_{2C}. The capacitor C_1 charges quickly and will remain charged until discharged by V_{1B}. This will occur some time after the signal has disappeared, because the audio was stepped up through T_1 and rectified in V_{2A}, and the resultant used to charge C_2. This voltage holds V_{1B} cut off for an appreciable time, until C_2 discharges through the 4.7-megohm resistor. The threshold of compression is set by adjusting the bias on the diodes (changing the value of the 3.3K or 100K resistors). There can be no d.c. return to ground from the a.g.c. line, because C_1 must be discharged only by V_{1B}. Even a v.t.v.m. across the a.g.c. line will be too low a resistance, and the operation of the system must be observed by the action of the S meter.

Occasionally a strong noise pulse may cause the a.g.c. to hang until C_2 discharges, but most of

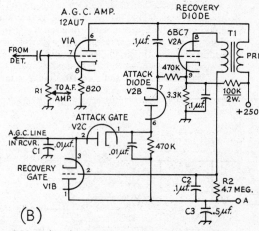

Fig. 5-18—Delayed automatic gain-control circuit using two diodes (A); B shows audio "hang" a.g.c. developed by W1DX. If manual control of gain is in i.f. and r.f. cathode circuits, point "A" is connected to chassis ground. If a negative supply is available, manual gain control can be negative bias applied between point "A" and ground.

R₁—Normal audio volume control in receiver.

T₁—1:3 step-up audio transformer.

The hang time can be adjusted by changing the value of the recovery diode time constant (4.7 megohms shown here). The a.g.c. line in the receiver must have no d.c. return to ground and the receiver should have good skirt selectivity.

the time the gain should return very rapidly to that set by the signal. A.g.c. of this type is very helpful in handling netted s.s.b. signals of widely varying strengths.

Additional information on a.g.c. for c.w. and s.s.b. can be found in the article "Better A.V.C. For S.S.B. and Code Reception," Goodman, *QST*, January 1957. Also, see "Improved A.V.C. For sideband And C.W.", Luick, *QST*, October 1957.

NOISE REDUCTION

Types of Noise

In addition to tube and circuit noise, much of the noise interference experienced in reception of high-frequency signals is caused by domestic or industrial electrical equipment and by automobile ignition systems. The interference is of two types in its effects. The first is the "hiss" type, consisting of overlapping pulses similar in nature to the receiver noise. It is largely reduced by high selectivity in the receiver, especially for code reception. The second is the "pistol-shot" or "machine-gun" type, consisting of separated impulses of high amplitude. The "hiss" type of interference usually is caused by commutator sparking in d.c. and series-wound a.c. motors, while the "shot" type results from separated spark discharges (a.c. power leaks, switch and key clicks, ignition sparks, and the like).

The only known approach to reducing tube and circuit noise is through better "front-end" design and through more over-all selectivity.

Impulse Noise

Impulse noise, because of the short duration of the pulses compared with the time between them, must have high amplitude to contain much average energy. Hence, noise of this type strong enough to cause much interference generally has an instantaneous amplitude much higher than that of the signal being received. The general principles of devices intended to reduce such noise is to allow the desired signal to pass through the receiver unaffected, but to make the receiver inoperative for amplitudes greater than that of the signal. The greater the amplitude of the pulse compared with its time of duration, the more successful the noise reduction.

Another approach is to "silence" (render inoperative) the receiver during the short duration time of any individual pulse. The listener will not hear the "hole" because of its short duration, and very effective noise reduction is obtained. Such devices are called **"blankers"** rather than "limiters."

In passing through selective receiver circuits, the time duration of the impulses is increased, because of the Q of the circuits. Thus the more selectivity ahead of the noise-reducing device, the more difficult it becomes to secure good pulse-type noise suppression.

Audio Limiting

A considerable degree of noise reduction in code reception can be accomplished by amplitude-limiting arrangements applied to the audio-output circuit of a receiver. Such limiters also maintain the signal output nearly constant during fading. These output-limiter systems are simple, and they are readily adaptable to most receivers without any modification of the receiver itself. However, they cannot prevent noise peaks from overloading previous stages.

NOISE-LIMITER CIRCUITS

Pulse-type noise can be eliminated to an extent which makes the reception of even the weakest of signals possible. The noise pulses can be clipped, or limited in amplitude, at either an r.f. or a.f. point in the receiver circuit. Both methods are used by receiver manufacturers; both are effective.

A simple audio noise limiter is shown at Fig. 5-19. It can be plugged into the headphone jack of the receiver and a pair of headphones connected to the output of the limiter. CR_1 and CR_2 are wired to clip both the positive and negative peaks of the audio signal, thus removing the high spikes of pulse noise. The diodes are back-biased

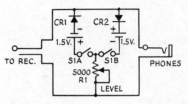

Fig. 5-19—Circuit of a simple audio limiter/clipper. It can be plugged into the headphone jack of the receiver. R_1 sets the bias on the diodes, CR_1 and CR_2, for the desired limiting level. S_1 opens the battery leads when the circuit is not being used. The diodes can be 1N34As or similar.

by 1.5-volt batteries to permit R_1 to serve as a clipping-level control. This circuit also limits the amount of audio reaching the headphones. When tuning across the band, strong signals will not be ear-shattering and will appear to be the same strength as the weaker ones. S_1 is open when the circuit is not in use to prevent battery drain. CR_1 and CR_2 can be germanium or silicon diodes, but 1N34As are generally used.

The usual practice in communications receivers is to use low-level limiting, Fig. 5-20. The limiting can be carried out at r.f. or a.f. points in the receiver, as shown. Limiting at r.f. does not cause poor audio quality as is sometimes experienced when using series or shunt a.f. limiters. The latter limits the normal a.f. signal peaks as well as the noise pulses, giving an unpleasant audio quality to strong signals.

In a series limiting circuit, a normally conducting element (or elements) is connected in the circuit in series and operated in such a manner that it becomes non-conductive above a given signal level. In a shunt limiting circuit, a nonconducting element is connected in shunt across the circuit and operated so that it becomes conductive above a given signal level, thus short-circuiting the signal and preventing its being transmitted to the remainder of the amplifier. The usual conducting element will be a forward-biased diode, and the usual non-conducting element will be a back-biased diode. In many applications the value of bias is set manually by the operator; usually the clipping level will be set at about 5 to 10 volts.

In the series-limiter circuit circuit of Fig. 5-20A V_1 is a vacuum-tube diode (½ of a 6AL5, or similar), but could be a silicon diode. Using tubes with a.c.-operated filaments in a low-level a.f. circuit sometimes introduces hum in the audio channel. For this reason, semiconductor diodes are usually preferred. S_1, when closed, disables the a.n.l. for normal receiver operation.

The a.f. shunt limiter at B, and the r.f. shunt limiter at C operate in the same manner. A pair of self-biased diodes are conected across the a.f. line at B, and across an r.f. inductor at C. When a steady c.w. signal is present the diodes barely conduct, but when a noise pulse rides in on the

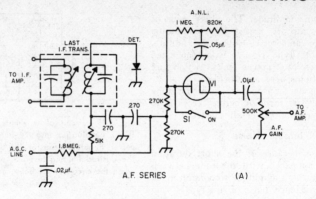

A.F. SERIES   (A)

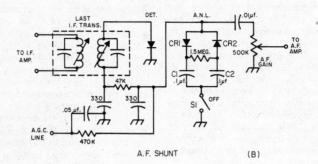

A.F. SHUNT   (B)

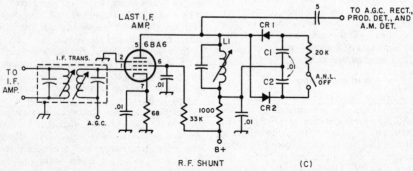

R.F. SHUNT   (C)

Fig. 5-20—Typical r.f. and a.f. a.n.l. circuits. At A, a tube-type diode works in a series audio a.n.l. arrangement. S_1 disables the clipper by shorting out V_1 when noise is not present; B shows the circuit of a
self-adjusting a.f. noise limiter. CR_1 and CR_2 are self-biased silicon diodes which limit both the positive and
negative audio and noise-pulse peaks. S_1 turns the limiter on or off; C shows an r.f. limiter of the same
type as B, but this circuit clips the positive and negative r.f. peaks and is connected to the last i.f. stage.
This circuit does not degrade the audio quality of the signal as do the circuits of A and B.

incoming signal it is heavily clipped because capacitors C_1 and C_2 tend to hold the diode bias
constant for the duration of the noise pulse. For
this reason the diodes conduct heavily in the
presence of noise and maintain a fairly constant
signal output level. Considerable clipping of s.s.b.
signal peaks occurs with this type of limiter, but
no apparent deterioration of the signal quality
results. L_1 at C is tuned to the i.f. of the receiver.
An i.f. transformer with a conventional secondary
winding could be used in place of L_1, the clipper
circuit being connected to the secondary winding;

the plate of the 6BA6 would connect to the primary winding in the usual fashion.

I.F. NOISE SILENCER

The i.f. noise silencer circuit shown in Fig.
5-21 is designed to be used in a receiver as far
along from the antenna stage as possible but
ahead of the high-selectivity section of the receiver. Noise pulses are amplified and rectified,
and the resulting negative-going d.c. pulses are
used to cut off an amplifier stage during the
pulse. A manual "threshold" control is set by the

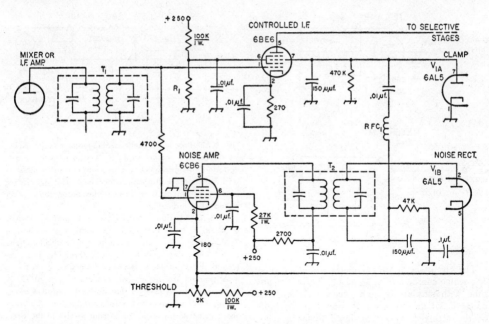

Fig. 5-21—Practical circuit diagram of an i.f. noise blanker. For best results the silencer should be used ahead of the high-selectivity portion of the receiver.
T₁—Interstage i.f. transformer

T₂—Diode i.f. transformer.
R₁—33,000 to 68,000 ohms, depending upon gain up to this stage.
RFC₁—R.f. choke, preferably self-resonant at i.f.

operator to a level that only permits rectification of the noise pulses that rise above the peak amplitude of the desired signal. The clamp diode, V_{1A}, short circuits the positive-going pulse "overshoots." Running the 6BE6 controlled i.f. amplifier at low screen voltage makes it possible for the No. 3 grid (pin 7) to cut off the stage at a lower voltage than if the screen were operated at the more-normal 100 volts, but it also reduces the available gain through the stage.

It is necessary to avoid i.f. feedback around the 6BE6 stage, and the closer RFC_1 can be to self-resonant at the i.f. the better will be the filtering. The filtering cannot be improved by increasing the values of the 150-pf. capacitors because this will tend to "stretch" the pulses and reduce the signal strength when the silencer is operative.

SIGNAL-STRENGTH AND TUNING INDICATORS

It is convenient to have some means by which to obtain *relative* readings of signal strength on a communications receiver. The actual meter readings in terms of S units, or decibels above S9, are of little consequence as far as a meaningful report to a distant station is concerned. Few signal-strength meters are accurate in terms of decibels, especially across their entire indicating range. Some manufacturers once established a standard in which a certain number of microvolts were equal to S9 on the meter face. Such calibration is difficult to maintain when a number of different receiver circuits are to be used. At best,

a meter can be calibrated for one receiver—the one in which it will be used. Therefore, most S meters are good only as relative indicating instruments for comparing the strength of signals at a given time, on a given amateur band. They are also useful for "on-the-nose-tuning" adjustments with selective receivers. If available, a signal generator with an accurate output attenuator can be used to calibrate an S meter in terms of microvolts, but a different calibration chart will probably be required for each band because of probable differences in receiver sensitivity from band to band. It is helpful to establish a 50-uv. reading at midscale on the meter so that the very strong signals will crowd the high end of the meter scale. The weaker signals will then be spread over the lower half of the scale and will not be compressed at the low end. Midscale on the meter can be called S9. If S units are desired across the scale, below S9, a marker can be established at every 6 db. point.

S-Meter Circuits

A very simple meter indicator is shown at Fig. 5-22B. Rectified r.f. is obtained by connecting CR_1 to the takeoff point for the detector. The d.c. is filtered by means of a 560-ohm resistor and a 0.05-uf. capacitor. A 10,000-ohm control sets the meter at zero reading in the absence of a signal and also serves as a "linearizing" resistor to help compensate for the nonlinear output from CR_1. The meter is a 50-ua. unit, therefore consuming but a small amount of current from the output of the i.f.

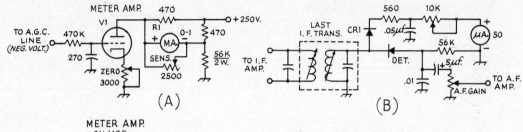

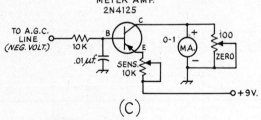

Fig. 5-22—Practical examples of S-meter circuits. At A, V_1 serves as a meter amplifier. As the negative a.g.c. voltage on its grid increases, its plate current diminishes and lessens the voltage drop across R_1. This permits increased current to flow through the meter, thus giving an up-scale indication.

At B the i.f. signal is rectified by CR_1 and is fed to a 50-ua. meter whose minus terminal is grounded. A 10,000-ohm control sets the sensitivity and also functions as a "linearizing" resistor to make the meter less subject to the square-law response from CR_1.

A bipolar transistor amplifies the a.g.c. at C. A p-n-p transistor is used so that normally-negative a.g.c. voltage will act as varying forward bias on the transistor to cause the collector current to rise in the presence of a signal. A 1-ma. meter reads the increasing current. The plus 9 volts can be taken from a small battery, or from the cathode of a tube-type audio output stage.

The circuit at A uses a meter amplifier tube, V_1, which can be a 6C4, ½ of a 12AU7A, or any tube with similar dynamic characteristics. The meter is set at zero with no signal at the input of the receiver. When a signal appears, a.g.c. voltage (negative) is developed and biases off the S-meter amplifier tube, thus reducing its plate current. When this happens, the voltage drop across R_1 decreases and permits more current to flow through the leg of the circuit which contains the meter, moving the needle toward the high end of the scale.

In the circuit at C, a p-n-p transistor is used to amplify the variations in a.g.c. voltage. The collector-current changes are read on a 1-ma. meter and the same calibration techniques mentioned earlier can be applied in this case. As the negative a.g.c. voltage increased, so does the forward bias on the transistor. This action causes a rise in collector current, in turn causing the meter reading to increase. If an n-p-n transistor is used, a plus a.g.c. voltage will be required.

IMPROVING RECEIVER SELECTIVITY

INTERMEDIATE-FREQUENCY AMPLIFIERS

One of the big advantages of the superheterodyne receiver is the improved selectivity that is possible. This selectivity is obtained in the i.f. amplifier, where the lower frequency allows more selectivity per stage than at the higher signal frequency. For normal a.m. (double-sideband) reception, the limit to useful selectivity in the i.f. amplifier is the point where too many of the high-frequency sidebands are lost. The limit to selectivity for a single-sideband signal, or a double-sideband a.m. signal treated as an s.s.b. signal, is about 1000 to 1500 Hz., but reception is much more normal if the bandwidth is opened up to 2000 or 2500 Hz. The correct bandwidth for f.m. or p.m. reception is determined by the deviation of the received signal; sideband cutting of these signals results in distortion. The limit to useful selectivity in code work is around 150 or 200 Hz. for hand-key speeds, but this much selectivity requires excellent stability in both transmitter and receiver, and a slow receiver tuning rate for ease of operation.

Single-Signal Effect

In heterodyne c.w. reception with a superheterodyne receiver, the beat oscillator is set to give a suitable audio-frequency beat note when the incoming signal is converted to the intermediate frequency. For example, the beat oscillator may be set to 454 kHz. (the i.f. being 455 kHz.) to give a 1000-Hz. beat note. Now, if an interfering signal appears at 453 kHz., or if the receiver is tuned to heterodyne the incoming signal to 453 kHz., it will also be heterodyned by the beat oscillator to produce a 1000-Hz. beat. Hence every signal can be tuned in at two places that will give a 1000-Hz. beat (or any other low audio frequency). This **audio-frequency image** effect can be reduced if the i.f. selectivity is such that the incoming signal, when heterodyned to 453 kHz., is attenuated to a very low level.

When this is done, tuning through a given signal will show a strong response at the desired beat note on one side of zero beat only, instead of the two beat notes on either side of zero beat characteristic of less-selective reception, hence the name: **single-signal reception**.

The necessary selectivity is not obtained with nonregenerative amplifiers using ordinary tuned circuits unless a low i.f. or a large number of circuits is used.

Regeneration

Regeneration can be used to give a single-signal effect, particularly when the i.f. is 455 kHz. or lower. The resonance curve of an i.f. stage at critical regeneration (just below the oscillating point) is extremely sharp, a bandwidth of kHz. at 10 times down and 5 kHz. at 100 times down being obtainable in one stage. The audio-frequency image of a given signal thus can be reduced by a factor of nearly 100 for a 1000-Hz. beat note (image 2000 Hz. from resonance).

Regeneration is easily introduced into an i.f. amplifier by providing a small amount of capacity coupling between grid and plate. Bringing a short length of wire, connected to the grid, into the vicinity of the plate lead usually will suffice. The feedback may be controlled by the regular cathode-resistor gain control. When the i.f. is regenerative, it is preferable to operate the tube at reduced gain (high bias) and depend on regeneration to bring up the signal strength. This prevents overloading and increases selectivity.

The higher selectivity with regeneration reduces the over-all response to noise generated in the earlier stages of the receiver, just as does high selectivity produced by other means, and therefore improves the signal-to-noise ratio. However, the regenerative gain varies with signal strength, being less on strong signals.

Crystal-Filters; Phasing

A simple means for obtaining high selectivity is by the use of a piezoelectric quartz crystal as a selective filter in the i.f. amplifier. Compared to a good tuned circuit, the Q of such a crystal is extremely high. The crystal is ground resonant at the i.f. and used as a selective coupler between i.f. stages. For single-signal reception, the audio-frequency image can be reduced by 50 db. or more. Besides practically eliminating the a.f. image, the high selectivity of the crystal filter provides good discrimination against adjacent signals and also reduces the noise.

BAND-PASS FILTERS

A single high-Q circuit (e.g., a quartz crystal or regenerative stage) will give adequate single-signal reception under most circumstances. For phone reception, however, either single-sideband or a.m., a **band-pass** characteristic is more desirable. A band-pass filter is one that passes without unusual attenuation a desired *band* of frequencies and rejects signals outside this band. A good band-pass filter for single-sideband reception might have a bandwidth of 2500 Hz. at -6 db. and 10 kHz. at -60 db.; a filter for a.m. would require twice these bandwidths if both sidebands were to be accommodated, thus assuring suitable fidelity.

The simplest band-pass crystal filter is one using two crystals, as in Fig. 5-23A. The two crystals are separated slightly in frequency. If the frequencies are only a few hundred Hz. apart the characteristic is a good one for c.w. reception. With crystals about 2 kHz. apart, a reasonable phone characteristic is obtained. Fig. 5-1 shows a selectivity characteristic of an amplifier with a bandpass (at -6 db.) of 2.4 kHz., which is typical of what can be expected from a two-crystal band-pass filter.

More elaborate crystal filters, using four and six crystals, will give reduced bandwidth at -60 db. without decreasing the bandwidth at -6 db. The resulting increased "skirt selectivity" gives better rejection of adjacent-channel signals. "Crystal-lattice" filters of this type are available commercially for frequencies up to 10 MHz. or so, and they have also been built by amateurs from inexpensive transmitting-type crystals. (See Vester, "Surplus-Crystal High-Frequency Filters," *QST*, January, 1959; Healey, "High-Frequency Crystal Filters for S.S.B.," *QST*, October, 1960.)

Two half-lattice filters of the type shown at Fig. 5-23A can be connected back to back as shown at B. The channel spacing of Y_1 and Y_2 will depend upon the receiving requirements as discussed in the foregoing text. Ordinarily, for s.s.b. reception (and non-stringent c.w. reception) a frequency separation of approximately 1.5 kHz. is suitable. The overall i.f. strip of the receiver is tuned to a frequency which is midway between Y_1 and Y_2. C_1 is tuned to help give the desired shape to the passband. L_1 is a bifilar-wound toroidal inductor which tunes to the i.f. frequency by means of C_1. The values of R_1 and R_2 are identical and are determined by the filter response desired. Ordinarily the ohmic value is on the order of 600 ohms, but values as high as 5000 ohms are sometimes used. The lower the value of resistance, the broader and flatter will be the response of the filter. Though the circuit at B is shown in a transistorized circuit, it can be used with vacuum tubes or integrated circuits as well. The circuit shows an i.f. frequency of 9 MHz., but the filter can be used at any desired frequency below 9 MHz. by altering the crystal frequencies and the tuned circuits. Commercial versions of the 9-MHz. lattice filter are available at moderate cost.[1] War-surplus FT-241 crystals in the 455-kHz. range are inexpensive and lend themselves nicely to this type of circuit.

Mechanical filters can be built at frequencies below 1 MHz. They are made up of three sections; an input transducer, a mechanically-resonant filter section, and an output transducer.

---

[1] International Crystal Co,. 10 N. Lee, Oklahoma City, Okla., 73102. Also, McCoy Electronics Co. Mount Holly Springs, Penna.

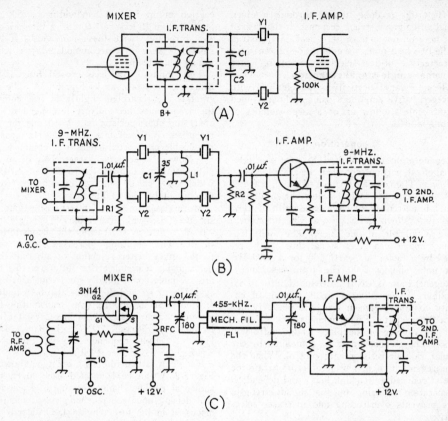

Fig. 5-23—A half-lattice bandpass filter at A; B shows two half-lattice filters in cascade; C shows a mechanical filter in a transistorized circuit.

The transducers use the principle of magneto-striction to convert the electrical signal to mechanical energy, then back again. The mechanically-resonant section consists of carefully-machined metal disks supported and coupled by thin rods. Each disk has a resonant frequency dependent upon the material and its dimensions, and the effective Q of a single disk may be in excess of 2000. Consequently a mechanical filter can be built for either narrow or broad bandpass with a nearly rectangular curve. Mechanical filters are available commercially and are used in both receivers and single-sideband transmitters. They are moderately priced.

The signal-handling capability of a mechanical filter is limited by the magnetic circuits to from 2 to 15 volts r.m.s., a limitation that is of no practical importance provided it is recognized and provided for. Crystal filters are limited in their signal-handling ability only by the voltage breakdown limits, which normally would not be reached before the preceding amplifier tube was overloaded. A more serious practical consideration in the use of any high-selectivity component is the prevention of coupling "around" the filter, externally, which can only degrade the action of the filter.

The circuit at Fig. 5-23C shows a typical hookup for a mechanical filter. FL_1 is a Collins 455-FB-21, which has a s.s.b. band-pass characteristic of 2.1 kHz. It is shown in a typical solid-state receiver circuit, but can be used equally as well in a tube-type application.

Placement of the b.f.o. signal with respect to the passbands of the three circuits at A, B, and C, is the same. Either a crystal-controlled or self-excited oscillator can be used to generate the b.f.o. signal and the usual practice is to place the b.f.o. signal at a frequency that falls at the two points which are approximately 20 db. down on the filter curve, dependent upon which sideband is desired. Typically, with the filter specified at C, the center frequency of FL_1 is 455 kHz. To place the b.f.o. at the 20-db. points (down from the center-frequency peak) a signal at 453 and 456 kHz. is required.

Q Multiplier

The "Q Multiplier" is a stable regenerative stage that is connected in parallel with one of the i.f. stages of a receiver. In one condition it narrows the bandwidth and in the other condition it produces a sharp "null" or rejection notch. A "tuning" adjustment controls the fre-

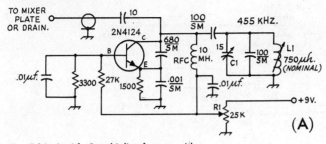

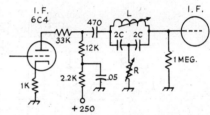

Fig. 5-24—An i.f. Q-multiplier for use with
a bipolar transistor (A). At B, a tube-type
r.f. Q-multiplier which can be used at the first stage of the
receiver. The antenna coil is used for feedback to V_1, which
then introduces "negative resistance" to L_2.

quency of the peak or null, moving it across the
normal pass band of the receiver i.f. amplifier.
The *shape* of the peak or null is always that of a
single tuned circuit (Fig. 2-50) but the effective
Q is adjustable over a wide range. A Q Multiplier is most effective at an i.f. of 500 kHz. or
less; at higher frequencies the rejection notch
becomes wide enough (measured in Hz.) to reject a major portion of a phone signal. Within its
useful range, however, the Q Multiplier will reject an interfering carrier without degrading the
quality of the desired signal.

In the "peak" condition the Q Multiplier can
be made to oscillate by advancing the "peak"
(regeneration) control far enough, and in this
condition it can be made to serve as a beat-
frequency oscillator. However, it cannot be made
to serve as a selective element and as a b.f.o.
at the same time. Some inexpensive receivers
may combine either a Q Multiplier or some other
form of regeneration with the b.f.o. function, and
the reader is advised to check carefully any inexpensive receiver he intends to buy that offers
a regenerative type of selectivity, in order to
make sure that the selectivity is available when
the b.f.o. is turned on.

A representative circuit for a transistorized
Q-multiplier is given in Fig. 5-24A. The constants
given are typical for i.f. operation at 455 kHz. L_1
can be a J. W. Miller 9002 or 9012 slug-tuned
inductor. A 25,000-ohm control, R_1, permits adjustment of the regeneration. C_1 is used to tune
the Q-multiplier frequency back and forth across
the i.f. passband for peaking or notching adjustments. With circuits of this type there is usually
a need to adjust both R_1 and C_1 alternately for
a peaking or notching, because the controls tend
to interlock as far as the frequency of oscillation
is concerned. A Q-multiplier should be solidly
built in a shielded enclosure to assure maximum
stability.

Q multipliers can be used at the front end of
a receiver also, as shown at B in Fig. 5-24. The
enhancement of the Q at that point in a receiver
greatly reduces image problems because the selectivity of the input tuned circuit is increased
markedly. The antenna coil, L_1, is used as a feedback winding to make V_1 regenerative. This in
effect adds "negative resistance" to L_2, increasing

its Q. A 20,000-ohm control sets the regeneration
of V_1, and should be adjusted to a point just under
regeneration for best results. R.f. Q multiplication is not a cure for a poor-quality inductor at
L_2, however.

Fig. 5-25—Typical T-notch (bridged-T) filter, to provide
a sharp notch at a low i.f.. Adjustment of L changes the
frequency of the notch; adjustment of R controls the
notch depth.

T-Notch Filter

At low intermediate frequencies $(50 - 100$
kHz.) the T-notch filter of Fig. 5-25 will provide
a sharp tunable null.

The inductor L resonates with C at the rejection frequency, and when $R = 4X_L/Q$ the rejection is maximum. (X_L is the coil reactance and Q
is the coil Q). In a typical 50-kHz. circuit, C
might be 3900 pf. making L approximately
2.6 mh. When R is greater than the maximum-
attenuation value, the circuit still provides some
rejection, and in use the inductor is detuned or
shorted out when the rejection is not desired.

At higher frequencies, the T-notch filter is not
sharp enough with available components to reject only a narrow band of frequencies.

RADIO-FREQUENCY AMPLIFIERS

While selectivity to reduce audio-frequency
images can be built into the i.f. amplifier, discrimination against radio-frequency images can
only be obtained in tuned circuits or other selective elements ahead of the first mixer or converter stage. These tuned circuits are usually
used as the coupling networks for one or more

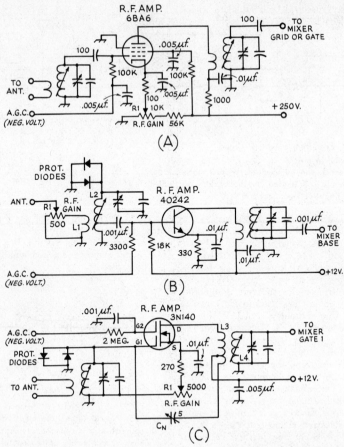

Fig. 5-26—Typical radio-frequency amplifier circuits. A.g.c. and manual r.f. gain provisions are shown for all three circuits. The circuits of B and C use protective diodes to prevent burnout from high r.f. levels. The dual-gate MOS FET at C is neutralized by means of C_n.

vacuum tubes or transistors, and the combinations of circuits and amplifying devices are called radio-frequency amplifiers. The tuned circuits contribute to the r.f. image rejection and the amplifying device(s) determines the noise figure of the receiver.

Knowing the Q of the coil in each tuned circuit between the antenna and the first mixer or converter stage, the image rejection capability can be computed by using the chart in Fig. 2-50. The Q of the input tuned circuit (coupled to the antenna) should be taken as about one-half the unloaded Q of that circuit, and the Q of any other tuned circuit can be assumed to be the unloaded Q to a first approximation (the vacuum tubes will reduce the circuit Q to some extent, especially at 14 MHz. and higher).

In general, receivers with an i.f. of 455 kHz. can be expected to have some noticeable image response at 14 MHz. and higher if there are only two tuned circuits (one r.f. stage) ahead of the mixer or converter. Regeneration in the r.f. amplifier will reduce image response, but regeneration usually requires frequent readjustment when tuning across a band. Regeneration is, however, a useful device for improving the selectivity of an r.f. amplifier without requiring a multiplicity of tuned circuits.

With three tuned circuits between the antenna and the first mixer, and an i.f. of 455 kHz., no images should be encountered up to perhaps 25 MHz. Four tuned circuits or more will eliminate any images at 28 MHz. when an i.f. of 455 kHz. is used.

Obviously, a better solution to the r.f. selectivity problem (elimination of image response) is to use an i.f. higher than 455 kHz., and most modern receivers use an i.f. of 1600 kHz. or higher. The owner of a receiver with a 455-kHz. i.f. amplifier can enjoy image-free reception on the higher frequencies by using a crystal-controlled converter ahead of the receiver and utilizing the receiver as a "tunable i.f. amplifier" at 3.5 or 7.0 MHz.

For best selectivity r.f. amplifiers should use high-Q circuits and tubes with high input and output resistance. Variable-μ pentodes and field-effect transistors (JFET and MOS FET) are practically always used, although triodes (neutralized or otherwise connected so that they won't oscillate) are often used on the higher frequencies because they introduce less noise. However, their lower plate resistance will load the tuned circuits. Pentodes and FETs are better where maximum image rejection is desired, because they have less loading effect on the tuned circuits.

Representative Circuits

An example of a typical vacuum-tube r.f. amplifier using a remote-cutoff pentode and a.g.c. is given in Fig. 5-26 at A. The Manual r.f. gain control, R_1, varies the bias on the stage, thereby changing the gain of the tube. Two such stages are sometimes connected in cascade at 21 MHz. and higher to minimize image response.

In the circuit at B, a bipolar transistor is used as an r.f. amplifier. Because of its dynamic characteristics, it cannot handle as high an input signal level as the circuits at A and C and is more subject to overloading. It has a.g.c. provisions and requires a negative a.g.c. voltage because the device is an n-p-n type. A positive a.g.c. voltage would be needed if a p-n-p transistor were used. R_1, the r.f. gain control, is simply a 500-ohm control inserted between the lo-Z antenna lead and the input link of the tuned circuit. Control over the r.f. gain can also be effected by supplying a variable negative voltage (from a fixed supply) to the base element by means of a potentiometer. Protective diodes, connected for opposite polarity, are bridged between the hi-Z end of L_2 and ground. When the signal level (positive or negative peaks) reaches the conduction point of the diodes (approximately 0.6 volt for silicon diodes) they short L_2 out and prevent damage to the transistor junction. High-speed switching diodes are frequently used for this application. For efficient operation as an r.f. amplifier, the transistor must have an f_T rating of at least 10 times that of the proposed operating frequency. Neutralization may be required if good circuit isolation between the input and output tuned circuits is not employed, or if transistors with exceptionally high beta ratings are used.

A dual-gate MOS FET is used at C. Gate 2 is used for a.g.c. and offers excellent control of the gain. A manual r.f. gain control, R_1, is shown in the source return of the FET. Protective diodes hold the gate voltage at a safe value when strong r.f. levels are present. The diodes are not recommended unless absolutely necessary. The same rule applies to the circuit at B.

Some form of neutralization is usually required when FETs are used as amplifiers, and the same rules that apply to triode tubes should be followed. In the circuit at C a small amount of r.f. voltage (opposite in phase to the feedthrough voltage between gate 1 and the drain) is taken from L_3 and is fed back to the gate by means of C_n—a variable capacitor which is adjusted for best stability of the stage. Additional information on neutralization is given in Chapter 6. The methods described are applicable to receivers.

FEEDBACK

Feedback giving rise to regeneration and oscillation can occur in a single stage or it may appear as an over-all feedback through several stages that are on the same frequency. To avoid feedback in a single stage, the output must be isolated from the input in every way possible, with the vacuum tube or transistor furnishing the only coupling between the two circuits. An oscillation can be obtained in an r.f. or i.f. stage if there is any undue capacitive or inductive coupling between output and input circuits, if there is too high an impedance between cathode and ground or screen and ground, or if there is any appreciable impedance through which the grid and plate currents can flow in common.

To avoid over-all feedback in a multistage amplifier, attention must be paid to avoid running any part of the output circuit back near the input circuit without first filtering it carefully. Since the signal-carrying parts of the circuit can't be filtered, the best design for any multistage amplifier is a straight line, to keep the output as far away from the input as possible. For example, an r.f. amplifier might run along a chassis in a straight line, run into a mixer where the frequency is changed, and then the i.f. amplifier could be run back parallel to the r.f. amplifier, provided there was a very large frequency difference between the r.f. the i.f. amplifiers. However, to avoid any possible coupling, it would be better to run the i.f. amplifier off at right angles to the r.f.-amplifier line, just to be on the safe side. Good shielding is important in preventing overall oscillation in high-gain-per-stage amplifiers, but it becomes less important when the stage gain drops to a low value. In a high-gain amplifier, the power leads (including the heater circuit) are common to all stages, and they can provide the overall coupling if they aren't properly filtered. Good bypassing and the use of series isolating resistors will generally eliminate any possibility of coupling through the power leads. R.f. chokes, instead of resistors, are used in the heater leads where necessary.

CROSS-MODULATION

Since a one- or two-stage r.f. amplifier will have a bandwidth measured in hundreds of kHz. at 14 MHz. or higher, strong signals will be amplified through the r.f. amplifier even though it is not tuned exactly to them. If these signals are strong enough, their amplified magnitude may be measurable in *volts* after passing through several r.f. stages. If an undesired signal is strong enough after amplification in the r.f. stages to shift the operating point of a tube or transistor (by driving the grid into the positive region), the undesired signal will modulate the desired signal. This effect is called **cross-modulation,** and if often encountered in receivers with several r.f. stages working at high gain. It shows up as a superimposed modulation on the signal being listened to, and often the effect is that a signal can be tuned in at several points. It can be reduced or eliminated by greater selectivity in the antenna and r.f. stages (difficult to obtain), the use of FETS or variable-μ tubes in the r.f. amplifier, reduced gain in the r.f. amplifier, or reduced antenna input to the receiver. The 6BJ6, 6BA6 and 6DC6 are recommended for r.f. amplifiers where cross-modulation may be a problem.

A receiver designed for minimum cross-modulation will use as little gain as possible ahead of the high-selectivity stages, to hold strong unwanted signals below the cross-modulation point. Cross-modulation often takes place in double-conversion superheterodynes at the *second* converter stage because there is insufficient selectivity up to this point and at this point the signals have quite appreciable amplitudes. Whenever interference drops out quite suddenly with a reduction in the setting of the gain control, cross-modulation should be suspected. Normally, of course, the interference would reduce in amplitude in proportion to the desired signal as the gain setting is reduced.

Gain Control

To avoid cross-modulation and other overload effects in the mixer and r.f. stages, the gain of the r.f. stages is usually made adjustable. This is accomplished by using variable-μ tubes and varying the d.c. grid bias, either in the grid or cathode circuit. If the gain control is automatic, as in the case of a.g.c., the bias is controlled in the grid circuit. Manual control of r.f. gain is generally done in the cathode circuit. A typical r.f. amplifier stages with the two types of gain control is shown in schematic form in Fig. 5-26. The a.g.c. control voltage (negative) is derived from rectified carrier or signal at the detector before the audio amplifier, or in the case of a c.w. or s.s.b. receiver it can be derived from rectified audio. The manual gain control voltage (positive with respect to chassis) is usually derived from a potentiometer across the B+ supply, since the bias can be changed even though little plate current is being drawn. The same manual gain-control techniques can be applied to solid-state r.f. amplifiers as shown in Fig. 5-26 at B and C.

Tracking

Tracking refers to the ability of a receiver to have all of its front-end stages—usually the r.f. amplifier, the mixer, and the oscillator—tune over a given range while each stage remains tuned to its proper frequency at any specified point in the tuning range. This arrangement provides a single tuning control for bandset and bandspread adjustments. To achieve proper tracking, it is usually necessary to have variable inductors and variable trimmer and padder capacitors for each of the tuned circuits. A two- or three-section variable capacitor is used for the tuning control.

Most modern receivers use a separate tuning control for the local oscillator and this is called the "main tuning." The r.f. and mixer stages are tracked and use a two-section variable for front-

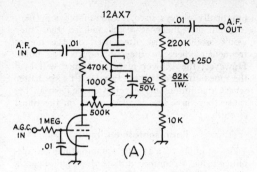

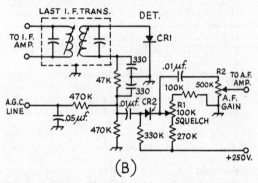

Fig. 5-27—Practical examples of squelch circuits for cutting off the receiver output when no signal is present.

end peaking adjustments. This control is frequently called "preselector tuning." If the main tuning control is moved, the preselector is readjusted for a peak signal response at the new frequency.

SQUELCH CIRCUITS

An audio squelch is one that cuts off the receiver output when no signal is coming through the receiver. A squelch is useful in mobile equipment where the no-signal receiver hiss noise may be as loud as some of the weak signals being copied. Noise of this kind, when listened to over a sustained period, can cause considerable operator fatigue. A squelch is useful with certain types of fixed-station equipment too, especially where continuous monitoring of a fixed v.h.f. or u.h.f. frequency is concerned.

A practical vacuum-tube squelch circuit is given in Fig. 5-27 at A. A twin triode (12AX7) serves as an audio amplifier and a control tube. When the a.g.c. voltage is low or zero, the lower (control) triode draws plate current. The consequent voltage drop across the adjustable resistor in the plate circuit cuts off the upper (amplifier) triode and no signal or noise is passed. When the a.g.c. voltage rises to the cut-off value of the control triode, the tube no longer draws current and the bias on the amplifier triode is now only its normal operating bias, furnished by the 1000-ohm resistor in the cathode circuit.

The tube now functions as an ordinary amplifier and passes signals. The relation between the a.g.c. voltage and the signal turn-on point is adjusted by varying the resistance in the plate circuit of the control triode.

A simple squelch arrangement is shown in the circuit of Fig. 5-27B. Here a silicon diode, CR_1, is used in the audio line from the detector. Adjustment of the squelch control, R_1, sets the diode

bias for a non-conducting condition. When an incoming signal reaches CR_2, it overcomes the fixed bias set by R_1 and allows the diode to conduct, thus passing the audio signal on to the subsequent stages. CR_1 is the detector diode and R_2 is the audio gain control. The values of the various squelch-circuit resistors will require modification if the circuit is used in receivers that operate from 9 or 12 volts.

IMPROVING RECEIVER SENSITIVITY

The sensitivity (signal-to-noise ratio) of a receiver on the higher frequencies above 20 MHz. is dependent upon the band width of the receiver and the noise contributed by the "front end" of the receiver. Neglecting the fact that image rejection may be poor, a receiver with no r.f. stage is generally satisfactory, from a sensitivity point, in the 3.5- and 7-MHz. bands. However, as the frequency is increased and the atmospheric noise becomes less, the advantage of a good "front end" becomes apparent. Hence at 14 MHz. and higher it is worth while to use at least one stage of r.f. amplification ahead of the first detector for best sensitivity as well as image rejection. The multigrid converter tubes have very poor noise figures, and even the best pentodes and triodes are three or four times noisier when used as mixers than they are when used as amplifiers.

If the purpose of an r.f. amplifier is to improve the receiver noise figure at 14 MHz. and higher, a good FET, or a high-g_m pentode or triode should be used. Among the pentodes, the best tubes are the 6EH7, 6BZ6, and 6AK5. Of the triodes, the 6AN4, 6CW4, and 6DS4 are best. Among the better field-effect transistors are the MPF105, 2N4417, 3N128, and 3N140.

When a receiver is satisfactory in every respect (stability and selectivity) except sensitivity on 14 through 30 MHz., the best solution for the amateur is to add a **preamplifier,** a stage of r.f. amplification designed expressly to improve the sensitivity. If image rejection is lacking in

the receiver, some selectivity should be built into the preamplifier (it is then called a preselector). If, however, the receiver operation is poor on the higher frequencies but is satisfactory on the lower ones, a "converter" is the best solution.

Some commercial receivers that appear to lack sensitivity on the higher frequencies can be improved simply by tighter coupling to the antenna. This can be accomplished by changing the antenna feed line to the right value (as determined from the receiver instruction book) or by using a simple matching device. Overcoupling the input circuit will often improve sensitivity but it will, of course, always reduce the image-rejection contribution of the antenna circuit.

Gain Control

In a receiver front end designed for best signal-to-noise ratio, it is advantageous in the reception of weak signals to eliminate the gain control from the first r.f. stage and allow it to run "wide open" all of the time. If the first stage is controlled along with the i.f. (and other r.f. stages, if any), the signal-to-noise ratio of the receiver will suffer. As the gain is reduced, the g_m of the first tube is reduced, and its noise figure becomes higher. A good receiver might well have two gain controls, one for the first r.f. stage and another for the i.f. (and any other r.f.) stages. The first r.f. stage gain would be reduced only for extremely strong signals, thus assuring a good noise figure.

TUNING A RECEIVER

C.W. Reception

In a receiver without selectivity, it doesn't much matter where the b.f.o. is set, so long as it is within the pass band of the receiver. However, in a receiver with selectivity, the b.f.o. should be offset, to give single-signal code reception. The proper setting of the b.f.o. is easy to find. In the absence of incoming signals, it will be found that, as the b.f.o. control is tuned, the pitch of the background noise will go from high to low and back to high again. The setting that gives the lowest pitch represents the setting of the b.f.o. in the *center* of the pass band. Setting the b.f.o. for a higher pitch (to the noise) will give more or less single-signal effect on incoming signals, depending upon the selectivity of the receiver. If the receiver uses a crystal filter that has a "re-

jection notch" or "phasing" control, setting the notch on the audio image will improve the single-signal effect.

The best receiver condition for the reception of code signals will have the first r.f. stage running at maximum gain, the following r.f., mixer and i.f. stages operating with just enough gain to maintain the signal-to-noise ratio, and the audio gain set to give comfortable headphone or speaker volume. The audio volume should be controlled by the audio gain control, not the i.f. gain control. Under the above conditions, the selectivity of the receiver is being used to best advantage, and cross-modulation is minimized. It precludes the use of a receiver in which the gains of the r.f. and i.f. stages are controlled simultaneously.

Single-Sideband Phone Reception

The receiver is set up for s.s.b. reception in a manner similar to that for single-signal code reception, except that a suitable band width for s.s.b. (2 to 3 kHz.) is used. The b.f.o. *must* be set off to one side of the pass band if good use is to be made of the selectivity. To determine which side to set it, remember this rule: A selective receiver can be set up for *lower*-sideband reception by setting the b.f.o. so that there is little or no signal on the *low*-frequency side of zero beat when tuning through a steady carrier or c.w. signal. Lower sideband is customarily used on 3.9 and 7 MHz., upper on the higher frequencies.

Unless the receiver has an a.g.c. system suitable for s.s.b. reception (fast attack, slow decay), the operator must be very careful not to let the receiver overload. If the receiver does overload, it will be impossible to obtain good s.s.b. reception. Run the receiver with as little i.f. gain as possible, consistent with a good signal-to-noise ratio, and run the audio gain high.

Carefully tune in an s.s.b. signal using only the main tuning dial. When the voice becomes natural sounding and understandable, the signal is properly tuned. If the incoming signal is on lower sideband, tuning the receiver to a lower frequency will make the voice sound lower pitched. An upper-sideband signal will sound higher pitched as the receiver is tuned to a lower frequency.

If the receiver has excellent selectivity, as 2.1 kHz. or less, it will be desirable to experiment slightly with the b.f.o. setting, remembering that each adjustment of the b.f.o. calls for a similar adjustment of the main tuning control. If the selectivity is quite high, setting the b.f.o. too far from the pass band will limit the incoming signal to the high audio frequencies only. Conversely, setting it too close will limit the response to the low audio frequencies.

A.M. Phone Reception

In reception of a.m. phone signals, the normal procedure is to set the r.f. and i.f. gain at maximum, switch on the a.g.c., and use the audio gain control for setting the volume. This insures maximum effectiveness of the a.g.c. system in compensating for fading and maintaining constant audio output on either strong or weak signals. On occasion a strong signal close to the frequency of a weaker desired station may take control of the a.g.c., in which case the weaker station may disappear because of the reduced gain. In this case better reception may result if the a.g.c. is switched off, using the manual r.f.

gain control to set the gain at a point that prevents "blocking" by the stronger signal.

When receiving an a.m. signal on a frequency within 5 to 20 kHz. from a single-sideband signal it may also be necessary to switch off the a.g.c. and resort to the use of manual gain control, unless the receiver has excellent skirt selectivity.

A crystal filter will help reduce interference in phone reception. Although the high selectivity cuts sidebands and reduces the audio output at the higher audio frequencies, it is possible to use quite high selectivity without destroying intelligibility. As in code reception, it is advisable to do all tuning with the filter in the circuit. Variable-selectivity filters permit a choice of selectivity to suit interference conditions.

An undesired carrier close in frequency to a desired carrier will heterodyne with it to produce a beat note equal to the frequency difference.

Spurious Responses

Spurious responses can be recognized without a great deal of difficulty. Often it is possible to identify an image by the nature of the transmitting station, if the frequency assignments applying to the frequency to which the receiver is tuned are known. However, an image also can be recognized by its behavior with tuning. If the signal causes a heterodyne beat note with the desired signal and is actually on the same frequency, the beat note will not change as the receiver is tuned through the signal; but if the interfering signal is an image, the beat will vary in pitch as the receiver is tuned. The beat oscillator in the receiver must be turned off for this test. Using a crystal filter with the beat oscillator on, an image will peak on the side of zero beat opposite that on which desired signals peak.

Harmonic response can be recognized by the "tuning rate," or movement of the tuning dial required to give a specified change in beat note. Signals getting into the i.f. via high-frequency oscillator harmonics tune more rapidly (less dial movement) through a given change in beat note than do signals received by normal means.

Harmonics of the beat oscillator can be recognized by the tuning rate of the beat-oscillator pitch control. A smaller movement of the control will suffice for a given change in beat note than that necessary with legitimate signals. In poorly-designed or inadequately-shielded and -filtered receivers it is often possible to find b.f.o. harmonics below 2 MHz., but they should be very weak or non-existent at higher frequencies.

ALIGNMENT AND SERVICING OF SUPERHETERODYNE RECEIVERS

I.F. Alignment

A calibrated signal generator or test oscillator is a useful device for alignment of an i.f. amplifier. Some means for measuring the output of

the receiver is required. If the receiver has a tuning meter, its indications will serve. Lacking an S meter, a high-resistance voltmeter or a vacuum-tube voltmeter can be connected across the second-detector load resistor, if the second detector is a diode. Alternatively, if the signal generator is a modulated type, an a.c. voltmeter can be connected across the primary of the transformer feeding the speaker, or from the plate of the last audio amplifier through a 0.1-μf. blocking capacitor to the receiver chassis. Lacking an a.c. voltmeter, the audio output can be judged by ear, although this method is not as accurate as the others. If the tuning meter is used as an indication, the a.g.c. of the receiver should be turned on, but any other indication requires that it be turned off. Lacking a test oscillator, a steady signal tuned through the input of the receiver (if the job is one of just touching up the i.f. amplifier) will be suitable. However, with no oscillator and tuning an amplifier for the first time, one's only recourse is to try to peak the i.f. transformers on "noise," a difficult task if the transformers are badly off resonance, as they are apt to be. It would be much better to haywire together a simple oscillator for test purposes.

Initial alignment of a new i.f. amplifier is as follows: The test oscillator is set to the correct frequency, and its output is coupled through a capacitor to the grid of the last i.f. amplifier tube. The trimmer capacitors of the transformer feeding the second detector are then adjusted for maximum output, as shown by the indicating device being used. The oscillator output lead is then clipped on to the grid of the next-to-the-last i.f. amplifier tube, and the second-from-the-last transformer trimmer adjustments are peaked for maximum output. This process is continued, working back from the second detector, until all of the i.f. transformers have been aligned. It will be necessary to reduce the output of the test oscillator as more of the i.f. amplifier is brought into use. It is desirable in all cases to use the minimum signal that will give useful output readings. The i.f. transformer in the plate circuit of the mixer is aligned with the signal introduced to the grid of the mixer. Since the tuned circuit feeding the mixer grid may have a very low impedance at the i.f., it may be necessary to boost the test generator output or to disconnect the tuned circuit temporarily from the mixer grid.

If the i.f. amplifier has a crystal filter, the filter should first be switched out and the alignment carried out as above, setting the test oscillator as closely as possible to the crystal frequency. When this is completed, the crystal should be switched in and the oscillator frequency varied back and forth over a small range either side of the crystal frequency to find the exact frequency, as indicated by a sharp rise in output. Leaving the test oscillator set on the crystal peak, the i.f. trimmers should be realigned for maximum output. The necessary readjustment should be small. The oscillator frequency should be checked frequently to make sure it has not drifted from the crystal peak.

A modulated signal is not of much value for aligning a crystal-filter i.f. amplifier, since the high selectivity cuts sidebands and the results may be inaccurate if the audio output is used as the tuning indication. Lacking the a.g.c. tuning meter, the transformers may be conveniently aligned by ear, using a weak unmodulated signal adjusted to the crystal peak. Switch on the beat oscillator, adjust to a suitable tone, and align the i.f. transformers for maximum audio output.

An amplifier that is only slightly out of alignment, as a result of normal drift or aging, can be realigned by using any steady signal, such as a local broadcast station, instead of the test oscillator. One's 100-kHz. standard makes an excellent signal source for "touching up" an i.f. amplifier. Allow the receiver to warm up thoroughly, tune in the signal, and trim the i.f. for maximum output as noted on the S meter, or by tuning for peak a.f. output.

R.F. Alignment

The objective in aligning the r.f. circuits of a gang-tuned receiver is to secure adequate tracking over each tuning range. The adjustment may be carried out with a test oscillator of suitable frequency range, with harmonics from your 100-kHz. standard or other known oscillator, or even on noise or such signals as may be heard. First set the tuning dial at the high-frequency end of the range in use. Then set the test oscillator to the frequency indicated by the receiver dial. The test-oscillator output may be connected to the antenna terminals of the receiver for this test. Adjust the oscillator trimmer capacitor in the receiver to give maximum response on the test-oscillator signal, then reset the receiver dial to the low-frequency end of the range. Set the test-oscillator frequency near the frequency indicated by the receiver dial and tune the test oscillator until its signal is heard in the receiver. If the frequency of the signal is indicated by the test-oscillator calibration is higher than that indicated by the receiver dial, more inductance (or more capacity in the tracking capacitor) is needed in the receiver oscillator circuit; if the frequency is lower, less inductance (less tracking capacity) is required in the receiver oscillator. Most commercial receivers provide some means for varying the inductance of the coils or the capacitance of the tracking capacitor, to permit aligning the receiver tuning with the dial calibration. Set the test oscillator to the frequency indicated by the receiver dial, and then adjust the tracking capacitance or inductance of the receiver oscillator coil to obtain maximum response. After making this adjustment, recheck the high-frequency end of the scale as previously described. It may be necessary to go back and forth between the ends of the range several times before the proper combination of inductance and capacitance is secured. In many cases, better overall tracking will result if frequencies near but not actually at the ends of the tuning range are selected, instead of taking the extreme dial settings.

After the oscillator range is properly adjusted, set the receiver and test oscillator to the high-frequency end of the range. Adjust the mixer trimmer capacitor for maximum hiss or signal, then the r.f. trimmers. Reset the tuning dial and test oscillator to the low-frequency end of the range, and repeat; if the circuits are properly designed, no change in trimmer settings should be necessary. If it is necessary to increase the trimmer capacitance in any circuit, more inductance is needed; conversely, if less capacitance resonates the circuit, less inductance is required.

Tracking seldom is perfect throughout a tuning range, so that a check of alignment at intermediate points in the range may show it to be slightly off. Normally the gain variation will be small, however, and it will suffice to bring the circuits into line at both ends of the range. If most reception is in a particular part of the range, such as an amateur band, the circuits may be aligned for maximum performance in that region, even though the ends of the frequency range as a whole may be slightly out of alignment.

RECEIVER SELECTION

Beginning amateurs often find themselves faced with the dilemma of choosing between a home-built or store-bought receiver. Ideally, the new ham would elect to build his own complete amateur station, extracting the maximum value from the project through the knowledge he would gain about electronics. Additionally, home-built equipment is more familiar in detail to its owner than is a manufactured receiver. Thus, he can service his unit more rapidly and does not have to consult with the manufacturer about servicing details. If he wishes to add new circuits to the home-built receiver, or to modify existing circuitry, he need not worry about destroying the resale value of the equipment. For this reason the owner may be encouraged to experiment more with circuits, enhancing his overall knowledge of electronics.

Conversely, single-lot quantities of small parts are quite expensive these days, sometimes causing the constructor to spend more money on a simple home-built receiver than he would on a complicated commercially-built unit. Modifications to factory-built ham gear generally degrade its resale value, discouraging the owner from making circuit improvements or improving his knowledge by experimenting.

The complexity of the receiver need only be such as to fill the operator's needs. Some very basic home-made receivers perform better than poorly-designed multi-tube commercial units. The receivers described later in this chapter have been designed with the radio amateur's needs in mind, yet no unnecessary circuitry has been added simply to make them appear to be highly sophisticated. Many of the parts used in these receivers can be obtained from junked TV sets, war surplus stores, junked war surplus equipment, and from the workshop junk box. These possibilities should not be overlooked, for a considerable amount of money can be saved by garnering small parts in this manner.

The final decision whether to buy or build will of course be up to the operator. If you're only interested in being a "communicator," then a store-bought receiver will probably suffice. If, however, you want to experience the thrill of communicating by means of home-constructed equipment, and if you want to *learn by doing,* then home-made receiving equipment should be considered. Such forthright endeavors are often the stepping stones to higher plateaus—a satisfying career in electronics, or the needed background to qualify for radio schooling when in the military service. Just having a good working knowledge of one's own station is rewarding in itself, and such knowledge contributes to an amateur's value during public service and emergency operations.

REDUCING BROADCAST STATION INTERFERENCE

Some receivers, particularly those that are lacking in front-end selectivity, are subject to cross-talk and overload from adjacent-frequency ham or commercial stations. This condition is particularly common with simple receivers that use bipolar transistors in the r.f. and mixer stages. With the latter, the range of linear operation is small compared to that of vacuum tubes. Large signals send the transistors into the nonlinear operating region, causing severe crosstalk.

The most common cross-talk problem in ham radio is that which caused by the presence of nearby broadcast stations in the 550- to 1600-Kc. range. In some regions, the ham bands—when tuned in on even the best receivers—are a mass of distorted "pop" music, garbled voices, and splatter. It should be pointed out at this juncture that the broadcast stations themselves seldom are at fault, (although in isolated instances they are capable of generating spurious output if operating in a faulty manner).

The most direct approach to the problem of broadcast-station interference is to install a rejection filter between the antenna feed line and the input terminals of the receiver. Such a filter, if capable of providing sufficient attenuation, prevents the broadcast-station signals from reaching the ham receiver's front end, thus solving the cross-talk problem.

An effective band-rejection filter, containing two m-derived pi sections in cascade, is shown in Fig. 5-28.[1] It offers sharp rejection to signals in the 500- to 1600-kc. range but does not impair reception above or below the broadcast band. It is designed for use in low-impedance lines, particularly those that are 50 or 75 ohms.

The band-rejection filter is housed in a $3\frac{1}{2} \times 2\frac{1}{8} \times 1\frac{5}{8}$-inch Minibox. Phono connectors are used for J_1 and J_2—an aid to cost reduction. Different-style fittings can be used if the builder

[1] Originally described in greater depth, and with examples of additional filter types, in *QST,* Dec., 1967.

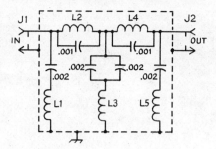

Fig. 5-28—Capacitance is in µf. Capacitors are disk or tubular ceramic.

J_1, J_2—Phono jack.

L_1, L_5—10-µh. inductor (Miller 70F105A1 suitable).

L_2, L_4—33-µh. inductor (Miller 70F335A1 suitable).

L_3—4.7-µh. inductor (Miller 70F476A1 suitable).

wishes. Standard-value components are used throughout the filter and the values specified must be used if good results are to be had.

In situations where a *single* broadcast station is involved in the cross-talk problem, a simple series- or parallel-tuned wave trap, tuned to the frequency of the interfering station, may prove adequate in solving the problem. Such a trap can be installed as shown in Fig. 5-29). The trap inductors can be made from ferrite-bar broadcast radio loop antennas and tuned to resonance by means of a 365-pf. Variable capacitor. Traps of this type should be enclosed in a metal box, as is true of the band-rejection filter.

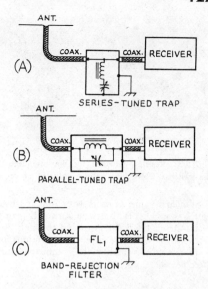

Fig. 5-29—Examples of series- and parallel-tuned single-frequency traps (installed) are shown at A and B. At C, FL_1 represents the band-rejection filter described in the text. If possible, the filter used should be bolted to the chassis or case of the receiver. The receiver should have a good earth ground connected to it.

FRONT-END OVERLOAD PROTECTION FOR THE RECEIVER

It is not uncommon to experience front-end overloading when the station receiver is subjected to an extremely strong signal. Frequently, it becomes necessary to install some type of external attenuator between the antenna and the input of the receiver to minimize the bad effects caused by the strong signal, or signals.[1] Ideally, such an attenuator should be designed to match the impedance of the antenna feed line and the input impedance of the receiver. Also, the attenuator should be variable, enabling the user to have some control over the amount of attenuation used. Manufacturer's of some modern receiving equipment build attenuators into the front end of their receivers, offering benefits that are not available from the normal r.f. gain-control circuit.

Examples of two such attenuators are given in Figs. 5-33 and 5-32. In Fig. 5-33 a ladder-type attenuator which gives a 0 to 40-decibel range of control in five steps.[2] A simple step attenuator is illustrated in Fig. 5-32.[3] The latter offers an attenuation range of 3 to 33 decibels in 3-db. steps by closing one or more of four slide switches. Both units are designed for use in low-impedance lines. The one in Fig. 5-33 is designed for a mid-range impedance of 60 ohms, making it satisfactory for use with receivers having a 50- or 75- ohm input. Although designed for an impedance of 50 ohms, the attenuator of Fig. 5-32 will work satisfactorily with 75-ohm receiver inputs for the purposes outlined here.

Fig. 5-30—Inside view of the attenuator box. The resistors are mounted directly on the switch, using short pigtails wherever possible. Wide strips of copper are used for the input and output leads.

[1]—Andrade, "Recent Trends in Receiver Front-End Design, *QST*, June 1962.

[2]—*QST*, Gimmicks and Gadgets, Nov., 1967.

[3]—*QST*, Gimmicks and Gadgets, August 1967.

Fig. 5-31—Resistor networks for the attenuator are mounted on the switches and grounded to lugs held by the switches. Note that outer conductor of coaxial cable is fanned out and grounded either side of switch.

Standard-value ½-watt resistors are used in both assemblies. Both attenuators will give good results from the broadcast band through 30 Mc. Isolation between the attenuator sections is not good enough to make either unit particularly effective above 30 MHz.

Either attenuator can be used ahead of the receiver, or can be built into the receiver as an integral part of the circuit. Such a device is particularly useful ahead of receivers that do not have an r.f. gain control, such as simple regenerative receiving sets.

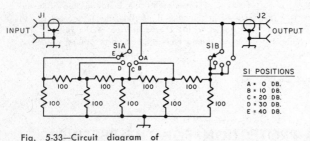

Fig. 5-32—Schematic of the attenuator. Resistance is in ohms. Resistors are ½-watt composition, 10% tolerance. S_1 is a phenolic rotary 1-section, 2-pole, 5-position switch. J_1 and J_2 are standard coax connectors. Approximate attenuation in decibels is given for each switch position.

SI POSITIONS

A = 0 DB.
B = 10 DB.
C = 20 DB.
D = 30 DB.
E = 40 DB.

Fig. 5-33—Circuit diagram of the step attenuator. All resistors are ½-watt composition. P_1, P_2—phono plugs, or similar. S_1–S_4—D.p.d.t. slide switch (Continental-Wirt or equiv.)

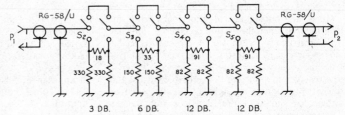

3 DB.   6 DB.   12 DB.   12 DB.

RECEPTION OF F.M. AND P.M. SIGNALS

Receivers for f.m. and p.m. signals differ from others principally in two features — there is no need for linearity preceding detection (in fact, it is advantageous if amplitude variations in signal and background noise can be "washed out"), and the detector must be capable of converting frequency variations in the incoming signal into amplitude variations.

Frequency- or phase-modulated signals can be received after a fashion on any ordinary receiver. The receiver is tuned to put the carrier frequency part-way down on one side of the selectivity curve. When the frequency of the sig-

nal varies with modulation it swings as indicated in Fig. 5-35A, resulting in an a.m. output varying between X and Y. This is then rectified as an a.m. signal.

With receivers having steep-sided selectivity curves, the method is not very satisfactory because the distortion is quite severe unless the frequency deviation is small, since the frequency deviation and output amplitude is linear over only a small part of the selectivity curve.

A detector designed expressly for f.m. or p.m. has a characteristic similar to that shown in Fig. 5-35B. The output is zero when the unmodulated

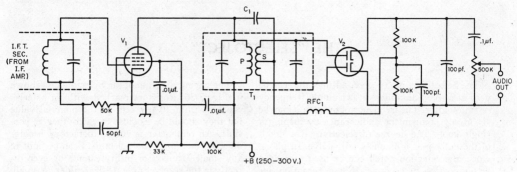

Fig. 5-34—Limiter-discriminator circuit.

C_1—About 500 ohms reactance at i.f.
T_1—Discriminator transformer for i.f. used. Push-pull diode transformer may be substituted.

RFC_1—High reactance at i.f.
V_1—Sharp-cutoff pentode.
V_2—Dual diode (6AL5).

carrier is tuned to the center, *0,* of the characteristic. When the frequency swings higher, the rectified output amplitude increases in the positive direction (as chosen in this example), and when the frequency swings lower the output amplitude increases in the negative direction. Over the range in which the characteristic is a straight line the conversion from f.m. to a.m. is linear and there is no distortion. One type of detector that operates in this way is the **frequency discriminator,** which combines the f.m.-

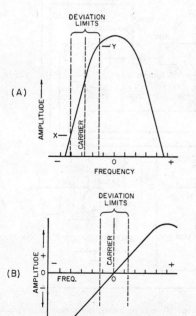

Fig. 5-35—F.m. or p.m. detection characteristics. A— "Slope detection," using the sloping side of the receiver's selectivity curve to convert f.m. or p.m. to a.m. for subsequent rectification. B—Typical discriminator characteristic. The straight portion of this curve between the two peaks is the useful region. The peaks should always lie outside the pass band of the receiver's selectivity curve.

to-a.m. conversion with rectification to give an a.f. output from the f.m. signal.

Limiter and Discriminator

A practical discriminator circuit is shown in Fig. 5-34. The f.m.-to-a.m. conversion takes place in transformer T_1, which operates at the intermediate frequency of a superheterodyne receiver. The voltage induced in the transformer secondary, S, is 90 degrees out of phase with the primary current. The primary voltage is introduced at the center tap on the secondary through C_1 and combines with the secondary voltages on each side of the center tap so that the resultant voltage on one side of the secondary leads the primary voltage and the voltage on the other side lags by the same phase angle, when the circuits are resonated to the unmodulated carrier frequency. When rectified, these two voltages are equal and of opposite polarity. If the frequency changes, there is a shift in the relative phase of the voltage components that results in an increase in output amplitude on one side of the secondary and a corresponding decrease in amplitude on the other side. Thus the voltage applied to one diode of V_2 increases while the voltage applied to the other diode decreases. The difference between these two voltages, after rectification, is the audio-frequency output of the detector.

The ouput amplitude of a simple discriminator depends on the amplitude of the input r.f. signal, which is undesirable because the noise-reducing benefits of f.m. are not secured if the receiving system is sensitive to amplitude variations. A discriminator is always preceded by some form of amplitude limiting, therefore. The conventional type of limiter also is shown in Fig. 5-34. It is simply a pentode i.f. amplifier, V_1, with its operating conditions chosen so that it "saturates" on a relatively small signal voltage. The limiting action is aided by grid rectification, with grid-leak bias developed in the 50,000-ohm resistor in the grid circuit. Another contributing factor is low screen voltage, the screen voltage-divider constants being chosen to result in about 50 volts on the screen.

THE "SELECTOJECT"

The Selectoject is a receiver adjunct that can be used as a sharp amplifier or as a single-frequency rejection filter. The frequency of operation may be set to any point in the audio range by turning a single knob. The degree of selectivity (or depth of the null) is continuously adjustable. In phone work, the rejection notch can be used to reduce or eliminate a heterodyne. In c.w. reception, interfering signals may be rejected or, alternatively, the desired signal may be picked out and amplified. The Selectoject may also be operated as a variable-frequency audio oscillator by advancing the "selectivity" control far enough in the selective-amplifier condition. The Selectoject is connected between the receiver headphone output connector and a pair of high-impedance headphones (4000-24,000 ohms). Its power requirement is only 2 ma. at 9 volts.

The wiring diagram of the Selectoject is shown in Fig. 5-36. Resistors marked with an asterisk can be within 10 per cent of the nominal value but they should be as close to each other as possible. An ohmmeter is quite satisfactory for doing the matching. The Selectoject can be built in any small Minibox or utility cabinet or even directly in the receiver as suits the builder. A small, self-contained transistor battery will easily power the unit.

In operation, overload of the receiver or the Selectoject should be avoided, or all the possible selectivity may not be realized.

The Selectoject is useful as a means of obtaining much of the performance of a "Q Multiplier" for a receiver lacking one. (*Built by Norman Posepanko, WA6KGP, and Walter Lange, W1YDS.*)

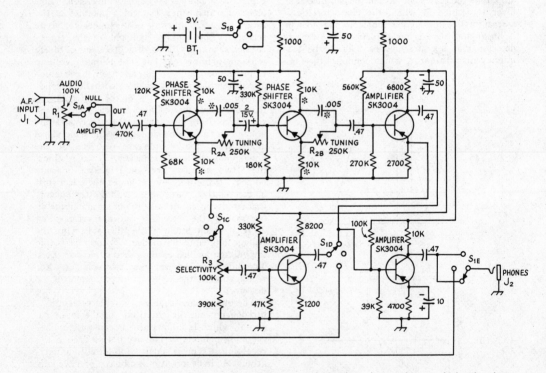

Fig. 5-36—Schematic diagram of Selectoject. Capacitors are rated 10 volts or better; those marked with polarity are electrolytic; capacitances are in microfarads (µf.) Unless specified otherwise, resistors are ½-watt, 10 per cent tolerance, resistances are in ohms. Resistors and capacitors marked with asterisk are matched as closely as possible.

BT₁—Nine-volt transistor battery (Eveready 216).
J₁—Phono jack.
J₂—Open circuit phone jack.
R₁—100,000-ohm control, audio taper (IRC CTS PQ13-128).
R₂—Ganged 250,000-ohm, linear taper potentiometers

(IRC CTS PQ11-130 with IRC CTS M11-130).
R₃—100,000-ohm control, linear taper (IRC CTS PQ11-128).
S₁—Five-pole 3-position ceramic rotary switch (Centralab PA-2015).

A SIMPLE AUDIO FILTER

Many receivers incorporate only one degree of selectivity, suitable for s.s.b. reception. Code reception can often be improved by the addition of an audio filter to the output of the receiver. The audio-filter circuit shown in Fig. 5-38 includes a power supply and an audio amplifier, and its use requires no change to the receiver itself. The tuned circuits, L_1C_2 and L_2C_3, use toroid transformers made for teletype units. These inexpensive inductors are available through several sources that advertise in *QST* Ham-Ads every month. If loudspeaker reception is not contemplated, T_1 can be omitted and the alternative output connection can be used.

Two degrees of selectivity are available. When S_3 is closed, two tuned circuits are active, and the bandwidth at 20 db. down is just a little over 100 Hz. With S_3 open, the bandwidth increase to about 1100 Hz. The peak frequency is about 750 Hz.

A $2 \times 5 \times 7$-inch chassis is sufficient to house the filter, or it might be built in a suitable Minibox. There is nothing very critical about the parts arrangement other than keeping the input and output circuits well isolated from each other. Machine screws $1\frac{1}{4}$ inches long, rubber grommets and washers can be used to hold the toroids.

With both tuned circuits working, the selectivity is extremely sharp, and some "ringing" will be apparent. This is perfectly normal, the inescapable result of confining the response to a narrow band of frequencies. If the ringing is considered excessive, try changing the value of C_3 slightly.

(From *QST*, December, 1966.)

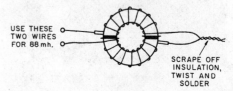

USE THESE TWO WIRES FOR 88 mh.

SCRAPE OFF INSULATION, TWIST AND SOLDER

Fig. 5-37—This drawing shows the method of connecting the windings of the 88-mh. toroid to obtain the required inductance.

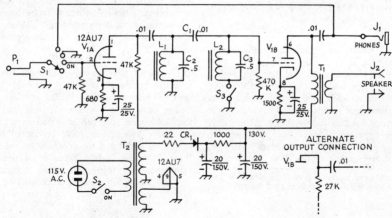

Fig. 5-38—Circuit diagram of the audio filter. All capacitances are in μf. Capacitors marked wth polarity are electrolytic. Resistances are in ohms; all resistors are ½-watt.

C_1—0.01 μf., disk ceramic.
C_2, C_3—0.5 μf., paper (see text).
CR_1—Silicon rectifier, 400 volts p.i.v. or more.
J_1—Headphone jack, open-circuit type.
J_2—Phone jack.
L_1, L_2—88-mh. toroid (see text).
P_1—Headphone plug.
S_1—Single-pole, four-position wafer switch, with a.c.

switch mounted on back (Centralab 1465 or similar).
S_2—See S_1.
S_3—Single-pole, single-throw toggle.
T_1—Output transformer, 10,000-ohm primary, 3.5-ohm secondary (Knight 54 A 1448 or equivalent).
T_2—Power transformer, 125 volts, 15 ma.; 6.3 volts, 0.06 amp. (Knight 54 A 1410 or equivalent).

A QRM FILTER FOR PHONE WORK

Audio filters are useful in reducing the level of unwanted energy which lies above and below the speech-frequency range used in communications work. The filter circuit of Fig. 5-40 rejects low-frequency rumble and high-frequency chatter, making phone reception somewhat less difficult during busy periods in the bands. The less selective the station receiver is, the more pronounced will be the effect of the Torofil.

The Circuit

The Torofil has a narrower passband than most audio filters. It is down 3 db. from peak output at 600 Hz. and again at 1900 Hz., and is reasonably flat in response from 700 to 1500 Hz. The low-frequency rolloff is very pronounced, being down some 10 db. at 500 Hz. This characteristic does not affect the intelligibility of a

Fig. 5-39—Parts arrangement inside the filter cabinet. The toroids are held in place by a long 6-32 screw, a washer, and a 6-32 hex nut. There is nothing critical about the layout.

impedance match between the filter and the 4-ohm terminations. The impedance of the filter at 1000 Hz. is approximately 500 ohms. This is a handy figure because it enables the builder to use standard 500-ohms-to-voice-coil transformers at T_1 and T_2.

S_1 has been included so the Torofoil can be taken out of the circuit at the operator's discretion. When it is switched to OUT, the filter elements are bypassed and normal operation is restored.

Construction

The circuit is built in a home-made box that measures $3 \times 5 \times 2$ inches. (A standard $3 \times 4 \times 5$ Minibox would allow ample room for all of the parts.) Rubber feet on the bottom cover of the box prevent damage to any equipment the filter is placed on.

The toroids are bolted to the chassis with $2\frac{1}{2}$-inch 6-32 machine screws. Plastic washers are used between the inductors, between the chassis and the inductor nearest the chassis, and between the remaining toroid and the metal washer that holds the assembly in place. The 6-32 toroid mounting bolt should have spaghetti tubing over it to prevent the bolt threads from damaging the insulation on the coil's windings. Use only enough tension to hold the inductors snugly in place.

Using the Filter

To install the Torofil disconnect the speaker from the receiver's voice-coil terminals then connect the filter in series with the speaker line.

For headphone operation a jack that matches the headphone plug can be wired in parallel with J_2. Some headphones have restricted frequency response, making it unnecessary to use an audio filter, but others—hi-fi types in particular—will reproduce everything that comes through the receiver's audio line. The Torofil will be a useful accessory when used with the latter.

phone signal, but it does impart a somewhat unnatural quality to it.

The Torofil is designed for use in 4-ohm speaker leads. The insertion loss is in the order of only 3 db., so no additional audio amplification is needed; most receivers have ample reserve gain to make up for the slight loss through the filter.

Telephone-type toroid inductors [1] are used for L_1 and L_2, Fig. 5-40. Transformers are used at the input and output of the filter to effect an

---

[1] These toroids are available from some electronic surplus outlets. Check the classified ads in *QST* for additional sources.

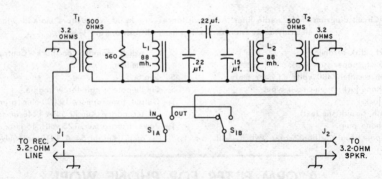

Fig. 5-40—Schematic of the audio filter. Capacitors are paper. The 560-ohm resistor is a ½-watt composition unit, and need not be included in the circuit. It was added experimentally to prevent "ringing," a condition that will not occur under normal circumstances.

J_1, J_2 — Phono connector.
L_1, L_2 — Telephone-style toroid inductor, 88 mh. If coil has 4 leads (2 windings), connect the windings in series.

S_1 — D.p.d.t. slide switch.
T_1, T_2 — 500-ohm to 3.2-ohm matching transformer (Stancor A-8101 or equivalent).

AN FET PRESELECTOR FOR 20, 15, AND 10

It is often necessary to put new life into tired old receivers, especially when operation is marginal on the three higher bands—14 through 30 MHz. A preselector of the type described here can pep up the front end of such receivers, while at the same time offering additional selectivity. The latter helps to reduce images, greatly improving reception on some of the low-cost receivers. Additional information on the construction of this unit, plus circuit-board layout data, is given in *QST*, August 1968.

Circuit Details

This preselector is completely self-contained, and no modifications are required in the receiver used. The circuit of the unit is shown in Fig. 5-42. The input circuit consists of L_1, L_2 and C_1. C_1 covers three bands, 20, 15 and 10, without bandswitching. An MPF104 field-effect transistor (FET) is used as a regenerative r.f. amplifier. By operating the transistor on the edge of self-oscillation maximum gain is obtained. Regeneration is controlled by C_2 and C_3. Output from the r.f. stage is fed to a source-follower, another MPF104. The source-follower serves to isolate the r.f. stage from the receiver front end. Without it, the r.f. stage might break into oscillation when the front-end tuning of the receiver is adjusted. Output from the follower is coupled to the receiver via C_7. S_1 serves to switch the unit into use, or to bypass it completely. Power is obtained from a 9-volt battery and total current drain is about 4 ma.

Constructional Information

The preamplifier was designed in such a way that it could be fitted into a $2\frac{1}{4} \times 2\frac{1}{4} \times 5$-inch Minibox. An etched-circuit board was used to mount all the components except C_1, C_2 and S_1. The circuit isn't critical at all; a bread board version with the components mounted on terminals on an insulated board will work just as well as the unit shown in the photo. If you decide on insulated-board type construction the only precaution you need observe is to mount the completed preamplifier in a metal box or enclosure to avoid stray signal feedthrough.

The only special items in construction are the two capacitors, C_1 and C_2. In order to keep the cost down two modified trimmer capacitors were used. As purchased, the trimmers have a screw adjustment. All that is required in the modification is to solder a length of $\frac{1}{4}$-inch diameter brass rod, 1 inch long, to the compression screw head. This provides a shaft that a knob can be mounted on. If your junk box happens to yield a couple of small variables with a maximum capacitance of 100 to 160 pf. these can be used for C_1 and C_2.

In soldering, whether or not you use an etched-circuit board or mount the components on tie points, always use a heat sink when soldering the transistor leads. Too much heat reaching the body of the transistor can ruin it.

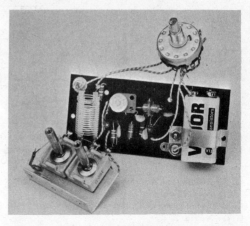

Fig. 5-41—At the left, on the circuit board, is the input coil combination L_1 and L_2. At the lower left is the mounting bracket for the two modified compression trimmers, C_1 and C_2. Just to the right of the coil assembly is C_3.

The two phono jacks, J_1 and J_2, are installed on the circuit board and the circuit board is mounted on the inside back of the Minibox. Two holes, large enough to clear the outside diameter of the phono jacks, were drilled in the back of the Minibox. In order to prevent the connections on the back of the etched board from being short-circuited, the board was mounted at each end with a $\frac{1}{8}$-inch spacer between the back of the board and the box. The two variables, C_1 and C_2, are mounted on an L-shaped bracket that measures $1\frac{1}{4}$ inches high and 2 inches long, with a $\frac{1}{2}$-inch wide foot. The bracket is mounted on the bottom of the Minibox and arranged so that the two capacitor shafts project out the front of the box by $\frac{5}{8}$ of an inch.

The battery, a 9-volt transistor radio type, is mounted on one end of the circuit board. Phono jacks, and L_1 and C_7 are connected to the appropriate switch terminals. S_1 is mounted on the front of the box.

Adjustment Procedures

When the unit is completed make up a length of coax, no longer than necessary to reach between the preamplifier and the receiver antenna terminal. Use either 50- or 70-ohm coax for this lead. Connect an antenna to J_1 and the unit is ready to test.

Turn the preselector on and tune the receiver to the 20-meter band, with the b.f.o. on. Tune C_1 through its range and listen for a loud rough note, indicating that the preselector is oscillating. If the unit doesn't oscillate, slowly decrease the capacitance of C_2 and go through the range of C_1 again. If you don't find a condition where the preamplifier oscillates, set C_2 at minimum capacitance and try another setting of C_3, retuning C_1 through its

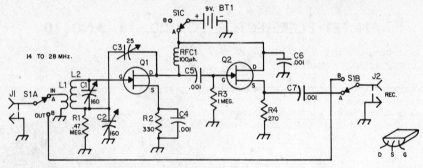

Fig. 5-42—Circuit diagram of the FET preselector. Resistances are in ohms; resistors are ½ watt. Fixed capacitors are disk ceramic. Circuit component designations not listed below are for etched circuit-board placement reference in QST.

C_1, C_2—160-pf. modified trimmer; see text (Miller 160-D, or similiar).

C_3—5-25-pf. trimmer (Erie NPO 5-25 or similar).

L_1, L_2—See Fig. 3.

Q_1, Q_2—Motorola MPF-104.

S_1—3-pole, 4-position wafer switch, 2 positions used (Mallory 3234J or similiar).

range. Once you find the setting of C_3, with C_2 at minimum capacitance, that makes the unit go into oscillation, slowly increase the capacitance of C_2 to the point where the oscillation stops. Under these conditions you should get a very pronounced increase in background noise or in signal strength from a signal tuned in, when C_1 is properly peaked. When you go to 15 meters, increase the capacitance of C_2 to prevent the unit from oscillating—likewise on 10 meters. However, no further adjustment of C_3 is required. While it isn't necessary to change the setting of C_2 when going across a band, C_1 should be repeaked when going from one end of a band to the other.

No doubt some readers may want to use this device with one of the transceivers that are on the market. If so, keep in mind that the preselector will *have* to be switched *out* of the antenna line when transmitting. Otherwise the transistors would be destroyed. If the transceiver has a sep-

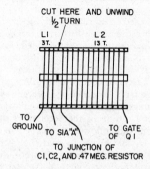

Fig. 5-43—This is the L_1L_2 coil assembly, made from a single length of B & W coil stock type 3007, ⅝-inch diameter, 16 turns per inch, No. 20.

arate receiving-antenna input, as some do, the preselector could be used without the necessity of being bypassed on transmitting.

A CRYSTAL-CONTROLLED CONVERTER FOR 20, 15 AND 10 METERS

The cure for most of the high-frequency ills of many receivers is the installation of a good crystal-controlled converter between the antenna and the receiver. The converter shown in Figs. 5-45 and 5-46 is intended to be used ahead of a receiver that tunes from 3.5 to 4.0 MHz. For example, on the 10-meter band, the 24.5 MHz. crystal heterodynes a 28.0-MHz. signal to 3.5 MHz., a 28.1-MHz. signal to 3.6 MHz., and so on. Used with a receiver that tunes the 80-meter band only, the 15- and 20-meter bands are covered with something left over, while only 500-kHz. segments of the 10-meter band can be covered without switching crystals.

Referring to Fig. 5-44, the converter consists of a 6BA6 r.f. amplifier and a triple-triode mixer, cathode follower and crystal oscillator. R.f. stage

gain is controlled by varying the cathode bias. The signal circuits, tuned by C_1 and C_2, cover 14 to 30 MHz. and are peaked by the operator for the band in use. Selector switch S_2 switches crystals and tuned circuits in the oscillator; on 10 meters the same tuned circuit is used with the two crystals. Mixer gain is improved by tuning the output with L_5, a broad setting that suffices for the 500-kHz. range. This converter is stable, and has good overall gain.

Construction

The converter is built on a 5 × 7 × 2-inch aluminum chassis. The 6BA6 socket is oriented so that pin 1 is closest to C_1, and the 6D10 socket should be arranged with pin 7 toward C_2. The most important wiring is at the 6BA6 socket.

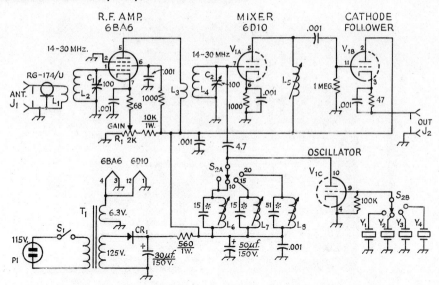

Fig. 5-44—Circuit diagram of the three-band crystal-controlled converter.

C₁, C₂—100-pf. midget variable (Hammarlund MAPC-1003).

CR₁—400 p.i.v. 750-ma. silicon diode.

J₁, J₂—Phono jack.

L₁—4 turns No. 20, ¾-inch diam., 16 t.p.i. (B&W 3011), ¼ inch from L₂.

L₂—9¾ turns No. 20, ¾-inch diameter, 16 t.p.i. (B&W 3011).

L₃—8½ turns No. 24, 1-inch diameter, 32 t.p.i. (B&W 3016).

L₄—8¼ turns No. 20, ¾-inch diameter, 16 t.p.i. (B&W 3011).

L₅—60-120 µh. (Miller 4511).

L₆—1.35-2.75 µh. (Miller 21A226RBI).

L₇—2.2-4.1 µh. (Miller 21A336RBI).

L₈—2.4-5.8 µh. (Miller 21A476RBI).

P₁—Fused line plug, ½-amp.

R₁—2000 ohms, linear taper, ½ watt (IRC Q11-110).

S₁—Part of R₁ (IRC 76-1).

T₁—125 v. at 50 ma., 6.3 v. at 2 amp.

Y₁—25.0 MHz. (International Crystal FA-9).

Y₂—24.5 MHz. (International Crystal FA-9).

Y₃—17.5 MHz. (International Crystal FA-9).

Y₄—10.5 MHz. (International Crystal FA-9).

Pin 2 and the center pin should be grounded to the chassis through a short lead. The 0.001-µf. cathode and screen bypass capacitors should be mounted over the socket, to provide further shielding for the grid and plate leads. Generous use throughout of tie points is advisable, so that both ends of resistors and capacitors will be supported.

Coils L_1 and L_2 are made from a piece of ¾-inch diameter 16 t.p.i. stock (B&W 3011 Miniductor). Space equivalent to 4 turns is left between the coils, by unwinding two turns in each direction from the point where the wire is cut. The near ends of L_1 and L_2 go to the outer conductor of the short length of RG-174/U and the rotor of C_1 respectively. The coils should be set in place parallel to the side wall of the chassis.

Coil L_4 is made of similar coil stock, and L_3 is made from larger stock (B&W 3016) that will slip over the smaller stock. For initial testing slip L_3 on to the ground end of L_4, so that the last turn of L_4 falls at the center of L_3. The outside end of L_3 (farthest from grid end of L_4) goes to the 6BA6 plate. L_3 and L_4 should be mounted parallel to the front of the chassis.

Fig. 5-45—"Backyard" view of the three-band converter. Simple construction (no panel) makes this unit easy to build. The r.f. amplifier tube is the miniature one at the right, just above the power transformer. The "Compactron" at the left is a triple triode, used as a mixer, cathode follower, and crystal-controlled oscillator. Converter output is in the 3.5-4.0-MHz. band.

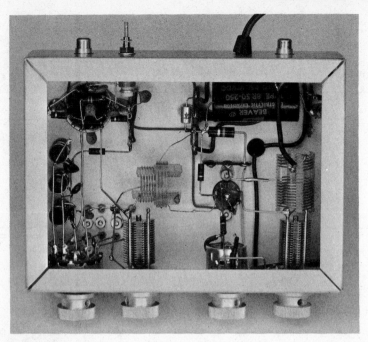

Fig. 5-46—The "works" of the converter are hidden beneath the chassis. Input circuit on right tunes 14 to 30 MHz. as does the mixer input at center. Coils are at right angles to avoid r.f.-stage oscillation. Coils at left are switched circuits for various crystals. Coil at upper left peaks mixer output for better overall gain.

Adjustment

When the wiring has been completed and checked, plug the tubes and crystals into their sockets and turn the adjustment screws of L_6, L_7 and L_8 so that the cores are as close to the chassis as possible. Use a length of coaxial line and suitable plugs to connect the output of the converter to the antenna terminals of the receiver. Plug in P_1 and turn on S_1. Monitor the oscillator action by temporarily measuring the voltage across the 1000-ohm resistor running to the base of L_6. Adjust each oscillator plate coil by setting S_2 to the proper point and then screw in the coil core until the voltage across the resistor takes a sudden rise. This indicates the stage has stopped oscillating. Back the core out at least a turn or two from this setting.

With an antenna connected to the converter, normal tuning of C_1 is sharp, while C_2 is less critical. The input circuit, L_1L_2, is intended for use with 50- or 75-ohm line from the antenna or antenna coupler. With a high-impedance antenna, such as a short wire, it is quite possible that the r.f. stage will oscillate; this is not an undesirable condition.

The coupling between L_3 and L_4 is best adjusted with a 68-ohm resistor temporarily connected at J_1. With R_1 set for maximum gain, swinging C_1 and C_2 around their maximum values should result in no r.f.-stage oscillation on 14 MHz. (Oscillation is indicated by harsh, rough sounds coming from the receiver, with the b.f.o. on.) Increasing the coupling by moving L_3 farther

on to L_4 should induce oscillation eventually; the desired setting is one that gives no oscillation. Check also on 21 and 28 MHz. When the converter is free from oscillation at maximum gain on every band, it may be found that removing the 68-ohm resistor will permit oscillation on one or more band. This is normal and nothing to worry about.

When a 10-meter signal is tuned in, the setting of C_2 may be exactly at minimum. If this occurs, the coupling between L_3 and L_4 will have to be reduced. When the tuning ranges of C_1 and C_2 have been checked, mark the tuning areas for ready reference, since the tuning is sharp. Finally, in the center of any band, peak L_5 on a signal.

Occasionally it may be found that the settings of C_1 and C_2 have no effect on the strength of an incoming signal. When this is the case, it is an 80-meter signal that is being copied. There are two ways the 80-meter signal can get through or around the converter. If the tunable receiver has a pair of terminals for the antenna connection, instead of a phono jack or coaxial receptacle, the signal may be getting in at the antenna terminals. If so, the solution is to provide better shielding at this point, by installing a phono jack or coaxial receptacle.

The second possibility is that an extremely strong signal can get through the converter by capacitive coupling through the coils and tubes. When this is the case, the signal can be minimized or eliminated by using a "wave trap" tuned to 80 meters.

A SIMPLE RECEIVER FOR THE BEGINNER

This battery-operated solid-state receiver will provide satisfactory general-coverage listening from 1.8 to 30 MHz. Battery operation makes it useful for portable work. Ham-band reception is satisfactory, making it possible to copy a.m., c.w., and s.s.b. signals without difficulty.

Circuit Information

Referring to Fig. 5-49, Q_1 is used in a tickler-coil type regenerative-detector circuit. The FET is used like a triode vacuum tube, the base element being like a grid, the drain acting as the plate, and the source serving like a cathode. C_1 is used to vary the antenna coupling and is set for the best sensitivity possible while still enabling Q_1 to oscillate freely (if too much coupling is used, the detector will not go into oscillation). C_3 is used for fine tuning (bandspread) and C_2 serves as a coarse-tuning control.

L_2, the tickler coil, provides feedback between the drain and base elements of Q_1 so that the detector can be made to regenerate (oscillate) when R_1 is set to increase the operating voltage on Q_1. If too few turns are used on L_2, if the spacing between L_1 and L_2 is too great, or if the polarity relationship between L_1 and L_2 is wrong,

Fig. 5-47—Beginner's solid-state receiver. The plug-in coils are at the left, plugged into a wooden base which serves as a coil rack. The battery pack is external.

the detector will not oscillate. Make sure that the coils are wound exactly as shown in Fig. 5-34.

Audio from the detector stage is taken from the drain circuit of Q_1 and routed through RFC_1 to AR_1, the IC audio amplifier. RFC_1 and its associated 560-pf. capacitors filter out any r.f. energy that may be present in the audio lead, thus preventing r.f. from reaching AR_1 and impairing its performance. The primary of T_1 is used as an audio choke, for coupling the a.f. signal to the following stage.

R_2 functions as an audio gain control and is adjusted for the desired headphone or loudspeaker level. R_3 is a bias resistor for AR_1 and can be obtained by placing two 1.2-ohm ½-watt resistors in parallel, or by winding approximately 6 feet of No. 30 enameled wire on a 1-megohm 1-watt resistor body—soldering the ends of the winding to the pigtails of the resistor—and using the wire's resistance for R_3.

Transformer T_2 matches the output impedance of AR_1 (125 ohms collector-to-collector) to a 4-ohm load such as a pair of low-impedance hi-fi phones or a 3.2-or 4-ohm speaker. A 10-ohm resistor is connected across J_3 to provide a constant load for AR_1 should the operator forget to plug in the speaker or phones when the set is turned on. Also, the resistor provides a mismatch safety factor when high-impedance phones are plugged directly into J_3, should the operator choose to do so. Hi-Z phones will work, but the audio output will be somewhat less because of the mismatch which will result. If hi-Z phones are used, better results will be had if a replacement tube-type output transformer of (2500- or 5000-ohm primary impedance, 4-ohm secondary) is used between the phones and J_3. The 4-ohm winding of the outboard transformer should plug into J_3 if this method is used.

Six size-D flashlight cells, series connected, provide the 9 volts that operate the receiver. Under no circumstances should the builder use a small 9-volt transistor battery, as the receiver

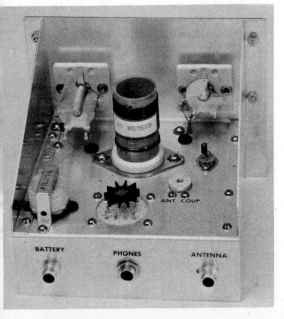

Fig. 5-48—Top-chassis view of the receiver. Q_1 is visible at the upper right, in front of the bandspread capacitor. The plug-in coil is at the center of the chassis, just to the left of Q_1. C_3, the main tuning capacitor, is at the left of the coil form. Output transformer T_2 is at the lower left of the chassis. AR_1 is just to the right of T_2, crowned by is radial-fin heat sink. J_1, J_2, and J_2 are on the rear lip of the chassis. C_1 is visible in the right foreground, ahead of, but between, the plug-in coil and Q_3.

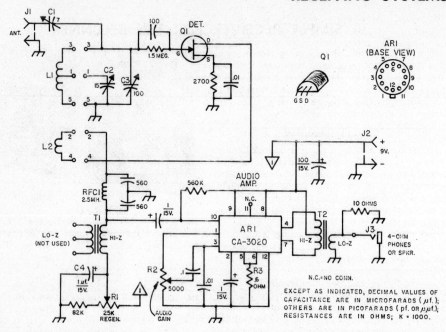

Fig. 5-49—Schematic of the GCR-2. Tapped-coil arrangement shown for L_1 is used on the 40-, 20-, and 10/15-meter coils Pin 1 connects directly to pin 3 of the coil form (inside the coil form by means of a jumper wire) for broadcast-band, 160-and 80-meter operation. There is no coil tap on these three bands. Fixed capacitors are disk ceramic. Polarized capacitors are electrolytic. Fixed resistors are ½-watt carbon.

AR_1—RCA CA-3020 integrated circuit.

C_1—1-5 to 7-pf. trimmer (Centralab 822-EZ used here. Elemenco 400 suitable and less costly, or make a "gimmick" capacitor by twisting two 1-inch lengths of insulated hookup wire together. Number of twists will determine degree of coupling).

C_2—15-pf. miniature variable (Millen 20015).

C_3—100-pf. miniature variable (Millen 20100).

J_1, J_2—Phono jack.

J_3—Two-conductor phone jack (Switchcraft type 11 suitable).

L_1, L_2—See Table 1.

Q_1—Motorola MPF-105 FET (MPF-102 or MPF-106 also suitable).

R_1—25,000-ohm linear-taper carbon control.

R_2—5000-ohm audio-taper carbon control.

R_2—See text.

RFC_1—2.5-mh. choke (Millen 34300-2500 or equivalent).

T_1—Any small transistor driver transformer with one winding of 10,000-ohms or greater. (Lo-Z winding not used.) Argonne AR-153 or similar.

T_2—Output transformer, primary 125 ohms c.t. to 4-ohm secondary (Argonne AR-174 or equal).

Knobs—Small knobs are Millen 10016. Large knobs with dial plates are Millen 1005-C.

drain will deplete it in a very short time. The battery is plugged into J_2 during operating periods. It should be unplugged when the receiver is not in use. *Make certain that the plus voltage connects to the center terminal of J_2.* The wrong battery polarity can immediately destroy Q_1 and AR_1.

Construction

The chassis and panel are homemade. The entire assembly, including the side brackets, was cut from an aluminum cookie sheet purchased from a local discount store. The stock used here is approximately ⅟₃₂ inch thick. The chassis was formed in a bench vise and measures 1½ × 4½ × 5 inches. A Bud CB-1629 open-end chassis can be used as a substitute (1½ by 4⅞ by 5¾ inches) if the builder wishes. The panel is 4½ inches high and 5¾ inches wide. If vernier dials are used with C_2 and C_3 a larger chassis and panel will be required, depending on the dimensions of the mechanisms used.

Side brackets prevent an annoying signal shift caused by mechanical instability when tuning the 20-, 15-, and 10-meter bands. They make tuning much easier on the higher bands.

AR_1 is mounted on a home-made terminal block. The IC is secured to a 1¼ by 1½-inch piece of perforated board into which 12 push-in terminals have been placed. The leads from AR_1 are soldered to the terminals on one side of the board and the circuit connections are made on the opposite side under the chassis. The IC assembly is centered over a 1⅛-inch diameter hole in the chassis. *Caution:* Use a heat sink each time a lead from AR_1 is soldered to a push-in terminal, or when soldering to the opposite ends of the push-in terminals. Heat can damage the IC. By grasping the leads with long-nose pliers, between the body of the IC and the point to be soldered, the heat will be drawn safely away.

RCA recommends the use of a heat sink on the case of AR_1 during operation at 9 volts. A

Wakefield Engineering NF-205 heat sink is shown in the photo; it is available from most wholesale outlets for approximately 30 cents. Any small heat sink that will fit a TO-5 transistor case can be used, however.

The plug-in coils are wound on Millen 45005 forms, which are 1⅝ inches high and have a diameter of 1 inch. The coils for the broadcast band and for 160-, 80-, and 40-meter reception are close-wound. The two high-band coils (8-30 Mc.) employ short lengths of air-wound (Miniductor) stock which are mounted inside the coil forms and cemented in place to assure good mechanical stability.

The builder may wish to experiment with the spacing between L_1 and L_2, or with the actual number of turns used for L_2, in the interests of smooth regeneration. The dimensions given here provide smooth operating conditions in this model, but may not be optimum in other versions because of FET characteristics. It is not essential for the builder to follow the layout to a fraction of an inch. The main consideration is that the r.f. leads be kept as short and direct as possible.

The completed coils should be coated with Q dope or Duco cement after they have been checked out in the receiver. This will tighten the windings and improve the overall stability of the receiver—important when tuning in weak c.w. or s.s.b. signals.

Testing and Operation

Initial checkout should start with a visual inspection of the completed unit, following the schematic diagram and tracing each lead to make sure the circuit is correctly wired. Look for mechanical short circuits caused by solder blobs or component leads that touch one another or the chassis. If all seems as it should be, the receiver can be given an on-the-air test.

Connect an antenna to J_1 and plug a pair of headphones into J_3. Next, connect the 9-volt battery pack to J_2. Turn R_1 toward maximum resistance until a "plop" is heard in the phones. This will indicate that Q_1 is going into oscillation. Tune C_3 until a c.w. signal is heard, then adjust R_2 for the desired listening volume. By varying the setting of the regeneration control, R_1, the pitch of the c.w. note can be changed. Also, the setting of R_1 will have a marked effect on the sensitivity of the receiver. The best setting for s.s.b. and c.w. reception is that which just permits Q_1 to go into oscillation. On very strong c.w. or s.s.b. signals it may be necessary to advance the setting of R_1 and make the detector oscillate

Fig. 5-50—Looking at the underside of the chassis, Q_1's socket is at the left, in front of R_1 and just to the left of the coil socket (Millen 33000 5-pin steatite). C_1 is just below the socket for Q_1 and connects to J_1 on the rear lip of the chassis by means of a short length of bare wire. R_2 is at the upper right, just ahead of T_1 and RFC_1. The homemade mount for AR_1 can be seen at the lower-center, directly under the phone jack, J_3.

slightly harder in order to get the required amount of beat-frequency signal. For a.m. reception R_1 should be adjusted to the point where oscillation just ceases. Changing the setting of R_1 will cause some shift in frequency, necessitating readjustment of the bandspread control.

By experimenting with the settings of C_1, a point should be found where a good compromise can be reached between good sensitivity and smooth regeneration. Its setting will depend upon the length of the antenna used, and the operating frequency. Generally, the longer the antenna the smaller will be the capacitance at C_1. If the builder does not have a doublet antenna available, an end-fed 50- or 100-foot length of wire will provide good results. An earth ground should be attached to the GCR-2 chassis for best results when short antennas are used.

The no-signal current drain of the receiver is approximately 25 ma. At high volume levels the circuit will draw as much as 250 ma. in the presence of strong signals.

ADAPTOR PLUG

The sketch shows an exploded view of an adaptor plug which adapts a conventional u.h.f. series connector for mating with a phono jack.

—*Robert J. Jarnutowski, K9ITS*

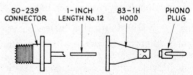

SO-239 CONNECTOR   1-INCH LENGTH No. 12   83-1H HOOD   PHONO PLUG

U.h.f. series-to-phono-plug adaptor.

THE MIGHTY-MIDGET RECEIVER

Somewhat more complex than the receiver just described, but easy for a beginner to build and get operating, this 80- and 40-meter tube-type receiver is suitable for use in a ham station. (From *QST*, April 1966.) For operation on the bands above 7 MHz., it can be used in combination with a simple crystal-controlled converter of the type described later in this chapter.

Circuit Details

Fig. 5-52 shows the circuit diagram of the two-band superhet. Three tubes are used in the unit, all are 6U8As. One advantage in using the same tubes for all functions is that you only need one spare tube not a variety of them. A 6U8 is actually two tubes in one envelope, a combination pentode-triode, so the receiver could be called a six-tube job.

The pentode section of V_{1A} is used as an r.f. amplifier. C_1 has sufficient range to cover both 80 and 40 meters so no bandswitching is required in either the r.f. or mixer stages. V_{2A} is the mixer with V_{2B} serving as the high-frequency (h.f.) oscillator. The intermediate frequency (i.f.) is 455 kHz. so the oscillator is operated at 455 kHz. above the signal frequency on both 80 and 40. Two tuning ranges are required in the h.f. oscillator and this is achieved by switching in the proper coil-capacitor combinations with S_1. Output from the h.f. oscillator is coupled to the cathode of the mixer. The mixer output at 455 kHz. is fed to a dual-crystal filter which provides excellent single-signal selectivity.

V_{3A} is the i.f. amplifier and output from T_1 is fed to the diode detector, CR_1. V_{1B} provides sufficient audio to run a pair of headphones. The phones are coupled to the plate of V_{1B} by L_6, the primary of an audio output transformer, and a 0.01-μf. capacitor. If 4- or 8-ohm phones are used, they should be connected to the voice-coil winding of L_6 for best results. If more audio output is desired, the builder can add another stage of amplification after V_{1B}. If this is done, L_6 and J_2 should be connected to the new (last) stage. A 47,000-ohm resistor would replace L_6 in the existing stage, V_{1B}. The new output stage could be a 6AV6, 6AT6, or a 6C4. The gain control, R_1, is in the cathode circuit of the r.f. stage. No audio gain control is required. V_{3B} is used for the beat-frequency oscillator (b.f.o.).

There is sufficient b.f.o. signal injection in V_{3A} without using a coupling capacitor, so none is used.

A half-wave rectifier, CR_3, is used in the power supply. The combination of C_3 and a 1000-ohm resistor provided adequate filtering. The voltage out of the filter is approximately 100.

Obtaining the Parts

Nearly all of the components used are standard items available from any of the mail-order houses. The homemade coils are wound on plastic pillboxes, $\frac{7}{8}$-inch diameter, $1\frac{1}{2}$-inches long. These

Fig. 5-51—The large vernier dial at the center of the panel is the main-tuning control. The on-off switch is at the lower left, the band switch at the lower center, and the gain control is at the lower right. A peaking control is directly above the gain control.

are obtainable from most drug stores for pennies and they make suitable coil forms.

Y_1 and Y_2 are surplus crystals. Any crystals in the range from 450 to 465 kHz. will be suitable. Good single-signal selectivity for c.w. reception is provided for with 454.166 kHz., Channel 327, and 453.704 kHz., Channel 45, crystals, approximately 400 Hz. separation. For phone reception, a Channel 327 and Channel 326, 452.777 kHz., made a good filter. This separation is approximately 1.4 kHz. In choosing your crystals, we would recommend about 400 Hz. separation for c.w., and about 1 kHz. for phone.

The dial and drive for the tuning capacitor is a National type AM, which provides a smooth action with no backlash. This dial costs a little more than some of the imported types, but the cost difference is well worthwhile.

Construction Tips

The cabinet is a Bud type AU1040HG. Unfortunately, there is no standard chassis that fits this cabinet. A chassis can be made up from a piece of aluminum cookie sheet, or from brass or copper. Fig. 5-52 gives the dimensions of the chassis.

We should point out that if you have a larger cabinet and chassis, there is no reason you have to duplicate *exactly* the unit shown in the photographs.

Refer to the top and bottom views when laying out the tube sockets and coils. Generally, construction isn't critical but one should avoid having any unnecessary coupling between the input and

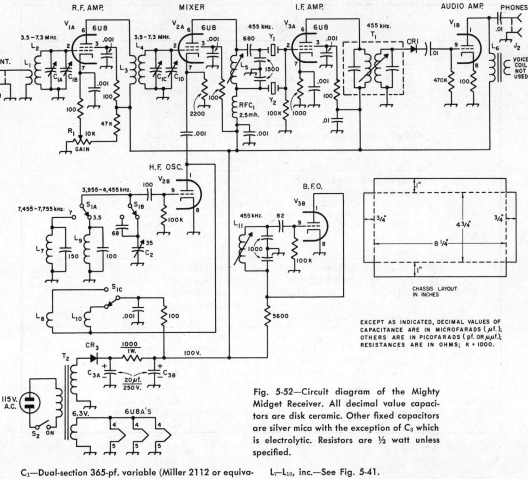

Fig. 5-52—Circuit diagram of the Mighty Midget Receiver. All decimal value capacitors are disk ceramic. Other fixed capacitors are silver mica with the exception of C_3 which is electrolytic. Resistors are ½ watt unless specified.

EXCEPT AS INDICATED, DECIMAL VALUES OF CAPACITANCE ARE IN MICROFARADS ($\mu f.$); OTHERS ARE IN PICOFARADS (pf. OR $\mu\mu f.$); RESISTANCES ARE IN OHMS; K = 1000.

C_1—Dual-section 365-pf. variable (Miller 2112 or equivalent). Sections B and D are trimmers furnished on capacitor.

C_2—35 pf. variable (Miller 19035).

$C_{3A, B}$—20 $\mu f.$, 250 volt electrolytic.

CR_1—1N34A germanium diode.

CR_3—Silicon rectifier, 400 volt p.i.v. minimum, 100 ma. (Barry Electronics 600/750).

J_1, J_2—Phono jacks.

L_1, L_3—5 turns wound directly below L_2 and L_4 respectively.

L_2, L_4—10 turns.

L_5, L_{11}—Approximately 300 $\mu h.$ slug-tuned (Miller 4411).

L_6—Standard type output transformer, any range from 2000 ohms to 10,000 ohms primary winding is suitable. Voice-coil winding not used.

L_7–L_{10}, inc.—See Fig. 5-41.

Note: L_1, L_2, L_3, L_4, L_7, L_8, L_9, L_{10} are all wound with No. 26 enamel wire, all turns are close spaced and are wound on plastic pill boxes, ⅞-inch diameter, 1½-inches long.

R_1—10,000 ohms, ½ watt control.

RFC_1—2.5 mh. R.f. choke.

S_1—3-Pole, 4-position rotary switch, 2 positions used (Mallory 3234J).

S_2—Single-pole, single-throw toggle.

T_1—I.f. transformer, output type, 455 kHz. (Miller 12-C2).

T_2—Power transformer, 125 v., 50 ma., 6.3 v., 2 amp. Chicago/Stancor PA-8421).

Y_1, Y_2—See text.

output of the crystal filter. This means between L_5 and the grid of V_{3A}. To much stray coupling will degrade the performance of the filter.

Coils and Coil Winding

When winding the coils, all turns must be put on the form in the same direction. For example, L_1 is the link, or antenna input coil and L_2 the secondary. L_1 consists of five close-spaced turns directly below L_2 and the two windings have no space between them. The turns should be put on in the same direction. L_3 and L_4 are duplicates of L_1 and L_2.

The other coils are for the high-frequency oscillator. Again, be sure that all coils are wound in the same direction. If the feedback windings, L_8 and L_{10} are not in the same direction as L_7 and L_9, the oscillator won't function.

COIL TABLE

Range (Mc.)	L_1	L_2	Tap
0.8–1.6	175 turns No. 36 enam. wire, close-wound.	25 turns No. 36 enam. close-would $\frac{1}{16}$ inch under L_1.	None
1.6–3.0	65 turns No. 30 enam. wire, close-wound.	6 turns No. 30 enam. wire, close-wound $\frac{1}{16}$ inch under L_1.	None
2.3–5.0	36 turns No. 30 enam. wire, close-wound.	3.5 turns No. 30 enam. wire, close-wound $\frac{1}{4}$ inch under L_1.	None
4.5–9.5	18 turns No. 20 enam. wire, close-wound.	$2\frac{1}{4}$ turns No. 20 enam. wire, close-wound $\frac{1}{4}$ inch under L_1.	9 turns
8.0–19	18 turns No. 18 bare wire, $\frac{5}{8}$ inch dia. by 1 inch long. (18-turn length of B&W Miniductor 3007, Air Dux 516T, or Polycoils 1736. Install inside coil form.	$2\frac{1}{2}$ turns No. 20 enam. wire, close-wound on outside of form, $\frac{1}{8}$ inch under ground end of L_1.	9 turns
16–30	$8\frac{1}{2}$ turns No. 18 bare wire, $\frac{5}{8}$-inch dia., 1 inch long. ($8\frac{1}{2}$ turns of B&W 3006 Miniductor stock, Air Dux 508T, or Polycoils 1734.	$2\frac{1}{2}$ turns No. 20 enam. wire, close-wound on outside of form, directly over ground end of L_1.	4 turns above ground end

All coil forms are Millen 45005 units. Coils that do not have a tap on L_1 should have a jumper wire connected between pins 1 and 3 inside the coil form. No other connection should go to pin 1 of such coils.

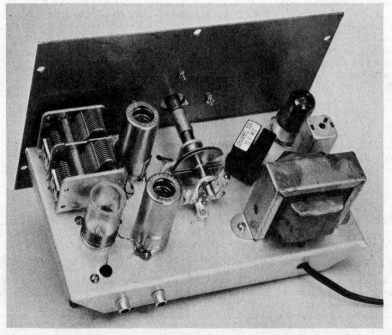

Fig. 5-53—This view shows the arrangement above deck. At the left is C_1 and L_1, L_2 coils just to the rear of the variable. The high-frequency oscillator tuning capacitor is at the center of the chassis.

Fig. 5-54—At the upper right on the panel is the r.f. gain control, R_1, and just to the rear of the control, the L_3 and L_4 coils. The output transformer L_6 is at the lower right and to its left is the socket for V_1. Directly behind the bandswitch, upper center, are the oscillator coils and the tube socket to its right is V_2. To the right of the octal socket used for holding the two crystals is L_5. At the upper left is the tube socket for V_3 and T_1 is just to the rear of the socket. The b.f.o. coil, L_{11}, is at the lower left.

The oscillator is designed to give 3500- to 4000-kHz. coverage on 80, and 7000 to about 7300 kHz. on 40. Because of stray capacitance or differences in wiring between your unit and the one described here, you may find that you don't get exactly the same coverage. If either band tunes too low in frequency you can move the oscillator frequency up by removing turns from L_7 or L_9, whichever band requires it. Only remove about ½ turn of wire at a time and remove the wire from the top of the coil, not at the point where the winding is next to the feedback winding. If the oscillator is tuning too high, add a half turn or so.

Tune-up Adjustments

In order to tune up the receiver a signal source will be needed. A transmitter or a grid-dip meter will provide an adequate signal for adjustment. Use a dummy load on the transmitter, such as a light bulb. If you have a d.c. voltmeter available capable of reading 150 volts, there are a few checks you can make before actually aligning the unit. Turn on the power, and first check to make sure the filaments in all the tubes are lit. If something starts to smoke, turn the receiver off ! You can usually spot the component that is getting hot and check the wiring around that portion of the circuit to make sure nothing is shorted. Assuming the heaters light up and there is no smoke, you

can make voltmeter checks to make sure the wiring is all complete. Check at the output side of the power supply to see if the voltage is about 100 volts. Next, check the plate and screen of each pentode section and the plate of each triode section

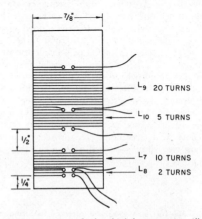

Fig. 5-55—Drawing of the high-frequency oscillator coils. All coils are wound with No. 26 enamel wire. The holes drilled in the coil form to hold the windings are 1/16th inch diameter. The same method is used in making the r.f. and mixer coils.

to see if the voltage is present. If there is a terminal or tube pin where there should be $+B$ and there isn't, check the wiring for open connections or a cold solder joint.

Assuming that everything checks out all right, tune up the transmitter on 80-meters, switch the receiver bandswitch S_1 to 80, and tune in the signal. You'll find that C_1 will peak with the plates about one-third meshed. You may hear the background noise peak up when tuning C_1. However, there should be enough pickup from the transmitter signal for you to hear it. Aligning the receiver is quite simple. With C_1 peaked, adjust the slug in the b.f.o. coil to the point where you hear an audio beat. Next, peak the slug in L_5 for maximum signal. At some point, you'll have to reduce the signal input because it will become too strong. You can move the transmitter away from the receiver—across the room or even into the next room. Also, reduce the r.f. gain control, R_1, to where the signal is just barely audible. Next, peak the top and bottom slugs in T_1, the i.f. transformer. At this point, one should be able to hear on-the-air signals. Put an antenna on the receiver and tune in an outside signal. Go back and forth over all the adjustments until you get the strongest possible peaking on the signal.

If you cannot hear any signal recheck your wiring to make sure there are no errors. Make sure the high-frequency oscillator is working. If you have one, or can borrow another receiver that tunes between 4 and 5 MHz. and 7.3 and 8, listen for the oscillator signal in the receiver. With the two receivers side by side, you should be able to hear the oscillator signal. Also, if you have an absorption wavemeter or a grid-dip meter couple either to the high-frequency oscillator coil, L_7, and you should get an indication when the wavemeter or grid-dipper is tuned to the oscillator range. Remember, the oscillator works at about 405 kHz. *above* the received signal range.

The Miller 2112 consists of two 365-pf. variables, C_{1A} and C_{1C}, and in parallel with each of these is a 3-30 pf. trimmer capacitor, C_{1B} and C_{1D}. Because the r.f. and mixer stages are gang-tuned, it is possible they won't track perfectly. However, the adjustment is quite simple. First, tune in a signal near the high end of the 3.5-MHz. band and peak C_1 for best signal strength. With the trimmer at maximum capacitance (the adjustment screws turned all the way down), slowly unscrew the trimmer across the r.f. stage while listening to the signal. At one point there may be a slight peak in the signal strength. If so, leave the trimmer at that setting. Do the same with the trimmer across the mixer capacitor.

Tune in the phone-band range until you hear an s.s.b. signal. In s.s.b., there is no carrier transmitted. *You* provide the carrier at your receiver, and in this case it is the b.f.o. signal. If the b.f.o. signal isn't in the correct relation to the incoming s.s.b. signal, the received signal will be garbled and almost impossible to copy. To adjust the b.f.o., reduce the r.f. gain control so that the incoming signal isn't too strong and then by carefully tuning C_1, the main tuning control and the slug in the b.f.o. coil, you should find a setting where the s.s.b. signal becomes good copy. Once you find that setting leave the b.f.o. slug alone. It will work equally well at that setting for c.w. and s.s.b.

AN ADVANCED 6-TUBE RECEIVER

This equipment is basically an 80-meter receiver, with crystal-controlled converters included for the bands 40 through 10 meters. It is an adaptation of the W1DX HB-67 receiver. This combination gives maximum frequency stability without complication. Considering first the basic 80-meter receiver, there are two tuned circuits between the antenna and the 7360 mixer grid. These are ganged with the 6C4 oscillator tuning to tune 3.5 to 4.1 MHz.; alignment of the ganged tuning is simplified through the use of adjustable inductors. A mechanical filter follows the mixer, providing good selectivity for s.s.b. reception. Its 2.0-kHz. bandwidth is more than optimum for code reception, but even so its excellent skirt selectivity will provide better protection against strong c.w. signals several kHz. away than anything except a narrower bandpass filter.

Fig. 5-56—This is a five-band receiver featuring a mechanical filter for selectivity. A two-speed dial (Miller MD-8) is fast enough for quick jumps around the band and slow enough for ease in tuning s.s.b. Audio-derived fast-attack slow-decay a.g.c. also contributes to ease of tuning.

Toggle switch to the right of the meter turns a.g.c. on. Two knobs below control i.f. gain and antenna tuning; bottom row controls audio gain, band switch, b.f.o., and A.C. on and off. The receiver is enclosed in a home-made aluminum cabinet.

Fig. 5-57—Top view of the receiver. Antenna jack, audio-output jack, and S-meter control are on rear apron of chassis. Note mechanical filter at right. The i.f. strip (7360 mixer, filter, 6BA6s, i.f. transformers and b.f.o. transformer) is built on a center line 5 inches from the front panel. Tunable oscillator, 6C4, is at right near panel; b.f.o. and a.g.c. V_2 can be seen in front of power transformer (near left).

The filter is followed by two i.f. amplifier stages, and the 455-kHz. section ends in a diode detector and a b.f.o. Audio gain and output are obtained from the triode and pentode sections of a 6T9 "Compactron." An audio-derived a.g.c. system is included; the a.g.c. voltage is applied to the two i.f. amplifier stages. When the a.g.c is applied, an "S meter" is switched in that monitors the cathode voltage of one of the i.f. stages. The a.g.c. is "fast attack, slow decay," well suited for s.s.b. and code reception. No envelope detector or carrier-derived a.g.c. is included; a.m. reception is obtained by treating an a.m. signal as an s.s.b. signal, and tuning to zero beat with the carrier.

The crystal-controlled converter section of the receiver is similar to the converter shown elsewhere in this chapter. However, it switches coils for each range rather than tuning several bands with a single coil. When tuning the 7-MHz. band, the "band tunes backwards" (7.0 MHz. is at 4.1 MHz., 7.1 is at 4.0, and so on), because an 11.1-MHz. crystal is used. To make it "tune right"

would require a 3.5-MHz. crystal, which would put a strong second-harmonic signal at 7.0 MHz. The slight inconvenience, or novelty, of the band tuning backward is quickly accepted, however.

The power supply uses a bridge silicon rectifier for the positive voltages. A negative voltage for the manual gain-control circuit is obtained from a voltage-doubling rectifier and the 6.3-volt heater supply.

Construction

The equipment is built on a 10 × 12 × 3-inch chassis. A ⅛-inch thick panel measures 8 × 14 inches. The panel is held to the chassis by the audio gain control, bandswitch and b.f.o. extension shaft bushings, and by the small screws that hold the tuning dial face.

Referring to Fig. 5-60, a strip of aluminum serves as a shield across the chassis. The strip also serves to reinforce the chassis and make it less susceptible to shock and vibration. It is held to the chassis at five points with 6-32 hardware.

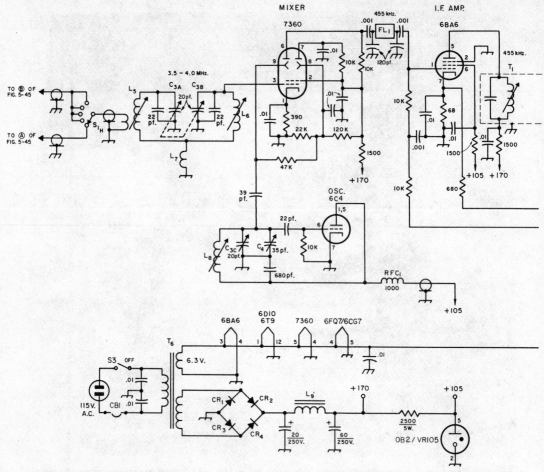

Fig. 5-58—Circuit diagram of the 80-meter and i.f. sections of the 6-tube receiver. Unless specified otherwise, all resistors are ½ watt, all capacitances are in μf. Capacitors marked with polarity are electrolytic; capacitors with values in pf. are silver mica or NP0 ceramic.

COIL TABLE

All primaries wound with No. 30 Nylclad or Formvar wire. Coils are closewound, starting at collar nearest mounting end of coil form.

	7 MHz.	14 MHz.	21 MHz.	28 MHz.
L_1	6.5 - 12:5 μh. (Miller 41A105CBI), shunted by 39 pf. Primary, 3⅜ t.	2.0 - 4.1 μh. (Miller 41A336CBI) Primary, 2⅛ turns.	1.2 - 1.9 μh. (Miller 41A156CBI) Primary, 1⅝ turns.	0.7 - 1.3 μh. (Miller 41A106CBI) Primary, 1¼ turns.
L_2	Same as L1, shunted by 39 pf. Primary, 15⅛ turns.	Same as L1. Primary, 14⅛ turn.	Same as L1. Primary 11⅛ t.	Same as L1. Primary 10⅛ t.
L_4	3.6 - 5.6 μh (Miller 20A476RBI	3.6 - 5.6 μh. (Miller 20A476RBI)	1.6 - 2.6 μh. (Miller 20A226RBI)	1.6 - 2.6 μh. (Miller 20A226RBI)
C_2	43 pf.	51 pf.	33 pf.	15 pf.
Y_1	11.100 MHz.	10.500 MHz.	17.500	24.500 MHz.

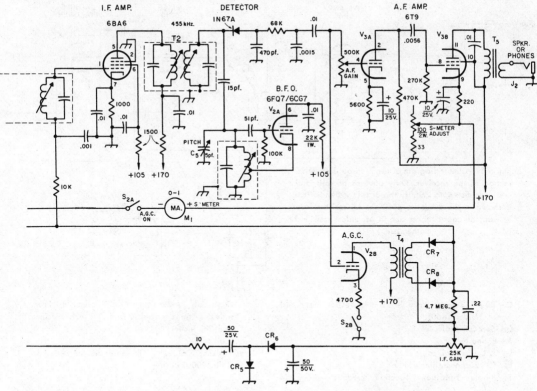

C_3—3-gang variable, 20 pf. per section (Miller 1460).

C_4—35-pf. midget variable (Millen 25035E).

C_5—2-plate variable (Millen 20015 with one rotor and two stator plates removed).

CB_1—2-amp. thermal breaker (Sylvania MB-316 Mite-T Breaker).

CR_1-CR_4—400 p.i.v. 750-ma. silicon.

CR_5-CR_8—200 p.i.v. 750-ma. silicon.

FL_1—455-kHz. mechanical filter, 2-kHz. bandwidth. (Collins 455-FB-21).

J_2—Phone jack.

L_5—26-41 μh. (Miller 41A335CBI) with 4½ turn primary.

L_6—26-41 μh. (Miller 41A335CBI).

L_7—1⅜ inches No. 22 wire. See text.

L_8—25-28 μh. (Miller 43A475CBI).

L_9—7—henry, 150-ma. filter choke.

M_1—0-1 milliammeter.

S_1—See Fig. 5-45.

S_2—D.p.s.t. toggle switch.

S_3—S.p.s.t (part of audio gain cont.).

T_1, T_2—455-kHz. i.f. transformer, interstage (Miller 1312-C2).

T_3—455-kHz. b.f.o. assembly (Miller 1727).

T_4—10K primary to 40K push-pull grids.

T_5—5K to voice coil, 40-ma. primary. (Stancor A-3877).

T_6—135 v. at 200 ma., 6.3 v. at 5.5 amp. (Triad R73B).

The end of the bandswitch is bolted to the shield, and the b.f.o. tuning capacitor is mounted alongside.

The tuning capacitors, C_1 and C_3, have three tapped holes for securing them to the chassis. Small washers were used between the chassis and the capacitors, for reasons that are obvious when one has the capacitor in hand. Care spent in aligning C_3 and the tuning dial will be well repaid in a smooth-tuning receiver. Check alignment by loosening the set screws on the insulating coupler; turning the dial should not cause the capacitor to turn.

Coils L_5 and L_6 are mounted ⅝ inch (center to center) apart. A common connection is made between the terminals nearest the mounting ends of the coil forms. From the center of this common

connection a 1⅜-inch length of No. 22 wire is run to a soldering lug under the rear screw for C_3. The inductive coupling between the coils consists of the coupling through their proximity plus the common inductance furnished by the short length of wire.

The power transformer, T_6, is mounted above the chassis on 1-inch long threaded round brass spacers, a catalog item. Mounting the transformer above the chassis saves having to cut a rectangular hole in the chassis, and it gives more room below the chassis. The rectangular hole for the mechanical filter was cut with a nibbling tool.

Multiple tie points are used in several spots as "sub assemblies," wired before being installed in the receiver. These include the four diodes in the power supply bridge rectifier, the gain-control

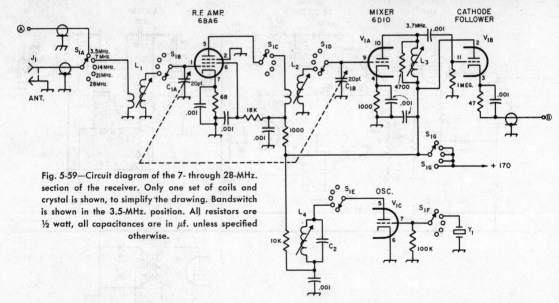

Fig. 5-59—Circuit diagram of the 7- through 28-MHz. section of the receiver. Only one set of coils and crystal is shown, to simplify the drawing. Bandswitch is shown in the 3.5-MHz. position. All resistors are ½ watt, all capacitances are in μf. unless specified otherwise.

C_1—20-pf. 3-gang variable, center section not used (Miller 1460).*

C_2—See coil table.

J_1—Phono jack.

L_1, L_2, L_4—See coil table.

L_3—60-120 μh. (Miller 4511).

S_1—8-pole 5-position 4-section ceramic rotary (4

Centralab PA-32 with PA-301 assembly). From index, sections spaced ¼ inch, 1¼ inch, 2¼ inch and 2¾ inches.

Y_1—See coil table.

* J. W. MILLER CO., 5917 S. Main St., Los Angeles, Calif. 90003.

bias supply, the a.g.c. rectifier assembly, and the detector and its associated filter.

To wind the primaries on L_5 and the various L_{1S} and L_{2S}, first cover the manufactured winding with a layer of Scotch tape. Thread the No. 30 wire through a hole in the collar nearest the mounting end of the coil form, and closewind the required number of turns toward the manufactured coil. Run the end of the wire through another hole and pull the winding tight. To finish off the coil, cover the primary winding with a strip of Scotch tape. All of the coils can be made single layer except the primary of the 7-MHz. L_2; here there isn't enough room for the turns without doubling up toward the finish.

Wiring can be kept neat by using small-diameter insulated wire for all of the d.c. and 60-Hz. a.c. wiring. Use RG-174 for all coaxial or shielded wiring. Signal-carrying r.f. and i.f. wiring is made as direct as possible. The 6BA6 r.f. and i.f amplifiers should have the center socket pins grounded. Run d.c. and other non-signal wiring along the sides of the chassis. Long audio runs, as to the audio gain control (500K potentiometer) should be in RG-174.

If the power supplies are wired first, followed by the audio amplifier and other portions of the 80-meter section, the receiver can be tested as one progresses. This makes it much easier to spot a wiring error.

Alignment

The alignment of the i.f. amplifier is simplified if a signal generator or other signal source is available. The b.f.o. is set at 455 kHz. (can be checked by listening for its second harmonic in the broadcast band), after which the i.f. transformers are peaked. Always work with the a.g.c. switched off and with as little signal input as convenient.

The oscillator tuning range should be set for 3.945 to 4.565 MHz. This can be done while listening for the oscillator on a general-coverage receiver, or it can be done a little more laboriously by adjusting the receiver tuning range to 3.49 to 4.11 MHz. The oscillator tuning range is controlled by setting L_8 at the low-frequency end (C_3 meshed) and setting C_4 at the high-frequency end of the range (C_3 unmeshed).

Once the oscillator range is set, the tracking of the input circuit should be checked. At the low-frequency end, tune in a signal and peak L_5 and L_6. Tune up to around 4.1 MHz. and peak the mica trimmers on C_{3A} and C_{3B}. Go back to 3.5 MHz. and check the settings of the cores in L_5 and L_6. After a few tries it will be found that neither the low-frequency inductor settings nor the high-frequency trimmer settings improve the signal. If a v.t.v.m. with r.f. probe is available, the r.f. voltage at the stator of C_4 will run about 2 to 5 volts across the range.

Fig. 5-60—View underneath the chassis shows the reinforcement/shield running the width of the chassis. The smaller shield near the front panel is held in place by one of the screws on the socket of the 6BA6 r.f. amplifier. Transformer tucked away at upper left is T_4, in the a.g.c. circuit.

With no antenna connected, switching to a.g.c. one should find that the tuning-meter reading changes with the i.f. gain control setting. The reading should be at zero when the gain control is almost fully advanced (maximum gain).

When the gain control is fully retarded, the meter reading should be about 0.9, and with the first i.f. amplifier tube removed from its socket, the meter reading should be 1.0. The S-meter zero-adjust control can be set for the desired reading.

Connecting an antenna and tuning the 80-meter band, the receiver should have good single-signal c.w. characteristics (if the b.f.o. is properly offset) and similarly good s.s.b. receiving qualities. The a.g.c. has a fast attack and a slow decay; it is useful on both code and sideband reception, but it may take a little "getting used to." If it holds in too long for a particular operator, the hold time can be decreased by substituting 0.1 μf. for the 0.22 μf. shown in Fig. 5-58.

Aligning the crystal-controlled portion of the receiver is quite straightforward. For any given band, crystal oscillation can be checked by using an r.f. probe with a v.t.v.m., a sensitive absorption

wavemeter, or by noting the rise in voltage at the plate supply end of the active L_4 as its iron core is withdrawn. L_1 and L_2 are peaked on a signal (or signal generator) in the band. Although C_{1A} and C_{1B} (the outside capacitors of the 3-gang unit) have different minimum capacitances (one has no trimmer) the tuning range is great enough so that no lack of tracking is encountered on the band in use.

On the 10-meter and 40-meter ranges, the ungrounded ends of L_2 and L_4 are connected by 4.7-pf. capacitors. However, on 20 and 15 meters the stray coupling within V_1 provides sufficient injection. Proper sensitivity is indicated on these bands by rotating C_1 with a 68-ohm resistor temporarily connected across J_1. On each band an increase in noise should be detected as C_1 is tuned through resonance, sufficient to wiggle the tuning meter.

The resistor across L_3 is included to reduce the converter gain and make the tuning meter usable on all bands. If it is omitted the amplified antenna noise from the converter will hold the tuning meter at half scale or better, rendering the meter practically useless.

Chapter 6

Oscillators, Multipliers and Power Amplifiers

Regardless of the transmission mode—code, a.m., single sideband, radioteletype, amateur TV—vacuum tubes and semiconductors are common elements to the transmitters. They are used as oscillators, amplifiers, frequency multipliers and frequency converters. These four building blocks, plus suitable power supplies, are basically all that is required to make any of the popular transmission systems.

The simplest code transmitter is a keyed oscillator working directly into the antenna; a more elaborate (and practical) code transmitter will include one or more frequency-multiplication stages and one or more power-amplifier stage. Any code transmitter will obviously require a means for keying it. The bare skeleton is shown in Fig. 6-1A. The r.f. generating and amplifying sections of a double-sideband 'phone transmitter (a.m. or f.m.) are similar to those of a code transmitter.

The over-all design depends primarily upon the bands in which operation is desired, and the power output. A simple oscillator with satisfactory frequency stability may be used as a transmitter at the lower frequencies, but the power output obtainable is small. As a general rule, the output of the oscillator is fed into one or more amplifiers to bring the power fed to the antenna up to the desired level.

An amplifier whose output frequency is the same as the input frequency is called a **straight amplifier**. A **buffer amplifier** is the term sometimes applied to an amplifier stage to indicate that its primary purpose is one of isolation, rather than power gain.

Because it becomes increasingly difficult to maintain oscillator frequency stability as the frequency is increased, it is most usual practice in working at the higher frequencies to operate the oscillator at a low frequency and follow it with one or more **frequency multipliers** as required to arrive at the desired output frequency. A frequency multiplier is an amplifier that delivers output at a multiple of the exciting frequency. A **doubler** is a multiplier that gives output at twice the exciting frequency; a **tripler** multiplies the exciting frequency by three, etc. From the viewpoint of any particular stage in a transmitter, the preceding stage is its **driver**.

As a general rule, frequency multipliers should not be used to feed the antenna system directly, but should feed a straight amplifier which, in turn, feeds the antenna system.

Good frequency stability is most easily obtained through the use of a **crystal-controlled oscillator**, although a different crystal is needed

for each frequency desired (or multiples of that frequency). A **self-controlled oscillator** or **v.f.o.** (variable-frequency oscillator) may be tuned to any frequency with a dial in the manner of a receiver, but requires great care in design and construction if its stability is to compare with that of a crystal oscillator.

In all types of transmitter stages, screen-grid tubes have the advantage over triodes that they require less driving power. With a lower-power exciter, the problem of harmonic reduction is made easier.

The best stage or stages to key in a code transmitter is a problem by itself, to be discussed in a later chapter. An f.m. transmitter (Fig. 6-1B) can only be modulated in the oscillator stage; a closely-allied type of transmitter (phase-modulated) can be modulated in a multiplier or amplifier stage. An a.m. 'phone transmitter, Fig. 6-1C, can only be modulated in the output stage, unless the modulated stage is followed by a linear amplifier. However, following an amplitude-modulated stage by a linear amplifier is an inefficient process, convenient as an expedient but not recommended for best efficiency.

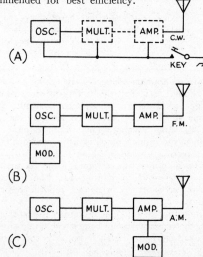

Fig. 6-1—Block diagrams showing the types of transmitters that typically use frequency multipliers followed by power amplifiers. The code transmitter (A) may or may not include multipliers and amplifiers. An f.m. transmitter must be modulated in the oscillator stage and is usually followed by several multiplier stages before the output amplifier. An a.m. 'phone transmitter is most efficient when modulated in the output stage, although it can be modulated in the driver stage and use a following linear amplifier on the same frequency.

Following the generation of a single-sideband 'phone signal, its frequency can be changed only by frequency conversion (not multiplication), in exactly the same manner that signals in a receiver are heterodyned to a different frequency.

CRYSTAL OSCILLATORS

The frequency of a crystal-controlled oscillator is held constant to a high degree of accuracy by the use of a quartz crystal. The frequency depends almost entirely on the dimensions of the crystal (essentially its thickness); other circuit values have comparatively negligible effect. However, the power obtainable is limited by the heat the crystal will stand without fracturing. The amount of heating is dependent upon the r.f. crystal current which, in turn, is a function of the amount of feedback required to provide proper excitation. Crystal heating short of the danger point results in frequency drift to an extent depending upon the way the crystal is cut. Excitation should always be adjusted to the minimum necessary for proper operation.

Crystal-Oscillator Circuits

The simplest crystal-oscillator circuit is shown in Fig. 6-2A. An equivalent circuit is shown in Fig. 6-2B, where C_4 represents the grid-

the oscillator itself is not entirely independent of adjustments made in the plate tank circuit when the latter is tuned near the fundamental frequency of the crystal, the effects can be satisfactorily minimized by proper choice of the oscillator tube.

The circuit of Fig. 6-3A is known as the Tritet. The oscillator circuit is that of Fig. 6-2C. Excitation is controlled by adjustment of the tank L_1C_1, which should have a low L/C ratio, and be tuned considerably to the high-frequency side of the crystal frequency (approximately 5 Mc. for a 3.5-Mc. crystal) to prevent over-excitation and high crystal current. Once the proper adjustment for average crystals has been found, C_1 may be replaced with a fixed capacitor of equal value.

The oscillator circuit of Fig. 6-3B is that of Fig. 6-2A. Excitation is controlled by C_9.

The oscillator of the grid-plate circuit of Fig. 6-3C is the same as that of Fig. 6-3B, except that the ground point has been moved from the cathode to the plate of the oscillator (in other words, to the screen of the tube). Excitation is adjusted by proper proportioning of C_6 and C_7.

When most types of tubes are used in the circuits of Fig. 6-3, oscillation will stop when the output plate circuit is tuned to the crystal fre-

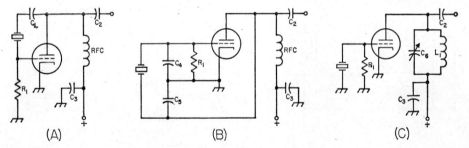

Fig. 6-2—Simple crystal oscillator circuits. A—Pierce. B—Equivalent of circuit A. C—Simple triode oscillator. C_1 is a plate blocking capacitor, C_2 an output coupling capacitor, and C_3 a plate bypass. C_4 and C_5 are discussed in the text. C_6 and L_1 should tune to the crystal fundamental frequency. R_1 is the grid leak.

cathode capacitance and C_5 indicates the plate-cathode, or output capacitance. The ratio of these capacitors controls the excitation for the oscillator, and good practice generally requires that both of these capacitances be augmented by external capacitors, to provide better control of the excitation.

The circuit shown in Fig. 6-2C is the equivalent of the tuned-grid tuned-plate circuit discussed in the chapter on vacuum-tube principles, the crystal replacing the tuned grid circuit.

The most commonly used crystal-oscillator circuits are based on one or the other of these two simple types, and are shown in Fig. 6-3. Although these circuits are somewhat more complicated, they combine the functions of oscillator and amplifier or frequency multiplier in a single tube. In all of these circuits, the screen of a tetrode or pentode is used as the plate in a triode oscillator. Power output is taken from a separate tuned tank circuit in the actual plate circuit. Although

quency, and it is necessary to operate with the plate tank circuit critically detuned for maximum output with stability. However, when the 6AG7, 5763, or the lower-power 6AH6 is used with proper adjustment of excitation, it is possible to tune to the crystal frequency without stopping oscillation. The plate tuning characteristic should then be similar to Fig. 6-4. These tubes also operate with less crystal current than most other types for a given power output, and less frequency change occurs when the plate circuit is tuned through the crystal frequency (less than 25 cycles at 3.5 Mc.).

Crystal current may be estimated by observing the relative brilliance of a 60-ma. dial lamp connected in series with the crystal. Current should be held to the minimum for satisfactory output by careful adjustment of excitation. With the operating voltages shown, satisfactory output should be obtained with crystal currents of 40 ma. or less.

In these circuits, output may be obtained at multiples of the crystal frequency by tuning the plate tank circuit to the desired harmonic, the output dropping off, of course, at the higher harmonics. Especially for harmonic operation, a low-C plate tank circuit is desirable.

For best performance with a 6AG7 or 5763, the values given under Fig. 6-3 should be followed closely.

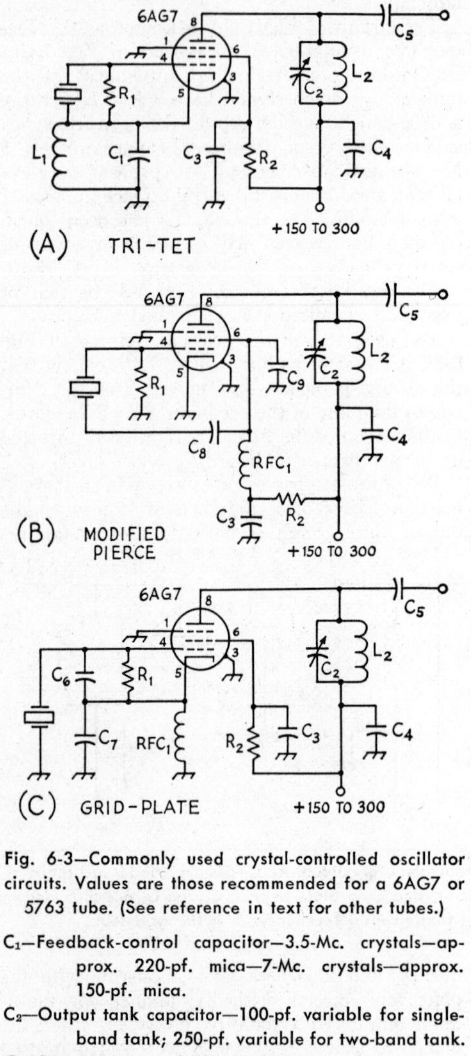

VARIABLE-FREQUENCY OSCILLATORS

The frequency of a v.f.o. depends entirely on the values of inductance and capacitance in the circuit. Therefore, it is necessary to take careful steps to minimize changes in these values not under the control of the operator. As examples, even the minute changes of dimensions with temperature, particularly those of the coil, may result in a slow but noticeable change in frequency called **drift**. The effective input capacitance of the oscillator tube, which must be connected across the circuit, changes with variations in electrode voltages. This, in turn, causes a change in the frequency of the oscillator. To make use of the power from the oscillator, a load, usually in the form of an amplifier, must be coupled to the oscillator, and variations in the load may reflect on the frequency. Very slight mechanical movement of the components may result in a shift in frequency, and vibration can cause modulation.

V.F.O. Circuits

Fig. 6-5 shows the most commonly used circuits. They are all designed to minimize the effects mentioned above. All are similar to the crystal oscillators of Fig. 6-3 in that the screen of a tetrode or pentode is used as the oscillator plate. The oscillating circuits in Figs. 6-5A and B are the Hartley type; those in C and D are Colpitts circuits. (See chapter on vacuum-tube principles.) In the circuits of A, B and C, all of the above-mentioned effects, except changes in inductance, are minimized by the use of a high-Q tank circuit obtained through the use of large tank capacitances. Any uncontrolled changes in capacitance thus become a very small percentage of the total circuit capacitance.

In the series-tuned Colpitts circuit of Fig. 6-5D (sometimes called the Clapp circuit), a high-Q circuit is obtained in a different manner. The tube is tapped across only a small portion of the oscillating tank circuit, resulting in very loose coupling between tube and circuit. The taps are provided by a series of three capacitors across the coil. In addition, the tube capacitances are shunted by large capacitors, so the effects of the tube — changes in electrode voltages and loading — are still further reduced. In contrast to the preceding circuits, the resulting tank circuit has a high L/C ratio and therefore the

---

(A) TRI-TET　　6AG7　　+150 TO 300

(B) MODIFIED PIERCE　　6AG7　　+150 TO 300

(C) GRID-PLATE　　6AG7　　+150 TO 300

Fig. 6-3—Commonly used crystal-controlled oscillator circuits. Values are those recommended for a 6AG7 or 5763 tube. (See reference in text for other tubes.)

C_1—Feedback-control capacitor—3.5-Mc. crystals—approx. 220-pf. mica—7-Mc. crystals—approx. 150-pf. mica.

C_2—Output tank capacitor—100-pf. variable for single-band tank; 250-pf. variable for two-band tank.

C_3—Screen bypass—0.001-μf. disk ceramic.

C_4—Plate bypass—0.001-μf. disk ceramic.

C_5—Output coupling capacitor—50 to 100 pf.

C_6—Excitation-control capacitor—30-pf. trimmer.

C_7—Excitation capacitor—220-pf. mica for 6AG7; 100-pf. for 5763.

C_8—D.c. blocking capacitor—0.001-μf. mica.

C_9—Excitation-control capacitor—220-pf. mica.

R_1—Grid leak—0.1 megohm, $\frac{1}{2}$ watt.

R_2—Screen resistor—47,000 ohms, 1 watt.

L_1—Excitation-control inductance—3.5-Mc. crystals—approx. 4 μh.; 7-Mc. crystals—approx. 2 μh.

L_2—Output-circuit coil—single band:—3.5 Mc.—17 μh.; 7 Mc.—8 μh.; 14 Mc.—2.5 μh.; 28 Mc.—1 μh. Two-band operation: 3.5 & 7 Mc.—7.5 μh.; 7 & 14 Mc.—2.5 μh.

RFC_1—2.5-mh. 50-ma. r.f. choke.

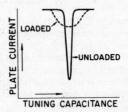

Fig. 6-4—Plate tuning characteristic of circuits of Fig. 6-3 with preferred types (see text). The plate-current dip at resonance broadens and is less pronounced when the circuit is loaded.

tank current is much lower than in the circuits using high-C tanks. As a result, it will usually be found that, other things being equal, drift will be less with the low-C circuit.

For best stability, the ratio of C_{12} or C_{13} (which are usually equal) to $C_{10} + C_{11}$ should be as high as possible without stopping oscillation. The permissible ratio will be higher the higher the Q of the coil and the mutual conductance of the tube. If the circuit does not oscillate over the desired range, a coil of higher Q must be used or the capacitance of C_{12} and C_{13} reduced.

Load Isolation

In spite of the precautions already discussed, the tuning of the output plate circuit will cause a noticeable change in frequency, particularly in the region around resonance. This effect can be reduced considerably by designing the oscillator for half the desired frequency and doubling frequency in the output circuit.

It is desirable, although not a strict necessity if detuning is recognized and taken into account, to approach as closely as possible the condition where the adjustment of tuning controls in the transmitter, beyond the v.f.o. frequency control, will have negligible effect on the frequency. This can be done by substituting a fixed-tuned circuit in the output of the oscillator, and adding isolating stages whose tuning is fixed between the oscillator and the first tunable amplifier stage in the transmitter. Fig. 6-6 shows such an arrangement that gives good isolation. In the first stage, a 6C4 is connected as a cathode follower. This

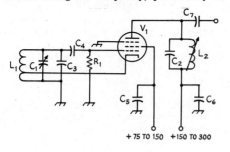

(A) HARTLEY

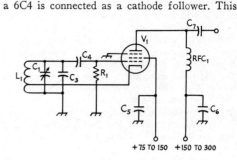

(B) HARTLEY – UNTUNED OUTPUT

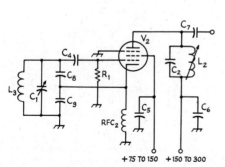

(C) COLPITTS

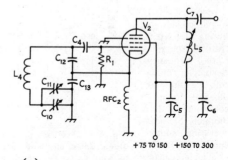

(D) SERIES – TUNED COLPITTS

Fig. 6-5—V.f.o. circuits. Approximate values for 3.5-4.0-Mc. output are given below. Grid circuits are tuned to half frequency (1.75 Mc.).

C_1—Oscillator bandspread tuning capacitor—200-pf. variable.

C_2—Output-circuit tank capacitor—47-pf.

C_3—Oscillator tank capacitor—600-pf. zero-temperature-coefficient mica.

C_4—Grid coupling capacitor—100-pf. zero-temperature-coefficient mica.

C_5—Screen bypass—0.001-μf. disk ceramic.

C_6—Plate bypass—0.001-μf. disk ceramic.

C_7—Output coupling capacitor—50 to 100-pf. mica.

C_8—Oscillator tank capacitor—750-pf. zero-temperature-coefficient mica.

C_9—Oscillator tank capacitor—0.0033-μf. zero-temperature-coefficient mica.

C_{10}—Oscillator bandspread padder—100-pf. variable air.

C_{11}—Oscillator bandspread tuning capacitor—50-pf. variable.

C_{12}, C_{13}—Tube-coupling capacitor—0.002-μf. zero-temperature-coefficient mica.

R_1—47,000 ohms, $\frac{1}{2}$ watt.

L_1—Oscillator tank coil—10 μh., tapped about one-third-way from grounded end.

L_2—Output-circuit tank coil—20-40 μh., adjustable.

L_3—Oscillator tank coil—10 μh.

L_3—Oscillator tank coil—10 μh.

L_4—Oscillator tank coil—70 μh.

L_5—Output coil—100-140 μh., adjustable.

RFC$_1$, RFC$_2$—100 μh. r.f. choke.

V_1—6AG7, 5763 or 6AH6 preferred; other types usable.

V_2—6AG7, 5763 or 6AH6 required for feedback capacitances shown.

drives a 5763 buffer amplifier whose input circuit is fixed-tuned to the v.f.o output band. For best isolation, the 6C4 should not be driven into grid current. This can be achieved by adding a 100-pf. capacitor from 6C4 grid to ground (to form, with the coupling capacitor, a voltage divider) or by reducing the oscillator supply voltages.

Chirp, Pulling and Drift

Any oscillator will change frequency with an extreme change in plate and screen voltages, and the use of stabilized sources for both is good practice. But steady source voltages cannot alter the fact of the extreme voltage changes that take place when an oscillator is keyed or heavily amplitude-modulated. Consequently some chirp or f.m. is the inescapable result of oscillator keying or heavy amplitude modulation.

A keyed or amplitude-modulated amplifier presents a variable load to the driving stage. If the driving stage is an oscillator, the keyed or modulated stage (the variable load) may "pull" the oscillator frequency during the keying or modulation. This may cause a "chirp" on c.w. or incidental f.m. on a.m. 'phone. In either case the cure is to provide one or more "buffer" or isolating stages between the oscillator stage and the varying load. If this is not done, the keying or modulation may be little better than when the oscillator itself is keyed or modulated.

Frequency **drift** is minimized by limiting the temperature excursions of the frequency-determining components to a minimum. This calls for good ventilation and a minimum of heat-generating components.

Variable capacitors should have ceramic insulation, good bearing contacts and should preferably be of the double bearing type. Fixed capacitors should have zero temperature coefficients. The tube socket should have ceramic insulation.

Temperature Compensation

If, despite the observance of good oscillator construction practice, the warm-up drift of an oscillator is too high, it is caused by high-temperature operation of the oscillator. If the ventilation cannot be improved (to reduce the ultimate temperature), the frequency drift of the oscillator can be reduced by the addition of a "temperature-coefficient capacitor". These are available in negative and positive coefficients, in contrast to the zero-coefficient "NPO" types.

Most uncorrected oscillators will drift to a lower frequency as the temperature rises. Such an oscillator can be corrected (at a frequency f) by adding an N750-type capacitor (-750 parts per million per ^{0}C) of a value determined by making two sets of measurements. Measure the drift f_1 from cold to stability (e.g., 1½ hours). To the cold (cooled-off) oscillator, add a *trial* N750 capacitor (e.g., 50 pf.) and retune the cold oscillator to frequency f (by retuning a padder capacitor or the tuning capacitor). Measure the new warm-up drift f_2 over the same period (e.g., 1½ hours). The required corrective N750 capacitor is then

$$\text{Corrective } C = C_{\text{trial}} \frac{f_1}{f_1 - f_2}$$

If the trial capacitor results in a drift to a higher frequency, the denominator becomes $f_1 + f_2$.

Oscillator Coils

The Q of the tank coil used in the oscillating portion of any of the circuits under discussion should be as high as circumstances (usually space) permit, since the losses, and therefore the heating, will be less. With recommended care in regard to other factors mentioned previously, most of the drift will originate in the coil. The coil should be well spaced from shielding and other large metal surfaces, and be of a type that radiates heat well, such as a commercial air-

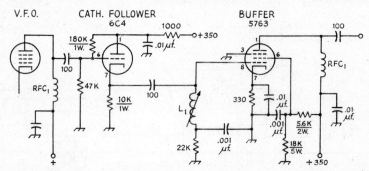

Fig. 6-6—Circuit of an isolating amplifier for use between v.f.o. and first tunable stage. Unless otherwise specified, all capacitances are in picofarads, all resistors are ½ watt. L_1, for the 3.5-Mc. band, consists of 100-140 μh. adjustable inductor. RFC$_1$ is 100 μh. All capacitors are disk ceramic.

wound type, or should be wound tightly on a threaded ceramic form so that the dimensions will not change readily with temperature. The wire with which the coil is wound should be as large as practicable, especially in the high-C circuits.

Mechanical Vibration

To eliminate mechanical vibration, components should be mounted securely. Particularly in the circuit of Fig. 6-5D, the capacitor should preferably have small, thick plates and the coil braced, if necessary, to prevent the slightest mechanical movement. Wire connections between tank-circuit components should be as short as possible and flexible wire will have less tendency to vibrate than solid wire. It is advisable to cushion the entire oscillator unit by mounting on sponge rubber or other shock mounting.

Tuning Characteristic

If the circuit is oscillating, touching the grid of the tube or any part of the circuit connected to it will show a change in plate current. In tuning the plate output circuit without load, the plate current will be relatively high until it is tuned near resonance where the plate current will dip to a low value, as illustrated in Fig. 6-4. When the output circuit is loaded, the dip should still be found, but broader and much less pronounced as indicated by the dashed line. The circuit should not be loaded beyond the point where the dip is still recognizable.

Checking V.F.O. Stability

A v.f.o. should be checked thoroughly before it is placed in regular operation on the air. Since succeeding amplifier stages may affect the signal characteristics, final tests should be made with the complete transmitter in operation. Almost any v.f.o. will show signals of good quality and stability when it is running free and not connected to a load. A well-isolated monitor is a necessity. Perhaps the most convenient, as well as one of the most satisfactory, well-shielded monitoring arrangements is a receiver combined with a crystal oscillator, as shown in Fig. 6-7. (See "Crystal Oscillators," this chapter.) The crystal frequency should lie in the band of the lowest frequency to be checked and in the frequency range where its harmonics will fall in the higher-frequency bands. The receiver b.f.o. is turned off and the v.f.o. signal is tuned to beat with the signal from the crystal oscillator instead. In this way any receiver instability caused by overloading of the input circuits, which may result in "pulling" of the h.f. oscillator in the receiver, or by a change in line voltage to the receiver when the transmitter is keyed, will not

affect the reliability of the check. Most crystals have a sufficiently low temperature coefficient to give a check on drift as well as on chirp and signal quality if they are not overloaded.

Harmonics of the crystal may be used to beat with the transmitter signal when monitoring at the higher frequencies. Since any chirp at the lower frequencies will be magnified at the higher frequencies, accurate checking can best be done by monitoring at a harmonic.

The distance between the crystal oscillator and receiver should be adjusted to give a good beat between the crystal oscillator and the transmitter signal. When using harmonics of the crystal oscillator, it may be necessary to attach a piece

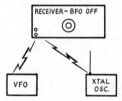

Fig. 6-7—Setup for checking v.f.o. stability. The receiver should be tuned preferably to a harmonic of the v.f.o. frequency. The crystal oscillator may operate somewhere in the band in which the v.f.o. is operating. The receiver b.f.o. should be turned off.

of wire to the oscillator as an antenna to give sufficient signal in the receiver. Checks may show that the stability is sufficiently good to permit oscillator keying at the lower frequencies, where break-in operation is of greater value, but that chirp becomes objectionable at the higher frequencies. If further improvement does not seem possible, it would be logical in this case to use oscillator keying at the lower frequencies and amplifier keying at the higher frequencies.

R.F. POWER-AMPLIFIER TANKS AND COUPLING

In the remainder of this chapter the vacuum tubes will be shown, for the most part, with indirectly-heated cathodes. However, many transmitting tubes use directly heated filaments for the cathodes; when this is done the filament "center-tap" connection will be used, as shown in Fig. 6-8.

PLATE TANK Q

R.f. power amplifiers used in amateur transmitters are operated under Class-C or -AB conditions (see chapter on tube fundamentals). The main objective, of course, is to deliver as much fundamental power as possible into a load, R, without exceeding the tube ratings. The load resistance R may be in the form of a transmission line to an antenna, or the grid circuit of another amplifier. A further objective is to minimize the harmonic energy (always generated by a Class C amplifier) fed into the load circuit. In attaining these objectives, the Q of the tank circuit is of importance. When a load is coupled inductively, as in Fig. 6-10, the Q of the tank circuit

will have an effect on the coefficient of coupling necessary for proper loading of the amplifier. In respect to all of these factors, a tank Q of 10 to 20 is usually considered optimum. A much lower Q will result in less efficient operation of the amplifier tube, greater harmonic output, and greater difficulty in coupling inductively to a load. A much higher Q will result in higher tank current with increased loss in the tank coil.

The Q is determined (see chapter on electrical

Fig. 6-8—Filament center-tap connections to be substituted in place of cathode connections shown in diagrams when filament-type tubes are substituted. T_1 is the filament transformer. Filament bypasses, C_1, should be 0.01-μf. disk ceramic capacitors. If a self-biasing (cathode) resistor is used, it should be placed between the center tap and ground.

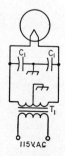

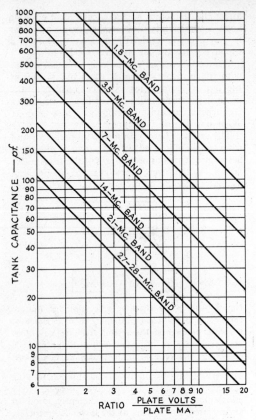

These values of capacitance include the output capacitance of the amplifier tube, the input capacitance of a following amplifier tube if it is coupled capacitively, and all other stray capacitances. At the higher plate-voltage/plate-current ratios, the chart may show values of capacitance, for the higher frequencies, smaller than those attainable in practice. In such a case, a tank Q higher than 10 is unavoidable.

INDUCTIVE-LINK COUPLING

Coupling to Flat Coaxial Lines

When the load R in Fig. 6-10 is located for convenience at some distance from the amplifier, or when maximum harmonic reduction is desired, it is advisable to feed the power to the load through a low-impedance coaxial cable. The shielded construction of the cable prevents radiation and makes it possible to install the line in any convenient manner without danger of unwanted coupling to other circuits.

If the line is more than a small fraction of a wavelength long, the load resistance at its output end should be adjusted, by a matching circuit if necessary, to match the impedance of the cable. This reduces losses in the cable and makes the coupling adjustments at the transmitter independent of the cable length. Matching circuits for use between the cable and another transmission line are discussed in the chapter on transmission lines, while the matching adjustments when the load is the grid circuit of a following

Fig. 6-9—Chart showing plate tank capacitance required for a Q of 10. Divide the tube plate voltage by the plate current in milliamperes. Select the vertical line corresponding to the answer obtained. Follow this vertical line to the diagonal line for the band in question, and thence horizontally to the left to read the capacitance. For a given ratio of plate-voltage/plate current, doubling the capacitance shown doubles the Q, etc. When a split-stator capacitor is used in a balanced circuit, the capacitance of each section may be one half of the value given by the chart.

laws and circuits) by the L/C ratio and the load resistance at which the tube is operated. The tube load resistance is related, in approximation, to the ratio of the d.c. plate voltage to d.c. plate current at which the tube is operated and can be computed from:

$$R_L = \frac{Plate\ volts \times 500}{Plate\ ma.}$$

The amount of C that will give a Q of 10 for various ratios is shown in Fig. 6-9. For a given plate-voltage/plate-current ratio, the Q will vary directly as the tank capacitance, twice the capacitance doubles the Q, etc. For the same Q, the capacitance of *each section* of a split-stator capacitor in a balanced circuit should be half the value shown.

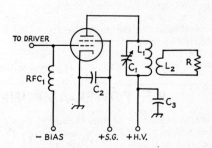

Fig. 6-10—Inductive-link output coupling circuits.

C_1—Plate tank capacitor—see text and Fig. 6-9 for capacitance, Fig. 6-33 for voltage rating.

C_2—Screen bypass—voltage rating depends on method of screen supply. See paragraphs on screen considerations. Voltage rating same as plate voltage will be safe under any condition.

C_3—Plate bypass—0.001-μf. disk ceramic or mica. Voltage rating same as C_1, plus safety factor.

L_1—To resonate at operating frequency with C_1. See LC chart and inductance formula in electrical-laws chapter, or use ARRL *Lightning Calculator*.

L_2—Reactance equal to line impedance. See reactance chart and inductance formula in electrical-laws chapter, or use ARRL *Lightning Calculator*.

R—Representing load.

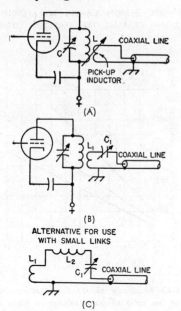

Fig. 6-11—With flat transmission lines, power transfer is obtained with looser coupling if the line input is tuned to resonance. C_1 and L_1 should resonate at the operating frequency. See table for maximum usable value of C_1. If circuit does not resonate with maximum C_1 or less, inductance of L_1 must be increased, or added in series at L_2.

amplifier are described elsewhere in this chapter.

Assuming that the cable is properly terminated, proper loading of the amplifier will be assured, using the circuit of Fig. 6-11A, if

1) The plate tank circuit has reasonably high value of Q. A value of 10 is usually sufficient.

2) The inductance of the pick-up or link coil is close to the optimum value for the frequency and type of line used. The optimum coil is one whose self-inductance is such that its reactance at the operating frequency is equal to the characteristic impedance, Z_0, of the line.

3) It is possible to make the coupling between the tank and pick-up coils very tight.

The second in this list is often hard to meet. Few manufactured link coils have adequate inductance even for coupling to a 50-ohm line at low frequencies.

Capacitance in pf. Required for Coupling to Flat Coaxial Lines with Tuned Coupling Circuit [1]		
Frequency	*Characteristic Impedance of Line*	
Band	52	75
Mc.	ohms	ohms
3.5	450	300
7	230	150
14	115	75
21	80	50
28	60	40

[1] Capacitance values are maximum usable.

Note: Inductance in circuit must be adjusted to resonate at operating frequency.

If the line is operating with a low s.w.r., the system shown in Fig. 6-11A will require tight coupling between the two coils. Since the secondary (pick-up coil) circuit is not resonant, the leakage reactance of the pick-up coil will cause some detuning of the amplifier tank circuit. This detuning effect increases with increasing coupling, but is usually not serious. However, the amplifier tuning must be adjusted to resonance, as indicated by the plate-current dip, each time the coupling is changed.

Tuned Coupling

The design difficulties of using "untuned" pick-up coils, mentioned above, can be avoided by using a coupling circuit tuned to the operating frequency. This contributes additional selectivity as well, and hence aids in the suppression of spurious radiations.

If the line is flat the input impedance will be essentially resistive and equal to the Z_0 of the line. With coaxial cable, a circuit of reasonable Q can be obtained with practicable values of inductance and capacitance connected in series with the line's input terminals. Suitable circuits are given in Fig. 6-11 at B and C. The Q of the coupling circuit often may be as low as 2, without running into difficulty in getting adequate coupling to a tank circuit of proper design. Larger values of Q can be used and will result in increased ease of coupling, but as the Q is increased the frequency range over which the circuit will operate without readjustment becomes smaller. It is usually good practice, therefore, to use a coupling-circuit Q just low enough to permit operation, over as much of a band as is normally used for a particular type of communication, without requiring retuning.

Capacitance values for a Q of 2 and line impedances of 52 and 75 ohms are given in the accompanying table. These are the *maximum* values that should be used. The inductance in the circuit should be adjusted to give resonance at the operating frequency. If the link coil used for a particular band does not have enough inductance to resonate, the additional inductance may be connected in series as shown in Fig. 6-11C.

Characteristics

In practice, the amount of inductance in the circuit should be chosen so that, with somewhat loose coupling between L_1 and the amplifier tank coil, the amplifier plate current will increase when the variable capacitor, C_1 is tuned through the value of capacitance given by the table. The coupling between the two coils should then be increased until the amplifier loads normally, without changing the setting of C_1. If the transmission line is flat over the entire frequency band under consideration, it should not be necessary to readjust C_1 when changing frequency, if the values given in the table are used. However, it is unlikely that the line actually will be flat over such a range, so some readjustment of C_1 may be needed to compensate for changes in the input impedance of the line. If the input impedance variations are not large, C_1 may be used as a loading control, no changes in the coupling between L_1 and the tank coil being necessary.

The degree of coupling between L_1 and the amplifier tank coil will depend on the coupling-circuit Q. With a Q of 2, the coupling should be tight — comparable with the coupling that is typical of "fixed-link" manufactured coils. With a swinging link it may be necessary to increase the Q of the coupling circuit in order to get sufficient power transfer. This can be done by increasing the L/C ratio.

PI-SECTION OUTPUT TANK

A pi-section tank circuit may also be used in coupling to an antenna or transmission line, as shown in Fig. 6-12. The optimum values of capacitance for C_1 and C_2, and inductance for L_1 are dependent upon values of tube power input and output load resistance.

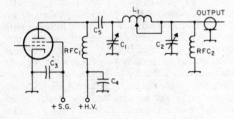

Fig. 6-12—Pi-section output tank circuit.

C_1—Input or plate tuning capacitor. See text or Fig. 6-13 for reactance. Voltage rating equal to d.c. plate voltage; twice this for plate modulation.

C_2—Output or loading capacitor. See text or Fig. 6-15 for reactance. See text for voltage rating.

C_3—Screen bypass. See Fig. 6-10.

C_4—Plate bypass. See Fig. 6-10.

C_5—Plate blocking capacitor—0.001-μf. disk ceramic or mica. Voltage rating same as C_1.

L_1—See text or Fig. 6-14 for reactance.

RFC_1—See later paragraph on r.f. chokes.

RFC_2—2.5-mh. receiving type (to reduce peak voltage across both C_1 and C_2 and to blow plate power supply fuse if C_5 fails).

Values of reactance for C_1, L_1 and C_2 may be taken directly from the charts of Figs. 6-13, 6-14 and 6-15 if the output load resistance is the usual 52 or 72 ohms. It should be borne in mind that these values apply only where the output load is resistive, i.e., where the antenna and line have been matched.

Output-Capacitor Ratings

The voltage rating of the output capacitor will depend upon the s.w.r. If the load is resistive, receiving-type air capacitors should be adequate for amplifier input powers up to 1 kw. with plate modulation when feeding 52- or 72-ohm loads. In obtaining the larger capacitances re-

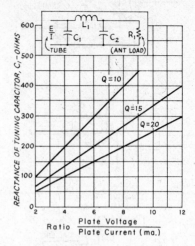

Fig. 6-13—Reactance of input capacitor, C_1, as a function the ratio of plate voltage to plate current.

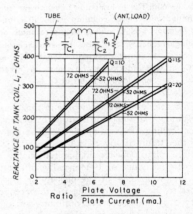

Fig. 6-14—Reactance of tank coil, L_1, as a function of plate voltage and current, for pi networks.

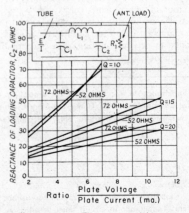

Fig. 6-15—Reactance of loading capacitor, C_2, as a function of plate voltage and current, for pi networks.

quired for the lower frequencies, it is common practice to switch fixed capacitors in parallel with the variable air capacitor. While the voltage rating of a mica or ceramic capacitor may not be exceeded in a particular case, capacitors of these types are limited in current-carrying capacity. Postage-stamp silver-mica capacitors should be adequate for amplifier inputs over the range from about 70 watts at 28 Mc. to 400 watts at 14 Mc. and lower. The larger mica capacitors (CM-45 case) having voltage ratings of 1200 and 2500 volts are usually satisfactory for inputs varying from about 350 watts at 28 Mc. to 1 kw. at 14 Mc. and lower. Because of these current limitations, particularly at the higher frequencies, it is advisable to use as large an air capacitor as practicable, using the micas only at the lower frequencies. Broadcast-receiver replacement-type capacitors can be obtained reasonably. Their insulation should be adequate for inputs of 500 watts or more.

Neutralizing with Pi Network

Screen-grid amplifiers using a pi-network output circuit may be neutralized by the system shown in Figs. 6-23 B and C.

TRANSISTOR OUTPUT CIRCUITS

Since r.f. power transistors have a low output impedance (on the order of 5 ohms or less), the problem of coupling the transistor to the usual 50-ohm load is the reverse of the problem with a vacuum-tube amplifier. The 50-ohm load must be transformed to a low resistance.

Two common circuits are shown in Fig. 6-16. That at A is the familiar pi network, differing only in the relative values. C_1 will be larger than the output loading capacitor, C_2, and L_1 will be small by comparison with the value used with vacuum tubes at the same frequency. The choke, RFC_1, should have an impedance no higher than 10 times the output impedance of the transistor, if low-frequency parasitics are to be avoided. See Chapter Two for pi network formulas.

A circuit with somewhat more harmonic attenuation is shown in Fig. 6-16B. In designing such a circuit, which is actually two pi networks in cascade, the first section is designed for, say, 5 to 16 ohms, and the second for 16 to 50. C_5 is then the sum of the output capacitance of the first network and the input of the second.

A third network, a variation of the L network, is shown in Fig. 6-16C. In this circuit, the effective inductance in the L network is the *net* inductive reactance in the L_1C_7 branch. Thus tuning C_7 has the effect of varying the inductance

in the L network. See Chapter Two for L network formulas. Output loading is controlled by C_9, but it will interlock with C_7 and C_8.

In a power r.f. common emitter transistor amplifier, the excitation is introduced between base and emitter. With minimum resistance in the d.c. circuit, the operation will be Class B. Adding a few ohms in series for bias will result in Class-C operation. The bias resistor should be bypassed for the operating frequency. If an r.f. choke is used, its impedance should be 5 to 50 times the transistor input impedance.

Parallel operation of power transistors is not recommended, because one transistor may "hog" the current. However, push-pull operation (and particularly Class-C) provides no such problems. It does compound the required tank-circuit components, however, unless one goes to single-inductor inductive coupling circuitry.

Early tests of transistor r.f. power amplifiers should be made with low voltage, a dummy load and no drive. Some form of output indicator should be included. When it has been established that no instability exists, the drive can be applied in increments and adjustment made for maximum output. The amplifier should never be operated at high voltage and no load.

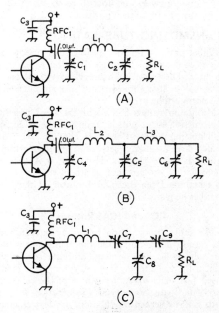

Fig. 6-16—Output circuits for use with r.f. power transistors. (A) Simple pi network. (B) Double pi network, for better harmonic attenuation. (C) L network.

R.F. AMPLIFIER-TUBE OPERATING CONDITIONS

In addition to proper tank and output-coupling circuits discussed in the preceding sections, an r.f. amplifier must be provided with suitable electrode voltages and an r.f. driving or excitation voltage (see vacuum-tube chapter).

All r.f. amplifier tubes require a voltage to operate the filament or heater (a.c. is usually permissible), and a positive d.c. voltage between the plate and filament or cathode (plate voltage). Most tubes also require a negative d.c. voltage (biasing voltage) between control grid (Grid No. 1) and filament or cathode. Screen-grid tubes require in addition a positive voltage (screen voltage or Grid No. 2 voltage) between screen and filament or cathode.

Biasing and plate voltages may be fed to the tube either in series with or in parallel with the associated r.f. tank circuit as discussed in the chapter on electrical laws and circuits.

It is important to remember that true plate, screen or biasing voltage is the voltage between the particular electrode and filament or cathode. Only when the cathode is directly grounded to the chassis may the electrode-to-chassis voltage be taken as the true voltage.

The required r.f. driving voltage is applied between grid and cathode.

Power Input and Plate Dissipation

Plate power input is the d.c. power input to the plate circuit (d.c. plate voltage × d.c. plate current).—Screen power input likewise is the d.c. screen voltage × the d.c. screen current.

Plate dissipation is the difference between the r.f. power delivered by the tube to its loaded plate tank circuit and the d.c. plate power input. The screen, on the other hand, does not deliver any output power, and therefore its dissipation is the same as the screen power input.

TRANSMITTING-TUBE RATINGS

Tube manufacturers specify the maximum values that should be applied to the tubes they produce. They also publish sets of typical operating values that should result in good efficiency and normal tube life.

Maximum values for all of the most popular transmitting tubes will be found in the tables of transmitting tubes in the last chapter. Also included are as many sets of typical operating values as space permits. However, it is recommended that the amateur secure a transmitting-tube manual from the manufacturer of the tube or tubes he plans to use.

CCS and ICAS Ratings

The same transmitting tube may have different ratings depending upon the manner in which the tube is to be operated, and the service in which it is to be used. These different ratings are based primarily upon the heat that the tube can safely dissipate. Some types of operation, such as with grid or screen modulation, are less efficient than others, meaning that the tube must dissipate more heat. Other types of operation, such as c.w. or single-sideband phone are intermittent in nature, resulting in less average heating than in other modes where there is a continuous power input to the tube during transmissions. There are also different ratings for tubes used in transmitters that are in almost constant use (CCS — Continuous Commercial Service), and for tubes that are to be used in transmitters that average only a few hours of daily operation (ICAS — Intermittent Commercial and Amateur Service). The latter are the ratings used by amateurs who

wish to obtain maximum output with reasonable tube life.

Maximum Ratings

Maximum ratings, where they differ from the values given under typical operating values, are not normally of significance to the amateur except in special applications. No single maximum value should be used unless all other ratings can simultaneously be held within the maximum values. As an example, a tube may have a maximum plate-voltage rating of 2000, a maximum plate-current rating of 300 ma., and a maximum plate-power-input rating of 400 watts. Therefore, if the maximum plate voltage of 2000 is used, the plate current should be limited to 200 ma. (instead of 300 ma.) to stay within the maximum power-input rating of 400 watts.

SOURCES OF ELECTRODE VOLTAGES

Filament or Heater Voltage

The heater voltage for the indirectly heated cathode-type tubes found in low-power classifications may vary 10 per cent above or below rating without seriously reducing the life of the tube. But the voltage of the higher-power filament-type tubes should be held closely between the rated voltage as a minimum and 5 per cent above rating as a maximum. Make sure that the plate power drawn from the power line does not cause a drop in filament voltage below the proper value when plate power is applied.

Thoriated-type filaments lose emission when the tube is overloaded appreciably. If the overload has not been too prolonged, emission sometimes may be restored by operating the filament at rated voltage with all other voltages removed for a period of 10 minutes, or at 20 per cent above rated voltage for a few minutes.

Plate Voltage

D.c. plate voltage for the operation of r.f. amplifiers is most often obtained from a transformer-rectifier-filter system (see power-supply chapter) designed to deliver the required plate voltage at the required current. However, batteries or other d.c.-generating devices are sometimes used in certain types of operation (see portable-mobile chapter).

Bias and Tube Protection

Several methods of obtaining bias are shown in Fig. 6-17. In A, bias is obtained by the voltage drop across a resistor in the grid d.c. return circuit when rectified grid current flows. The proper value of resistance may be determined by dividing the required biasing voltage by the d.c. grid current at which the tube will be operated. Then, so long as the r.f. driving voltage is adjusted so that the d.c. grid current is the recommended value, the biasing voltage will be the proper value. The tube is biased only when excitation is applied, since the voltage drop across the resistor depends upon grid-current flow. When excitation is removed, the bias falls to

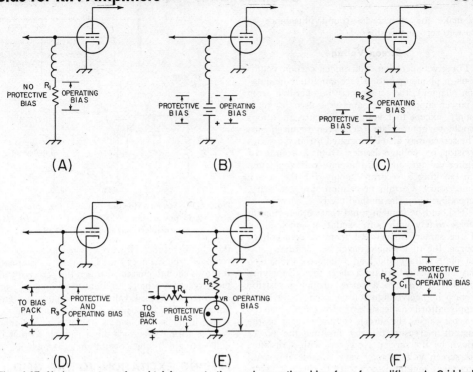

Fig. 6-17—Various systems for obtaining protective and operating bias for r.f. amplifiers. A—Grid-leak. B—Battery. C—Combination battery and grid leak. D—Grid leak and adjusted-voltage bias pack. E—Combination grid leak and voltage-regulated pack. F—Cathode bias.

zero. At zero bias most tubes draw power far in excess of the plate-dissipation rating. So it is advisable to make provision for protecting the tube when excitation fails by accident, or by intent as it does when a preceding stage in a c.w. transmitter is keyed.

If the maximum c.w. ratings shown in the tube tables are to be used, the input should be cut to zero when the key is open. Aside from this, it is not necessary that plate current be cut off completely but only to the point where the rated dissipation is not exceeded. In this case plate-modulated phone ratings should be used for c.w. operation, however.

With triodes this protection can be supplied by obtaining all bias from a source of fixed voltage, as shown in Fig. 6-17B. It is preferable, however, to use only sufficient fixed bias to protect the tube and obtain the balance needed for operating bias from a grid leak, as in C. The grid-leak resistance is calculated as above, except that the fixed voltage is subtracted first.

Fixed bias may be obtained from dry batteries or from a power pack (see power-supply chapter). If dry batteries are used, they should be checked periodically, since even though they may show normal voltage, they eventually develop a high internal resistance. Grid-current flow through this battery resistance may increase the bias considerably above that anticipated. The life of batteries in bias service will be approximately the same as though they were subject to a drain equal to the grid current, despite the fact that the grid-current flow is in such a direction as to charge the battery, rather than to discharge it.

In Fig. 6-17F, bias is obtained from the voltage drop across a resistor in the cathode (or filament center-tap) lead. Protective bias is obtained by the voltage drop across R_5 as a result of plate (and screen) current flow. Since plate current must flow to obtain a voltage drop across the resistor, it is obvious that cut-off protective bias cannot be obtained. When excitation is applied, plate (and screen) current increases and the grid current also contributes to the drop across R_5, thereby increasing the bias to the operating value. Since the voltage between plate and cathode is reduced by the amount of the voltage drop across R_5, the over-all supply voltage must be the sum of the plate and operating-bias voltages. For this reason, the use of cathode bias usually is limited to low-voltage tubes when the extra voltage is not difficult to obtain.

The resistance of the cathode biasing resistor R_5 should be adjusted to the value which will give the correct operating bias voltage with rated grid, plate and screen currents flowing with the amplifier loaded to rated input. When excitation is removed, the input to most types of tubes will fall to a value that will prevent damage to the tube, at least for the period of time required to remove plate voltage. A disadvantage of this biasing system is that the cathode r.f. connection to ground depends upon a bypass capacitor. From the consideration of v.h.f. harmonics and stability with high-perveance tubes, it is preferable to make the cathode-to-ground impedance as close to zero as possible.

Screen Voltage

For c.w. operation, and under certain conditions of phone operation (see amplitude-modulation chapter), the screen may be operated from a power supply of the same type used for plate supply, except that voltage and current ratings should be appropriate for screen requirements. The screen may also be operated through a series resistor or voltage-divider from a source of higher voltage, such as the plate-voltage supply, thus making a separate supply for the screen unnecessary. Certain precautions are necessary, depending upon the method used.

It should be kept in mind that screen current varies widely with both excitation and loading. If the screen is operated from a fixed-voltage source, the tube should never be operated without plate voltage and load, otherwise the screen may be damaged within a short time. Supplying the screen through a series dropping resistor from a higher-voltage source, such as the plate supply, affords a measure of protection, since the resistor causes the screen voltage to drop as the current increases, thereby limiting the power drawn by the screen. However, with a resistor, the screen voltage may vary considerably with excitation, making it necessary to check the voltage at the screen terminal under actual operating conditions to make sure that the screen voltage is normal. Reducing excitation will cause the screen current to drop, increasing the voltage; increasing excitation will have the opposite effect. These changes are in addition to those caused by changes in bias and plate loading, so if a screen-grid tube is operated from a series resistor or a voltage divider, its voltage should be checked as one of the final adjustments after excitation and loading have been set.

An approximate value for the screen-voltage dropping resistor may be obtained by dividing the voltage *drop* required from the supply voltage (difference between the supply voltage and rated screen voltage) by the rated screen current in decimal parts of an ampere. Some further adjustment may be necessary, as mentioned above, so an adjustable resistor with a total resistance above that calculated should be provided.

Protecting Screen-Grid Tubes

Considerably less grid bias is required to cut off an amplifier that has a fixed-voltage screen supply than one that derives the screen voltage through a high value of dropping resistor. When a "stiff" screen voltage supply is used, the necessary grid cut-off voltage may be determined from an inspection of the tube curves or by experiment.

When the screen is supplied from a series dropping resistor, the tube can be protected by the use of a clamper tube, as shown in Fig. 6-18. The grid-leak bias of the amplifier tube with excitation is supplied also to the grid of the clamper tube. This is usually sufficient to cut off

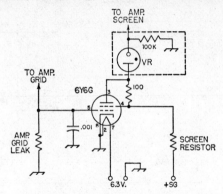

Fig. 6-18—Screen clamper circuit for protecting screen-grid power tubes. The VR tube is needed only for complete screen-voltage cut-off.

the clamper tube. However, when excitation is removed, the clamper-tube bias falls to zero and it draws enough current through the screen dropping resistor usually to limit the input to the amplifier to a safe value. If complete screen-voltage cut-off is desired, a VR tube may be inserted in the screen lead as shown. The VR-tube voltage rating should be high enough so that it will extinguish when excitation is removed.

FEEDING EXCITATION TO THE GRID

The required r.f. driving voltage is supplied by an oscillator generating a voltage at the desired frequency, either directly or through intermediate amplifiers or frequency multipliers.

As explained in the chapter on vacuum-tube fundamentals, the grid of an amplifier operating under Class C conditions must have an exciting voltage whose peak value exceeds the negative biasing voltage over a portion of the excitation cycle. During this portion of the cycle, current will flow in the grid-cathode circuit as it does in a diode circuit when the plate of the diode is positive in respect to the cathode. This requires that the r.f. driver supply power. The power required to develop the required peak driving voltage across the grid-cathode impedance of the amplifier is the r.f. driving power.

The tube tables give approximate figures for the grid driving power required for each tube under various operating conditions. These figures, however, do not include circuit losses. In general, the driver stage for any Class C amplifier should be capable of supplying at least three times the driving power shown for typical operating conditions at frequencies up to 30 Mc., and from three to ten times at higher frequencies.

Since the d.c. grid current relative to the biasing voltage is related to the peak driving voltage, the d.c. grid current is commonly used as a convenient indicator of driving conditions. A driver adjustment that results in rated d.c. grid current when the d.c. bias is at its rated value, indicates proper excitation to the amplifier when it is fully loaded.

In coupling the grid input circuit of an amplifier to the output circuit of a driving stage the

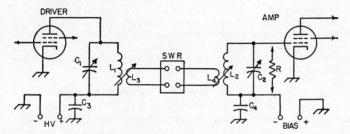

Fig. 6-19—Coupling excitation to the grid of an r.f. power amplifier by means of a low-impedance coaxial line.

C_1, C_3, L_1, L_3—See corresponding components in Fig. 6-10.

C_2—Amplifier grid tank capacitor—see text and Fig. 6-20 for capacitance, Fig. 6-34 for voltage rating.

C_4—0.001-μf. disk ceramic.

L_2—To resonate at operating frequency with C_2. See LC chart inductance formula in electrical-laws chapter, or use ARRL *Lightning Calculator*.

L_4—Reactance equal to line impedance—see reactance chart and inductance formula in electrical-laws chapter, or use ARRL *Lightning Calculator*.

R is used to simulate grid impedance of the amplifier when a low-power s.w.r. indicator, such as a resistance bridge, is used. See formula in text for calculating value. Standing-wave indicator SWR is inserted only while line is made flat.

objective is to load the driver plate circuit so that the desired amplifier grid excitation is obtained without exceeding the plate-input ratings of the driver tube.

Driving Impedance

The grid-current flow that results when the grid is driven positive in respect to the cathode over a portion of the excitation cycle represents an average resistance across which the exciting voltage must be developed by the driver. In other words, this is the load resistance into which the driver plate circuit must be coupled. The approximate grid input resistance is given by:

$$Input\ impedance\ (ohms)$$
$$= \frac{driving\ power\ (watts)}{d.c.\ grid\ current\ (ma.)^2} \times 620{,}000$$

For normal operation, the driving power and grid current may be taken from the tube tables.

Since the grid input resistance is a matter of a few thousand ohms, an impedance step-down is necessary if the grid is to be fed from a low-impedance transmission line. This can be done by the use of a tank as an impedance-transforming device in the grid circuit of the amplifier as shown in Fig. 6-19. This coupling system may be considered either as simply a means of obtaining mutual inductance between the two tank coils, or as a low-impedance transmission line. If the line is longer than a small fraction of a wave length, and if a s.w.r. bridge is available, the line is more easily handled by adjusting it as a matched transmission line.

Inductive Link Coupling with Flat Line

In adjusting this type of line, the object is to make the s.w.r. on the line as low as possible over as wide a band of frequencies as possible so that power can be transferred over this range without retuning. It is assumed that the output coupling considerations discussed earlier have been observed in connection with the driver plate

circuit. So far as the amplifier grid circuit is concerned, the controlling factors are the Q of the tuned grid circuit, L_2C_2, (see Fig. 6-20) the inductance of the coupling coil, L_4, and the degree of coupling between L_2 and L_4. Variable coupling between the coils is convenient, but not strictly necessary if one or both of the other factors can be varied. An s.w.r. indicator (shown as "SWR" in the drawing) is essential. An indi-

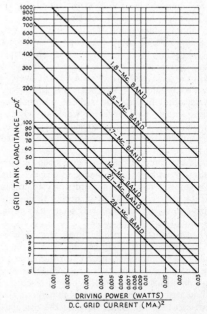

Fig. 6-20—Chart showing required grid tank capacitance for a Q of 12. To use, divide the driving power in watts by the square of the d.c. grid current in milliamperes and proceed as described under Fig. 6-9. Driving power and grid current may be taken from the tube tables. When a split-stator capacitor is used in a balanced grid circuit, the capacitance of *each section* may be half that shown.

cator such as the "Micromatch" (a commercially available instrument) may be connected as shown and the adjustments made under actual operating conditions; that is, with full power applied to the amplifier grid.

Assuming that the coupling is adjustable, start with a trial position of L_4 with respect to L_2, and adjust C_2 for the lowest s.w.r. Then change the coupling slightly and repeat. Continue until the s.w.r. is as low as possible; if the circuit constants are in the right region is should not be difficult to get the s.w.r. down to 1 to 1. The Q of the tuned grid circuit should be designed to be at least 10, and if it is not possible to get a very low s.w.r. with such a grid circuit the probable reason is that L_4 is too small. Maximum coupling, for a given degree of physical coupling will occur when the inductance of L_4 is such that its reactance at the operating frequency is equal to the characteristic impedance of the link line. The reactance can be calculated as described in the chapter on electrical fundamentals if the inductance is known; the inductance can either be calculated from the formula in the same chapter or measured as described in the chapter on measurements.

Once the s.w.r. has been brought down to 1 to 1, the frequency should be shifted over the band so that the variation in s.w.r. can be observed, without changing C_2 or the coupling between L_2 and L_4. If the s.w.r. rises rapidly on either side of the original frequency the circuit can be made "flatter" by reducing the Q of the tuned grid circuit. This may be done by decreasing C_2 and correspondingly increasing L_2 to maintain resonance, and by tightening the coupling between L_2 and L_4, going through the same adjustment process again. It is possible to set up the system so that the s.w.r. will not exceed 1.5 to 1 over, for example, the entire 7-Mc. band and proportionately on other bands. Under these circumstances a single setting will serve for work anywhere in the band, with essentially constant power transfer from the line to the power-amplifier grids.

If the coupling between L_2 and L_4 is not adjustable the same result may be secured by varying the L/C ratio of the tuned grid circuit — that is, by varying its Q. If any difficulty is encountered it can be overcome by changing the number of turns in L_4 until a match is secured. The two coils should be tightly coupled.

When a resistance-bridge type s.w.r. indicator (see measurements chapter) is used it is not possible to put the full power through the line when making adjustments. In such case the operating conditions in the amplified grid circuit can be simulated by using a *carbon resistor* (½ or 1 watt size) of the same value as the calculated amplifier grid impedance, connected as indicated by the arrows in Fig. 6-19. In this case the amplifier tube *must* be operated "cold"— without filament or heater power. The adjustment process is the same as described above, but with the driver power reduced to a value suitable for operating the s.w.r. bridge.

When the grid coupling system has been ad-

justed so that the s.w.r. is close to 1 to 1 over the desired frequency range, it is certain that the power put into the link line will be delivered to the grid circuit. Coupling will be facilitated if the line is tuned as described under the earlier section on output coupling systems.

Link Feed with Unmatched Line

When the system is to be treated without regard to transmission-line effects, the link line must not offer appreciable reactance at the operating frequency. Any appreciable reactance will in effect reduce the coupling, making it impossible to transfer sufficient power from the driver to the amplifier grid circuit. Coaxial cables especially have considerable capacitance for even short lengths and it may be more desirable to use a spaced line, such as Twin-Lead, if the radiation can be tolerated.

The reactance of the line can be nullified only by making the link resonant. This may require changing the number of turns in the link coils, the length of the line, or the insertion of a tuning capacitance. Since the s.w.r. on the link line may be quite high, the line losses increase because of the greater current, the voltage increase may be sufficient to cause a breakdown in the insulation of the cable and the added tuned circuit makes adjustment more critical with relatively small changes in frequency.

These troubles may not be encountered if the link line is kept very short for the highest frequency. A length of 5 feet or more may be tolerable at 3.5 Mc., but a length of a foot at 28 Mc. may be enough to cause serious effects on the functioning of the system.

Adjusting the coupling in such a system must necessarily be largely a matter of cut and try. If the line is short enough so as to have negligible reactance, the coupling between the two tank circuits will increase within limits by adding turns to the link coils, or by coupling the link coils more tightly, if possible, to the tank coils. If it is impossible to change either of these, a variable capacitor of 300 μμf. may be connected in series with or in parallel with the link coil at the driver end of the line, depending upon which connection is the most effective.

If coaxial line is used, the capacitor should be connected in series with the inner conductor. If the line is long enough to have appreciable reactance, the variable capacitor is used to resonate the entire link circuit.

The size of the link coils and the length of the line, as well as the size of the capacitor, will affect the resonant frequency, and it may take an adjustment of all three before the capacitor will show a pronounced effect on the coupling.

When the system has been made resonant, coupling may be adjusted by varying the link capacitor.

Simple Capacitive Interstage Coupling

The capacitive system of Fig. 6-21A is the simplest of all coupling systems. In this circuit, the plate tank circuit of the driver, C_1L_1, serves

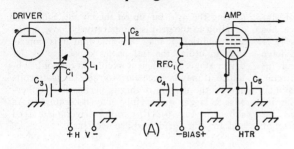

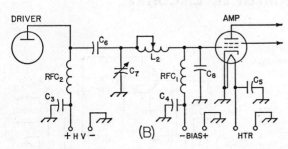

Fig. 6-21—Capacitive-coupled amplifiers.
A—Simple capacitive coupling. B—Pi-section coupling.

C$_1$—Driver plate tank capacitor—see text and Fig. 6-9 for capacitance, Fig. 6-33 for voltage rating.
C$_2$—Coupling capacitor—50 to 150 pf. mica, as necessary for desired coupling. Voltage rating sum of driver plate and amplifier biasing voltages, plus safety factor.
C$_3$—Driver plate bypass capacitor—0.001-μf. disk ceramic or mica. Voltage rating same as plate voltage.
C$_4$—Grid bypass—0.001-μf. disk ceramic.
C$_5$—Heater bypass—0.001-μf. disk ceramic.
C$_6$—Driver plate blocking capacitor—0.001-μf. disk ceramic or mica. Voltage rating same as C$_2$.
C$_7$—Pi-section input capacitor—see text referring to Fig. 6-12 for capacitance. Voltage rating—see Fig. 6-33A.
C$_8$—Pi-section output capacitor—100-pf. mica. Voltage rating same as driver plate voltage plus safety factor.
L$_1$—To resonate at operating frequency with C$_1$. See LC chart and inductance formula in electrical-laws chapter, or use ARRL Lightning Calculator.
L$_2$—Pi-section inductor—See Fig. 6-12. Approx. same as L$_1$.
RFC$_1$—Grid r.f. choke—2.5-mh.
RFC$_2$—Driver plate r.f. choke—2.5 mh.

also as the grid tank of the amplifier. Although it is used more frequently than any other system, it is less flexible and has certain limitations that must be taken into consideration.

The two stages cannot be separated physically any appreciable distance without involving loss in transferred power, radiation from the coupling lead and the danger of feedback from this lead. Since both the output capacitance of the driver tube and the input capacitance of the amplifier are across the single circuit, it is sometimes difficult to obtain a tank circuit with a sufficiently low Q to provide an efficient circuit at the higher frequencies. The coupling can be varied by altering the capacitance of the coupling capacitor, C$_2$. The driver load impedance is the sum of the amplifier grid resistance and the reactance of the coupling capacitor in series, the coupling capacitor serving simply as a series reactor. The driver load resistance increases with a decrease in the capacitance of the coupling capacitor.

When the amplifier grid impedance is lower than the optimum load resistance for the driver, a transforming action is possible by tapping the grid down on the tank coil, but this is not recom-mended because it invariably causes an increase in v.h.f. harmonics and sometimes sets up a parasitic circuit.

So far as coupling is concerned, the Q of the circuit is of little significance. However, the other considerations discussed earlier in connection with tank-circuit Q should be observed.

Pi-Network Interstage Coupling

A pi-section tank circuit, as shown in Fig. 6-21B, may be used as a coupling device between screen-grid amplifier stages. The circuit can also be considered a coupling arrangement with the grid of the amplifier tapped down on the circuit by means of a capacitive divider. In contrast to the tapped-coil method mentioned previously, this system will be very effective in reducing v.h.f. harmonics, because the output capacitor, C$_8$, provides a direct capacitive shunt for harmonics across the amplifier grid circuit.

To be most effective in reducing v.h.f. harmonics, C$_8$ should be a mica capacitor connected directly across the tube-socket terminals. Tapping down on the circuit in this manner also helps to stabilize the amplifier at the operating frequency because of the grid-circuit loading provided by C_8. For the purposes both of stability and harmonic reduction, experience has shown that a value of 100 pf. for C_8 usually is sufficient. In general, C_7 and L_2 should have values approximating the capacitance and inductance used in a conventional tank circuit. A reduction in the inductance of L_2 results in an increase in coupling because C_7 must be increased to retune the circuit to resonance. This changes the ratio of C_7 to C_8 and has the effect of moving the grid tap up on the circuit. Since the coupling to the grid is comparatively loose under any condition, it may be found that it is impossible to utilize the full power capability of the driver stage. If sufficient excitation cannot be obtained, it may be necessary to raise the plate voltage of the driver, if this is permissible. Otherwise a larger driver tube may be required. As shown in Fig. 6-21B, parallel driver plate feed and amplifier grid feed are necessary.

R.F. POWER AMPLIFIER CIRCUITRY

STABILIZING AMPLIFIERS

A straight amplifier operates with its input and output circuits tuned to the same frequency. Therefore, unless the coupling between these two circuits is brought to the necessary minimum, the amplifier will oscillate as a tuned-plate tuned-grid circuit. Care should be used in arranging components and wiring of the two circuits so that there will be negligible opportunity for coupling external to the tube itself. Complete shielding between input and output circuits usually is required. All r.f. leads should be kept as short as possible and particular attention should be paid to the r.f. return paths from plate and grid tank circuits to cathode. In general, the best arrangement is one in which the cathode connection to ground, and the plate tank circuit are on the same side of the chassis or other shielding. The "hot" lead from the grid tank (or driver plate tank) should be brought to the socket through a hole in the shielding. Then when the grid tank capacitor or bypass is grounded, a return path through the hole to cathode will be encouraged, since transmission-line characteristics are simulated.

A check on external coupling between input and output circuits can be made with a sensitive indicating device, such as the one diagrammed in Fig. 6-22. The amplifier tube is removed from its socket and if the plate terminal is at the

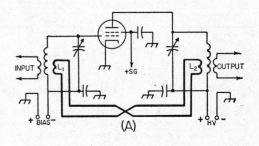

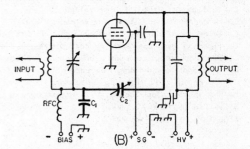

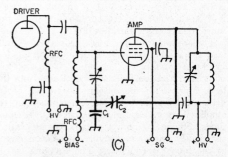

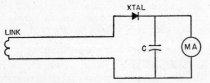

Fig. 6-22—Circuit of sensitive neutralizing indicator. Xtal is a 1N34 germanium diode, MA a 0-1 direct-current milliammeter and C a 0.001-μf. mica bypass capacitor.

socket, it should be disconnected. With the driver stage running and tuned to resonance, the indicator should be coupled to the output tank coil and the output tank capacitor tuned for any indication of r.f. feedthrough. Experiment with shielding and rearrangement of parts will show whether the isolation can be improved.

Screen-Grid Tube Neutralizing Circuits

The plate-grid capacitance of screen-grid tubes is reduced to a fraction of a micromicrofarad by

Fig. 6-23—Screen-grid neutralizing circuits. A—Inductive neutralizing. B-C—Capacitive neutralizing.

C_1—Grid bypass capacitor—approx. 0.001-μf. mica. Voltage rating same as biasing voltage in B, same as driver plate voltage in C.

C_2—Neutralizing capacitor—approx. 2 to 10 μμf.—see text. Voltage rating same as amplifier plate voltage for c.w., twice this value for plate modulation.

L_1, L_2—Neutralizing link—usually a turn or two will be sufficient.

the interposed grounded screen. Nevertheless, the power sensitivity of these tubes is so great that only a very small amount of feedback is necessary to start oscillation. To assure a stable amplifier, it is usually necessary to load the grid circuit, or to use a neutralizing circuit.

Fig. 6-23A shows how a screen-grid amplifier may be neutralized by the use of an inductive link line coupling the input and output tank circuits in proper phase. If the initial connection proves to be incorrect, connections to one of the link coils should be reversed. Neutralizing is adjusted by changing the distance between the link coils and the tank coils.

A capacitive neutralizing system for screen-grid tubes is shown in Fig. 6-23B. C_2 is the neutralizing capacitor. The capacitance should be chosen so that at some adjustment of C_2,

$$\frac{C_2}{C_1} = \frac{\text{Tube grid-plate capacitance (or } C_{gp})}{\text{Tube input capacitance (or } C_{IN})}$$

The grid-cathode capacitance must include all strays directly across the tube capacitance, including the capacitance of the tuning-capacitor stator to ground. This may amount to 5 to 20 $\mu\mu f$. In the case of capacitance coupling, as shown in Fig. 6-23C, the output capacitance of the driver tube must be added to the grid-cathode capacitance of the amplifier in arriving at the value of C_2.

Neutralizing a Screen-Grid Amplifier Stage

There are two general procedures available for indicating neutralization in a screen-grid amplifier stage. If the screen-grid tube is operated with or without grid current, a sensitive output indicator can be used. If the screen-grid tube is operated with grid current, the grid-current reading can be used as an indication of neutralization. When the output indicator is used, both screen and plate voltages must be removed from the tubes, but the d.c. circuits from plate and screen to cathode must be completed. If the grid-current reading is used, the plate voltage may remain on but the screen voltage must be zero, with the d.c. circuit completed between screen and cathode.

The immediate objective of the neutralizing process is reducing to a minimum the r.f. driver voltage fed from the input of the amplifier to its output circuit through the grid-plate capacitance of the tube. This is done by adjusting carefully, bit by bit, the neutralizing capacitor or link coils until an r.f. indicator in the output circuit reads minimum, or the reaction of the unloaded plate-circuit tuning on the grid-current value is minimized.

The device shown in Fig. 6-22 makes a sensitive neutralizing indicator. The link should be coupled to the output tank coil at the low-potential or "ground" point. Care should be taken to make sure that the coupling is loose enough at all times to prevent burning out the meter or the rectifier. The plate tank capacitor should be readjusted for maximum reading after each change in neutralizing.

When the grid-current meter is used as a neutralizing indicator, the screen should be grounded for r.f. and d.c., as mentioned above. There will be a change in grid current as the unloaded plate tank circuit is tuned through resonance. The neutralizing capacitor (or inductor) should be adjusted until this deflection is brought to a minimum. As a final adjustment, screen voltage should be returned and the neutralizing adjustment continued to the point where minimum plate current, maximum grid current and maximum screen current occur simultaneously. An increase in grid current when the plate tank circuit is tuned slightly on the high-frequency side of resonance indicates that the neutralizing capacitance is too small. If the increase is on the low-frequency side, the neutralizing capacitance is too large. When neutralization is complete, there should be a slight decrease in grid current on either side of resonance.

Grid Loading

The use of a neutralizing circuit may often be avoided by loading the grid circuit if the driving stage has some power capability to spare. Loading by tapping the grid down on the grid tank coil (or the plate tank coil of the driver in the case of capacitive coupling), or by a resistor from grid to cathode is effective in stabilizing an amplifier, but either device may increase v.h.f. harmonics. The best loading system is the use of a pi-section filter, as shown in Fig. 6-21B. This circuit places a capacitance directly between grid and cathode. This not only provides the desirable loading, but also a very effective capacitive short for v.h.f. harmonics. A 100-pf. mica capacitor for C_8, wired directly between tube terminals, will usually provide sufficient loading to stabilize the amplifier.

V.H.F. Parasitic Oscillation

Parasitic oscillation in the v.h.f. range will take place in almost every r.f. power amplifier. To test for v.h.f. parasitic oscillation, the grid tank coil (or driver tank coil in the case of ca-

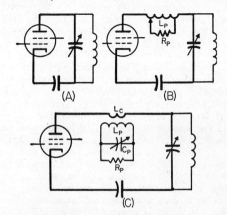

Fig. 6-24—A—Usual parasitic circuit. B—Resistive loading of parasitic circuit. C—Inductive coupling of loading resistance into parasitic circuit.

pacitive coupling) should be short-circuited with a clip lead. This is to prevent any possible t.g.t.p. oscillation at the operating frequency which might lead to confusion in identifying the parasitic. Any fixed bias should be replaced with a grid leak of 10,000 to 20,000 ohms. All load on the output of the amplifier should be disconnected. Plate and screen voltages should be reduced to the point where the rated dissipation is not exceeded. If a Variac is not available, voltage may be reduced by a 115-volt lamp in series with the primary of the plate transformer.

With power applied only to the amplifier under test, a search should be made by adjusting the input capacitor to several settings, including minimum and maximum, and turning the plate capacitor through its range for each of the grid-capacitor settings. Any grid current, or any dip or flicker in plate current at any point, indicates oscillation. This can be confirmed by an indicating absorption wavemeter tuned to the frequency of the parasitic and held close to the plate lead of the tube.

The heavy lines of Fig. 6-24A show the usual parasitic tank circuit, which resonates, in most cases, between 150 and 200 Mc. For each type of tetrode, there is a region, usually below the parasitic frequency, in which the tube will be self-neutralized. By adding the right amount of inductance to the parasitic circuit, its resonant frequency can be brought down to the frequency at which the tube is self-neutralized. However, the resonant frequency should not be brought down so low that it falls close to TV Channel 6 (88 Mc.). From the consideration of TVI, the circuit may be loaded down to a frequency not lower than 100 Mc. If the self-neutralizing frequency is below 100 Mc., the circuit should be loaded down to somewhere between 100 and 120 Mc. with inductance. Then the parasitic can be suppressed by loading with resistance, as shown in Fig. 6-24B. A coil of 4 or 5 turns, $\frac{1}{4}$ inch in diameter, is a good starting size. With the tank capacitor turned to maximum capacitance, the circuit should be checked with a g.d.o. to make sure the resonance is above 100 Mc. Then, with the shortest possible leads, a noninductive 100-ohm 1-watt resistor should be connected across the entire coil. The amplifier should be tuned up to its highest-frequency band and operated at low voltage. The tap should be moved a little at a time to find the minimum number of turns required to suppress the parasitic. Then voltage should be increased until the resistor begins to feel warm after several minutes of operation, and the power input noted. This input should be compared with the normal input and the *power* rating of the resistor increased by this proportion; i.e., if the power is half normal, the wattage rating should be doubled. This increase is best made by connecting 1-watt *carbon* resistors in parallel to give a resultant of about 100 ohms. As power input is increased, the parasitic may start up again, so power should be applied only momentarily until it is made certain that the parasitic is still suppressed. If the parasitic starts

up again when voltage is raised, the tap must be moved to include more turns. So long as the parasitic is suppressed, the resistors will heat up only from the operating-frequency current.

Since the resistor can be placed across only that portion of the parasitic circuit represented by L_p, the latter should form as large a portion of the circuit as possible. Therefore, the tank and bypass capacitors should have the lowest possible inductance and the leads shown in heavy lines should be as short as possible and of the heaviest practical conductor. This will permit L_p to be of maximum size without tuning the circuit below the 100-Mc. limit.

Another arrangement that has been used successfully is shown in Fig. 6-24C. A small turn or two is inserted in place of L_p and this is coupled to a circuit tuned to the parasitic frequency and loaded with resistance. The heavy-line circuit should first be checked with a g.d.o. Then the loaded circuit should be tuned to the same frequency and coupled in to the point where the parasitic ceases. The two coils can be wound on the same form and the coupling varied by sliding one of them. Slight retuning of the loaded circuit may be required after coupling. Start out with low power as before, until the parasitic is suppressed. Since the loaded circuit in this case carries much less operating-frequency current, a single 100-ohm 1-watt resistor will often be sufficient and a 30-pf. mica trimmer should serve as the tuning capacitor, C_p.

Low-Frequency Parasitic Oscillation

The screening of most transmitting screen-grid tubes is sufficient to prevent low-frequency parasitic oscillation caused by resonant circuits set up by r.f. chokes in grid and plate circuits. Should this type of oscillation (usually between 200 and 1200 kc.) occur, see paragraph under triode amplifiers.

PARALLEL AND PUSH-PULL AMPLIFIERS

The circuits for parallel-tube amplifiers are the same as for a single tube, similar terminals of the tubes being connected together. The grid impedance of two tubes in parallel is half that of a single tube. This means that twice the grid tank capacitance shown in Fig. 6-20 should be used for the same Q.

The plate load resistance is halved so that the plate tank capacitance for a single tube (Fig. 6-10) also should be doubled. The total grid current will be doubled so to maintain the same grid bias, the grid-leak resistance should be half that used for a single tube. The required driving power is doubled. The capacitance of a neutralizing capacitor, if used, should be doubled and the value of the screen dropping resistor should be cut in half.

In treating parasitic oscillation, it is often necessary to use a choke in each plate lead, rather than one in the common lead to avoid building in a push-pull type of v.h.f. circuit, a factor in obtaining efficient operation at higher frequencies.

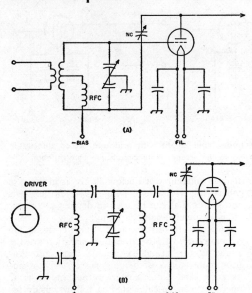

Fig. 6-25—When a pi-network output circuit is used with a triode, a balanced grid circuit must be provided for neutralizing. A—Inductive-link input. B—Capacitive input coupling.

Basic push-pull circuits are shown in Fig. 6-26C and D. Amplifiers using this circuit are cumbersome to bandswitch and consequently are not very popular below 30 Mc. However, since the push-pull configuration places tube input and output capacitances in series, the circuit is widely used at 50 Mc. and higher.

TRIODE AMPLIFIERS

Circuits for triode amplifiers are shown in Fig. 6-26. All triode straight amplifiers (not multipliers) must be neutralized. From the tube tables, it will be seen that triodes require considerably more driving power than screen-grid tubes. However, they also have less power sensitivity, so that greater feedback can be tolerated without the danger of instability.

Triode amplifiers can be neutralized using either the sensitive output rectifier or the grid-current meter as an indicator. In either case, the plate voltage must be zero and the d.c. circuit complete between plate and cathode.

Low-Frequency Parasitic Oscillation

When r.f. chokes are used in both grid and plate circuits of a triode amplifier, the split-stator tank capacitors combine with the r.f. chokes to form a low-frequency parasitic circuit,

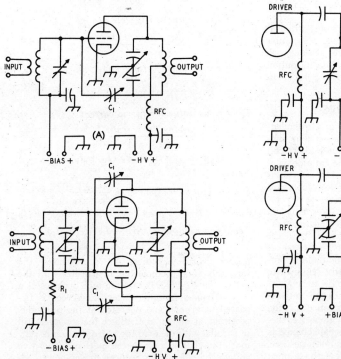

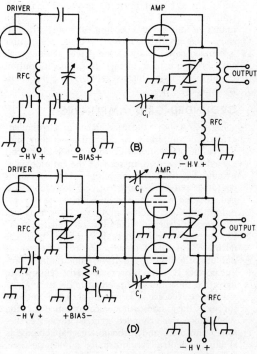

Fig. 6-26—Triode amplifier circuits. A—Link coupling, single tube. B—Capacitive coupling, single tube. C—Link coupling, push-pull. D—Capacitive coupling, push-pull. Aside from the neutralizing circuits, which are mandatory with triodes, the circuits are the same as for screen-grid tubes, and should have the same values throughout. The neutralizing capacitor, C_1, should have a capacitance somewhat greater than the grid-plate capacitance of the tube. Voltage rating should be twice the d.c. plate voltage for c.w., or four times for plate modulation, plus safety factor. The resistance R_1 should be at least 100 ohms and it may consist of part or preferably all of the grid leak. For other component values, see similar screen-grid diagrams.

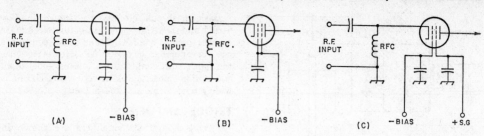

Fig. 6-27—A—Grounded-grid triode input circuit. B—Tetrode input circuit with grid and screen directly in parallel. C—Tetrode circuit with d.c. voltage applied to the screen. Plate circuits are conventional.

unless the amplifier circuit is arranged to prevent it. In the circuit of Fig. 6-26B, the amplifier grid is series fed and the driver plate is parallel fed. For low frequencies, the r.f. choke in the driver plate circuit is shorted to ground through the tank coil. In Figs. 6-26C and D, a resistor is substituted for the grid r.f. choke. This resistance should be at least 100 ohms. If any grid-leak resistance is used for biasing, it should be substituted for the 100-ohm resistor.

Triode Amplifiers with Pi-Network Output

Pi-network output tanks, designed as described earlier for screen-grid tubes, may also be used with triodes. However, in this case, a balanced input circuit must be provided for neutralizing. Fig. 6-25A shows the circuit when inductive-link input coupling is used, while B shows the circuit to be used when the amplifier is coupled capacitively to the driver. Pi-network circuits cannot be used in *both* input and output circuits, since no means is provided for neutralizing.

GROUNDED-GRID AMPLIFIERS

Fig. 6-27A shows the input circuit of a grounded-grid triode amplifier. In configuration it is similar to the conventional grounded-cathode circuit except that the grid, instead of the cathode, is at ground potential. An amplifier of this type is characterized by a comparatively low input impedance and a relatively high driver-power requirement. The additional driver power is not consumed in the amplifier but is "fed through" to the plate circuit where it combines with the normal plate output power. The total r.f. power output is the sum of the driver and amplifier output powers less the power normally required to drive the tube in a grounded-cathode circuit.

Positive feedback is from plate to cathode through the plate-cathode capacitance of the tube. Since the grounded grid is interposed between the plate and cathode, this capacitance is small, and neutralization usually is not necessary.

In the grounded-grid circuit the cathode must be isolated for r.f. from ground. This presents a practical difficulty especially in the case of a filament-type tube whose filament current is large. In plate-modulated phone operation the driver power fed through to the output is not modulated.

The chief application for grounded-grid amplifiers in amateur work below 30 Mc. is in the case where the available driving power far exceeds the power that can be used in driving a conventional grounded-cathode amplifier.

D.c. electrode voltages and currents in grounded-grid triode-amplifier operation are the same as for grounded-cathode operation. Approximate values of driving power, driving impedance, and total power output in Class C operation can be calculated as follows, using information normally provided in tube data sheets. R.m.s. values are of the fundamental components:

E_p = r.m.s. value of r.f. plate voltage =

$$\frac{d.c.\ plate\ volts + d.c.\ bias\ volts - peak\ r.f.\ grid\ volts}{1.41}$$

I_p = r.m.s. value of r.f. plate current

$$= \frac{rated\ power\ output\ watts}{E_p}$$

E_g = r.m.s. value of grid driving voltage

$$= \frac{peak\ r.f.\ grid\ volts}{1.41}$$

I_g = r.m.s. value of r.f. grid current

$$= \frac{rated\ driving\ power\ watts}{E_g}$$

Driving power (watts) $= E_g\ (I_p + I_g)$

Then

Driving impedance (ohms) $= \dfrac{E_g}{I_g + I_p}$

Power fed through from driver stage (watts) $= E_g I_p$

Total power output (watts) $= I_p\ (E_g + E_p)$

Screen-grid tubes are also used sometimes in grounded-grid amplifiers. In some cases, the screen is simply connected in parallel with the grid, as in Fig. 6-27B, and the tube operates as a high-μ triode. In other cases, the screen is bypassed to ground and operated at the usual d.c. potential, as shown at C. Since the screen is still in parallel with the grid for r.f., operation is very much like that of a triode except that the positive voltage on the screen reduces driver-power requirements. Since the information usually furnished in tube-data sheets does not apply to triode-type operation, operating conditions are usually determined experimentally. In general, the bias is adjusted to produce maximum output (within the tube's dissipation rating) with the driving power available.

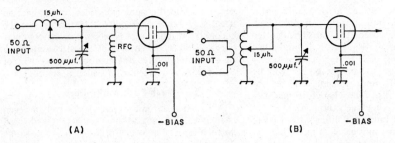

Fig. 6-28—Two ways to couple a low-impedance driver to a grounded-grid input. A—L network. B — Link - coupled tank circuit.

(A) (B)

Fig. 6-28 shows two methods of coupling a grounded-grid amplifier to the 50-ohm output of an existing transmitter. At A an L network is used, while a conventional link-coupled tank is shown at B. The values shown will be approximately correct for most triode amplifiers operating at 3.5 Mc. Values should be cut in half each time frequency is doubled, i.e., 250 $\mu\mu$f. and 7.5 μh. for 7 Mc., etc.

Filament Isolation

In indirectly-heated cathode tubes, the low heater-to-cathode capacitance will often provide enough isolation to keep r.f. out of the heater transformer and the a.c. lines. If not, the heater voltage must be applied through r.f. chokes.

In a directly-heated cathode tube, the filament must be maintained above r.f. ground. This can be done by using a pair of filament chokes or by using the input tank circuit, as shown in Fig. 6-29. In the former method, a double solenoid (often wound on a ferrite core) is generally used, although separate chokes can be used. When the tank circuit is used, the tank inductor is wound from two (insulated) conductors in parallel or from an insulated conductor inside a tubing outer conductor.

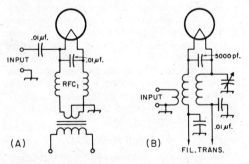

Fig. 6-29—Methods of isolating filament from ground. A—R.f. chokes in filament circuit. B—Filament fed through input tank inductor.

OUTPUT POWER AMPLIFIERS FOR TRANSMITTERS

C.w. or F.M.: In a c.w. or f.m. transmitter, any class of amplifier can be used as an output or intermediate amplifier. (For reasonable efficiency, a frequency multiplier *must* be operated Class C.) Class-C operation of the amplifier gives the highest efficiency (65 to 75 per cent), but it is likely to be accompanied by appreciable harmonics and consequent TVI possibilities. If the excitation is keyed in a c.w. transmitter, Class-C operation of subsequent amplifiers will, under certain conditions, introduce key clicks not present on the keyed excitation (see chapter on "Code Transmission"). The *peak envelope power* (p.e.p.) input or output of any c.w. (or f.m.) transmitter is the "key-down" input or output.

A.M.: In an amplitude-modulated phone transmitter, plate modulation of a Class-C output amplifier results in the highest output for a given input to the output stage. The efficiency is the same as for c.w. or f.m. with the same amplifier, from 65 to 75 per cent. (In most cases the manufacturer rates the *maximum allowable input* on plate-modulated phone at about 2/3 that of c.w. or f.m.). A plate-modulated stage running 100 watts input will deliver a carrier output of from 65 to 75 watts, depending upon the tube, frequency and circuit factors. The p.e.p. output of any a.m. signal is four times the carrier output power, or 260 to 300 watts for the 100-watt input example.

Grid- (control or screen) modulated output amplifiers in a.m. operation run at a carrier efficiency of 30 to 35 per cent, and a grid-modulated stage with 100 watts input has a carrier output of 30 to 35 watts. (The p.e.p. output, four times the carrier output, is 120 to 140 watts.

Running the legal input limit in the United States, a plate-modulated output stage can deliver a carrier output of 650 to 750 watts, while a screen- or control-grid-modulated output amplifier can deliver only a carrier of 300 to 350 watts.

S.S.B.: Only *linear* amplifiers can be used to amplify s.s.b. signals without distortion, and this limits the choice of output amplifier operation to Classes A, AB_1, AB_2 and B. The efficiency of operation of these amplifiers runs from about 20 to 65 per cent. In all but Class-A operation the indicated (by plate-current meter) input will vary with the signal, and it is not possible to talk about relative inputs and outputs as readily as it is with other modes. Therefore linear amplifiers are rated by p.e.p. (input or output) at a given distortion level, which indicates not only how much s.s.b. signal they will deliver but also how effective they will be in amplifying an a.m. signal.

LINEAR AMPLIFIERS FOR A.M.: In considering the practicality of adding a linear output amplifier to an existing a.m. transmitter, it is necessary to know the carrier output of the a.m. transmitter and the p.e.p. output rating of the linear amplifier. Since the p.e.p. output of an a.m. signal is four times the carrier output, it is obvious that a linear with a p.e.p. output rating of only four times the carrier output of the a.m. transmitter is no amplifier at all. If the linear amplifier has a p.e.p. output rating of *8* times the a.m. transmitter carrier output, the output power will be doubled and a 3-db. improvement will be obtained. In most cases a 3-db. change is *just discernible* by the receiving operator.

By comparison, a linear amplifier with a p.e.p. output rating of four times an existing s.s.b., c.w. or f.m. transmitter will *quadruple* the output, a 6-db. improvement. It should be noted that the linear amplifier must be rated for the mode (s.s.b., c.w. or f.m.) with which it is to be used.

GROUNDED-GRID AMPLIFIERS: The preceding discussion applies to vacuum-tube amplifiers connected in grounded-cathode or grounded-grid circuits. However, there are a few points that apply only to grounded-grid amplifiers.

A tube operated in a given class (AB_1, B, C) will require more driving power as a grounded-grid amplifier than as a grounded-cathode amplifier. This is not because the grid losses run higher in the grounded-grid configuration but because some of the driving power is coupled directly through the tube and appears in the plate load circuit. Provided enough driving power is available, this increased requirement is of no concern in c.w. or linear operation. In a.m. operation, however, the fed-through power prevents the grounded-grid amplifier from being fully modulated (100 per cent).

FREQUENCY MULTIPLIERS

Single-Tube Multiplier

Output at a multiple of the frequency at which it is being driven may be obtained from an amplifier stage if the output circuit is tuned to a harmonic of the exciting frequency instead of to the fundamental. Thus, when the frequency at the grid is 3.5 Mc., output at 7 Mc., 10.5 Mc., 14 Mc., etc., may be obtained by tuning the plate tank circuit to one of these frequencies. The circuit otherwise remains the same as that for a straight amplifier, although some of the values and operating conditions may require change for maximum multiplier efficiency.

A practical limit to efficiency and output within normal tube ratings is reached when the multiplier is operated at maximum permissible plate voltage and maximum permissible grid current. The plate current should be reduced as necessary to limit the dissipation to the rated value by increasing the bias and decreasing the loading.

Multiplications of four or five sometimes are used to reach the bands above 28 Mc. from a lower-frequency crystal, but in the majority of lower-frequency transmitters, multiplication in a single stage is limited to a factor of two or three. Screen-grid tubes make the best multipliers because their high power-sensitivity makes them easier to drive properly than triodes.

Since the input and output circuits are not tuned close to the same frequency, neutralization usually will not be required. Instances may be encountered with tubes of high trans-conductance, however, when a doubler will oscillate in t.g.t.p. fashion. The link neutralizing system of Fig. 6-23A is convenient in such a contingency.

Push-Push Multipliers

A two-tube circuit which works well at even harmonics, but not at the fundamental or odd harmonics, is shown in Fig. 6-30. It is known as the **push-push** circuit. The grids are connected in push-pull while the plates are connected in parallel. The efficiency of a doubler using this circuit approaches that of a straight amplifier.

This arrangement has an advantage in some applications. If the heater of one tube is turned off, its grid-plate capacitance, being the same as that of the remaining tube, serves to neutralize

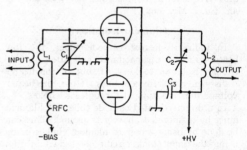

Fig. 6-30—Circuit of a push-push frequency multiplier for even harmonics.
C_1L_1 and C_2L_2—See text.
C_3—Plate bypass—0.001-μf. disk ceramic or mica.

the circuit. Thus provision is made for either straight amplification at the fundamental with a single tube, or doubling frequency with two tubes.

The grid tank circuit is tuned to the frequency of the driving stage and should have the same constants as indicated in Fig. 6-20 for balanced grid circuits. The plate tank circuit is tuned to an even multiple of the exciting frequency, and should have the same values as a straight amplifier for the harmonic frequency (see Fig. 6-10), bearing in mind that the total plate current of both tubes determines the C to be used.

Push-Pull Multiplier

A single- or parallel-tube multiplier will deliver output at either even or odd multiples of the exciting frequency. A push-pull stage does not work as a doubler or quadrupler but it will work as a tripler.

METERING

Fig. 6-31 shows how a voltmeter and milliammeter should be connected to read various voltages and currents. Voltmeters are seldom installed permanently, since their principal use is in preliminary checking. Also, milliammeters are not normally installed permanently in all of the positions shown. Those most often used are the

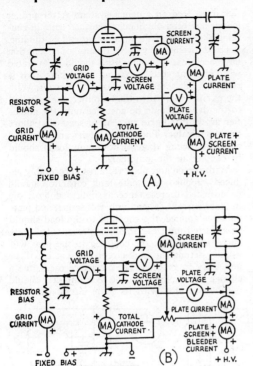

(A)

(B)

Fig. 6-31—Diagrams showing placement of voltmeter and milliammeter to obtain desired measurements. A—Series grid feed, parallel plate feed and series screen voltage-dropping resistor. B—Parallel grid feed, series plate feed and screen voltage divider.

ones reading grid current and plate current, or grid current and cathode current.

Milliammeters come in various current ranges. Current values to be expected can be taken from the tube tables and the meter ranges selected accordingly. To take care of normal overloads and pointer swing, a meter having a current range of about twice the normal current to be expected should be selected.

Grid-current meters connected as shown in Fig. 6-31 and meters connected in the cathode circuit need no special precautions in mounting on the transmitter panel so far as safety is concerned. However, milliammeters having zero-adjusting screws on the face of the meter should be recessed behind the panel so that accidental contact with the adjusting screw is not possible, if the meter is connected in any of the other positions shown in Fig. 6-31. The meter can be mounted on a small subpanel attached to the front panel with long screws and spacers. The meter opening should be covered with glass or celluloid. Illuminated meters make reading easier. Reference should also be made to the TVI chapter of this *Handbook* in regard to wiring and shielding of meters to suppress TVI.

Meter Switching

Milliammeters are expensive items and therefore it is seldom feasible to provide metering of

grid, screen and plate currents of all stages. The exciter stages in a multistage transmitter often do not require metering after initial adjustments. It is common practice to provide a meter-switching system by which a single milliammeter may be switched to read currents in as many circuits as desired. Two such meter-switching circuits are shown in Fig. 6-32. In Fig. 6-32A the resistors R (there could be more, of course) are connected in the various circuits in place of the milliammeters shown in Fig. 6-31. If the resistance of R is much higher than the internal resistance of the milliammeter, it will have no practical effect upon the reading of the meter. Care should be taken to observe proper polarity in making the connections between the resistors and the switch, and the switch should have adequate insulation and be of the "non-shorting" type. The circuit is used when the currents to be metered are of the same order.

When the meter must read currents of widely differing values, a low-current meter should be used as a voltmeter to measure the voltage drop across a resistor of, say, 10 to 100 ohms. An example of this circuit is shown in Fig. 6-32B; the resistor in series with the meter serves as the voltmeter multiplier (see chapter on measurements). Both the line resistor and the higher multiplier can be varied, to give a wide range for the single meter. Standard values of resistors can usually be found for any desired range.

AMPLIFIER ADJUSTMENT

Earlier sections in this chapter have dealt with the design and adjustment of input (grid) and

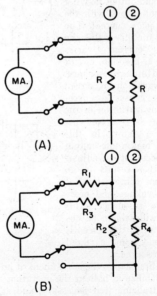

(A)

(B)

Fig. 6-32—Two circuits for switching a single milliammeter. (A) Where all currents are of the same order, the single meter is switched across resistors having 10 to 20 times the internal resistance of the meter. (B) Where a wide range of currents is to be metered, a low-current meter is used as a voltmeter.

output (plate) coupling systems, the stabilization of amplifiers, and the methods of obtaining the required electrode voltages. Reference to these sections should be made as necessary in following a procedure of amplifier adjustment.

The objective in the adjustment of an intermediate amplifier stage is to secure adequate excitation to the following stage. In the case of the output or final amplifier, the objective is to obtain maximum power output to the antenna. The adjustment must be consistent with the tube's voltage, current and dissipation ratings.

Adequate drive to a following amplifier is normally indicated when rated grid current in the following stage is obtained with the stage operating at rated bias, the stage loaded to rated plate current, and the driver stage tuned to resonance. In a final amplifier, maximum output is normally indicated when the output coupling is adjusted so that the amplifier tube draws rated plate current when it is tuned to resonance.

Resonance in the plate circuit is normally indicated by the dip in plate-current reading as the plate tank capacitor is tuned through its range. When the stage is unloaded, or lightly loaded, this dip in plate current will be quite pronounced. As the loading is increased, the dip will become less noticeable. See Fig. 6-4. However, in the base of a screen-grid tube whose screen is fed through a series resistor, maximum output may not be simultaneous with the dip in plate current. The reason for this is that the screen current varies widely as the plate circuit is tuned through resonance. This variation in screen current causes a corresponding variation in the voltage drop across the screen resistor. In this case, maximum output may occur at an adjustment that results in an optimum combination of screen voltage and nearness to resonance. This effect will seldom be observed when the screen is operated from a fixed voltage source.

The first step in the adjustment of an amplifier is to stabilize it, both at the operating frequency by neutralizing it if necessary, and at parasitic frequencies by introducing suppression circuits.

If "flat" transmission-line coupling is used, the output end of the line should be matched, as described in this chapter for the case where the amplifier is to feed the grid of a following stage, or in the transmission-line chapter if the ampli-

fier is to feed an antenna system. After proper match has been obtained, all adjustments in coupling should be made at the *input* end of the line.

Until preliminary adjustments of excitation have been made, the amplifier should be operated with filament voltage on and fixed bias, if it is required, but screen and plate voltages off. With the exciter coupled to the amplifier, the coupling to the driver should be adjusted until the amplifier draws rated grid current, or somewhat above the rated value. Then a load (the antenna grid of the following stage, or a dummy load) should be coupled to the amplifier.

With screen and plate voltages (preferably reduced) applied, the plate tank capacitor should be adjusted to resonance as indicated by a dip in plate current. Then, with full screen and plate voltages applied, the coupling to the load should be adjusted until the amplifier draws rated plate current. Changing the coupling to the load will usually detune the tank circuit, so that it will be necessary to readjust for resonance each time a change in coupling is made. An amplifier should not be operated with its plate circuit off reso-

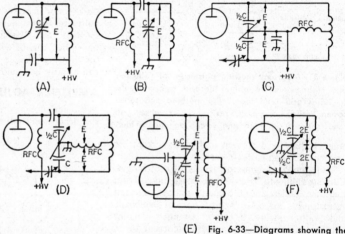

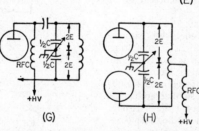

Fig. 6-33—Diagrams showing the peak voltage for which the plate tank capacitor should be rated for c.w. operation with various circuit arrangements. E is equal to the d.c. plate voltage. The values should be doubled for plate modulation. The circuit is assumed to be fully loaded. Circuits A, C and E require that the tank capacitor be insulated from chassis or ground, and from the control.

nance for any except the briefest necessary time, since the plate dissipation increases greatly when the plate circuit is not at resonance. Also, a screen-grid tube should not be operated without normal load for any appreciable length of time, since the screen dissipation increases.

It is normal for the grid current to decrease when the plate voltage is applied, and to decrease again as the amplifier is loaded more heavily. As the grid current falls off, the coupling to the driver should be increased to maintain the grid current at its rated value.

COMPONENT RATINGS AND INSTALLATION

Plate Tank-Capacitor Voltage

In selecting a tank capacitor with a spacing between plates sufficient to prevent voltage breakdown, the peak r.f. voltage across a tank circuit under load, but without modulation, may be taken conservatively as equal to the d.c. plate voltage. If the d.c. plate voltage also appears across the tank capacitor, this must be added to the peak r.f. voltage, making the total peak voltage twice the d.c. plate voltage. If the amplifier is to be plate-modulated, this last value must be doubled to make it four times the d.c. plate voltage, because both d.c. and r.f. voltages double with 100-per-cent plate modulation. At the higher plate voltages, it is desirable to choose a tank circuit in which the d.c. and modulation voltages do not appear across the tank capacitor, to permit the use of a smaller capacitor with less plate spacing. Fig. 6-33 shows the peak voltage, in terms of d.c. plate voltage, to be expected across the tank capacitor in various circuit arrangements. These peak-voltage values are given assuming that the amplifier is loaded to rated plate current. Without load, the peak r.f. voltage will run much higher.

The plate spacing to be used for a given peak voltage will depend upon the design of the variable capacitor, influencing factors being the mechanical construction of the unit, the insulation used and its placement in respect to intense fields, and the capacitor plate shape and degree of polish. Capacitor manufacturers usually rate their products in terms of the peak voltage between plates. Typical plate spacings are shown in the following table.

Typical Tank-Capacitor Plate Spacings					
Spacing (In.)	Peak Voltage	Spacing (In.)	Peak Voltage	Spacing (In.)	Peak Voltage
0.015	1000	0.07	3000	0.175	7000
0.02	1200	0.08	3500	0.25	9000
0.03	1500	0.125	4500	0.35	11000
0.05	2000	0.15	6000	0.5	13000

Plate tank capacitors should be mounted as close to the tube as temperature considerations will permit, to make possible the shortest capacitive path from plate to cathode. Especially at the higher frequencies where minimum circuit capacitance becomes important, the capacitor should be mounted with its stator plates well spaced from the chassis or other shielding. In circuits where the rotor must be insulated from ground, the capacitor should be mounted on ceramic insulators of size commensurate with the plate voltage involved and — most important of all, from the viewpoint of safety to the operator — a well-insulated coupling should be used between the capacitor shaft and the dial. *The sec-*

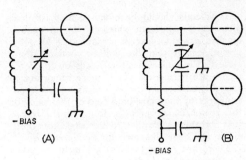

Fig. 6-34—The voltage rating of the grid tank capacitor in A should be equal to the biasing voltage plus about 20 per cent of the plate voltage.

tion of the shaft attached to the dial should be well grounded. This can be done conveniently through the use of panel shaft-bearing units.

Grid Tank Capacitors

In the circuit of Fig. 6-34A, the grid tank capacitor should have a voltage rating approximately equal to the biasing voltage plus 20 per cent of the plate voltage. In the balanced circuit of B, the voltage rating of *each section* of the capacitor should be this same value.

The grid tank capacitor is preferably mounted with shielding between it and the tube socket for isolation purposes. It should, however, be mounted close to the socket so that a short lead can be passed through a hole to the socket. The rotor ground lead or bypass lead should be run directly to the nearest point on the chassis or other shielding. In the circuit of Fig. 6-34A, the same insulating precautions mentioned in connection with the plate tank capacitor should be used.

Plate Tank Coils

The inductance of a manufactured coil usually is based upon the highest plate-voltage/plate-current ratio likely to be used at the maximum power level for which the coil is designed. Therefore in the majority of cases, the capacitance shown by Figs. 6-9 and 6-20 will be greater than that for which the coil is designed and turns must be removed if a Q of 10 or more is needed. At 28 Mc., and sometimes 21 Mc., the value of capacitance shown by the chart for a high plate-voltage/plate-current ratio may be lower than that attainable in practice with the components available. The design of manufactured coils usually takes this into consideration also and it may be found that values of capacitance greater than those shown (if stray capacitance is included) are required to tune these coils to the band.

Manufactured coils are rated according to the plate-power input to the tube or tubes when the stage is loaded. Since the circulating tank current is much greater when the amplifier is unloaded, care should be taken to operate the amplifier conservatively when unloaded to prevent damage to the coil as a result of excessive heating.

Tank coils should be mounted at least their diameter away from shielding to prevent a marked loss in Q. Except perhaps at 28 Mc., it is not important that the coil be mounted quite close to the tank capacitor. Leads up to 6 or 8 inches are permissible. It is more important to keep the tank capacitor as well as other components out of the immediate field of the coil. For this reason, it is preferable to mount the coil so that its axis is parallel to the capacitor shaft, either alongside the capacitor or above it.

There are many factors that must be taken into consideration in determining the size of wire that should be used in winding a tank coil. The considerations of form factor and wire size that will produce a coil of minimum loss are often of less importance in practice than the coil size that will fit into available space or that will handle the required power without excessive heating. This is particularly true in the case of screen-grid tubes where the relatively small driving power required can be easily obtained even if the losses in the driver are quite high. It may be considered preferable to take the power loss if the physical size of the exciter can be kept down by making the coils small.

The accompanying table shows typical conductor sizes that are usually found to be adequate for various power levels. For powers under 25 watts, the minimum wire sizes shown are largely a matter of obtaining a coil of reasonable Q. So far as the power is concerned, smaller wire could be used.

Wire Sizes for Transmitting Coils		
Power Input (Watts)	Band (Mc.)	Wire Size
1000	28-21	6
	14-7	8
	3.5-1.8	10
500	28-21	8
	14-7	12
	3.5-1.8	14
150	28-21	12
	14-7	14
	3.5-1.8	18
75	28-21	14
	14-7	18
	3.5-1.8	22
25 or less*	28-21	18
	14-7	24
	3.5-1.8	28

*Wire size limited principally by consideration of Q.

Space-winding the turns invariably will result in a coil of higher Q, especially at frequencies above 7 Mc., and a form factor in which the turns spacing results in a coil length between 1 and 2 times the diameter is usually considered satisfactory. Space winding is especially desirable at the higher power levels because the heat developed is dissipated more readily. The power lost in a tank coil that develops appreciable heat

at the higher-power levels does not usually represent a serious loss percentagewise. A more serious consequence, especially at the higher frequencies, is that coils of the popular "air-wound" type supported on plastic strips may deform. In this case, it may be necessary to use wire (or copper tubing) of sufficient size to make the coil self-supporting. Coils wound on tubular forms of ceramic or mica-filled bakelite will also stand higher temperatures.

Plate-Blocking and Bypass Capacitors

Plate-blocking and bypass capacitors should have low inductance. Between 3.5 and 30 Mc. a capacitance of 0.001 μf. is commonly used. The voltage rating should be 50% above the peak supply voltage.

Disk ceramic capacitors are to be preferred as bypass capacitors, since when they are applied correctly (see TVI chapter), they are series resonant in the TV range and thus very useful in filtering power leads.

R. F. Chokes

The characteristics of any r.f. choke will vary with frequency, from characteristics resembling those of a parallel-resonant circuit, of high impedance, to those of a series-resonant circuit, where the impedance is lowest. In between these extremes, the choke will show varying amounts of inductive or capacitive reactance.

In series-feed circuits, these characteristics are of relatively small importance because the r.f. voltage across the choke is negligible. In a parallel-feed circuit, however, the choke is shunted across the tank circuit, and is subject to the full tank r.f. voltage. If the choke does not present a sufficiently high impedance, enough power will be absorbed by the choke to cause it to burn out.

To avoid this, the choke must have a sufficiently high reactance to be effective at the lowest frequency, and yet have no series resonances near the higher-frequency bands.

Universal pie-wound chokes of the "receiver" type (2.5 mh., 125 ma.) are usually satisfactory if the plate voltage does not exceed 750. For higher voltages, a single-layer solenoid-type choke of correct design has been found satisfactory. The National type R-175A and Raypar RL-100, RL-101 and RL-102 are representative manufactured types.

Since the characteristics of a choke will be affected by any metal in its field, it should be checked when mounted in the position in which it is to be used, or in a temporary set-up simulating the same conditions. The plate end of the choke should not be connected, but the power-supply end should be connected directly, or bypassed, to the chassis. The g.d.o. should be coupled as close to the ground end of the choke as possible. Series resonances, indicating the frequencies of greatest loss, should be checked with the choke short-circuited with a short piece of wire. Parallel resonances, indicating frequencies of least loss, are checked with the short removed.

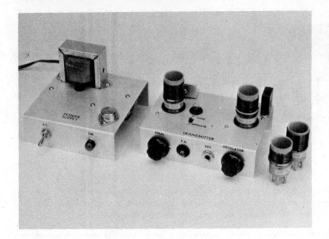

Fig. 6-35—Top-chassis layout of the transmitter and power supply. The oscillator stage is at the right of the transmitter chassis, the tune-operate switch is at the top-center of the chassis, and the p.a. stage is at the left. The heat sink for Q_2 is visible at the far left corner of the transmitter chassis—just behind the p.a. coil. Q_1 is behind the plug-in coil at the right rear of the chassis.

A TRANSISTOR 5-WATTER FOR 80 AND 40

This transmitter is capable of spanning great distances with its signal if used with a good antenna. It is easy to build and get operating, and at moderate cost. (Originally described in *QST*, June 1967.) Because it operates from 12 or 28 volts d.c., it is useful not only in a fixed station, but as a portable c.w. rig. It can be used to drive a vacuum-tube amplifier if higher power is desired.

The R.F. Circuit

In the circuit of Fig. 6-36, Q_1 serves as a modified Pierce oscillator with the crystal Y_1 connected between its base and collector. A 1000-pf. silver-mica capacitor is used between the base of Q_1 and ground to regulate feedback. The d.c. supply lead is broken at J_1 for keying, and a 100-ohm resistor and 10-μf. capacitor form a shaping network to give a click-free c.w. signal.

Q_1 and Q_2 are 5-watt n.p.n. transistors selected because of their low cost and reasonably-high upper-frequency limit ($f_T = 100$ Mc.). Many other types could be made to work in the circuit, probably with greater output and better efficiency. However, the 2N2102s do a fine job here even though the efficiency falls off slightly at 40 meters.

Equal outputs on both 80 and 40 meters no doubt could be obtained if u.h.f.-type transistors were used, but these are far more costly than the 2N2102s. Among the "hotter" transistors are the 2N3553, 40280, 40290, 2N3118, and others. If the builder is not experienced with transistor circuit design, it would be best to stick to the 2N2102s. Other types would require different bias resistor values, different driving-power levels, and different impedance-matching taps on the tuned circuits. Also, the "hotter" transistors might cause circuit instability, which is sometimes hard to cure in transistor rigs.

L_1L_2 is a plug-in coil assembly wound for a good impedance match between the collector of Q_1 and the base of Q_2. A 33-ohm resistor and 0.01-μf. capacitor are connected between the cold end of L_2 and ground. The resistor permits Q_2 to be driven farther into the class-C bias region than

would be possible without it, adding somewhat to the efficiency of the stage. Depending on the transistor used, the value of the base-leak resistor could be something other than 33 ohms for best efficiency. Ordinarily, the value will be somewhere between 10 and 100 ohms. If the builder wishes he can use a 100-ohm potentiometer in place of the fixed resistor and adjust it for optimum transmitter output.

A 56-ohm resistor is shown bridged across the base winding, L_2. This resistor was added to "load" the input circuit of Q_2 when a slight amount of instability was noted on 40 meters. The resistor cured the problem, but it may not be necessary to use it in other models. It can be eliminated if there is no instability.

The collector of Q_2 is tapped down on L_3, a plug-in coil, to provide a suitable impedance match to the antenna circuit, thus assuring maximum power transfer. L_4 is wound to match 50 ohms, but will work into a 75-ohm termination too. To use the transmitter with random-wire antennas, or feed lines of higher impedance than 75 ohms, a transmatch can be employed.[1]

A 250-ma. pilot lamp, I_1, is connected in series with the d.c. collector lead to Q_2, serving not only as a fuse but as a current indicator. Because the bulb causes a voltage drop of approximately 10 volts (key down) it limits the power input to Q_2 during tuneup. The bulb is shorted out by S_{1A} in normal operation. A No. 47 bulb, I_2, in series with the ground return side of L_4 serves as an r.f. output indicator for tuneup, and is shorted out by S_{1B} for normal operation. It lights to full brilliance when the transmitter is working into a proper load.

Power Supply Circuit

The power supply circuit of Fig. 6-39, takes advantage of the "electronic-filtering" concept

---

[1] See Chapter 13 for examples of transmatch construction and use.

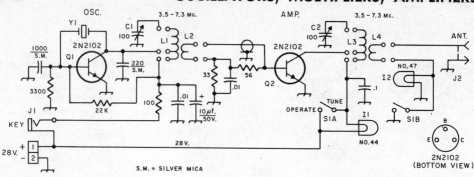

Fig. 6-36—Schematic diagram of the two-transistor transmitter. Except as indicated, decimal-value capacitances are in μf; others are in pf. Polarized capacitors are electrolytic; other fixed capacitors are disk ceramic. Resistances are in ohms (k = 1000). Resistors are ½-watt composition.

C_1, C_2—100-pf. miniature variable (Millen 20100).

I_1—250-ma. pilot lamp.

I_2—150-ma. pilot lamp.

J_1—Open-circuit jack.

J_2—Phono connector.

L_1—80 meters = 36 turns No. 24 enam. on 1-inch dia. form, close-wound. Tap 15¾ turns from C_1 end.

    40 meters = 18 turns No. 20 enam. close-wound on 1-inch dia. form. Tap at 5¾ turns from C_1 end.

L_2—80 meters = 6 turns No. 24 enam. close-wound over cold end of L_1.

    40 meters = 4 turns No. 20 enam. close-wound over cold end of L_1.

L_3—80 meters = 36 turns No. 24 enam. close-wound on 1-inch dia. form. Tap 12 turns from cold end.

    40 meters = 18 turns No. 20 enam. wire, close-wound on 1-inch dia. form. Tap 6 turns from cold end.

L_4—80 meters = 5 turns No. 24-enam., close-wound over cold end of L_3

    40 meters = 4 turns No. 20-enam., close-wound over cold end of L_3

S_1—D.p.s.t. slide switch.

Y_1—3.5- or 7.0-Mc. fundamental-cut crystal.

described in other *QST* articles.[2,3] Although at first glance the circuit may look like that of a regulated power supply, it isn't. For good d.c. regulation, Q_3 would need a voltage reference between its base and the negative side of the supply. However, the circuit offers some regulation and performs far better in that respect than would be the case if the operating voltage were taken directly from the bridge rectifier and filter capacitor.

The regulation is sufficient for the transmitter of Fig. 6-36. From no load to full-load current of about 250 ma. the voltage drop is approximately four volts—from 28 volts to 24 volts. Better regulation could be had by reducing the value of the 220-ohm resistor between the collector and base of Q_3, but this would increase the ripple in the output of the supply. The values given represent a good compromise. The r.f. output of the transmitter is free of noticeable a.c. ripple when operated from this power supply.

Assembling the Equipment

Home-made open-end aluminum chassis are used for both the power supply and the transmitter. The transmitter is built on a base which measures 1 × 4 × 5 inches. A Bud CB-1620 would be a suitable substitute. The power supply chassis measures 1 × 5 × 5 inches; a Bud CB-

1629 would work nicely there. A single chassis could contain the entire lash-up.

A heat sink is used to cool Q_2, and details of the home-made model are given in Fig. 6-38. The main body of the heat sink is a piece of aluminum angle, available from most hardware stores. The transistor is press-fit into

Fig. 6-37—Underside of the transmitter chassis. The oscillator circuit is at the right. The p.a. stage is at the left. Connection to I_1 and I_2 are soldered directly to the bases of the bulbs.

---

[2] "A Transistor Power Supply", *QST*, June 1962.

[3] "Galeski, The Imp TR", *QST*, Dec. 1961, page 10.

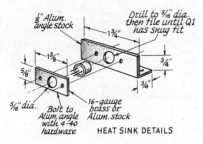

Fig. 6-38—Layout and assembly details of the home-made heat sink for Q₂. The completed assembly is insulated from the main chassis of the transmitter by using insulating washers or rubber grommets (see text).

a hole bored in the angle stock. A thin coating of silicone grease can be spread over the case of the transistor to provide more efficient heat transfer to the heat sink.[4] The complete transistor heat sink assembly is electrically isolated from the main chassis of the transmitter by means of insulating washers. Small rubber grommets (two) will work equally as well. No need to worry about the dielectric quality of the insulating material if rubber or fiber is used. At 80 and 40 meters there will be no measurable r.f. loss because the collector of Q_2 is operating at low impedance. Under normal conditions, the heat sink does not get hot enough to cause deterioration of rubber grommets if they are used.

Pilot lamps I_1 and I_2 are held in place by inserting them into ⅜-inch-diameter rubber grommets, as shown in the photos. The connections to the bulbs are soldered directly to their bases.

Transistor Q_3 is insulated from the power-supply chassis by a mica spacer and two nylon washers. The mounting hardware is furnished with the transistor. A thin layer of silicone grease is used between the transistor and the mica spacer, and between the spacer and the chassis. The chassis provides sufficient surface area to perform well as a heat sink for Q_3.

Winding the Coils

The coils are hand-wound on Millen 45005 mica-filled forms.[5] Small-diameter holes are drilled in the forms to allow the ends of the windings to be passed through to the inside and then down into the base pins, where they are soldered in place. The ends of the windings should be brought into the coil forms directly over the base pins in which the wires will be soldered; this will assure the shortest possible leads and will prevent the wires from crossing over one another inside

the coil form. The main windings are wound first. The secondary windings, L_2 and L_4, are wound *over* the cold ends of their respective primary windings to assure tight coupling—necessary in this circuit for optimum power transfer. A single layer of masking tape is used between the primary and secondary windings to prevent the possibility of short circuiting. The completed coils can be coated with coil cement to hold the turns firmly in place.

Operation

With the power supply connected to the transmitter, a dummy load connected to J_2, and a crystal plugged in at Y_1, apply power and key the transmitter. With S_1 in the TUNE position, adjust C_1 and C_2 for maximum brightness of I_2. Normally, this point will *not* occur when the collector current is at its absolute dip (minimum value of current). While tuning C_2, watch for a point at which I_2 shows maximum brightness with the least amount of brightness at I_1. Get as close as possible to the minimum-current condition at I_1 without sacrificing lamp brilliance at I_2. In other words, do not let Q_2 draw any more current than is necessary for maximum r.f. output. If the circuit is performing properly, Q_2 will draw between 200 and 225 ma. after tuneup. At this current, I_1 will be lit to normal brightness, or nearly so.

The next step is to adjust C_1 while monitoring the c.w. signal from the transmitter. It should be

A look into the underside of the power supply. The silicon rectifiers are mounted between two insulated terminal strips (right). The filter capacitors are installed in a similar fashion.

---

[4] Silicone grease is generally available from electronics supply houses for approximately $2.00 per tube. It is a worthwhile investment for those who experiment with power transistors.

[5] The Millen coil forms listed here, and other single-lot Millen components, can be purchased directly from the manufacturer, the James Millen Mfg. Co., Inc., 150 Exchange Street, Malden, Mass.

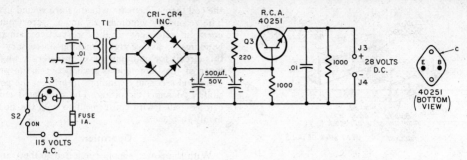

Fig. 6-39—Schematic diagram of the 28-volt power supply. Capacitance is in μf. Capacitors are disk ceramic except those with polarity marking, which are electrolytic. Resistance is in ohms; resistors are ½-watt composition.

CR_1-CR_4, inc.—750-ma. 50-p.i.v. top-hat rectifiers.

I_3—Neon panel-lamp assembly with built-in dropping resistor.

J_3, J_4—Insulated banana jack, one red (positive) and one black (negative).

S_2—S.p.s.t. toggle switch.

T_1—25.2 volt, 1-ampere filament transformer (Stancor P-6469 or equivalent).

possible to secure a clickless, chirp-free note. The transmitter should be in the OPERATE position for this test and the r.f. gain in the receiver should be retarded until the c.w. signal is coming in at $S9$ or less. Also, the receiver's a.g.c. should be disabled for this check.

Following these adjustments, the transmitter can be put into service. Tuneup into an antenna system should be done in the same manner as into the dummy load. I_2 can again be used during adjustment to indicate maximum transmitter output.

To protect the transistor, S_1 should always be in the TUNE position while the transmitter is being tuned up.

Some Final Comments

The transmitter was tried with a 12-volt power supply and it fired up without difficulty. The power output was a bit less than one-half the amount available with the 28-volt supply. (Output at 28 volts was 3.2 watts on 80 and 2.6 watts on 40.) In fact, the circuit performed satisfactorily at 6 volts, but the power output was less than one watt.

This transmitter is not practical for use on frequencies above 40 meters. The limiting factor here is the transistor type. With v.h.f. power transistors in the circuit, 20-meter operation should be possible.

USING A.M. WITH TRANSISTOR RIGS

When amplitude modulating transistorized transmitters, certain rules must be followed. The collector supply voltage of the stage, or stages, being modulated should be set no higher than one fourth the safe maximum collector-to-emitter voltage specified by the transistor manufacturer. This will allow for the four-times collector-voltage swing which occurs during the peak of the modulation cycle. With the 5-watter in the foregoing text, no more than 20 volts should be used to supply Q_2 if it is to be modulated. Also, modulation should not be applied unless the transmitter is properly loaded into a dummy or an antenna. Without a suitable load, the modulator will develop high peaks of voltage, which can in turn destroy the transistor stage being modulated.

The same rules apply for transistor rigs as do for vacuum-tube types when it comes to effecting an impedance match between the modulator and the modulated stages of the transmitter; use an audio power equal to one half the d.c. input

to the modulated stages. If 100-percent modulation is to be obtained, it is usually necessary to modulate the driver stage as well as the p.a., when a driver stage is used after the oscillator. If the p.a. runs at 5 watts input, the modulator should deliver at least 2.5 watts of undistorted audio output for good modulation. Push-pull class AB- or B-type modulators (transistorized) are recommended.

The modulator load impedance can be calculated by dividing the collector supply voltage by the collector current (loaded) in amperes. At 5 watts input (20-volt collector supply), the transmitter in the preceding text will present an 80-ohm load to the modulator. With no driver stage to modulate, 80-percent modulation is about the best that can be expected because of r.f. feedthrough from the oscillator stage.

The tuning of the driver and p.a. stages will usually have a marked effect on the quality of the modulated signal. It is suggested that an oscilloscope be used when tuning for the best waveform obtainable during modulation.

A ONE-TUBE TRANSMITTER FOR "80" AND "40"

Probably the simplest transmitter a beginner could build to get started in ham radio with is a one-tube crystal-controlled oscillator. This is a description of such a rig. It operates on the 80- and 40-meter bands. The transmitter can be run at about 35 watts input, which is more than enough power for making "solid" contacts around the country.

Circuit Details

The one-tuber is a grid-plate oscillator utilizing fundamental crystals for both bands (Fig. 6-40). A pi-network tank is used in the plate circuit of the 6146, and is designed to work into a 50- to 70-ohm load. Keying is accomplished by opening and closing the cathode circuit at J_1. R_2 and C_3 comprise a key-click filter.

The power supply uses full-wave rectification; diodes CR_1 and CR_2 are used for rectifiers. The filter network consists of C_7, R_3, and C_6. V_2 provides a regulated 105 volts for the oscillator screen.

Getting the Parts

All of the items (except L_1 and T_1) should be obtainable from any radio-parts distributor. V_1 is a 6146, but the 6146A and 6146B can also be used.

The one-tuber makes a neat package. The plate-tuning capacitor is just to the right of the meter. The loading capacitor is at the far right. Across the bottom from the left are the a.c. switch, key jack, and crystal socket, in that order.

T_1 is a commercially-available transformer, but a power transformer could be taken from an old TV set and used instead. A TV transformer

The tank-circuit components are grouped in the front left corner, just in front of the 6146. M_1 is at the upper right on the panel. At the rear is the power transformer with the regulator tube mounted just to the left of T_1.

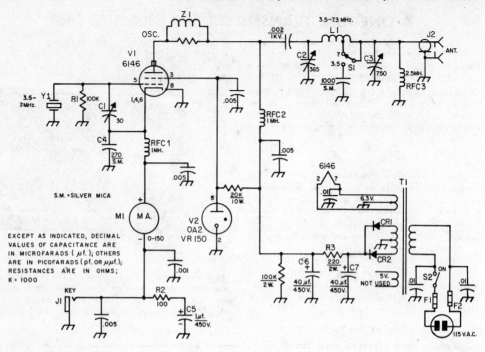

Fig. 6-40—Circuit diagram of the one-tube transmitter. Unless specified, all resistors are 1-watt. All decimal-value capacitors are disk ceramic. Capacitors with polarity marking are electrolytic.

C_1—2-30-pf. trimmer.

C_2—365-pf. variable (Miller 2111).

C_3—730-pf. varible (dual 365-pf.) stators connected in parallel (Miller 2112).

C_4—270-pf. silver mica.

C_5—1-uf. 450-volt electrolytic.

C_6, C_7—40-uf. 450-volt electrolytic.

CR_1, CR_2—600-volt p.i.v., 1-amp. silicon rectifier.

F_1, F_2—2-amp. fuse, type 3AG.

J_1—Open-circuit phone jack.

J_2—Coax chassis connector, type SO-239.

L_1—26 turns No. 16 enam., 8 turns per inch, 1¼-inch diam. (B & W 3018, Illumitronics 1008T). The 7-MHz. tap is 7 turns from the C_3 end of the coil.

M_1—0-150-ma. d.c.

R_1—100,000 ohms, 1 watt.

R_2—100 ohms, 1 watt.

R_3—220 ohms, 2 watts.

RFC_1, RFC_2—1-mh. r.f. choke (Millen 34200-1000, or similar).

RFC_3—2.5-mh. r.f. choke (Millen 34300-2500, or similar).

S_1—Phenolic rotary, 1 section, 1 pole, 11 positions, 2 positions used (Centralab type PA 2001 or similar).

S_2—S.p.s.t. toggle.

T_1—540 volts center-tapped, 120 ma., 6.3 volts, 3.5 amp., 5 volts, 3 amp. not used (Allied-Knight 61G466 or similar).

Z_1—10 turns No. 18 enam. space-wound on a 100-ohm 1-watt resistor.

would be larger than the part specified, but there is adequate chassis space for a larger unit. L_1 is a length of manufactured coil stock. However, there isn't any reason one couldn't wind his own coil on a suitable form—on a plastic pillbox, for example.

A standard aluminum chassis, 2 x 7 x 9 inches, is used to mount the parts. The front panel, 6 by 9 inches, the sides, and the bottom plate are made from a sheet of Reynolds "do-it-yourself" aluminum. Reynolds perforated aluminum stock is used for the top and back shielding. While TVI shouldn't be a problem with 80- and 40-meter

operation, shielding the rig will help in keeping harmonics from being radiated.

Construction Notes

Layout of the parts is not critical, but one should follow the general arrangement shown in the photographs. While it isn't so important in an oscillator such as this unit, one should always follow a set pattern in constructing radio gear. This is true for receivers and transmitters. All components associated with the grid (or input) circuit should be installed on the grid or input side of the tube and not mixed in with the

The 6146 socket is visible at the upper left corner. To the right of the tube socket are the two filter capacitors for the power supply. Just to the front of these are the key-click filter components.

components on the output side. In this rig, the grid components are mounted below the chassis. The pi-network tank-circuit components, C_2, L_1, S_1 and C_3, are mounted above deck and are grouped together.

Wiring

It is a good idea to follow a logical sequence in doing the job. The power supply can be wired first, and if a voltmeter is available the supply can be checked out to make sure it is functioning properly before proceeding to the next stage. After the supply is wired, the heaters can be connected and then the rest of the wiring completed.

Tuning Up

A 40-watt lamp bulb can be used for a dummy load during testing. Connect the shell of the bulb to the chassis and the base pin of the bulb to the inner terminal of J_2. Plug a key into J_1 and a 40-meter crystal into the crystal socket. Turn on the power and let the rig warm up (key open). Next, set C_3 at maximum capacitance (plates fully meshed). Close the key and tune C_2 for a dip in cathode current, as indicated on M_1. The dip shows when the oscillator is tuned to resonance. It is also a good idea to have the receiver turned on and tuned to the crystal frequency of the transmitter. Reduce the r.f. and audio gain controls on the receiver to prevent the receiver from overloading. If you do not get a dip, or cannot hear the transmitter frequency in your receiver, adjust C_1, the oscillator feedback capacitor, and try tuning C_3 again. At some setting of C_1, the transmitter will go into oscillation. When making these tests do not hold the key closed any longer than necessary as the tube can overheat. By decreasing the capacitance of C_3 and redipping C_2, it should be possible to load the light bulb up to near full brilliance. The same procedure can be followed for tuning up on 3.5 MHz., using an 80-meter crystal and changing the band switch to that band.

Antennas

This transmitter is designed to work into a 50- to 70-ohm load. This doesn't mean the load has to be *exactly* in this range for the rig to work. One of the multiband antennas described in Chapter 14 should provide good results with this transmitter.

To tune up with the antenna attached to the rig, simply follow the procedure outlined with the dummy load. Set C_3 at maximum capacitance, close the key, and dip the final with C_2. Gradually decrease the capacitance of C_3, redipping C_2 until a loading of about 100 ma. is achieved.

A FIVE-BAND "FIFTY WATTER"

The transmitter shown in Figs. 6-41 through 6-45 is easy to construct and to get working. Metal work is minimized by using a "box-on-chassis" arrangement. This complete enclosure also provides good shielding, a "must" in avoiding TVI.

Referring to the circuit diagram, Fig. 6-42, a 12BY7 is used as a crystal oscillator stage. Fundamental or harmonic energy from the crystal is selected by the setting of S_1. The coils of L_1 through L_5 are adjusted only during the initial test procedure. Eighty-meter crystals are used for operation on 80 and 40 meters; 7-Mc. crystals are used on 7, 14, 21, and 28 Mc.

The 6DQ6B is used as a straight-through amplifier at all times. Its output circuit is a pi network designed to work into loads of 50 to 75 ohms. Switch S_2 selects the correct number of turns in L_5 for each band, and it also adds capacitance across both C_3 and C_5 in the 3.5-Mc. position. RFC_4 is a safety device that will blow the fuse if by any chance the 0.01-μf. plate blocking capacitor should fail. The 6DQ6B is a high-gain tube, and both a neutralizing circuit (C_1, C_2) and a parasitic suppressor (RFC_6) are included to insure a clean signal.

The function switch, S_3, selects the type of operation desired. In the TUNE position, the amplifier screen is grounded, to limit plate current during the tune-up procedure. In the BOTH position, both oscillator and amplifier are keyed, for break-in operation. In CAL, the amplifier cathode is removed from the keying line, and only the oscillator operates when the key is pressed. This permits the operator to locate his frequency in the band with respect to other signals. In AMP, the oscillator runs continuously, and only the amplifier is keyed. This is recommended operation on the higher frequencies, where oscillator keying may become chirpy. The 68-ohm resistor and the 10-μf. capacitor at the key jack shape the keying and minimize key clicks; the 0.01-μf. capacitor and the 47-ohm resistor also help.

The 0-1 milliammeter is connected as a voltmeter to read the voltage drops across resistors in the grid, plate and screen leads. With the values shown, this gives a full-scale reading of the currents in those leads of 5, 200 and 20 ma., respectively. By using every other position on S_4, the insulation between contacts is increased.

Two power supplies are used. The first supply, using T_1 and a full-wave bridge circuit, supplies 170 volts to the amplifier screen grid and to the oscillator plate and screen. The second supply (T_2 and a full-wave rectifier) delivers 460 volts to the amplifier plate. The supplies are turned on by switch S_5, and the neon lamp, I_1, warns the operator when power is present.

Construction

A 12 × 7 × 3-inch aluminum chassis is used as the base for the transmitter. Placed on top of this, and held by six 6-32 screws is a 12 × 6 × 7-inch aluminum box (Premier AC-1276). For ventilation three rows of holes (3/16" diameter on 3/8" centers) are drilled on the box sides and the rear wall. Reynolds perforated aluminum is used as a top cover. One of the aluminum panels supplied with the box is used as a bottom plate. Four rubber feet are mounted on the bottom plate to avoid scratching the operating table.

Although layout is not critical (except for the mounting of C_2), it is advisable to follow the photographs as closely as possible. 4-40 hardware

Fig. 6-41—The five-band 50-watt transmitter is a two-tube unit much superior to the "simple 1-tube" transmitters often recommended for newcomers to amateur radio. The cabinet combines a chassis and an aluminum "utility box."

Switch under meter permits reading grid, screen and plate current of output stage. From left to right along base: neon bulb indicator, a.c. switch, quartz crystal, grid bandswitch, function switch, key jack. Lower knob at right is loading control, upper knob is for plate tuning.

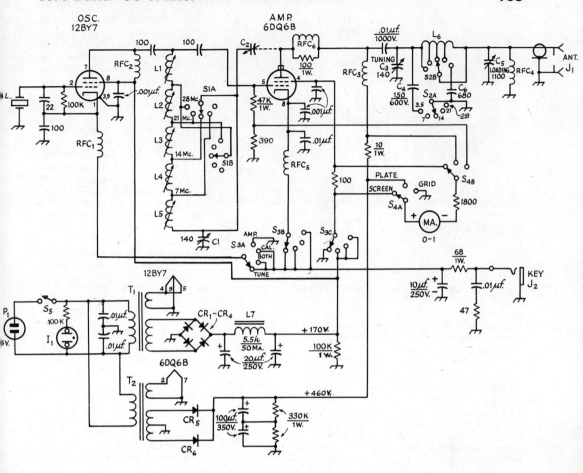

Fig. 6-42—Circuit diagram of the five-band 50 watter. Unless indicated otherwise, capacitances are in pf. and resistances are in ohms, ½-watt. Capacitors marked with polarity are electrolytic; capacitors with decimal value of μf. are disc ceramic.

C₁—140-pf. variable (Hammarlund APC-140).

C₂—One-inch wide aluminum strip. See Fig. 6-43.

C₃—140-pf. variable (Hammarlund) HFA-140-A).

C₄—150-pf. zero-temp.-coefficient (Centralab type TCZ).

C₅—1100-pf. variable. 3-section, 365 pf. per section, stator sections connected in parallel, trimmers removed (Allied Radio 43A3522).

C₆—680 pf., 500 volts, dipped mica.

CR₁-CR₄—400 p.i.v. 750-ma. silicon diode.

CR₅, CR₆—1000 p.i.v. 400-ma. silicon diode (1N3563).

I₁—Neon indicator (Drake R-117-603).

J₁—Coaxial receptacle SO-239.

J₂—Open-circuit phone jack.

L₁—.68-1.25 μh. adjustable (Miller 21A106RBI).

L₂—.68-1.25 μh. adjustable (Miller 21A106RBI).

L₃—1.35-2.75 μh. adjustable (Miller 21A226RBI).

L₄—9.4-15.0 μh. adjustable (Miller 21A155RBI).

L₅—27.5-58 μh. adjustable (Miller 21A475RBI).

L₆—31½ turns No. 16, 8 t.p.i., 1¼ inch diameter (B&W 3018) tapped from C₃ end: 2¾, 6¾, 10¾, 22¾ turns.

L₇—5.5-henry 50-ma. choke (Allied Radio 54A2135).

M₁—0-1 milliammeter (Lafayette 99G5040).

P₁—Fused plug, 1½-amp. fuses.

RFC₁-RFC₅—1-mh. 125-ma. r.f. choke (Miller 4662).

RFC₆—7 turns No. 18 space-wound on 100-ohm 1-watt composition resistor.

S₁—2-pole 6-position (5 used) rotary switch (Mallory 3226J).

S₂—2-pole 6-position (4 used) rotary switch (Centralab PA-2003).

S₃—3-pole 4-position rotary switch (Mallory 3234J).

S₄—2-pole 6-position (1, 3, 5, used) rotary switch (Mallory 3226J).

S₅—S.p.s.t. toggle.

T₁—125-volt 50-ma., 6.3-volt 2-amp. transformer (Knight 54A1411).

T₂—700 v.c.t. 90-ma., 6.3-volt 3.5-amp. transformer (Knight 54A1429).

(Knight products handled by Allied Radio, Chicago.)

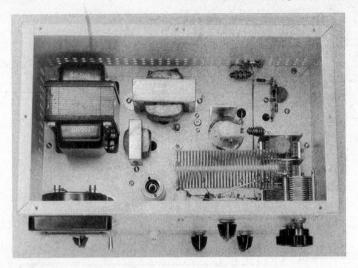

Fig. 6-43—Top view of the 50 watter shows the two power transformers (left rear) and the smaller filter choke. The 12BY7 crystal-oscillator tube (left of coil) has a tube shield around it. The coil is supported at left end by ceramic standoff insulator, at right end by plate tuning capacitor. Plate choke to the 6DQ6 is masked by parasitic suppressor, RFC_6, to right of tube.

The one-inch wide strip of aluminum alongside the 6DQ6, together with the 6DQ6 plate, is neutralizing capacitor C_2. The strip extends up from the chassis 3 inches; it is supported at the bottom by a ceramic feedthrough insulator.

is required at the 12BY7 socket and the crystal socket, otherwise 6-32 hardware is standard.

Liberal use has been made of tie points, solder lugs, and grommets. Make sure that each component is supported at both ends. Short r.f. leads are essential. Bypassing is done from the tube socket pin directly to a ground lug with as short leads as possible. Care should be taken to obtain good solder joints. Avoid excess heat in soldering any of the coils used. L_6 uses the entire B & W stock specified. Before tapping the coil, unwind ½ turn from each end. Indent the turn each side of the desired tap by pushing gently with a screw driver. One end of L_6 is supported by by C_3, the other end by a 1-inch ceramic standoff insulator. The unused 5-volt winding of T_2 is taped and tucked along the side of the chassis. Be sure to observe proper polarity on all diodes and electrolytic capacitors.

Operation

Connect a 50-watt lamp at J_1 with a suitable connector. Plug in a 40-meter crystal in the appropriate socket and a key in the key jack. Set both bandswitches to the 28 Mc. position, the function switch to the TUNE position, and the meter switch to the GRID position. Plug in the a.c. line cord and turn on the transmitter with S_5. Allow 30 seconds or so for the heaters of the tubes to light. Then press the key and adjust L_1 for 1.0 ma. of drive (0.2 on the meter). Now is the correct time to neutralize the final amplifier. With the operating controls in the positions stated, and the key depressed, tune C_3 for a dip in grid current. The object is to adjust C_1 so that swinging C_3 results in a minimum dip in grid current (one meter division or less). During the neutralization process it will be necessary to repeak L_1 to yield the specified grid current. Once the resonance dip in grid current is minimized, the transmitter may be considered neutralized.

With the transmitter still in the TUNE condition, switch to 21 Mc. and adjust L_2 for 1.0 ma. grid current. Do the same on 14 Mc. adjusting L_3; similarly adjust L_4 for 7 Mc. Then plug in an 80-meter crystal and adjust L_5 for 1.0 ma. grid current on 3.5 Mc.

Choose a given band to check out the final amplifier. Insert the proper crystal and switch S_1 and S_2 to the band of operation. With S_3 still in the TUNE position, switch S_4 to read plate current. Close the key and tune C_3 until a dip is noted. Then switch S_3 to the BOTH position. Check the dip by tuning C_3. Proceed to load the amplifier by decreasing the capacitance of C_5 until the plate current is 120 ma., (0.6 on the meter). Dip again using C_3, and load again to 120 ma. using C_5. During the tuning process the lamp should get progressively brighter.

As a final check on proper amplifier operation, switch S_4 to SCREEN. Screen current should be between 8 and 10 ma. (0.4 and 0.5 on the meter). If screen current is higher, the cause may be two fold; either there is a mismatch in the output circuit or grid drive is not properly adjusted. The latter can be remedied by adjusting L_1-L_5 until the screen current is of the proper value.

Working into an antenna is similar to the light bulb, although control settings may vary. When working into an antenna, check the amplifier screen current, as it will give you a good indication as to how well everything is working.

Keying Monitor

The optional r.f.-powered keying monitor, shown in Fig. 6-45, uses a small portion of the r.f. output to power an audio oscillator. With this simple addition, the operator can follow his sending and be sure at all times that his code is similar to the published one. While the monitor does not disclose chirps and clicks on the transmitted signals, it does tell the truth about the relative lengths of dots, dashes and spaces.

The monitor can be assembled on a single tiepoint strip (right, Fig. 6-44). The receiver output is fed to J_1 (J_2 and J_3 if the receiver output is ungrounded, as in the regenerative receiver, Chapter

Fig. 6-44—View under chassis of 50 watter shows how tie points are used to support components. Silicon-diode rectifiers are mounted on strips at lower left. Strip assembly at extreme right is optional keying monitor (see Fig. 6-45). Use of rubber grommets when leads pass through chassis is considered good practice.

Five). The headphones are plugged in at J_4. When the transmitter is on and power is delivered to the antenna, a fraction of the power is rectified and powers the monitor.

If the monitor circuit is used with a higher-powered transmitter, the value of R_1 should be adjusted to give approximately —6 volts at the point marked in Fig. 6-45.

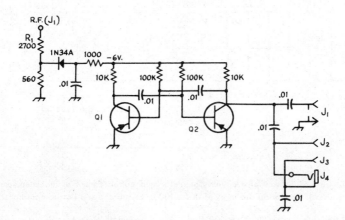

Fig. 6-45—Circuit diagram of the r.f.-powered keying monitor. Point marked "RF" connects to ungrounded lead of J_1 (Fig. 6-42). This circuit can be used with any transmitter, simply by selecting an input resistor, R_1, that gives about —6 volts at the point shown.

J_1—Phono jack, for grounded receiver input.
J_2, J_3—Tip jacks, for receiver with ungrounded output.
J_4—Phone jack (insulated from chassis) for headphone output.
Q_1, Q_2—2N406, SK3003, or equivalent.

A STABLE F.E.T. V.F.O.

The v.f.o. shown in Figs. 6-46 through 6-50 furnishes output from 3.5 to 4, 5.0 to 5.5, and from 8 to 9 Mc. and first appeared in *QST*, Dec. 1966. Output is on the order of two volts, peak value. Consequently, it is necessary to use the v.f.o. with transmitters that do not require an excitation voltage in excess of the amount stated. If more v.f.o. output is needed, the unit can be used to drive an outboard class A buffer stage, vacuum-tube or solid-state type, to build up the peak output to the level required by the transmitter.

This v.f.o. is extremely stable and is useful as a frequency-controlling device for an 80-meter transmitter, a single-sideband transmitter with a 9-Mc. i.f., or it can be used to control the frequency of a 6- or 2-meter transmitter. Coil data for each of these ranges is given in the accompanying table.

Fig. 6-46—The FET v.f.o. The panel is ⅛-inch aluminum, 7 by 10 inches. (*Designed and built by G. D. Hanchett, W2YM.*)

Mechanical Details

Like a vacuum-tube unit, the MOS v.f.o. requires great care in the mounting of the oscillator components. The complete v.f.o. is housed in a 4 × 5 × 6-inch aluminum utility box. The MOS oscillator, less its tuned circuits, is mounted on an H. H. Smith No. 1070 terminal strip, as shown in the bottom view. The two-stage amplifier is mounted on a similar strip.

Power is carried to the closed unit by means of 1500-pf. feed-through capacitors mounted at the rear of the utility box along with the 25-pf. frequency-setting capacitor. The tuning capacitor should be a high-quality, two-bearing type; in this particular oscillator, a Millen 23100 MKF was used.

Maximum rigidity of the oscillator circuit is obtained by the use of a special bracket formed from one of the utility box covers. The box cover material is soft aluminum and can be bent easily

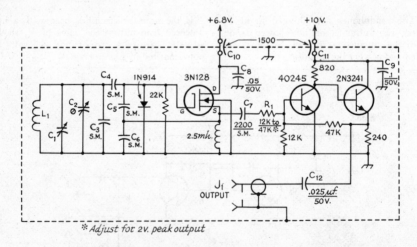

Adjust for 2v. peak output

Fig. 6-47—Circuit diagram of the variable-frequency oscillator and buffer. Except as indicated, capacitances are in pf. (μμf.). Resistances are in ohms (K = 1000); resistors are ½-watt composition.

C_1—Double-bearing variable (Millen 23100 or 23050—see table below).

C_2—25-pf. air trimmer (Hammarlund APC-25 or equivalent).

C_3, C_4, C_5, C_6—Silver mica; see table below for values.

C_7—2200-pf. silver mica.

C_8, C_9, C_{12}—Ceramic disk.

C_{10}, C_{11}—Feedthrough type.

J_1—Coaxial connector, chassis mounting.

L_1—See table below.

R_1—12,000 to 47,000 ohms; select for 2-volt peak output level at input to transmitter.

RFC₁—Miniature 2.5-mh. r.f. choke, iron core (Millen J300-2500).

with the aid of wood blocks and a vise. Hardwood blocks and a hammer are used to make the bends square and sharp. When bolted securely to the front and back of the oscillator box, the bracket not only supports the circuit components but helps stiffen the box itself.

To facilitate mounting the variable capacitor, the holes for the mounting feet are slotted. In addition, during assembly the shaft nut and mounting spacers are tightened to the side of the box first, and then the 6-32 screws for the feet are tightened. Special clamps designed to hold the coil are cut from thin lucite or polystyrene in strips ¼ inch wide and 2½ inches long. Holes are drilled at both ends of each strip so that they can be bolted to the standoff insulators.

The silver-mica capacitors, which form a part of the tuned circuit, must be mounted so that there is no possibility of motion. Small feed-through insulators are used as tie points to hold them as shown in the inside top view. For maximum reinforcement of the entire unit, new covers were cut from ⅛-inch aluminum panel stock and fastened to the boxes with a liberal number of self-tapping screws.

Although any suitable dial and panel arrangement could be used, the particular one shown employs a Millen 10037 "no string" panel dial. The dial is mounted on a small panel and the assembly in turn is bolted to the v.f.o. box with 1¼-inch metal pillars. Though large, the dial is

Tuned-Circuit Table			
	3.5–4.0 Mc.	5.0–5.5 Mc.	8.0–9.0 Mc.
L_1 — No. of turns	17*	14¾*	11½**
Wire size	20	20	18
Turns/inch	16	16	8
Diam., inches	1	1	1
C_1, pf.	100	50	50
C_2, pf.	25	25	25
C_3, pf.	100	None	None
C_4, pf.	390	390	270
C_5, pf.	680	680	560
C_6, pf.	680	680	560

* B & W 3015, Polycoils 1748, AirDux 816T.

** B & W 3014, Polycoils 1746, AirDux 808T.

free from any noticeable backlash and provides adequate illumination and an easy-to-read scale.

The panel is provided with a single-pole, double-throw switch, which can be connected so that in the "spot" position only the v.f.o. supply can be turned on, but in the transmit position this function is transferred to the main transmitter power-supply control so that it is activated by the transmit/receive switch.

Fig. 6-48—The tuned circuit is supported by a bent aluminum steel extending from the front to the rear of the 4 by 5 by 6-inch box. The trimmer capacitor, C_2, is mounted on the rear wall, as are also the coaxial output connector and feed-through bypass capacitors for the power leads.

Fig. 6-49—Circuit of regulated power supply for the FET v.f.o. Capacitances are in $\mu f.$, capacitors are electrolytic. Resistors are ½-watt. For mobile use, a 12-volt car battery may be substituted for rectifier/filter supply to the left of line AB.

CR₁—12-volt 1-watt Zener diode.
CR₂—6.8 volt 1-watt Zener diode.
T₁—6.3-volt 1.2 amp. filament transformer.

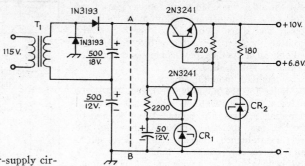

Fig. 6-49 shows a suggested power-supply circuit for 120-volt, 60-cycle operation. The regulator in this circuit also can be used for mobile work. A vacuum-tube v.f.o. article prompted many requests for information on how the unit could be adapted for use at other frequencies.[1] Generally speaking, this MOS transistor circuit is useful at any frequency up to and including the 144-Mc. band. Coil and capacitor information is provided for three frequency ranges: a 3.5 to 4.0-mc. range for 80-meter transmitters, a 5 to 5.5-Mc. range for s.s.b transmitters, and an 8- to 9-MC. range for 50- and 144-Mc. transmitters.

Adjustment

Output from the v.f.o. can be monitored on a general-coverage communications receiver by connecting a coax lead from J_1 of the v.f.o. to the

[1] Hanchett, "Stability with Simplicity", *QST*, Oct. 1960.

antenna terminals of the receiver. The signal will be quite strong, so turn the receiver r.f. gain control down until a moderately-strong v.f.o. signal is heard. The signal should be clean and stable.

C_2 should be adjusted to provide the desired v.f.o. coverage over the chosen frequency range. The dial can be calibrated by comparing it with the dial on the receiver. If more accurate calibration is desired—provided the test receiver is not accurate enough—a BC-221 or similar frequency standard can be used to establish check points for dial calibration.

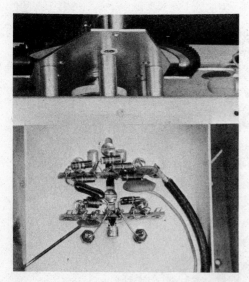

Fig. 6-50—Oscillator and buffer components are mounted on two tie-point strips underneath the tuned circuit. The lower strip supports the oscillator components, with the 3N128 projecting downward from the center of the strip in this view. The upper strip is for the two-stage buffer; in this case the transistors project upward on either side of the mounting screw. The short length of coax cable runs to the connector on the rear of the shield box.

160-METER OPERATION WITH THE FET V.F.O.

The following information is given for those who may want to operate the W2YM v.f.o. between 1.8 and 2.0 Mc. These component values were tried with the circuit of Fig. 6-47 and provided stable operation. The tuning range of the v.f.o. covers from approximately 1775 to 2050 kc. Greater bandspread can be obtained, if desired, by making C_1 smaller and by increasing the value of C_3. Capacitors C_4, C_5, and C_6 have the same value that is recommended for 80-meter operation, though increasing their capacitance values could lead to even greater frequency stability during 160-meter operation.

The modification requires that a 20-uh. inductor be used at L_1. The new coil can be wound on a James Millen 45000 1-inch diameter coil form, or equal. It should consist of 45 turns of No. 18 enamel wire, close-wound. A suitable amount of Miniductor stock can be substituted if desired. C_1 will be 100 pf., C_2 will remain a 25-pf. trimmer, and C_3 will be a 100-pf. silver-mica unit. $C_4 = 390$ pf., C_5 and C_6 are each 680 pf. All three are silver-mica capacitors. C_8 should be changed to a 0.1-$\mu f.$ disk ceramic for operation in the 1.8 to 2.0-Mc. range.

GENERAL-PURPOSE V.F.O.

The v.f.o. described here is capable of delivering approximately 3 volts peak output into a low-impedance load. It can be fed into a vacuum-tube or transistor amplifier stage if additional output is required. Coil data is given for the popular tuning ranges used with most modern communications equipment.

Circuit Details

Two bipolar transistors, Q_1 and Q_2 (Fig. 9-52), are used. Q_1 is used in a Colpitts circuit; Q_2 performs as an emitter-follower stage for purposes of isolation. R_4 is a parasitic-suppressor resistor and was required to clean up some random oscillation which resulted from the use of a high-beta transistor at Q_1.

Though the circuit is shown for use from a 150-volt d.c. line (VR-150/0A2 regulator line recommended) in the station receiver or exciter, it can be operated from a 12-volt source as well. If this is done, the 7500-ohm 10-watt resistor between the power supply and CR_1 should be changed to a 100-ohm 1-watt unit. Similarly, other operating voltages can be used if the dropping resistor is changed to a value that enables CR_1 to draw approximately 20 milliamperes of current. C_{11}, the feed-through capacitor, should be mounted on the v.f.o. case and used as a B-plus connector, thus helping to filter the power lead at r.f. level.

Construction

Mechanical rigidity is always the keynote if a v.f.o. is to be a good tool to work with. In the accompanying photos it can be seen that considerable attention has been given to the matter of

Fig. 6-51—View of the back side of the v.f.o. A phono connector is used as an output jack. A feedthrough capacitor is used as a B-plus connector, and is located just above the output jack. L_1 is mounted to the right of J_1, just below trimmer capacitor C_6. Trimmer capacitor C_7 is accessible from the top of the case.

structural soundness. Aluminum sheeting, $\frac{1}{16}$ inch thick, was used to form the chassis and side plates for the v.f.o. All bending was done on a sheet-metal brake, but the parts could have been formed by hand while using a rawhide hammer and a bench vise. A local machine- or sheet-metal shop will often bend a chassis for a couple of dollars or less if the stock is precut and marked when they receive it. Alternatively, a utility box can be used as a v.f.o. housing and its walls reinforced

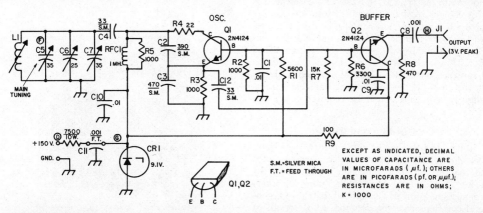

Fig. 6-52—Schematic diagram of the v.f.o. Fixed-value capacitors are disk ceramic except C_{11} which is a feed-through type. Resistors are ½-watt composition unless noted otherwise. All parts carry numbers for identification purposes on the circuit-board template. Significant parts are listed below.

C_5—Miniature double-bearing 35-pf. capacitor (James Millen 21035 MK). See text.

C_6—5 to 25-pf. ceramic trimmer, type NPO. (Erie type 557).

C_7—Miniature 35-pf. variable (James Millen 26035).

CR_1—9.1-volt 1-watt Zener diode (GE Z4XL9.1 or similar).

J_1—Phono connector, chassis mount type.

L_1—See Table 9-00.

RFC_1—Subminiature 1-mh. r.f. choke (J. W. Miller 73F103AF).

Coil And Capacitor Table				
Freq. in MHz.	*L_1 (uh.)*	*Miller No.*	*C_2 (pf.)*	*C_3 (pf.)*
1.7 to 2.1*	54 to 125	42A104CBI	820	1000
3.0 to 4.0	12.9 to 27.5	42A225CBI	390	470
5.0 to 6.0	9.4 to 18.7	42A155CBI	390	470
6.5 to 7.5	6.05 to 12.5	42A105CBI	390	470
7.5 to 9.0	2.4 to 5.8	42A476CBI	390	470

Coil, capacitor, and frequency-range data for the solid-state v.f.o. Frequency can be extended beyond both the upper and lower limits given here for each range, by adjustment of L_1 and C_7. Ranges given include popular v.f.o. ranges for s.s.b. receivers and exciters using 455-kHz. and 9-MHz. filters. Data is also given for 160-, 80-, and 40-meter v.f.o. operation. The 7.5- to 9.0-MHz. range covers the common v.f.o. tuning range for v.h.f. operation (8 to 8.5-MHz.). *Use 2.5-mh. r.f. choke for 160-meter operation at RFC_1.

by adding thick aluminum covers in place of those supplied. The actual size of the v.f.o. case is not particularly important provided all of the parts can be installed conveniently. The box shown here is 2-¾ inches high, 2½ inches wide, and 3½ inches long. The etched-circuit board measures 2½ x 2-¾ inches.[1]

V.f.o. inductor L_1 is mounted on the rear wall of the box, but is insulated from the enclosure by mounting it in a small piece of insulating board which is centered over a ⅝-inch diameter hole. This was done to prevent the slug of L_1 from being affected by chassis heating when the v.f.o. is used as an integral part of a vacuum-tube exciter or receiver. If the thermal path is not broken up in this fashion, a drift problem often results.

A James Millen 39016 anti-backlash flexible coupling is used between the shaft of C_5 and the dial mechanism to lessen stress on the v.f.o. box and main-tuning capacitor. A Millen 10037 slide-rule dial drive can be used with this v.f.o. as was done with the W2YM IGFET v.f.o. elsewhere in this chapter. A dial mechanism from a war surplus TU-17 tuning unit can also be used if a less-costly, more-compact dial is desired. A smoother-tuning assembly will result if a Millen 28035 MKBB variable is used for C_5 in place of the less-expensive Millen 21035 MK which is shown in the photo. If the ball-bearing variable is used, slightly more space will be required inside the box.

Testing and Use

Initial testing can be done before the circuit board is installed in the box. It can be connected to the rest of the components, temporarily, by using short lengths of insulated wire for inter-connection. With power applied, listen on a general-coverage receiver for the v.f.o. signal. It should be quite loud if a lead is run from J_1 to the antenna post of the receiver. If the v.f.o. is operating, mount the board permanently in the box. If not, check for shorts between the etched-circuit lines, and look for poor solder joints, or improper wiring. Make sure the rotors of C_5, C_6, and C_7 are grounded to the chassis.

With the v.f.o. in its case, and with the bottom enclosed by the main chassis or an aluminum plate, again apply voltage and listen for the signal in the receiver. Set C_6 for approximately mid-range. C_5 should be fully meshed and C_7 should be approximately half meshed. Adjust the slug in L_1 until the v.f.o. signal is heard at the lowest desired frequency. Next, tune C_5 to minimum capacitance (unmeshed) and tune the receiver until the signal is heard. If it falls near the desired *upper* range, no additional adjustments will be necessary. If it falls too high, or too low to give the necessary v.f.o. tuning range, juggle the settings of C_7 and L_1 until the desired bandspread is obtained. If the v.f.o. is to be used on the higher frequencies listed in the table, the builder may wish to remove plates from C_5 and increase the capacitance of C_7 to limit the tuning range of the v.f.o.

Some suggested circuits for increasing the output from the v.f.o. are given in Fig. 9-54.

Fig. 6-53—Bottom view of the completed v.f.o. The circuit board is mounted by means of small aluminum L brackets (far right). L_1 is mounted on a small square of insulating board (see text) at lower left. C_5 is directly opposite L_1. C_7 is to the right of C_5, but is mounted on the top wall of the box.

[1] A scale-size template showing component placement is available from ARRL for 25 cents. Send SASE with order.

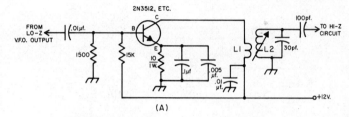

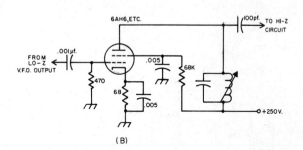

Fig. 6-54—Typical circuits for amplifying the v.f.o. output. At A, a transistor amplifier. L_1 is a low-impedance winding on the B-plus end of L_2. L_2 provides high-impedance output and is tuned to the v.f.o. frequency. A low-C circuit will give greatest bandwidth but will result in less peak voltage because of reduced Q.

A similar circuit is shown at B, but uses a vacuum-tube amplifier. A 470-ohm grid resistor provides a low-impedance load for the v.f.o. for better isolation between the tuned circuits, thus reducing "pulling" effects.

A LOW-POWER PHONE/C.W. RIG FOR 1.8 MHZ.

This equipment is intended, primarily, for use as a low-power mobile or fixed-station transmitter with an input power of approximately 15 watts. It can be used as an exciter to drive a linear amplifier, or it can be used as an integral part of a higher-power transmitter which uses a class-C final stage. It features push-to-talk operation and has shaped keying to assure a clean c.w. note. Transmitters in this power class have been used during many coast-to-coast 160-meter contacts. Many DX contacts have been made with foreign amateurs when power levels of this type were involved.

The Circuit

Three tubes are used in the circuit of Fig. 6-56. The r.f. section is a single compactron whose triode section, V_{1A}, operates as a crystal-controlled oscillator. Y_1 is a fundamental-cut FT-243 style crystal. The 39-pf. capacitor between one end of Y_1 and ground is part of the feedback circuit and is necessary for reliable oscillator starting. A pi-network tank circuit connects the oscillator stage to the amplifier section, V_{1B}. This method was chosen to permit C_1 to be used for "grid loading", an aid to stability of the p.a. stage when a neutralization circuit is not employed. Though grid loading reduces the amount of drive available at the input of the driven stage, it does not detract from the proper performance of this transmitter.

Output from the p.a. is routed to K_{1A}, the changeover relay, through a standard pi-network plate tank. K_{1A} and K_{1B}, the relay contacts, switch the antenna from the transmitter to the receiver during standby, and mute the receiver when its standby terminals are attached to J_4. The push-to-talk mike switch operates K_1, or it can

Fig. 6-55—The midget-size 160-meter phone/c.w. transmitter is dwarfed by the microphone next to it. A minimum number of controls are used; all are located on the front panel. A low-cost power supply for fixed-station use is shown at the right of the transmitter.

be operated by a switch on the power supply chassis. The power supply is activated by a third set of relay contacts, K_{1C}.

A high-impedance crystal, dynamic, or ceramic microphone can be used with this transmitter. Its output is amplified by V_{2A} and is then amplified further by V_{2B}. The triode section of V_{3A}, another 6T9 compactron, provides additional amplification of the speech signal. A single-ended modulator, V_{3B}, is coupled to the p.a. by means of T_1, a replacement type push-pull audio output transformer. This provides a 1:1 impedance ratio—a good match for this circuit. No connections are made to the voice-coil winding of T_1 (secondary). S_1 is used to disconnect the modulator sec-

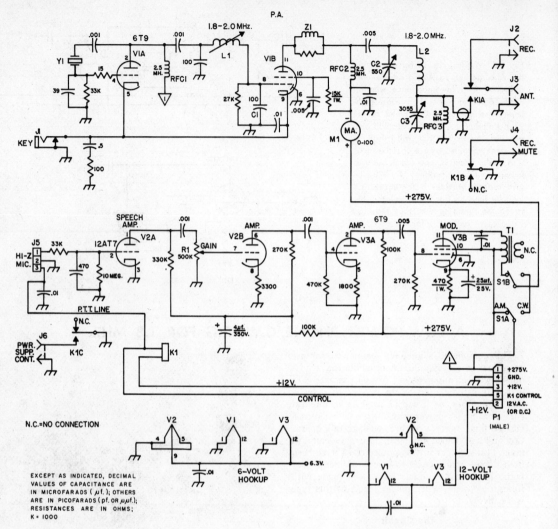

Fig. 6-56—Schematic diagram of the transmitter. Fixed-value capacitors are disk ceramic. Fixed-value resistors are ½-watt composition unless noted differently. Capacitors with polarity marking are electrolytic.

C₁—See text.

C₂—115 to 550-pf. padder (Elmenco 304 or similar).

C₃—1400 to 3055-pf. padder (Elmenco 315 or similar).

J₁—Closed-circuit phone jack.

J₂-J₄, inc.—Phono jack.

J₅—Two-circuit (plus ground) microphone jack.

J₆—Phono jack.

K₁—3-pole, double-throw, 12-volt d.c. relay (Potter & Brumfield KA14DY suitable).

L₁—120- to 190-uh. adjustable inductor (J. W. Miller 4512).

L₂—25-uh. fixed-value inductor. 45 turns No. 24 enam. wire close-wound on 1-inch dia. low-loss form

(James Millen 45000 coil form used here).

M₁—1½-inch, 0 to 100-ma., d.c. meter.

P₁—5-pin male chassis-mount plug (see text).

R₁—0.5-megohm, audio-taper control.

RFC₁-RFC₃, inc.—2.5-mh., 125-ma. r.f. choke (James Millen 34300-2500 suitable).

S₁—D.p.d.t. slide switch.

T₁—5-watt, push-pull output transformer (Stancor A-3831 or similar).

Y₁—Fundamental-cut 1.8-MHz. crystal (JAN Crystals).

Z₁—Parasitic suppressor. 8 turns No.-26 enam. wire spaced over the body of a 56-ohm, 1-watt carbon resistor.

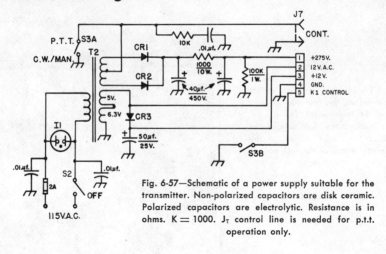

Fig. 6-57—Schematic of a power supply suitable for the transmitter. Non-polarized capacitors are disk ceramic. Polarized capacitors are electrolytic. Resistance is in ohms. K = 1000. J7 control line is needed for p.t.t. operation only.

CR₁, CR₂—1000 p.r.v., 1-amp. silicon diode.
CR₃—100 p.r.v., 1-amp. silicon diode.
I₁—Neon panel-lamp assembly with built-in resistor for 115-volt a.c. operation.
J₇—Phono jack.
J₈—Female 5-pin chassis connector.
R₂—Adjustable resistor. Set for 275 volts of B-plus with

transmitter operating at normal power input, on phone.
S₂—S.p.s.t. toggle.
S₃—D.p.s.t. toggle.
T₁—Power transformer, 520 volts c.t. at 90 ma., 6.3 v. at 3 amps., 5 volts at 2 amps. (Stancor PC-8404 or similar).

tion during c.w. operation. Circuits are given in Fig. 6-56 for 6- and 12-volt filament operation.

Assembly Information

The unit is assembled on a home-made aluminum chassis which is 6 inches deep, 5 inches wide,

and 1½ inches high. It was formed in a bench vise with the aid of a rawhide hammer. The stock was cut from an aluminum cookie sheet which was purchased at a hardware store. Similarly, the cabinet was fashioned from two U-shaped pieces of stock (see Fig. 6-55) which are held together

Fig. 6-58—A top-chassis view of the transmitter. L₂, the p.a. tank coil, is behind the panel, directly adjacent to the tank capacitors, C₂ and C₃ (left foreground). V₁ is to the right of L₂, and K₁ is to the right of V₁. M₁, R₁, V₂, and V₃ are along the far side of the chassis.

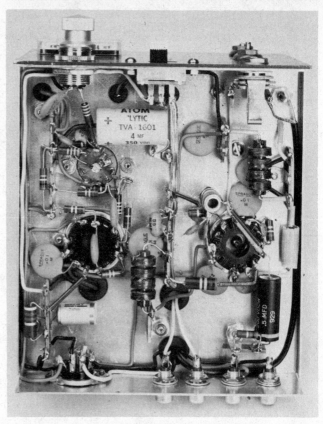

Fig. 6-59—Looking into the bottom of the chassis, the four phono jacks are at the lower right. The r.f. circuitry is along the right side of the chassis. The audio portion of the transmitter occupies the left half of the chassis.

by means of 1-inch wide aluminum strips and 4-40 hardware, inside the cabinet. The strips mount over the joints where the cabinet halves meet. The chassis and cabinet have been soaked in a mild lye-bath solution which imparted the satin finish to the aluminum. The panel measures 5 x 5¼ inches and is painted dark gray to contrast with the cabinet. White decals identify the controls.

Short, direct wiring is used throughout the transmitter. The audio section occupies one half of the chassis. The r.f. circuit is located on the remaining half of the chassis. P_1, and J_1 through J_4, are located on the rear apron of the chassis. If a power plug is used instead of a grommet and cable for connection to the power supply, P_1 should be a *male* type (not as shown in the photo) to reduce shock hazard from accidental contact to the power-supply cable end (which would be a male type if a female chassis connector were used). In this model, the power-supply cable plug was epoxy-cemented to the mating socket on the transmitter chassis after the equipment was installed, thus, preventing future shock hazard.

Although compression-type padders are used for C_2 and C_3, there is no reason why the layout could not be altered to make room for standard tuning capacitors with shafts if the builder desired. Compression padders are compact and in-expensive, hence, were chosen because of crowded conditions in the mobile installation.

Checkout and Operation

With the power supply connected, and with a low-impedance dummy load connected at J_3 (four No.-47 pilot lamps in series suitable), depress the mike switch and observe the plate current on M_1. If the oscillator does not start, the meter reading will be quite high—approximately 80 ma. (100 ma. full scale). If this happens, adjust L_1 until the meter reading drops to a lower reading, indicating that drive is present at V_{1B}. Adjust the slug of L_1, further, until no additional decrease in p.a. current is noted. Next, adjust C_2 for maximum transmitter output. C_3 is the loading capacitor and should be adjusted, alternately, with C_2, for maximum transmitter output. The dipped, loaded plate current will be approximately 40 ma. on phone, and will be near 50 ma. for c.w. operation. Do not hold the key down for long periods of time during c.w. as it may damage V_{1B}.

If the c.w. note of this transmitter is a bit "chirpy", or if the oscillator is slow in starting, it may be helpful to experiment with the slug settings of L_1. Also, the value of the feedback capacitor at Y_1 may need to be slightly greater (or smaller) for the best sounding note.

A SWEEP-TUBE LINEAR AMPLIFIER

This simple 1200-watt p.e.p. sweep-tube amplifier is designed for use on the 80-, 40-, and 20-meter bands. Though coil dimensions are not given for 15- and 10-meter operation, the amplifier can be used on the two higher bands if coils similar in proportion to those described are wound. Copper tubing, $\frac{1}{4}$ inch in diameter, should be used for L_2 if this is done. Coils for the two higher bands were not built because the amplifier was intended, primarily, for use with a popular series of low-cost transceivers which cover only the three lower bands.

A power supply for this amplifier is described in Chapter 12 ("A 900-Volt General-Purpose Supply") and can be used if the builder does not wish to design his own unit. This amplifier is not for use on a.m. This circuit is an adaptation of one described in July 1968 *QST*, page 30.

Circuit Data

Four 6KD6 color-TV sweep tubes are used in parallel in the circuit of Fig. 6-62. This grounded-grid amplifier operates in the Class-AB region.

HBA-4 AMPLIFIER

Fig. 6-60—The amplifier has one vent hole on each side of the home-made cabinet, and four holes on the top. Each hole, and the back side of the cabinet, is enclosed by means of perforated aluminum. The cabinet was formed by making two U-shaped sections of $\frac{1}{16}$-inch thick aluminum and mating them. They are held together by means of two 1-inch wide aluminum strips (inside) and 4-40 hardware.

The extremely low plate-load impedance of this amplifier—approximately 500 ohms—requires that special measures be taken to match the plate circuit to the load. A tapped-coil arrangement at L_2 aids in obtaining a suitable match.

Individual 10-ohm resistors are used in each cathode lead to permit balancing the tubes for equal resting plate currents during initial check-out. Bias is fed to each grid by means of bias-adjust controls R_1 through R_4. Without drive applied at J_1, each tube is set for 20 ma. by reading the voltage drop across each resistor with a VTVM (0.2 volts). All operating voltages are applied during the balancing adjustments. *Beware of high voltage.*

K_1 provides a "switch-through" feature which permits the antenna to be used during receive.

Fig. 6-61—Top view of the chassis. RFC_3 is centered between the four tubes. The high voltage is brought to the bottom of the choke through a chassis feed-through bushing. The $\frac{3}{8}$-inch dia. hole on the chassis near the edge, and close to two of the 6KD6s, was used for mounting an a.l.c. control which was later eliminated.

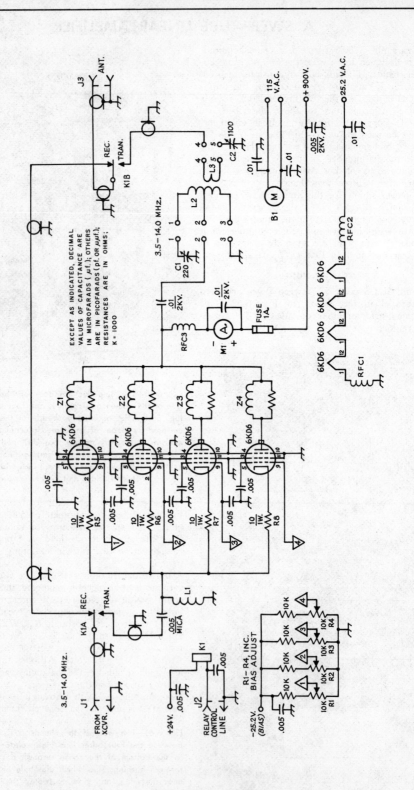

Fig. 6-62—Schematic of the linear amplifier. Fixed-value capacitors are disk ceramic unless otherwise indicated. Fixed-value resistors are ½-watt composition unless noted otherwise. R_5-R_8, inc., are 5% tolerance.

B₁—High-speed fan (see text). Barber-Coleman DYAF 761-110 suitable. Use Barber-Coleman AYFA-403 (190 c.f.m.) fan blades.

C₁—200-pf. transmitting variable, ⅛-inch plate spacing (see text).

C₂—3-section broadcast variable, 365 pf. per section. All sections parallel-connected. (J. W. Miller 2113 or equiv.)

J₁, J₂—Phono connector.

J₃—SO-239-type chassis connector.

K₁—D.p.d.t. 24-volt d.c. relay with 10-ampere contacts.

L₁—65 turns No. 24 enam. wire, close-wound on 4-inch length of ½-inch diameter ferrite rod, 200 uh. (Lafayette Radio rod No. 32H6103 suitable.)

L₂—80 meters—18 turns No. 12 wire, 2-½ inch dia., 3 inches long, made from Polycoils 1774 stock. Tap 6 turns down from C₁ end.
40 meters—12 turns No. 12 wire, 2-½ inch dia., 3 inches long, made from Polycoils stock. Tap 3 turns down from C₁ end.
20 meters—8 turns No. 10 wire, 1-¼ inch i.d., 3 inches long. Tap 3 turns from C₁ end.

L₃—80 meters—5 turns No. 14 wire, 3-inch diameter, approx. ¾ inch long. Mount over outside of L₂ at ground end.
40 meters—3 turns No. 14 wire, 3-inch dia. Mount over ground end of L₂.
20 meters—2 turns No. 12 wire, 2 inches dia. Mount over ground end of L₂.

M₁—0 to 1-ampere d.c. meter (Simpson 1227 used here).

R₁-R₄, inc.—10,000-ohm linear-taper carbon control.

RFC₁, RFC₂—65 turns No. 20 enam. wire, close-wound on 4-inch length of ½-inch dia. ferrite rod, 200 uh. (Same type rod as used for L₁. See text.)

RFC₃—See text and Fig. 6-63.

Z₁-Z₄, inc.—Parasitic choke. 8 turns No. 24 enam. wound on body of 56-ohm 1-watt carbon resistor. Use resistor pigtails as solder terminals for ends of windings. Mount near plate caps.

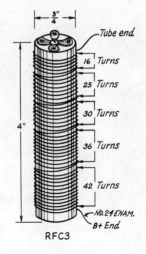

RFC3

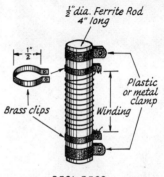

RFC1, RFC2

Fig. 6-63—Details for winding the plate choke, RFC₃. Sketch also shows how RFC₁ and RFC₂ are assembled.

Also, by not activating K_1 the transceiver can be used (bypassing the amplifier) while the amplifier is kept ready for use. If the operator does not plan to use this amplifier with a transceiver, the relay contacts can be rewired for antenna changeover—the usual arrangement for separate transmitter and receiver setups.

Construction

The general layout can be seen in the photographs. The equipment is built on an 8 x 12 x 3-inch aluminum chassis. The panel and cabinet are home made and were cut from 1/16-inch thick aluminum stock. The panel is 8 inches wide and 9½ inches high. Vent holes are located on the top and sides of the cabinet. These holes, and the back of the cabinet, are enclosed by means of perforated aluminum (Reynolds) to offer TVI shielding.

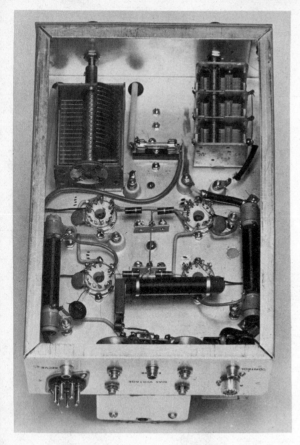

Fig. 6-64—Looking into the bottom of the amplifier chassis. C_1 and C_2 are located near the front panel. A 1-ampere meter-protection fuse is mounted between C_1 and C_2. RFC_1 and RFC_2 are mounted along the sides of the chassis. L_1 is between the rear of the chassis and the tube sockets.

Inductors L_1, RFC_1, RFC_2, and RFC_3 are hand-wound. RFC_3, the plate r.f. choke, is wound for operation at low impedance over the range from 3.5 to 30 MHz. It was designed with the aid of an RX meter and "looks" like 100,000 ohms on all bands but 10 meters. On ten meters it looks like 25,000 ohms—ample for the 500-ohm plate-load impedance of the four 6KD6s. L_1, RFC_1, and RFC_2 consist of 65 turns of enameled wire on lengths of $\frac{1}{2}$-inch diameter ferrite rod. Homemade brass anchors, $\frac{1}{8}$-inch wide, are snapped onto each end of each rod and are used as tie points for the ends of the windings. RFC_1 and RFC_2 are attached to chassis standoff posts by means of plastic cable clamps. L_1 is mounted by means of stiff bus-wire pigtails. RFC_3 is wound on a piece of $\frac{3}{4}$-inch diameter polystyrene rod. A steatite rod can also be used. (An H. H. Smith 2630 standoff would be suitable, and has a threaded hole at each end for attaching terminals.)

L_2 and L_3 are made up as plug-in assemblies so that the amplifier can be used as a single-band unit. Band-switching arrangements would not be practical with the type of tank circuit used. A pi-network tank could be used, and switched, but because of the very low impedance of the plate circuit, the amount of capacitance required for the input and output capacitors of the pi-section tank would be impractical if a satisfactory Q were to result on 80 and 40 meters. The plug-in coils are wound on James Millen 41305 jack-bar plugs.

C_1 is a 200-pf. transmitting-type variable taken from an old Command transmitter. Any variable capacitor with similar capacitance and plate spacing (approximately $\frac{1}{8}$ inch) can be substituted.

A high-speed cooling fan is used to keep the tube envelopes at a safe temperature. The forced-air cooling also helps to prevent damage to the plates of the tubes from excessive heating. The fan blades should be mounted close to the tubes and should be capable of providing 100 c.f.m., or better.

Operation

Approximately 50 watts of peak driving power are required to operate this amplifier at its rated 1200 watts (p.e.p.) input. If the transceiver being used as a driver has more power output than 50 watts, merely turn the transceiver's audio-gain control down until the power output is correct.

With a 50-ohm dummy load attached to J_3 (after making the bias adjustments described earlier in the text), and with operating voltages applied, apply a small amount of drive until an increase in plate current is evident (approximately 100 ma.). Adjust C_1 until a dip in plate current occurs. Increase drive until 300 ma. of plate current is indicated on M_1. Quickly dip the plate current and remove drive. Warning: *Do not allow continuous plate current in excess of 100 ma. to flow for more than 30 seconds at one time.* Allow 30 seconds for cooling between tests. Next, apply drive until approximately 600 ma. (667 ma. for 1200 watts p.e.p.) of plate current is obtained at dip. C_2 should be adjusted for proper loading, making the dip in plate current somewhat broad and shallow. The amplifier is now ready for use and will have a d.c. input of 600 watts (single tone or c.w.) at this setting. Tests made with a spectrum analyzer showed that the IMD (intermodulation distortion) was very good at this power level. The third-order products were down some 30 decibels, and the fifth-order products were down in excess of 50 db. At 800 watts input the third-order products were still acceptable—25 db. down. If the operator does not mind the risk of shortened tube life, the power level can be 1600 watts p.e.p. input (800 watts c.w. input). The efficiency of the amplifier is approximately 65 percent.

Other types of tubes can be substituted in this circuit, but few will permit the power level discussed here. A good substitute might be the 6LQ6.

A 2-KILOWATT P.E.P. AMPLIFIER

This linear amplifier operates in a grounded-grid circuit and uses two Eimac 3-500Z zero-bias triodes. It is capable of the maximum legal power input level, 1000 watts d.c., and can develop up to 2000 watts peak input during s.s.b. operation. The amplifier is intended for use on c.w. and s.s.b., but it is not recommended for a.m. This amplifier requires a driver that can deliver at least 65 watts p.e.p. Actually, it is best to use a driver that is capable of 100 watts p.e.p., to assure that sufficient driving power is available on 21 and 28 MHz., the frequencies at which the efficiency of coupling circuits is often poor in comparison to that of the lower bands. This amplifier is designed to operate from the same power supply circuit that is used for the 3-1000Z amplifier described elsewhere in this chapter.

In the circuit of Fig. 6-66 a pi-network input circuit (C_1, C_2, and L_1) is used to aid linearity and to lessen the driving power requirements. Only one tuned circuit is shown in the diagram for reasons of clarity. The remaining tuned circuits (described in the coil table) are connected to the rest of the contacts shown for S_1. Relay K_1 routes the input (J_1) around the amplifier to J_2, thus enabling the operator to keep the amplifier in standby while transmitting around it with his exciter or transceiver when low-power operation desired. Also, this switching arrangement connects the antenna to the transceiver during receive periods, bypassing the amplifier. The changeover relay, K_1, and the bias control relay, K_2, are controlled by external means; J_4 connects to the VOX or push-to-talk circuit of the driver. The input tuned circuit is connected to the filament r.f. choke, a bifilar-wound inductor consisting of 28 turns (double) of No. 10 Formvar-insulated wire. The turns are close-wound on a $\frac{1}{2}$-inch diameter ferrite rod, $7\frac{1}{2}$ inches long.

An Air-Dux 195-2 tank coil is used in the plate circuit of the amplifier. The capacitance of C_4 is sufficient for all bands except 3.5 MHz. For 80-meter operation an additional capacitor, C_3, is switched in parallel with C_4 (S_{2B}).

An r.f. sampling circuit is connected to the output of the amplifier (CR_2). Rectified r.f. is fed to M_3 through the sensitivity control, R_1, for tuning adjustments. There is no reason why this circuit could not be replaced by a Monimatch-type s.w.r. bridge so that reflected-power readings could be used for Transmatch adjustments.

Bias resistor R_2 is used to cut the amplifier off during standby periods. During transmit it is shorted out by the contacts on K_2. Forced-air cooling is provided by B_1, a 100-c.f.m. muffin fan. S_4 turns on the filaments supply, relay supply, and blower fan. S_3 activates the power supply to provide B-plus voltage for the 3-500Zs.

Construction Notes

This equipment is built on a standard 13 x 17 x 4-inch aluminum chassis. The panel and cabinet

Fig. 6-65—Outside view of the amplifier. Vent holes permit the free flow of air for efficient cooling. The two screened windows in the front panel permit the operator to observe the tubes for plate color. The large dial at the left, a James Millen 10008, is the plate tuning. To the right, and lower, is the band switch, and to its right is the loading control. The large rocker switches are Carling No. TILA50s. Designed and built by Carl Smith, W1ETU.

are home made. A standard rack panel can be used, if desired. The assembly is enclosed in a cover made of sections of aluminum sheeting and perforated aluminum material (Reynolds). This was done for TVI reasons, and to prevent accidental contact with r.f. and d.c. voltages within. The bottom of the assembly is enclosed by means of an aluminum plate. Forced-air cooling is effected by mounting B_1, a muffin fan, on the bottom plate of the chassis, under the Eimac SK-410 tube sockets. Four feet, each 1 inch high, are attached to the bottom plate to allow sufficient air intake for proper cooling. The corners of the chassis are plugged with epoxy cement to prevent air from escaping through paths other than the intended one. Each tube has an Eimac SK-406 chimney, assuring that the air stream is directed along the sides of the tubes. Heat-dissipating plate caps are used as anode connectors.

All non-signal leads, except the high-voltage bus, are bypassed where they enter the chassis in the interest of TVI prevention. In actual service, each panel meter is enclosed in a shield can. The cans were left off for the photographs so that the wiring details could be seen. It was found that by removing the rolled lips from three aluminum Vienna sausage cans (obtained at the local supermart) and cutting four $\frac{1}{4}$-inch square tabs in the stock at the open ends of the cans—the tabs to line up with the meter-mounting studs

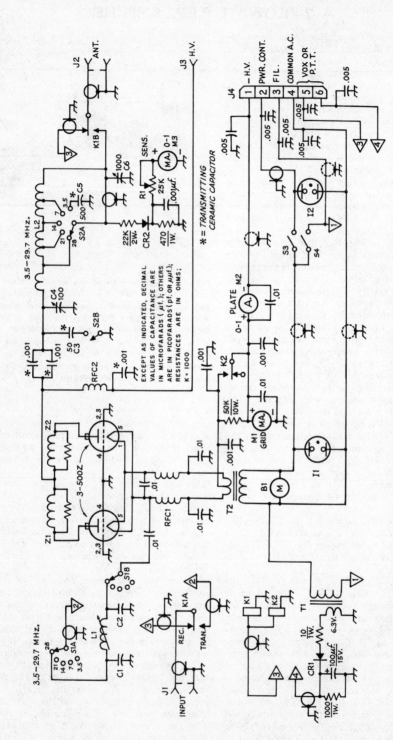

Fig. 6-66—Schematic diagram of the 3-500Z amplifier. Fixed-value capacitors are 1000-volt disk ceramic unless noted otherwise. C_7 is electrolytic. Capacitors marked with * are Centralab Series-850 transmitting-type ceramic.

B₁—115 v.a.c., 100-c.f.m. muffin fan (Rotron Gold Seal).

C_1, C_2—See coil table.

C_3, C_5—For text discussion.

C_4—100-pf. transmitting variable (E. F. Johnson 154-14).

C_6—1000-pf. transmitting variable (E. F. Johnson 154-30).

C_7—Miniature electrolytic, 100uf., 15 V.

CR_1—100 p.r.v., 1-ampere silicon diode.

CR_2—1N34A.

I_1, I_2—Panel-lamp indicator (neon) with built-in resistor for 115-v.a.c. use.

J_1, J_2—SO-239 style chassis fitting.

J_3—James Millen 37001 high-voltage connector.

J_4—Male octal connector (Amphenol 86-CP8 in Amphenol 61-61 shell).

K_1—D.p.d.t. 6-volt d.c. relay (Potter & Brumfield KT-11D).

K_2—S.p.d.t. 6-volt d.c. relay, one contact unused (Potter & Brumfield KM5D).

L_1—See coil table.

L_2—Air-Dux 195-2 inductor assembly. Tap as follows: 3.5 MHz.—Use entire coil. 7.0 MHz.—Tap 9½ turns from C_6 end. 14 MHz.—Tap at junction of tubing and main coil. 21 MHz.—Tap two turns up on tubing from main coil junction. 28 MHz.—Use all four turns of flat coil (right angle to main coil section).

M_1—0 to 500-ma. d.c. meter (Simpson type 1227).

M_2—0 to 1-ampere d.c. meter (Simpson type 1227).

M_3—0 to 1-ma. d.c. meter (Simpson type 1227).

R_1—25,000-ohm, linear-taper carbon control.

R_2—For text discussion.

RFC_1—Bifilar filament choke wound on Lafayette Radio ½-inch diameter ferrite rod (Lafayette 32H6103 part). See text for full data.

RFC_2—National Radio r.f. choke No. R175A.

S_1—2-pole 6-position (5 used) ceramic rotary switch, single wafer. (Centralab PA-2003).

S_2—Single-pole, double-contact, 6-position heavy-duty ceramic switch. 5 poles used. (Radio Switch Corp. type 86-B, Marlboro, New Jersey). See text.

S_3, S_4—S.p.s.t. rocker switch (Carling No. T1LA50).

T_1—5-volt, 30-amp. filament transformer (Stancor P-6468).

T_2—6.3-volt, 1.2 amp. filament transformer (Stancor P-8190).

Z_1, Z_2—Parasitic suppressor (Ohmite P-300).

L_1 COIL TABLE		
Band	C_1, C_2	L_1
80	1600 pf. (Arco VCM-35B162K)	16 t., closewound
40	910 pf. (Arco VCM-20B911K)	8 t., closewound
20	430 pf. (Arco VCM-20B431K)	6 t., closewound
15	300 pf. (Arco VCM-20B301K)	4 t., closewound
10	220 pf. (Arco VCM-20B221K)	4 t., spaced to fill form.

Capacitors are 1000-v. silver mica. Inductors wound with No. 16 Formvar or Nylclad on ½-inch diam. slug-tuned form (No. 69046—James Millen Co., 150 Exchange St., Malden, Mass.)

—the cans served as excellent covers. A hole is drilled in each tab to permit the shield cans to be bolted to the panel by means of the meter bolts. A hole and rubber grommet in the side of each can enables the meter wires to enter the shields.

Switch S_{2B} is a home-made addition to S_{2A}. It was needed to permit an additional 50-pf. of capacitance to be switched in parallel with C_4 during 80-meter operation. C_3 was bolted to a 1 by 2-inch piece of ¼-inch thick Plexiglas. A small angle bracket is bolted to one edge of the Plexiglas block so that it can be mounted on the main chassis near the shaft of S_{2A}. To provide the movable contact of S_{2B} a ½-inch steel cable clamp was attached to S_{2A}'s rotor-shaft bushing (near the chassis) by means of the existing set screws. Another cable clamp was attached to the free end of C_3, to provide the fixed contact of S_{2B}, then soldered securely. The entire assembly on which C_3 was mounted should be bolted to the chassis near S_{2A} in such a manner to permit the two clamps to mate *firmly* when S_{2A} is placed in the 3.5-MHz. position. Other methods could no doubt be worked out, but this was satisfactory. Perhaps a piece of brass spring stock could be used in lieu of the clamps, if available. Some hardware stores and lumber yards stock this material for preventing windows and doors from rattling.

When winding RFC_1 it is suggested that a piece of ⁷⁄₁₆-inch diameter wooden dowel be used as a form. After the coil has been wound, slip it off the dowel and mount it on the ferrite rod. Because of the stress needed when winding the No. 10 wire, the ferrite might break if used as a former.

Adjustment and Performance

Although any voltage between 2000 and 3000 can be used with this amplifier, the latter is recommended for best efficiency with this circuit; the *L-C* ratio in the plate tank is designed for 3000-volt operation. One must always be mindful that *lethal voltage* is being used here. *Never apply the high voltage while the top or bottom covers are removed.* Do not handle the power supply

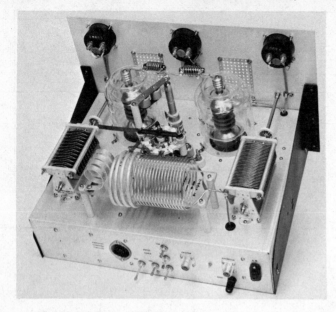

Fig. 6-67—Top view of the 3-500Z amplifier. The plate-tuning control is at the far left, the tank inductor is at the lower center of the photo, and the loading capacitor is to the right of the tank coil. The two paralleled plate-blocking capacitors are mounted on the copper strap which is attached to the top of the plate r.f. choke (between the two 3-500Zs). Each tube uses a heat-dissipating anode connector and a glass chimney. Metal cans enclose the backs of the panel meters, but these were removed for the photo.

until it is turned off and unplugged from the a.c. outlet. Allow plenty of time for the filter capacitors to bleed off, using a shorting stick to discharge them as a final safety measure.

Resting plate current (no signal) for this amplifier will be approximately 300 ma. with R_2 shorted out. As much as 200 ma. of grid current can flow during peak drive periods. In practice, with 3000 volts on the plates, approximately 150 ma. of grid current was noted when the full legal power input was being run.

With the amplifier's covers in place, a dummy load connected to the output, and an s.w.r. indicator connected between the driver and the input jack, J_1, apply a small amount of drive (single-tone) and adjust L_1 for minimum reflected power (low). Adjust C_4 and C_6 for maximum output as indicated on M_3. Gradually apply more drive until the plate current is 330 ma. at the dip. This will correspond to 990 watts input; the output power will be approximately 650 watts. At this level the p.e.p. input can rise to as high as 1980 watts on s.s.b., depending upon the actual voice characteristics of the operator.

Tests performed on this amplifier indicated that the IMD (intermodulation distortion) was down in excess of 30 db. at 1000 watts input (3000-volt plate supply) (third- and fifth-order products). Harmonic output from the amplifier was down some 50 db.

Fig. 6-68—Looking into the under side of the amplifier chassis, the filament transformer is at the lower right of the photo. The filament choke is to the left of the transformer. A right-angle drive (National Type RAD) connects the shafts of S_1 and S_2 and is visible near the center of the chassis. S_1 is mounted on an aluminum bracket near the rear-center of the chassis, just ahead of the slug-tuned input coils. Relay K_1 is mounted on the rear wall of the chassis, just to the left of the coils. K_2 is barely visible between the 3-500Z sockets. The blower fan is mounted on the bottom cover of the chassis (far left of photo) and plugs into a socket under the chassis. T_1 is on the right wall of the chassis.

A COMPACT 3-400Z GROUNDED-GRID AMPLIFIER

The amplifier shown in Figs. 6-69 through 6-73 easily handles a kilowatt p.e.p. input at 3000 volts. It has been designed with ease of construction and operation in mind, and to this end as few special parts and machine operations as possible are required. Probably the major operation is adding an arm to the band switch, to ground a plate padding capacitor in the 3.5-Mc. position. This enables a smaller plate tuning capacitor to be used than would be the case if the variable were required to furnish all of the capacitance on this lowest-frequency band.

Referring to the wiring diagram in Fig. 6-70, the circuit is about as simple as it could be made. No tuned input circuit is used, since it was found that any of the s.s.b. units in the 75- to 100-watts output class could drive it without any trouble. If drive were marginal, as when only 35 watts peak were available, a coupling network might offer a slight advantage. Two r.f. chokes and a 1000-pf. bypass are used in the high-voltage lead because a high-impedance circuit like this is harder to filter than one where the current is higher and the voltage is lower. The plate coil is a standard 500-watt unit that runs cold at a kilowatt c.w. or s.s.b.

The 50,000-ohm resistor in the center tap of the filament transformer biases the tube to cut-off during "stand-by" periods and eliminates the "diode noise" caused by the static plate current. Leads to J_4 and J_5 from the VOX or other control short the resistor during transmit periods.

The connections on J_6 are similar to those on the 3-1000Z amplifier shown later in this chapter,

with the exception of the lead marked "vm". This variation permits mounting the voltmeter on the transmitter panel instead of in the power supply. The power supply design is similar to that for the larger amplifier, with the exception of more filter capacitance and more compact rectifiers.

Front and back panels and base plate are all standard unfinished ⅛-inch thick aluminum rack panels. They are trimmed to 15 inches. The angle stock holding the pieces together, and furnishing the faces for support of the cover, are ¾ × ¾ × 1/16-inch Reynolds stock. A short piece is also used for supporting the fan, cut away as shown in Fig. 6-71.

The tube socket (Eimac SK-410) is held to the tapped base plate by long 6-32 screws. Prior to installation, one-half of the skirt is removed, so that the fan can move air under the socket and cool the pins (see Fig. 6-73). The three grid pins are grounded to individual soldering lugs.

To conserve space, the filament transformer must be modified so that the leads come out the side. This is done by removing the end bells and drilling a hole in the side through which the leads can be threaded.

To modify switch S_1, first remove the rear shaft bearing and replace the ceramic insulators with shorter (½-inch) ones. Two pairs of ⅛-inch polystyrene washers (Millen 38601) can be to expose the end of the switch shaft. A brass shaft coupling, cut to a length of 7/16 inch, is drilled and tapped 6-32 at right angles to the normal set-screw hole. The spring stock (0.20 x ⅜ silver solder) is wrapped half around the

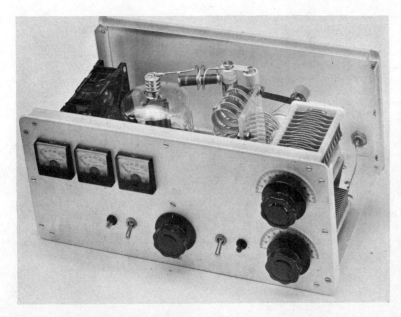

Fig. 6-69—The compact kilowatt amplifier with its perforated-metal cover removed. Using a 3-400Z in a grounded-grid circuit, it handles a kilowatt p.e.p. input at 3000 volts with ease. The (2-inch) meters monitor plate voltage, grid current and plate current. Panel is 7 X 15 inches; the bottom plate is 8¾ inches wide. (Built by Robert Smith, WILLF, Simsbury, Conn.)

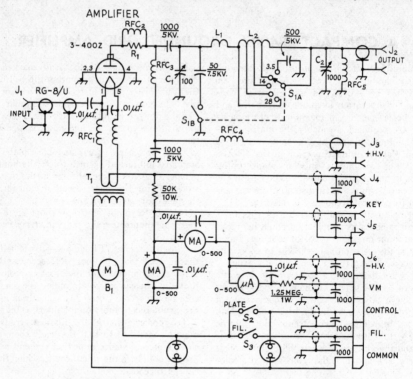

Fig. 6-70—Circuit diagram of the kilowatt grounded-grid amplifier.
Unless specified otherwise, capacitances are in picofarads.

B₁—65 c.f.m. fan (Rotron Whisper, with Rotron 16415 plug-in cord assembly).

C₁—100-pf. variable, 0.125-inch spacing (Johnson 154-14).

C₂—1000-pf. variable, 0.045-inch spacing (Johnson 154-30, available direct from manufacturer).

J₁, J₂—Coaxial receptacle (Dow-Key DK-60P).

J₃—Coaxial receptacle UG-560/U (Amphenol 82-805).

J₄, J₅—Phono jack.

J₆—Octal male connector (Amphenol 86-CP8 in 61-61 shell).

L₁—4 turns ⅜-inch strap, 1⅜ diam.

L₂—20 turns No. 10, 3-inch diam. 11 turns at L₁ end, 4 t.p.i.; remainder 6 t.p.i. Tapped 1, 3, 5 and 11 turns from L₁ end. (L₁ and L₂: Illumitronics 195-1).

R₁—Two 43-ohm thermistors in series (CG 25-926).

RFC₁—24 double turns No. 14 Formvar or Nyclad, close-wound on 5¾-inch length of ½-inch diam. ferrite rod (Lafayette Radio 32 R 6103).

RFC₂—2 turns No. 14, 1¼ inch diam., 2 t.p.i., on R₁.

RFC₃—90-μh. 500-ma. r.f. choke (B & W 800).

RFC₄, RFC₅—2.5-mh. 300-ma. (National R-300U).

S₁—2-pole 6-position (5 used) heavy-duty ceramic switch (Radio Switch Corp. type 86-B, Marlboro, N.J.) See text.

S₂, S₃—Heavy-duty toggle switch.

T₁—5-v. 13-ampere transformer (Triad F-9A). See text.

50-pf. 7½-kv. capacitor is Centralab 850S-50Z.
500- and 1000-pf. 5-kv. capacitors are Centralab 858S.
1000-pf. and 0.01-μf. capacitors are disc ceramic.
Meters are Simpson Model 1212. Dial lights are Drake Econoglow 117 with 100K resistor.

coupling and fastened at two points with short 6-32 screws through the new hole. The original set screw is left exposed. (Silver solder is available at welding supply houses; the type used here is called "Handy Harmon Easy Flow"). The fixed contact is supported by a ceramic insulator mounted on the base plate. "Time" the switch so that it engages as the switch is rotated from the 7- to the 3.5-Mc. position.

Adjustment

An output indicator is a useful adjunct when tuning a grounded-grid linear. The amplifier should be tested with a dummy load, to acquaint the builder with the tuning. If the drive is a steady carrier, adjust the amplifier for 330 ma. plate current (at 3000 volts) and 100 ma. grid current. If sufficient test equipment is available for the "two-tone test", this adjustment can be confirmed or modified accordingly. With a dummy load connected and with C_2 half meshed, switching to 28 Mc. and setting C_1 at minimum capacitance should give no indication of grid current (with no excitation). If there is an indication of grid current, it indicates the existence of a parasitic oscillation, and a turn may have to be added to RFC_2.

Fig. 6-71—The rear wall of the compact kilowatt has been removed to reveal the "works." Coaxial receptacles at left are output and input jacks; receptacle at center (near tube) is high-voltage connector. A 50-pf. 3.5-Mc. plate loading capacitor can be seen mounted on the plate tuning capacitor (upper left); the 500-pf. 3.5-Mc. output loading capacitor is mounted on the base behind the coil (just visible to right of variable loading capacitor).

Fig. 6-72—Power supply for the 3-400Z amplifier.

Fig. 6-72—The power supply for the 3-400Z amplifier (Shown on the previous page) is built on a 12-inch length of 8¾-inches high rack panel. The four sides, which take a protective cover of perforated aluminum, are made from ¾ x ¾ aluminum angle.

A junction box to which the four primary leads are connected, is supported by the aluminum bracket on the upper left of the transformer. The bolts that hold this bracket support the Vectorboard on the right that carries the two current-limiting resistors.

As a safety precaution, to alert the operator that the primary is energized (relays do stick on occasion), a pilot light is connected across the primary leads.

Circuit diagram is similar to Fig. 6-90, with exception of transformer used (BTC 6181) and voltmeter connected noted in text.

Fig. 6-73 (above)—Close-up view with the tube and fan removed discloses details of switch S_{1B}. It is made from a brass shaft coupling and a length of silver solder; in the 3.5-Mc. position it contacts a fixed arm and grounds the 50-pf. fixed capacitor (upper left).

Mounting plate for fan is trimmed away for maximum ventilation under tube socket. The fan is mounted on a piece of ¼-inch foam rubber and held in position by two screws through rubber grommets in the vertical plate.

Chapter 7

Code Transmission

Keying a transmitter properly involves much more than merely turning it on and off with a fast manually-operated switch (the key). If the output is permitted to go from zero to full instantaneously (zero "rise" time), side frequencies, or **key clicks,** will be generated for many kilocycles either side of the transmitter frequency, at the instant the key is closed. Similarly, if the output drops from full to zero instantaneously (zero "decay" time), side frequencies will be generated at the instant of opening the key. The amplitude of the side-frequency energy decreases with the frequency separation from the transmitter frequency. To avoid key clicks and thus to comply with the FCC regulations covering spurious radiations, the transmitter output must be "shaped" to provide finite rise and decay times for the envelope. The longer the rise and decay times, the less will be the side-frequency energy and extent.

Since the FCC regulations require that ". . . the frequency of the emitted wave shall be as

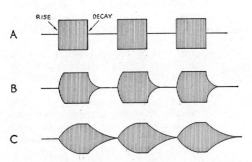

Fig. 7-1—Typical oscilloscope displays of a code transmitter. The rectangular-shaped dots or dashes (A) have serious key clicks extending many kc. either side of the transmitter frequency. Using proper shaping circuits increases the rise and decay times to give signals with the envelope form of B. This signal would have practically no key clicks. Carrying the shaping process too far, as in C, results in a signal that is too "soft" and is not quite as easy to copy as B.

Oscilloscope displays of this type are obtained by coupling the transmitter r.f. to the vertical plates (Chapter 11) and using a slow sweep speed synchronized to the dot speed of an automatic key.

constant as the state of the art permits", there should be no appreciable change in the transmitter frequency while energy is being radiated. A *slow* change in frequency, taking place over minutes of time, is called a frequency **drift;** it is usually the result of thermal effects on the oscillator. A *fast* frequency change, observable

during each *dit* or *dah* of the transmission, is called a **chirp.** Chirp is usually caused by a non-constant load on the oscillator or by d.c. voltage changes on the oscillator during the keying cycle. Chirp may or may not be accompanied by drift.

If the transmitter output is not reduced to zero when the key is up, a **backwave** (sometimes called a "spacing wave") will be radiated. A backwave is objectionable to the receiving operator if it is readily apparent; it makes the signal slightly harder to copy. However, a slight backwave, 40 db. or more below the key-down signal, will be discernible only when the signal-to-noise ratio is quite high. Some operators lis-

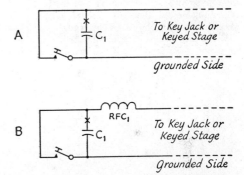

Fig. 7-2—Typical filter circuits to apply at the key (and relay, if used) to minimize r.f. clicks. The simplest circuit (A) is a small capacitor mounted at the key. If this proves insufficient, an r.f. choke can be added to the ungrounded lead (B). The value of C_1 is .001 to .01 μf., RFC_1 can be 0.5 to 2.5 mh., with a current-carrying ability sufficient for the current in the keyed circuit. In difficult cases another small capacitor may be required on the other side of the r.f. choke. In all cases the r.f. filter should be mounted right at the key or relay terminals; sometimes the filter can be concealed under the key. When cathode or center-tap keying is used, the resistance of the r.f. choke or chokes will add cathode bias to the keyed stage, and in this case a high-current low-resistance choke may be required, or compensating reduction of the grid-leak bias (if it is used) may be needed. Shielded wire or coaxial cable makes a good keying lead.

A visible spark on "make" can often be reduced by the addition of a small (10 to 100 ohms) resistor in series with C_1 (inserted at point "x"). Too high a value of resistor reduces the arc-suppressing effect on "break."

tening in the shack to their own signals and hearing a backwave think that the backwave can be heard on the air. It isn't necessarily so, and the best way to check is with an amateur a

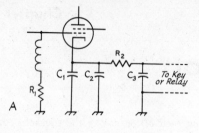

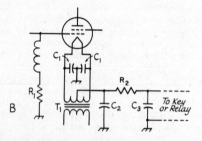

Fig. 7-3—The basic cathode (A) and center-tap (B) keying circuits. In either case C_1 is the r.f. return to ground, shunted by a larger capacitor, C_2, for shaping. Voltage ratings at least equal to the cut-off voltage of the tube are required. T_1 is the normal filament transformer. C_1 and C_3 can be about 0.01 μf.

The shaping of the signal is controlled by the values of R_2 and C_2. Increased capacitance at C_2 will make the signal softer on break; increased resistance at R_2 will make the signal softer on make.

Values at C_2 will range from 0.5 to 10 $\mu f.$, depending upon the tube type and operating conditions. The value of R_2 will also vary with tube type and conditions, and may range from a few to one hundred ohms. When tetrodes or pentodes are keyed in this manner, a smaller value can sometimes be used at C_2 if the screen-voltage supply is fixed and not obtained from the plate supply through a dropping resistor. If the resistor decreases the output (by adding too much cathode bias) the value of R_1 should be reduced.

Oscillators keyed in the cathode can't be softened on break indefinitely by increasing the value of C_2 because the grid-circuit time constant enters into the action.

mile or so away. If he doesn't find the backwave objectionable on the S9+ signal, you can be sure that it won't be when the signal is weaker.

When any circuit carrying d.c. or a.c. is closed or opened, the small or large spark (depending upon the voltage and current) generates r.f. during the instant of make or break. This r.f. click covers a frequency range of many megacycles. When a transmitter is keyed, the spark at the key (and relay, if one is used) causes a click in the receiver. *This click has no effect on the transmitted signal.* Since it occurs at the same time that a click (if any) appears on the transmitter output, it must be eliminated if one is to listen critically to his own signal within the shack. A small r.f. filter is required at the contacts of the key (and relay); typical circuits and values are shown in Fig. 7-2. To check the effectiveness of the r.f. filter, listen on a band lower in frequency than the one the transmitter is tuned to, with a short receiving antenna and the receiver gain backed off.

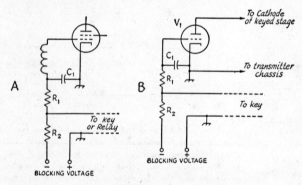

Fig. 7-4—The basic circuit for blocked-grid keying is shown at A. R_1 is the normal grid leak, and the blocking voltage must be at least several times the normal grid bias. The click on make can be reduced by making C_1 larger, and the click on break can be reduced by making R_2 larger. Usually the value of R_2 will be 5 to 20 times the resistance of R_1. The power supply current requirement depends upon the value of R_2, since closing the key circuit places R_2 across the blocking voltage supply.

An allied circuit is the vacuum-tube keyer of B. The tube V_1 is connected in the cathode circuit of the stage to be keyed. The values of C_1, R_1 and R_2 determine the keying envelope in the same way that they do for blocked-grid keying. Values to start with might be 0.47 megohm for R_1, 4.7 megohm for R_2 and 0.0047 $\mu f.$ for C_1.

The blocking voltage supply must deliver several hundred volts, but the current drain is very low. The 2A3 or other low plate-resistance triode is suitable for V_1. To increase the current-carrying ability of a tube keyer, several tubes can be connected in parallel.

A vacuum-tube keyer adds cathode bias and drops the supply voltages to the keyed stage and will reduce the output of the stage. In oscillator keying it may be impossible to use a v.t. keyer without changing the oscillator d.c. grid return from ground to cathode.

What Transmitter Stage To Key

A satisfactory code signal, free from chirp and key clicks, can be amplified by a *linear* amplifier without affecting the keying characteristics in any way. If, however, the satisfactory signal is amplified by one or more non-linear stages (e.g., a Class-C multiplier or amplifier), the signal envelope will be modified. The rise and decay times will be decreased, possibly introducing significant key clicks that were not present on the signal before amplification. It is possible to compensate for the effect by using longer-than-normal rise and decay times in the excitation and letting the amplifier(s) modify the signal to an acceptable one.

Many two-, three- and even four-stage v.f.o.-controlled transmitters are

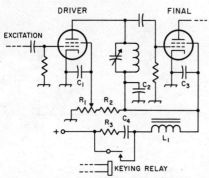

Fig. 7-5—When the driver-stage plate voltage is roughly the same as the screen voltage of a tetrode final amplifier, combined screen and driver keying is an excellent system. The envelope shaping is determined by the values of L_1, C_4, and R_3, although the r.f. bypass capacitors C_1, C_2 and C_3 also have a slight effect. R_1 serves as an excitation control for the final amplifier, by controlling the screen voltage of the driver stage. If a triode driver is used, its plate voltage can be varied for excitation control.

The inductor L_1 will not be too critical, and the secondary of a spare filament transformer can be used if a low-inductance choke is not available. The values of C_4 and R_3 will depend upon the inductance and the voltage and current levels, but good starting values are 0.1 μf. and 50 ohms.

To minimize the possibility of electrical shock, it is recommended that a keying relay be used in this circuit, since both sides of the circuit are "hot." As in any transmitter, the signal will be chirp-free only if keying the driver stage has no effect on the oscillator frequency.

(The Sigma 41FZ-35-ACS-SIL 6-volt a.c. relay is well-suited for keying applications.)

incapable of chirp-free output-amplifier keying because keying the output stage has an effect on the oscillator frequency and "pulls" it. Keying the amplifier presents a variable load to its driver stage, which in turn is felt as a variable load on the previous stage, and so on back to the oscillator. Chances of **pulling** are especially high when the oscillator is on the same frequency as the keyed output stage, but frequency multiplication is no guarantee against pulling. Another source of reaction is the variation in oscillator supply voltage under keying conditions, but this can usually be handled by stabilizing the oscillator supply with a VR tube. If the objective is a completely chirp-free transmitter, the first step is to make sure that keying the amplifier stage

(or stages) has no effect on the frequency. This can be checked by listening on the oscillator frequency while the amplifier stage is keyed. Listen for chirp on either side of zero beat, to eliminate the possibility of a chirpy receiver (caused by line-voltage changes or b.f.o. pulling).

An amplifier can be keyed by any method that reduces the output to zero. Neutralized stages can be keyed in the cathode circuit, although where powers over 50 or 75 watts are involved it is often desirable to use a keying relay or vacuum tube keyer, to minimize the chances for electrical shock. Tube keying drops the supply voltages and adds cathode bias, points to be considered where maximum output is required. Blocked-grid keying is applicable to many neutralized stages, but it presents problems in high-powered amplifiers and requires a source of negative voltage. Output stages that aren't neutralized, such as many of the tetrodes and pentodes in widespread use, will usually leak a little and show some backwave regardless of how they are keyed. In a case like this it may be necessary to key two stages to eliminate backwave. They can be keyed in the cathodes, with blocked-grid keying, or in the screens. When screen keying is used, it is not always sufficient to reduce the screen voltage to zero; it may have to be taken to some negative value to bring the key-up plate current to zero, unless fixed negative control-grid bias is used. It should be apparent that where two stages are keyed, keying the earlier stage must have no effect on the oscillator frequency if completely chirp-free output is the goal.

Shaping of the keying is obtained in several ways. Vacuum-tube keyers, blocked-grid and cathode-keyed systems get suitable shaping with proper choice of resistor and capacitor values, while screen-grid keying can be shaped by using inductors or resistors and capacitors. Sample circuits are shown in Figs. 7-3, 7-4 and 7-5, together with instructions for their adjustment. There is no "best" adjustment, since this is a matter of personal preference and what you want your signal to sound like. Most operators seem to like the make to be heavier than the break. All of the circuits shown here are capable of a wide range of adjustment.

If the negative supply in a grid-block keyed stage fails, the tube will draw excessive key-up current. To protect against tube damage in this eventuality, an overload relay can be used or, more simply, a fast-acting fuse can be included in the cathode circuit.

OSCILLATOR KEYING

One may wonder why oscillator keying hasn't been mentioned earlier, since it is widely used. A sad fact of life is that excellent oscillator keying is infinitely more difficult to obtain than is excellent amplifier keying. If the objective is no detectable chirp, it is probably *impossible* to obtain with oscillator keying, particularly on the higher frequencies. The reasons are simple. Any

keyed-oscillator transmitter requires shaping at the oscillator, which involves changing the operating conditions of the oscillator over a significant period of time. The output of the oscillator doesn't rise to full value immediately so the drive on the following stage is changing, which in turn may reflect a variable load on the oscillator. No oscillator has been devised that has no change

Fig. 7-6—Simple differential-keying circuit for a crystal-controlled oscillator and power-amplifier transmitter.

Most simple crystal-controlled transmitters, commercial or home-built, return the oscillator grid-lead resistor, R_1, to chassis, and "cathode keying" is used on the oscillator and amplifier stages. By returning the oscillator grid leak to the cathode, as shown here, negative-power-supply-lead keying is used on the oscillator. A good crystal oscillator will operate with only 5 to 10 volts applied to it.

Using the above circuit, the signal is controlled by the shaping circuit, $C_4 R_3$. Increasing the value of R_3 will make the signal "softer" on make; increasing the capacitance at C_4 will make the signal softer on make and break. The oscillator will continue to operate after the amplifier has cut off, until the charge in C_4 falls below the minimum operating voltage for the oscillator.

The 0.01-μf. capacitor and 47-ohm resistor reduce the spark at the key contacts and minimize "key clicks" heard in the receiver and other nearby receivers. They *do not* control the key clicks associated with the signal miles away; these clicks are reduced by increasing the values of R_3 and C_4.

Since the oscillator may hold in between dots and dashes, a back wave may be present if the amplifier stage is not neutralized.

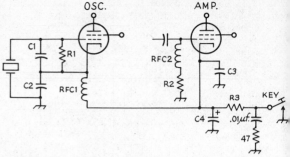

C_1, C_2—Normal oscillator capacitors.
C_3—Amplifier r.f. cathode bypass capacitor.
C_4—Shaping capacitor, typically 1 to 10 μf., 250 volts.
R_1—Oscillator grid leak, returned to cathode instead of chassis ground.
R_2—Normal amplifier grid leak; no change.
R_3—Typically 47 to 100 ohms.
RFC_1, RFC_2—As in transmitter, no change.

in frequency over its entire operating voltage range and with a changing load. Furthermore, the shaping of the keyed-oscillator envelope usually has to be exaggerated, because the following stages will tend to sharpen up the keying and introduce clicks unless they are operated as linear amplifiers.

Break-In Keying

The usual argument for oscillator keying is that it permits break-in operation (see subsequent sections, also Chapter 22). If break-in operation is not contemplated and as near perfect keying as possible is the objective, then keying an amplifier or two by the methods outlined earlier is the solution. For operating convenience, an automatic transmitter "turner-onner" (see Campbell, *QST*, Aug., 1956), which will turn on the power supplies and switch antenna relays and receiver muting devices, can be used. The station switches over to the complete "transmit" condition where the first dot is sent, and it holds in for a length of time dependent upon the setting of the delay. It is equivalent to voice-operated phone of the type commonly used by s.s.b. stations. It does not permit hearing the other station whenever the key is up, as does full break-in.

Full break-in with excellent keying is not easy to come by, but it is easier than many amateurs think. Many use oscillator keying and put up with a second-best signal.

Differential Keying

The principle behind "differential" keying is to turn the oscillator on fast before a keyed amplifier stage can pass any signal and turn off the oscillator fast after the keyed amplifier stage has cut off. A number of circuits have been devised for accomplishing the action. The simplest, which should be applied *only* to a transmitter using a voltage-stable (crystal-controlled) oscillator is shown in Fig. 7-6. Many "simple" and kitted Novice transmitters can be modified to use this system, which approaches the performance of the "turner-onner" mentioned above insofar as the transmitter performance is concerned. With separate transmitting and receiving antennas, the performance is comparable.

A simple differential-keying circuit that can be applied to any grid-block keyed amplifier or tube-keyed stage by the addition of a triode and a VR tube is shown in Fig. 7-7. Using this keying system for break-in, the keying will be chirp-free if it is chirp-free with the VR tube removed from its socket, to permit the oscillator to run all of the time. If the transmitter can't pass this test, it indicates that more isolation is required between keyed stage and oscillator.

Another VR-tube differential keying circuit, useful when the screen-grid circuit of an amplifier is keyed, is shown in Fig. 7-8. The normal screen keying circuit is made up of the shaping capacitor C_1, the keying relay (to remove dangerous voltages from the key), and the resistors R_1 and R_2. The + supply should be 50 to 100 volts higher than the normal screen voltage, and the — voltage should be sufficient to ignite the VR tube, V_2, through the drop in R_2 and R_3. Current through R_2 will be determined by voltage required to cut off oscillator; if 10 volts will do it the current will be 1 ma. For a desirable keying characteristic, R_2 will usually have a higher value than R_1. Increasing the value of C_1 will soften both "make" and "break."

The tube used at V_2 will depend upon the available negative supply voltage. If it is between 120 and 150, a 0A3/VR75 is recommended. Above this a 0C3/VR105 can be used. The diode, V_1, can be any diode operated within ratings. A 6AL5 will suffice with screen voltages under 250 and bleeder currents under 5 ma. For maximum life a separate heater transformer should be used for the diode, with the cathode connected to one side of the heater winding.

Clicks in Later Stages

It was mentioned earlier that key clicks can be generated in amplifier stages following the keyed stage or stages. This can be a puzzling problem to an operator who has spent considerable time adjusting the keying in his exciter unit for click-less keying, only to find that the clicks are bad when the amplifier unit is added. There are two possible causes for the clicks: low-frequency parasitic oscillations and amplifier "clipping."

Under some conditions an amplifier will be momentarily triggered into low-frequency parasitic oscillations, and clicks will be generated when the amplifier is driven by a keyed exciter. If these clicks are the result of low-frequency

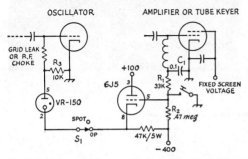

Fig. 7-7—When satisfactory blocked-grid or tube keying of an amplifier stage has been obtained, this VR-tube break-in circuit can be applied to the transmitter to furnish differential keying. The constants shown here are suitable for blocked-grid keying of a 6146 amplifier; with a tube keyer the 6J5 and VR tube circuitry would be the same.

With the key up, sufficient current flows through R_3 to give a voltage that will cut off the oscillator tube. When the key is closed, the cathode voltage of the 6J5 becomes close to ground potential, extinguishing the VR tube and permitting the oscillator to operate. Too much shunt capacity on the leads to the VR tube, and too large a value of grid capacitor in the oscillator, may slow down this action, and best performance will be obtained when the oscillator (turned on and off this way) sounds "clicky." The output envelope shaping is obtained in the amplifier, and it can be made softer by increasing the value of C_1. If the keyed amplifier is a tetrode or pentode, the screen voltage should be obtained from a fixed voltage source or stiff voltage divider, not from the plate supply through a dropping resistor.

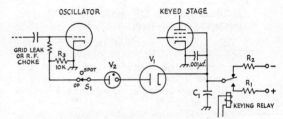

Fig. 7-8—VR-tube differential keying in an amplifier screen circuit.

With key up and current flowing through V_1 and V_2, the oscillator is cut off by the drop through R_3. The keyed stage draws no current because its screen grid is negative. C_1 is charged negatively to the value of the — source. When the relay is energized, C_1 charges through R_1 to a + value. Before reaching zero (on its way +) there is insufficient voltage to maintain ionization in V_2, and the current is broken in R_3, turning on the oscillator stage. As the screen voltage goes positive, the VR tube, V_2, cannot reignite because the diode, V_1, will not conduct in that direction. The oscillator and keyed stage remain on as long as the relay is closed. When the relay opens, the voltage across C_1 must be sufficiently negative for V_2 to ionize before any bleeder current will pass through R_3. By this time the screen of the keyed stage is so far negative that the tube has stopped conducting. (See Fig. 7-5 for suitable relay.)

parasitic oscillations, they will be found in "groups" of clicks occurring at 50- to 150-kc. intervals either side of the transmitter frequency. Of course low-frequency parasitic oscillations can be generated in a keyed stage, and the operator should listen carefully to make sure that the output of the exciter is clean before he blames a later amplifier. Low-frequency parasitic oscillations are usually caused by poor choice in r.f. choke values, and the use of more inductance in the plate choke than in the grid choke for the same stage is recommended.

When the clicks introduced by the addition of an amplifier stage are found only near the transmitter frequency, amplifier "clipping" is indicated. It is quite common when fixed bias is used on the amplifier and the bias is well past the "cut-off" value. The effect can usually be minimized by using a combination of fixed and grid-leak bias for the amplifier stage. The fixed bias should be sufficient to hold the key-up plate current only to a low level and not to zero.

A linear amplifier (Class AB_1, AB_2 or B) will amplify the excitation without adding any clicks, and if clicks show up a low-frequency parasitic oscillation is probably the reason.

KEYING SPEEDS

In radio telegraphy the basic code element is the dot, or unit pulse. The time duration of a dot and a space is that of two unit pulses. A dash is three unit pulses long. The space between letters is three unit pulses; the space between words is seven unit pulses. A speed of one **baud** is one pulse per second.

Assuming that a speed key is adjusted to give the proper dot, space and dash values mentioned above, the code speed can be found from

$$Speed \text{ (w.p.m.)} = \frac{dots/min.}{25}$$

E.g.: A properly adjusted electronic key gives a string of dots that counts to 10 dots per second. Speed = (60 × 10) ÷ 25 = 24 w.p.m.

OSCILLOGRAMS OF SHAPED AND UNSHAPED KEYING

These photos show how the driving signal compares to the p.a. output as observed on a dual-trace oscilloscope. The five-band 50-watt c.w. transmitter described in Chapter 6 was used to obtain these waveforms. Differential keying is used in that circuit.

At A, the driving signal is shown at the p.a. grid without shaping being applied to the keying circuit. The waveform at B shows the output of the p.a. without shaping. The waveform is relatively square in shape and has sharp corners which show the rapid transitions between key-up and key-down conditions. These transitions are a source of clicks.

Shown at C is the waveform at the grid of the p.a. stage, with shaping. Note that the oscillator is still on after the key is open, thus helping to provide the differential action. At D, the shaped output of the p.a. is illustrated. Observe the rounded corners of the waveform on both the leading and trailing edges (make and break). The waveform at D should be established to assure clean keying.

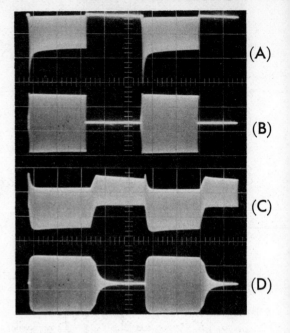

(A)

(B)

(C)

(D)

A SOLID-STATE KEYER

This circuit is a modern version of a keyer that was invented by W9TO.[1] It is compact, inexpensive to build (under $25), and easy to construct. It employs both integrated circuits (ICs) and bipolar transistors. The complete package measures $4 \times 5 \times 6$ inches when fully assembled.

The Circuit

The logic functions in the Micro-TO keyer (Fig. 7-10) are performed by silicon integrated circuits. The boxes labeled FF_1 and FF_2 (μL923) are called J-K flip-flops, and contain some 15 transistors and 17 resistors; the details of the inner workings need not concern us. For our purposes, the flip-flops behave in the following way: Whenever the trigger input (Pin 2) is brought from positive (more than 0.7 volt) to ground (less than 0.2 volt) the flip-flop can go into a new state. If both the inputs (Pins 1 and 3) are held at ground during the negative-going trigger pulse, the outputs (Pins 5 and 7) will complement (assume opposite states), while if Pin 3 is grounded and Pin 1 is held positive the flip-flop will go into the state in which Pin 5 is grounded no matter what the initial state. Whenever the dot lever is closed and Pin 1 of the dot flip-flop FF_1 thereby grounded, the pulse generator, which will be discussed in

greater detail below, begins to deliver a string of pulses into the dot flip-flop trigger input. Grounding the dash contact also grounds the dot contact through CR_2. A series of dots will appear at the dot flip-flop outputs as long as one of the levers is closed. The output of the dot flip-flop feeds through some gates in G_1, μL914 (which consists of two pairs of paralleled transistors) to key the

Fig. 7-9—This electronic speed keyer is 100 percent solid state and uses both integrated circuits and bipolar transistors. It operates over a speed range of 10 to 50 w.p.m. and contains its own built-in monitor.

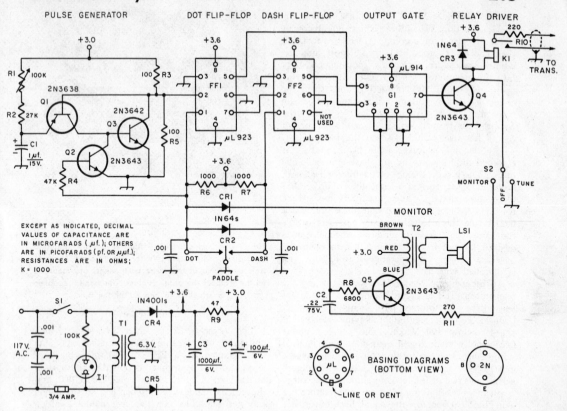

PULSE GENERATOR   DOT FLIP-FLOP DASH FLIP-FLOP   OUTPUT GATE   RELAY DRIVER

EXCEPT AS INDICATED, DECIMAL
VALUES OF CAPACITANCE ARE
IN MICROFARADS (μf.); OTHERS
ARE IN PICOFARADS (pf. OR μμf.);
RESISTANCES ARE IN OHMS;
K = 1000

BASING DIAGRAMS
(BOTTOM VIEW)

LINE OR DENT

Fig. 7-10—Schematic of the Micro-TO keyer. Capacitances are in μf., polarity indicates electrolytic, others are ceramic. Resistances are in ohms ($K = 1000$); resistors are ½-watt. Component designations not listed below are for identification in board layout.

CR_1, CR_2—Must be germanium diodes.
FF_1, FF_2—J-K flip-flop (Fairchild μL923).
G_1—Dual-input gate (Fairchild μL914).
I_1—Neon glow pilot lamp.
K_1—S.p.s.t. reed relay (Magnecraft W102X1).
LS_1—3-inch 10-ohm speaker (Philmore).
Q_1–Q_5, incl.—Must be silicon transistors with beta of 10 or greater. 2N4125 (p-n-p) and 2N4123 (n-p-n) suitable.

R_1—100,000-ohm control, linear taper, 2 watts, composition.
S_1—S.p.s.t. switch on R_1.
S_2—S.p.s.t. center-off toggle switch.
T_1—6.3-volt 0.6-amp. filament transformer (Stancor P6465 or equivalent).
T_2—Transistor output transformer, 500 ohms c.t. to 16 ohms (Argonne AR-118).

relay. When the dash lever is closed, Pin 1 on the dash flip-flop FF_2 is also grounded and this flip-flop is ready to change state whenever Pin 7 of the dot flip-flop goes to ground. Thus, when the dash lever is closed, the dot flip-flop changes state with the first trigger pulse and this in turn triggers the dash flip-flop. At the end of the first dot, the dash flip-flop is still set and holds the relay in via the output gate. CR_1 keeps the dot generator going even if the dash lever is released, and the keyer goes on to make a second dot. This time when Pin 7 goes to ground it resets the dash flip-flop and, finally, after the end of the second dot the relay opens and the keyer is ready to generate the next character. A little thought will reveal that once a character has started it is impossible to alter it with the keyer paddle. Also, there is no space in the middle of a dash,

as is found in some keyers, so dashes are self-completing without a need for filters on the paddle leads (except, of course, for some 0.001's to keep r.f. out of the keyer).

The pulse generator is somewhat novel. Ignoring Q_2 for the moment, the combination of Q_1 and Q_3 resembles a unijunction transistor. Both Q_1 and Q_3 are normally off, and the base of Q_1 sits at 1.5 volts as determined by the 100-ohm divider resistors. C_1 charges through R_1 until the Q_1 emitter reaches about 2.1 volts (1.5 volts plus the base-emitter voltage drop), at which point Q_1 begins to turn on. Current begins to flow into the base of Q_3 and it also begins to turn on. This lowers the base voltage on Q_1, making it come on a little more; Q_1 then feeds more current to Q_3, making it come on harder, and so on: a cataclysmic collapse occurs which discharges

C_1 and generates the negative pulse required by the dot flip-flop. When there is not enough charge on C_1 to keep things going, Q_1 and Q_3 turn off, the base of Q_1 goes back to 1.5 volts, and the whole process repeats. Now putting Q_2 back into the circuit, we see that with the key levers open it is normally conducting and, since the collector-emitter voltage on a saturated silicon transistor is less than the base-emitter drop required to turn it on, it diverts any current that otherwise would go into the base of Q_3. The collapsing process cannot begin, and C_1 is clamped at 2.1 volts by the base-emitter diode of Q_1. The instant the dot on dash lever is closed, however, Q_2 is turned off and the collapse takes place immediately. The circuit is insensitive to dirty paddle contacts, and once the clock has started the interval between pulses is always the same. If a free-running pulse generator is desired, a switch can be installed to open the base lead of Q_2. A speed range of 10 to 50 w.p.m. is obtained with the constants shown.

An inexpensive reed relay is used to key the transmitter. It has operate and release times of less than 1 millisecond, including contact bounce, causing negligible keying delays at speeds below 100 w.p.m. The relay contacts occasionally stick together if the relay is used with transmitter keying lines having large bypass capacitors. A 220-ohm resistor has been added in series with one of the leads to eliminate the surge that causes the sticking. This small resistance has a negligible effect on the usual high-impedance grid-block keying line. The relay is not recommended for use with cathode-keyed transmitters running much more than 30 watts.

The monitor is a makeshift affair depending on speaker resonance and transformer inductance to generate an audio tone. The values indicated work for the particular speaker-transformer combination indicated; if other parts are used the values of the 6800-ohm resistor and 0.22-μf. capacitor will probably need to be changed. The waveform is a series of pulses which are damped out by the speaker resonance, and the resulting tone, while rough, is not annoying. The waveform can be made sinusoidal, but the keying then becomes clicky. The volume is determined by the value of the 100-ohm resistor in the Q_5 emitter lead.

Fig. 7-11—Components for the keyer are mounted on a piece of perforated Vector circuit board. The controls and some of the large components are mounted on the walls of the utility cabinet. The monitor speaker is attached to one lid of the box.

Construction

The keyer is housed in a 3 × 4 × 5-inch aluminum utility cabinet. The small components are mounted on a 2⅜ × 4¹³⁄₁₆-inch piece of Vectorbord. The speaker is bolted to the bottom of the box, in which a few holes are drilled, and the box is mounted on rubber feet so the sound can get out. The controls are mounted along the lower part of the box, and the wiring board is fastened with small brackets near the top so it will clear the controls and speaker. The relay is held to the side of the cabinet with a pair of cable clamps.

The Fairchild economy epoxy-cased integrated circuits used may be hard to find. The name of the nearest distributor can be obtained from Fairchild Semiconductor, Marketing Services Dept., P.O. Box 1058, Mountain View, California. The Motorola HEP integrated circuit line, which is available at many electronics stores, could probably be used if the power supply and relay voltages were changed. Other silicon transistor types could be substituted. The total cost of the keyer, including the monitor, is under $25.00.

R.F.-POWERED C.W. MONITOR

This monitor is powered by rectified r.f. from the transmitter. The pickup wire can be a small probe placed near the feed line or near the p.a. tank of the transmitter—*danger, high voltage!*

Fig. 7-11A—R.f.-powered c.w. monitor. CR_1 is a 1N34A diode. The transistor is a 2N1178, 2N4125, or similar. T_1 is a 12,000-ohm primary to 3.2-ohm secondary transformer (Thordarson 22S48 or equal).

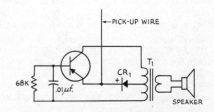

RELAY DRIVER FOR USE WITH SOLID-STATE KEYERS

Some of today's transistorized electronic keyers will not operate with all transmitters because of the limitations of the transistor in the switching stage of the keyer. In many cases, voltages above minus 100 volts and currents greater than 30 to 40 ma. will damage the switching transistor.

One solution (Fig. 7-12) to this problem is the addition of an external circuit to actuate a keying relay. The relay contacts then key the transmitter. In the normal state, V_1 is cut off by the negative voltage from the power supply and the tube does not conduct, leaving the keying circuit open. When the electronic keyer circuit closes, the grid of V_1 is at zero volts and the tube conducts, energizing the relay and closing the keying circuit of the transmitter.

Construction

The keyer in the photograph is built on a homemade chassis, but any chassis about $4 \times 6 \times 2$ inches will do. A smaller chassis could be used if power for the circuit is obtained from the transmitter. The wiring and layout are not critical. To keep down the noise, the relay should be mounted on rubber grommets or similar cushioning material.

Although other relays will work in the circuit, the one specified is designed for high-speed operation. Most ordinary relays will cause keying problems at high speeds because of contact bounce. The relay used here will have no problem following speeds of at least 40 to 50 w.p.m.

With the addition of three parts, the relay driver can be used to key a transmitter from a tape recorder or other audio source. For contest work, a CQ tape could be made up and a switch would select either the electronic keyer or the tape recorder with the CQ tape.

The circuit (Fig. 7-13) uses the audio voltage from the output of a tape recorder, which is stepped up by T_2 and rectified. This d.c. voltage is then fed to the input of the relay driver and overrides the negative voltage at the grid of the tube.

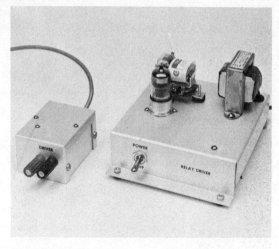

Fig. 7-12—The relay driver is at the right and is a self-contained unit. The smaller assembly at the left is the tape-recorder adaptor of Fig. 7-13B.

Parts layout is not critical. The adapter may be put on the same chassis as the relay driver or a $2\frac{3}{4} \times 2\frac{1}{8} \times 1\frac{5}{8}$-inch Minibox may be used.

To operate, the tape recorder is connected to TB_3 and the output (TB_4) is connected to TB_1 of the relay driver. The volume control of the tape recorder should be adjusted to provide enough audio to follow the keying.

Caution: This circuit is designed for use with only those keyers that are set up to switch a *negative* voltage, Heath HD-10, etc.

Fig. 7-13—Schematic of the relay driver is shown at A. The tape-recorder adaptor is at B. Capacitance is in µf. The polarized capacitor is electrolytic. The 0.01-µf. unit is a disk ceramic. Resistance is in ohms, K = 1000. Resistors are ½ watt composition unless otherwise noted.

CR₁, CR₂—Silicon diode, 400 p.r.v., 100 ma. or more.

CR₃—Silicon diode, 200 p.r.v., 100 ma. or more.

K₁—1000-ohm keying relay, s.p.s.t. contacts (Sigma 41F 1000S-SIL).

S₁—S.p.s.t. toggle.

T₁—125 volts, 15 ma., 6.3 volts, 0.6 amp. (Stancor PS-8415).

T₂—Output Transformer, 5000 ohms to 3.2 ohms.

TB₁-TB₄, inc.—2-lug terminal strip (Millen E-302 or similar).

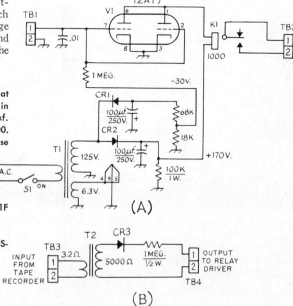

BREAK-IN OPERATION

Smooth c.w. break-in operation involves protecting the receiver from permanent damage by the transmitter power and insurance that the receiver will "recover" fast enough to be sensitive between dots and dashes, or at least between letters and words. Few of the available antenna transfer relays is fast enough to follow keying, so the simplest break-in system is the use of a separate receiving antenna. If the transmitter power is low (25 or 50 watts) and the isolation between transmitting and receiving antennas is good, this method can be satisfactory. Best isolation is obtained by mounting the antennas as far apart as possible and at right angles to each other. Feedline pick-up should be minimized, through the use of coaxial cable or 300-ohm Twin-Lead. If the receiver recovers fast enough but the transmitter clicks are bothersome (they may be caused by the receiver overload and so exist only in the receiver) their effect on the operator can be minimized through the use of an output limiter (see Chapter Five).

When powers above 25 or 50 watts are used, or where two antennas are not available, special treatment is required for quiet break-in on the transmitter frequency. A means must be provided for limiting the power that reaches the receiver input; this can be either a direct short-circuit or a limiting device like an electronic TR switch (see Chapter Twenty two). Further, a means must be provided for momentarily reducing the gain through the receiver, which enables the receiver to "recover" faster.

The system shown in Fig. 7-14 permits quiet break-in operation of high-powered stations. It may require a simple operation on the receiver, although many commercial receivers already provide the connection and require no internal modification. The circuit for use with a separate receiving antenna is shown in Fig. 7-12A; the slight change for use with a TR switch and a single antenna is shown in B. R_1 is the regular receiver r.f. and i.f. gain control. The ground lead is run to chassis ground through a rheostat, R_2. A wire from the junction runs to the keying relay, K_1. When the key is up, the ground side of R_1 is connected to ground through the relay arm, and the receiver is in its normal operating condition. When the key is closed the relay closes, which breaks the ground connection from R_1 and applies additional bias to the tubes in the receiver. This bias is controlled by R_2. When the relay closes, it also closes the circuit to the transmitter keying circuit. A simple r.f. filter at the key suppresses the local clicks caused by the relay current. This circuit is superior to any working on the a.g.c. line of the receiver because the cathode circuit(s) have shorter time constants than the a.g.c. circuits and will recover faster.

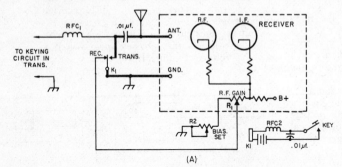

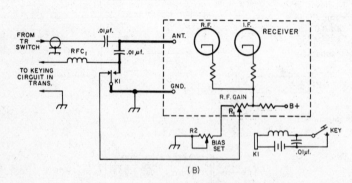

Fig. 7-14—Two variations of a circuit for smooth break-in operation, using (A) separate receiving antenna or (B) an electronic TR switch. The leads shown as heavy lines should be kept as short as possible, to minimize direct transmitter pick-up.

R_1—Receiver manual gain control.

R_2—5000- or 10,000-ohm wire-wound potentiometer.

RFC_1, RFC_2—1- to $2\frac{1}{2}$-mh. r.f. choke, current rating adequate for application.

K_1—S.p.d.t. keying relay (Sigma 41FZ-35-ACS-SIL or equiv.). Although battery and d.c. relay are shown, any suitable a.c. or d.c. relay and power source can be used.

Chapter 8

Audio Amplifiers and Double-Sideband Phone

The audio amplifiers used in radiotelephone transmitters operate on the principles outlined earlier in this book in the chapter on vacuum tubes. The design requirements are determined principally by the type of modulation system to be used and by the type of microphone to be employed. It is necessary to have a clear understanding of modulation principles before the problem of laying out a speech system can be approached successfully. Those principles are discussed under appropriate headings.

The present chapter deals with the design of audio amplifier systems for communication purposes. In voice communication the primary objective is to obtain the most *effective* transmission; i.e., to make the message be understood at the receiving point in spite of adverse conditions created by noise and interference. The methods used to accomplish this do not necessarily coincide with the methods used for other purposes,

such as the reproduction of music or other program material. In other words, "naturalness" in reproduction is distinctly secondary to intelligibility.

The fact that satisfactory intelligibility can be maintained in a relatively narrow band of frequencies is particularly fortunate, because the width of the channel occupied by a phone transmitter is directly proportional to the width of the audio-frequency band. If the channel width is reduced, more stations can occupy a given band of frequencies without mutual interference.

In speech transmission, amplitude distortion of the voice wave has very little effect on intelligibility. The importance of such distortion in communication lies almost wholly in the fact that many of the audio-frequency harmonics caused by it lie outside the channel needed for intelligible speech, and thus will create unnecessary interference to other stations.

SPEECH EQUIPMENT

In designing speech equipment it is necessary to know (1) the amount of audio power the modulation system must furnish and (2) the output voltage developed by the microphone when it is spoken into from normal distance (a few inches) with ordinary loudness. It then becomes possible to choose the number and type of amplifier stages needed to generate the required audio power without overloading or undue distortion anywhere in the system.

MICROPHONES

The level of a microphone is its electrical output for a given sound intensity. The level varies somewhat with the type. It depends to a large extent on the distance from the sound source and the intensity of the speaker's voice. Most commercial transmitters are designed for the median level. If a high-level mike is used, care should be taken not to overload the input amplifier stage. Conversely, a microphone of too low a level must be boosted by a preamplifier.

The frequency response (fidelity) of a microphone is its ability to convert sound uniformly into alternating current. For high articulation it is desirable to reproduce a frequency range of from 200-3500 Hz. When all frequencies are reproduced equally, the microphone is considered "flat." Flat response is highly desirable as peaks (sharp rises in the reproduction curve) limit the swing or modulation to the maximum drive voltage, whereas the usable energy is contained in the flat part of the curve.

Microphones are generally omnidirectional,

and respond to sound from all directions, or unidirectional, picking up sound from one direction. If a microphone is to be used close to the operator's mouth, an omnidirectional microphone is ideal. If, however, speech is generated a foot or more from the microphone, a unidirectional microphone will reduce reverberation by a factor of 1.7:1. Some types of unidirectional microphones have proximity effect in that low frequencies are accentuated when the microphone is too close to the mouth.

Carbon Microphones

The carbon microphone consists of a metal diaphragm placed against a cup of loosely packed carbon granules. As the diaphragm is actuated by the sound pressure, it alternately compresses and decompresses the granules. When current is flowing through the button, a variable d.c. will correspond to the movement of the diaphragm. This fluctuating d.c. can be used to provide grid 11-11 cathode voltage corresponding to the sound pressure which is then amplified.

The output of a carbon microphone is extremely high, but nonlinear distortion and instability has reduced its use. The circuit shown in Fig. 8-1A will deliver 20-30 volts at the transformer secondary.

Piezoelectric Microphones

Piezoelectric microphones make use of the phenomena by which certain materials produce a voltage by mechanical stress or distortion of the material. A diaphragm is coupled to a small bar of material such as Rochelle salt or ceramics made of barium titanate or lead zirconium titanate. The diaphragm motion is thus translated into electrical energy.

Rochelle-salt crystals are damage susceptible to high temperatures, excessive moisture, or extreme dryness. Although the output level is higher, their use is declining because of their fragility.

Ceramic microphones are impervious to temperature and humidity. The output level is adequate for most modern amplifiers. They are capacitive devices and the output impedance is high.

The load impedance will affect the low frequencies. To provide attentuation, it is often desirable to reduce it to 0.25 megohm or even lower, to maximize performance when operating s.s.b., thus eliminating much of the unwanted low-frequency response.

Dynamic Microphones

The dynamic microphone somewhat resembles a dynamic loudspeaker. A lightweight coil, usually made of aluminum wire, is attached to a diaphragm. This coil is suspended in a magnetic circuit. When sound impinges on the diaphragm, it moves the coil through the magnetic field, generating an alternating voltage.

Dynamic microphones are essentially low-impedance devices. For vacuum-tube input circuits, they are generally supplied in high-impedance (25,000 ohms) output. Transistor circuitry usually requires a relatively low impedance to supply power rather than voltage. In either instance, a built-in transformer provides the impedance match.

Whenever long lines are necessary, a low-impedance microphone with suitable coupling transformers should be used.

THE SPEECH AMPLIFIER

The a.f. amplifier stage that causes the r.f. output to be varied is called the **modulator**, and all the amplifier stages preceding it comprise the **speech amplifier**. Depending on the modulator used, the speech amplifier may be called upon to deliver power ranging from zero (only voltage required) to 20 or 30 watts.

Before starting the design of a speech amplifier, therefore, it is necessary to have selected a suitable modulator for the transmitter. This selection must be based on the power required to modulate the transmitter; this power in turn is determined by the mode of transmission and the particular method of modulation. With the modulator determined, its **driving-power** requirements (audio power required to excite the modulator to full output) can be determined from the tube tables in a later chapter. Generally speaking, it is advisable to choose a tube or tubes (or semiconductors) for the last stage of the speech amplifier that will be capable of developing at least 50 percent more power than the rated driving power of the modulator. This will provide a factor of safety so that losses in coupling transformers, etc., will not upset the calculations.

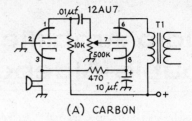

(A) CARBON

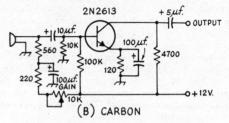

(B) CARBON

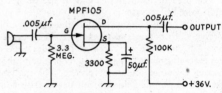

(C) CRYSTAL, CERAMIC, OR HI-Z DYNAMIC

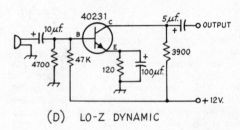

(D) LO-Z DYNAMIC

Fig. 8-1—Speech circuits for use with standard-type microphones. Typical parts values are given.

Voltage Amplifiers

If the modulator stage is a Class AB_2 or B amplifier, the last stage of the speech amplifier must deliver power enough to drive it. However, if the modulator is operated Class A or AB_1, the preceding stage can be simply a voltage amplifier. From there on back to the microphone, all stages are voltage amplifiers.

The important characteristics of a voltage amplifier are its **voltage gain,** maximum undistorted **output voltage,** and its **frequency response.** The voltage gain is the voltage-amplification ratio of the stage. The output voltage is the maximum a.f. voltage that can be secured from the stage without distortion. The amplifier frequency response should be adequate for voice reproduction; this requirement is easily satisfied.

The voltage gain and maximum undistorted output voltage depend on the operating conditions of the amplifier. The output voltage is in terms of *peak* voltage rather than r.m.s.; this makes the rating independent of the waveform.

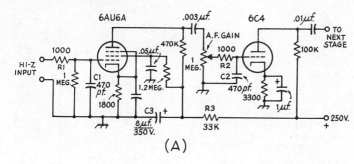

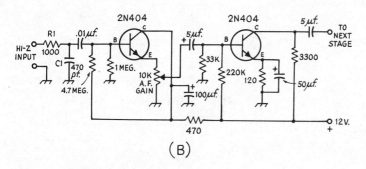

Fig. 8-2—Resistance-coupled speech amplifiers. Component values are representative of typical circuits.

Exceeding the peak value causes the amplifier to distort, so it is more useful to consider only peak values in working with amplifiers.

Resistance Coupling

Resistance coupling generally is used in voltage-amplifier stages. It is relatively inexpensive, good frequency response can be secured, and there is little danger of hum pick-up from stray magnetic fields. It is the most satisfactory type of coupling for the output circuits of pentodes and high-μ triodes, because with transformers a sufficiently high load impedance cannot be obtained without considerable frequency distortion. Typical circuits are given in Fig. 8-2.

Transformer Coupling

Transformer coupling between stages ordinarily is used only when power is to be transferred (in such a case resistance coupling is very inefficient), or when it is necessary to couple between a single-ended and a push-pull stage. Triodes having an amplification factor of 20 or less are used in transformer-coupled voltage amplifiers. With transformer coupling, tubes should be operated under the Class A conditions given in the tube tables at the end of this book.

Circuits for coupling single-ended to push-pull stages is shown in Fig. 8-3. The transformer primary is in series with the plate of the tube, or the collector of the transistor, and thus must carry the plate or collector current. When the following amplifier operates without grid current, the voltage gain of the stage is practically equal to the μ of the tube multiplied by the transformer ratio. This circuit also is suitable for transferring power (within the capabilities of the tube) to a following Class AB_2 or Class B stage.

Phase Inversion

Push-pull output may be secured with resistance coupling by using **phase-inverter** or **phase-splitter** circuits as shown in Fig. 8-4.

The circuits shown in Fig. 8-4 are of the "self-balancing" type. In A, the amplified voltage from V_1 appears across R_5 and R_7 in series. The drop across R_7 is applied to the grid of V_2, and the amplified voltage from V_2 appears across R_6

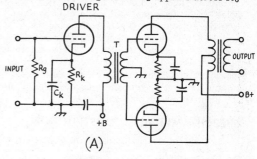

(A)

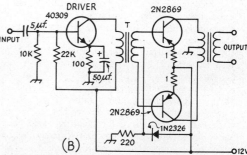

(B)

Fig. 8-3—Transformer-coupled amplifier circuits. Parts values used will depend upon the tubes or transistors used, and upon the frequency response desired.

and R_7 in series. This voltage is 180 degrees out of phase with the voltage from V_1, thus giving push-pull output. The part that appears across R_7 from V_2 opposes the voltage from V_1 across R_7, thus reducing the signal applied to the grid of V_2. The negative feedback so obtained tends to regulate the voltage applied to the phase-inverter tube so that the output voltages from both tubes are substantially equal. The gain is slightly less than twice the gain of a single-tube amplifier using the same operating conditions.

In the single-tube circuit shown in Fig. 8-4B the plate load resistor is divided into two equal parts, R_9 and R_{10}, one being connected to the plate in the normal way and the other between cathode and ground. Since the voltages at the plate and cathode are 180 degrees out of phase, the grids of the following tubes are fed equal a.f. voltages in push-pull. The grid return of V_3 is made to the junction of R_8 and R_{10} so normal bias will be applied to the grid. This circuit is highly degenerative because of the way R_{10} is connected. The voltage gain is less than 2 even when a high-μ triode is used at V_3. A typical transistorized phase splitter is shown at Fig. 8-4C.

Gain Control

A means for varying the over-all gain of the amplifier is necessary for keeping the final output at the proper level for modulating the transmitter. The common method of gain control is to adjust the value of a.c. voltage applied to the base or grid of one of the amplifiers by means of a voltage divider or potentiometer.

The gain-control potentiometer should be near the input end of the amplifier, at a point where the signal voltage level is so low there is no danger that the stages ahead of the gain control will be overloaded by the full microphone output. In a high-gain amplifier it is best to operate the first stage at maximum gain, since this gives the best signal-to-hum ratio. The control is usually placed in the input circuit of the second stage.

SPEECH-AMPLIFIER CONSTRUCTION

Once a suitable circuit has been selected for a speech amplifier, the construction problem resolves itself into avoiding two difficulties — excessive hum, and unwanted feedback. For reasonably humless operation, the hum voltage should not exceed about 1 per cent of the maximum audio output voltage — that is, the hum and noise should be at least 40 db. below the output level.

Unwanted feedback, if negative, will reduce the gain below the calculated value; if positive, is likely to cause self-oscillation or "howls." Feedback can be minimized by isolating each stage with decoupling resistors and capacitors, by avoiding layouts that bring the first and last stages near each other, and by shielding of "hot" points in the circuit, such as grid leads in low-level stages.

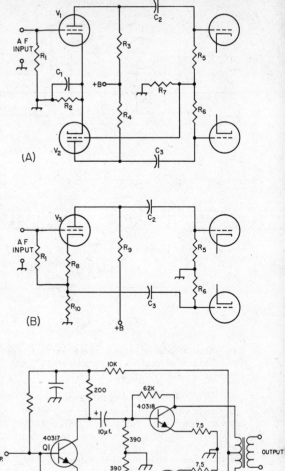

Fig. 8-4—Typical phase-inverter circuits for tube and transistor applications. V_1, V_2, and V_3 can be tubes such as the 12AX7, 12AT7, or 12AU7. Component values should be selected from the tube charts in the RCA Tube Manual and will depend on the frequency response and operating conditions needed.

Speech-amplifier equipment, especially voltage amplifiers, should be constructed on metal chassis, with all wiring kept below the chassis to take advantage of the shielding afforded. Exposed leads, particularly to the grids of low-level high-gain tubes, are likely to pick up hum from the electric field that usually exists in the vicinity of house wiring. Even with the chassis, additional shielding of the input circuit of the first tube in a high-gain amplifier usually is necessary. In addition, such circuits should be separated as much as possible from power-supply transformers and chokes and also from any audio transformers that operate at fairly high power levels; this will minimize magnetic coupling to the grid circuit and thus reduce hum or audio feedback.

The microphone and cable usually are constructed with suitable shielding; this should be connected to the speech-amplifier chassis, and it may be necessary to connect the chassis to a ground such as a water pipe.

Heater wiring should be kept as far as possible from grid leads, and either the center-tap or one side of the heater-transformer secondary winding should be connected to the chassis. If the center-tap is grounded, the heater leads to each tube should be twisted together to reduce the magnetic field from the heater current. With either type of connection; it is advisable to lay heater leads in the corner formed by a fold in the chassis, bringing them out from the cor-

ner to the tube socket by the shortest possible path.

Tubes used in the low-level stages of high-gain amplifiers must be shielded; tube shields are obtainable for that purpose. It is a good plan to enclose the entire amplifier in a metal box, or at least provide it with a cane-metal cover, to avoid feedback difficulties caused by the r.f. field of the transmitter. R.f. picked up on exposed wiring, leads or tube elements causes overloading, distortion, and self-oscillation of the amplifier.

When using paper capacitors as bypasses, be sure that the terminal marked "outside foil" is connected to ground. This utilizes the outside foil of the capacitor as a shield around the "hot" foil. When paper capacitors are used for coupling between stages, always connect the outside foil terminal to the side of the circuit having the lower impedance to ground. Usually, this will be the plate side rather than the following-grid side.

AMPLITUDE MODULATORS AND THEIR DRIVERS

CLASS AB AND B MODULATORS

Class AB or B modulator circuits are basically identical no matter what the power output of the modulator. The diagrams of Fig. 8-5 therefore will serve for any modulator of this type that the amateur may elect to build. The triode circuit is

given at A and the circuit for tetrodes at B. When small tubes with indirectly heated cathodes are used, the cathodes should be connected to ground.

Modulator Tubes

The audio ratings of various types of transmitting tubes are given in the chapter containing the tube tables. Choose a pair of tubes that is capable of delivering sine-wave audio power equal to somewhat more than half the d.c. input to the modulated Class C amplifier. It is sometimes convenient to use tubes that will operate at the same plate voltage as that applied to the Class C stage, because one power supply of adequate current capacity may then suffice for both stages.

In estimating the output of the modulator, remember that the figures given in the tables are for the tube output only, and do not include output-transformer losses. To be adequate for modulating the transmitter, the modulator should have a theoretical power capability 15 to 25 per cent greater than the actual power needed for modulation.

Matching to Load

In giving audio ratings on power tubes, manufacturers specify the plate-to-plate load impedance into which the tubes must operate to deliver the rated audio power output. This load impedance seldom is the same as the modulating impedance of the Class C r.f. stage, so a match must be brought about by adjusting the turns ratio of the coupling transformer. The required turns ratio, primary to secondary, is

$$N = \sqrt{\frac{Z_p}{Z_m}}$$

where N = Turns ratio, primary to secondary

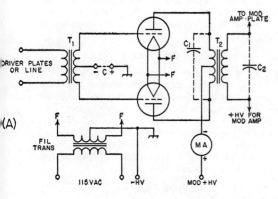

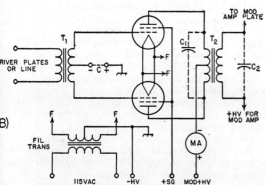

Fig. 8-5—Amplitude-modulator circuit diagrams. Tubes and circuit considerations are discussed in the text.

Z_m = Modulating impedance of Class C r.f. amplifier

Z_p = Plate-to-plate load impedance for Class B tubes

Example: The modulated r.f. amplifier is to operate at 1250 volts and 300 ma. The power input is

$$P = EI = 1250 \times 0.3 = 375 \text{ watts}$$

so the modulating power required is $375/2 = 188$ watts. Increasing this by 25% to allow for losses and a reasonable operating margin gives $188 \times 1.25 = 236$ watts. The modulating impedance of the Class C stage is

$$Z_m = \frac{E}{I} = \frac{1250}{0.3} = 4167 \text{ ohms.}$$

From the *RCA Transmitting Tube Manual* a pair of 811As at 1250 plate volts will deliver 235 watts to a load of 12,400 ohms, plate-to-plate. The primary-to-secondary turns ratio of the modulation transformer therefore should be

$$\sqrt{\frac{Z_p}{Z_m}} = \sqrt{\frac{12,400}{4170}} = \sqrt{2.97} = 1.72:1.$$

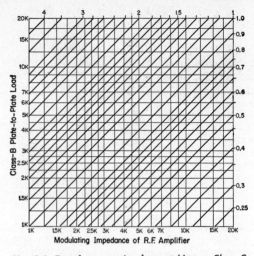

Fig. 8-6—Transformer ratios for matching a Class C modulating impedance to the required plate-to-plate load for the Class B modulator. The ratios given on the curves are from total primary to secondary. Resistance values are in kilohms.

The required transformer ratios for the ordinary range of impedances are shown graphically in Fig 8-6.

Many modulation transformers are provided with primary and secondary taps, so that various turns ratios can be obtained to meet the requirements of particular tube combinations. However, it may be that the exact turns ratio required cannot be secured, even with a tapped modulation transformer. *Small* departures from the proper turns ratio will have no serious effect if the modulator is operating well within its capabilities; if the actual turns ratio is within 10 per cent of the ideal value, the system will operate satisfactorily. Where the discrepancy is larger, it is usually possible to choose a new set of operating conditions for the Class C stage to give a modulating impedance that can be matched by the turns ratio of the available transformer. This may require operating the Class C amplifier at higher voltage and less plate current, if the modulating impedance must be increased, or at lower voltage and higher current if the modulating impedance must be decreased. However, this process cannot be carried very far without exceeding the ratings of the Class C tubes for either plate voltage or plate current, even though the power input is kept at the same figure.

Suppressing Audio Harmonics

Distortion in the driver or modulator will cause a.f harmonics that may lie outside the desired frequency band for intelligible speech.

Capacitors C_1 and C_2 of Fig. 8-5 reduce the strength of the h.f. components in the modulation by acting with the leakage inductance of the transformer windings to form a simple low-pass filter. The values depend upon the load impedance of the Class C amplifier. The capacitors will usually be between 0.001 and 0.01 μf. The large values will be used when low values of load resistance are encountered. A better arrangement is to use a low-pass filter at the output of the modulator, Fig. 8-10.

Grid Bias

Some triode modulator tubes operate at zero grid bias. Others, pentodes and triodes, require a specific value of fixed bias. An a.c.-operated bias supply is used with most modern circuits. Examples of bias supplies are given in Chap. 12. The bias supply should be fairly "stiff" (10 percent regulation or better) for best operation. A regulated bias supply is recommended where large amounts of grid current flow.

Plate Supply

As is true of the modulator's bias supply, the plate voltage supply should have good regulation. If the regulation is such that a significant voltage drop occurs at peak plate current, the lowest voltage figure is that which must be used when calculating the modulator power input.

Good dynamic regulation—i.e., with suddenly applied loads—is equally important as is true of linear r.f. amplifiers. An instantaneous drop in supply voltage on voice peaks will limit the output and cause distortion. The output capacitor of the power supply should be as large as practical to assure good dynamic regulation. The use of silicon rectifiers is also desirable to minimize voltage drop in that part of the supply. The screen supply of AB2 modulators should be well regulated also and should be set near the value recommended (but not higher) for the tubes used.

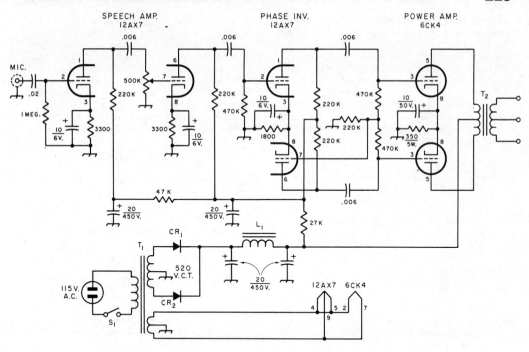

Fig. 8-7—Typical speech-amplifier driver for 5-10 watts output. Capacitances are in μf. Resistors are ½ watt unless specified otherwise. Capacitors with polarity indicated are electrolytic.

CR₁, CR₂—Silicon diode, 800 p.i.v.
L₁—10h., 110-ma. filter choke.
T₂—Class-B driver transformer, 3000 ohms plate-to-plate; secondary impedance as required by

Class-B tubes used; 15-watt rating.
T₁—Power transformer, 520 volts c.t., 90 ma.; 6.3 volts, 3 amp.

Load Precautions

Excitation should never be applied to a modulator until the final amplifier of the transmitter is turned on and operating into a proper load. With no load to absorb the power, the primary impedance of the transformer rises to a high value, permitting peak voltages high enough to break down the transformer insulation.

DRIVERS FOR CLASS-B MODULATORS

Class AB₂ and Class B amplifiers are driven into the grid-current region, so power is consumed in the grid circuit. The preceding stage or driver must be capable of supplying this power at the required peak audio-frequency grid-to-grid voltage. Both of these quantities are given in the manufacturer's tube ratings. The grids of the Class B tubes represent a varying load resistance over the audio-frequency cycle, because the grid current does not increase directly with the grid voltage. To prevent distortion, therefore, it is necessary to have a driving source that will maintain the wave form of the signal without distortion even though the load varies. That is, the driver stage must have good regulation. To this end, it should be capable of delivering somewhat more power than is consumed by the Class B grids, as previously described in the discussion on speech amplifiers.

Driver Tubes

To secure good voltage regulation the internal impedance of the driver, as seen by the modulator grids, must be low. The principal component of this impedance is the plate resistance of the driver tube or tubes as reflected through the driver transformer. Hence for low driving-source impedance the effective plate resistance of the driver tubes should be low and the turns ratio of the driver transformer, primary to secondary, should be as large as possible. The maximum turns ratio that can be used is that value which just permits developing the modulator grid-to-grid a.f. voltage required for the desired power output. The rated tube output (see tube tables) should be reduced by about 20 per cent to allow for losses in the Class B input transformer.

Low-μ triodes such as the 6CK4 have low plate resistance and are therefore good tubes to use as drivers for Class AB₂ or Class B modulators. Tetrodes such as the 6V6 and 6L6 make very poor drivers in this respect when used without negative feedback, but with such feedback the effective plate resistance can be reduced to a value comparable with low-μ triodes.

In a push-pull driver stage using cathode bias, if the amplifier operates Class A the cathode resistor need not be bypassed, because the a.f. currents from each tube flowing in the cathode resistor are out of phase and cancel each other.

However, in Class AB operation this is not true; considerable distortion will be generated at high signal levels if the cathode resistor is not by-passed. The bypass capacitance required can be calculated by a simple rule: the cathode resistance in ohms multiplied by the bypass capacitance in microfarads should equal at least 25,000. The voltage rating of the capacitor should be equal to the maximum bias voltage. This can be found from the maximum-signal plate current and the cathode resistance.

Example: A pair of 6CK4s is to be used in Class AB_1 self-biased. From the tube tables, the cathode resistance should be 350 ohms and the maximum-signal plate current 80 ma. From Ohm's Law,

$$E = RI = 350 \times 0.08 = 27 \text{ volts}$$

From the rule mentioned previously, the by-pass capacitance required is

$$C = 25,000/R = 25,000/350 = 71 \text{ } \mu f.$$

A 100-μf. 50-volt electrolytic capacitor would be satisfactory.

Fig. 8-7 is a typical circuit for a speech amplifier suitable for use as a driver for a Class AB_2 or Class B modulator. An output of about 10 watts can be realized with the power supply circuit shown (or any similar well-filtered supply delivering 300 volts under load). This is sufficient for driving any of the power triodes commonly used as modulators. The 6CK4s in the output stage are operated Class AB_1. The circuit provides several times the voltage gain needed for crystal or ceramic microphones.

The two sections of a 12AX7 tube are used in the first two stages of the amplifier. These are resistance coupled, the gain control being in the grid circuit of the second stage.

The third stage uses a medium-μ triode which is coupled to the 6CK4 grids through a transformer having a push-pull secondary. The ratio may be of the order of 2 to 1 (total secondary to primary) or higher; it is not critical since the gain is sufficient without a high step-up ratio.

The turns ratio of transformer T_2, for the primary to one-half secondary, is approximated by

$$N = \sqrt{\frac{PZ}{0.35 \text{ } E_s}}$$

where P = driving power required by modulator tubes

Z = plate load impedance of driver tube(s)

E_s = peak grid-to-grid voltage for driven tubes

(This approximation is useful for any driver tube, or tubes, driving Class AB_2 or Class B modulators. Select driver tube(s) capable of delivering 1½ times the grid-driving power required.)

In the case of AB_1 6CK4s with fixed bias and 300 plate volts, $Z = 3000$ ohms.

Grid bias for the 6CK4s is furnished by a separate supply using a silicon rectifier and a TV "booster" transformer, T_4. The bias should be set to −62 volts or to obtain a total plate current of 80 ma.

In building an amplifier of this type the constructional precautions outlined earlier should be observed. The Class AB_1 modulators described subsequently in this chapter are representative of good constructional practice.

INCREASING THE EFFECTIVENESS OF THE PHONE TRANSMITTER

The effectiveness of a Phone transmitter can be increased to a considerable extent by taking advantage of speech characteristics. Measures that may be taken to make the modulation more effective include band compression (filtering), volume compression, and speech clipping.

Compressing the Frequency Band

Most of the intelligibility in speech is contained in the medium band of frequencies; that is, between about 500 and 2500 Hz. On the other hand, a large portion of speech power is normally found below 500 Hz. If these low frequencies are attenuated, the frequencies that carry most of the actual intelligence can be increased in amplitude without exceeding 100 percent modulation, and the effectiveness of the transmitter is correspondingly increased.

One simple way to reduce low-frequency response is to use small values of coupling capacitance between resistance-coupled stages. A time constant of 0.0005 second for the coupling capacitor and following-stage grid, gate, or base resistor will have little effect on the amplification

at 500 Hz., but will practically halve it at 100 Hz. In two cascaded stages the gain will be down about 5 db. at 200 Hz. and 10 db. at 100 Hz.

The high-frequency response can be reduced by using "tone control" methods, utilizing a capacitor in series with a variable resistor connected across an audio impedance at some point in the speech amplifier. A good spot for the tone control is across the primary of the output transformer of the speech amplifier. The capacitor should have a reactance at 1000 Hz. about equal to the load resistance required by the amplifier tube or tubes, or transistors while the variable resistor in series may have a value equal to four or five times the load resistance. The control can be adjusted while listening to the amplifier, the object being to cut the high-frequency response without unduly sacrificing intelligibility.

Restricting the frequency response not only puts more modulation power in the optimum frequency band but also reduces hum, because the low-frequency response is reduced, and helps reduce the width of the channel occupied by the

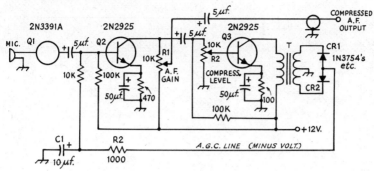

Fig. 8-8—Typical solid-state compressor circuit. C_1 and R_2 determine the hold-in time.

transmission, because of the reduction in the amplitude of the high audio frequencies.

Volume Compression

Although it is obviously desirable to modulate the transmitter as completely as possible, it is difficult to maintain constant voice intensity when speaking into the microphone. To overcome this variable output level, it is possible to use automatic gain control that follows the *average* (not instantaneous) variations in speech amplitude. This can be done by rectifying and filtering some of the audio output and applying the rectified and filtered d.c. to a control electrode in an early stage in the amplifier.

A practical example of a compressor circuit is shown in Fig. 8-8. Q_1 is a low-noise microphone amplifier stage which drives Q_2, another audio amplifier. Output to the succeeding audio amplifier stages is taken from R_1. Some of the output is taken from the collector of Q_2 and is amplified further by Q_3. Transformer T has a 1000-ohm primary impedance, and the secondary impedance is 10,000 ohms. It is used to couple the output of Q_3 to the a.g.c. diodes, CR_1 and CR_2. The diodes rectify the amplified a.f. signal and feed a minus a.g.c. voltage to the base element of Q_2. Since Q_2 is an n-p-n transistor the minus a.g.c. voltage reverse biases Q_2 and lowers its gain. The amount of compression obtained depends upon the setting of R_2. The gain reduction from the a.g.c. action is substantially proportional to the average output of the microphone and thus tends to hold the amplifier output at a constant level.

A suitable time constant for voice operation is established by C_1 and R_2. They have a sufficiently long time constant to hold the a.g.c. voltage at a reasonably steady value between syllables and words. The overall gain of the system must be high enough to assure full output at a moderately-low voice level. Vacuum-tube compressors operate on the same principle. This circuit is especially suited to s.s.b., a.m., and f.m. modulators.

Speech Clipping and Filtering

In speech wave forms the average power content is considerably less than in a sine wave of

the same peak amplitude. Since modulation percentage is based on peak values, the modulation or sideband power in a transmitter modulated 100 percent by an ordinary voice wave form will be considerably less than the sideband power in the same transmitter modulated 100 percent by a sine wave. The modulation percentage with voice wave forms is determined by peaks having relatively low average power content.

If the low-energy peaks are clipped off, the remaining wave form will have a considerably higher ratio of average power to peak amplitude. More sideband power will result, therefore, when such a clipped wave is used to modulate the transmitter 100 percent. Although clipping distorts the wave form and the result therefore does not sound exactly like the original, it is possible to secure a worth-while increase in modulation power without sacrificing intelligibility. Once the system is properly adjusted *it will be impossible to overmodulate the transmitter* because the maximum output amplitude is fixed.

By itself, clipping generates the same high-order harmonics that overmodulation does, and therefore will cause splatter. To prevent this, the audio frequencies above those needed for intelligible speech must be filtered out, *after* clipping and *before* modulation. The filter required for this purpose should have relatively little attenuation below about 2500 Hz., but high attenuation for all frequencies above 3000 Hz.

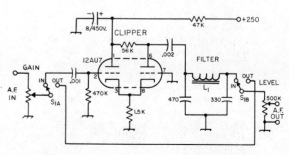

Fig. 8-9—Circuit of a typical vacuum-tube speech clipper.

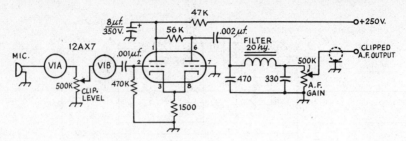

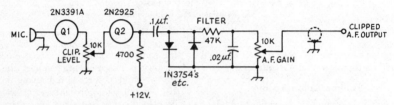

Fig. 8-10—Upper diagram shows where tube-type clipper is connected in typical speech amplifier. Lower drawing illustrates use of silicon diodes to clip positive and negative voice peaks.

The values of L and C should be chosen to form a low-pass filter section having a cut-off frequency of about 2500 Hz., using the modulating impedance of the r.f. amplifier as the load resistance. For this cut-off frequency the formulas are

$$L_1 = \frac{R}{7850} \quad \text{and} \quad C_1 = C_2 = \frac{63.6}{R}$$

where R is in ohms, L_1 in henrys, and C_1 and C_2 in microfarads. Bypass capacitors in the plate circuit of the r.f. amplifier should be included in C_2. Voltage ratings for C_1 and C_2 must be at least twice the d.c. voltage applied to the plate of the modulated amplifier.

It is possible to use as much as 25 db. of clipping before intelligibility suffers; that is, if the original peak amplitude is 10 volts, the signal can be clipped to such an extent that the resulting maximum amplitude is less than one volt. If the original 10-volt signal represented the amplitude that caused 100-percent modulation on peaks, the clipped and filtered signal can then be amplified up to the same 10-volt peak level for modulating the transmitter.

There is a loss in naturalness with "deep" clipping, even though the voice is highly intelligible. With moderate clipping levels (6 to 12 db.) there is almost no change in "quality" but the voice power is increased considerably.

Before drastic clipping can be used, the speech signal must be amplified several times more than is necessary for normal modulation. Also, the hum and noise must be much lower than the tolerable level in ordinary amplification, because the noise in the output of the amplifier increases in proportion to the gain.

One type of clipper-filter system is shown in Fig. 8-9. The clipper is a peak-limiting rectifier of the same general type that is used in receiver noise limiters. It must clip both positive and negative peaks. The gain or clipping control sets the amplitude at which clipping starts. Following the low-pass filter for eliminating the harmonic distortion frequencies is a second gain control, the "level" or modulation control. This control is set initially so that the amplitude-limited output of the clipper-filter cannot cause more than 100-percent modulation.

In the circuit of Fig. 8-10 a simple diode clipper is shown following a two-transistor preamplifier section. The 1N3754s conduct at approximately 0.7 volt of audio and provide positive- and negative-peak clipping of the speech waveform. A 47,000-ohm resistor and a 0.02-μf. capacitor follow the clipper to form a simple R-C filter for attenuating the high-frequency components generated by the clipping action, as discussed earlier. Any top-hat or similar silicon diodes can be used in place of the 1N3754s. Germanium diodes (1N34A type) can also be used, but will clip at a slightly lower peak audio level.

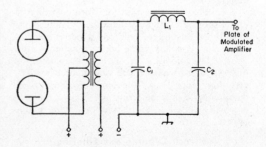

Fig. 8-11—Splatter-suppression filter for use at high level.

A LOW-POWER MODULATOR

A modulator suitable for plate modulation of low-power transmitters, or for screen or control-grid modulation of high-power amplifiers, is pictured in Figs. 8-12 and 8-13. The undistorted output of the amplifier is approximately 8 watts. This is sufficient for modulating the plate of an r.f. amplifier running up to 16 watts input, or for modulating the control or screen grids of r.f. amplifier tubes having plate-dissipation ratings up to 250 watts.

The Circuit

Referring to Fig. 8-14, T_1 is an audio step-down transformer which couples the audio signal from a high-impedance microphone into the base of the first transistor amplifier, Q_1. R.f. filtering is provided in the base circuit of Q_1 (100-ohm resistor and the 470-pf. capacitor). R_1 controls the output level of the modulator.

Q_2, the second preamplifier transistor, increases the amplitude of the audio signal to a level sufficient enough to drive a complementary amplifier consisting of Q_3 and Q_4. The complementary amplifier eliminates the need for an audio transformer by taking advantage of the individual characteristics of an n-p-n- (Q_3) and a p-n-p. (Q_4) transistor. During the positive half of the cycle, Q_3 conducts, and during the negative half cycle, Q_4 conducts.

The audio power amplifier consists of two 40310 transistors (Q_5, Q_6) series-connected, operating in class B push-pull. Such an arrangement provides low distortion as well as low idling current. The output of the amplifier stage is capacity-coupled via C_1 to T_2, which matches the modulator output impedance (8 ohms) to the impedance presented by the transmitter.

As shown in Fig. 8-14, a 5.0 v. to 115-volt filament transformer is used as a modulation transformer with the primary winding connected to J_2. This transformer will match a load of 5000 ohms impedance to the 8-ohm amplifier output impedance. For a load of 2700 ohms, a 6.3 v. to 115-volt filament transformer may be used. Another al-

Fig. 8-12—Top view of the modulator chassis. The audio section is mounted along the left side of the chassis. T_2 is mounted at the left rear. The power supply is located at the right rear of the chassis with the core of T_3 mounted at right angles to that of T_2 to avoid hum pick-up.

ternative would be to use an 18-watt universal output transformer [1] with its primary winding (high impedance) connected to J_2. The proper transformer taps in this case will have to be determined experimentally.

A 0.01-uf. capacitor is connected across the output of T_2 to help reduce undesirable high-frequency audio response. In addition, the 68,000 ohm resistor connected to T_2, feeds back a small amount of out-of-phase audio voltage to the base of Q_2, thereby reducing the chance of overdriving the modulator. Thermal stability is maintained through the use of diodes CR_1 and CR_2.

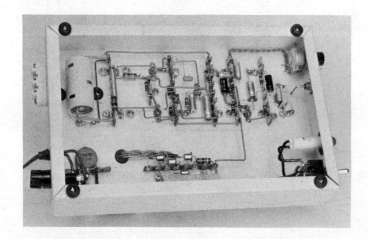

Fig. 8-13—Bottom view of the modulator chassis. T_1 is mounted just to the left of the microphone jack J_1 at the right of the chassis. The power supply components are mounted on a single terminal strip located in the lower center portion of the chassis. C_1 is the large capacitor at the upper left of the chassis.

The power supply, utilizing a 26.8-volt filament transformer, is connected as a full-wave bridge circuit. A single high-capacitance filter is used, which provides good filtering and adequate dynamic regulation.

Construction

Both the modulator and its power supply are built on a single 11 x 7 x 2-inch aluminum chassis using conventional wiring techniques. Transistor sockets are used for Q_1-Q_4, inc., to avoid heat damage during construction. Q_5 and Q_6 are mounted using the hardware provided by the manufacturer. A homemade mounting for T_1 is constructed by physically inverting the transformer assembly in its mounting frame. A small copper strap is then soldered to the frame. The copper strap (along with the transformer) is then fastened to the chassis using two machine screws. Care should be taken to observe proper electrolytic capacitor and diode polarity. Also, make sure that the transistors are properly connected.

In testing the unit, at no time should the modulator be operated without a load, whether it be a resistive dummy load, or the transmitter. Adjust the gain control R_1, until the level of audio is sufficient for proper modulation. If available, an oscilloscope should be used to determine the proper percentage of modulation.

[1] Stancor A3852, Stancor A3870, Knight 54A2022, etc.

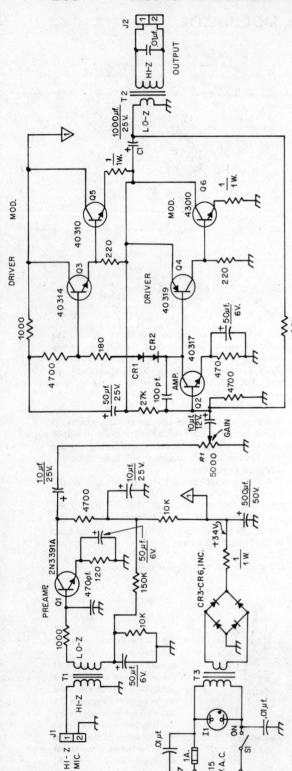

Fig. 8-14—Circuit of the speech amplifier and modulator. Capacitors with polarities marked are electrolytic, others are disk ceramic. Resistors are ½-watt except as noted. Resistance is in ohms, K = 1000.

C_1—For text reference.

CR_1, CR_2—1N3754 diode. (50 p.r.v., 1 amp.)

CR_3-CR_6, inc.—50 p.r.v., 1 amp. silicon.

I_1—Neon panel assembly with resistor (designed for 115 v.a.c. use).

J_1—Microphone connector (Amphenol 75-PC1M).

J_2—Terminal strip (Millen 37302).

Q_1—2N3391A (G.E.).

Q_2—40317 (RCA).

Q_3—40314 (RCA).

Q_4—40319 (RCA).

Q_5, Q_6—40310 (RCA).

R_1—5000-ohm control, audio taper.

S_1—S.p.s.t. toggle.

T_1—200,000-ohm to 1000-ohm miniature audio transformer. (Argonne AR-100 or equal.)

T_2—5.0-volt filament transformer (see text).

T_3—26.8-volt 1-amp. filament transformer (Knight 54D-4145 or similar).

A 50-WATT A.M. MODULATOR

Although the trend is toward s.s.b. telephony, particularly below 30 Mc., there are still many applications for a.m., on any amateur band. The modulator to be described is intended for the amateur who wants a complete station, ready for any occasion. Several up-to-the-minute features have been included in the circuit, so that it reflects the most modern thinking about a.m. techniques. Speech clipping and filtering is used, to maximize the effective "talk power" without causing adjacent-channel QRM. Control circuits enable the operator to choose between manual operation, push-to-talk or foot-switch control when activating the transmitter and modulator. During c.w. operation of the transmitter, footswitch control is still available by merely throwing the phone-c.w. switch on the modulator to the c.w. position. Jacks located on the rear of the modulator chassis make available the necessary connections to external control circuits.

For the modern look, rocker-type switches are used for a.c. and d.c. control of the power supply. To match the switches, rectangular pilot-lamp assemblies are used as indicators.

Circuit

Referring to the circuit diagram, Fig. 8-16, the input circuit is intended for use with the normal high-impedance microphone. R.f. filtering is included, to minimize the chances for r.f. feedback and its resultant howls and squeals. After amplification through V_{1A} and V_{1B}, the signal is clipped by CR_1 and CR_2. The clipping level is set by R_1. The setting of R_2 determines the output level of the modulator after clipping takes place. Audio harmonics generated by the clipper are filtered out by L_1 and the associated filter capacitors. The signal is amplified further by V_2 and then transformer-coupled to the grids of V_3 and V_4.

Clipping and filtering maintains the average modulation level higher than it would be in the absence of clipping. It improves the effectiveness of a.m. without detracting noticeably from the intelligibility.

Although a Stancor P-6315 power transformer is used in the power-supply section of the modulator, an old TV-set transformer could be substituted for T_3. Most TV sets use transformers of similar specifications and these will do a good job. The rest of the power supply is of common design. Bias is developed by borrowing voltage from the secondary winding of T_4, and rectifying it through CR_7 and CR_9, a voltage doubler. Approximately −30 volts is needed at the 7027A grids to establish the correct operating conditions. If the builder prefers to have adjustable bias a 100,000-ohm, 2-watt control can be installed in place of R_3, and the bias voltage taken from the arm of the control.

Fig. 8-15—A look at the top of the modulator chasis. The power supply is located on the right, the speech amplifier tubes are at the upper left, and the modulation transformer is at the lower left. The control relay, K_1, is at the center of the chassis, just behind the meter.

Because silicon rectifiers are used for CR_3 through CR_6, and because capacitor-input filtering is employed, the power supply delivers approximately 450 volts. A 600-volt capacitor is used at C_1 to allow adequate safety margin for the surge voltage of the supply.

Rectified voltage from CR_8 is used to operate relay K_1. The relay is used to break the center-tap connection of T_3, to turn off the supply. The relay can be manually activated by S_4 when S_3 is in the MANUAL position. When S_3 is in the P.T.T. position, K_1 can be controlled by the microphone switch or by a foot switch which connects to J_5. During c.w. operation, S_2 is turned to the c.w. position and the foot switch can be employed to activate the control circuits of an r.f. deck, and the antenna relay, by using it to short circuit J_4's control line. When operating c.w., the secondary winding of T_2 is switched out of the B-plus line at J_2, by switch S_2. A spare set of relay contacts is connected to J_6 and can be used to control other external devices, should the need arise.

Construction

The general layout is shown in Figs. 8-15 and 8-17. A 10 × 17 × 3-inch aluminum chassis serves as a foundation for the modulator. A 7-inch aluminum rack panel is made fast to the chassis by attaching it with a pair of steel chassis brackets. The brackets give added rigidity to the chassis —a necessity because of the heavy transformers used.

Square holes for mounting T_2 and T_3 were cut in the chassis with a hand nibbling tool. A saber saw or keyhole saw would work just as well. The holes for the rocker switches and the indicator lamps were made in the panel and chassis by first

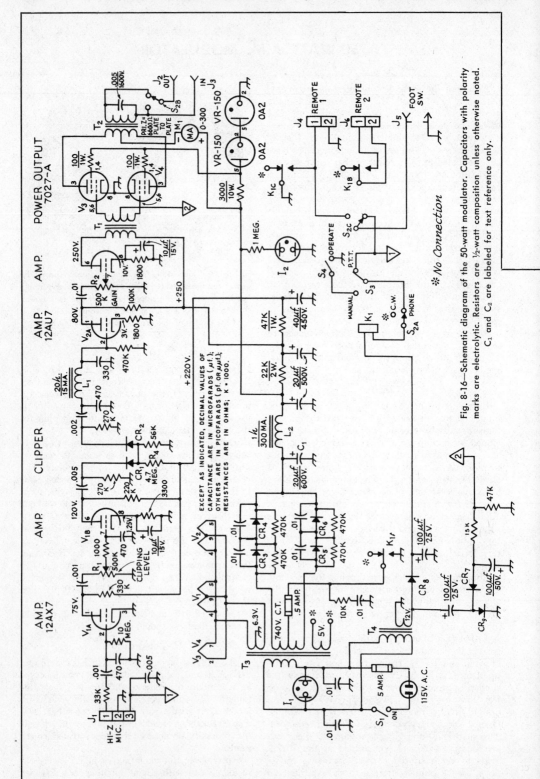

Fig. 8-16—Schematic diagram of the 50-watt modulator. Capacitors with polarity marks are electrolytic. Resistors are ½-watt composition unless otherwise noted. C_1 and C_2 are labeled for text reference only.

Fig. 8-17—A bottom-chassis view of the 50-watt modulator. The power supply section is at the left, the speech amplifier and clipper circuits are at the upper right, and the terminal block of the modulation transformer is at the lower right. The phone-c.w. switch is visible at the top-center of the chassis, just above the relay socket.

drilling numerous small holes around the desired cut-out area, knocking the resulting slug out of the metal, and then filing the holes to size. If a 2¼-inch punch is not available for making the meter hole in the panel, a fly cutter can be used. If neither tool is available, the system used for cutting the switch and pilot-light holes can be employed.

Operation

The plate-to-plate load impedance for the modulator tubes is 6600 ohms with the voltages used. Once the load into which the modulator will work is determined, the matching sheet which is supplied with the modulation transformer can be consulted for the correct primary and secondary connections.

Because of the resistance and capacitance values used in the speech-amplified stages of the modulator, and because of the characteristics of the clipper-filter, the audio response is reasonably flat from 300 to 3000 c.p.s., falling off rapidly above and below that range. This feature will help to keep the on-the-air signal narrow and clean.

The idling current of the modulator output tubes is approximately 70 ma. The maximum plate current on voice peaks should not exceed 200 ma.

The microphone connector, J_1, can be selected to match the user's microphone plug. Any 3-terminal type will be satisfactory if push-to-talk operation is desired.

The amount of clipping used will be pretty much the choice of the operator. Between 6 and 10 decibels of clipping seems best. Some may prefer to clip as much as 12 or 15 db., but the more clipping that is used, the bassier the audio will seem to be, at times impairing the readability of the signal. By setting R_1 far in a counter-clockwise position and advancing R_2 for near-maximum gain, the clipper will be effectively disabled. An oscilloscope is useful for determining the various settings of R_1 and R_2 that will be desired by the operator. These set-things can be logged for future use.

A word of caution: Do not attempt to operate the modulator without a proper load. Operating without a secondary load can destroy the modulation transformer.

CR_1, CR_2—Small-signal silicon diode. (1N914A suitable.)
CR_3-CR_6, inc.—Silicon rectifier, 800 p.r.v., 500 ma. (1 N3256 suitable.)
CR_7, CR_8, CR_9—Silicon rectifier, 50 p.r.v., 750ma. (1N-2858 suitable.)
F_1—1-amp. fuse.
I_1—Neon panel lamp assembly, amber. (Leecraft 31-2113).
I_2—Neon panel lamp assembly, red (Leecraft 31-2111).
J_1—3-terminal microphone jack (see text).
J_2, J_3—Millen high-voltage jack, type 37001.
J_4, J_5—2-terminal connector (Millen E-302A).
J_5—Phono connector.
K_1—3-p.d.t. 12-volt d.c. relay. (Guardian 1225-3C-12D with matching Guardian relay socket.)
L_1—20 h., 15 ma. filter choke (Stancor C-1515).
L_2—1 h., 300 ma. choke (Stancor C-2326).
M_1—0-300 ma. d.c. meter (Simpson Model 1227 shown).
R_1, R_2—500,000-ohm control, audio taper.
R_3—See text.
R_4—See footnote 1.
S_1—S.p.s.t. rocker switch (Carling TILA50-BL).
S_2—Ceramic rotary, 1-section, 3-pole, 3-position switch. 2 positions used. (Centralab 2506.)
S_3—S.p.d.t. toggle.
S_4—S.p.s.t. rocker switch (Carling TILA50-RD).
T_1—Interstage transformer, 1:3 ratio (Stancor A-63-C).
T_2—50-watt, vari-match modulation transformer (U.T.C. S-20).
T_3—740 volts c.t. at 275 ma., 6.3 volts c.t. at 7 amperes. 5-volt winding not used. (Stancor P-6315).
T_4—12.6 volts at 1.5 amperes (Knight 6-K-94 HF).

TRANSISTORIZED CLIPPER/AMPLIFIER

An a.m. signal can be made more effective by employing speech compression or clipping in the modulator circuit. The average voice power can be increased by as much as 12 or 15 db. without serious impairment of the audio quality. Under weak-signal conditions, such an increase is extremely worthwhile. Clippers of the type described here are not satisfactory for use with s.s.b. transmitters because of the distortion that they introduce. This unit is self-contained and can be installed between the microphone and the audio input jack of most a.m. or d.s.b. transmitters.

The Circuit

The circuit (Fig. 8-20B) uses three transistors When no clipping is used, the transistors work as straight amplifiers. Gain for the circuit is adjusted by R_2. The maximum gain is about 15 db. if R_1 is set just below the clipping point. To use the circuit as a clipper, R_1 is adjusted for the amount of clipping desired. The silicon diodes, CR_1, CR_2, will begin clipping at an audio level of about 0.6 volt peak. Q_3 makes up for the gain lost by clipping.

Construction

The clipper is built in the top of a $3 \times 4 \times 5$-inch Minibox. The input jack, audio gain control and clipping control are mounted on one end, with the output strip on the other end. A three-terminal strip is used for the output connection to permit the clipper to be used with a push-to-talk microphone. Cables can be made up to fit the type of input connector used on the transmitter.

The remainder of the circuit is mounted on an etched circuit board.[1] Standard layout can be used

Fig. 8-18—Inside view showing the etched circuit board. The clipper diodes are near the upper edge of the board in this view. Q_3 is at the left, Q_2 is at the right, and Q_1 is below Q_2 with a paper capacitor in between.

by those who do not wish to make up an etched board.[2] The battery is held in place with a Keystone No. 95 battery clamp. The circuit board is mounted on 1-inch spacers. Rubber feet prevent the cabinet from scratching desk tops.

In use, R_1 is adjusted to the desired level of clipping and R_2 is set for the audio output level needed for full modulation of the transmitter. The adjustment may be made either with an oscilloscope or by on-the-air checks.

---

[1] A full-size template for the etched circuit board is available for 25 cents from the American Radio Relay League, 225 Main St., Newington, Conn. 06111.

[2] Etched-Circuit processing is described in detail in Chap. 20.

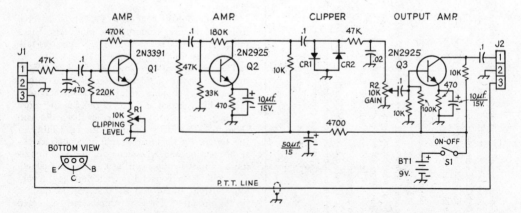

Fig. 8-19—Circuit diagram of the speech-amplifier/clipper. Capacitances are in pf. unless noted differently; capacitors with polarity indicated are electrolytic; 0.1-μf. capacitors are paper (Sprague 4PS-P10); 0.02-μf. capacitor is disk ceramic. Fixed resistors are ½-watt; resistances are in ohms (K = 1000).

CR_1, CR_2—Any type silicon diode.
J_1—3-conductor microphone jack.

J_2—3-terminal strip (Millen E-303).
R_1, R_2—10,000-ohm control, linear taper.

AMPLITUDE MODULATION

As described in the chapter on circuit fundamentals, the process of modulation sets up groups of frequencies called **sidebands**, which appear symmetrically above and below the frequency of the unmodulated signal or **carrier**. If the instantaneous values of the amplitudes of all these separate frequencies are added together, the result is called the **modulation envelope**. In **amplitude modulation (a.m.)** the modulation envelope follows the amplitude variations of the signal that is used to modulate the wave.

For example, modulation by a 1000-Hz. tone will result in a modulation envelope that varies in amplitude at a 1000-Hz. rate. The actual r.f. signal that produces such an envelope consists of three frequencies — the carrier, a side frequency 1000 Hz. higher, and a side frequency 1000 Hz. lower than the carrier. These three frequencies easily can be separated by a receiver having high selectivity. In order to reproduce the original modulation the receiver must have enough bandwidth to accept the carrier and the sidebands simultaneously. This is because an a.m. detector responds to the modulation envelope rather than to the individual signal components, and the envelope will be distorted in the receiver unless all the frequency components in the signal go through without change in their amplitudes.

In the simple case of tone modulation the two side frequencies and the carrier are constant in amplitude — it is only the envelope amplitude that varies at the modulation rate. With more complex modulation such as voice or music the amplitudes and frequencies of the side frequencies vary from instant to instant. The amplitude of the modulation envelope varies from instant to instant in the same way as the complex audio-frequency signal causing the modulation. Even in this case the *carrier* amplitude is constant if the transmitter is properly modulated.

A.M. Sidebands and Channel Width

Speech can be electrically reproduced, with high intelligibility, in a band of frequencies lying between approximately 100 and 3000 Hz. When these frequencies are combined with a radio-frequency carrier, the sidebands occupy the frequency spectrum from about 3000 Hz. below the carrier frequency to 3000 Hz. above—a total band or **channel** of about 6 kHz.

Actual speech frequencies extend up to 10,000 Hz. or more, so it is possible to occupy a 20-kHz. channel if no provision is made for reducing its width. For communication purposes such a channel width represents a waste of valuable spectrum space, since a 6-kHz. channel is fully adequate for intelligibility. Occupying more than the minimum channel creates unnecessary interference. Thus speech equipment design and transmitter adjustment and operation should be pointed toward minimum channel width.

THE MODULATION ENVELOPE

In Fig. 8-20 the drawing at A shows the unmodulated r.f. signal, assumed to be a sine wave of the desired radio frequency. The graph can be taken to represent either voltage or current.

In B, the signal is assumed to be modulated by the audio frequency shown in the small drawing above. This frequency is much lower than the carrier frequency, a necessary condition for good modulation. When the modulating voltage is "positive" (above its axis) the envelope amplitude is increased *above* its unmodulated amplitude; when the modulating voltage is "negative" the envelope amplitude is *decreased*. Thus the envelope grows larger and smaller with the polarity and amplitude of the modulating voltage.

The drawings at C shows what happens with stronger modulation. The envelope amplitude is doubled at the instant the modulating voltage reaches its positive peak. On the negative peak of the modulating voltage the envelope amplitude just reaches zero.

Percentage of Modulation

When a modulated signal is detected in a receiver, the detector output follows the modulation envelope. The stronger the modulation, therefore, the greater is the useful receiver output. Obviously, it is desirable to make the modulation as strong or "heavy" as possible. A wave modulated as in Fig. 8-21C would produce more useful audio output than the one shown at B.

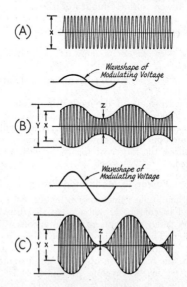

Fig. 8-20—Graphical representation of (A) r.f. output unmodulated, (B) modulated 50%, (C) modulated 100%. The modulation envelope is shown by the thin outline on the modulated wave.

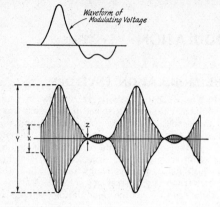

Fig. 8-21—Modulation by an unsymmetrical wave form. This drawing shows 100% downward modulation along with 300% upward modulation. There is no distortion, since the modulation envelope is an accurate reproduction of the wave form of the modulating voltage.

The "depth" of the modulation is expressed as a percentage of the unmodulated carrier amplitude. In either B or C, Fig. 8-20, X represents the unmodulated carrier amplitude, Y is the maximum envelope amplitude on the modulation up-peak, and Z is the minimum envelope amplitude on the modulation downpeak.

In a properly operating modulation system the modulation envelope is an accurate reproduction of the modulating wave, as can be seen in Fig. 8-20 at B and C by comparing one side of the outline with the shape of the modulating wave. (The lower outline duplicates the upper, but simply appears upside down in the drawing.)

The **percentage of modulation** is

$$\% \text{ Mod.} = \frac{Y-X}{X} \times 100 \text{ (upward modulation), or}$$

$$\% \text{ Mod.} = \frac{X-Z}{X} \times 100 \text{ (downward modulation)}$$

If the wave shape of the modulation is such that its peak positive and negative amplitudes are equal, then the modulation percentage will be the same both up and down. If the two percentages differ, the larger of the two is customarily specified.

Power in Modulated Wave

The amplitude values shown in Fig. 8-20 correspond to current or voltage, so the drawings may be taken to represent instantaneous values of either. The power in the wave varies as the *square* of either the current or voltage, so at the peak of the modulation up-swing the instantaneous power in the envelope of Fig. 8-20 is four times the unmodulated carrier power (because the current and voltage both are doubled). At the peak of the down-swing the power is zero, since the amplitude is zero. These statements are true of 100-percent modulation no matter what

the wave form of the modulation. The instantaneous envelope power in the modulated signal is proportional to the square of its envelope amplitude at every instant. This fact is highly important in the operation of every method of amplitude modulation.

It is convenient, and customary, to describe the operation of modulation systems in terms of sine-wave modulation. Although this wave shape is seldom actually used in practice (voice wave shapes depart very considerably from the sine form) it lends itself to simple calculations and its use as a standard permits comparison between systems on a common basis. With sine-wave modulation the *average* power in the modulated signal over any number of full cycles of the modulation frequency is found to be 1½ times the power in the unmodulated carrier. In other words, the power output increases 50 percent with 100-percent modulation by a sine wave.

This relationship is very useful in the design of modulation systems and modulators, because any such system that is capable of increasing the *average* power output by 50 percent with sine-wave modulation automatically fulfills the requirement that the *instantaneous* power at the modulation up-peak be four times the carrier power. Consequently, systems in which the additional power is supplied from outside the modulated r.f. stage (e.g., plate modulation) usually are designed on a sine-wave basis as a matter of convenience. Modulation systems in which the additional power is secured from the modulated r.f. amplifier (e.g., grid modulation) usually are more conveniently designed on the basis of peak envelope power rather than average power.

The extra power that is contained in a modulated signal goes entirely into the sidebands, half in the upper sideband and half into the lower. As a numerical example, full modulation of a 100-watt carrier by a sine wave will add 50 watts of sideband power, 25 in the lower and 25 in the upper sideband. Supplying this additional power for the sidebands is the object of all of the various systems devised for amplitude modulation.

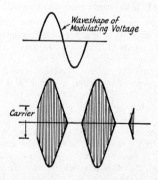

Fig. 8-22—An overmodulated signal. The modulation envelope is not an accurate reproduction of the wave form of the modulating voltage. This or any type of distortion occurring during the modulation process generates spurious sidebands or "splatter."

No such simple relationship exists with complex wave forms. Complex wave forms such as speech do not, as a rule, contain as much average power as a sine wave. Ordinary speech wave forms have about half as much average power as a sine wave, for the same peak amplitude in both wave forms. Thus for the same modulation percentage, the sideband power with ordinary speech will average only about half the power with sine-wave modulation, since it is the peak envelope amplitude, not the average power, that determines the percentage of modulation.

Unsymmetrical Modulation

In an ordinary electric circuit it is possible to increase the amplitude of current flow indefinitely, up to the limit of the power-handling capability of the components, but it cannot very well be decreased to less than zero. The same thing is true of the amplitude of an r.f. signal; it can be modulated *upward* to any desired extent, but it cannot be modulated *downward* more than 100 percent.

When the modulating wave form is unsymmetrical it is possible for the upward and downward modulation percentages to be different. A simple case is shown in Fig. 8-21. The positive peak of the modulating signal is about 3 times the amplitude of the negative peak. If, as shown in the drawing, the modulating amplitude is adjusted so that the peak downward modulation is just 100 percent ($Z = 0$) the peak upward modulation is 300 percent ($Y = 4X$). The carrier amplitude is represented by X, as in Fig. 8-20. The modulation envelope reproduces the wave form of the modulating signal accurately, hence there is no distortion. In such a modulated signal the increase in power output with modulation is considerably greater than it is when the modulation is symmetrical and therefore has to be limited to 100 percent both up and down. In Fig. 8-21 the peak envelope amplitude, Y, is four times the carrier amplitude, X, so the peak-envelope power is 16 times the carrier power. When the upward modulation is more than 100 percent the power capacity of the modulating system obviously must be increased sufficiently to take care of the much larger peak amplitudes.

Overmodulation

If the amplitude of the modulation on the downward swing becomes too great, there will be a period of time during which the r.f. output is entirely cut off. This is shown in Fig. 8-22. The shape of the downward half of the modulating wave is no longer accurately reproduced by the modulation envelope, consequently the modulation is distorted. Operation of this type is called **overmodulation.**

The distortion of the modulation envelope causes new frequencies (harmonics of the modulating frequency) to be generated. These combine with the carrier to form new side frequencies that widen the channel occupied by the modulated signal. These spurious frequencies are commonly called "splatter."

It is important to realize that the channel occupied by an amplitude-modulated signal is dependent *on the shape of the modulation envelope.* If this wave shape is complex and can be resolved into a wide band of audio frequencies, then the channel occupied will be correspondingly large. An overmodulated signal splatters and occupies a much wider channel than is necessary because the "clipping" of the modulating wave that occurs at the zero axis changes the envelope wave shape to one that contains high-order harmonics of the original modulating frequency. These harmonics appear as side frequencies separated by, in some cases, many kHz. from the carrier frequency.

Because of this clipping action at the zero axis, it is important that care be taken to prevent applying too large a modulating signal in the downward direction. Overmodulation downward results in more splatter than is caused by most other types of distortion in a phone transmitter.

GENERAL REQUIREMENTS

For proper operation of an amplitude-modulated transmitter there are a few general requirements that must be met no matter what particular method of modulation may be used. Failure to meet these requirements is accompanied by distortion of the modulation envelope. This in turn increases the channel width as compared with that required by the legitimate frequencies contained in the original modulating wave.

Frequency Stability

For satisfactory amplitude modulation, the carrier *frequency* must be entirely unaffected by modulation. If the application of modulation causes a change in the carrier frequency, the frequency will wobble back and forth with the modulation. This causes distortion and widens the channel taken by the signal. Thus unnecessary interference is caused to other transmissions.

In practice, this undesirable frequency modulation is prevented by applying the modulation to an r.f. amplifier stage that is isolated from the frequency-controlling oscillator by a **buffer amplifier.** Amplitude modulation applied directly to an oscillator always is accompanied by frequency modulation. Under existing FCC regulations amplitude modulation of an oscillator is permitted only on frequencies above 144 MHz. Below that frequency the regulations require that an amplitude-modulated transmitter be completely free from frequency modulation.

Linearity

At least up to the limit of 100 percent upward modulation, the amplitude of the r.f. output should be directly proportional to the amplitude of the modulating wave. Fig. 8-23 is a graph of an ideal **modulation characteristic,** or curve showing the relationship between r.f. output amplitude and instantaneous modulation amplitude. The modulation swings the r.f. amplitude back and forth along the curve A, as the modulating

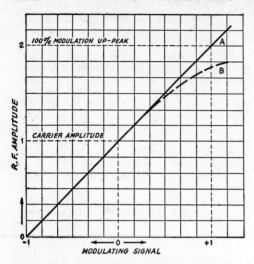

Fig. 8-23—The modulation characteristic shows the relationship between the instantaneous envelope amplitude of the r.f. output (or voltage) and the instantaneous amplitude of the modulating voltage. The ideal characteristic is a straight line, as shown by curve A.

voltage alternately swings positive and negative. Assuming that the negative peak of the modulating wave is just sufficient to reduce the r.f. output to zero (modulating voltage equal to −1 in the drawing), the same modulating voltage peak in the *positive* direction (+1) should cause the r.f. amplitude to reach twice its unmodulated value. The ideal is a straight line, as shown by curve *A*. Such a modulation characteristic is perfectly **linear**.

A **nonlinear** characteristic is shown by curve *B*. The r.f. amplitude does not reach twice the unmodulated carrier amplitude when the modulating voltage reaches its positive peak. A modulation characteristic of this type gives a modulation envelope that is "flattened" on the up-peak; in other words, the modulation envelope is not an exact reproduction of the modulating wave. It is therefore distorted and harmonics

are generated, causing the transmitted signal to occupy a wider channel than is necessary. A nonlinear modulation characteristic can easily result when a transmitter is not properly designed or is misadjusted.

The **modulation capability** of the transmitter is the maximum percentage of modulation that is possible without objectionable distortion from nonlinearity. The maximum capability can never exceed 100 percent on the down-peak, but it is possible for it to be higher on the up-peak. The modulation capability should be as close to 100 percent as possible, so that the most effective signal can be transmitted.

Plate Power Supply

The d.c. power supply for the plate or plates of the modulated amplifier should be well filtered; if it is not, plate-supply ripple will modulate the carrier and cause annoying hum. The ripple voltage should not be more than about 1 percent of the d.c. output voltage.

In amplitude modulation the plate current of the modulated r.f. amplifier varies at an audio-frequency rate; in other words, an alternating current is superimposed on the d.c. plate current. The output filter capacitor in the plate supply must have low reactance, at the lowest audio frequency in the modulation, if the transmitter is to modulate equally well at all audio frequencies. The capacitance required depends on the ratio of d.c. plate current to plate voltage in the modulated amplifier. The requirements will be met satisfactorily if the capacitance of the output capacitor is at least equal to

$$C = 25\frac{I}{E}$$

where C = Capacitance of output capacitor in μf.
I = D.c. plate current of modulated amplifier in milliamperes
E = Plate voltage of modulated amplifier

Example: A modulated amplifier operates at 1250 volts and 275 ma. The capacitance of the output capacitor in the plate-supply filter should be at least

$$C = 25\frac{I}{E} = 25 \times \frac{275}{1250} = 25 \times 0.22 = 5.5 \ uf.$$

AMPLITUDE MODULATION METHODS

MODULATION SYSTEMS

As explained in the preceding section, amplitude modulation of a carrier is accompanied by an increase in power output, the additional power being the "useful" or "talk power" in the sidebands. This additional power may be supplied from an external source in the form of audio-frequency power. It is then added to the unmodulated power input to the amplifier to be modulated, after which the combined power is converted to r.f. This is the method used in

plate modulation. It has the advantage that the r.f. power is generated at the high efficiency characteristic of Class C amplifiers — of the order of 65 to 75 percent—but has the accompanying disadvantage that generating the audio-frequency power is rather expensive.

An alternative that does not require relatively large amounts of audio-frequency power makes use of the fact that the power output of an amplifier can be controlled by varying the potential of a tube element — such as a control grid or a screen grid — that does not, in itself, consume

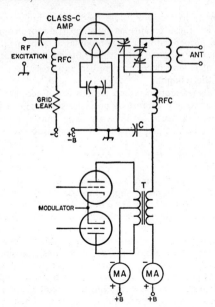

Fig. 8-24—Plate modulation of a Class C r.f. amplifier. The r.f. plate bypass capacitor, C, in the amplifier stage should have reasonably high reactance at audio frequencies. A value of the order of 0.001 μf. to 0.005 μf. is satisfactory in practically all cases.

appreciable power. In this case the additional power during modulation is secured by sacrificing carrier power; in other words, a tube is capable of delivering only so much total power within its ratings, and if more must be delivered at full modulation, then less is available for the unmodulated carrier. Systems of this type must of necessity work at rather low efficiency at the unmodulated carrier level. As a practical working rule, the efficiency of the modulated r.f. amplifier is of the order of 30 to 35 percent, and the unmodulated carrier power output obtainable with such a system is only about one-fourth to one-third that obtainable from the same amplifier with plate modulation.

It is well to appreciate that no simple modulation scheme that purports to get around this limitation of grid modulation ever has actually done so. Methods have been devised that have resulted in modulation at high over-all efficiency, without requiring audio power, by obtaining the necessary additional power from an auxiliary r.f. amplifier. This leads to circuit and operating complexities that make the systems unsuitable for amateur work, where rapid frequency change and simplicity of operation are almost always essential.

The method discussed in this section are the basic ones. Variants that from time to time attain passing popularity can readily be appraised on the basis of the preceding paragraphs. A simple

grid modulation system that claims high efficiency should be looked upon with suspicion, since it is almost certain that the high efficiency, if actually achieved, is obtained by sacrificing the linear relationship between modulating signal and modulation envelope that is the first essential of a good modulation method.

PLATE MODULATION

Fig. 8-24 shows the most widely used system of plate modulation, in this case with a triode r.f. tube. A balanced (push-pull Class A, Class AB or Class B) **modulator** is transformer-coupled to the plate circuit of the modulated r.f. amplifier. The audio-frequency power generated by the modulator is combined with the d.c. power in the modulated-amplifier plate circuit by transfer through the coupling transformer, T. For 100 percent modulation the audio-frequency power output of the modulator and the turns ratio of the coupling transformer must be such that the voltage at the plate of the modulated amplifier varies between zero and twice the d.c. operating plate voltage, thus causing corresponding variations in the amplitude of the r.f. output.

Audio Power

As stated earlier, the average power output of the modulated stage must increase during modulation. The modulator must be capable of supplying to the modulated r.f. stage sine-wave audio power equal to 50 percent of the d.c. plate input. For example, if the d.c. plate power input to the r.f. stage is 100 watts, the sine-wave audio power output of the modulator must be 50 watts.

Modulating Impedance; Linearity

The **modulating impedance**, or load resistance presented to the modulator by the modulated r.f. amplifier, is equal to

$$Z_m = \frac{E_b}{I_p} \times 1000 \, \text{ohms}$$

where E_b = D.c. plate voltage
I_p = D.c. plate current (ma.)
E_b and I_p are measured without modulation.

The power output of the r.f. amplifier must vary as the square of the instantaneous plate voltage (the r.f. output voltage must be proportional to the plate voltage) for the modulation to be linear. This will be the case when the amplifier operates under Class C conditions. The linearity depends upon having sufficient grid excitation and proper bias, and upon the adjustment of circuit constants to the proper values.

Adjustment of Plate-Modulated Amplifiers

The general operating conditions for Class C operation are described in the chapter on transmitters. The grid bias and grid current required for plate modulation usually are given in the operating data supplied by the tube manufacturer; in general, the bias should be such as to give an operating angle of about 120 degrees at the d.c. plate voltage used, and the grid excita-

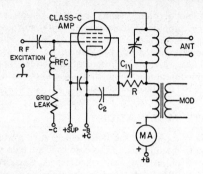

Fig. 8-25—Plate and screen modulation of a Class C r.f. amplifier using a screen-grid tube. The plate r.f. bypass capacitor, C_1, should have reasonably high reactance at all audio frequencies; a value of 0.001 to 0.005 μf. is generally satisfactory. The screen bypass, C_2, should not exceed 0.002 μf. in the usual case.

When the modulated amplifier is a beam tetrode the suppressor connection shown in this diagram may be ignored. If a base terminal is provided on the tube for the beam-forming plates, it should be connected as recommended by the tube manufacturer.

tion should be great enough so that the amplifier's plate efficiency will stay constant when the plate voltage is varied over the range from zero to twice the unmodulated value. For best linearity, the grid bias should be obtained from a fixed-bias source of about the cut-off value, supplemented by enough grid-leak bias to bring the total up to the required operating bias.

The maximum permissible d.c. plate power input for 100-percent modulation is twice the sine-wave audio-frequency power output available from the modulator. This input is obtained by varying the loading on the amplifier (keeping its tank circuit tuned to resonance) until the product of d.c. plate voltage and plate current is

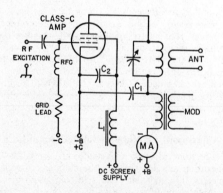

Fig. 8-26—Plate modulation of a beam tetrode, using an audio impedance in the screen circuit. The value of L_1 discussed in the text. See Fig. 8-25 for data on bypass capacitors C_1 and C_2.

the desired power. The modulating impedance under these conditions must be transformed to the proper value for the modulator by using the correct output-transformer turns ratio. This point is considered in detail in an earlier section in this chapter.

Neutralization, when triodes are used, should be as nearly perfect as possible, since regeneration may cause nonlinearity. The amplifier also must be completely free from parasitic oscillations.

Although the total power input (d.c. plus audio-frequency a.c.) increases with modulation, the d.c. plate current of a plate-modulated amplifier should not change when the stage is modulated. This is because each increase in plate voltage and plate current is balanced by an equivalent decrease in voltage and current on the next half-cycle of the modulating wave. D.c. instruments cannot follow the a.f. variations, and since the average d.c. plate current and plate voltage of a properly operated amplifier do not change, neither do the meter readings. A change in plate current with modulation indicates nonlinearity. On the other hand, a thermocouple r.f. ammeter connected in the antenna or transmission line will show an increase in r.f. current with modulation, because instruments of this type respond to power rather than to current or voltage.

Screen-Grid Amplifiers

Screen-grid tubes of the pentode or beam-tetrode type can be used as Class C plate-modulated amplifiers by applying the modulation to both the plate and screen grid. The usual method of feeding the screen grid with the necessary d.c. and modulation voltages is shown in Fig. 8-27. The dropping resistor, R, should be of the proper value to apply normal d.c. voltage to the screen under steady carrier conditions. Its value can be calculated by taking the difference between plate and screen voltages and dividing it by the rated screen current.

The modulating impedance is found by dividing the d.c. plate voltage by the sum of the plate and screen currents. The plate voltage multiplied by the sum of the two currents gives the power input to be used as the basis for determining the audio power required from the modulator.

Modulation of the screen along with the plate is necessary because the screen voltage has a much greater effect on the plate current than the plate voltage does. The modulation characteristic is nonlinear if the plate alone is modulated. However, some beam tetrodes can be modulated satisfactorily by applying the modulating power to the plate circuit alone, provided the screen is connected to its d.c. supply through an audio impedance. Under these conditions the screen becomes self-modulating, because of the variations in screen current that occur when the plate voltage is varied. The circuit is shown in Fig. 8-26. The choke coil L_1 is the audio impedance in the screen circuit; its inductance should be large enough to have a reactance (at the lowest desired audio frequency) that is not less than the

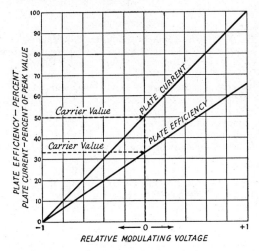

Fig. 8-27—In a perfect grid-modulated amplifier both plate current and plate efficiency would vary with the instantaneous modulating voltage as shown. When this is so the modulation characteristic is as given by curve A in Fig. 8-23, and the peak envelope output power is four times the unmodulated carrier power. The variations in plate current with modulation, indicated above, do not register on a d.c. meter, so the plate meter shows no change when the signal is modulated.

impedance of the screen. The screen impedance can be taken to be approximately equal to the d.c. screen voltage divided by the d.c. screen current in amperes.

GRID MODULATION

The principal disadvantage of plate modulation is that a considerable amount of audio power is necessary. This requirement can be avoided by applying the modulation to a grid element in the modulated amplifier. However, serious disadvantages of grid modulation are the reduction in the carrier power output obtainable from a given r.f. amplifier tube and the more rigorous operating requirements and more complicated adjustment.

The term "grid modulation" as used here applies to all types — control grid, screen, or suppressor — since the operating principles are exactly the same no matter which grid is actually modulated. (Screen-grid modulation is the most commonly used technique of the three types listed here.) With grid modulation the plate voltage is constant, and the increase in power output with modulation is obtained by making both the plate current and plate efficiency vary with the modulating signal as shown in Fig. 8-27. For 100 percent modulation, both plate current and efficiency must, at the peak of the modulation up-swing, be twice their carrier values. Thus at the modulation-envelope peak the power input

is doubled, and since the plate efficiency also is doubled at the same instant the peak envelope output power will be four times the carrier power. The efficiency obtainable at the envelope peak depends on how carefully the modulated amplifier is adjusted, and sometimes can be as high as 80 percent. It is generally less when the amplifier is adjusted for good linearity, and under average conditions a round figure of ⅔, or **66** percent, is representative. The efficiency without modulation is only half the peak efficiency, or about 33 percent. This low average efficiency reduces the permissible carrier output to about one-fourth the power obtainable from the same tube in c.w. operation, and to about one-third the carrier output obtainable from the tube with plate modulation.

The modulator is required to furnish only the audio power dissipated in the modulated grid under the operating conditions chosen. A speech amplifier capable of delivering 3 to 10 watts is usually sufficient.

Grid modulation does not give quite as linear a modulation characteristic as plate modulation, even under optimum operating conditions. When misadjusted the nonlinearity may be severe, resulting in bad distortion and splatter.

Plate-Circuit Operating Conditions

The d.c. plate power input to the grid-modulated amplifier, assuming a round figure of ⅓ (33 per cent) for the plate efficiency, should not exceed 1½ times the plate dissipation rating of the tube or tubes used in the modulated stage. Use the maximum plate voltage permitted by the manufacturer's ratings, because the optimum operating conditions are more easily achieved with high plate voltage and the linearity also is improved.

Example: Two tubes having plate dissipation ratings of 55 watts each are to be used with grid modulation.
The maximum permissible power input, at 33% efficiency, is
$P = 1.5 \times (2 \times 55) = 1.5 \times 110 = 165$ watts
The maximum recommended plate voltage for these tubes is 1500 volts. Using this figure, the average plate current for the two tubes will be

$$I = \frac{P}{E} = \frac{165}{1500} = 0.11 \text{ amp.} = 110 \text{ ma.}$$

At 33% efficiency, the carrier output to be expected is 55 watts.
The plate-voltage/plate-current ratio at *twice* carrier plate current is

$$\frac{1500}{220} = 6.8$$

The tank-circuit L/C ratio should be chosen on the basis of *twice* the average or carrier plate current. If the L/C ratio is based on the plate voltage/plate current ratio under carrier conditions the Q may be too low for good coupling to the output circuit.

Screen Grid Modulation

Screen modulation is probably the simplest and most popular form of grid modulation, and the least critical of adjustment. The most satisfactory way to apply the modulating voltage to the screen is through a transformer, as shown in Fig. 8-28. With practical tubes it is necessary to drive the screen somewhat negative with respect to the cathode to get complete cut-off of r.f. output. For this reason the peak modulating voltage required for 100-percent modulation is usually 10 percent or so greater than the d.c. screen voltage. The latter, in turn, is approximately half the rated screen voltage recommended by the manufacturer under maximum ratings for radiotelegraph operation.

The audio power required for 100-percent modulation is approximately one-fourth the d.c. power input to the screen in c.w. operation, but varies somewhat with the operating conditions. A receiving-type audio power amplifier will suffice as the modulator for most transmitting tubes. The relationship between screen voltage and screen current is not linear, which means that the load on the modulator varies over the audio-frequency cycle. It is therefore highly advisable to use negative feedback in the modulator circuit. If excess audio power is available, it is also advisable to load the modulator with a resistance (R in Fig. 8-28) its value being adjusted to dissipate the excess power. There is no simple way to determine the proper resistance except experimentally, by observing its effect on the modulation envelope with the aid of an oscilloscope.

On the assumption that the modulator will be fully loaded by the screen plus the additional load resistor R, the turns ratio required in the coupling transformer may be calculated as follows:

$$N = \frac{E_d}{2.5\sqrt{PR_L}}$$

where N is the turns ratio, secondary to primary; E_d is the rated screen voltage for c.w. operation; P is the rated audio power output of the modulator; and R_L is the rated load resistance for the modulator.

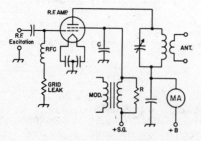

Fig. 28—Screen-grid modulation of beam tetrode. Capacitor C is an r.f. bypass capacitor and should have high reactance at audio frequencies. A value of 0.002 μf. is satisfactory. The grid leak can have the same value that is used for c.w. operation of the tube.

Adjustment

A screen-modulated amplifier should be adjusted with the aid of an oscilloscope connected to give a trapezoid pattern (see Chapter Eleven). A tone source for modulating the transmitter is a convenience, since a steady tone will give a steady pattern on the oscilloscope. A steady pattern is easier to study than one that flickers with voice modulation.

Having determined the permissible carrier plate current as previously described, apply r.f. excitation and d.c. plate and screen voltages. Without modulation, adjust the plate loading to give the required plate current, keeping the plate tank circuit tuned to resonance. Next, apply modulation and increase the modulating voltage until the modulation characteristic shows curvature. If curvature occurs well below 100-percent modulation, the plate efficiency is too high at the carrier level. Increase the plate loading slightly and readjust the r.f. grid excitation to maintain the same plate current; then apply modulation and check the characteristic again. Continue until the characteristic is as linear as possible from zero to twice the carrier amplitude.

In general, the amplifier should be heavily loaded. Under proper operating conditions the plate-current dip as the amplifier plate circuit is tuned through resonance will be little more than just discernible. Operate with the grid current as low as possible, since this reduces the screen current and thus reduces the amount of power required from the modulator.

With proper adjustment the linearity is good up to about 90-percent modulation. When the screen is driven negative for 100-percent modulation there is a kink in the modulation characteristic at the zero-voltage point. This introduces a small amount of envelope distortion. The kink can be removed and the over-all linearity improved by applying a small amount of modulating voltage to the control grid simultaneously with screen modulation.

In an alternative adjustment method not requiring an oscilloscope the r.f. amplifier is first tuned up for maximum output without modulation and the rated d.c. screen voltage (from a fixed-voltage supply) for c.w. operation applied. Use heavy loading and reduce the grid excitation until the output just starts to fall off, at which point the resonance dip in plate current should be small. Note the plate current and, if possible, the r.f. output current, and then reduce the d.c. screen voltage until the plate current is one-half its previous value. The r.f. output current should also be one-half its previous value at this screen voltage.

The amplifier is then ready for modulation, and the modulating voltage may be increased until the plate current just starts to shift upward, which indicates that the amplifier is modulated 100 percent. With voice modulation the plate current should remain steady, or show just an occasional small upward kick on intermittent peaks.

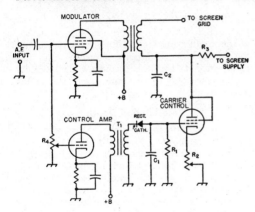

Fig. 8-29—Circuit for carrier control with screen modulation. A small triode such as the 6C4 can be used as the control amplifier and a 6Y6G is suitable as a carrier-control tube. T_1 is an interstage audio transformer having a 1-to-1 or larger turns ratio. R_4 is a 0.5-megohm volume control and also serves as the grid resistor for the modulator. A germanium crystal may be used as the rectifier. Other values are discussed in the text.

Controlled Carrier

As explained earlier, a limit is placed on the output obtainable from a grid-modulation system by the low r.f. amplifier plate efficiency (approximately 33 percent) under unmodulated carrier conditions. The plate efficiency increases with modulation, since the output increases while the d.c. input remains constant, and reaches a maximum in the neighborhood of 50 percent with 100 percent sine-wave modulation. If the power input to the amplifier can be reduced during periods when there is little or no modulation, thus reducing the plate loss, advantage can be taken of the higher efficiency at full modulation to obtain higher effective output. This can be done by varying the d.c. power input to the modulated stage in accordance with *average* variations in voice intensity, in such a way as to maintain just sufficient carrier power to keep the modulation high, but not exceeding 100 percent, under all conditions. Thus the carrier amplitude is controlled by the average voice intensity. Properly utilized, controlled carrier permits increasing the carrier output at maximum level to a value about equal to the rated plate dissipation of the tube, twice the output obtainable with constant carrier.

It is desirable to control the power input just enough so that the plate loss, without modulation, is safely below the tube rating. Excessive control is disadvantageous because the distant receiver's a.v.c. system must continually follow the variations in average signal level. The circuit of Fig. 8-29 permits adjustment of both the maximum and minimum power input, and although somewhat more complicated than some circuits that have been used is actually simpler to operate because it separates the functions of modulation and carrier control. A portion of the audio voltage at the modulator grid is applied to a Class A "control amplifier" which drives a rectifier circuit to produce a d.c. voltage negative with respect to ground. C_1 filters out the audio variations, leaving a d.c. voltage proportional to the average voice level. This voltage is applied to the grid of a "clamp" tube to control the d.c. screen voltage and thus the r.f. carrier level. Maximum output is obtained when the carrier-control tube grid is driven to cut-off, the voice level at which this occurs being determined by the setting of R_4. The input without modulation is set to the desired level (usually about equal to the plate dissipation rating of the modulated stage) by adjusting R_2. R_3 may be the normal screen-dropping resistor for the modulated beam tetrode, but in case a separate screen supply is used the resistance need be just large enough to give sufficient voltage drop to reduce the no-modulation power input to the desired value.

C_1R_1 and C_2R_3 should have a time constant of about 0.1 second. An oscilloscope is required for proper adjustment.

FREQUENCY AND PHASE MODULATION

It is possible to convey intelligence by modulating any property of a carrier, including its frequency and phase. When the frequency of the carrier is varied in accordance with the variations in a modulating signal, the result is **frequency modulation (f.m.).** Similarly, varying the phase of the carrier current is called **phase modulation (p.m.).**

Frequency and phase modulation are not independent, since the frequency cannot be varied without also varying the phase, and vice versa. The difference is largely a matter of definition.

The effectiveness of f.m. and p.m. for communication purposes depends almost entirely on the receiving methods. If the receiver will respond to frequency and phase changes but is insensitive to amplitude changes, it will discriminate against most forms of noise, particularly impulse noise such as is set up by ignition systems and other sparking devices. Special methods of detection are required to accomplish this result.

Modulation methods for f.m. and p.m. are simple and require practically no audio power.

There is also the advantage that, since there is no amplitude variation in the signal, interference to broadcast reception resulting from rectification of the transmitted signal in the audio circuits of the BC receiver is substantially eliminated. These two points represent the principal

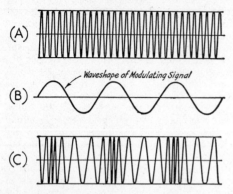

Fig. 8-30—Graphical representation of frequency modulation. In the unmodulated carrier at A, each r.f. cycle occupies the same amount of time. When the modulating signal, B, is applied, the radio frequency is increased and decreased according to the amplitude and polarity of the modulating signal.

reasons for the use of f.m. and p.m. in amateur work.

Frequency Modulation

Fig. 8-30 is a representation of frequency modulation. When a modulating signal is applied, the carrier frequency is increased during one half-cycle of the modulating signal and decreased during the half-cycle of opposite polarity. This is indicated in the drawing by the fact that the r.f. cycles occupy less time (higher frequency) when the modulating signal is positive, and more time (lower frequency) when the modulating signal is negative. The change in the carrier frequency (**frequency deviation**) is proportional to the instantaneous amplitude of the modulating signal, so the deviation is small when the instantaneous amplitude of the modulating signal is small, and is greatest when the modulating signal reaches its peak, either positive or negative.

As shown by the drawing, the amplitude of the signal does not change during modulation.

Phase Modulation

If the phase of the current in a circuit is changed there is an instantaneous frequency change during the time that the phase is being shifted. The amount of frequency change, or deviation, depends on how rapidly the phase shift is accomplished. It is also dependent upon the total amount of the phase shift. In a properly operating p.m. system the amount of phase shift is proportional to the instantaneous amplitude of the modulating signal. The rapidity of the phase shift is directly proportional to the frequency of the modulating signal. Conse-

quently, the frequency deviation in p.m. is proportional to both the amplitude and frequency of the modulating signal. The latter represents the outstanding difference between f.m. and p.m., since in f.m. the frequency deviation is proportional only to the amplitude of the modulating signal.

Modulation Depth

Percentage of modulation in f.m. and p.m. has to be defined differently than for a.m. Practically, "100 percent modulation" is reached when the transmitted signal occupies a channel just equal to the bandwidth for which the *receiver* is designed. If the frequency deviation is greater than the receiver can accept, the receiver distorts the signal. However, on another receiver designed for a different bandwidth the same signal might be equivalent to only 25 percent modulation.

In amateur work "narrow-band" f.m. or p.m. (frequently abbreviated n.b.f.m.) is defined as having the same channel width as a properly modulated a.m. signal. That is, the effective channel width does not exceed twice the highest audio frequency in the modulating signal. n.b.f.m. transmissions based on an upper audio limit of 3000 Hz. therefore should occupy a channel not significantly wider than 6 kHz.

F.M. and P.M. Sidebands

The sidebands set up by f.m. and p.m. differ from those resulting from a.m. in that they occur at integral multiples of the modulating frequency on either side of the carrier rather than, as in a.m., consisting of a single set of side frequencies for each modulating frequency. An f.m. or p.m. signal therefore inherently occupies a wider channel than a.m.

The number of "extra" sidebands that occur in f.m. and p.m. depends on the relationship between the modulating frequency and the frequency deviation. The ratio between the frequency deviation, in cycles per second, and the modulating frequency, also in cycles per second, is called the **modulation index**. That is,

$$Modulation\ index = \frac{Carrier\ frequency\ deviation}{Modulating\ frequency}$$

Example: The maximum frequency deviation in an f.m. transmitter is 3000 Hz. either side of the carrier frequency. The modulation index when the modulating frequency is 1000 Hz. is

$$Modulation\ index = \frac{3000}{1000} = 3$$

At the same deviation with 3000-Hz. modulation the index would be 1; at 100 Hz. it would be 30, and so on.

In p.m. the modulation index is constant regardless of the modulating frequency; in f.m. it varies with the modulating frequency, as shown in the above example. In an f.m. system the ratio of the *maximum* carrier-frequency deviation to the *highest* modulating frequency used is called the **deviation ratio**.

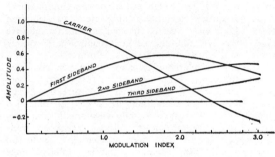

Fig. 8-31—How the amplitude of the pairs of sidebands varies with the modulation index in an f.m. or p.m. signal. If the curves were extended for greater values of modulation index it would be seen that the carrier amplitude goes through zero at several points. The same statement also applies to the sidebands.

Fig. 8-31 shows how the amplitudes of the carrier and the various sidebands vary with the modulation index. This is for single-tone modulation; the first sideband (actually a pair, one above and one below the carrier) is displaced from the carrier by an amount equal to the modulating frequency, the second is twice the modulating frequency away from the carrier, and so on. For example, if the modulating frequency is 2000 Hz. and the carrier frequency is 29,500 kHz., the first sideband pair is at 29,498 kHz. and 29,502 kHz., the second pair is at 29,496 kHz. and 29,504 kc., the third at 29,494 kc. and 29,506 kHz., etc. The amplitudes of these sidebands depend on the modulation index, not on the frequency deviation.

Note that, as shown by Fig. 8-31, the carrier strength varies with the modulation index. (In amplitude modulation the carrier strength is constant; only the sideband amplitude varies.) At a modulation index of approximately 2.4 the carrier disappears entirely. It then becomes "negative" at a higher index, meaning that its phase is reversed as compared to the phase without modulation. In f.m. and p.m. the energy that goes into the sidebands is taken from the carrier, the *total* power remaining the same regardless of the modulation index.

Since there is no change in amplitude with modulation, an f.m. or p.m. signal can be amplified without distortion by an ordinary Class C amplifier. The modulation can take place in a very low-level stage and the signal can then be amplified by either frequency multipliers or straight amplifiers.

If the modulated signal is passed through one or more frequency multipliers, the modulation index is multiplied by the same factor that the carrier frequency is multiplied. For example, if modulation is applied on 3.5 MHz. and the final output is on 28 MHz. the total frequency multiplication is 8 times, so if the frequency deviation is 500 Hz. at 3.5 MHz. it will be 4000 Hz. at 28 MHz. Frequency multiplication offers a means for obtaining practically any desired amount of frequency deviation, whether or not the modulator itself is capable of giving that much deviation without distortion.

Narrow-Band F.M. and P.M.

"Narrow-band" f.m. or p.m., the only type that is authorized by FCC for use on the lower frequencies where the phone bands are crowded, is defined as f.m. or p.m. that does not occupy a wider channel than an a.m. signal having the same audio modulating frequencies.

If the modulation index (with single-tone modulation) does not exceed 0.6 or 0.7, the most important extra sideband, the second, will be at least 20 db. below the unmodulated carrier level, and this should represent an effective channel width about equivalent to that of an a.m. signal. In the case of speech, a somewhat higher modulation index can be used. This is because the energy distribution in a complex wave is such that the modulation index for any one frequency component is reduced, as compared to the index with a sine wave having the same peak amplitude as the voice wave.

The chief advantage of narrow-band f.m. or p.m. for frequencies below 30 MHz. is that it eliminates or reduces certain types of interference to broadcast reception. Also, the modulating equipment is relatively simple and inexpensive. However, assuming the same unmodulated carrier power in all cases, narrow-band f.m. or p.m. is not as effective as a.m. *with the methods of reception used by most amateurs.* As shown by Fig. 8-31, at an index of 0.6 the amplitude of the first sideband is about 25 percent of the unmodulated-carrier amplitude; this compares with a sideband amplitude of 50 percent in the case of a 100 percent modulated a.m. transmitter. When copied on an a.m. receiver, a narrow-band f.m. or p.m. transmitter is about equivalent to a 100 percent modulated a.m. transmitter operating at one-fourth the carrier power. On a suitable (f.m.) receiver, f.m. is as good or better than a.m., watt for watt.

Comparison of F.M. and P.M.

Frequency modulation cannot be applied to an amplifier stage, but phase modulation can; p.m. is therefore readily adaptable to transmitters employing oscillators of high stability such as the crystal-controlled type. The amount of phase shift that can be obtained with good linearity is such that the maximum practicable modulation index is about 0.5. Because the phase shift is proportional to the modulating frequency, this index can be used only at the highest frequency present in the modulating signal, assuming that all frequencies will at one time or another have equal amplitudes. Taking 3000 Hz. as a suitable upper limit for voice work, and setting the modulation index at 0.5 for 3000

Hz., the frequency response of the speech-amplifier system above 3000 Hz. must be sharply attenuated, to prevent sideband splatter. Also, if the "tinny" quality of p.m. as received on an f.m. receiver is to be avoided, the p.m. must be changed to f.m., in which the modulation index decreases in inverse proportion to the modulating frequency. This requires shaping the speech-amplifier frequency-response curve in such a way that the output voltage is inversely proportional to frequency over most of the voice range. When this is done the maximum modulation index can only be used at some relatively low audio frequency, perhaps 300 to 400 Hz. in voice transmission, and must decrease in proportion to the increase in fre-quency. The result is that the maximum linear frequency deviation is only one or two hundred Hz., when p.m. is changed to f.m. To increase the deviation for n.b.f.m. requires a frequency ·multiplication of 8 times or more.

It is relatively easy to secure a fairly large frequency deviation when a self-controlled oscillator is frequency-modulated directly. (True frequency modulation of a crystal-controlled oscillator results in only very small deviations and so requires a great deal of frequency multiplication.) The chief problem is to maintain a satisfactory degree of carrier stability, since the greater the inherent stability of the oscillator the more difficult it is to secure a wide frequency swing with linearity.

METHODS OF FREQUENCY AND PHASE MODULATION

A simple and satisfactory device for producing f.m. in the amateur transmitter is the reactance modulator. This is a vacuum tube connected to the r.f. tank circuit of an oscillator in such a way as to act as a variable inductance or capacitance.

Fig. 8-32 is a representative circuit. The control grid of the modulator tube is connected across the oscillator tank circuit, $C_1 L_1$, through resistor R_1 and blocking capacitor C_2. C_8 represents the input capacitance of the modulator tube. The resistance of R_1 is made large compared to the reactance of C_8, so the r.f. current through $R_1 C_8$ will be practically in phase with the r.f. voltage appearing at the terminals of the tank circuit. However, the voltage across C_8 will lag the current by 90 degrees. The r.f. current in the plate circuit of the modulator will be in phase with the grid voltage, and consequently is 90 degrees behind the current through C_8, or 90 degrees behind the r.f. tank voltage. This lagging current is drawn through the oscillator tank, giving the same effect as though an inductance were connected across the tank. The frequency increases in proportion to the amplitude of the lagging plate current of the modulator. The audio voltage, introduced through a radio-frequency choke, RFC_1, varies the transconductance of the tube and thereby varies the r.f. plate current.

The modulated oscillator usually is operated on a relatively low frequency, so that a high order of carrier stability can be secured. Frequency multipliers are used to raise the frequency to the final frequency desired.

A reactance modulator can be connected to a crystal oscillator as well as to the self-controlled type. However, the resulting signal is more phase-modulated than it is frequency-modulated, for the reason that the frequency deviation that can be secured by varying the tuning of a crystal oscillator is quite small.

The sensitivity of the modulator (frequency change per unit change in grid voltage) depends on the transconductance of the modulator tube.

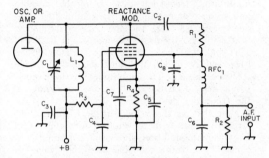

Fig. 8-32—Reactance modulator using a high-transconductance pentode (6BA6, 6CL6, etc.).

C_1—R.f. tank capacitance (see text).
C_2, C_3—0.001-μf. mica.
C_4, C_5, C_6—0.0047-μf. mica.
C_7—10-μf. electrolytic.
C_8—Tube input capacitance.
R_1—47,000 ohms.
R_2—0.47 megohm.
R_3—Screen dropping resistor; to give proper screen voltage on modulator tube.
R_4—Cathode bias resistor; Class-A operation.
L_1—R.f. tank inductance.
RFC_1—2.5-mh. r.f. choke.

It increases when R_1 is made smaller in comparison with C_8. It also increases with an increase in L/C ratio in the oscillator tank circuit. However, for highest carrier stability it is desirable to use the largest tank capacitance that will permit the desired deviation to be secured while keeping within the limits of linear operation.

A change in *any* of the voltages on the modulator tube will cause a change in r.f. plate current, and consequently a frequency change. Therefore it is advisable to use a regulated power supply for both modulator and oscillator. At the low voltage used (250 volts or less) the required stabilization can be secured by means of gaseous regulator tubes.

Speech Amplification

The speech amplifier preceding the modulator follows ordinary design, except that no power is taken from it and the a.f. voltage required by the modulator grid usually is small — not more than 10 or 15 volts, even with large modulator tubes. Because of these modest requirements, only a few speech stages are needed; a two-stage amplifier consisting of two bipolar transistors, both resistance-coupled, will more than suffice for crystal ceramic or hi-z dynamic microphones.

PHASE MODULATION

The same type of reactance-tube circuit that is used to vary the tuning of the oscillator tank in f.m. can be used to vary the tuning of an amplifier tank and thus the phase of the tank current for p.m. Hence the modulator circuit of Fig. 8-32 can be used for p.m. if the reactance tube works on an amplifier tank instead of directly on a self-controlled oscillator.

The phase shift that occurs when a circuit is detuned from resonance depends on the amount of detuning and the Q of the circuit. The higher the Q, the smaller the amount of detuning needed to secure a given number of degrees of phase shift. If the Q is at least 10, the relationship between phase shift and detuning (in kHz. either side of the resonant frequency) will be substantially linear over a phase-shift range of about 25 degrees. From the standpoint of modulator sensitivity, the Q of the tuned circuit on which the modulator operates should be as high as possible. On the other hand, the effective Q of the circuit will not be very high if the amplifier is delivering power to a load since the load resistance reduces the Q. There must therefore be a compromise between modulator sensitivity and r.f. power output from the modulated amplifier. An optimum figure for Q appears to be about 20; this allows reasonable loading of the modulated amplifier and the necessary tuning variation can be secured from a reactance modulator without difficulty. It is advisable to modulate at a low power level, as in a stage where receiving-type tubes are used.

Reactance modulation of an amplifier stage usually also results in simultaneous amplitude modulation because the modulated stage is detuned from resonance as the phase is shifted. This must be eliminated by feeding the modulated signal through an amplitude limiter or one or more "saturating" stages — that is, amplifiers that are operated Class C and driven hard enough so that variations in the amplitude of the grid excitation produce no appreciable variations in the final output amplitude.

For the same type of reactance modulator, the speech-amplifier gain required is the same for p.m. as for f.m. However, as pointed out earlier, the fact that the actual frequency deviation increases with the modulating audio frequency in p.m. makes it necessary to cut off the frequencies above about 3000 Hz. before modulation takes place. If this is not done, unnecessary sidebands will be generated at frequencies considerably away from the carrier.

F.M. FROM CRYSTAL OSCILLATORS

A practical way to obtain f.m. with transmitters that use crystal oscillators is to employ the method shown in Fig. 8-33. The junction capacitance of CR_1 is varied by the incoming audio voltage. As the capacitance of CR_1 changes, the oscillator frequency varies because the crystal is "pulled" by the action of the Varactor diode. Only a few volts of audio are needed to provide the necessary frequency swing. A simple transistorized audio amplifier of two or three stages is usually sufficient for this purpose. The amount of frequency swing is controlled by the setting of the audio-gain control (deviation control).

This type of circuit is useful with transmitters operating at 50 Mc. and higher. The oscillator is followed by additional frequency-multiplier stages, thus assuring ample frequency deviation to provide a suitable f.m. signal. This technique can be used with overtone crystal oscillators as well, provided the order of frequency multiplication in the transmitter is high enough to give ample frequency swing at the carrier frequency.

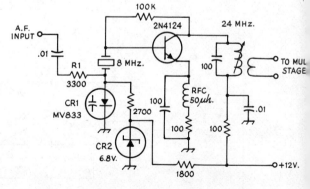

Fig. 8-33—Schematic of a transistor oscillator whose frequency is "pulled" by means of a variable-capacitance diode to obtain f.m. R_1 is an r.f. isolating resistor. CR_1 is a small Varactor diode. In some circuits a high-frequency small-signal silicon diode (or v.h.f. silicon transistor) is used for this same purpose. CR_2 is a Zener diode.

Chapter 9

Single-Sideband Phone

GENERATING THE S.S.B. SIGNAL

A fully modulated a.m. signal has two-thirds of its power in the carrier and only one-third in the sidebands. The sidebands carry the intelligence to be transmitted; the carrier "goes along for the ride" and serves only to demodulate the signal at the receiver. By eliminating the carrier and transmitting only the sidebands, or just one sideband, the available transmitter power is used to greater advantage. To recover the intelligence being transmitted, the carrier must be reinserted at the receiver, but this is no great problem with a proper detector circuit.

Assuming that the same final-amplifier tube or tubes are used either for normal a.m. or for single sideband, carrier suppressed, it can be shown that the use of s.s.b. can give an effective gain of up to 9 db. over a.m. — equivalent to increasing the transmitter power 8 times. Eliminating the carrier also eliminates the heterodyne interference that so often spoils communication in congested phone bands.

Balanced Modulators

The carrier can be suppressed or nearly eliminated by using a balanced modulator or an extremely sharp filter. In s.s.b. transmitters it is common practice to use both devices. The basic principle of any balanced modulator is to introduce the carrier in such a way that it does not appear in the output, but so that the sidebands will. The type of balanced-modulator circuit chosen by the builder will depend upon the constructional considerations, cost, and whether tubes or transistors (or both) are to be employed.

In any balanced-modulator circuit there will be no output with no audio signal. When audio is applied, the balance is upset, and one branch will conduct more than the other. Since any modulation process is the same as "mixing" in receivers, sum and difference frequencies (sidebands) will be generated. The modulator is not balanced for the sidebands, and they will appear in the output.

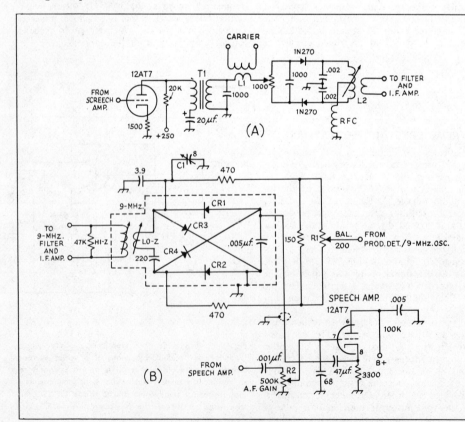

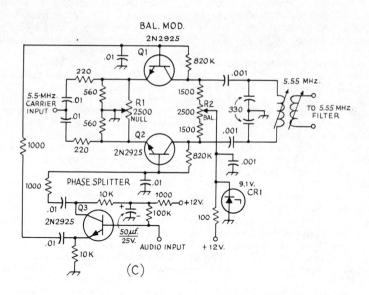

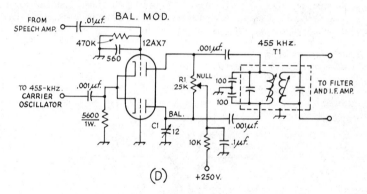

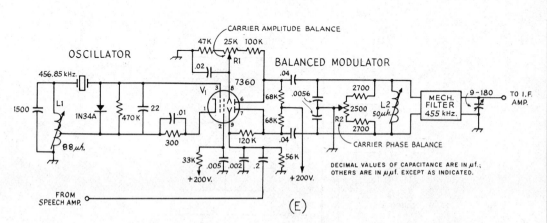

Fig. 9-1—Typical circuits of balanced modulators. Representative parts values are given and should serve as a basis for designing one's own equipment.

In the rectifier-type balanced modulators shown in Fig. 9-1, at A and B, the diode rectifiers are connected in such a manner that, if they have equal forward resistances, no r.f. can pass from the carrier source to the output circuit via either of the two possible paths. The net effect is that no r.f. energy appears in the output. When audio is applied, it unbalances the circuit by biasing the diode (or diodes) in one path, depending upon the instantaneous polarity of the audio, and hence some r.f. will appear in the output. The r.f. in the output will appear as a double-sideband suppressed-carrier signal. (For a more complete description of diode-modulator operation, see *Single Sideband for the Radio Amateur,* 4th Edition, pp. 25-28.)

In any diode modulator, the r.f. voltage should be at least 6 or 8 times the peak audio voltage, for minimum distortion. The usual operation involves a fraction of a volt of audio and several volts of r.f. The diodes should be matched as closely as possible — ohmmeter measurements of their forward resistances is the usual test.

One of the most simple diode balanced modulators in use is that of Fig. 9-1A. Its use is usually limited to low-cost portable equipment in which a high degree of carrier suppression is not vital. A ring balanced modulator is shown in Fig. 9-1B and offers excellent carrier suppression at low cost. This circuit has been used by the R. L. Drake Co. Diodes CR_1 through CR_4 should be well matched and can be 1N270s or similar. C_1 is adjusted for best r.f. phase balance as

evidenced by maximum carrier null. R_1 is also adjusted for the best carrier null obtainable. It may be necessary to adjust each control several times to secure optimum suppression.

A bipolar-transistor balanced modulator is shown in Fig. 9-1C. This circuit is similar to one used by Galaxy Electronics and uses closely matched transistors at Q_1 and Q_2. A phase splitter (inverter), Q_3, is used to feed audio to the balanced modulator in push pull. The carrier is supplied to the circuit in parallel and the output is taken in push pull. CR_1 is a Zener diode and is used to stabilize the d.c. voltage. Controls R_1 and R_2 are adjusted for best carrier suppression.

Two practical vacuum-tube balanced modulators are illustrated in Fig. 9-1 at D and E. In the circuit at D the audio is effectively applied in push pull, the carrier is injected in parallel, and the output is in push pull. C_1 is adjusted for best r.f. phase balance and may have to be connected between the opposite plate and ground in actual practice. This will depend upon the overall circuit balance. As in the other circuits C_1 and R_1 are adjusted for best carrier suppression. T_1 can be a standard input i.f. transformer to which two 100-pf. capacitors are externally connected to the primary winding as shown. These capacitors help effect r.f. phase balance. The circuit at E offers superior carrier suppression to that of D and uses a 7360 beam-deflection tube as a balanced modulator. This tube is capable of providing as much as 60 db. of carrier suppression. When used with mechanical or crystal-lattice filters the total

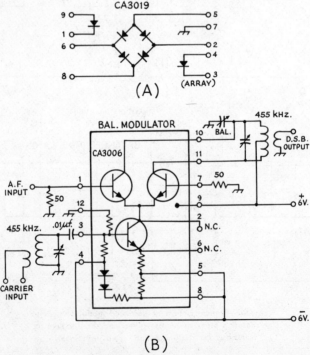

Fig. 9-2—Additional balanced-modulator circuits in which integrated circuits are used.

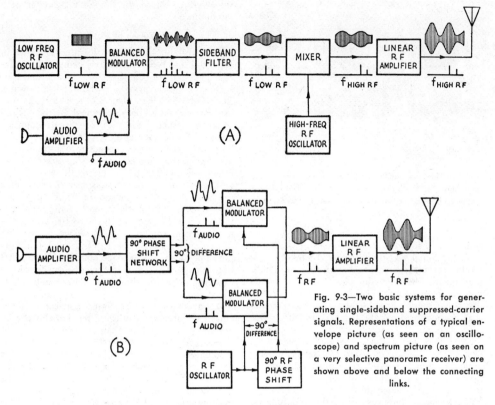

Fig. 9-3—Two basic systems for generating single-sideband suppressed-carrier signals. Representations of a typical envelope picture (as seen on an oscilloscope) and spectrum picture (as seen on a very selective panoramic receiver) are shown above and below the connecting links.

carrier suppression can be as great as 80 db. Most well-designed balanced modulators can provide between 30 and 50 db. of carrier suppression, hence the 7360 circuit is highly desirable for optimum results. An in-depth treatment of this tube and its application in s.s.b. circuits is given in *Single Sideband for the Radio Amateur,* 4th Edition, page 29.

Integrated circuits (ICs) are presently available for use in balanced-modulator and mixer circuits. A diode array such as the RCA CA3019, Fig. 9-2, is ideally suited for use in circuits such as that of Fig. 9-1B. Since all diodes are formed on a common silicon chip, their characteristics are extremely well matched. This fact makes the IC ideal in circuits where optimum balance is required. Alternatively, a differential amplifier IC such as the RCA CA3006 can be used effectively as a balanced modulator by employing it as shown in Fig. 9-2B. If attention is given to good external circuit symmetry, the double-sideband suppressed-carrier output will be at least 25 db. greater in level than the carrier input when applying 31 millivolts of carrier at T_1 and 10 millivolts of audio at terminal 1. Detailed information on IC balanced modulators is given in *RCA Linear Integrated Circuit Fundamentals,* Tech. Series IC-41. Additional information on balanced mixers and other s.s.b. circuits is given in *Single Sideband Principles And Circuits,* Pappenfus, Bruene, and Shoenike (McGraw-Hill Publishing Co.).

SINGLE-SIDEBAND GENERATORS

Two basic systems for generating s.s.b. signals are shown in Fig. 9-3. One involves the use of a bandpass filter having sufficient selectivity to pass one sideband and reject the other. "Mechanical" filters are available for frequencies below 1 MHz. From 0.2 to 10 MHz., good sideband rejection can be obtained with filters using four or more quartz crystals. Oscillator output at the filter frequency is combined with the audio signal in a balanced modulator, and only the upper and lower sidebands appear in the output. One of the sidebands is passed by the filter and the other rejected, so that an s.s.b. signal is fed to the mixer. The signal is there mixed with the output of a high-frequency r.f. oscillator to produce the desired output frequency. For additional amplification a linear r.f. amplifier must be used. When the s.s.b. signal is generated around 500 kHz. it may be necessary to convert twice to reach the operating frequency, since this simplifies the problem of rejecting the "image" frequencies resulting from the heterodyne process. The problem of image frequencies in the frequency conversions of s.s.b. signals differs from the problem in receivers because the beating-oscillator frequency becomes important. Either balanced modulators or sufficient selectivity must be used to attenuate these frequencies in the output and hence minimize the possibility of unwanted radiations. (Examples of filter-type ex-

Fig. 9-4—This 4-crystal lattice filter is built in modular form and uses the circuit of Fig. 9-5. It is suitable for use in s.s.b. exciters, or it can be used in the i.f. strip of a s.s.b. receiver.

the overall cost of the home-built exciter at a minimum.

Types of Filters

A home-built 4-crystal lattice filter is shown in Figs. 9-4 and 9-5. This unit is composed of cascaded half-lattice bandpass filters (two) and uses surplus FT-241 crystals in the 455-kHz. range. Standard 455-kHz. input i.f. transformers are used for coupling. They are tuned for the desired bandpass response for s.s.b. operation—approximately 2.7 kHz. at the 6 db. points on the curve. The skirt selectivity is dependent to a greater extent upon the number of crystals used in the filter—the more used the steeper the sides of the passband curve. The crystals used in this filter can be obtained at frequencies in the i.f. range, and ones that are within the ranges of the i.f. transformers will be satisfactory. Two 100-pf. capacitors are connected across the secondary winding of two of the transformers to give push-pull output. The crystals should be obtained in pairs 1.8 kHz. apart. The i.f. transformers can be either capacitor-tuned as shown, or they can be slug-tuned.

citers can be found in various issues of *QST* and in *Single Sideband for the Radio Amateur*.)

The second system is based on the phase relationships between the carrier and sidebands in a modulated signal. As shown in the diagram, the audio signal is split into two components that are identical except for a phase difference of 90 degrees. The output of the r.f. oscillator (which may be at the operating frequency, if desired) is likewise split into two separate components having a 90-degree phase difference. One r.f. and one audio component are combined in each of two separate balanced modulators. The carrier is suppressed in the modulators, and the relative phases of the sidebands are such that one sideband is balanced out and the other is augmented in the combined output. If the output from the balanced modulators is high enough, such an s.s.b. exciter can work directly into the antenna, or the power level can be increased in a following amplifier.

Generally, the filter-type exciter is easier to adjust than is the phasing exciter. Most home-built s.s.b. equipment uses commercially-made filters these days. The alignment is done at the factory, thus relieving the amateur of the sometimes tedious task of adjusting the filter for suitable bandpass characteristics. Filter-type exciters are more popular than phasing units and offer better carrier suppression and alignment stability. It is still practical for the builder to fabricate his own crystal-lattice filter by utilizing low-cost surplus crystals. This possibility should not be overlooked if the builder is interested in keeping

A variable-frequency signal generator is required for alignment of the filter, but this can be nothing more elaborate than a shielded b.f.o. unit. The signal should be introduced at the balanced modulator, and an output indicator connected to the plate circuit of the vacuum tube following the filter. With the crystals out of the circuit, the transformers can be brought close to frequency by plugging in small capacitors (2 to 5 pf.) in one crystal socket in each stage and then tuning the transformers for peak output at one of the two crystal frequencies. The small capacitors can then be removed and the crystals replaced in their sockets.

Tuning the signal source slowly across the pass band of the filter and watching the output indicator will show the selectivity characteristic of the filter. The objective is a fairly flat response for about two kHz. and a rapid drop-off outside this range. It will be found that small changes in the tuning of the transformers will change the shape of the selectivity characteristic, so it is wise to make a small adjustment of one trimmer, swing the frequency across the band, and observe the characteristic. After a little experimenting it will be found which way the trimmers must be moved to compensate for the peaks that will rise when the filter is out of adjustment.

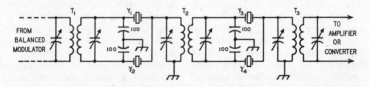

Fig. 9-5—Schematic diagram of the filter shown in Fig. 9-4. Low-frequency surplus-type 450-kHz. crystals are used. Y_1 and Y_3 should be the same frequency and Y_2 and Y_4 should be 1.8 kHz. higher. T_1, T_2, and T_3 are standard input i.f. transformers for 455 kHz.

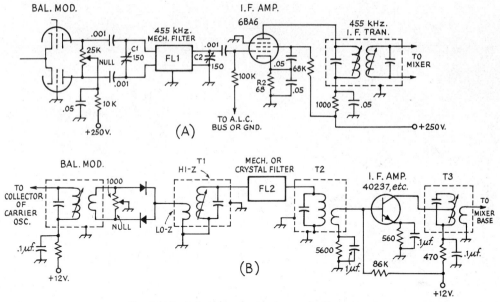

Fig. 9-6—Typical circuits showing how s.s.b. filters are connected in the circuit.

The (suppressed) carrier frequency must be adjusted so that it falls properly on the slope of the filter characteristic. If it is too close to the filter mid-frequency the sideband rejection will be poor; if it is too far away there will be a lack of "lows" in the signal.

Ordinarily, the carrier is placed on one side of the curve, depending upon which sideband is desired, which is approximately 20 db. down from the' peak. It is sometimes helpful to make provisions for "rubbering" the crystal of the carrier oscillator so that the most natural voice quality can be realized when making initial adjustments. Considerable information of the design and adjustment of crystal lattice filters is given in *Single Sideband For The Radio Amateur*.

Using Commercial Crystal Filters

Some builders may not have adequate testing facilities for building and aligning their own filters. In such instances it is possible to purchase ready-made units which are prealigned and come equipped with crystals for upper- and lower-sideband use. The International Crystal Company[1] has three types for use at 9'MHz. Another manufacturer, McCoy Electronics Co.,[2] sells two different 9-MHz. models for amateur use.

Mechanical Filters

Mechanical filters contain elements that vibrate and establish resonance mechanically. In crystal filters the coupling between filter sections is achieved by electrical means. In mechanical filters, mechanical couplers are used to transfer the vibrations from one resonant section to the next. At

[1] International Crystal Mfg. Co., Inc., 10 North Lee, Oklahoma City, Oklahoma 73102.
[2] McCoy Electronics Co., Mt. Holly Springs, Pa.

the input and output ends of the filter are transducers which provide for electrical coupling to and from the filter. Most mechanical filters are designed for use from 200 to 600 kHz., the range near 455 kHz. being the most popular for amateur use. Mechanical filters suitable for amateur radio circuits are manufactured by the Collins Radio Co. and can be purchased from some dealers in amateur radio equipment. A circuit using a mechanical filter is described later in this chapter.

FILTER APPLICATIONS

Methods for using typical sideband filters are shown in block-diagram form in Fig. 9-3A, and schematically in Fig. 9-6. In the circuit of Fig. 9-6A a 455-kHz. mechanical filter is coupled to the balanced modulator by means of two d.c. isolating capacitors. C_1 is used to tune the input of FL_1 to resonance (if a Collins type 455-FB-21 is used). Frequently, a fixed-value 120-pf. capacitor will suffice at each end of the filter. C_2 tunes the output of the filter. A stage of i.f. amplification usually follows the filter, as shown, to compensate for the insertion loss of the filter and to provide a stage to which a.g.c. can be applied for a.l.c. (automatic level control) purposes. In the circuit shown the operator can ground R_1 if a.l.c. is not used. R_2 can be lifted from ground and a 5000-ohm control can be placed between it and ground to provide a means of manual gain control for providing the desired signal level to the mixer.

In the circuit of Fig. 9-6B a simple diode balanced modulator is shown coupled to FL_2 which can be any crystal or mechanical filter which has high-impedance input and output characteristics. T_1, T_2, and T_3 are tuned to the filter frequency. Most commercial s.s.b. filters are supplied with

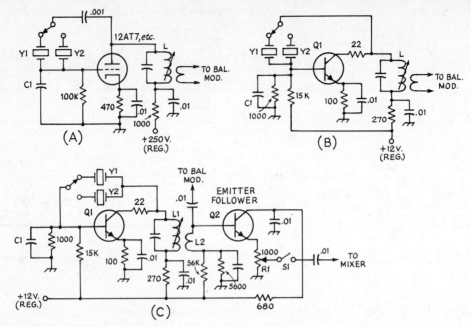

Fig. 9-7—Schematic diagrams of practical crystal oscillators for generating the carrier in s.s.b. exciters. Each circuit has two crystals, permitting upper- and lower-sideband operation.

a data sheet which shows recommended input and output circuits for matching the impedance of the filter. All are adaptable to use with tubes or transistors.

Carrier Oscillators

It is desirable to have provisions for switching from upper to lower sideband when the need arises. On some of the amateur bands the lower sideband is preferred, while the upper sideband is commonly used on some of the other bands. For this reason it is helpful to have two crystals for the carrier oscillator as shown in Fig. 9-7, permitting operation on either sideband at the flip of a switch. At A, a triode oscillator provides the carrier. Y_1 and Y_2 are selected for upper- and lower-sideband operation. C_1 is part of the feedback circuit and is chosen for the frequency of operation. At 455 kHz. it is usually between 10 and 33 pf. Smaller values will be needed for higher operating frequencies. L is tuned to resonance at the crystal frequency. In the circuit at B a bipolar transistor is used. C_1 will be on the order of 500 pf. for operation at 455 kHz. The 22-ohm resistor in the collector lead is for parasitic suppression. A high C-L ratio should be used in the collector tuned circuit to reduce harmonic currents. In the circuit of Fig. 9-7C a bipolar transistor oscillator is followed by an emitter-follower stage to permit carrier insertion around the filter, to the mixer stage, for tune-up purposes. S_1 can be part of R_1, the level control, and will assure that the carrier-insertion line is open during normal operation. This method of carrier insertion can be applied to the circuit of

Fig. 9-7A by utilizing a cathode follower after the oscillator. This method need not be used if the equipment has a means by which the balanced modulator can be unbalanced for tuning up or zero beating. The circuit at C is handy for c.w., permitting the operator to insert carrier as needed. Q_1 and Q_2 can be any n-p-n transistors whose beta is 20 or better, and whose f_T is 10 times or more the proposed oscillator frequency.

Mixer Circuits

After the s.s.b. suppressed-carrier signal is generated, then amplified by the i.f. stage, it is ready to be mixed with local-oscillator signal to provide the desired transmitter output frequency. For proper operation, the mixer must be able to convert the two signals to the desired sum or difference frequency without generating additional unwanted products in the output by intermodulation distortion (IMD) between the signal components. For this reason it is important to pay attention to the signal-level ratios applied to the mixer, and to make certain that the selectivity following the mixer is of a sufficient order to pass only the desired band of frequencies. The use of a balanced mixer is desirable but not imperative. The latter will help reduce the level of local-oscillator signal from the p.t.o. or v.f.o. at the mixer output, thus helping to greatly reduce spurious responses in the output.

Some typical mixer circuits are illustrated in Fig. 9-8. Ideally, though not necessary, a mixer stage should have some gain. The circuits of Fig. 9-8 meet this requirement. At A, a single-ended mixer uses a 6BA7 in a conventional circuit. A

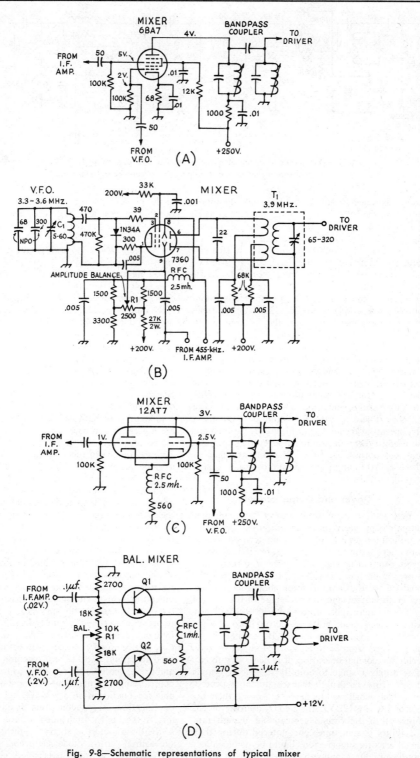

Fig. 9-8—Schematic representations of typical mixer circuits for s.s.b. exciters.

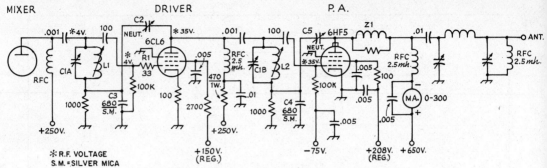

Fig. 9-9—Schematic diagram of a typical driver and p.a. stage for a s.s.b. exciter. Neutralization and parasitic-suppression circuits have been included.

bandpass tuned circuit is used to couple the mixer output to the following stage. In the circuit at B, a 7360 beam-deflection tube is utilized to provide up to 40 db. of carrier balance when carefully adjusted. The tube doubles as the v.f.o. in this circuit. Additional data on this circuit is given in the ARRL's *Single Sideband For The Radio Amateur,* 4th Edition.

In the circuit of Fig. 9-8C a twin triode is employed as a simple balanced mixer. Other tubes of the same general type can also be used in this circuit. This circuit is not as effective at balancing out the carrier as is the circuit at B, but it is somewhat superior to the circuit at A. The illustration at D shows how two n-p-n bipolar transistors can be used in a balanced-mixer circuit. The transistors should be closely matched for best results, and should have a beta of 40 or greater. Their f_T ratings should be well above the operating frequency. A high C-L ratio should be used in the collector tuned circuit to minimize spurious output. R_1 varies the forward bias on the transistors and is set for the best d.c. balance it will provide.

Driver and Output Stages

Few s.s.b. transmitting mixers have sufficient output to properly drive an output stage of any significant power level. Most modern-day linear amplifiers require at least 30 to 100 watts of exciter output power to drive them to their rated power input level. It follows, then, that an intermediate stage of amplification should be used between the mixer and the p.a. stage of the exciter.

The vacuum-tube mixers of Fig. 9-8 will provide 3 or 4 peak volts of output into a high-impedance load. Since most AB1 exciter output stages need from 25 to 50 volts of swing on their grids for normal operation, it is necessary to employ a driver stage to amplify the mixer output. There are several high-transconductance pentode tubes that work well as drivers. Among them are the 6CL6, the 12BY7, the 6EH7, and the 6GK6. Since all of these tubes are capable of high gain, instability is sometimes encountered during their use. Parasitic suppression should be included as a matter of course, and can take the form of a low-value noninductive resistor in series with the grid, or a standard parasitic choke installed directly

at the plate of the tube. Some form of neutralization is recommended and is preferred to resistive loading of the tuned circuits. The latter method lowers the tuned-circuit Q. This in turn lowers the stage selectivity and permits spurious responses from the mixer to be passed on to the following stage of the exciter.

A typical driver and p.a. stage for modern exciters is shown in Fig. 9-9. The p.a. is set up for AB_1 amplification. The AB_1 mode is preferred because it results in less distortion than does the AB_2 or Class-B modes, and because driving power is not needed for AB_1 operation. TV sweep tubes are used in the output stages of most commercial exciters because they are easy to obtain, are low cost, and have excellent power sensitivity. Some are capable of producing less IMD than others, but if not overdriven most of them are satisfactory for ham use. The 6146 series of tubes are excellent for use in p.a. stages of s.s.b. exciters and have excellent IMD characteristics. Among the sweep tubes useful as AB_1 amplifiers are the following: 6DQ5, 6GB5, 6GE5, 6HF5, 6JE6, 6JS6, 6KD6, 6KG6, and 6LQ6.

In the circuit of Fig. 9-9, a 6CL6 and a 6HF5 are shown in a typical driver-amplifier arrangement. Each stage is stabilized by means of R_1 in the driver grid, and Z_1 in the p.a. plate, both for parasitic suppression. C_2 and C_5 are neutralizing capacitors and can take the form of stiff wires placed adjacent to, and in the same place as the tube anode. Varying the spacing between the neutralizing stubs and the tube envelopes provides the adjustment of these capacitors. Parallel d.c. feed is used in the mixer and driver stages to prevent the tuned-circuit Q from being lowered by d.c. current flow through L_1 and L_2. C_{1A} and C_{1B} are ganged, and slug-tuned inductors are used at L_1 and L_2 to permit tracking of the mixer and driver plate tanks. C_3 and C_4 form part of the neutralizing circuits. The values shown are suitable for operation on 3.5 MHz. but may require modification for use on other bands. Regulated d.c. voltage is recommended for the screen grids of the driver and p.a. stages. Typical r.f. voltages (measured with a diode r.f. probe and v.t.v.m.) are identified with an asterisk. A circuit of this type is capable of up to 80 watts p.e.p. output. As many as four tubes can be operated in parallel.

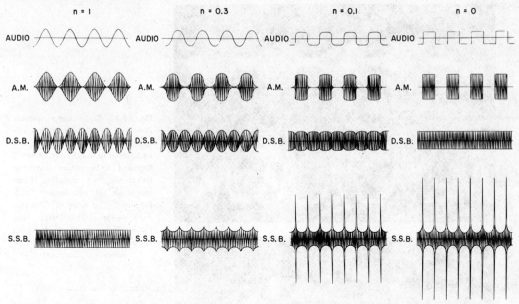

Fig. 9-10—The same audio signal gives widely-different envelope patterns, depending upon the type of transmitter. Various audio waveforms are shown in the top line; the resulting envelopes for 100 percent a.m., double-sideband suppressed carrier, and single-sideband suppressed carrier are shown below. The various audio waveforms are obtained by substituting values shown for n in $\sin^n \alpha$.

SPEECH AMPLIFICATION FOR S.S.B. EXCITERS

Speech amplifiers are used in s.s.b. exciters to increase the amplitude of the microphone output to a suitable level for operating the s.s.b. generator. In contrast to the speech requirements for a.m. operation, very little audio power is needed for s.s.b. equipment. The audio amplifier stage or stages need only have sufficient power to operate the balanced modulators discussed earlier in this chapter. It is important to design the audio amplifier section for minimum IM or harmonic distortion so that spurious components will not fall within the passband of the exciter, thus assuring the utmost purity of the output signal. Spurious components from the foregoing causes will be passed without attenuation by the exciter. For this reason it is advisable to limit hum, distortion, and noise to the lowest practical level when designing any s.s.b. audio section.

It is not difficult to keep distortion and harmonics minimized in the speech stages of the exciter if the tubes or transistors are not overdriven. Hum can be nearly eliminated by proper placement of the signal leads and through the use of shielded audio leads wherever applicable. The frequency response of the audio section should be restricted to only the usable speech frequencies for communications—approximately 400 to 3000 Hz. The frequency response over this range should be reasonably flat, within 3 db. Inverse feedback is frequently employed to help assure good audio characteristics. The speech-amplifier circuits shown in the early part of Chapter 8 are typical of those used in s.s.b. exciters. The actual

R and C values should be chosen for reasonably flat response from 400 to 3000 Hz.

Speech Processing

Although audio speech clipping has been effectively employed in a.m. transmitters for many years, little success has been obtained with similar schemes applied to s.s.b. generators. The use of automatic level control improves s.s.b. performance mostly through making the transmitter (or exciter) easier to adjust for maximum peak power without serious "flat-topping," while providing a measure of speech compression. However, it cannot substantially increase the average-to-peak power ratio as can a well-designed audio clipper/filter in a.m. Audio compressors suffer similarly in that they operate on the *integrated* audio waveform rather than on a cycle-to-cycle basis as does a clipper.

The difficulty in applying audio clipping to an s.s.b. system is a *fundamental* one; it is not a problem of refined circuitry or ingenious gadgetry. It has been known for some time that it is essentially *impossible* to increase the average-to-peak power ratio in the resulting s.s.b. signal *by any form of audio clipping*.

The big difference (as far as special processing is concerned) between a.m. and s.s.b. lies in the fact that in s.s.b. the envelope bears no simple relationship to the audio waveform used to generate it. In a.m. the radiated envelope is *identical* to the audio waveform (assuming linear, distortion-free modulation). If the audio waveform is a sine wave, the a.m. envelope is a sine wave. If the audio waveform is a square wave, the a.m. envelope is a square wave. In s.s.b. if the audio

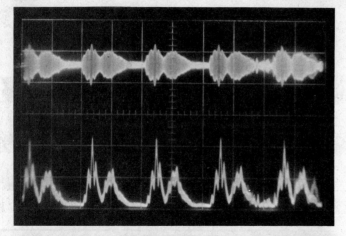

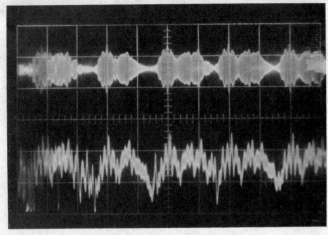

Fig. 9-11—Oscilloscope photos showing the clipper action. In each picture the top trace is the s.s.b. input to the clipper. (Above) Rectified s.s.b. output from the transceiver, no clipping. Peak power is set just below "flat-topping." The word is, "Hello." Zero power is the bottom line. (Below) Same as above, but with clipping. The increase in average power is apparent.

waveform is a sine wave, the s.s.b. envelope is that of a c.w. carrier. If the audio waveform is a square wave, the s.s.b. envelope contains a peak value that goes to *infinity,* with a waveform bearing no resemblance to the input square wave.

This situation can be seen more clearly in Fig. 9-10, which shows the r.f. envelopes for a.m., d.s.b. and s.s.b. for audio waveforms ranging from a sine wave to a square wave.[3] It can be seen that as the audio is clipped (made more nearly a square wave), the s.s.b. average-to-peak power actually *decreases!* In fact, in the extreme case of a perfectly square wave, the s.s.b. transmitter would require an *infinitely large peak power output* to accurately reproduce it. This inability to improve s.s.b. performance by clipping techniques suitable for a.m. (and d.s.b.) has been established more rigorously, and quantitative relationships between the modulating (audio) waveform and the resulting average-to-peak power ratios have been published.[4] It is clear that another approach is required.

[3] Courtesy of E. Bedrosian.
[4] Squires and Bedrosian, "The Computation of Single Sideband Peak Power," *Proc. I.R.E.,* January 1960.

A Practical Method

Since operations on the audio waveform are so unrewarding, it is logical to attempt operations on the s.s.b. waveform itself. In fact, an obvious attempt to do just this is made by anyone who "talks up" his s.s.b. transmitter to the "flat-topping" point. The average power *is* increased, but the resulting splatter, distortion products and unwanted sideband energy bring complaints from neighbors, more conservative amateurs and certain regulatory bodies.

Logically, the s.s.b. signal is formed in the usual way, *with as little distortion as possible.* It is important that a good s.s.b. signal be formed. The carrier and unwanted sideband should be well down, and the wanted sideband should be properly bandwidth-shaped with a good filter. This s.s.b. envelope is then amplitude clipped. The resulting waveform which now contains spectral components in the unwanted sideband (and everywhere else) is filtered *again,* preferably with a filter as good or better than the filter used to form the original s.s.b. signal. What results is a true s.s.b. signal with much increased average-to-peak power, but no out-of-band dis-

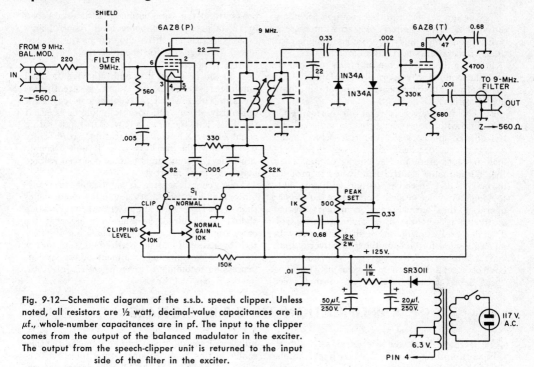

Fig. 9-12—Schematic diagram of the s.s.b. speech clipper. Unless noted, all resistors are ½ watt, decimal-value capacitances are in µf., whole-number capacitances are in pf. The input to the clipper comes from the output of the balanced modulator in the exciter. The output from the speech-clipper unit is returned to the input side of the filter in the exciter.

tortion products, which can be amplified and transmitted in the usual way. Typical waveforms as the signal passes through this process are shown in the oscilloscope photos of Fig. 9-11.

Before proceeding to a specific design, several conditions must be noted:

1) System gain must be increased by whatever amount of clipping is taken. E.g., if 20 db. of clipping is performed, over-all gain must be increased by 20 db. to regain the previous (non-clipped) *peak* power.

2) As system gain is increased, hum and noise must be controlled, just as in a.m. clipping. In addition, carrier suppression must be improved (if inadequate) by the same degree to which clipping is performed.

3) High-level stages must have increased *average* power capability. Many linear amplifiers which perform creditably on "normal" s.s.b. exceed power supply and tube ratings on clipped s.s.b. since the *average* power requirement can be increased by 10 to 20 db. On some voices, with heavy clipping, the average input power may be only a few decibels below the peak power!

A Practical Circuit

The speech-processor circuit of Fig. 9-12 was described in July 1964 *QST* by Squires and Clegg, W2PUL and W2LOY, and was designed to operate with a commercial s.s.b. transceiver. This transceiver forms an s.s.b. signal at 9.0-MHz. i.f. and the s.s.b. speech clipper was designed to operate following the 9.0-MHz. balanced modulator.

The output from the balanced modulator is applied to a crystal bandpass filter having a 560-ohm input/output impedance and a 3.1-kHz. (−6 db.) bandwidth. At the output of this filter, the resulting s.s.b. voltage is amplified by a 6AZ8 remote cutoff pentode to provide the increase in system gain required. The gain of this stage can be adjusted independently in either "clipping" or "normal" mode. In the "clipping" mode the gain setting controls the degree of clipping, and in the "normal" mode it resets the system gain to its original (without clipper) value.

After amplification the s.s.b. signal is clipped by a full-wave diode pair whose threshold is set by the "peak set" control. This control establishes the maximum output voltage, and peak power level, attainable in the clipping mode. Once properly set for maximum peak power without power-amplifier "flat-topping," no increase in audio gain, or shouting, can produce a higher *peak* power level—or cause "flat-topping."

The output of the clipper is impedance-matched to the second s.s.b. filter (identical to the first) by the 6AZ8 triode section. This filter does not show on the schematic since it is the s.s.b. filter normally used in the transceiver itself. In the transceiver, the 9-MHz. filter output drives a 12AU6 mixer which, with a 5.0-5.5-MHz. v.f.o. injection frequency, converts to 14.0-14.5-MHz. output.

Construction of the unit is completely straightforward. The only precautions necessary are to shield the input from the output of the first filter (to obtain good skirt selectivity) and to thoroughly shield the entire unit to avoid any pickup and possible r.f. feedback.

The design is typical of that required for many different s.s.b. transmitters. Its adjustment procedure would also apply to versions designed for other transmitters and is as follows:

1) Using the 9-MHz. output of the transceiver, with the modulator temporarily unbalanced, T_1 is adjusted for maximum carrier output (in "normal" position).

2) The transceiver is reset for normal s.s.b. operation with the carrier properly nulled. With the clipper in "normal," the transceiver audio gain is advanced, usually to "full on" if no overload in stages preceding the clipper occurs. Then the "normal gain" control is adjusted to produce normal s.s.b. transceiver output with no "flat-topping" on voice peaks. For future *no-clipper* operation the "normal gain" control is treated as though it were the usual audio gain control. The above adjustments are best carried out with an oscilloscope for viewing the transceiver output.

3) Switched to "clipping," the "clipping level" control is set full on, or at maximum gain. The "peak level" control is now set so that voice peaks are at the same output level as established in (2) above. The "clipping level" control now establishes the depth of clipping to the desired level. No further adjustment of the "peak set" control is necessary.

It should be noted that with clipping the final amplifier average power input is greatly increased. Tubes which ran cool before may glow ominously when "full-bore" clipping is used. If the final amplifier has a c.w. d.c. input rating equal to its s.s.b. d.c. input rating, no difficulty will occur. The same is true of power-supply capability; in some units plate and screen voltage may have to be improved.

This general scheme is applicable to transmitters which use filters for other frequencies than 9 MHz. Only slight circuit modification should be required, keeping in mind that the capacitor values may require changing if effective bypassing is to be realized at some other frequencies. Additional treatment of the speech-processing technique is given in *QST*, July 1967, by W. Sabin, WØIYH.

AMPLIFICATION OF S.S.B. SIGNALS

To increase the power level of an s.s.b. signal, a **linear amplifier** must be used. A linear amplifier is one that operates with low distortion, and the low distortion is obtained by the proper choice of tube and operating conditions. Physically there is little or no difference between a linear amplifier and any other type of r.f. amplifier stage. The circuit diagram of a tetrode r.f. amplifier is shown in Fig. 9-13; it is no different basically than the similar ones in Chapter Six. The practical differences can be found in the supply voltages for the tube and their special requirements. The proper voltages for a number of suitable tubes can be found in the tube tables in this book. Filament-type tubes will require the addition of the filament bypass capacitors C_9 and C_{10} and the completion of the filament circuit by grounding the filament-transformer center tap. The grid bias, E_1, is furnished through an r.f. choke, although a resistor can be used if the tube is operated in Class AB_1 (no grid current). The screen voltage, E_2, must be supplied from a "stiff" source (little or no voltage change with current change) which eliminates the use of a dropping resistor from the plate supply unless a voltage-regulator tube is used.

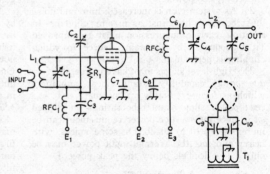

Fig. 9-13—Circuit diagram of a tetrode linear amplifier using link-coupled input tuning and pi network output coupling. The grid, screen and plate voltages (E_1 E_2 and E_3) are given in Table 9-1 for a number of tubes. Although the circuit is shown for an indirectly-heated cathode tube, the only change required when a filament type tube is used is the addition of the filament bypass capacitors C_9 and C_{10}.

Minimum voltage ratings for the capacitors are given in terms of the power supply voltages.

C_1—Grid tuning capacitor, $3E_1$.

C_2—Neutralizing capacitor, $2E_3$.

C_3—Grid-circuit bypass capacitor, part of neutralizing circuit, $3E_1$.

C_4—Plate tuning capacitor, $1.5E_3$.

C_5—Output loading capacitor. 0.015 spacing for kilowatt peak.

C_6—Plate coupling capacitor, $2E_3$.

C_7—Screen bypass capacitor, $2E_2$.

C_8—H.v. bypass capacitor, $2E_3$.

C_9, C_{10}—Filament bypass capacitor.

L_1—Grid inductor.

L_2—Plate inductor.

R_1—Grid circuit swamping resistor, required for AB_2. See text.

RFC_1—Grid-circuit r.f. choke.

RFC_2—Plate r.f. choke.

T_1—Filament transformer.

Any r.f. amplifier circuit can be adapted to linear operation through the proper selection of operating conditions. For example, the tetrode circuit in Fig. 9-13 might be modified by the use of another neutralizing scheme, but the resultant amplifier would still be linear if the proper operating conditions were observed. A triode or pentode amplifier circuit would differ only in detail; circuits can be found in Chapter Six.

The simplest linear amplifier is the Class-A amplifier, which is used almost without exception throughout receivers and low-level speech amplifiers. (See Chapter Three for an explanation of the classes of amplifier operation.) While its linearity can be made relatively good, it is inefficient. The theoretical limit of efficiency is 50 percent, and most practical amplifiers run about 25 percent at full output. At low levels this is not worth worrying about, but when the 2- to 10-watt level is exceeded the efficiency should be considered, in view of the tube, power-supply and operating costs.

Class-AB_1 operation provides excellent linear amplifiers if suitable tubes are used. Primary advantages of Class-AB_1 amplifiers are that they give greater output than straight Class-A amplifiers using the same tubes, and they too do not require any grid driving power (no grid current drawn at any time). Triodes can be used in Class AB_1 but tetrodes or pentodes are to be preferred. Class-AB_1 operation requires high peak plate current without grid current, which is easier to obtain with multigrid tubes (tetrodes and pentodes) than with triodes.

Maximum linear output is obtained from tetrodes, pentodes and most triodes when they are operated class AB_2. This operation, however, increases the driving-power requirements and, what is more important, requires that driver regulation (ability to maintain wave form under varying load) be good or excellent. This is not an easy requirement to meet, and the current trend is to use tetrodes or pentodes in AB_1 or zero-bias Class-B triodes.

Class-B amplifiers are theoretically capable of 78.5 percent efficiency at full output, and practical amplifiers run at 60–70 percent efficiency at full output. Triodes normally designed for Class-B audio work can be used in r.f. linear amplifiers and will operate at the same power rating and efficiency provided, of course, that the tube is capable of operation at the radio frequency. The operating conditions for r.f. are substantially the same as for audio work — the only difference is that the input and output transformers are replaced by suitable r.f. tank circuits. Further, in r.f. circuits it is readily possible to operate only one tube if only half the power is wanted — push-pull is not a necessity in Class-B r.f. work.

For proper operation of grounded-cathode Class-B amplifiers, and to reduce harmonics and facilitate coupling, the input and output circuits should not have a low C-to-L ratio. A good guide to the proper size of tuning capacitor will be found in Chapter Six; use the voltage-to-current ratio of p.e.p. conditions. It is essential that the amplifier be so constructed, wired and neutralized that no trace of regeneration or parasitic instability remains. Needless to say, this also applies to the preceding stages.

In a Class-AB_1 amplifier, the control-grid bias supply can be anything. However, the screen supply should have good regulation; its voltage should remain constant under the varying current demands. If the maximum screen current does not exceed 30 or 35 ma., a string of VR tubes in series can be used to regulate the screen voltage. If the current demand is higher, it may be necessary to use an electronically regulated power supply or a heavily bled power supply with a current capacity of several times the current demand of the screen circuit.

Where VR tubes are used to regulate the screen supply, they should be selected to give a regulated voltage as close as possible to the tube's rated voltage, but it does not have to be exact. Minor differences in idling plate current can be made up by readjusting the grid bias.

The plate voltage applied to the linear amplifier should be held as constant as possible under the varying current-demand conditions. This condition can be met by using low-resistance transformers and inductors and by using a large value of output capacitor in the power-supply filter. An output capacitor value three or four times the minimum required for normal filtering is reasonable.

Grounded-grid operation of zero-bias triodes is popular among s.s.b. operators. A zero-bias triode that requires 10 or 15 watts driving power in a grounded-cathode circuit will need several times this for full output in the grounded-grid configuration. This is not because the grid losses increase—they don't—but in grounded-grid operation a large portion of the input signal finds its way to the output. Since many of the sideband-exciter designs that one starts with are in the 50- to 100-watt output class, a grounded-grid amplifier makes better use of the exciter output than would a Class-AB_1 amplifier.

It is not necessary to use indirectly-heated cathode type tubes in grounded-grid circuits; filament-type tubes can be used just as effectively. However, it is necessary to raise the filament above r.f. ground with filament chokes between the filament transformer and the tube socket. The inductance of the r.f. chokes does not have to be very high, and 5 to 10 μh. will usually suffice from 80 meters on down.

The current-carrying capacities of the r.f. chokes must be adequate for the tube or tubes in use, and if the resistance of the chokes is too high the filament voltage *at the tube socket* may be too low and the tube life will be endangered. In such a case, a higher-voltage filament transformer can be used, with its primary voltage cut down until the voltage at the tube socket is within the proper limits.

Although filament chokes can be wound on wooden or ceramic forms (e.g., large cylindrical ceramic antenna insulators), they can be made more compact and with lower resistance (less voltage drop) by winding them on ferrite rods. Individual chokes for each side of the filament are desirable if they must be wound on wood or ceramic, but when wound on ferrite a dual winding is satisfactory. The single winding choke(s) should be wound with heavy wire spaced (with string) one-half to one wire diameter. In the ferrite-cored choke the two parallel enameled wires are treated as one wire; see Chapter Six for examples of homemade filament chokes.

When considerable power is available for driving the grounded-grid stage, the matching between driver stage and the amplifier is not too important. However, when the driving power is marginal or when the driver and amplifier are to be connected by a long length of coaxial cable, a matching circuit can be used in the input of the grounded-grid amplifier.

The input impedance of a grounded-grid amplifier is in the range of 50 to 400 ohms, depending upon the tube or tubes and their operating conditions. When data for grounded-grid operation is available the input impedance can be computed from

$$Z = \frac{(peak\ r.f.\ driving\ voltage)^2}{2 \times driving\ power}$$

From this and the equations for a pi or L network, a suitable matching circuit can be devised. It should have a low Q, about 3 or 4.

Getting the most out of a linear amplifier is done by increasing the peak power without exceeding the average plate dissipation over any appreciable length of time. This can be done by raising the plate voltage or the peak current (or both), provided the tube can withstand the increase. However, the manufacturers have not released any data on such operation, and any extrapolation of the audio ratings is at the risk of the amateur. A 35- to 50-percent increase above plate-voltage ratings should be perfectly safe in most cases. In a tetrode or pentode, the peak plate current can be boosted some by raising the screen

voltage. In all instances there will be an optimum set of driving and loading conditions for any given set of plate and grid (and screen) voltages, but the tube manufacturer can obviously give only a few (and they are likely to be conservative). The *only* dependable approach to determining the proper conditions for an "unknown" linear-amplifier (one operating at other than manufacturer's ratings) is by using an oscilloscope and dummy load.

When running a linear amplifier at considerably higher than the audio ratings, the "two-tone test signal" should never be applied at full amplitude for more than a few seconds at any one time. The above statements about working tubes above ratings apply only when a voice signal is used—a prolonged whistle or two-tone test signal may damage the tube. It is possible, however, to "key" or "pulse" the two-tone test signal so that the linearity of an amplifier can be checked at high peak-to-average plate dissipation ratios. For example, an electronic "bug" key can be used to switch the two-tone test signal on and off at a rapid rate (a string of "dots"). This will reduce the average-to-peak plate-dissipation ratio to a low figure. (For another method of adjusting linear amplifiers safely at high input, see Goodman, "Linear Amplifiers and Power Ratings," *QST,* August, 1957.)

Linear amplifiers are rated in "p.e.p. input" or "p.e.p. output." The "p.e.p." stands for **peak envelope power**. P.e.p. input is not indicated by the maximum reading the plate milliammeter kicks to; it is the input that would be indicated by the plate milliammeter and voltmeter *if* the amplifier were driven continuously by a single r.f. signal of the peak amplitude the amplifier can handle within its allowable distortion limits. In other words, it is the "key-down input" within the allowable distortion limits. The p.e.p. output is the r.f. output under these same conditions. As implied in the preceding paragraph, it may be impossible to measure the p.e.p. input or output directly without injuring the tube or tubes.

PROTECTING LINEARITY OF AMPLIFIERS

The signal-handling ability of a linear amplifier can be held at maximum by several methods. One is to use *compression* in the early stages of the exciter. This is similar to the *automatic gain control* used in most receivers; a large signal causes the gain to be reduced through the system, and the gain reduction is at a syllabic rate.

A method in vogue in many s.s.b. systems is automatic level control (ALC), which insures that the output amplifier is not driven beyond linearity. This assumes that the exciter is well within its limits of linearity, an obvious qualification.

One form of ALC, readily adaptable for use with a Class AB_1 linear amplifier, uses a high

resistance in the d.c. grid return of the linear amplifier. If the amplifier is driven into grid current, a voltage will be developed across the grid resistor. This voltage is rectified and fed to the grid of a low-level amplifier in the sideband exciter. While the action is a lot like "closing the barn door after the horse is stolen", the method is effective.

Another method, applicable to any class of linear-amplifier operation, uses a back-biased diode to meter the r.f. voltage at the grid or the output of the amplifier. When the voltage exceeds the bias, and the diode conducts, the resultant d.c. is applied to a low-level stage (or several stages) to reduce the gain.

SINGLE SIDEBAND TRANSCEIVERS

A "transceiver" combines the functions of transmitter and receiver in a single package. In contrast to a packaged "transmitter-receiver", it utilizes many of the active and passive elements for both transmitting and receiving. S.s.b. transceiver operation enjoys widespread popularity for several justifiable reasons. In most designs the transmissions are on the same (suppressed-carrier) frequency as the receiver is tuned to. The only practical way to carry on a rapid multiple-station "round table" or net operation is for all stations to transmit on the same frequency. Transceivers are ideal for this, since once the receiver is properly set the transmitter is also. Transceivers are by nature more compact than transmitter-receivers, and thus lend themselves well to mobile and portable use.

Although the many designs available on the market differ in detail, there are of necessity many points of similarity. All of them use the filter type of sideband generation, and the filter unit furnishes the receiver i.f. selectivity as well. The carrier oscillator doubles as the receiver (fixed) b.f.o. One or more mixer or i.f. stage or stages will be used for both transmitting and receiving. The receiver S meter may become the transmitter plate-current or output-voltage indicator. The v.f.o. that sets the receiver frequency also determines the transmitter frequency. The same signal-frequency tuned circuits may be used for both transmission and reception, including the transmitter pi-network output circuit.

Usually the circuits are switched by a multiple-contact relay, which transfers the antenna if necessary and also shifts the biases on several stages. Most commercial designs offer **VOX** (voice-controlled operation) and **MOX** (manual operation). Which is preferable is a controversial subject; some operators like VOX and others prefer MOX.

The complexity of a multiband s.s.b. transceiver is such that most amateurs buy them fully built and tested. There are, however, some excellent designs available in the kit field, and any amateur able to handle a soldering iron and follow instructions can save himself considerable money by assembling an s.s.b. transceiver kit.

Some transceivers include a feature that permits the receiver to be tuned a few kc. either side of the transmitter frequency. This consists of a voltage-sensitive capacitor, which is tuned by varying the applied d.c. voltage. This can be a useful device when one or more of the stations in a net drift slightly. Other transceivers include provision for a crystal-controlled transmitter frequency plus full use of the receiver tuning. This is useful for "DXpeditions" where net operation (on the same frequency) may not be desirable.

A.L.C. CIRCUITS

Automatic level control—or automatic load control, as it is called alternatively—is a form of delayed automatic gain control applied to a transmitter. Its purpose is to prevent modulation peaks from exceeding the linear range of operation. The principle is quite similar to that of a.g.c. as used in receivers. That is, some of the output of the last stage is rectified to develop a d.c. voltage that can be used to control the gain of an earlier low-level stage in such a way that the final output level will not rise above a predetermined value.

In the single-sideband transmitter the a.l.c. circuit is designed to allow modulation peaks to reach the linear peak-envelope level, but not to exceed it. To achieve this, the circuit is adjusted so that it comes into operation only when the amplitude is close to the peak-envelope value; that is, the gain control is delayed until the point of maximum output is almost reached, but then comes into action rapidly so the amplitude cannot reach the "flattening" point.

Rectification of Plate Output

Typical circuits are shown in Fig. 9-14. The circuit at A can be applied to amplifiers using any type of tube or circuit—i.e., triode or tetrode, grid-driven or cathode-driven. It works directly from the plate of the amplifier, taking a relatively-small sample of the r.f. voltage through the capacitive voltage divider C_1C_2. This is rectified by the diode of CR_1 to develop a control voltage, negative with respect to ground, across the 1-megohm load resistor. The diode is back biased from a positive voltage source, the bias voltage being adjustable by means of the "level-set" potentiometer R_1. CR_1 will be unable to rectify until the r.f. voltage exceeds the bias voltage, and by setting R_1 properly no gain-control voltage will develop until the r.f. amplitude is close to the peak-envelope point.

The d.c. control voltage is used to increase the negative bias on a low-level amplifier or mixer, preferably the former, as shown at C. The controlled tube should be of the variable-μ type. The time constant of the control-voltage circuit should be such that the control voltage will rise rapidly when rectification begins, but will hold down the gain during syllables of speech. The time constant can be adjusted by shunting additional capacitance. C_3, across the 1-megohm resistor, R_2, in Fig. 9-14A (the 0.01μf. capacitor is simply an r.f. bypass). A value of about 0.1 μf. is representative.

The capacitive divider C_1C_2 should be designed to apply about 20 volts peak to CR_1 when the amplifier is delivering peak-envelope output. The total capacitance of C_1 and C_2 in series should not exceed 5 to 10 p.f.—i.e., should be small in comparison with the tank tuning capacitance so tuning will not be seriously affected. For estimating values, the amplifier peak output r.f. voltage can be assumed to be equal to 75 percent of the d.c. plate voltage.

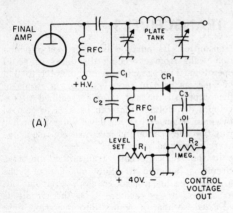

(A)

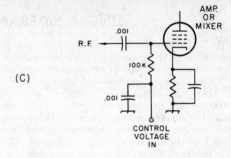

(C)

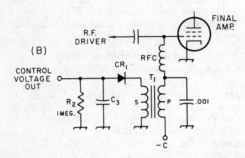

(B)

Fig. 9—14—(A) Control voltage obtained by sampling the r.f. output voltage of the final amplifier. The diode back bias, 40 volts or so maximum, may be taken from any convenient positive voltage source in the transmitter. R_1 may be a linear control having a maximum resistance of the order of 50,000 ohms. CR_1 may be a 1N34A or similar germanium diode. Other values are discussed in the text.

(B) Control voltage obtained from grid circuit of a Class AB_1 tetrode amplifier. T_1 is an interstage audio transformer having a turns ratio, secondary to primary, of 2 or 3 to 1. An inexpensive transformer may be used since the primary and secondary currents are negligible. CR_1 may be a 1N34A or similar; time constant of R_2C_3 is discussed in the text.

(C) Applying control voltage to the controlled amplifier or mixer.

For example, if the amplifier d.c. plate voltage is 1500, the peak r.f. voltage will be of the order of $0.75 \times 1500 = 1100$ volts, approximately. Since about 20 volts is required, the divider ratio would be 1100/20, or 55 to 1. This is also (approximately) the ratio of the capacitance of C_2 to that of C_1. Thus if C_1 is 5 pf., C_2 should be $5 \times 55 = 270$ pf.

Tetrode Grid Rectification

The circuit of Fig. 9-14B is less flexible and can be used only with grid-driven tetrodes operated Class AB_1. It makes use of the fact that a small amount of rectification occurs in the grid-cathode circuit of a tetrode AB_1 amplifier before the driving voltage actually causes the net grid voltage to be zero and the grid current becomes large enough to cause flattening. This rectification causes a small audio-frequency current to flow in the grid circuit.

In the circuit shown, the current causes an a.f. voltage to be developed in the secondary of transformer T_1; this voltage is rectified by CR_1 and filtered to negative d.c. by R_2 and C_3. The resultant d.c. voltage is used to control an amplifier or mixer as in Fig. 9-14C. The time constant of R_2C_3 should be chosen as described

above. Resistance-capacitance coupling can be substituted for the transformer, although when this is done a voltage-doubling rectifier is generally used so the control voltage will be stepped up. Alternatively, an audio amplifier can be inserted between the grid circuit and the rectifier.

Controlled Stage

The circuits shown here can be modified as necessary to suit individual amplifier and exciter circuits. The details will vary with the actual equipment, but should not be difficult to work out if the principles of the system are understood. Either circuit is capable of developing the few volts of control voltage necessary to prevent the amplifier from being driven into the nonlinear region. The greater the gain between the control amplifier and the stage at which the control voltage is taken off (usually the final amplifier) the less control voltage required. That is, the control voltage should be applied to an early stage in the exciter. Preferably, too, the stage should be one operating on a frequency different from that of the final stage, to reduce the possibility of unwanted feedback.

TESTING A SIDEBAND TRANSMITTER

Many amateurs are still afraid to adjust their sideband transmitters. Granted, a sideband rig is a complex piece of equipment, but that is no reason why a hands-off attitude should be so dominant. A large number of amateurs just do not take the time to become familiar with sideband techniques. With a small investment in test equipment and a little practice, any amateur can keep his transmitter in top condition.

Even if the transmitter never fails to operate, component aging, tube changes and the difference in temperature in your shack between winter and summer will affect the performance of balanced modulators and phase-shift networks. These circuits *will* require readjustment from time to time. And, too, even a perfect transmitter can be operated in such a way that it sounds horrible. The damage has been done if you wait until others on the band (or the FCC) inform you that something is wrong with your transmitter.

Test Equipment

To observe the rapidly-changing levels in a sideband transmitter an oscilloscope is absolutely necessary. No meter can keep up with the dynamic variations encountered with the human voice. There are monitor scopes sold that will fill the bill completely, or any shop-type scope which has an internal horizontal sweep generator and external vertical deflection-plate connections may be used with the tuning unit to be described. Several inexpensive scope kits are also available.

An audio generator is the other piece of test equipment required. The standard sort of audio generator will do; one often can be borrowed from local RTTYers or high-fi buffs, or a simple audio generator may be constructed to give a selection of frequencies.[1]

The generator should have good sine-wave output and low distortion. A two-tone generator makes testing even easier.

For the service-type oscilloscope an r.f. pickup unit is used to sample the output of the transmitter, and a tuned circuit builds up the r.f. voltage to provide adequate vertical deflection

[1] Baxter, "A Transistor Audio Oscillator," *QST*, February, 1965.

for the scope. See Figs. 9-10 and 9-11. The pickup unit is constructed in a $4 \times 2\frac{1}{2} \times 2\frac{1}{2}$-inch Minibox. The tuning unit has link-coupled input; each link is made by winding two turns of hookup wire around the center of the coil and cementing it down. Solder lugs are used on the ends of the leads from the Miniductor coil and link to facilitate coil changing. The shaft of the variable capacitor must be insulated from ground. In the unit in the photograph, the capacitor is mounted on a $\frac{3}{4}$-inch stand-off insulator, as is the terminal strip. The chassis of the tuning unit is made from a 4×8-inch piece of aluminum sheet stock, although a wooden block would do just as well, as you would not need to use the stand-off insulators.

Only a small amount of energy is used by the tuning unit, so the pickup may be left in the transmitter output line for on-the-air monitoring.

A typical test setup is shown in Fig. 9-15. All testing should be done with a dummy load. The audio or two-tone generator is connected to the microphone jack of the transmitter, except when a mike is used for speech patterns. The generator should be adjusted so that its output is about at the level of the microphone you normally use. Gain adjustments should be made at the transmitter with the mike gain control. The pickup unit is inserted between the transmitter and dummy load, and the tuning unit should be placed so short connections can be made to the scope. Don't forget to ground the scope to the tuning unit. A length of RG-58/U or RG-59/U is used to connect the tuning unit to the pickup unit.

The transmitter to be tested should be tuned up in the c.w. position, or in the sideband position with a single audio tone injected for normal input. Then adjust the tuning unit to give about half-scale deflection on the scope face, and turn on the horizontal sweep generator in the oscilloscope. Then you are ready to start testing.

Speech Patterns

Speech patterns offer rather a poor way of telling what is going on in the sideband transmitter because they come and go so fast. Yet with a little experience one can learn to recognize

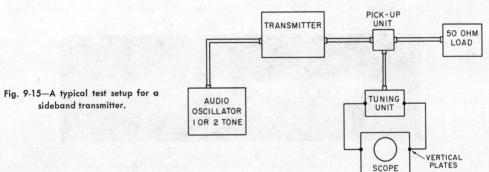

Fig. 9-15—A typical test setup for a sideband transmitter.

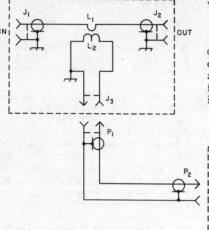

Fig. 9-16—R.f. sampling and tuning units to provide deflection voltage for the vertical plates of an oscilloscope.

the balanced modulator, which is covered later will be necessary.

Two-Tone Tests

A sideband transmitter should be a linear device from mike jack to output connector—for each audio frequency put in you should get out an r.f. frequency, with no distortion of the waveform. The basis of a two-tone test is that you inject two audio signals, from which you should

signs of transmitted carrier and flattening. These are useful later in monitoring on-the-air operation with a scope.

Connect a microphone to the transmitter, set the oscilloscope sweep for about 30 c.p.s. and say a few words. The number "five" will produce a "Christmas tree" pattern similar to Fig 9-9A. Each different word will produce a different pattern, which is one of the reasons why speech patterns are so hard to interpret. The important thing here is to observe the peaks to see if they are sharp, as in Fig. 9-17A. Fig. 9-17B is the number "five" again but this time the mike gain is set way too high; the final stage is being overdriven resulting in clipping of the voice peaks as the final tube reaches plate-current saturation. Underloading the final stage will produce the same result. Operating a transmitter this way will produce a lot of splatter, making you unpopular with your neighbors on the band. Usually, reducing the gain control a little will remove all signs of flattening. Try different settings of the gain control until you can tell a correct pattern from one showing clipping.

If, when the mike gain is reduced to zero, the scope pattern shows you still have some output, you may be transmitting carrier. Adjustment of

get out only two r.f. signals. No tube is ever perfectly linear, so some mixing of the two tones will occur, but all of the new signals produced should be so weak in comparison with the main output of the transmitter that you cannot detect their presence in a scope pattern. What you will see is the pattern of two sine-wave signals as they add and subtract, forming peaks and valleys.

A two-tone test's main advantage is that it will produce a stationary pattern that may be examined for defects. It is not easy to tell with your eye exactly what is a pure sine wave on a scope. Complex patterns are even more difficult, so it is a good idea to draw the correct pattern carefully on a piece of tracing paper, which they may be placed over the actual pattern on the scope face for comparison. Remember that this test will show major defects in the transmitter only.

To make the test, apply the output of the two-tone generator to the mike jack, set the 'scope sweep for about 200 c.p.s., and check the pattern to see that both tones are of equal level. If they are not equal level, the valleys of the waveform will not meet at a single point on the zero line. Fig. 9-18A shows the correct pattern; note that the crossover is in the form of an X. Another way to obtain a two-tone test signal is to use a single

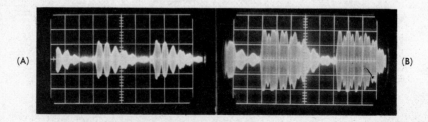

Fig. 9-17—(A) Speech pattern of a correctly adjusted sideband transmitter. (B) The same transmitter with excessive drive causing peak clipping in the final amplifier.

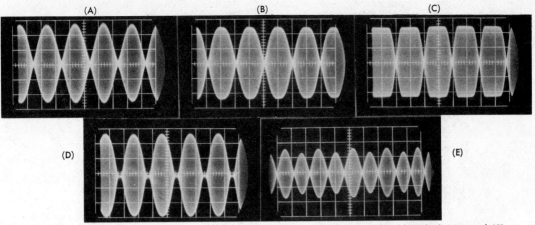

Fig. 9-18—Sideband two-tone test patterns: (A) a correctly adjusted transmitter, (B) mild peak clipping and (C) severe peak clipping caused by excessive drive or underloading of the amplifier, (D) incorrect amplifier bias causing rounding of the crossover points, (E) pattern with modulation caused by carrier leak-through.

audio tone and unbalance the carrier to the point where it forms the pattern shown in Fig. 9-18A.

Examine closely Fig. 9-18A—this is the correct pattern. Note the clean rounded peaks and straight sides of the envelopes, and again how an X is formed at the crossover. Fig. 9-18B shows mild flattening of the peaks, and 9-18C severe flattening. The cause is the same: an amplifier stage being overdriven or underloaded. Cutting the drive level or increasing the loading should result in the Fig. 9-18A pattern.

Incorrect bias adjustment can also cause a stage to be nonlinear. This defect will show up as rounding of the crossover points as in Fig. 9-18D. The manufacturer's instruction manual should be consulted for the proper bias value and the location of the bias control. This control should be adjusted for the proper operating bias. Incorrect bias will also show up as high or low values of

resting plate current. If a correct resting current and pattern cannot be obtained the tube may be bad and should be replaced.

Fig. 9-18E indicates what happens when an external two-tone generator is used and carrier leak-through is also present. The carrier causes the peaks of the two-tone pattern to have different heights. If this happens, you should first null out the carrier, then go back to the two-tone testing.

Carrier Balance

For carrier balance adjustments only one tone is used. The carrier shows up as a sine-wave modulation, similar to what you may have seen in a.m. The carrier-balance control(s) should be adjusted until the sine-wave modulation disappears. Fig. 9-19A shows the single-tone test with sine-wave modulation caused by a partially

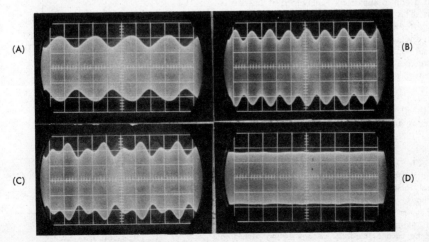

Fig. 9-19—Phasing-type exciter patterns with single-tone input and constant oscilloscope sweep frequency: (A) carrier leak-through, (B) insufficient unwanted-sideband suppression, (C) both carrier leak-through and unwanted sideband, (D) correct pattern for single-tone input.

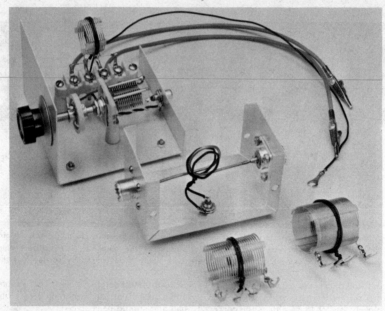

Fig. 9-20—The variable capacitor is used to adjust the vertical deflection on the scope. The tuning unit should be mounted near the oscilloscope so short leads to the deflection plates may be used. An extra lead is provided to ground the tuning unit to the scope.

suppressed carrier, and Fig. 9-19D shows the pattern after the carrier has been balanced out.

The location of the carrier-balance controls may be found in the instruction manual if they are not located on the front panel. Phasing rigs usually have two controls, while the filter types have one control and a variable capacitor. In either case the action of these adjustments is somewhat interlocking. The first should be adjusted, then the second, repeating in turn until the carrier is nulled out.

Carrier balance may also be adjusted with the aid of a communications receiver if it has an S meter. The receiver should be coupled to the transmitter so you have a strong, S9 signal. Then adjust the balanced modulator as before for the least amount of indicated signal on the S meter. During this test the mike gain should be reduced to zero, so no modulation appears on the carrier.

The Phasing Exciter

With a single-tone input, the phasing-type exciter owner may find he has a pattern resembling Fig. 9-19C. This pattern is formed when you

have carrier leak-through and also the unwanted sideband is only partially suppressed. The unwanted sideband, like the carrier, shows up as sine-wave modulation, but at twice the frequency. For a scope sweep of about 400 c.p.s. Fig. 9-19A shows carrier unbalance, Fig. 9-19B insufficient unwanted-sideband suppression, and Fig. 9-19C is a combination of the two.

If you need to realign a phasing-type exciter, read carefully the manufacturer's instructions.

Fig. 9-21—Oscilloscope modification for making r.f. connections to deflection plates without going through internal amplifiers. A—Representative amplifier-r.f. coupling. B—Modified for alternative connection to external source. R_1 and R_2 should be 1 megohm or more, 1-watt rating. For vertical r.f. deflection C_1 and C_2 should be mica or ceramic, voltage rating according to plate voltage on vertical amplifiers; capacitance may be 500 pf. or more. For audio input to horizontal plates, C_1 and C_2 should be 0.1-μf. paper, 600 volts.

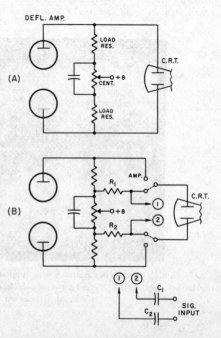

Different models will require different procedures, so we shall only go over the high points.

Use a single-tone test, and null out the carrier. Carrier balance should be checked again during the alignment of the phasing generator, for it will upset your pattern if any carrier creeps in.

The phasing generator will have audio balance and r.f. phasing adjustments, which may number two, three or four. Injecting a single tone, these controls are manipulated until the unwanted sideband is suppressed, as indicated by the disappearance of ripple from the scope pattern. You should achieve a pattern like Fig. 9-19D. Then the transmitter should be switched to the other sideband and checked again for suppression of the unwanted. No doubt you will see some sign that in this position you do not have complete suppression of the unwanted sideband. This is probably due to the stray effects in the sideband

switching. Thus you must reach a compromise in the setting of the audio balance and r.f. phase that gives good suppression of the unwanted when the transmitter is operated on either sideband. If you have achieved a pattern like Fig. 9-19D you have carrier and unwanted-sideband suppression of 35 to 40 db. This is about the limit of suppression you can see on an oscilloscope.

If your transmitter has passed all the above tests, you can be sure it is working well. Further tests that will show the small distortion that you cannot see on a scope will require much more advanced techniques, and are beyond the scope of this article.[2] In most cases, anything that does not show up in these tests will never be noticed on the air.

---

[2] For more information see *Single Sideband Principles and Circuits*, Pappenfus, Bruene, and Schoenike, McGraw-Hill, Inc., 1964.

TRANSISTORIZED VOX

The circuit of Fig. 9-23 can be used with any s.s.b. transmitter that does not have VOX provisions. Many commercial transmitters and transceivers are designed for push-to-talk operation, only. This VOX unit can be used with such equipment, or incorporated into the circuit of any home-built s.s.b. exciter.

The Hookup

Operation of the VOX circuit is simple. Audio from a high-impedance microphone is amplified by Q_1, Q_2, and Q_3. Next, it is rectified, then applied to the base of Q_4 which operates the relay, K_1. Contacts on the relay are connected to the push-to-talk circuit of the transmitter. Once the relay has closed, it will hold in for any desired amount of time, up to several seconds. In Fig. 9-30, transistor Q_1 is operated as an emitter follower to present a high impedance to the microphone and to act as a relatively low-impedance source for driving Q_2. Transistors Q_2 and Q_3 are audio amplifiers. Audio output from Q_3 feeds into the VOX rectifier, CR_2, which is part of a control circuit similar to that described by W3UWV several years ago.[2]

The negative bias developed at R_1 is applied to the base of Q_4 through CR_4. This increases Q_4's collector current and closes the relay, K_1. Diode CR_4 acts as a gate to prevent any positive-going signal from getting to the base of Q_4.

To prevent signals from the shack speaker from triggering the VOX, an anti-trip circuit is built in. Some of the output from the receiver (which can be taken from the speaker connection at the receiver) is rectified by CR_3, which is

Fig. 9-22—The completed VOX unit. It goes between the microphone and the transmitter. The miniature knobs are Johnson Collet type 116-603.

connected so that it produces a positive bias to buck the negative bias from CR_2 developed through the VOX stages.

The transistors used in this circuit can be most any of the available small-signal audio types. The ones shown here were chosen because they are all available for about 35 cents each.

Power for the VOX unit is a 15-volt battery, BT_1, regulated at 10 volts by a Zener diode, CR_1. It was found to be absolutely necessary to use the Zener diode, especially in mobile service, since the relay hold-in delay time will change with battery voltage. The Zener diode shown is a

---

[1] Campbell, " 'Tattoo'—Automatic C.W. Transmitter Control," *QST*, August 1956, p. 18.

[2] Packham, "A Transistorized Control Unit," *QST*, November 1955, p. 32.

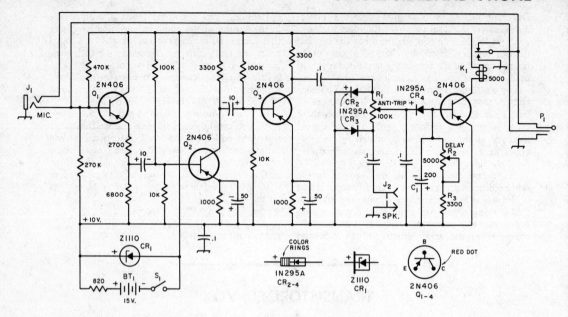

Fig. 9-23—Circuit diagram of the VOX unit. Capacitances are in $\mu f.$; resistances are in ohms; K = 1000. Resistors are ½-watt. Capacitors with polarity marking are electrolytic.

BT₁—15-volt battery (Burgess K10).

C₁—200-$\mu f.$ subminiature electrolytic capacitor (Sprague TE-1119.6).

CR₁—10-volt Zener diode (International Rectifier Z1110 or equiv.).

CR₂₋₄—1N295A crystal diodes.

J₁—3-conductor military type phone jack (Switchcraft C-12B).

J₂—Phono jack.

K₁—5000-ohm relay (Advance RC1C5000D or Argonne AR-21).

P₁—3-cond. military type phone plug (Switchcraft 480).

Q₁-Q₄, inc.—2N406 transistors (See text).

R₁—100,000-ohm miniature control (Mallory MLC-15L).

R₂—5000-ohm miniature control (Mallory MLC-53L).

R₃—3300-ohm, ½-watt resistor.

S₁—Miniature toggle switch.

one-watt unit available for less than two dollars from Allied Radio. Actually, a ¼-watt unit will do and can be used instead of the one specified. If the VOX device is to be used exclusively for mobile work, the car battery can be used instead of the dry-cell battery. The circuit is designed for voltages between 12 and 15 volts and for either positive or negative battery grounds.

Construction

The case for the VOX is a Minibox that measures 2¼ × 2¼ × 5 inches (Bud 3004A). Close inspection of Fig. 9-31 will show where most of the components are mounted although more conventional construction and layout can be used in a larger chassis or box. Only two lug-type terminal strips (H. H. Smith 830) were necessary. One is a strain reliever for the output cable and the other is a tie point for mounting the Zener diode. The battery holder is a modified Keystone type 166. Originally, this holder had a spring clip on both sides to help hold the battery in place. However, the battery used here is too wide for the holder and the side clips must be removed.

The end clips with the terminals have sufficient holding power to keep the battery in place.

Most of the components—resistors, capacitors, transistors, and diodes—are mounted on 1¾ × 2-inch prepunched terminal boards (Vector 85G24EP). The boards are attached to one side of the Minibox case (see Fig. 9-31) with small angle brackets (General Cement H570-F). All of the electrolytic capacitors used here are Sprague type TE 10-volt subminiatures. Layout of the components on the terminal boards is not critical, except from a mechanical standpoint. That is, junctions and connections should be arranged so that it will be convenient to make board-to-board or board-to-external-component connections.

The two controls, DELAY and ANTI-TRIP, must be insulated from the Minibox chassis if their cases are used as tie points, as in Fig. 4. This can be done easily by using extruded fibre washers with ¼-inch holes (General Cement 6528-C) and flat fibre washers with ¼-inch holes (General Cement 6516-C). Finally, the 5000-ohm relay is attached to the Minibox with its own mounting

Fig. 9-24—The finished VOX unit with its cover removed takes on a compact look, although a large part of the space inside the classis actually is taken up by the battery and its holder. This view also shows the phono connector and the output cable.

screw. The relay is designed for use in radio-controlled models and has a pull-in current of about 1.5 ma.

The project is completed by putting small rubber feet on the Minibox bottom.

Operation

Using the VOX is a simple matter of plugging the microphone into the VOX unit and plugging the VOX cable into the microphone jack of the transmitter. There are no gain controls on the unit; it runs wide open all the time.

Delay between the time of the last word spoken into the mike and the time the relay opens can be adjusted from almost zero to several seconds with control R_2. The time constant is determined by the value of capacitor C_1 and the resistance, $R_2 R_3$, across it. It may be necessary to juggle these values around somewhere to get the desired range of delay.

To use the device for semibreak-in operation on c.w., connect the relay terminals to the send-receive control circuits of the transmitter-receiver. A tone source (code practice oscillator, signal generator, etc.) must be keyed in parallel with the transmitter. The keyed tone is fed to the microphone input of the VOX unit. Fig. 9-25 shows a typical hookup for this kind of operation.

T_1 is a filament transformer or an output transformer with the low-impedance side connected to the VOX unit. This is necessary since the VOX will trip when its input is connected to an unshielded high-impedance circuit, because of hum or electrical noise pickup. Capacitor C_1 is used to isolate the d.c. keying circuit in the transmitter. The value of C_1 is not critical; something like 0.01 μf. will do.

When using the VOX on c.w., the first dot or dash made with the key will close the VOX relay, turning on the transmitter. The relay will remain closed (the transmitter will stay on) between characters and words or even sentences, if desired. After a pause in keying, the relay will open and turn off the transmitter. The amount of delay is adjustable with the DELAY control. Other control circuits can be added to the system for receiver muting, antenna switching, or similar.

It is also possible to remove C_1 completely so that there is, for all practical purposes, no delay at all. When a keyed tone is fed into the VOX unit from a tape recorder or a receiver, the relay, K_1, will be keyed along with it. This way, a tape recorder or receiver can key the station transmitter.

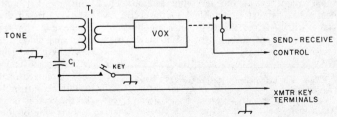

Fig. 9-25—A keyed tone, fed into the VOX unit, will give semibreak-in operation for the station c.w. rig. T_1 is a filament or output transformer. C_1 is .01 μf.

A 50-WATT P.E.P. OUTPUT TRANSCEIVER FOR 75

This easy-to-build s.s.b. transceiver uses low-cost components, many of which should be available in the builder's junk box. Although some of the circuitry is a bit unorthodox, on-the-air testing of several units that used the circuit of Fig. 9-28 [1] indicated that the design is thoroughly practical. Commonly-available tube types are used, and a simple sideband filter using surplus crystals provides good suppression in the transmit mode, and a fairly narrow pass-band for reception. Only four crystals are needed, in all.

Circuit Principles

The complete wiring diagram of the transmitter (save for the heater wiring shown in Fig. 9-29) appears in Fig. 9-28. Several features were taken from a *QST* article [2], so any similarity is *not* coincidental. When receiving, the incoming 4-Mc. signal is amplified in the 6AU6A r.f. stage, and then combined in the 6BE6 receiver mixer with a 3545-kc. signal from the v.f.o. to produce a signal at 455 kc. in the output of the mixer. This signal is fed through the selective crystal filter (Y_2Y_3) to a single i.f. stage using another 6AU6A. The amplified 455-kc. signal is coupled into the 1N34A diode detector where it is combined with the signal from the 455-kc. crystal-controlled 6C4 b.f.o. to produce audio output. The audio signal is amplified in the triode section of the 6EB8, and brought up to speaker level in the pentode section of the same tube. The r.f. gain control, R_3, which is applied to the r.f. and i.f. stages, provides smooth control of audio output, so a separate audio gain control was not deemed necessary.

When transmitting, the crystal-controlled b.f.o. serves as the carrier generator at 455 kc. The oscillator signal is fed to a balanced modulator using a 12AT7. When the output circuit is adjusted for balance by potentiometer R_2, the carrier is suppressed. The application of audio from the speech amplifier results in a double-sideband suppressed-carrier signal at 455 kc. which is fed to a crystal filter consisting of T_5, Y_4, T_2, Y_2 and Y_3. (The 6BE6 receiver mixer is not active on transmit.) The filter attenuates the upper sideband by 20 to 30 db. The remaining lower-sideband signal is amplified in the i.f. stage, and passed along to the transmitter mixer, a 6CS6. Here it is combined with the 3545-kc. signal from the v.f.o. to produce mixer output at 4 Mc.—the same frequency as the receiving section. The 4-Mc. l.s.b. signal is amplified in the 12BY7A stage which drives the 6146 final amplifier. A pi-section output circuit provides a match to a low-impedance load.

[1] This unit originally described in *QST,* June 1967, page 29.

[2] Taylor, "A 75-Meter S.S.B. Transceiver", *QST,* April, 1961.

Fig. 9-26—This model was constructed by W5RQJ. The dial is homemade, but may be replaced by a conventional type. At the left-hand end of the panel are the loading and tuning controls of the pi-net-work output circuit; at the right-hand end are controls for receiver and transmitter audio. Along the bottom, from left to right, are receiver r.f. trimmer, mobile power relay switch, buffer tuning control, and modulator balance control.

Control Circuit

Reviewing the foregoing, it will be seen that three stages are common to the receiving and transmitting sections. These are the v.f.o., the b.f.o./carrier oscillator, and the i.f. amplifier with its crystal filter. Other stages are switched in and out, as necessary, by the four-pole double-throw relay, K_1, which also switches the antenna. On receive, 250 volts is applied to the r.f. amplifier, r.f. gain control, receiving mixer, detector, and receiving audio. (The mixer is switched in the cathode circuit by a separate relay pole to avoid diode mixing in the receiver mixer while transmitting.) In addition, another pole of the relay disconnects the two 8-μf. bypass capacitors in the speech amplifier. This was found to be necessary to avoid audio oscillation in the speech amplifier which occurred as the capacitor discharged after removal of voltage from the amplifier when switching from transmit back to receive.

When transmitting, voltage is removed from the stages mentioned above, and applied to the balanced modulator, the speech amplifier, transmitter mixer, and driver stage. The cathode resistor of the i.f. amplifier is switched to ground to remove it from the influence of the r.f. gain control and place it at full gain on transmit. (This switching also grounds the cathode resistor of the r.f. stage, of course, but since plate voltage has been removed from this stage, complications that might arise from this source are avoided.) Power to the final is not switched.

One side of the relay coil is connected to the

250-volt line through a 10,000-ohm series resistor. The coil circuit is completed to ground through the p.t.t. switch at the microphone.

The V.F.O.

A variation of the Vackar circuit, first noted in *QST* several years ago, is used in this important part of the transceiver. This circuit is easily adjusted, and provides constant output and adequate drive through very small coupling capacitances, with a plate voltage of only 108 volts. This voltage is regulated by an 0B2 fed from the 250-volt supply through a 7000-ohm resistor. One section of a 12AT7 (V_{3A}) is used in the oscillator, while the other section (V_{3B}) is in a cathode follower driven by the oscillator. The latter serves to isolate the v.f.o. from the two mixers which it feeds. With this configuration, frequency shift is a matter of only a few cycles, comparing very favorably in this respect to commercial gear. No v.f.o. temperature compensation is included; drift is nominal after a thorough warm-up.

Crystals

Surplus crystals in the 455-kc. range are used. The low-numbered FT-241 crystals, from Channel 38 to about Channel 75, are in a range that can be tuned to with ordinary ¾-inch 455-kc. i.f. transformers. Two Channel 45 crystals (Y_2 and Y_4), and one Channel 44 crystal (Y_3) are used in the filter. These crystals are fairly close to 455 Kc. and Y_3 differs from the other two by about 1852 cycles. Using a Channel 45 crystal at Y_1 in the b.f.o./carrier oscillator, and tuning as described presently, lower-sideband output will be produced. For those unable to obtain the surplus crystals, Texas Crystals, Fort Myers, Florida, or JAN Crystals, also of Fort Myers, advertises crystals in the 455-kc. range, 25-cycle tolerance, in FT-241 holders. Three crystals of the same frequency are needed—two for the filter and one for the b.f.o. The additional crystal for the filter should be approximately 1800 to 2000 cycles lower in frequency.

Construction and Adjustment

An 8 × 12 × 2-inch chassis provides enough space to avoid crowding of components if the layout shown in the photos is followed reasonably closely. A panel 5½ inches high will provide clearance for the 6146 without submounting the socket. The dial is home-brew. The gearing was salvaged from old Command-set mechanisms. However, a National 5-to-1-ratio planetary-drive dial, or any similar conventional dial, may be used.

Careful orientation of the tube sockets will furnish convenient tie points for resistors and bypass capacitors and hold wiring between stages to a minimum. Low-potential wiring can be run around the edges of the chassis in bends and corners for neater appearance. As indicated in the diagram, shielded wire should be used for the connections to the microphone jack and gain control in the speech amplifier, for the balanced-modulator output connection, and in the coupling line between the i.f. amplifier and the transmitter mixer. Shielded wire is also preferable for heater circuits and other low-potential wiring.

The transceiver can be built a stage or section at a time, testing each as it is completed. It is suggested that the v.f.o. be constructed first, using short leads. The tuning capacitor, C_4, is placed above the chassis in a shielding box, with a connecting wire running through a small hole to the coil, which is enclosed in a second shielding box on the underside of the chassis. Coil turns may have to be pruned, and capacitance juggled, to achieve the proper 200-kc. tuning range for the v.f.o. Assuming that the carrier-oscillator crystal is for Channel 45 (about 455 kc.), the upper limit

Fig. 9-27—Grouped at left center are T_1, R_2 and C_9, the latter two mounted on a shielding bracket. L_5 is below the bracket. To the right is the box shielding the coil and other components of the v.f.o./cathode follower. Below the box are L_6 and driver tuning capacitor, C_6. L_1/L_2 and C_2 are in the shielding compartment in the upper right-hand corner, and L_3 is to the immediate left.

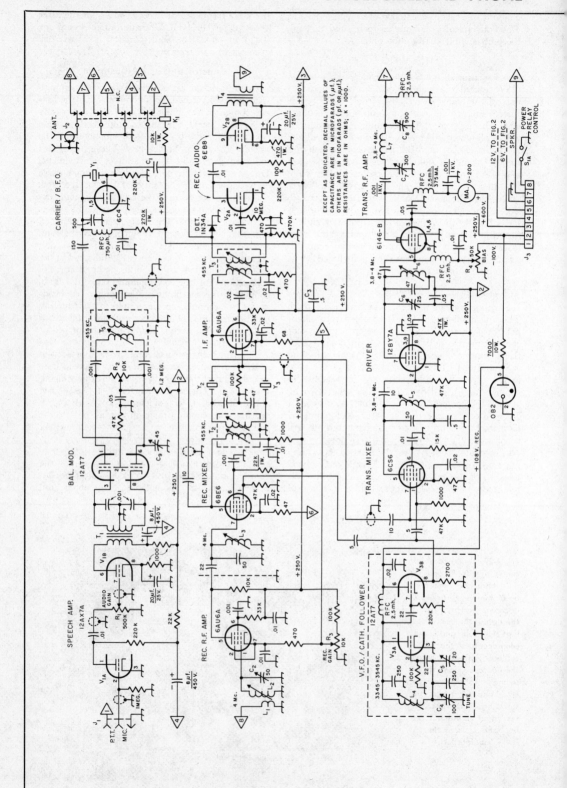

Fig. 9-28—Circuit of the 75-meter transceiver. Fixed capacitors of decimal value, unless listed below or indicated otherwise, are disk ceramic and, unless indicated otherwise, are 500-volt. Others are silver mica or NPO ceramic, 500-volt, except where polarity indicates electrolytic. Unless indicated otherwise, resistors are ½-watt.

C₁—"Gimmick" capacitor made by twisting two short lengths of insulated wire together.

C₂—Air trimmer (Hammarlund APC-50-B).

C₃—Mylar capacitor.

C₄—Midget air variable (Johnson 167-11, or similar).

C₅—Miniature air trimmer (Johnson 160-110).

C₆—Air trimmer (Millen 19325, or similar; see text).

C₈—Three-section broadcast-band t.r.f. variable capacitor, sections in parallel.

C₉—7-45-pf. ceramic trimmer.

J₁—Three-circuit microphone connector.

J₂—Chassis-mounting coaxial receptacle.

J₃—8-contact chassis-mounting male connector (Cinch-Jones).

K₁—Four-pole double-throw relay, 115 volts, d.c. (Potter & Brumfield KL17D, or similar).

L₁—10 turns No. 30 enameled, wound over ground end of L₂.

L₂, L₃, L₅, L₆—35 turns No. 30 enameled, wound on ⅜-inch ceramic iron-slug form.

L₄—28 turns No. 26 enameled on ⅜-inch ceramic iron-slug form, wound tightly and doped.

L₇—24 turns No. 22 enameled on ⅞-inch ceramic form (surplus form).

R₁—Audio-taper control.

R₂, R₃, R₄—Linear control.

S₁—D.p.s.t. rotary switch (see Fig. 2 for second section).

T₁—Interstage audio transformer, single plate to p-p. grids (Stancor A-63-C).

T₂, T₅—Miniature 455-kc. i.f. input transformer (Miller 12-C1).

T₃—Miniature 455-kc. i.f. output transformer (Miller 12-C2).

T₄—Audio output transformer, 5000 ohms to voice coil.

Y₁, Y₂, Y₄—455-kc. crystal (see text).

Y₃—453.148-kc. crystal (see text).

---

of the v.f.o. range would be 3545 kc. to tune the transceiver to 4000 kc. The lower end of the range would be 3345 kc., to tune the transceiver to 3800 kc. Keeping the v.f.o. frequency on the lower side of the incoming signal seems to result in less drift than when the v.f.o. is tuned to the upper side. Listening on a receiver while adjusting the v.f.o. will assist the builder in getting the circuit into the proper tuning range.

After the v.f.o. is working, the receiver section can be constructed. To align the i.f. amplifier stage, couple output from a modulated signal generator to the receiver mixer stage with all four crystals in place. Tune the signal generator exactly to the frequency of the b.f.o. crystal. Remove this crystal, and peak i.f. transformers T_2 and T_3 for maximum audio output. Replace the b.f.o. crystal. Final alignment of the crystal-filter and i.f. stage can be done after construction of the transmitter stages.

Now peak the receiver mixer coil, L_3, at 3900 kc. (A grid-dip oscillator will be helpful in rough tuning of circuits in the transmitter as well as in the receiver section.) The r.f. stage is rough-tuned by the slug of L_1L_2, and the circuit is peaked by the 50-pf. trimmer, C_2, which should be mounted on the panel.

After the receiving section is working, the transmitter section should be checked out. Peak the transmitter mixer coil, L_5, at 3900 kc. In operation, the output of the mixer will fall off some at either end of the band, but should still be adequate for full drive to the final. Peak L_6 at

Fig. 9-29—Heater wiring diagram for either 6- or 12-volt operation. I_1 is a No. 47 6.3-volt 0.15-ampere pilot bulb. For 12-volt operation, the 12-volt terminal should be connected to Pin 4 of the plug for J₃, Fig. 9-15, Gnd. to Pin 6, no connection to the 6-volt terminal. For 6-volt operation, S₁B should be transferred to the 6-volt line at X, the 6-volt terminal should be connected to Pin 5, the 12-volt terminal and Gnd. to Pin 6.

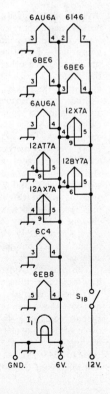

Fig. 9-30—Lined up along the rear edge of the chassis, from right to left, are the 6AU6 receiver r.f-amplifier tube, 6BE6 receiver mixer tube, T_2, Y_2 and Y_3, the 6AU6A i.f. tube, T_3, the 6EB8 receiving-audio tube, 6C4 carrier/b.f.o., and Y_1. L_1/L_2 is to the right of output connector, and L_3 to the left. The 12AT7 v.f.o. tube is immediately to the rear of the box shielding the v.f.o. tuning capacitor, C_4. The adjusting screw of L_4 and the screwdriver shaft of trimmer C_5 are discernible to the right of the 12AT7. The tube above and to the left of the box is the 12BY7A driver. L_6 is mounted between the box and the panel, and cannot be seen. Grouped at the upper left are the 12AX7 transmitting audio tube (above T_4), the 6CS6 transmitting mixer (below the meter), T_5 and Y_4, and the 12AT7 balanced-modulator tube. L_5 is to the right of the meter. At the upper right are the 6146 and components of the pi network. L_7 is mounted on the output capacitor C_8. The tube to the right of the changeover relay is the 0B2 regulator. On the rear apron are the power connector, J_3, and the shaft of the bias control, R_4.

3900 kc. with C_6 set at mid capacitance. It will be noticed that part of the tuning capacitance in this stage is fixed to confine the tuning range to the vicinity of 4 Mc., thus avoiding the possibility of tuning to some other response in the output of the mixer. Those more mechanically able could gang-tune the mixer and driver stages by adding a small variable capacitor across the mixer coil, and coupling its shaft to that of the driver tuning capacitor, C_6, to obtain full output across the band.

No special constructional precautions are necessary in the driver and final stages, except that a shield should be placed across the 12BY7A socket. Pins 3 and 9 of this tube are grounded, and the shield can be placed across these two pins when the socket is properly oriented on the chassis. The relay should be mounted on the chassis reasonably close to the pi-network components, since one pole of the relay switches the antenna.

The biasing control, R_4 should be set for a final-amplifier idling current of 25 to 30 ma.

If the transceiver has been constructed in sections, as suggested, proper alignment of the filter system, consisting of the three filter crystals and three i.f. transformers, can now best be done by feeding a sine-wave audio signal at low level, 1000 to 2000 cycles, into the microphone input, and observing the output wave form on a scope.

A little *careful* twisting on the i.f. transformer slugs will produce the proper pattern on the scope, indicating when the pass band of the filter is adjusted for maximum suppression of the unwanted sideband, and the carrier.

Additional information on filter alignment will be found in *Single Sideband for the Radio Amateur*.

In actual operation, transmitter adjustment is very simple. Press the push-to-talk switch. Set the v.f.o. to frequency, turn the carrier-balance control to one side, tune the final for maximum output, then adjust R_2 and C_9 for minimum final-amplifier idling current. If C_9 has no effect when connected to one plate of the 12AT7, it should be transferred to the other plate. That's all there is to it.

A field-strength meter can be used when tuning the final, but the plate-current dip is a fairly satisfactory indicator. During adjustment with the scope, the proper setting of the gain control to prevent overdrive and splatter should be determined.

Power Supply

For home-station operation, a power supply delivering 600 volts at 150 ma., 250 volts at 75 ma., and 100 volts of bias can be used. The Heath HP-10 supply can be used for mobile work. The heater wiring diagram of Fig. 9-29 provides for either 6- or 12-volt operation.

A 175-WATT MECHANICAL-FILTER EXCITER

This 3.5 to 4.0-MHz. s.s.b./c.w. transmitter can be used by itself, or it can be used to drive any of the amplifiers described in Chapter 6. It will drive most commercially-built amplifiers also. The power output from this unit, while maintaining an acceptable IMD level (intermodulation distortion) is 100 watts, p.e.p.

Block diagrams have been added to each schematic illustration to help the reader understand how the circuit operates. The power supply, "A 650-Volt General-Purpose Supply," is shown in Chapter 12. Information on building the modular solid-state v.f.o. is given in Chapter 5 ("A General-Purpose V.F.O."). This transmitter was designed to be used with these two units.

This exciter has effective a.l.c., which helps to maintain a high average talk-power level. Grid-block keying is used for c.w. The keying is shaped to provide a clean, clickless note. If low-power a.m. operation is desired, carrier can be inserted for this purpose. The power input to the p.a. must be limited to approximately 25 watts if this is done, and the output signal will be *single-side-band* a.m.

Circuit Information

In the circuit of Fig. 9-31, output from a hi-impedance microphone is amplified by V_1 and fed to a twin-triode balanced-modulator, V_2. The 455-kHz. carrier is generated by V_{3A} and routed to V_2. The double-sideband suppressed-carrier a.m. signal from V_2 is next passed through FL_1 where it becomes a s.s.b.

suppressed-carrier signal; the sideband (upper or lower) depends upon the crystal selected at V_{3A}. Output from FL_1 is amplified by V_4, whose actual gain at a given instant is dependent upon the level of the minus-polarity a.l.c. voltage supplied to its grid; the lower the a.l.c. voltage, the higher will be the gain of V_4. V_{3B} is used as a cathode-follower to supply carrier (455 kHz.) to V_5 for tuneup, c.w., or a.m. operation, thus bypassing the mechanical filter and balanced-modulator with some of the signal. The carrier-insertion level is controlled by R_3. S_2, a part of R_3, opens that branch of the circuit during s.s.b. operation to minimize carrier leak-through from V_{3B} to V_5.

A transistorized v.f.o. is used to beat a 3045 to 3545-kHz. signal against the 455-kHz. s.s.b. signal at V_5. The *sum* frequency from the mixer provides the desired 3.5 to 4.0-MHz. transmitter output frequency. Output from the v.f.o. is filtered by L_4, L_5, and their related network capacitors. The filtering keeps spurious output from the v.f.o. from reaching the balanced mixer and generating unwanted frequencies. A vacuum-tube buffer stage, V_8, is used between the v.f.o. and V_5 to reduce "pulling" and to transform the v.f.o.'s low output impedance to a higher impedance for feeding the grid of the balanced mixer. L_6 is broadbanded (no parallel capacitor) to assure fairly constant mixer injection across the entire tuning range of the v.f.o.

The mixer tuned circuit, L_1-C_{2A}, is connected to the grid of the driver stage, V_6. The plate cir-

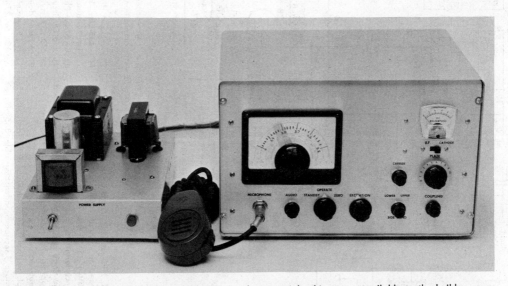

The exciter is housed in a home-made cabinet. Several commercial cabinets are available to the builder, many of which are similar in size and style to this one. An LMB type W-2J would be a good choice, and could be ventilated. Black decals are used for identifying the controls on the satin-finish aluminum panel. The panel was soaked in a lye bath to get the dull finish, then sprayed with clear lacquer.

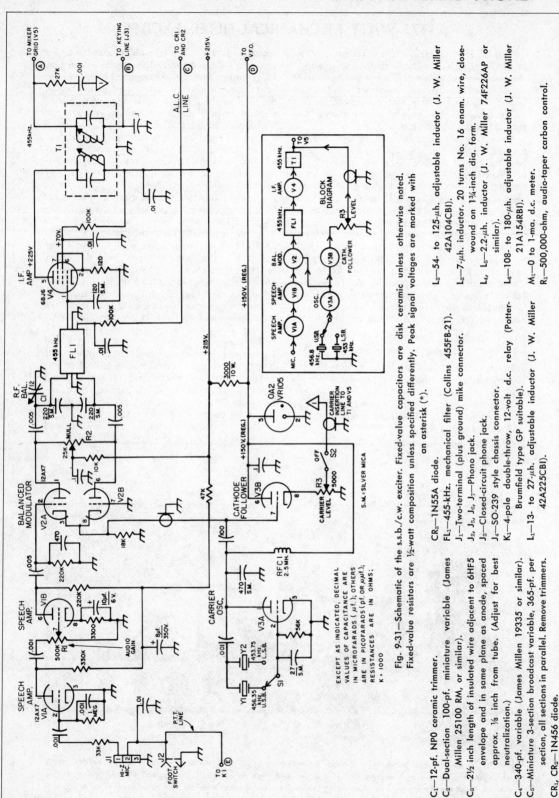

Fig. 9-31—Schematic of the s.s.b./c.w. exciter. Fixed-value capacitors are disk ceramic unless otherwise noted. Fixed-value resistors are ½-watt composition unless specified differently. Peak signal voltages are marked with an asterisk (*).

C_1—12-pf. NPO ceramic trimmer.

C_2—Dual-section 100-pf. miniature variable (James Millen 25100 RM, or similar).

C_3—2½ inch length of insulated wire adjacent to 6HF5 envelope and in same plane as anode, spaced approx. ⅛ inch from tube. (Adjust for best neutralization.)

C_4—340-pf. variable (James Millen 19335 or similar).

C_5—Miniature 3-section broadcast variable, 365-pf. per section, all sections in parallel. Remove trimmers.

CR_1, CR_2—1N456 diode.

CR_3—1N55A diode.

FL_1—455-kHz. mechanical filter (Collins 455FB-21).

J_1—Two-terminal (plus ground) mike connector.

J_2, J_5, J_6, J_7—Phono jack.

J_3—Closed-circuit phone jack.

J_4—SO-239 style chassis connector.

K_1—4-pole double-throw, 12-volt d.c. relay (Potter-Brumfield type GP suitable).

L_1—13- to 27-μh. adjustable inductor (J. W. Miller 42A225CBI).

L_2—54- to 125-μh. adjustable inductor (J. W. Miller 42A104CBI).

L_3—7-μh. inductor. 20 turns No. 16 enam. wire, close-wound on 1¾-inch dia. form.

L_4, L_5—2.2-μh. inductor (J. W. Miller 74F226AP or similar).

L_6—108- to 180-μh. adjustable inductor (J. W. Miller 21A154RBI).

M_1—0 to 1-ma. d.c. meter.

R_1—500,000-ohm, audio-taper carbon control.

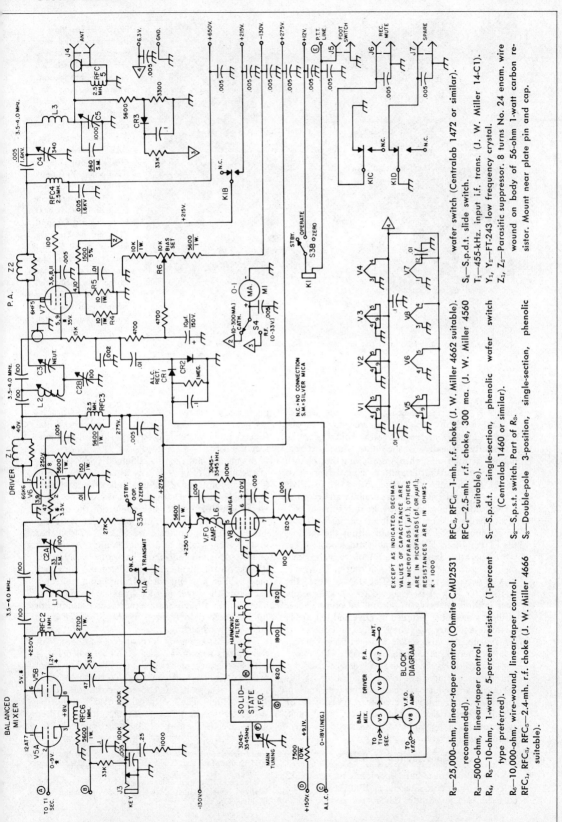

EXCEPT AS INDICATED, DECIMAL VALUES OF CAPACITANCE ARE IN MICROFARADS (μf.); OTHERS ARE IN PICOFARADS (pf. or μμf.); RESISTANCES ARE IN OHMS;
K = 1000

N.C = NO CONNECTION
S.M = SILVER MICA

BLOCK DIAGRAM

R$_2$—25,000-ohm, linear-taper control (Ohmite CMU2531 recommended).

R$_3$—5000-ohm, linear-taper control.

R$_4$, R$_5$—10-ohm, 1-watt, 5-percent resistor (1-percent type preferred).

R$_6$—10,000-ohm, wire-wound, linear-taper control.

RFC$_1$, RFC$_3$, RFC$_5$—2.4-mh. r.f. choke (J. W. Miller 4666 suitable).

RFC$_2$, RFC$_6$—1-mh. r.f. choke (J. W. Miller 4662 suitable).

RFC$_4$—2.5-mh. r.f. choke, 300 ma. (J. W. Miller 4560 suitable).

S$_1$—S.p.d.t. single-section, phenolic wafer switch (Centralab 1460 or similar).

S$_2$—S.p.s.t. switch. Part of R$_3$.

S$_3$—Double-pole 3-position, single-section, phenolic wafer switch (Centralab 1472 or similar).

S$_4$—S.p.d.t. slide switch.

T$_1$—455-kHz. input i.f. trans. (J. W. Miller 14-C1).

Y$_1$, Y$_2$—FT-243 low frequency crystal.

Z$_1$, Z$_2$—Parasitic suppressor. 8 turns No. 24 enam. wire wound on body of 56-ohm 1-watt carbon resistor. Mount near plate pin and cap.

Fig. 9-32—Top view of the chassis. The p.a. compartment is at one end of the chassis. V_3, Y_1, and Y_2 are located where the p.a. compartment and panel meet. L_2, V_6, and R_6 are adjacent to the p.a. compartment. The OA2 is between the v.f.o. assembly and the front panel. V_8 is near the v.f.o. on the opposite side, directly in front of T_1. V_5 is next to T_1 (toward R_6), and V_4 is on the opposite side of T_1. V_1, V_2, R_2, and FL_1 are along the side of the chassis next to the v.f.o. assembly. M_1, C_4, and S_4 are mounted on the front panel, inside the p.a. compartment.

cuit of V_6 is series-tuned by C_{2B}. Adjustment of C_2 tunes both the mixer and driver stages at one time, and serves as the excitation control for the transmitter. Ideally, it should be tuned to resonance at all times, thus minimizing the chance of spurious transmitter output. The driver feeds power to V_7, the p.a. stage. An a.l.c. rectifier, CR_1-CR_2, works as a voltage doubler and rectifies audio which appears in the grid return of V_7. Minus voltage from this circuit varies with the power input level of V_7, controlling the gain of the i.f. amplifier, V_4. A suitable time constant for voice operation is set by the 0.1-uf. capacitor and the 1-megohm resistor at the output of CR_1.

A pi-network tank is used at the output of the transmitter, V_7. It is designed to work into any load impedance between 40 and 90 ohms. Some of the r.f. output is sampled by CR_3 and fed to M_1 through S_4, thus providing r.f. output metering for tuneup. M_1 also reads total cathode current for V_7 when S_4 is switched to read 0–300 ma.

A control relay, K_1, operates from 12-volts d.c. and serves during push-to-talk operation. It has extra contacts which are used for receiver muting, linear-amplifier control, antenna-relay control, or whatever external functions are required. A jack, J_5, provides a terminal for foot-switch control during c.w. operation.

Construction Notes

This equipment is built on a home made $8 \times 12 \times 2$-inch aluminum chassis. A Bud AC-1419 can be used as a substitute. The panel is also home

made and measures $8 \times 12\frac{1}{2}$ inches. Panel brackets have been added (also home made) to make the assembly more rigid—an aid to good mechanical stability.

Stages V_1 and V_2 are shielded from the rest of the circuit (Fig. 9-31) by a partition which is 6 inches long and 2 inches high. Similarly, the underside of the p.a. section is divided off by a shield which runs the entire depth of the chassis. The top side of the p.a. end of the chassis is enclosed in a home-made cage which is $7\frac{3}{4}$ inches long, 3 inches wide, and 5 inches high. A coating of heat-resistant dull-black barbeque spray paint is used on the inside and outside of the compartment. This prevents heat from being reflected back into the envelope of V_7, and helps the compartment to absorb heat. A perforated aluminum lid is attached to the top of the p.a. cage after completion of testing.

The v.f.o. assembly is mounted on the top of the chassis near to V_1 and V_2. The dial drive is a two-speed vernier with a shallow front-panel profile. No backlash could be detected in several models tried, so it was chosen for the job. It is a J. W. Miller MD-4 with ratios of 6:1 and 36:1, the latter for easy zero beating.[1] James Millen knobs are used on all of the panel controls.[2]

[1] If J. W. Miller components are not available from your distributor, write directly to: J. W. Miller Co., 5917 South Main St., Los Angeles, Calif. 90003. Request catalog.

[2] James Millen components available factory-direct. Write: James Millen Mfg. Co., 150 Exchange St., Malden, Mass.

Checkout and Operation

Remove V_6 and V_7 from their sockets during initial testing. Make sure that the v.f.o. and carrier oscillator, V_{3A}, are operating properly. This can be done by listening to the second harmonic of V_{3A} on a broadcast receiver (900 kHz.), or making sure that pin 2 has a negative voltage on it. (Use a v.t.v.m. for this test, reading between 15 and 25 minus volts for normal operation.) Place an r.f. probe—a length of coax line with a one-turn link on the sampling end—near L_1. Tune in the signal on the 80-meter band of a communications receiver. S_2 should be in the off position. Peak C_2, T_1, and L_6 for maximum indicated output from V_5. Next, null the carrier by alternately adjusting R_2 and C_1 for minimum received signal. A sharp null should result. If C_1 does not provide a null, move it to the opposite side of the filter input and repeat the foregoing. After nulling the balanced modulator, connect a microphone to J_1 and listen to your s.s.b. signal in the receiver. It should sound clean and should have very little carrier energy if all stages are working satisfactorily. If trouble is encountered in nulling the carrier, chances are that the 220-pf. silver-mica capacitors are poorly matched, or that V_2 does not have similar characteristics in both triode sections. Similarly, the 0.005-uf. coupling capacitors to FL_1 should be matched within 20 percent—the usual tolerance. Symmetrical wiring in that part of the circuit is also helpful in obtaining a good null.

The next step is to plug V_6 into its socket and place the r.f. probe near L_2. Tune in the signal and tune C_2 through its range. No "birdies" or popping should be noted if the stage is stable.

Next, tune the exciter to 3.5 MHz. Set C_2 at maximum capacitance and alternately adjust L_1 and L_2 for maximum output signal from V_6. Check at 4 MHz. to see if the tuning tracks. If not, it will be close. Some operators may wish to adjust L_1 and L_2 for maximum output at the center of their favorite section of the band.

Final testing will be done with V_7 installed. A dummy load should be attached to J_4 and the meter should be switched to read cathode current. With S_3 in the OPERATE position (no audio or carrier insertion being used), depress the mike button and observe the cathode current. Adjust the bias control, R_6, for a reading of 30 ma. resting current. Next, insert only enough carrier (R_3) to bring the cathode current up to approximately 60 ma. Switch S_4 to read r.f. and tune C_4 for a peak meter reading. C_5 should be fully meshed, or nearly so. Adjust the excitation (C_2) for maximum meter reading. By inserting maximum carrier, the cathode current should rise to approximately 150 ma. *Do not maintain a steady cathode current in excess of 60 ma. for more than 30 seconds at a time.* The 6HF5 will be damaged if this rule is not followed.

The transmitter is now ready for operation. With S_2 turned off for s.s.b. operation, audio can be applied to J_1 and the cathode current of V_7 should swing to as high as 150 ma. For c.w. operation, turn S_2 on and insert sufficient carrier to provide the output power required. It is not recommended that the cathode current of V_7 be allowed to exceed 110 ma. during c.w. operation.

For zero beating, place S_3 in the ZERO position and insert carrier until the required level is attained for a good beat note. Remove the carrier before transmitting in the s.s.b. mode.

Fig. 9-33—Looking at the bottom of the unit, the p.a. section is shielded from the rest of the chassis by a full-length divider. Similarly, the speech and balanced-modulator section is shielded by a smaller divider. C_2 is near the rear-center of the chassis, with K_1 between it and the audio compartment. L_1 is adjacent to the rear section of C_2. L_2 is housed in a small shield can (J. W. Miller S-34) and mounted on top of the chassis for reasons of isolation. C_5 is near the front panel, inside the p.a. compartment. Signal leads from V_3 are subminiature coax with the shield grounded at each end. The B-plus and filament leads of V_3 are shielded audio cable.

A 2-METER S.S.B./C.W. TRANSMITTING CONVERTER

This transmitting converter is designed to be used with any 14-MHz. s.s.b. exciter capable of delivering approximately 20 watts, peak, output. It is stable both in terms of frequency and general operating conditions. It can provide up to 20 watts peak output at 144 MHz.—sufficient, say, for driving a pair of 4CX250 tubes in Class C for c.w. operation, or the same pair of tubes can be operated AB_1 to provide 1200 watts p.e.p. input with this unit as a driver. The output signal is clean and TVI should not be experienced under normal operating conditions.

It is not recommended that beginners attempt this project since v.h.f. circuits require special care in their construction and operation, sometimes a requirement that is a bit beyond the inexperienced builder.

How It Operates

Starting with V_{1A}, the oscillator, Fig. 9-35, a 43.333-MHz. overtone crystal is used at Y_1 to provide the local-oscillator signal for the exciter. Output from V_{1A} is amplified by V_{1B} to a suitable level for driving the tripler, V_2. 130-MHz. energy is fed to the grids of V_3, a 6360 mixer, by means of a bandpass tuned circuit, L_3C_1, and L_4C_2. The selectivity of this circuit is high, thus reducing unwanted spurious energy at the mixer grids.

Output from the 14-MHz. exciter is supplied through an attenuator pad at J_1 and is injected to the mixer, V_3, at its cathode circuit, across a 270-ohm resistor. The attenuator pad can be eliminated if a very low-power exciter is to be used. The values shown in Fig. 9-35 were chosen for operation with a Central Electronics 20-A exciter operating at full input, or nearly so. The amount of driving power needed at the cathode of V_3 is approximately 4 or 5 watts p.e.p.

After the 130-MHz. and 14 MHz. signals are mixed at V_3, the *sum* frequency of 144-MHz. is coupled to the grids of V_4, the p.a. stage, by means of another bandpass tuned circuit—further reducing spurious output from the exciter. P.a. stage V_4 operates in the AB_1 mode. Its idling plate current is approximately 25 ma. The plate current rises to approximately 100 ma. at full input.

If c.w. operation is desired, the grid-block keying circuit in the mixer stage (J_3) can be included. If s.s.b. operation is all that is contemplated, the minus 100-volt bias line can be eliminated along with J_3, R_1, and the shaping network at J_3. In that case the 15,000-ohm. grid resistor from the center tap of L_4 would be grounded to the chassis.

Construction Notes

The photographs show the construction techniques that should be followed for duplicating this equipment. The more seasoned v.h.f. builder should have no difficulty changing the prescribed layout to fit his particular needs, but the shield-

Fig. 9-34—Top view of the 2-meter transmitting converter. This version is patterned after a model designed and built by K9UIF, and was built from information supplied by him. The on-off switches for a.c. and d.c. sections of the power supply are mounted on the front panel of the unit as are the pilot lamps and plate meter for the p.a. stage. The power connector and key jack are on one side of the chassis. The tuning controls for the various stages are accessible from the top of the chassis. The input and output jacks are on the top-rear surface of the unit. The key jack was added after the photo was taken. It mounts adjacent to the power plug.

ing and bypassing methods used here should be adhered to even if changes are made.

An $8 \times 12 \times 3$-inch aluminum chassis is used for this equipment. An internal chassis, 5 inches wide, 3 inches deep, and 12 inches long, is made from flashing copper and installed along one edge of the main chassis. This method makes it possible to solder directly to the chassis for making positive ground connections rather than rely on mechanical joints. Shield partitions are made of copper and are soldered in place as indicated on the schematic diagram and in the photo. An aluminum bottom plate is used to enclose the underside of the chassis for confining the r.f.

A large number of feedthrough capacitors are used to bring power leads into the copper compartment. Though this adds somewhat to the overall cost of the project, it provides excellent bypassing and decoupling, thus reducing unwanted interstage coupling. It also contributes to TVI reduction. Most surplus houses stock feedthrough capacitors, and offer them at reasonable cost.

Operation

The equipment can be powered by the circuit of Fig. 9-36, or the builder can design a supply of his own choice. Regulated voltages are recommended for best operation.

With a dummy load connected to J_2, apply operating voltage to the exciter, but not 14-MHz.

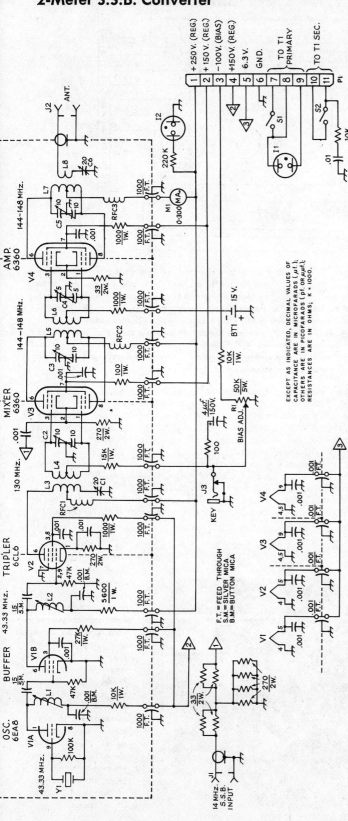

Fig. 9-35—Schematic diagram of the transmitting converter. Fixed-value capacitors are disk ceramic unless otherwise noted. Fixed-value resistors are ½-watt carbon unless otherwise noted. The polorized capacitor is electrolytic. Capacitance values marked with an asterisk differently.

EXCEPT AS INDICATED, DECIMAL VALUES OF CAPACITANCE ARE IN MICROFARADS ($\mu f.$); OTHERS ARE IN PICOFARADS (pf. OR $\mu\mu f$); RESISTANCES ARE IN OHMS; K = 1000.

F.T. = FEED THROUGH
S.M. = SILVER MICA
B.M. = BUTTON MICA

B₁—Small 15-volt battery.

C₁—20-pf. miniature variable (E. F. Johnson 160-110 suitable).

C₂, C₃, C₅—10-pf. per section miniature butterfly (E. F. Johnson 167-21 suitable).

C₄—5-pf. per section miniature butterfly (E. F. Johnson 160-205 suitable).

C₆—20-pf. miniature variable (same as C₁).

I₁, I₂—115-v.a.c. neon panel lamp assembly.

J₁, J₂—SO-239-style coax connector.

J₃—Closed-circuit phone jack.

L₁—15 turns No. 28 enam. wire, close-wound, on ¼-inch dia. slug-tuned form (Millen 69058 form suitable).

L₂—12 turns No. 28 enam. wire, close-wound, on same type form as L₁.

L₃—6 turns No. 18 wire space-wound to ⅞-inch length, ½-inch dia., center-tapped.

L₄—3 turns No. 18 wire, ½-inch dia., ⅜-inch long, center-tapped.

L₅—5 turns No. 18 wire, ½-inch dia., ⅝-inch long, center-tapped.

L₆—3 turns No. 18 wire, ½-inch dia., ⅜-inch long, center-tapped.

L₇—4 turns No. 18 wire, ½-inch dia., ½-inch long, center-tapped.

L₈—1-turn link of insulated hookup wire, ½-inch dia., inserted in center of L₇.

M₁—0 to 200-ma. d.c. meter.

P₁—11-pin chassis-mount male plug (Amphenol 86PM11).

R₁—50,000-ohm linear-taper, 5-watt control.

RFC₁–RFC₃, inc.—2.7-μh. r.f. choke (Millen 34300-2.7).

S₁, S₂—S.p.s.t. rocker-type switch (Carling TIGK60).

Y₁—43.333-MHz. third-overtone crystal (International Crystal Co., Oklahoma City, Okla.).

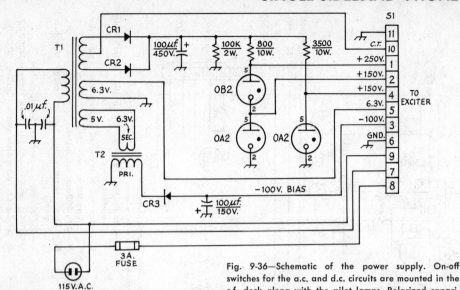

Fig. 9-36—Schematic of the power supply. On-off switches for the a.c. and d.c. circuits are mounted in the r.f. deck along with the pilot lamps. Polarized capacitors are electrolytic, others are disk ceramic. CR_1 and CR_2 are 1000-volt, 1-ampere silicon diodes. CR_3 is a 200 p.r.v. 600-ma. silicon diode. T_1 is a power transformer with a 540-volt c.t. secondary at 120 ma. Filament windings are 5 volts at 3 A., and 6.3 volts at 3.5 A. T_2 is a 6.3-volt, 1-ampere filament transformer connected back to back with the 5-volt winding of T_1. S_1 is an 11-pin socket (female). A 10,000-ohm resistor and a 0.01-μf. disk capacitor are connected in series between the center tap of T_1's secondary and ground for transient suppression when S_2 is switched to on. The suppressor is mounted at S_2, in the r.f. deck.

drive. Couple a wavemeter to L_1 and tune the oscillator plate for maximum output. Then, detune the slug of L_1 slightly (toward minimum inductance) to assure reliable oscillator starting. Couple the wavemeter to L_2 and tune for peak output. With the wavemeter coupled to L_4, adjust C_1 and C_2 for maximum indicated output.

The next step is to connect the 14-MHz. exciter to J_1 and supply just enough drive to cause a rise in p.a. plate current of a few milliamperes. Tune C_3 and C_4 for maximum indicated plate current at M_1, then adjust C_5 and C_6 for maximum

power output to the dummy load. C_1, C_2, C_3 and C_4 should be readjusted at this point for maximum plate current of the p.a. stage. Use only enough 14-MHz. drive to bring the p.a. plate current up to 100 ma. at maximum d.c. input power.

A closed-circuit keying jack is used at J_3 so that the mixer stage is not biased to cutoff during voice operation. Inserting the key permits full bias to be applied, thus cutting off V_3. R_1 should be adjusted for complete cutoff of V_3 when the key is open.

Fig. 9-37—Looking into the bottom of the chassis, the r.f. section is enclosed in a shield compartment made from flashing copper. Additional divider sections isolate the input and output tuned circuits of the last three stages of the exciter. Feedthrough capacitors are mounted on one wall of the copper compartment to provide decoupling of the power leads. The cluster of resistors at the rear-center is used in an attenuator pad at the input to the mixer.

A TRANSCEIVING CONVERTER FOR 1.8 MHz.

For quite some time it has been practical to generate s.s.b. signals in the v.h.f. and u.h.f. regions of the spectrum by using transmitting converters in combination with an existing 14- or 28-MHz. s.s.b. transmitter. The low-band transmitter signal is taken at low power (usually under 5 watts) and mixed with a crystal-controlled oscillator signal to produce the desired *sum* frequency, e.g., a 14-MHz. s.s.b. signal is beat with a crystal-controlled 130-MHz. signal to produce 144-MHz. s.s.b. energy. Getting from the 75-meter band to 1.8 MHz. can be done in a like manner by using the *difference* frequency of a 5800-kHz. crystal-controlled oscillator and that of a 3.8-MHz. s.s.b. transceiver. This combination results in a frequency of 2000 kHz. Moving the transceiver's frequency to 4.0 MHz. results in a difference frequency of 1.8 MHz., the low end of the 160-meter band. This method is used with the simple 3-tube circuit described here (from *QST*, Nov. 1968). Receiving is handled in the same manner, beating the incoming 1.8-MHz. signal with the 5800-kHz. energy to produce an i.f. of 4 MHz., thus utilizing the 75-meter transceiver's receiver section for listening to the 160-meter signals.

Fig. 9-38—The transceiving converter is housed in a homemade aluminum cabinet which measures 8 × 8 × 12 inches. Perforated aluminum is used for the top and back sides of the cabinet to assure good ventilation.

Circuit Data

Looking at the circuit of Fig. 9-40, V_{1A} operates as a crystal-controlled oscillator to produce a 5800-kHz. local-oscillator signal for transmitting and receiving. This stage operates continuously. Output from V_{1A} is fed to the transmitting mixer, V_{1B}, and to the receiving mixer, V_3. V_{1B} is turned off by means of K_{1C}, the changeover relay, during receive. During transmit, 3.5-MHz. s.s.b. or c.w. energy is supplied to the cathode of V_{1B}, across a 470-ohm resistor. This is mixed with the 5800-kHz. local-oscillator output at V_{1B} and re-

sults in a 160-meter signal at the output of V_{1B}. A high-Q tuned circuit couples the mixer output to the grid of the power amplifier, V_2. The 6146B p.a. stage amplifies the 1.8-MHz. Signal input power is approximately 35 watts p.e.p.

During receive the local-oscillator energy is fed to the receiving mixer grid (V_3) and beats with the incoming 160-meter signal to produce a receiving i.f. of 3.5 to 4 MHz., depending upon the dial setting of the 75-meter transceiver. Output from the mixer is routed to the transceiver through K_{1A} and J_1. During transmit, V_3 is turned off by K_{1C}. A double-tuned high-Q input circuit is used at V_3 to reduce images, and to lessen the chances of front-end overload from strong local b.c. stations. A band-pass tuned circuit is used at the output of V_3 to assure that only the desired i.f. signal reaches the input of the 75-meter transceiver.

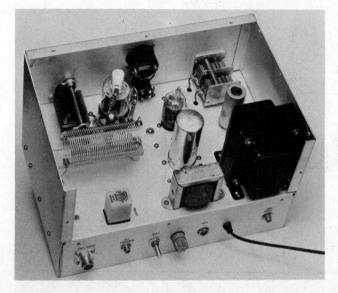

Fig. 9-39—Looking into the top of the transceiving converter, the power supply is at the lower right. Directly ahead of the power transformer is the receiving mixer, V_3, and its tuning capacitor, C_6. V_1 is to the left of V_3, just ahead of the filter capacitor. The p.a. section of the unit is at the upper left. C_5 is below the chassis, directly under C_4. C_3, the neutralizing wire, is encased in spaghetti tubing and is visible adjacent to the 6146B tube. Relay K_1 is at the lower left.

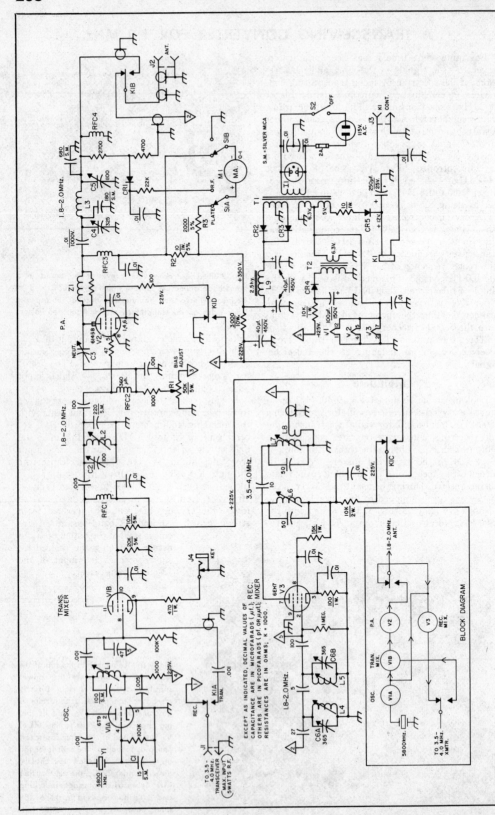

Fig. 9-40—Schematic diagram of the 160-meter equipment. Fixed decimal-value capacitors are disk ceramic unless otherwise noted. Polarized capacitors are electrolytic. Fixed-value resistors are ½-watt composition unless indicated otherwise. A block diagram is included to show the direction of signal flow.

C_1—Feedback capacitor. (May require slightly more or less capacitance, experimentally, for best oscillator for starting.)

C_2—100-pf. variable (Hammarlund HFA-100A).

C_3—See text.

C_4—325-pf. variable (Hammarlund MC-325M).

C_5—3-section broadcast-type variable, all sections in parallel (J. W. Miller 2113).

C_6—Two section broadcast-type variable (J. W. Miller 2112).

CR_1—1N34A germanium diode.

CR_2, CR_3—1000 p.r.v., 1-ampere silicon diode.

CR_4—600 p.r.v., 750 ma. silicon diode.

CR_5—50 p.r.v., 2-ampere silicon diode.

I_1—115-v.a.-c. neon indicator (part of S_2).

J_1, J_3—RCA phono connector.

J_2—SO-239 style coax connector.

J_4—Closed-circuit phone jack.

K_1—4-pole double-throw 12-volt d.c. relay (Potter & Brumfield KHP17D11).

RFC_1—1-mh., 75-ma. r.f. choke (National R-50 or equiv.).

RFC_2—360-μh. r.f. choke (Millen J300-360 suitable).

RFC_3, RFC_4—2.5-mh., 250-ma. r.f. choke (Millen 34102).

S_1—D.p.d.t. toggle.

S_2—S.p.s.t. rocker switch with built-in pilot lamp (Carling Electric Co. Type LTILA50). Carling Electric Co., 505 New Park Ave., West Hartford, Conn. 06110 (catalog available).

L_1—5- to 8-μh. adjustable inductor (J. W. Miller 21A-686RBI).

L_2—12.9- to 27.5-μh. adjustable inductor (J. W. Miller 42A225CBI).

L_3—20-μh. inductor; 35 turns No. 18 wire, spaced one wire diameter between turns, 1½ inch diameter. Use 35 turns of Polycoils No. 1759 inductor.

L_4, L_5—12.9- to 27.5-μh. variable inductor (J. W. Miller 42A225CBI).

L_6, L_7—23.8- to 39.6-μh. adjustable inductor (J. W. Miller 21A335RBI). J. W. Miller Co., 5917 S. Main St., Los Angeles, Calif. 90003.

L_8—6 turns small-diameter insulated wire wound over ground end of L_7.

L_9—2.5-hy. 100-ma. filter choke.

M_1—0 to 1-ma. d.c. panel meter.

R_1—50,000-ohm, linear-taper, 5-watt control.

R_2, R_3—See text.

T_1—Power transformer. 540 volts c.t. at 120 ma., 5 volts at 3 amps., 6.3 volts at 3.5 amps. (Allied-Knight 54C1466 or equivalent).

T_2—6.3-volt, 1-amp. filament transformer, reverse connected.

Y_1—5800-kHz. fundamental-type crystal (International Crystal Co.).

Z_1—Parasitic suppressor; 5 turns No. 18 wire over body of 47-ohm, 1-watt resistor.

Straightforward design is used in the power supply. The 6.3- and 5-volt windings of T_1 are series-connected to provide approximately 12 volts for the relay, K_1. They must be phased properly to prevent cancellation of the voltages. If no output is obtained, merely reverse one of the windings. The 12 volts a.c. is rectified by CR_5 to provide d.c. voltage for K_1.

Bias voltage is obtained for V_2 by connecting a small 6.3-volt filament transformer back-to-back fashion with the 6.3-volt winding of T_1. The 125-volt a.c. output from T_2 is rectified and filtered, then routed to R_1, the bias-adjust control. It is set to establish a resting plate current of 25 ma. for V_2.

The metering circuit reads plate current—200 ma. full scale—by measuring the voltage drop across a 10-ohm 5-percent resistor, R_2. The 2000-ohm 5-percent metering resistor, R_3, provides a full-scale meter reading of 2 volts, corresponding to 200 ma. of current flow through R_1. M_1 is a 0 to 1-ma. instrument. It reads relative r.f. output voltage when S_1 is switched to r.f. A resistive divider is connected to the output line of the p.a. stage and CR_1 rectifies the r.f. which appears at the junction of the two resistors. A 22,000-ohm "linearizing" resistor helps to make the meter respond more uniformly to the changes in r.f. voltage. If greater accuracy is desired for the plate-metering circuit, 1-percent resistors can be used at R_2 and R_3, though the 5-percent resistors should be suitable for this application.

A probe-type neutralizing circuit is used at V_2. C_3 is actually a stiff piece of bus wire, three inches in length, which is fed through the chassis by means of an insulating bushing. The wire is placed adjacent to the tube's anode, and is in the same plane as the anode. It is moved to and from the tube envelope to vary the capacitance between it and the tube plate. Adjustment of C_3 is discussed later.

Construction

An aluminum chassis which measures 12 × 8 × 2½ inches is used as the base for this equipment. A home-made panel and cabinet is used to enclose the unit. The panel is 8 inches high and is 12 inches wide. The top cover is fashioned from perforated aluminum material which was obtained from the hardware store (Reynolds aluminum).

The layout should be apparent from the accompanying photographs. All long runs of r.f. wiring should be made with subminiature coax cable (RG-174/U), grounding the shield braid at each end of the cable.

Checkout and Tune Up

Some provision should be made to reduce the power output of the 75-meter transceiver to be used with this equipment. No more than 5 watts of drive should be necessary; too much drive can damage V_{1B}. Approximately 30 r.f. volts will appear between the transmitting mixer cathode and ground when normal 3.8-MHz. drive is ap-

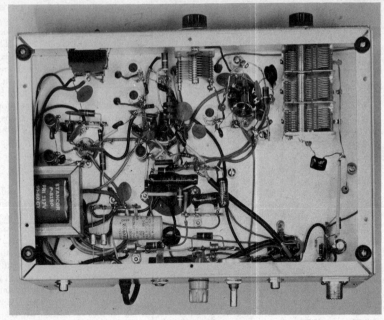

Fig. 9-41—Looking into the bottom of the chassis. C_5 is at the upper right. The 6146B socket is to its left. C_2 is visible at the upper center of the chassis. V_3 is at the far left of the chassis.

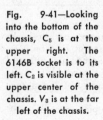

plied. Some transceivers are capable of supplying sufficient output on 3.8 MHz. by removing the screen voltage from the p.a. stage. Or, it may be practical to disable the p.a. and borrow some output from the driver stage by means of link coupling. The stout-of-heart may wish to merely turn down the speech gain of the transceiver until the desired power level is reached. This method was used in the ARRL lab while working with a KWM-2, but could lead to disaster if the audio level was inadvertently turned up beyond the desired point.

Before testing the 160-meter unit, make sure that the changeover relay, K_1, is connected to the remote keying terminals of the 75-meter equipment by means of J_3. Then, connect a 160-meter antenna to J_2 and listen for 160-meter signals, atmospheric noise, or Loran pulses. Peak the incoming signal by means of C_6. For reception on the low end of the 160-meter band, C_6 should be almost fully meshed. The slugs of L_4 and L_5 should then be adjusted for best signal response. When receiving near the high end of the band, C_6 should be near midrange. Coils L_6 and L_7 form a bandpass circuit and should be stagger-tuned to give uniform response across any desired segment of the 160-meter band, e.g., 1800 to 1900 kHz., or 1900 to 2000 kHz. If the receiving section is performing properly, one should be able to copy a 0.3-μv. c.w. signal without difficulty in areas where minimum atmospheric and man-made noise levels prevail. Ordinarily, however, noise levels prevent such weak-signal reception. If no signals can be heard, check V_{1A} to make certain it is working properly. The 5800-kHz. signal can be monitored on a general-coverage receiver to determine if the oscillator is operating.

Attach a 50-ohm dummy load to J_2 before testing the transmitter section of the equipment. Set

R_1 for a resting plate current of 25 ma. for V_2. This adjustment should be made without drive applied at J_1, but with K_1 energized. Next, apply approximately 2 watts of 3.8-MHz. (carrier) drive at J_1. Switch S_1 to read r.f. voltage, then tune C_2, C_4, and C_5 for maximum meter reading. Next, L_1 can be peaked for maximum oscillator output, while still observing the meter. After the foregoing adjustments are made monitor the plate current and tune for a dip the p.a. plate current by adjusting C_4. C_5 is the loading control, and it should be adjusted so that the dip in plate current is rather broad to assure tight coupling to the antenna—necessary if a good-quality signal is to be had. When the p.a. is properly adjusted the plate current should be approximately 100 ma.

If the 6146B stage is stable there will be no changes in plate current, other than the normal dip, as C_4 is tuned through its range. If additional peaks or dips occur, adjust the spacing between the neutralizing wire and the tube's anode until no instability is noted. With the drive disconnected from J_1, tune C_4 through its range and observe the plate current. Only the resting plate current should be registered if the amplifier is stable. By coupling a sensitive wavemeter to L_3 during the latter test,[1] self-oscillation will be apparent as r.f. output when C_4 is tuned. Fine adjustments to C_3 can then be made until no spurious output is noted.

When operating c.w., insert sufficient carrier to bring the p.a. plate current up to 100 ma. at dip. The key can be plugged into the exciter's key jack, or into J_4. Since K_1 is not designed for high-speed keying, it might be best to use J_4 as the keying terminal.

[1] "Are You Putting Out On The Correct Band?" *QST*, March 1967, p. 25.

Chapter 10

Specialized Communications Systems

The field of specialized amateur communications systems includes radioteletype, amateur television, amateur facsimile, and repeaters (fixed and mobile). Radio control of models is not a "communications" system in the amateur (two-way) sense. The specialized hobby of radio control has a large following, but "citizen-band" provisions for frequency allocations and operator registrations divorce if from the strictly ham-radio field (unless one wishes to avoid the QRM). By far the greatest activity in the specialized fields is to be found in radioteletype (RTTY).

Activity in amateur TV (**ATV**) can be found primarily in a number of population centers around the country. Most of the work is based on converted entertainment receivers and manufacturer's-surplus camera tubes (Vidicons). ATV is permitted on the amateur bands above 420 Mc., and this and the broadband nature of the transmissions precludes extensive DX work. (See *QST*, November, 1962).

"Slow-scan TV" is essentially facsimile and a narrow-band system that is permitted in any of the 'phone bands. It is a completely electronic system, however; no photographic techniques are required. Depending upon the definition (number of lines) and the bandwidth, pictures can be transmitted in 6 seconds or less. (See *QST*, Aug., 1958; Jan., 1961; March, 1964).

Hilltop-located unmanned repeater stations make extended-range v.h.f. contacts readily possible with normal equipment. Ten or so such stations are scattered around the country. Each one is a special problem, involving satisfying the FCC that all legal requirements (no unauthorized access, log-keeping, master control) be met. (See Green, *QST*, July, 1962.)

An earth-orbiting satellite 144-Mc. repeater (OSCAR III) was successfully used in early 1965; OSCAR IV was put in orbit in Dec., 1965. *QST* carries up-to-date reports on the progress of and means for utilizing and tracking OSCARs.

RADIOTELETYPE

Radioteletype (abbreviated **RTTY**) is a form of telegraphic communication employing typewriter-like machines for 1) generating a coded set of electrical impulses when a typewriter key corresponding to the desired letter or symbol is pressed, and 2) converting a received set of such impulses into the corresponding printed character. The message to be sent is typed out in much the same way that it would be written on a typewriter, but the printing is done at the distant receiving point. The teletypewriter at the sending point also prints the same material, for checking and reference.

The machines used for RTTY are far too complex mechanically for home construction, and if purchased new would be highly expensive. However, used teletypewriters in good mechanical condition are available at quite reasonable prices. These are machines retired from commercial service but capable of entirely satisfactory operation in amateur work. They may be obtained from several sources on condition that they will be used purely for amateur purposes and will not be resold for commercial use.

A number of RTTY societies and clubs exist around the country, and some of them publish bulletins giving technical and operating information. Some of them have also accepted responsibility to help in club distribution of certain

The Model 15 page printer, shown here with table, is used in a great many RTTY stations.

Western Union surplus teletypewriter equipment. For an up-to-date list of these clubs and sources of equipment, send a self-addressed stamped envelope and your request to:

American Radio Relay League
RTTY T.I.S.
225 Main Street
Newington, Conn. 06111

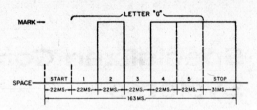

Fig. 10-1—Pulse sequence in the teletype code. Each character begins with a start pulse, always a "space," and ends with a "stop" pulse, always a "mark." The distribution of marks and spaces in the five elements between start and stop determines the particular character transmitted.

Types of Machines

There are two general types of machines, the **page printer** and the **tape printer.** The former prints on a paper roll about the same width as a business letterhead. The latter prints on paper tape, usually gummed on the reverse side so it may be cut to letter-size width and pasted on a sheet of paper in a series of lines. The page printer is the more common type in the equipment available to amateurs.

The operating speed of most machines is such that characters are sent at the rate of about 60 words per minute. Ordinary teletypewriters are of the **start-stop** variety, in which the pulse-forming mechanism (motor driven) is at rest until a typewriter key is depressed. At this time it begins operating, forms the proper pulse sequence, and then comes to rest again before the next key is depressed to form the following

character. The receiving mechanism operates in similar fashion, being set into operation by the first pulse of the sequence from the transmitter. Thus, although the actual transmission speed cannot exceed about 60 w.p.m. it can be considerably slower, depending on the typing speed of the operator.

It is also possible to transmit by using perforated tape. This has the advantage that the complete message may be typed out in advance of actual transmission, at any convenient speed; when transmitted, however, it is sent at the machine's normal maximum speed. A special transmitting head and tape perforator are required for this process. A **reperforator** is a device that may be connected to the conventional teletypewriter for punching tape when the machine is operated in the regular way. It may thus be used either for an original message or for "taping" an incoming message for retransmission.

Teletype Code

In the special code used for teletype every character has five "elements" sent in sequence. Each element has two possible states, either "mark" or "space," which are indicated by different types of electrical impulses (i.e., mark might be indicated by a negative voltage and space by a positive voltage). In customary practice each element occupies a time of 22 milliseconds. In addition, there is an initial "start" element (space), also 22 milliseconds long, to set the sending and receiving mechanisms in operation, and a terminal "stop" element (mark) 31 milliseconds long, to end the operation and ready the machine for the next character.

This sequence is illustrated in Fig. 10-1, which shows the letter G with its start and stop elements. The letter code as it would appear on perforated tape is shown in Fig. 10-2, where the black dots indicate marking pulses. Figures and arbitrary signs — punctuation, etc. — use the same set of code impulses as the alphabet, and are selected by shifting the carriage as in the case of an ordinary typewriter. The carriage shift is accomplished by transmitting

The Model 32 page printer is one of the newer types; it can be obtained directly from the manufacturer at a price that is reasonably attractive to the amateur.

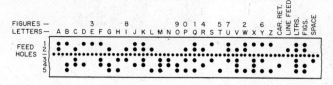

There are no lower-case letters on a teletypewriter. Where blanks appear in the above chart in the "FIGS" line, characters may differ on different machines.

either the "LTRS" or "FIGS" code symbol as required. There is also a "carriage return" code character to bring the carriage back to the starting position after the end of the line is reached on a page printer, and a "line feed" character to advance the page to the next line after a line is completed.

Additional System Requirements

To be used in radio communication, the pulses (d.c.) generated by the teletypewriter must be utilized in some way to key a radio transmitter so they may be sent in proper sequence and usable form to a distant point. At the receiving end the incoming signal must be converted into d.c. pulses suitable for operating the printer. These functions, shown in block form in Fig. 10-3, are performed by electronic units known respectively as the **keyer** and **receiving converter**.

The radio transmitter and receiver are quite conventional in design. Practically all the special features needed can be incorporated in the keyer and converter, so that any ordinary amateur equipment is suitable for RTTY with little modification.

Transmission Methods

It is quite possible to transmit teletype signals by ordinary "on-off" or "make-break" keying such as is used in regular hand-keyed c.w. transmission. In practice, however, **frequency-shift keying** is preferred because it gives definite pulses on both mark and space, which is an advantage in printer operation. Also, since f.s.k. can be received by methods similar to those used for f.m. reception, there is considerable discrimination against noise, both natural and man-made, distributed uniformly across the receiver's pass band, when the received signal is not too weak. Both factors make for increased reliability in printer operation.

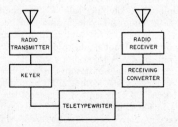

Fig. 10-3—Radioteletype in block form.

Frequency-Shift Keying

General practice with f.s.k. is to use a frequency shift of 850 cycles per second, although FCC regulations permit the use of any value of frequency shift up to 900 cycles. The smaller values of shift have been shown to have a signal-to-noise-ratio advantage in commercial circuits, and are currently being experimented with by amateurs. At present, however, the major part of amateur RTTY work is done with the 850-cycle shift. This figure also is used in much commercial work. The nominal transmitter frequency is the mark condition and the frequency is shifted 850 cycles (or whatever shift may have been chosen) lower for the space signal.

On the v.h.f. bands where A2 transmission is permitted **audio frequency-shift keying** (a.f.s.k.) is generally used. In this case the r.f. carrier is transmitted continuously, the pulses being transmitted by frequency-shifted tone modulation. The audio frequencies used have been more-or-less standardized at 2125 and 2975 cycles per second, the shift being 850 cycles as in the case of straight f.s.k. (These frequencies are the 5th and 7th harmonics, respectively, of 425 cycles, which is half the shift frequency, and thus are convenient for calibration and alignment purposes.) With a.f.s.k. the lower audio frequency is customarily used for mark and the higher for space.

THE RECEIVING CONVERTER

The very simple "starter" converter circuit shown in Fig. 10-4 is only an afternoon's project, but will enable the beginning RTTYer to get his feet wet practically as soon as he has a machine. Only the space pulses are used in this converter. The 5763 keyer tube, V_1, draws enough current to hold the printer magnets closed when there is no audio at J_1. When a signal is heard its voltage is stepped up in the transformer and rectified by CR_1, giving a negative-going pulse for each audio tone received. Thus the machine magnets are held in the mark condition until a space signal is received; the 5763 is then biased to cutoff by the negative pulse, and the magnet current is cut off. When the space pulse ends, the mark current again flows. In this way the machine receives the pulses as sent, and prints a letter. The circuit is self-limiting, in that plate current ceases the instant the negative pulse reaches the tube's cutoff bias, so all pulses strong enough to reach cutoff

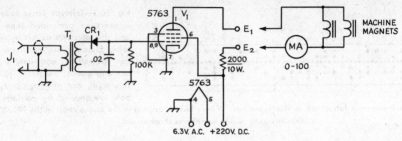

Fig. 10-4—Circuit diagram of the simple converter. The 100,000 ohm resistor is ½-watt composition, and the 0.02-μf. capacitor may be ceramic or Mylar type.

CR₁—Silicon diode, 400 volts p.i.v., 750 ma. (GE504, 1N540, etc.).

E₁, E₂—Binding posts.

J₁—Phono jack.

T₁—Audio output transformer, 5000-ohm primary, 3-ohm secondary (Knight 62 G 064 or an equivalent output transformer salvaged from a b.c. receiver may be used).

cause the plate-current pulse to be square-topped at a constant amplitude.

The circuit may be constructed in a $4 \times 2 \times 1\frac{1}{2}$-inch Minibox or other convenient housing. The 10-watt resistor should be mounted for best cooling as it gets quite warm in operation. Care should be used in soldering the silicon diode, since excess heat may damage it. Otherwise, there are no special precautions to be taken.

After checking the wiring, connect the unit to a power supply and place a 0–100 milliammeter between binding posts E_1 and E_2. After warm-up, the meter should show about 60 ma. plate current to the 5763 (for parallel operation of the magnets). If the current is much higher than 60 ma., enough resistance should be added in the B-plus lead to reduce the current to 60 ma. If the current initially is below 55 ma. with a 220-volt supply, the tube probably has weak emission and will not draw enough current to key the selector magnets.

Audio from the speaker jack of the receiver to be used should be connected to J_1. Tune in a strong, steady carrier with the b.f.o. turned on. Turn on the receiver audio gain and watch the current meter. As the audio gain is advanced, the current should drop until finally it is reduced to zero. If the current increases with audio, diode CR_1 is wired in reverse.

For best operation the selector magnets of the Teletype machine should be wired in parallel. Connect the magnets to the binding posts with the 100-ma. meter in series as shown in Fig. 1. The meter is an aid to tuning the signal correctly. Another good tuning indicator is an oscilloscope, if you have one. The vertical plates should be connected to the plate and cathode of the 5763. With the horizontal sweep set for about 30 cycles, it is possible to observe the output pulses directly.

Pick a strong commercial f.s.k. station that is testing at a steady rate to start with. Set your receiver to maximum selectivity, and tune through the RTTY signal. You will notice that the signal is made up of pulses on two frequencies, one 850 cycles or less lower in frequency than the other. Only one of the signals has the

space information that will provide correct copy with this system. It may be necessary to try both pulse signals to find the correct one. In receivers with no sharp c.w. selectivity the mark signal may be set to zero beat, where it will cause no interference to the space signal.

Turn on the machine. It will "run open" until the converter is turned on. The machine should then be silent until the audio gain is advanced, when it should start to print. Adjust the audio gain of the receiver for best copy, or for the squarest-looking pulse on the scope. By trial and error adjustment of the audio note and the audio gain it is possible to get quite good Teletype copy. Remember that any QRM or noise will upset the apple cart, as the converter can not discriminate between them and the wanted signal. The converter shown in Fig. 10-5 is a development of the W2PAT circuit with changes to operate the magnets directly. Considering its moderate cost and relatively simple construction it will provide good, trouble-free operation.

This circuit uses both components of the f.s.k. signal. The two audio tones resulting from b.f.o. detection in the receiver are taken from the speaker output jack, and are clipped to a maximum amplitude of about ½ volt by silicon diodes CR_1 and CR_2. This clipped signal is next amplified by V_1, with some additional limiting through grid saturation, and is then applied through R_1 to two tuned audio circuits consisting of L_1 and L_2 with their associated capacitors. These are adjusted for 850 cycles difference in frequency. L_1 and L_2 are TV width coils, which work very well in this application. The signals peaked by the tuned circuit are applied, respectively, to detectors V_{2A} and V_{2B}. The outputs of the detectors are coupled to a combiner tube, V_3, through neon lamps. The lamps provide a sharp make-break characteristic as they fire and extinguish, and are mounted on the front panel to do double duty as tuning indicators. A reversing switch is included at this point as an aid in tuning the RTTY signal. The combined signals form a single amplified output pulse in V_3. This is used to control the keyer tube V_4 in the same way as the 5763 described in the "starter" converter. The meter M_1 may be

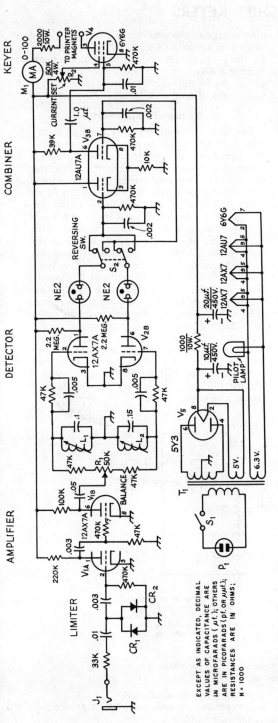

Fig. 10-5—Receiving demodulator for f.s.k. Teletype signals. Unless otherwise noted, resistors are ½-watt composition; capacitors of 0.01 µf. or less may be mica or ceramic; larger values are 450-volt paper. Capacitors with polarities indicated are electrolytic.

CR₁, CR₂—Silicon diode, 50 volts or more p.i.v.

J₁—Phone jack.

L₁, L₂—TV width coils, about 30 mh. (Miller 6319, Thordarson WC-19, Meissner 20-1034).

M₁—0-100 milliammeter.

P₁—Chassis-mounting a.c. connector, male.

R₁—50,000-ohm control, linear taper.

R₂—50,000-ohm control, linear taper, 4 watts.

S₁—S.p.s.t. toggle.

S₂—D.p.d.t. toggle.

T₁—Power transformer, 700 volts c.t., 100 ma.; 6.3 volts, 3 amp.; 5 volts, 2 amp. (Stancor PC8409 or PC8411).

omitted to save cost, but if it is, a 0–100 milliammeter should be connected in series with the lead to the machine magnets, for initial testing. The shack v.o.m. may be used.

When power is applied to the converter the neon lamps should first fire, and then die out as V_2 starts to draw current. An audio oscillator should be connected to J_1 and the tuned circuits adjusted for resonance on the frequencies chosen. (If the shack doesn't have an audio oscillator check with the local hi-fi bugs — they often have one.) For v.h.f., where the keying is audio frequency, the standard frequencies of 2125 and 2975 c.p.s. should be used. However, if operation is intended only on the h.f. bands, the tones may be any pair that can be passed by the receiver audio section without attenuation, are separated by 850 cycles, and are not harmonically related. Several sets of frequencies were tried with this converter, and all seemed to work equally well. As each tuned circuit is resonated, its associated neon lamp should first.

Connect the machine magnets to the converter and adjust R_2 for 30 or 60 ma., depending on whether the magnets are in series or parallel. Then tune in a signal on the receiver with the b.f.o. on, to provide an audio beat with the incoming signal. Set the balance control, R_1, so that the lamps have equal brightness. If the signal is correctly tuned, both neons should be flickering on and off with the Teletype pulses. If the machine prints garbled letters, throw the reversing switch to the other position and try again. If you still can not copy anything, the station may have a shift other than 850 cycles, or some other speed than 60 w.p.m. Many commercial services do not use these standards any more, but most amateur stations do. After a few days' practice, one can guess whether a station has the correct shift and speed by listening to the audio output of the receiver.

FREQUENCY-SHIFT KEYERS

The keyboard contacts of the teletypewriter actuate a direct-current circuit that operates the printer magnets, and a pair of terminals is provided that connect to a key. In the "resting" condition the contacts are closed (mark). In operation the contacts open for "space." These contacts may be used to operate a keyer circuit of the radio transmitter, provided it is not "loaded" to such an extent that it affects the operation of the printer.

Perhaps the simplest satisfactory circuit for frequency-shift keying a v.f.o. is the one shown in Fig. 10-6. This uses a diode to switch a capacitor in and out of the circuit. Although shown for 455 kc., the v.f.o. can be made to operate on any reasonable frequency by substituting suitable inductance and capacitance values.

The triode oscillator uses the series-tuned Colpitts circuit, with the actual frequency adjustment done by changing the inductance. The closed contacts of the printer complete the voltage-dividing circuit (1000- and 100K resistors), and the 1N67 is heavily back-biased. The effect is to open the circuit between C_1 and C_2, and C_2 is substantially out of the circuit.

When the contacts open, the 1N67 no longer conducts. The net capacitance that is inserted, determined by the setting of C_1, the shift adjustment.

A buffer amplifier follows the v.f.o., with a capacitance voltage divider reducing the available voltage to the amplifier but furnishing further buffer action. At 455 kc., it should be possible to short circuit the output terminals without shifting the oscillator frequency more than a few cycles. As in any oscillator, solid construction and the use of good components is recommended.

Frequency Adjustment

The frequency shift, whatever the type of circuit, should be made as nearly exact as available equipment will permit, since the shift must match the frequency difference between the filters in the receiving converter if the signals are to be usable at the receiving end. An accurately calibrated audio oscillator is useful for this purpose. To check, the mark frequency should be tuned in on the station receiver, with the b.f.o. on, and the receiver set to exact zero beat. (See Chapter 21 on measurements for identification of exact zero beat). The space frequency should then be adjusted to exactly the desired shift. This may be done by adjusting for an auditory zero beat between the beat tone from the receiver and the tone from the audio oscillator. If an oscilloscope is available, the frequency adjustment may be accomplished by feeding the receiver tone to the vertical plates and the audio-oscillator tone to the horizontal plates, and then adjusting the space frequency for the elliptical pattern that indicates the two frequencies are the same.

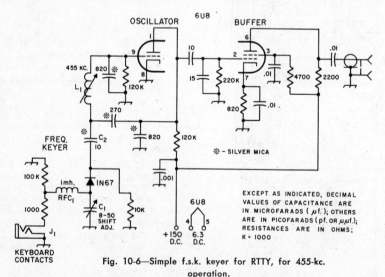

Fig. 10-6—Simple f.s.k. keyer for RTTY, for 455-kc. operation.

C_1—8-50-pf. trimmer (Centralab 822-AN)
C_2—10-pf. silver mica
RCF$_1$—1-mh. subminiature choke (Millen J300-1000)
J$_1$—Shorting type headphone jack
L$_1$—430-850-μh. adjustable coil (Miller 42A684CBI)

A comprehensive series of articles on RTTY, far beyond the possible scope of this Handbook, was carried monthly in QST during 1965 and 1966. Written by Irvin Hoff, K8DKC, and starting in the January 1965 issue, they are recommended reading for any RTTY enthusiast.

F.M. COMMUNICATIONS

There is an increasing interest in the use of f.m. as a means of amateur radio communications, particularly in the v.h.f. and u.h.f. portions of the spectrum. Mobile stations are finding effective use of this mode by virtue of extended range, channelized operation, and the reduction in pulse-noise response from automobile ignition systems. A typical installation consists of a transmitter and receiver, or a transceiver, and an antenna system. Typically, both the transmitter and receiver are crystal controlled for operation on a selected frequency. Most mobile equipment is modified commercial gear. Some home-built equipment is being used, especially in the area of control circuitry, and this approach should not be overlooked by the f.m. operator. While not currently in vogue, it might be prudent to include provisions for making the receiver tunable, as well as crystal controlled, so that fixed-frequency operation will not be mandatory. Fig. 10-7 illustrates the basic system for fixed-station or mobile operation.

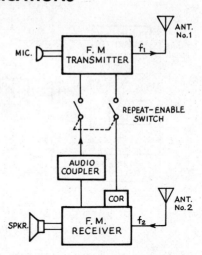

Fig. 10-8—Block diagram showing how a basic f.m. station can be made to serve as a repeater.

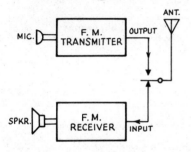

Fig. 10-7—Block diagram of a basic f.m. station.

A considerable amount of older-type commercial gear is being used by amateurs for f.m. service (mostly pre-1963 vintage). Much of it is wideband equipment with ± 15-kHz. deviation. Some of the newer gear being used has a ± 5-kHz. deviation factor. It is expected that some amateur work will eventually utilize the ± 5-kHz. deviation.

Most operators use crystal control for receiving and transmitting, hence they need only to concern themselves with "getting on frequency" and staying there. Normally, the oscillator circuits have crystal-padding capacitors which enable the operator to hit the desired frequency. Good quality crystals should be used to assure frequency stability. Used equipment can often be purchased from war surplus dealers, two-way radio service organizations, and from dealers who advertise in the various radio magazines.

REPEATERS

Repeaters are amateur radio stations which are used to extend the range of mobile and other base stations. The repeater is located at a geographically superior site (high hill or mountain top) and receives signals on one frequency, then re-transmits them on another frequency. Fig. 10-8

shows how an amateur f.m. station can be converted to a simple repeater. Separate antennas are used so that the receiver and transmitter may operate simultaneously, or a duplexer can be used to permit the station to transmit and receive at the same time with a single antenna. If two antennas are used, the vertical separation between them should be as great as practical to reduce transmitter interference to the receiver. Greater frequency separation between transmitter and receiver also helps reduce interference, but is limited by the capability of the mobile equipment using the repeater.

The repeater receiver is equipped with a carrier-operated relay (COR). It is connected to the "repeat-enable" switch so that the operator of the repeater station has absolute control over the transmissions he is repeating. The receiver's audio output is fed through an audio coupler to the audio input of the transmitter. The operator can use the station in a conventional manner if he wishes, and not as a repeater. When he wants the station to repeat, he closes the switch and permits the COR to be operated by an incoming signal, thus keying the transmitter.

When a repeater is not located where an operator is on duty, it may be operated by remote control under the provisions of Section 97.43 of the FCC rules. Control may be either by wire, or by radio means on amateur frequencies above 220 MHz. Audio tones are generally used to provide the control information. The operator must be present at the authorized remote control point, and must always have the ability to stop the transmissions (see Fig. 10-9).

As this data is released (late 1968) there are proposals pending with FCC to permit automatic operation of amateur repeaters without the need for an operator on duty. (Write to ARRL for

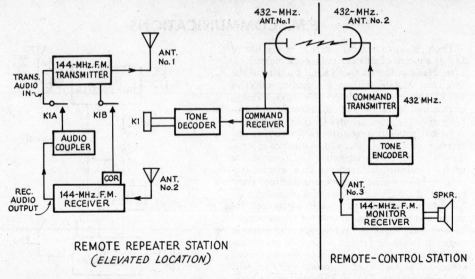

REMOTE REPEATER STATION
(ELEVATED LOCATION)

REMOTE-CONTROL STATION

Fig. 10-9—Block diagram illustrating how a repeater station can be controlled from a remote point by means of command link, operator on duty. The arrows indicate the direction of the signal.

possible late information.) The newcomer to f.m. may obtain a considerable amount of useful information from the references listed here. Many of the two-way radio maintenance men in your area are amateurs and can be called upon for information.

Most of the information compiled here was provided by H. W. Middleton, Jr., W4DYE/W8-CXD, T. A. McKee, K4ZAD, and the General Electric Co. The GE Company *does not* furnish parts, used equipment, or instruction books to amateurs. You may write for their Publication Order form, however, listed in the bibliography section of this text.

Bibliography

QST, July 1960, Aagaard, "Two-Meter F.M. for Noise-Free Local Communication."

QST, July 1962, "U.H.F. Repeater Problems and Possibilities," J. Green, K6QNY.

QST, August 1968, "Converting Wide-Band F.M. Equipment for 420-MHZ. Service," G. Poland, W8FWF.

F.M. Magazine, 2005 Hollywood St., Grosse Pointe, Michigan 48236.

F.M. Simplified, Kiver, 3rd Edition, VanNostrand Co., Inc.

The Radio Amateur's V.H.F. Manual, 2nd Edition, ARRL.

GE Publication Order form ECP-227 lists books and other material on f.m. which can be ordered. Write GE Co., Mountain View Road, Lynchburg, Va. 24502.

Standards for VHF Amateur FM Operation
Recommended by Lynchburg, Va, Area Amateurs

Antenna Polarization— Vertical.

Deviation— ± 15 kHz. max. Should tend toward ± 5 kHz. max. in the future (See text).

Freq. Netting— Equipment should have crystal trimmers to permit precise frequency adjustment.

Channel Spacing—

6—Meters— 40 kHz. channels beginning with 52.56 MHz. plus the national channel of 52.525 MHz.

2—Meters— 60 kHz.—channel increments each side of the 146.94 MHz.—national channel.

3/4—Meters— 100 kHz. channels on the tenths of MHz.

Crystals— Buy quality crystals correlated for your equipment.

Fig. 10-10—A chart showing the recommendations for f.m. repeater operation as recommended by the Lynchburg, Va. area amateurs.

SPACE COMMUNICATIONS

The use of v.h.f. and u.h.f. frequencies for intermediate and long distance communications has become possible through space communications techniques. There are basically two types of systems: passive and active. A passive system uses a celestial object such as the moon or an artificial reflecting satellite to return signals to earth. An active system consists of a space vehicle carrying an electronic repeater. Commercial and military communicators currently have in everyday use both passive and active space communications systems; amateur efforts, however, are still in experimental stages.

MOONBOUNCE

Use of the moon as a passive reflector is increasing in popularity among amateurs. Such a communications system requires high antenna gain and receiving sensitivity, and at least a moderate amount of transmitter power to overcome the extreme earth-moon-earth (e.m.e.) path attenuation involved. To date, most amateur e.m.e. work has been at 144 MHz. Although, contacts have been made at 432 MHz. and with increasing interest, at 1296 MHz. Moonbounce is not an area in which a beginner can find easy success. However, with a station, in terms of transmitter power, receiver quality, and antenna size, equal to that used in many advanced h.f. amateur installations, international communications can be achieved at v.h.f. and u.h.f. frequencies.

SATELLITES

Four satellites designed and built by amateurs have been orbited through cooperation of the U.S. government. This activity has been conducted under the direction of Project Oscar (Orbiting Satellite Carrying Amateur Radio) Inc., an ARRL-affiliated organization. Oscars III and IV, both orbited in 1965, were communications satellites carrying repeaters for relaying amateur signals. Conventional v.h.f. and u.h.f. amateur stations are suitable for Oscar communications. However, it is desirable to have an antenna which can move in azimuth and elevation to track the satellite.

Late Information

QST carries information about recent developments in Oscar and moonbounce communications. On request, ARRL will send a bibliography of *QST* Oscar or moonbounce articles.

Chapter 11

Testing and Monitoring Transmissions

Testing and measuring of power output and frequency are not treated in this chapter, since they are treated elsewhere. It should be pointed out, however, that the fine points of frequency measurement become increasingly important as one operates closer to a band edge.

A little knowledge of how to test one's own equipment is worth more than most of the solicited reports obtained over the air during a lifetime. *Un*solicited *adverse* criticism is something else again; it usually indicates a signal so bad that it is a menace to the welfare of the band, not to mention the long and continued life of one's license!

"Testing" involves the checking of new or modified equipment, to determine if it is working as it should. "Monitoring" is the continuous checking during every transmission, to insure that nothing has failed or that inherent limits have not been exceeded. Obviously the fields are overlapping, and "checking" procedures may be used for continuous monitoring.

TESTING KEYING

The easiest way to find out what your keyed signal sounds like on the air is to trade stations with a near-by ham friend some evening for a short QSO. If he is a half mile or so away, that's fine, but any distance where the signals are still S9 will be satisfactory.

After you have found out how to work his rig, make contact and then have him send slow dashes, with dash spacing. (The letter "T" at about 5 w.p.m.) With minimum selectivity, cut the r.f. gain back just enough to avoid receiver overloading (the condition where you get crisp signals instead of mushy ones) and tune slowly from out of beat-note range on one side of the signal through to zero and out the other side. Knowing the tempo of the dashes, you can readily identify any clicks in the vicinity as yours or someone else's. A good signal will have a thump on "make" that is perceptible only where you can also hear the beat note, and the click on "break" should be practically negligible at any point. If your signal is like that, it will sound good, provided there are no chirps. Then have your friend run off a string of fast dots with the bug — if they are easy to copy, your signal has no "tails" worth worrying about and is a good one for any speed up to the limit of manual keying. Make one last check with the selectivity in, to see that the clicks off the signal frequency are negligible even at high signal level.

If you don't have any friends with whom to trade stations, you can still check your keying, although you have to be a little more careful. The first step is to get rid of the r.f. click at the key. This requires an r.f. filter (see Chapter 7).

With no click from a spark at the key, disconnect the antenna from your receiver and short the antenna terminals with a short piece of wire. Tune in your own signal and reduce the r.f. gain to the point where your receiver doesn't overload. Detune any antenna trimmer the receiver may have. If you can't avoid overload within the r.f. gain-control range, pull out the r.f. amplifier tube and try again. If you still can't avoid overload, listen to the second harmonic as a last resort. An overloaded receiver can generate clicks.

Describing the volume level at which you should set your receiver for these "shack" tests is a little difficult. The r.f. filter should be effective with the receiver running wide open and with an antenna connected. When you turn on the transmitter and take the steps mentioned to reduce the signal in the receiver, run the audio up and the r.f. down to the point where you can just hear a little "rushing" sound with the b.f.o. off and the receiver tuned to the signal. This is with the selectivity in. At this level, a properly adjusted keying circuit will show no clicks off the rushing-sound range. With the b.f.o. on and the same gain setting, there should be no clicks outside the beat-note range. When observing clicks, make the slow-dash and dot tests outlined previously.

Now you know how your signal sounds on the air, with one possible exception. If keying your transmitter makes the lights blink, you may not be able to tell too accurately about the chirp on your signal. However, if you are satisfied with the absence of chirp when tuning *either side of zero beat,* it is safe to assume that your receiver isn't chirping with the light flicker and that the observed signal is a true representation. No chirp either side of zero beat is fine. Don't try to make these tests without first getting rid of the r.f. click at the key, because clicks can mask a chirp.

The least satisfactory way to check your keying is to ask another ham on the air how your keying sounds. It is the least satisfactory because most hams are reluctant to be highly critical of another amateur's signal. In a great many cases they don't actually know what to look for or how to describe any aberrations they may observe.

MONITORING OF KEYING

In general, there are two common methods for monitoring one's "fist" and signal. The first type involves the use of an audio oscillator that is keyed simultaneously with the transmitter.

The second method is one that permits receiving the signal through one's receiver, and this generally requires that the receiver be tuned to the transmitter (not always convenient unless working on the same frequency) and that some method be provided for preventing overloading of the receiver, so that a good replica of the transmitted signal will be received. Except where quite low power is used, this usually involves a relay for simultaneously shorting the receiver input terminals and reducing the receiver gain. Methods are shown in Chapter 5.

An alternative is to use an r.f.-powered audio oscillator. This follows the keying very closely (but tells nothing about the quality—chirps or clicks—of the signal).

THE "MATCHTONE"

The "Matchtone" is a c.w. tone-generating monitor using a transistor audio oscillator. A diode rectifier in the antenna circuit or the d.c. from a "Monimatch" (see Chap. 13) serves as the keyed source of d.c. power. In addition to the usual function it can be used by the sightless amateur as an audible transmitter-antenna tuning indicator.

While direct monitoring of c.w. transmissions via the receiver is a preferred method because it can reveal much about the keying characteristics, transmissions offset from the receiving frequency call for a separate monitor. The self-powered transistorized monitor fills the bill nicely. The use of the r.f bridge, already connected in the r.f. transmission line, as a source of power for the monitor is a logical choice.

The circuit of the Matchtone and the connections to the Monimatch and the receiver are shown in Fig. 11-1. A small 2- or 3-to-1 push-pull grid-to-plate audio interstage transformer is used for feedback as well as for coupling to the receiver. If a transformer having a p.p. grid winding is not available from the junk box, the audio coupling to the receiver can be obtained by connecting C_2 to the ungrounded end of R_1. While use of a low value of capacitance for C_2 is necessary to avoid excessive shunting of the high impedance receiver audio circuit, the value shown will provide sufficient coupling for a good audio tone level from the monitor. A third possibility for the audio out-put connection from the monitor is to substitute the headphones for R_1, together with a single-pole double-throw switch or relay to switch the phones between the monitor and the receiver. The on-off switch, S_1, can be made a part of R_2 by use of a volume control switch attachment.

The value shown for C_1 gives an audio pitch in the 500–1000 cycle range, depending somewhat on the particular transformer, the setting of R_2 and the transmitter output power. Other values of C_1 can be used to adjust the pitch to the

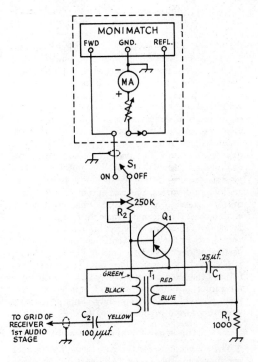

Fig. 11-1—Circuit of the Matchtone. Section enclosed in dashed line is the Monimatch and its indicating circuit; a simple r.f. rectifier will also serve as the d.c. source. Braid of shielded lead to audio grid should connect to receiver chassis.

C_1—Paper.

C_2—Mica or ceramic.

Q_1—2N109, CK722 or similar.

R_1—1000 ohms, ½ watt.

R_2—0.25-megohm volume control.

S_1—S.p.s.t. toggle.

T_1—Push-pull interstage audio transformer, 2:1 or 3:1 total grid to plate.

operator's individual preference. R_2 may be adjusted to compensate for the changes in the d.c. current from the rectifier or Monimatch caused by a change in transmitter frequency band or power. Using a 2N109 transistor, the circuit should oscillate with usable audio level with as little as 0.1 ma. d.c. flowing to ground through the monitor. Other low-cost transistors such as the 2N107 and the 2N170 should work equally well in the circuit.

Because the pitch of the audio tone is to some degree dependent upon the d.c. voltage obtained from the source, the pitch gives a reasonably accurate indication of correct final amplifier plate circuit tuning (maximum power output) and, if an antenna tuner is used, will also indicate resonance of the tuner to the transmitter output frequency. This characteristic of the Matchtone should be of considerable aid to sightless amateurs. (From *QST*, January, 1958.)

CHECKING A.M. PHONE OPERATION

USING THE OSCILLOSCOPE

Proper adjustment of a phone transmitter is aided immeasurably by the oscilloscope. The scope will give more information, more accurately, than almost any collection of other instruments that might be named. Furthermore, an oscilloscope that is entirely satisfactory for the purpose is not necessarily an expensive instrument; the cathode-ray tube and its power supply are about all that are needed. Amplifiers and linear sweep circuits are by no means necessary.

In the simplest scope circuit, radio-frequency voltage from the modulated amplifier is applied to the vertical deflection plates of the tube, usually through blocking capacitors as shown in the oscilloscope circuit in the chapter on measurements, and audio-frequency voltage from the modulator is applied to the horizontal deflection plates. As the instantaneous amplitude of the audio signal varies, the r.f. output of the transmitter likewise varies, and this produces a wedge-shaped pattern or **trapezoid** on the screen. If the oscilloscope has a built-in horizontal sweep, the r.f. voltage can be applied to the vertical plates as before (never through an amplifier) and the sweep will produce a pattern that follows the modulation envelope of the transmitter output, provided the sweep frequency is lower than the modulation frequency. This produces a **wave-envelope** modulation pattern.

The Wave-Envelope Pattern

The connections for the wave-envelope pattern are shown in Fig. 11-2A. The vertical deflection plates are coupled to the amplifier tank coil (or an antenna coil) through a low-impedance (coax, twisted pair, etc.) line and pick-up coil. As shown in the alternative drawing, a resonant circuit tuned to the operating frequency may be connected to the vertical plates, using link coupling between it and the transmitter. This will eliminate r.f. harmonics, and the tuning control is a means for adjustment of the pattern height.

If it is inconvenient to couple to the final tank coil, as may be the case if the transmitter is tightly shielded, the pick-up loop may be coupled to the tuned tank of a matching circuit or antenna coupler. Any method (even a short antenna

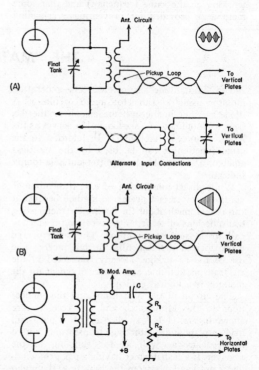

Fig. 11-2—Methods of connecting the oscilloscope for modulation checking. A—connections for wave-envelope pattern with any modulation method; B—connections for trapezoidal pattern with plate or screen modulation.

coupled to the tuned circuit shown in the "alternate input connections" of Fig. 11-2A) that will pick up enough r.f. to give a suitable pattern height may be used.

The position of the pick-up coil should be varied until an unmodulated carrier pattern, Fig. 11-3B, of suitable height is obtained. The horizontal sweep voltage should be adjusted to make the width of the pattern somewhat more than half the diameter of the screen. When voice modulation is applied, a rapidly changing pattern of varying height will be obtained. When the

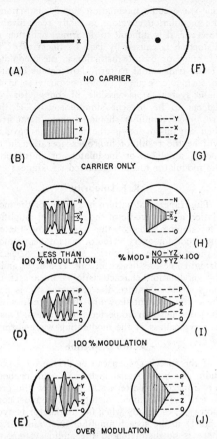

Fig. 11-3—Wave-envelope and trapezoidal patterns representing different conditions of modulation.

adjustable so a suitable pattern width can be obtained; a 0.25-megohm volume control can be used at R_2 for this purpose.

The resistance required at R_1 will depend on the d.c. voltage on the modulated element. The total resistance of R_1 and R_2 in series should be about 0.25 megohm for each 100 volts. For example, if a plate-modulated amplifier operates at 1500 volts, the total resistance should be 3.75 megohms, 0.25 megohm at R_2 and the remainder, 3.5 megohms, in R_1. R_1 should be composed of individual resistors not larger than 0.5 megohm each, in which case 1-watt resistors will be satisfactory.

For adequate coupling at 100 cycles the capacitance, in microfarads, of the blocking capacitor, C, should be at least $0.05/R$, where R is the total resistance $(R_1 + R_2)$ in megohms. In the example above, where R is 3.75 megohms, the capacitance should be $0.05/3.75 = 0.013$ μf. or

maximum height of this pattern is just twice that of the carrier alone, the wave is being modulated 100 percent. This is illustrated by Fig. 11-3D, where the point X represents the horizontal sweep line (reference line) alone, YZ is the carrier height, and PQ is the maximum height of the modulated wave.

If the height is greater than the distance PQ, as illustrated in E, the wave is overmodulated in the upward direction. Overmodulation in the downward direction is indicated by a gap in the pattern at the reference axis, where a single bright line appears on the screen. Overmodulation in either direction may take place even when the modulation in the other direction is less than 100 per cent.

The Trapezoidal Pattern

Connections for the trapezoid or wedge pattern as used for checking a.m. are shown in Fig. 11-6B. The vertical plates of the c.r. tube are coupled to the transmitter tank through a pick-up loop, preferably using a tuned circuit, as shown in the upper drawing, adjustable to the operating frequency. Audio voltage from the modulator is applied to the horizontal plates through a voltage divider, R_1R_2. This voltage should be

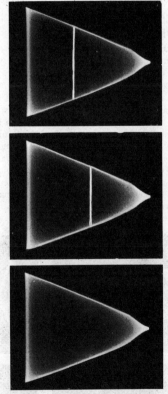

Fig. 11-4—Top—A typical trapezoidal pattern obtained with screen modulation adjusted for optimum conditions. The sudden change in slope near the point of the wedge occurs when the screen voltage passes through zero. Center—If there is no audio distortion, the unmodulated carrier will have the height and position shown by the white line superimposed on the sine-wave modulation pattern. Bottom—Even-harmonic distortion in the audio system, when the audio signal applied to the speech amplifier is a sine wave, is indicated by the fact that the modulation pattern does not extend equal horizontal distances on both sides of the unmodulated carrier.

more. The voltage rating of the capacitor should be at least twice the d.c. voltage applied to the modulated element.

Trapezoidal patterns for various conditions of modulation are shown in Fig. 11-3 at F to J, each alongside the corresponding wave-envelope pattern. With no signal, only the cathode-ray spot appears on the screen. When the unmodulated carrier is applied, a vertical line appears; the length of the line should be adjusted, by means of the pick-up coil coupling, to a convenient value. When the carrier is modulated, the wedge-shaped pattern appears; the higher the modulation percentage, the wider and more pointed the wedge becomes. At 100 percent modulation it just makes a point on the axis, X, at one end, and the height, PQ, at the other end is equal to twice the carrier height, YZ. Overmodulation in the upward direction is indicated by increased height over PQ, and downward by an extension along the axis X at the pointed end.

CHECKING A.M. TRANSMITTER PERFORMANCE

The trapezoidal pattern is generally more useful than the wave-envelope pattern for checking the operation of a phone transmitter. However, both types of patterns have their special virtues, and the best test setup is one that makes both available. The trapezoidal pattern is better adapted to showing the performance of a modulated amplifier from the standpoint of inherent linearity, without regard to the wave form of the audio modulating signal, than is the wave-envelope pattern. Distortion in the audio signal also can be detected in the trapezoidal pattern, although experience in analyzing scope patterns is required to recognize it.

If the wave-envelope pattern is used with a sine-wave audio modulating signal, distortion in the modulation envelope is easily recognizable; however, it is difficult to determine whether the distortion is caused by lack of linearity of the r.f. stage or by a.f. distortion in the modulator. If the trapezoidal pattern shows good linearity in such a case the trouble obviously is in the audio system. It is possible, of course, for both defects to be present simultaneously. If they are, the r.f. amplifier should be made linear first; then any distortion in the modulation envelope will be the result of improper operation in the speech amplifier or modulator, or in coupling the modulator to the modulated r.f. stage.

R. F. Linearity

The trapezoidal pattern is a graph of the modulation characteristic of the modulated amplifier. The sloping sides of the wedge show the r.f. amplitude for every value of instantaneous modulating voltage. If these sides are perfectly straight lines, as drawn in Fig. 11-3 at H and I, the modulation characteristic is linear. If the sides show curvature, the characteristic is nonlinear to an extent shown by the degree to which the sides depart from perfect straightness. This is true regardless of the modulating wave form.

Audio Distortion

If the speech system can be driven by a good audio sine-wave signal instead of a microphone, the trapezoidal pattern also will show the presence of even-harmonic distortion (the most common type, especially when the modulator is overloaded) in the speech amplifier or modulator. If there is no distortion in the audio system, the trapezoid will extend horizontally equal distances on each side of the vertical line representing the unmodulated carrier. If there is even-harmonic

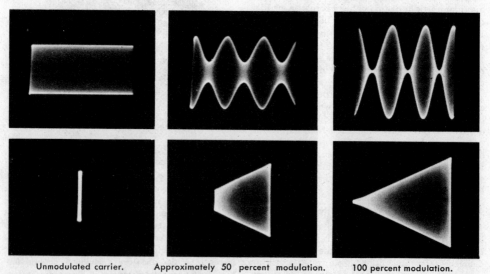

Unmodulated carrier.   Approximately 50 percent modulation.   100 percent modulation.

Fig. 11-5—Oscilloscope patterns showing proper modulation of a plate-and-screen modulated tetrode r.f. amplifier. Upper row, trapezoidal patterns; lower row, corresponding wave-envelope patterns. In the latter a linear sweep having a frequency one-third that of the sine-wave audio modulating frequency was used, so that three cycles of the modulation envelope show in the pattern.

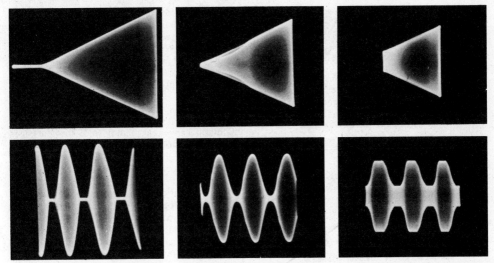

Modulation over 100 per cent.   Improper screen-circuit time constant.   Insufficient audio power.

Fig. 11-6—Improper operation or design. These pictures are to the same scale as those in Fig. 11-9, on the same transmitter and with the same test setup.

distortion the trapezoid will extend farther to one side of the unmodulated-carrier position than to the other. This is shown in Fig. 11-4. The probable cause is inadequate power output from the modulator, or incorrect load on the modulator.

An audio oscillator having reasonably good sine-wave output is highly desirable for testing both speech equipment and the phone transmitter as a whole. With an oscillator and the scope, the pattern is steady and can be studied closely to determine the effects of adjustments.

In the case of the wave-envelope pattern, distortion in the audio system will show up in the modulation envelope (with a sine-wave input signal) as a departure from the sine-wave form, and may be checked by comparing the envelope with a drawing of a sine-wave. Attributing any such distortion to the audio system assumes, of course, that a check has been made on the linearity of the modulated r.f. amplifier, preferably by use of the trapezoidal pattern.

Typical Patterns

Figs. 11-4, 11-5 and 11-6 show some typical scope patterns of modulated signals for different conditions of operation. The screen-modulation patterns, Fig. 11-4, also show how the presence of even-harmonic audio distortion can be detected in the trapezoidal pattern. The pattern to be sought in adjusting the transmitter is the one at the top in Fig. 11-5, where the top and bottom edges of the pattern continue in straight lines up to the point representing 100 percent modulation. If these edges tend to bend over toward the horizontal at the maximum height of the wedge the amplifier is "flattening" on the modulation up-peaks. This is usually caused by attempting to get too large a carrier output, and can be corrected by tighter coupling to the antenna or by a decrease in the d.c. screen voltage.

Fig. 11-5 shows patterns indicating proper operation of a plate-and-screen modulated tetrode r.f. amplifier. The slight "tailing off" at the modulation down peak (point of the wedge) can be minimized by careful adjustment of excitation and plate loading.

Several types of improper operation are shown in Fig. 11-6. In the photos at the left the linearity of the r.f. stage is good but the amplifier is being modulated over 100 percent. This is shown by the maximum height of the pattern (compare with the unmodulated carrier of Fig. 11-5) and by the bright line extending from the point of the wedge (or between sections of the envelope).

The patterns in the center, Fig. 11-6, show the effect of a too-long time constant in the screen circuit, in an amplifier getting its screen voltage through a dropping resistor, both plate and screen being modulated. The "double-edged" pattern is the result of audio phase shift in the screen circuit combined with varying screen-to-cathode resistance during modulation. The overall effect is to delay the rise in output amplitude during the up-sweep of the modulation cycle, slightly distorting the modulation envelope as shown in the wave-envelope pattern. This effect, which becomes more pronounced as the audio modulating frequency is increased, is usually absent at low modulation percentages but develops rapidly as the modulation approaches 100 percent. It can be reduced by reducing the screen bypass capacitance, and also by connecting resistance (to be determined experimentally, but of the same order as the screen dropping resistance) between screen and cathode.

The right-hand pictures in Fig. 11-6 show the effect of insufficient audio power. Although the trapezoidal pattern shows good linearity in the r.f. amplifier, the wave-envelope pattern shows flattened peaks (both positive and negative) in

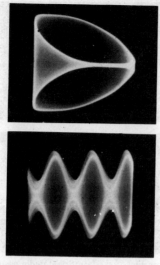

Fig. 11-7—Upper photo—Audio phase shift in coupling circuit between transmitter and horizontal deflection plates. Lower photo—Hum on vertical deflection plates.

the modulation envelope even though the audio signal applied to the amplifier was a sine wave. More speech-amplifier gain merely increases the flattening without increasing the modulation percentage in such a case. The remedy is to use a larger modulator or less input to the modulated r.f. stage. In some cases the trouble may be caused by an incorrect modulation-transformer turns ratio, causing the modulator to be overloaded before its maximum power output capabilities are reached.

Faulty Patterns

The pattern defects shown in Fig. 11-6 are only a few out of many that might be observed in the testing of a phone transmitter, all capable of being interpreted in terms of improper operation in some part of the transmitter. However, it is not always the transmitter that is at fault when the scope shows an unusual pattern. The trouble may be in some defect in the test setup.

Patterns representative of two common faults of this nature are shown in Fig. 11-7. The upper picture shows the trapezoidal pattern when the audio voltage applied to the horizontal plates of the c.r. tube is not exactly in phase with the modulation envelope. The normal straight edges of the wedge are transformed into ellipses which in the case of 100 percent modulation (shown) touch at the horizontal axis and reach maximum heights equal to the height of the normal wedge at the modulation up-peak. Such a phase shift can occur (and usually will) if the audio voltage applied to the c.r. tube deflection plates is taken from any point in the audio system other than where it is applied to the modulated r.f. stage. The coupling capacitor shown in Fig. 11-2 must have very low reactance compared with the resistance of R_1 and R_2 in series — not larger than a few percent of the sum of the two resistances.

The wave-envelope pattern in Fig. 11-7 shows the effect of hum on the vertical deflection plates. This may actually be on the carrier or may be introduced in some way from the a.c. line through stray coupling between the scope and the line or because of poor grounding of the scope, transmitter or modulator.

It is important that r.f. from the *modulated stage only* be coupled to the oscilloscope, and then only to the vertical plates. If r.f. is present also on the horizontal plates, the pattern will lean to one side instead of being upright. If the oscilloscope cannot be moved to a position where the unwanted pick-up disappears, a small bypass capacitor (10 $\mu\mu$f. or more) should be connected across the horizontal plates as close to the cathode-ray tube as possible. An r.f. choke (2.5 mh. or smaller) may also be connected in series with the ungrounded horizontal plate.

CHECKING F.M. AND P.M. TRANSMITTERS

Accurate checking of the operation of an f.m. or p.m. transmitter requires different methods than the corresponding checks on an a.m. set. This is because the common forms of measuring devices either indicate amplitude variations only (a d.c. milliammeter, for example), or because their indications are most easily interpreted in terms of amplitude. There is no simple measuring instrument that indicates frequency deviation directly.

However, there is one favorable feature in f.m. or p.m. checking. The modulation takes place at a very low level and the stages following the one that is modulated do not affect the linearity of modulation so long as they are properly tuned. Therefore the modulation may be checked *without putting the transmitter on the air,* or even on a dummy antenna. The power is simply cut off the amplifiers following the

modulation stage. A selective receiver is an essential part of the checking equipment of an f.m. or p.m. transmitter, particularly for narrow-band f.m. or p.m.

The quantities to be checked in an f.m. or p.m. transmitter are the linearity and frequency deviation. The methods of checking differ in detail.

Reactance-Tube F.M.

It is possible to calibrate a reactance modulator by applying an adjustable d.c. voltage to the modulator grid and noting the change in oscillator frequency as the voltage is varied. A suitable circuit for applying the adjustable voltage is shown in Fig. 11-8. The battery voltage is 3 to 6 volts (two or more dry cells in series). The arrows indicate clip connections so that the battery polarity can be reversed.

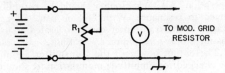

Fig. 11-8—D.c. method of checking frequency deviation. R_1 is 500 to 1000 ohms.

The oscillator frequency deviation should be measured by using a receiver in conjunction with an accurately calibrated frequency meter, or by any means that will permit accurate measurement of frequency differences of a few hundred cycles. One simple method is to tune in the oscillator on the receiver (disconnecting the receiving antenna, if necessary, to keep the signal strength well below the overload point) and then set the receiver b.f.o. to zero beat. Then increase the d.c. voltage applied to the modulator grid from zero in steps of about ½ volt and note the beat frequency at each change. Then reverse the battery terminals and repeat. The frequency of the beat note may be measured by comparison with a calibrated

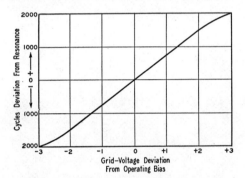

Fig. 11-9—A typical curve of frequency deviation vs. modulator grid voltage.

audio-frequency oscillator. Note that with the battery polarity positive with respect to ground the radio frequency will move in one direction when the voltage is increased, and in the other direction when the polarity is reversed. When several readings have been taken a curve may be plotted to show the relationship between grid voltage and frequency deviation.

A sample curve is shown in Fig. 11-9. The usable portion of the curve is the center part which is essentially a straight line. The bending at the ends indicates that the modulator is no longer linear; this departure from linearity will cause harmonic distortion and will broaden the channel occupied by the signal. In the example, the characteristic is linear 1.5 kc. on either side of the center or carrier frequency.

A good modulation indicator is a "magic-eye" tube such as the 6E5. This should be connected across the grid resistor of the reactance modulator as shown in Fig. 11-10. Note its de-

flection (using the d.c. voltage method as in Fig. 11-8) at the maximum deviation to be used. For narrow-band f.m. the proper deviation is approximately 2000 cycles (this maximum deviation is based on an upper a.f. limit of 3000 cycles and a deviation ratio of 0.7) at the *output* frequency. This deflection represents "100 per cent modulation" and with speech input the gain should be kept at the point where it is just reached on voice peaks. If the transmitter is used on more than one band, the gain control should be marked at the proper setting

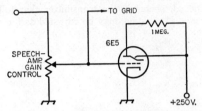

Fig. 11-10—6E5 modulation indicator for f.m. or p.m. modulators. To insure sufficient grid voltage for a good deflection, it may be necessary to connect the gain control in the modulator grid circuit.

for each band, because the signal amplitude that gives the correct deviation on one band will be either too great or too small on another.

Checking with a Selective Receiver

With p.m. the d.c. method of checking just described cannot be used, because the frequency deviation at zero frequency (d.c.) also is zero. For narrow-band p.m. it is necessary to check the actual width of the channel occupied by the transmission. (The same method also can be used to check f.m.) For this purpose it is necessary to have a selective receiver and a 3000-cycle audio oscillator or generator.

Keeping the signal intensity in the receiver at a medium level, tune in the carrier at the *output* frequency. Do not use the a.v.c. Switch on the beat oscillator, and set the receiver filter at its sharpest. Peak the signal on the crystal and adjust the b.f.o. for any convenient beat note. Then apply the 3000-cycle tone to the speech amplifier (through an attenuator, if necessary, to avoid overloading) and increase the audio gain until there is a small amount of modulation. Tuning the receiver near the carrier frequency will show the presence of sidebands 3 kc. from the carrier. With low input, these two should be the only sidebands detectable.

Now increase the audio gain and tune the receiver over a range of about 10 kc. on both sides of the carrier. When the gain becomes high enough, a second set of sidebands spaced 6 kc. on either side of the carrier will be detected. The signal amplitude at which these sidebands become detectable is the maximum speech amplitude that should be used.

When this method of checking is used with a reactance-tube-modulated f.m. (not p.m.) transmitter, the linearity of the system can be checked by observing the *carrier* as the a.f. gain is slowly increased. The beat-note frequency will stay constant so long as the modulator is linear, but nonlinearity will be accompanied by a shift in the average carrier frequency that will cause the beat note to change in frequency. If such a shift occurs at the same time that the 6-kc. sidebands appear, the extra sidebands may be caused by modulator distortion rather than by an excessive modulation index.

R.F. Amplifiers

The r.f. stages in the transmitter that follow the modulated stage may be adjusted as for c.w.

operation. All tank circuits should be carefully tuned to resonance. With f.m. or p.m., all r.f. stages in the transmitter can be operated at the manufacturer's maximum c.w. ratings.

The output power of the transmitter should be checked for amplitude modulation. It should not change from the unmodulated-carrier value when the transmitter is modulated. If no output indicator is available, a flashlight lamp and loop can be coupled to the final tank coil to serve as a current indicator. If the carrier amplitude is constant, the lamp brilliance will not change with modulation. If a.m. is indicated, the cause is almost certain to be nonlinearity in the modulator.

Chapter 12

Power Supplies

RECTIFIER CIRCUITS

Half-Wave Rectifier

Fig. 12-1 shows three rectifier circuits covering most of the common applications in amateur equipment. Fig. 12-1A is the circuit of a half-wave rectifier. The rectifier is a device that will conduct current in one direction but not in the other. During one half of the a.c. cycle the rectifier will conduct and current will flow through the rectifier to the load. During the other half of the cycle the rectifier does not conduct and no current flows to the load. The shape of the output wave is shown in (A) at the right. It shows that the current always flows in the same direction but that the flow of current is not continuous and is pulsating in amplitude.

The average output voltage—the voltage read by the usual d.c. voltmeter—with this circuit (no filter connected) is 0.45 times the r.m.s. value of the a.c. voltage delivered by the transformer secondary. Because the frequency of the pulses is relatively low (one pulsation per cycle), considerable filtering is required to provide adequately smooth d.c. output, and for this reason this circuit is usually limited to applications where the current involved is small, such as supplies for cathode-ray tubes and for protective bias in a transmitter.

The *peak reverse voltage,* the voltage the rectifier must withstand when it isn't conducting, varies with the load. With a resistive load it is the peak a.c. voltage ($1.4\ E_{\mathrm{RMS}}$) but with a capacitor load drawing little or no current it can rise to $2.8\ E_{\mathrm{RMS}}$.

Another disadvantage of the half-wave rectifier circuit is that the transformer must have a considerably higher primary volt-ampere rating (approximately 40 percent greater), for the same d.c. power output, than in other rectifier circuits.

Full-Wave Center-Tap Rectifier

The most universally used rectifier circuit is shown in Fig. 12-1B. Essentially an arrangement in which the outputs of two half-wave rectifiers are combined, it makes use of both halves of the a.c. cycle. A transformer with a center-tapped secondary is required with the circuit.

The average output voltage is 0.9 times the r.m.s. voltage of half the transformer secondary; this is the maximum voltage that can be obtained with a suitable choke-input filter. The peak output voltage is 1.4 times the r.m.s. voltage of half the transformer secondary; this is the maximum voltage that can be obtained from a capacitor-input filter (at little or no load).

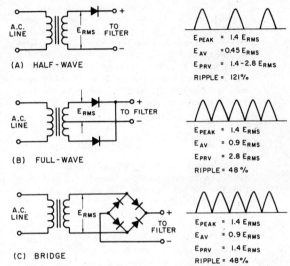

(A) HALF-WAVE

$E_{\mathrm{PEAK}}\ =\ 1.4\ E_{\mathrm{RMS}}$
$E_{\mathrm{AV}}\ =0.45\ E_{\mathrm{RMS}}$
$E_{\mathrm{PRV}}\ =\ 1.4\text{-}2.8\ E_{\mathrm{RMS}}$
RIPPLE $=\ 121\%$

(B) FULL-WAVE

$E_{\mathrm{PEAK}}\ =\ 1.4\ E_{\mathrm{RMS}}$
$E_{\mathrm{AV}}\ =\ 0.9\ E_{\mathrm{RMS}}$
$E_{\mathrm{PRV}}\ =\ 2.8\ E_{\mathrm{RMS}}$
RIPPLE $=\ 48\%$

(C) BRIDGE

$E_{\mathrm{PEAK}}\ =\ 1.4\ E_{\mathrm{RMS}}$
$E_{\mathrm{AV}}\ =\ 0.9\ E_{\mathrm{RMS}}$
$E_{\mathrm{PRV}}\ =\ 1.4\ E_{\mathrm{RMS}}$
RIPPLE $=\ 48\%$

Fig. 12-1—Fundamental rectifier circuits. A—Half-wave ($E_{\mathrm{PRV}} = 1.4\ E_{\mathrm{RMS}}$ with resistive load, $= 2.8\ E_{\mathrm{RMS}}$ with capacitor-input filter). B—Full-wave. C—Full-wave bridge. Output voltage values do not include rectifier voltage drops.

The peak reverse voltage across a rectifier unit is 2.8 times the r.m.s. voltage of half the transformer secondary.

As can be seen from the sketches of the output wave form in (B) to the right, the frequency of the output pulses is twice that of the half-wave rectifier. Therefore much less filtering is required. Since the rectifiers work alternately, each handles half of the load current, and the load-current rating of each rectifier need be only half the total load current drawn from the supply.

Two separate transformers, with their primaries connected in parallel and secondaries connected in series (with the proper polarity) may be used in this circuit. However, if this substitution is made, the primary volt-ampere rating must be reduced to about 40 percent less than twice the rating of one transformer.

Full-Wave Bridge Rectifier

Another full-wave rectifier circuit is shown in Fig. 12-1C. In this arrangement, two rectifiers operate in series on each half of the cycle, one rectifier being in the lead to the load, the other being in the return lead. The current flows

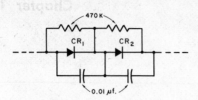

Fig. 12-2—When silicon rectifiers are connected in series for high-voltage operation, the reverse voltage drops can be equalized by using equalizing resistors of about one-half megohm. To protect against voltage "spikes" that may injure an individual rectifier, each rectifier should be bypassed by a 0.01-μf. capacitor. Connected as shown, two 400-p.i.v. silicon rectifiers can be used as an 800-p.i.v. rectifier, although it is preferable to include a safety factor and call it a "750-p.i.v." rectifier. The rectifiers, CR_1 and CR_2, should be the same type (same type number and ratings).

through two rectifiers during one half of the cycle and through the other two rectifiers during the other half of the cycle. The output wave shape (C), to the right, is the same as that from the simple center-tap rectifier circuit. The maximum output voltage into a resistive load or a properly-designed choke-input filter is 0.9 times the r.m.s. voltage delivered by the transformer secondary; with a capacitor-input filter and a very light load the output voltage is 1.4 times the secondary r.m.s. voltage. The peak reverse voltage per rectifier is 1.4 times the secondary r.m.s. voltage. Each rectifier in a bridge circuit should have a minimum load-current rating of one-half the total load current to be drawn from the supply.

Semiconductor Rectifiers

Selenium and silicon rectifiers are being used almost exclusively in power supplies for amateur equipment, and they will eventually supplant high-vacuum and mercury-vapor rectifiers. The semiconductors have the advantages of compactness, low internal voltage drop, low operating temperature and high current-handling capability. Also, no filament transformers are required.

In general, selenium rectifiers find their primary application at relatively low voltages (130 r.m.s. or less) and for load currents up to about one ampere. They too are rapidly being replaced by silicon diodes.

Silicon rectifiers are available in a wide range of voltage and current ratings. In peak inverse voltage (p.i.v.) ratings of 600 and less, silicon rectifiers carry current ratings as high as 400 amperes, and at 1000 p.i.v. the current ratings may be 1.5 amperes or so. The extreme compactness of silicon types makes feasible the stacking of several units in series for higher voltages. Standard stacks are available that will handle up to 10,000 p.i.v. at a d.c. load current of 500 ma., although they are comparatively expensive and the amateur can do much better by stacking the rectifiers him-

self. To equalize the p.i.v. drops and to guard against transient voltage spikes, it is good practice to shunt each rectifier with a half-megohm resistor and a 0.01-μf. capacitor, as shown in Fig. 12-2. Silicon rectifiers carry surge-current ratings, and series limiting resistors are required if the transformer winding resistance and reactance are too low to limit the current to a suitable value.

High-Vacuum Rectifiers

High-vacuum rectifiers depend entirely upon the thermionic emission from a heated filament

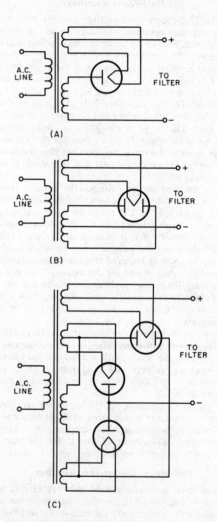

Fig. 12-3—The fundamental rectifier circuits of Fig. 12-1 redrawn for use with hot-cathode rectifiers. In many applications the filament transformer would be separate from the high-voltage transformer, and in many applications the full-wave rectifier in a single envelope would be replaced by two half-wave rectifiers. Low-voltage bridge circuits sometimes use rectifiers with indirectly-heated cathodes that have high heater-to-cathode voltage ratings; this reduces the number of cathode-heating windings required for the power supply.

and are characterized by a relatively high internal resistance. For this reason, their application usually is limited to low power, although there are a few types designed for medium and high power in cases where the relatively high internal voltage drop may be tolerated. This high internal resistance make them less susceptible to damage from temporary overload and they are free from the bothersome electrical noise sometimes associated with other types of rectifiers.

Some rectifiers of the high-vacuum full-wave type in the so-called receiver-tube class will handle up to 275 ma. at 400 to 500 volts d.c. output. Those in the higher-power class can be used to handle up to 500 ma. at 2000 volts d.c. in full-wave circuits. Most low-power high-vacuum rectifiers are produced in the full-wave type, while those for greater power are invariably of the half-wave type, two tubes being required for a full-wave rectifier circuit. A few of the lower-voltage types have indirectly heated cathodes, but are limited in heater-to-cathode voltage rating.

Mercury-Vapor Rectifiers

The voltage drop through a mercury-vapor rectifier is practically constant regardless of the load current. It ranges from 10 to 15 volts, depending upon the tube type. Rectifiers of this type, however, have a tendency toward a type of oscillation which produces noise in nearby receivers, sometimes difficult to eliminate. R.f. filtering in the primary circuit and at the rectifier plates as well as shielding may be required. As with high-vacuum rectifiers, full-wave types are available in the lower-power ratings only. For higher power, two tubes are required in a full-wave circuit.

Rectifier Ratings

All rectifiers are subject to limitations as to breakdown voltage and current-handling capability. Some tube types are rated in terms of the maximum r.m.s. voltage that should be applied to the rectifier plate. This is sometimes dependent on whether a choke- or capacitive-input filter is used. Others, particularly mercury-vapor and semiconductor types, are rated according to maximum *peak inverse voltage* (**p.i.v.**)—the peak voltage between anode and cathode while the rectifier is not conducting.

Rectifiers are rated also as to maximum d.c. load current, and some may carry peak-current ratings in addition. To assure normal life, all ratings should be carefully observed.

Operation of Hot-Cathode Rectifiers

In operating rectifiers requiring filament or cathode heating, as shown in Fig. 12-3, care should be taken to provide the correct filament voltage at the tube terminals. Low filament voltage can cause excessive voltage drop in high-vacuum rectifiers and a considerable reduction in the inverse peak-voltage rating of a mercury-vapor tube. Filament connections to the rectifier socket should be firmly soldered, particularly in the case of the larger mercury-vapor tubes whose filaments operate at low voltage and high current. The socket should be selected with care, not only as to contact surface but also as to insulation, since the filament usually is at full output voltage to ground. Phenolic sockets will serve at voltages up to 500 or so, but ceramic sockets, well spaced from the chassis, always should be used at the higher voltages. Special filament transformers with high-voltage insulation between primary and secondary are required for rectifiers operating at potentials in excess of 1000 volts inverse peak. In a supply furnishing a + voltage with respect to ground, the insulation must at least be able to withstand any possible voltage, plus 1000 or 2000 volts safety factor. Most rectifier filament transformers intended for high-voltage service carry 5000- or 10,000-volt insulation ratings.

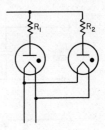

Fig. 12-4—Connecting mercury-vapor rectifiers in parallel for heavier currents. R_1 and R_2 should have the same value, between 50 and 100 ohms, and corresponding filament terminals should be connected together.

The rectifier tubes should be placed in the equipment with adequate space surrounding them to provide for ventilation. When mercury-vapor tubes are first placed in service, and each time after the mercury has been disturbed, as by removal from the socket to a horizontal position, they should be run with filament voltage *only* for 30 minutes before applying high voltage. After that, a delay of 30 seconds is recommended each time the filament is turned on.

Hot-cathode rectifiers may be connected in parallel for current higher than the rated current of a single unit. This includes the use of the sections of a double diode for this purpose. With mercury-vapor types, equalizing resistors of 50 to 100 ohms should be connected in series with each plate, as shown in Fig. 12-4, to maintain an equal division of current between the two rectifiers. If one tube tends to "hog" the current, the increased voltage drop across its resistor will decrease the voltage applied to the tube.

FILTERING

The pulsating d.c. waves from the rectifiers shown in Fig. 12-1 are not sufficiently constant in amplitude to prevent hum corresponding to the pulsations. Filters consisting of capacitances (and sometimes inductances) are required between the rectifier and the load to smooth out the pulsations to an essentially constant d.c. voltage. Also, upon the design of the filter depends to a large extent the d.c. voltage output, the *voltage regulation* of the power supply and the maximum load current that can be drawn from the supply without exceeding the peak-current rating of the rectifier.

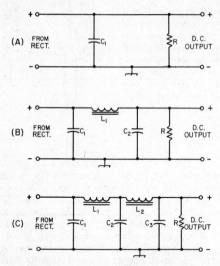

Fig. 12-5.—Capacitive-input filter circuits. A—Simple capacitive. B—Single-section. C—Double-section.

Load Resistance

In discussing the performance of power-supply filters, it is sometimes convenient to express the load connected to the output terminals of the supply in terms of resistance. The load resistance is equal to the output voltage divided by the total current drawn, including the current drawn by the bleeder resistor.

Type of Filter

Power-supply filters fall into two classifications, capacitor input and choke input. Capacitor-input filters are characterized by relatively high output voltage in respect to the transformer voltage. Advantage of this can be taken when silicon rectifiers are used or with any rectifier when the load resistance is high. Silicon rectifiers have a higher allowable peak-to-d.c. ratio than do thermionic rectifiers. This permits the use of capacitor-input filters at ratios of input capacitor to load resistance that would seriously shorten the life of a thermionic rectifier system. When the series

resistance through a rectifier and filter system is appreciable, as when high-vacuum rectifiers are used, the voltage regulation (see subsequent section) of a capacitor-input power supply is poor.

The output voltage of a properly-designed choke-input power supply is less than would be obtained with a capacitor-input filter from the same transformer.

Voltage Regulation

The output voltage of a power supply always decreases as more current is drawn, not only because of increased voltage drops on the transformer, filter chokes and the rectifier (if high-vacuum rectifiers are used) but also because the output voltage at light loads tends to soar to the peak value of the transformer voltage as a result of charging the first capacitor. By proper filter design the latter effect can be eliminated. The change in output voltage with load is called *voltage regulation* and is expressed as a percentage.

$$Percent\ regulation = \frac{100\ (E_1 - E_2)}{E_2}$$

Example: No-load voltage = E_1 = 1550 volts.
Full-load voltage = E_2 = 1230 volts.

$$Percentage\ regulation = \frac{100\ (1550 - 1230)}{1230}$$

$$= \frac{32,000}{1230} = 26\ percent.$$

A steady load, such as that represented by a receiver, speech amplifier or unkeyed stages of a transmitter, does not require good (low) regulation so long as the proper voltage is obtained under load conditions. However, the filter capacitors must have a voltage rating safe for the highest value to which the voltage will soar when the external load is removed.

A power supply will show more (higher) regulation with long-term changes in load resistance than with short temporary changes. The regulation with long-term changes is often called the **static regulation**, to distinguish it from the **dynamic regulation** (short temporary load changes). A load that varies at a syllabic or keyed rate, as represented by some audio and r.f. amplifiers, usually requires good dynamic regulation (15 percent or less) if distortion products are to be held to a low level. The dynamic regulation

Fig. 12-6—D.c. output voltages from a full-wave rectifier circuit as a function of the filter capacitance and load resistance. R_s includes transformer winding resistance and rectifier forward resistance. For the ratio R_s/R, both resistances are in ohms; for the RC product, R is in thousands of ohms.

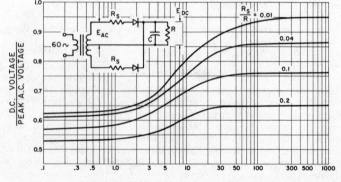

RC (R in thousands of ohms, C in µf.)

of a power supply is improved by increasing the value of the output capacitor.

When essentially constant voltage, regardless of current variation is required (for stabilizing an oscillator, for example), special voltage-regulating circuits described elsewhere in this chapter are used.

Bleeder

A bleeder resistor is a resistance connected across the output terminals of the power supply. Its functions are to discharge the filter capacitors as a safety measure when the power is turned off and to improve voltage regulation by providing a minimum load resistance. When voltage regulation is not of importance, the resistance may be as high as 100 ohms per volt. The resistance value to be used for voltage-regulating purposes is discussed in later sections. From the consideration of safety, the power rating of the resistor should be as conservative as possible, since a burned-out bleeder resistor is more dangerous than none at all !

Ripple Frequency and Voltage

The pulsations in the output of the rectifier can be considered to be the resultant of an alternating current superimposed upon a steady direct current. From this viewpoint, the filter may be considered to consist of shunting capacitors which short-circuit the a.c. component while not interfering with the flow of the d.c. component, and series chokes which pass d.c. readily but which impede the flow of the a.c. component.

The alternating component is called the ripple. The effectiveness of the filter can be expressed in terms of percent ripple, which is the ratio of the r.m.s. value of the ripple to the d.c. value in terms of percentage. Any multiplier or amplifier supply in a code transmitter should have less than 5 percent ripple. A linear amplifier can tolerate about 3 percent ripple on the plate voltage. Bias supplies for linears, and modulator and modulated-amplifier plate supplies, should have less than 1 percent ripple. V.f.o.s, speech amplifiers and receivers may require a ripple reduction to 0.01 percent.

Ripple frequency is the frequency of the pulsations in the rectifier output wave—the number of pulsations per second. The frequency of the ripple with half-wave rectifiers is the same as the frequency of the line supply—60 Hz. with 60-Hz. supply. Since the output pulses are doubled with a full-wave rectifier, the ripple frequency is doubled—to 120 Hz. with 60-Hz. supply.

The amount of filtering (values of inductance and capacitance) required to give adequate smoothing depends upon the ripple frequency, more filtering being required as the ripple frequency is lowered.

Transformer Winding Resistance

The effective transformer secondary resistance is given by

$$R_{tr} = R_{sec} + N^2 R_{pri}$$

where N is the transformer turns ratio, secondary to primary (voltage ratio at no load), and R_{pri} and R_{sec} are the primary and secondary resistances respectively. In the case of a full-wave rectifier circuit, N is the ratio of one-half secondary to primary and R_{sec} is the resistance of half of the secondary winding.

CAPACITIVE-INPUT FILTERS

Capacitive-input filter systems are shown in Fig. 12-5. Disregarding voltage drops in the chokes, all have the same characteristics except in respect to ripple. Better ripple reduction will be obtained when LC sections are added, as shown in Figs. 12-5B and C.

Output Voltage

To determine the approximate d.c. voltage output when a capacitive-input filter is used, reference should be made to the graph of Fig. 12-6.

Example:

> Transformer r.m.s. voltage—350
> Peak a.c. voltage = 1.4 × 350 = 495
> Load resistance—2000 ohms
> Series resistance—200 ohms
> 200 ÷ 2000 = 0.1
> Input capacitor C = 20 μf.
> R (thousands) × C = 2 × 20 = 40
> From curve 0.1 and RC = 40, d.c. voltage
>   = 495 × 0.75 = 370

Regulation

If a bleeder resistance of 20,000 ohms is used in the example above, when the load is removed and R becomes 20,000, the d.c. voltage will rise to 470. For minimum regulation with a capacitor-input filter, the bleed resistance should be as high as possible, or the series resistance should be low and the filter capacitance high, without exceeding the transformer or rectifier ratings.

Maximum Rectifier Current

The maximum current that can be drawn from a supply with a capacitive-input filter without exceeding the peak-current rating of the rectifier may be estimated from the graph of Fig. 12-7. Using values from the preceding example, the ratio of peak rectifier current to d.c. load current for 2000 ohms, as shown in Fig. 12-7, is 3. Therefore, the maximum load current that can be drawn without exceeding the rectifier rating is ⅓ the peak rating of the rectifier. For a load current of 185 ma., as above, the rectifier peak current rating should be at least 3 × 185 = 555 ma.

With bleeder current only, Fig. 12-7 shows that the ratio will increase to 7½. But since the bleeder draws 23.5 ma. d.c., the rectifier peak current will be only 176 ma.

Ripple Filtering

The approximate ripple percentage after the simple capacitive filter of Fig. 12-5A may be determined from Fig. 12-8. With a load resistance of 2000 ohms, for instance, the ripple will be approximately 10% with an 8-μf. capacitor or 20% with a 4-μf. capacitor. For other capacitances, the ripple will be in inverse proportion to

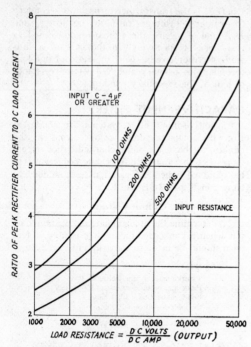

Fig. 12-7—Graph showing the relationship between the d.c. load current and the rectifier peak plate current with capacitive input for various values of load and input resistance.

the capacitance, e.g., 5% with 16 μf., 40% with 2 μf., and so forth.

The ripple can be reduced further by the addition of *LC* sections as shown in Figs. 12-5B and C. Fig. 12-9 shows the factor by which the ripple from any preceding section is reduced depending on the product of the capacitance and inductance added. For instance, if a section composed of a choke of 5 h. and a capacitor of 4 μf. were to be added to the simple capacitor of Fig. 12-5A, the product is $4 \times 5 = 20$. Fig. 12-9 shows that the original ripple (10% as above with 8 μf. for example) will be reduced by a factor of about 0.09. Therefore the ripple percentage after the new section will be approximately $0.09 \times 10 = 0.9\%$. If another section is added to the filter, its reduction factor from Fig. 12-9 will be applied to the 0.9% from the preceding section; $0.9 \times 0.09 = 0.081\%$ (if the second section has the same *LC* product as the first).

CHOKE-INPUT FILTERS

With thermionic rectifiers better voltage regulations results when a choke-input filter, as shown in Fig. 12-10, is used. Choke input permits better utilization of the thermionic rectifier, since a higher load current usually can be drawn without exceeding the peak current rating of the rectifier.

Minimum Choke Inductance

A choke-input filter will tend to act as a capacitive-input filter unless the input choke has at least a certain minimum value of inductance called the **critical** value. This critical value is given by

$$L_{\text{crit}} \text{ (henries)} = \frac{E \text{ (volts)}}{I \text{ (ma.)}}$$

where E is the output voltage of the supply, and I is the current being drawn through the filter.

If the choke has at least the critical value, the output voltage will be limited to the average value of the rectified wave at the input to the choke (see Fig. 12-1) when the current drawn from the supply is small. This is in contrast to the capacitive-input filter in which the output voltage tends to soar toward the peak value of the rectified wave at light loads. Also, if the input choke has at least the critical value, the rectifier peak current will be limited to about twice the d.c. current drawn from the supply. Most thermionic rectifiers have peak-current ratings of three to four times their maximum d.c. output-current ratings. Therefore, with an input choke of at least critical inductance, current up to the maximum output-current rating of the thermionic rectifier may be drawn from the supply without exceeding the peak-current rating of the rectifier.

Minimum-Load—Bleeder Resistance

From the formula above for critical inductance, it is obvious that if no current is drawn from the supply, the critical inductance will be infinite. So that a practical value of inductance may be used, some current must be drawn from the supply at all times the supply is in use. From the formula we find that this minimum value of current is

$$I \text{ (ma.)} = \frac{E \text{ (volts)}}{L_{\text{crit}}}$$

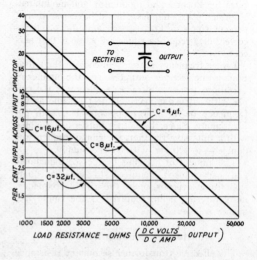

Fig. 12-8—Showing approximate 120-Hz. percentage ripple across filter input capacitor for various loads.

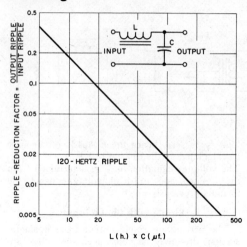

Fig. 12-9—Ripple-reduction factor for various values of L and C in filter section. Output ripple = input ripple × ripple factor.

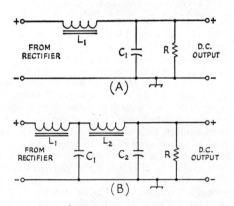

Fig. 12-10—Choke-input filter circuits. A—Single-section. B—Double-section.

400 ma., the choke need have an inductance of only 5 h. to maintain the critical value. This is fortunate, because chokes having the required inductance for the bleeder load only and that will maintain this value of inductance for much larger currents are very expensive.

Swinging Chokes

Less costly chokes are available that will maintain at least critical value of inductance over the range of current likely to be drawn from practical supplies. These chokes are called **swinging chokes.** As an example, a swinging choke may have an inductance rating of 5/25 h. and a current rating of 200 ma. If the supply delivers 1000 volts, the minimum load current should be 1000/25 = 40 ma. When the full load current of 200 ma. is drawn from the supply, the inductance will drop to 5 h. The critical inductance for 200 ma. at 1000 volts is 1000/200 = 5 h. Therefore the 5/25-h. choke maintains the critical inductance at the full current rating of 200 ma. At all load currents between 40 ma. and 200 ma., the choke will adjust its inductance to the approximate critical value.

Table 12-I shows the maximum supply output voltage that can be used with commonly-available swinging chokes to maintain critical inductance at the maximum current rating of the choke. These chokes will also maintain critical inductance for any lower values of voltage, or current down to the required minimum drawn by a proper bleeder as discussed above.

In the case of supplies for higher voltages in particular, the limitation on maximum load resistance may result in the wasting of an appreciable portion of the transformer power capacity in the bleeder resistance. Two input chokes in series will permit the use of a bleeder of twice the resistance, cutting the wasted current in half. Another alternative that can be used in a c.w. transmitter is to use a very high-resistance bleeder for protective purposes and only sufficient fixed bias on the tubes operating from the supply to bring the total current drawn from the

Thus, if the choke has an inductance of 20 h., and the output voltage is 2000, the minimum load current should be 100 ma. This load may be provided, for example, by transmitter stages that draw current continuously (stages that are not keyed). However, in the majority of cases it will be most convenient to adjust the bleeder resistance so that the bleeder will draw the required minimum current. In the above example, the bleeder resistance should be 2000/0.1 = 20,000 ohms.

From the formula for critical inductance, it is seen that when more current is drawn from the supply, the critical inductance becomes less. Thus, as an example, when the total current, including the 100 ma. drawn by the bleeder, rises to

TABLE 12-I				
L_h	Max. ma.	Max. volts	Max. R^1	Min. ma.[2]
3.5/13.5	150	525	13.5K	39
2/12	200	400	12K	33
5/25	200	1000	25K	40
2/12	250	500	12K	42
4/20	300	1200	20K	60
5/25	300	1500	25K	60
4/20	400	1600	20K	80
5/25	500	2500	25K	100

[1] Maximum bleeder resistance for critical inductance.

[2] Minimum current (bleeder) for critical inductance.

Fig. 12-11—Diagram showing various voltage drops that must be taken into consideration in determining the required transformer voltage to deliver the desired output voltage.

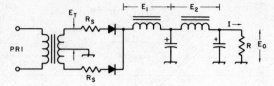

supply, when the key is open, to the value of current that the required bleeder resistance should draw from the supply. Operating bias is brought back up to normal by increasing the grid-leak resistance. Thus the entire current capacity of the supply (with the exception of the small drain of the protective bleeder) can be used in operating the transmitter stages. With this system, it is advisable to operate the tubes at phone, rather than c.w., ratings, since the average dissipation is increased.

Output Voltage

Provided the input-choke inductance is at least the critical value, the output voltage may be calculated quite closely by the following equation:

$$E_o = 0.9E_t - (I_B + I_L)(R_1 + R_2) - E_r$$

where E_o is the output voltage; E_t is the r.m.s. voltage applied to the rectifier (r.m.s. voltage between center-tap and one end of the secondary in the case of the center-tap rectifier); I_B and I_L are the bleeder and load currents, respectively, in amperes; R_1 and R_2 are the resistances of the first and second filter chokes; and E_r is the voltage drop across the rectifier. The various voltage drops are shown in Fig. 12-11. At no load I_L is zero, hence the no-load voltage may be calculated on the basis of bleeder current only. The voltage regulation may be determined from the no-load and full-load voltages using the formula previously given.

Ripple with Choke Input

The percentage ripple output from a single-section filter may be determined to a close approximation from Fig. 12-12.

> Example: $L = 5$ h., $C = 4$ μf., $LC = 20$. From Fig. 12-12, percentage ripple = 7 percent.

> Example: $L = 5$ h. What capacitance is needed to reduce the ripple to 1 percent? Following the 1-percent line to its intersection with the diagonal, thence down to the LC scale, read $LC = 120$. $120/5 = 24$μf.

In selecting values for the first filter section, the inductance of the choke should be determined by the considerations discussed previously. Then the capacitor should be selected that when combined with the choke inductance (minimum inductance in the case of a swinging choke) will bring the ripple down to the desired value. If it is found impossible to bring the ripple down to the desired figure with practical values in a single section, a second section can be added, as shown in Fig. 12-10B and the reduction factor from Fig. 12-9 applied as discussed under capacitive-input filters. The second choke should not be of the swinging type, but one having a more or less constant inductance with changes in current (smoothing choke).

OUTPUT CAPACITOR

If the supply is intended for use with a Class-A a.f. amplifier, the reactance of the output capacitor should be low for the lowest audio frequency; 16 μf. or more is usually adequate. When the supply is used with a Class-B amplifier (for modulation or for s.s.b. amplification) or a c.w. transmitter, increasing the output capacitance will result in improved dynamic regulation of the supply. However, a region of diminishing returns can be reached, and 20 to 30 μf. will usually suffice for any supply subjected to large changes at a syllabic (or keying) rate.

RESONANCE

Resonance effects in the series circuit across the output of the rectifier which is formed by the first choke and first filter capacitor must be avodied, since the ripple voltage would build up to large values. This not only is the opposite action to that for which the filter is intended, but

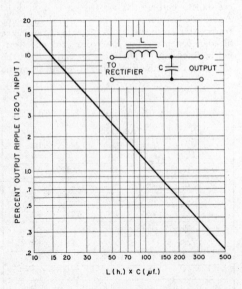

Fig. 12-12—Graph showing combinations of inductance and capacitance that may be used to reduce 120-Hz. ripple with a single-section choke-input filter.

also may cause excessive rectifier peak currents and abnormally high inverse peak voltages. For full-wave rectification the ripple frequency will be 120 Hz. for a 60-Hz. supply, and resonance will occur when the product of choke inductance in henrys time capacitor capacitance in microfarads is equal to 1.77. The corresponding figure for 50-Hz supply (100-Hz. ripple frequency) is 2.53, and for 25-Hz. supply (50-Hz. ripple frequency) 13.5. At least twice these products of inductance and capacitance should be used to ensure against resonance effects. With a swinging choke, the minimum rated inductance of the choke should be used.

RATINGS OF FILTER COMPONENTS

In a power supply using a choke-input filter and properly-designed choke and bleeder resistor, the no-load voltage across the filter capacitors will be about nine-tenths of the a.c. r.m.s. voltage. Nevertheless, it is advisable to use capacitors rated for the *peak* transformer voltage. This large safety factor is suggested because the voltage across the capacitors can reach this peak value if the bleeder should burn out and there is no load on the supply.

In a capacitive-input filter, the capacitors should have a working-voltage rating at least as high, and preferably somewhat higher, than the peak-voltage rating of the transformer. Thus, in the case of a center-tap rectifier having a transformer delivering 550 volts each side of the center-tap, the minimum safe capacitor voltage rating will be 550 × 1.41 or 775 volts. An 800-volt capacitor should be used, or preferably a 1000-volt unit.

Filter Capacitors in Series

Filter capacitors are made in several different types. Electrolytic capacitors, which are available for peak voltages up to about 800, combine high capacitance with small size, since the dielectric is an extremely thin film of oxide on aluminum foil. Capacitors of this type may be connected in series for higher voltages, although the filtering capacitance will be reduced to the resultant of the two capacitances in series. If this arrangement is used, it is important that *each* of the capacitors be shunted with a resistor of about 50 ohms per volt of supply voltage, with a power

rating adequate for the total resistor current at that voltage. These resistors may serve as all or part of the bleeder resistance (see choke-input filters). Capacitors with higher-voltage ratings usually are made with a dielectric of thin paper impregnated with oil. The **working voltage** of a capacitor is the voltage that it will withstand continuously.

Filter Chokes

The input choke may be of the swinging type, the required minimum no-load and full-load inductance values being calculated as described above. For the second choke **(smoothing choke)** values of 4 to 20 henrys ordinarily are used. When filter chokes are placed in the positive leads, the negative being grounded, the windings should be insulated from the core to withstand the full d.c. output voltage of the supply and be capable of handling the required load current.

Filter chokes or inductances are wound on iron cores, with a small gap in the core to prevent magnetic saturation of the iron at high currents. When the iron becomes saturated its permeability decreases, consequently the inductance also decreases. Despite the air gap, the inductance of a choke usualy varies to some extent with the direct current flowing in the winding; hence it is necessary to specify the inductance at the current which the choke is intended to carry. Its inductance with little or no direct current flowing in the winding will usually be considerably higher than the value when full load current is flowing.

NEGATIVE-LEAD FILTERING

For many years it has been almost universal practice to place filter chokes in the positive leads of plate power supplies. This means that the insulation between the choke winding and its core (which should be grounded to chassis as a safety measure) must be adequate to withstand the output voltage of the supply. This voltage requirement is removed if the chokes are placed in the negative lead as shown in Fig. 12-13. With this connection, the capacitance of the transformer secondary to ground appears in parallel with the filter chokes tending to bypass the chokes. However, this effect will be negligible in practical application except in cases where the output ripple must be reduced to a very low figure. Such applications are usually limited to low-voltage devices such as receivers, speech amplifiers and v.f.o.'s where insulation is no problem and the chokes may be placed in the positive side in the conventional manner. In higher-voltage applications, there is no reason why the filter chokes should not be placed in the negative lead to reduce insulation requirements. Choke terminals, negative capacitor terminals and the transformer center-tap terminal should be well protected against accidental contact, since these will assume full supply voltage to chassis should a choke burn out or the chassis connection fail.

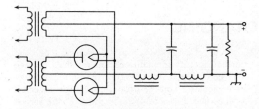

Fig. 12-13—In most applications, the filter chokes may be placed in the negative instead of the positive side of the circuit. This reduces the danger of a voltage breakdown between the choke winding and core.

PLATE AND FILAMENT TRANSFORMERS

Output Voltage

The output voltage which the plate transformer must deliver depends upon the required d.c. load voltage and the type of filter circuit.

With a choke-input filter, the required r.m.s. secondary voltage (each side of center-tap for a center-tap rectifier) can be calculated by the equation:

$$E_t = 1.1 \left[E_o + I(R_1 + R_2 + R_s) \right]$$

where E_o is the required d.c. output voltage, I is the load current (including bleeder current) in amperes, R_1 and R_2 are the d.c. resistances of the chokes, and R_s is the series resistance (transformer and rectifier) rectifier. E_t is the open-circuit r.m.s. voltage.

The approximate transformer output voltage required to give a desired d.c. output voltage with a given load with a capacitive-input filter system can be calculated with Fig. 12-11.

Example:
Required d.c. output volts — 500
Load current to be drawn — 100 ma. (0.1 amp)

Load resistance = $\frac{500}{0.1}$ = 5000 ohms.

Input capacitor — 10 µf.
If the series resistance is 200 ohms, Fig. 12-6 shows that the ratio of d.c. volts to the required transformer peak voltage is 0.85. The ratio to the r.m.s. voltage is 0.85 × 1.414 = 1.2.
The required transformer terminal voltage under load with chokes of 200 and 300 ohms is

$$E_t = \frac{E_o + I\left(R_1 + R_2 + R_s \right)}{1.2}$$

$$= \frac{500 + 0.1\left(200 + 300 + 200 \right)}{1.2}$$

$$= \frac{570}{1.2} = 473 \text{ volts.}$$

Volt-Ampere Rating

The volt-ampere rating of a transformer depends upon the type of filter (capacitor or choke input) used, and upon the type of rectifier used (full-wave center tap, or full-wave bridge). With a capacitive-input filter the heating effect in the secondary is higher because of the high ratio of peak to average current, consequently the volt-amperes handled by the transformer may be several times the watts delivered to the load. With a choke-input filter, provided the input choke has at least the critical inductance, the secondary volt-amperes can be calculated quite closely by the equation:

$$\text{(Full-wave C.T.) } Sec. \; V.A. = \frac{.707 \; EI}{1000}$$

$$\text{(Full-wave bridge) } Sec. \; V.A. = \frac{EI}{1000}$$

where E is the *total* r.m.s. voltage of the secondary (between the outside ends in the case of a center-tapped winding) and I is the d.c. output current in milliamperes (load current plus bleeder current). The primary volt-amperes will be somewhat higher because of transformer losses.

Broadcast & Television Replacement Transformers in Amateur Transmitter Service

Small power transformers of the type sold for replacement in broadcast and television receivers are usually designed for service in terms of use for several hours continuously with capacitor-input filters. In the usual type of amateur transmitter service, where most of the power is drawn intermittently for periods of several minutes with equivalent intervals in between, the published ratings can be exceeded without excessive transformer heating.

With capacitor input, it should be safe to draw 20 to 30 percent more current than the rated value. With a choke-input filter, an increase in current of about 50 percent is permissible. If a bridge rectifier is used, the output voltage will be approximately doubled. In this case, it should be possible in amateur transmitter service to draw the rated current, thus obtaining about twice the rated output power from the transformer.

This does not apply, of course, to amateur transmitter plate transformers which are usually already rated for intermittent service.

VOLTAGE CHANGING

Series Voltage-Dropping Resistor

Certain plates and screens of the various tubes in a transmitter or receiver often require a variety of operating voltages differing from the output voltage of an available power supply. In most cases, it is not economically feasible to provide a separate power supply for each of the required voltages. If the current drawn by an electrode, or combination of electrodes operating at the same voltage, is reasonably constant under normal operating conditions, the required voltage may be obtained from a supply of higher voltage by means of a voltage-dropping resistor in series, as shown in Fig. 12-14A. The value of the series, resistor, R_1, may be obtained from Ohm's Law, $R = \frac{E_d}{I}$, where E_d is the voltage *drop* required from the supply voltage to the desired voltage and I is the total rated current of the load.

Example: The plate of the tube in one stage and the screens of the tubes in two other stages require an operating voltage of 250. The nearest available supply voltage is 400 and the total of the rated plate and screen currents is 75 ma. The required resistance is

$$R = \frac{400-250}{0.075} = \frac{150}{0.075} = 2000 \text{ ohms.}$$

The power rating of the resistor is obtained from P (watts) = I^2R = $(0.075)^2$ (2000) = 11.2 watts. A 20-watt resistor is the nearest safe rating to be used.

Voltage Dividers

The regulation of the voltage obtained in this manner obviously is poor, since any change in current through the resistor will cause a directly proportional change in the voltage drop across the resistor. The regulation can be improved somewhat by connecting a second resistor from the low-voltage end of the first to the negative power-supply terminal, as shown in Fig. 12-14B. Such an arrangement constitutes a voltage **divider**. The second resistor, R_2, acts as a constant load for the first, R_1, so that any variation in current from the tap becomes a smaller percentage of the total current through R_1. The heavier the current drawn by the resistors when they alone are connected across the supply, the better will be the voltage regulation at the tap.

Such a voltage divider may have more than a single tap for the purpose of obtaining more than one value of voltage. A typical arrangement is shown in Fig. 12-14C. The terminal voltage is E, and two taps are provided to give lower voltages, E_1 and E_2, at currents I_1 and I_2 respectively. The smaller the resistance between taps in proportion to the total resistance, the lower the voltage between the taps. For convenience, the voltage divider in the figure is considered to be made up of separate resistances R_1, R_2, R_3, between taps. R_3 carries only the bleeder current, I_3; R_2 carries

I_2 in addition to I_3; R_1 carries I_1, I_2 and I_3. To calculate the resistances required, a bleeder current, I_3, must be assumed; generally it is low compared with the total load current (10 percent or so). Then the required values can be calculated as shown in the caption of Fig. 12-14C, I being in decimal parts of an ampere.

The method may be extended to any desired number of taps, each resistance section being calculated by Ohm's Law using the needed voltage drop across it and the total current through it. The power dissipated by each section may be calculated by multiplying I and E or I^2 and R.

The "Economy" Power Supply

In many transmitters of the 100-watt class, an excellent method for obtaining plate and screen voltages without wasting power in resistors is by the use of the "economy" power-supply circuit. Shown in Fig. 12-15, it is a combination of the full-wave and bridge-rectifier circuits. The voltage at E_1 is the normal voltage obtained with the full-wave circuit, and the voltage at E_2 is that obtained with the bridge circuit (see Fig. 12-1). The *total* d.c. power obtained from the transformer is, of course, the same as when the transformer is used in its normal manner. In c.w. and s.s.b. applications, additional power can usually be drawn without excessive heating, especially if the transformer has a rectifier filament winding that isn't being used.

VOLTAGE-MULTIPLYING CIRCUITS

Although vacuum-tube rectifiers can be used in voltage-multiplying circuits, semiconductor rectifiers are recommended.

A simple half-wave rectifier circuit is shown in Fig. 12-16. Strictly speaking this is not a voltage-multiplying circuit. However, if the current demand is low (a milliampere or less), the d.c. output voltage will be close to the peak voltage of the source, or $1.4 E_{rms}$. A typical applica-

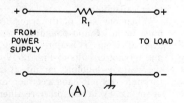

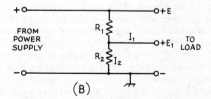

Fig. 12-14—A—A series voltage-dropping resistor. B—Simple voltage divider.

$$R_2 = \frac{E_1}{I_2}; \quad R_1 = \frac{E - E_1}{I_1 + I_2}$$

I_2 must be assumed.
C—Multiple divider circuit.

$$R_3 = \frac{E_2}{I_3}; R_2 = \frac{E_1 - E_2}{I_2 + I_3}; R_1 = \frac{E - E_1}{I_1 + I_2 + I_3}$$

I_3 must be assumed.

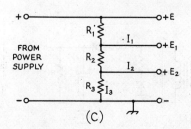

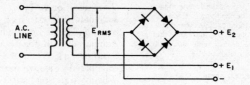

Fig. 12-15—The "economy" power supply circuit is a combination of the full-wave and bridge-rectifier circuits.

tion of the circuit would be to obtain a low bias voltage from a heater winding; the + side of the output can be grounded by reversing the polarity of the rectifier and capacitor. As with all half-wave rectifiers, the output voltage drops quickly with increased current demand.

The resistor R_1 in Fig. 12-16 is included to limit the current through the rectifier, in accordance with the manufacturer's rating for the diode. If the resistance of the transformer winding is sufficient, R_1 can be omitted.

Resistors R_1 in Fig. 12-17 are used to limit the surge currents through the rectifiers. Their values are based on the transformer voltage and the rectifier surge-current rating, since at the instant the power supply is turned on the filter capacitors look like a short-circuited load. Provided the limiting resistors can withstand the surge current, their current-handling capacity is based on the maximum load current from the supply.

Output voltages approaching twice the peak voltage of the transformer can be obtained with

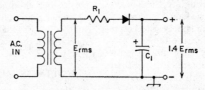

Fig. 12-16—If the current demand is low, a simple half-wave rectifier will deliver a voltage increase. Typical values, for $E_{rms} = 117$ and a load current of 1 ma.:
C_1—50-μf., 250-v. electrolytic.
E_{output}—160 volts.
R_1—22 ohms.

Several types of voltage-doubling circuits are in common use. Where it is not necessary that one side of the transformer secondary be at ground potential, the voltage-doubling circuit of Fig. 12-17 is used. This circuit has several advantages over the voltage-doubling circuit to be described later. For a given output voltage, compared to the full-wave rectifier circuit (Fig. 12-1B), this full-wave doubler circuit requires only half the p.i.v. rating. Again for a given output voltage, compared to a full-wave bridge circuit (Fig. 12-1C) only half as many rectifiers (of the same p.i.v. rating) are required.

the voltage-doubling circuit of Fig. 12-17. Fig. 12-18 shows how the voltage depends upon the ratio of the series resistance to the load resistance, and the product of the load resistance times the filter capacitance.

When one side of the transformer secondary must be at ground potential, as when the a.c. is derived from a heater winding, the voltage-multiplying circuits of Fig. 12-19 can be used. In the voltage-doubling circuit at A, C_1 charges through the left-hand rectifier during one half of the a.c. cycle; the other rectifier is nonconductive during this time. During the other half of the

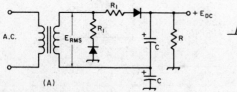

(A)

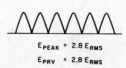

$E_{PEAK} = 2.8 E_{RMS}$
$E_{PRV} = 2.8 E_{RMS}$

Fig. 12-17—Full-wave voltage-doubling circuit. Values of limiting resistors, R_1, depend upon allowable surge currents of rectifiers.

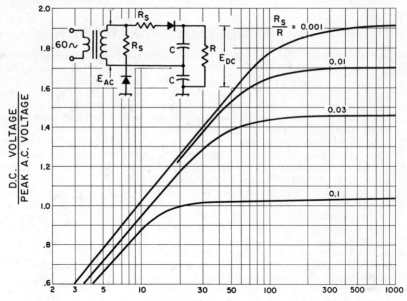

Fig. 12-18—D.c. output voltages from a full-wave voltage-doubling circuit as a function of the filter capacitances and load resistance. For the ratio R_s/R, both resistances are in ohms; for the RC product, R is in thousands of ohms.

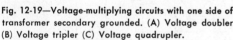

RC (R in thousands of ohms, C in μf.)

cycle the right-hand rectifier conducts and C_2 becomes charged; they see as the source the transformer plus the voltage in C_1. By reversing the polarities of the capacitors and rectifiers, the − side of the output can be grounded.

A voltage-tripling circuit is shown in Fig. 12-19B. On one-half of the a.c. cycle C_1 is charged to the source voltage through the left-hand rectifier. On the opposite half of the cycle the middle rectifier conducts and C_2 is charged to twice the source voltage, because it sees the transformer plus the charge in C_1 as the source. At the same time the right-hand rectifier conducts and, with the transformer and the charge in C_2 as the source, C_3 is charged to three times the transformer voltage. The − side of the output can be grounded if the polarities of all of the capacitors and rectifiers are reversed.

The voltage-quadrupling circuit of Fig. 12-19C works in substantially similar fashion.

In any of the circuits of Fig. 12-19, the output voltage will approach an exact multiple (2, 3 or 4, depending upon the circuit) of the peak a.c. voltage when the output current drain is low and the capacitance values are high.

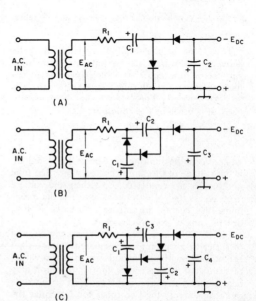

Fig. 12-19—Voltage-multiplying circuits with one side of transformer secondary grounded. (A) Voltage doubler (B) Voltage tripler (C) Voltage quadrupler.

Capacitances are typically 20 to 50 μf., depending upon output current demand. D.c. ratings of capacitors are related to E_{peak} (1.4 E_{ac}):

C_1—Greater than E_{peak}
C_2—Greater than $2E_{peak}$
C_3—Greater than $3E_{peak}$
C_4—Greater than $4E_{peak}$

VOLTAGE STABILIZATION

Gaseous Regulator Tubes

There is frequent need for maintaining the voltage applied to a low-voltage low-current circuit at a practically constant value, regardless of the voltage regulation of the power supply or variations in load current. In such applications, gaseous regulator tubes (0B2/VR105, 0A2/VR150, etc.) can be used to good advantage. The voltage drop across such tubes is constant over a moderately wide current range. Tubes are available for regulated voltages near 150, 105, 90 and 75 volts.

The fundamental circuit for a gaseous regulator is shown in Fig. 12-20A. The tube is connected in series with a **limiting resistor**, R_1, across a source of voltage that must be higher than the **starting** voltage. The starting voltage is about 30 to 40 percent higher than the operating voltage. The load is connected in parallel with the tube. For stable operation, a minimum tube current of 5 to 10 ma. is required. The maximum permissible current with most types is 40 ma.; consequently, the load current cannot exceed 30 to 35 ma. if the voltage is to be stabilized over a range from zero to maximum load current.

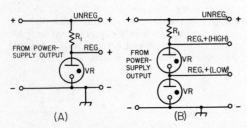

(A)   (B)

Fig. 12-20—Voltage stabilization circuits using VR tubes.

The value of the limiting resistor must lie between that which just permits minimum tube current to flow and that which just passes the maximum permissible tube current when there is no load current. The latter value is generally used. It is given by the equation:

$$R = \frac{(E_s - E_r)}{I}$$

where R is the limiting resistance in ohms, E_s is the voltage of the source across which the tube and resistor are connected, E_r is the rated voltage drop across the regulator tube, and I is the maximum tube current in amperes, (usually 40 ma., or 0.04 amp.).

Fig. 12-20B shows how two tubes may be used in series to give a higher regulated voltage than is obtainable with one, and also to give two values of regulated voltage. The limiting resistor may be calculated as above, using the sum of the voltage drops across the two tubes for E_r. Since the

upper tube must carry more current than the lower, the load connected to the low-voltage tap must take small current. The total current taken by the loads on both taps should not exceed 30 to 35 ma. Regulation of the order of 1 percent can be obtained with these regulator circuits.

The capacitance in shunt with a VR tube should be limited to 0.1 μf. or less. Larger values may cause the tube drop to oscillate between the operating and starting voltages.

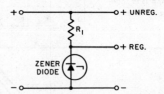

Fig. 12-21—Zener-diode voltage regulation.

A single VR tube may also be used to regulate the voltage to a load current of almost any value so long as the *variation* in the current does not exceed 30 to 35 ma. If, for example, the average load current is 100 ma., a VR tube may be used to hold the voltage constant provided the current does not fall below 85 ma. or rise above 115 ma. In this case, the resistance should be calculated to drop the voltage to the VR-tube rating at the maximum load current to be expected plus 5 ma. Under constant load, effects of line-voltage changes may be eliminated by basing the resistance on load current plus 15 ma.

Zener Diode Regulation

A Zener diode (named after Dr. Carl Zener) can be used to stabilize a voltage source in much the same way as when the gaseous regulator tube is used. The typical circuit is shown in Fig. 12-21. Note that the bar or cathode side of the diode is connected to the positive side of the supply.

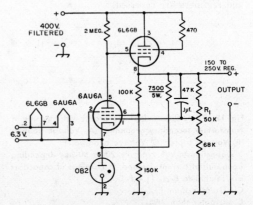

Fig. 12-22—Electronic voltage-regulator circuit. Resistors are ½ watt unless specified otherwise.

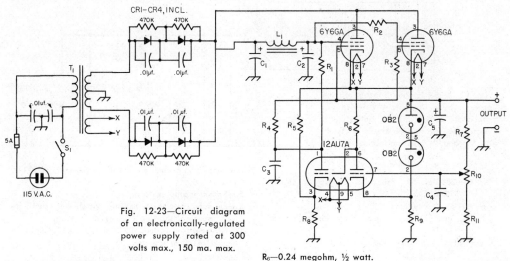

Fig. 12-23—Circuit diagram of an electronically-regulated power supply rated at 300 volts max., 150 ma. max.

C_1, C_2, C_5—16-μf. 600-volt electrolytic.
C_3—0.015-μf. paper.
C_4—0.1-μf. paper.
CR_1-CR_4, incl.—1000 p.r.v., 1-Amp. silicon diode.
R_1—0.3 megohm, $\frac{1}{2}$ watt.
R_2, R_3—100 ohms, $\frac{1}{2}$ watt.
R_4—510 ohms, $\frac{1}{2}$ watt.
R_5, R_8—30,000 ohms, 2 watts.

R_6—0.24 megohm, $\frac{1}{2}$ watt.
R_7—0.15 megohm, $\frac{1}{2}$ watt.
R_9—9100 ohms, 1 watt.
R_{10}—0.1-megohm linear-taper control.
R_{11}—43,000 ohms, $\frac{1}{2}$ watt.
L_1—8-hy., 40-ma. filter choke.
S_1—S.p.s.t. toggle.
T_1—Power transformer: 375-375 volts r.m.s., 160 ma.; 6.3 volts, 3 amps.; (Thor. 22R33).

Zener diodes are available in a wide variety of voltages and power ratings. The voltages range from 3 or 4 to 200, while the power ratings (power diode can dissipate) run from less than 0.25 watt to 50 watts. The ability of the Zener diode to stabilize a voltage is dependent upon the conducting impedance of the diode, which can be as low as one ohm or less in a low-voltage high-power diode to as high as a thousand ohms in a low power high-voltage diode.

More information on Zener (or voltage-reference) diodes is given in Chapter 4.

Electronic Voltage Regulation

Several circuits have been developed for regulating the voltage output of a power supply electronically. While more complicated than the VR-tube circuits, they will handle higher voltages currents and the output voltage may be varied continuously over a wide range. In the circuit of Fig. 12-22, the OB2 regulator tube supplies a reference of approximately +105 volts for the 6AU6A control tube. When the load connected across the output terminals increases, the output voltage tends to decrease. This makes the voltage on the control grid of the 6AU6A less positive, causing the tube to draw less current through the 2-megohm plate resistor. As a consequence the grid voltage on the 6L6GB series regulator becomes more positive and the voltage drop across the 6L6GB decreases, compensating for the reduction in output voltage. With the values shown, adjustment of R_1 will give a regulated output

from 150 to 250 volts, at up to 60 or 70 ma. The available output current can be increased by adding tubes in parallel with the series regulator tube. When this is done, 100-ohm resistors should be wired to each control grid and plate terminal, to reduce the chances for parasitic oscillations.

Another regulator circuit is shown in Fig. 12-23. The principal difference is that screen-grid regulator tubes are used. The fact that a screen-grid tube is relatively insensitive to changes in plate voltage makes it possible to obtain a reduction in ripple voltage adequate for many purposes simply by supplying filtered d.c. to the screens with a consequent saving in weight and cost. The accompanying table shows the performance of the circuit of Fig. 12-23. Column I shows various output voltages, while Column II shows the maximum current that can be drawn at that voltage with negligible variation in output voltage. Column III shows the measured ripple at the maximum current. The second part of the table shows the variation in ripple with load current at 300 volts output.

Table of Performance for Circuit of Fig. 12-23				
I	II	III	Output voltage — 300	
450 v.	22 ma.	3 mv.	150 ma.	2.3 mv.
425 v.	45 ma.	4 mv.	125 ma.	2.8 mv.
400 v.	72 ma.	6 mv.	100 ma.	2.6 mv.
375 v.	97 ma.	8 mv.	75 ma.	2.5 mv.
350 v.	122 ma.	9.5 mv.	50 ma.	3.0 mv.
325 v.	150 ma.	3 mv.	25 ma.	3.0 mv.
300 v.	150 ma.	2.3 mv.	10 ma.	2.5 mv.

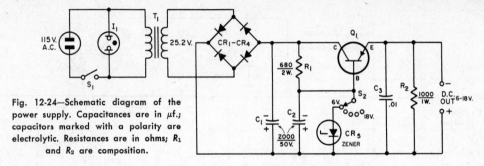

Fig. 12-24—Schematic diagram of the power supply. Capacitances are in μf.; capacitors marked with a polarity are electrolytic. Resistances are in ohms; R_1 and R_2 are composition.

C_1, C_2—2000-μf. 50 volts d.c. electrolytic (Mallory CG23U5OC1).

C_3—0.01-μf. disk ceramic.

CR_1–CR_4, inc.—50 p.i.v. 3-amp. silicon diode (Motorola 1N4719).

CR_5—Voltage regulator diode.

I_1—Neon lamp assembly with resistor (Leecraft 32-2111).

Q_1—2N1970.

S_1—S.p.s.t. toggle switch.

S_2—Phenolic rotary, 1 section, 2-pole (1 used), 6-position, shorting (Mallory 3126J).

T_1—Filament transformer, 25.2 volts, 2 amp. (Knight 54 D 4140 or similar).

Low-Voltage Regulators

Most transistorized amateur equipment requires a power supply voltage of between 6 and 28 volts, at currents up to 2 amperes. It is desirable to use voltage regulation to assure good stability of operating conditions.

One of the simplest forms of low-voltage regulation is shown at Fig. 12-24. A bridge rectifier supplies 25 volts d.c. to a series regulator transistor, Q_1, whose base bias is established by means of a Zener diode, CR_5, providing a voltage reference of a more or less fixed level. C_1 is the input capacitor for the filter and C_2 filters out the ripple which appears across CR_5. R_1 is chosen to establish a safe Zener diode current, which is dependent upon the wattage rating of the diode. A 1-watt Zener diode is adequate for the circuit of Fig. 12-24. R_2 is a bleeder resistor and C_3 is an r.f. bypass. If several output voltages are desired, say from 6 to 18 volts, Zener diodes from 6 to 18 volts can be wired to S_2 as shown.

When a 2N1970 is used at Q_1, the value of R_1 will be 680 ohms. This value offers a compromise for the 5 reference diodes used (6, 9, 12, 15, and 18 volts).

The output of the supply is equal to the Zener voltage minus the emitter-to-base bias voltage of Q_1. Both the Zener voltage and bias voltage change with load variations. The bias voltage will be approximately zero with only R_2 as a load, but will rise to roughly 0.3 volts with a 1-ampere load connected to the output. An increase in load current lowers the unregulated d.c. input voltage which appears across CR_5 and R_1. Zener current is reduced, decreasing the voltage at which the diode regulates. How much the voltage drops depends upon the characteristics of the particular Zener employed.

This power supply has very low output ripple. The main limitation of this circuit is the possibility of destroying Q_1, the series-regulator transistor, when a dead short or heavy overload is

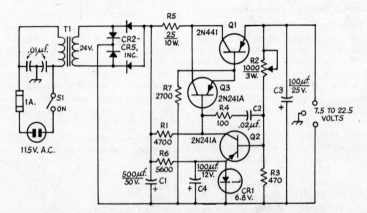

Fig. 12-25—Circuit of the improved regulator. Resistance is in ohms. Fixed-value resistors are ½-watt composition unless otherwise noted. Polarized capacitors are electrolytic. CR_1 is a 1N754 Zener diode, or equal. CR_2–CR_5, incl., are 1N191s or equiv. T_1 is a 24-volt, 1-ampere transformer.

Table of operating conditions for Fig. 12-25.

E_o Volts	I_o[1] Ma.	E_{AC}[2] Mv. R.M.S.	E_1[3] Mv.	E_s[4] Mv.
7.5	300	3.3	75	25
10.0	250	4.2	85	30
12.5	230	4.6	95	35
15.0	170	5.0	100	45
17.5	135	5.3	100	55
20.0	100	6.0	100	65
22.5	90	8.0	110	90

[1] Maximum load current with 115 v. a.c. input.
[2] Output ripple voltage at maximum load, 115 v. a.c. input.
[3] Change in output voltage as output current is varied from no load to full load with constant 115 v. a.c. input.
[4] Change in output voltage with a constant load corresponding to one half that of Column 2 as the line voltage is varied from 105 to 125 volts.

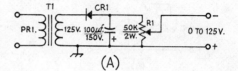

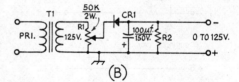

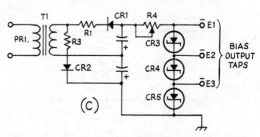

Fig. 12-26—Circuits of typical bias supplies using solid-state rectifiers. Zener-diode regulation is shown at C.

connected across the output of the supply. To protect Q_1 during normal operation, it should be mounted on a fairly large heat sink which is thermally-coupled to the main chassis of the supply. The transistor should be insulated from the sink by means of a mica spacer and a thin layer of silicone grease. The sink can then be bolted directly to the chassis.

AN IMPROVED TRANSISTOR REGULATOR

A versatile, yet simple, regulated low-voltage supply is shown in the practical circuit of Fig. 12-25. A current-limiting resistor, R_5, is connected between the unregulated d.c. and Q_1 to protect against current overloads. The addition of R_5 does not have a significant effect upon the regulation of the supply. R_6 supplies current to CR_1 and is set to provide approximately 5 ma. Q_1 and Q_3 are connected in what is called a Darlington pair. At first approximation, Q_3 can be regarded as a current amplifier which also raises the base impedance of Q_1 as seen by the collector circuit of Q_2. C_2 and R_4 prevent high-frequency oscillation from occurring. C_3 helps to improve the transient response and R_2 has been made variable to provide a means for adjusting the output voltage. C_4 reduces ripple across CR_1, thus greatly reducing the ripple in the regulator output. R_7 prevents Q_3 from being cut off at low output currents. As in the supply of Fig. 12-24, Q_1 should be mounted on a fairly large heat sink, preferably above the chassis, and R_5 should also be in the clear. These two components should be spaced well away from Q_2, Q_3, and CR_1 to prevent their heat from affecting the latter three components. The accompanying table shows typical operating conditions for this regulator.

BIAS SUPPLIES

Bias supplies are used to provide grid voltage to the p.a. and modulator stages of amateur transmitters, to supply grid voltage to linear amplifiers, and to provide control voltage for cutting off receiver and transmitter output. Negative supply voltage is also used for grid-block keying in most modern amateur exciters.

Typical circuits for bias supplies are shown in Fig. 12-26. At A, a simple half-wave rectifier (CR_1) provides d.c. voltage to R_1 which is adjusted for the desired output. If the bias is being fed to a class C amplifier, the circuit at B is preferred. R_1 is used to set the bias voltage at the desired level and R_1 is the value that would ordinarily be used as a grid-leak resistor for the class-C stage. No other grid resistor should be used.

A voltage-doubler bias supply is shown at C. T_1 is chosen to provide the desired output voltage, when doubled, while allowing for the voltage drop across R_4. Zener diodes are connected in series (CR_3 through CR_5, incl.) to offer regulation and to enable the user to obtain three different bias voltages. The Zener diodes are selected for the operating voltages required. Fewer, or more, Zener diodes can be connected in the string, or a single Zener diode can be used. R_4 is adjusted to provide the proper Zener-diode current for the string, and its wattage must be sufficient to handle the current flowing through it. R_2 and R_3 are current-limiting resistors to protect CR_1 and CR_2. More information on Zener-diode use is given in Chapter 4. A discussion of voltage doublers is presented earlier in this chapter.

Of course, full-wave center-tapped and full-wave bridge rectifiers can be used in place of the half-wave examples shown in Fig. 12-26. Similarly, voltage triplers can be used in bias supplies. The full-wave rectifiers are easier to filter and may be preferred for some applications.

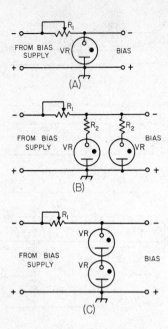

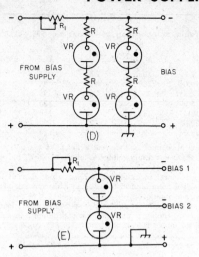

Fig. 12-27—Illustrating the use of VR tubes in stabilizing protective-bias supplies. R_1 is a resistor whose value is adjusted to limit the current through each VR tube to 5 ma. before amplifier excitation is applied. R and R_2 are current-equalizing resistors of 50 to 1000 ohms.

Gaseous Voltage Regulators

Standard VR tubes can be used as bias-voltage regulators in a manner similar to Zener diodes. Some typical circuits are given in Fig. 12-27. A VR tube with a voltage rating anywhere between the biasing-voltage value which will reduce the input to the amplifier to a safe level when excitation is removed, and the operating value of bias, should be chosen. R_1 is adjusted, without amplifier excitation, until the VR tube ignites and draws about 5 ma. Additional voltage to bring the bias up to the operating value when excitation is applied can be obtained from a grid leak resistor, as discussed in the transmitter chapter.

Each VR tube will handle 40 ma. of grid current. If the grid current exceeds this value under any condition, similar VR tubes should be added in parallel, as shown in Fig. 12-27B, for each 40 ma., or less, of additional grid current. The resistors R_2 are for the purpose of helping to maintain equal currents through each VR tube, and should have a value of 50 to 1000 ohms, or more.

If the voltage rating of a single VR tube is not sufficiently high for the purpose, other VR tubes may be used in series (or series-parallel if required to satisfy grid-current requirements) as shown in the diagrams of Fig. 12-27C and D.

If a single value of fixed bias will serve for more than one stage, the biasing terminal of each such stage may be connected to a single supply of this type, provided only that the total grid current of all stages so connected does not exceed the current rating of the VR tube or tubes.

Providing the VR-tube current rating is not exceeded, a series arrangement may be tapped for lower voltage, as shown at E.

PROTECTION OF SILICON POWER DIODES

The important specifications of a silicon diode are:

1) P.I.V. (or p.r.v.), the peak inverse (or peak reverse) voltage.

2) I_0, the average d.c. current rating.

3) I_{REP}, the peak repetitive forward current, and

4) I_{SURGE}, the peak one-cycle surge current. The first two specifications appear in most catalogs. The last two often do not, but they are very important.

Since the rectifier never allows current to flow more than half the time, when it does conduct it has to pass at least twice the average d.c. current. With a capacitor-input filter, the rectifier conducts much less than half the time, so that when it does conduct, it may pass as much as ten to twenty times the average d.c. current, under certain conditions. This peak current is I_{REP}, the peak repetitive forward current.

Also, when the supply is first turned on, the discharged input capacitor looks like a dead short, and the rectifier passes a very heavy current. This is I_{SURGE}. The maximum I_{SURGE} rating is usually for a duration of one cycle (at 60 Hz.), or about 16.7 milliseconds.

If you don't have a manufacturer's data sheet, you can make an educated guess about your diode's capability by using these rules of thumb for silicon diodes of the type commonly used in amateur power supplies:

Rule 1) The maximum I_{REP} rating can be assumed to be approximately four times the maximum I_0 rating.

Rule 2) The maximum I_{SURGE} rating can be assumed to be approximately twelve times the maximum I_O rating. (This should provide a reasonable safety factor. Silicon rectifiers with 750-ma. d.c. ratings, as an example, seldom have 1-cycle surge ratings of less than 15 amperes; some are rated up to 35 amperes or more.) From this then, it can be seen that the rectifier should be selected on the basis of I_{SURGE} and not on I_O ratings.

THERMAL PROTECTION

The junction of a diode is quite small, hence it must operate at a high current density. The heat-handling capability is, therefore, quite small. Normally, this is not a prime consideration in high-voltage, low-current supplies. When using high-current rectifiers at or near their maximum ratings, usually 2-ampere (or larger) stud-mount rectifiers, some form of heat sinking is usually necessary. Frequently, mounting the rectifier on the main chassis—directly, or by means of thin mica insulating washers—will suffice. If insulated from the chassis, a thin layer of silicone grease should be used between the diode and the insulator, and between the insulator and the chassis to assure good heat conduction. Large high-current rectifiers often require special heat sinks to maintain a safe operating temperature. Forced-air cooling is sometimes used as a further aid. Safe case temperatures are usually given in the manufacturer's data sheets and should be observed if the maximum capabilities of the diode are to be realized.

SURGE PROTECTION

Each time the power supply is activated, assuming the input filter capacitor has been discharged, the rectifiers must look into what represents a dead short, as discussed earlier. Some form of surge protection is usually necessary to protect the diodes until the input capacitor becomes nearly charged. Although the d.c. resistance of the transformer secondary can be relied upon in some instances to provide ample surge-current limiting, it is seldom enough on high-voltage power supplies to be suitable. Series resistors can be installed between the secondary and the rectifier strings as illustrated in Fig. 12-17, but are a deterrent to good voltage regulation. By installing a surge-limiting device in the primary circuit of the plate transformer, the need for series resistors in the secondary circuit can be avoided. Two practical methods for primary-circuit surge control are shown in Fig. 12-28. At A, R_s introduces a voltage drop in the primary feed to T_1 until C is nearly charged. Then, after C becomes partially charged, the voltage drop across R_s lessens and allows K_1 to pull in, thus applying full primary power to T_1 as K_{1A} shorts out R_s. R_s is usually a 25-watt resistor whose resistance is somewhere between 15 and 50 ohms, depending upon the power supply characteristics. A practical example of this is given in *QST*, October 1967, page 18.

A simplified version of surge protection is shown at B. Here a 115-volt light bulb is inserted in one leg of the primary. S_1 is kept open until the input filter capacitor is nearly charged, then it is closed to short out I_1. I_1 can be a 40- or 60-watt lamp for most power supplies. A practical example of this circuit is given later in this chapter.

Transient Problems

A common cause of trouble is transient voltages on the a.c. power line. These are short spikes, mostly, that can temporarily increase the voltage seen by the rectifier to values much higher than the normal transformer voltage. They come from distant lightning strokes, electric motors turning on and off, and so on. Transients cause unexpected, and often unexplained, loss of silicon rectifiers.

It's always wise to suppress line transients, and it can be easily done. Fig. 12-29A shows one way. C_1 looks like 280,000 ohms at 60 Hz., but to a sharp transient (which has only high-frequency components), it is an effective bypass. C_2 pro-

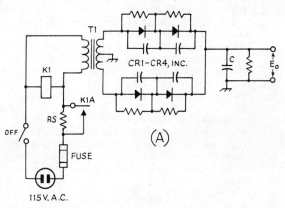

(A)

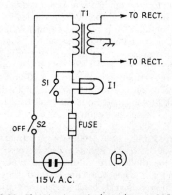

(B)

Fig. 12-28—The circuit at A shows how a 115-volt a.c. relay and a series dropping resistor, R_s, can provide surge protection while C charges. A simplified, manually-operated surge-protection system is shown at B. A switch and a light bulb provide protection to the rectifiers as C charges.

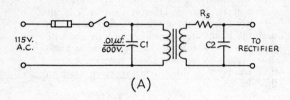

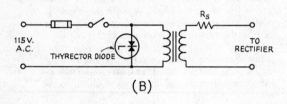

Fig. 12-29—Methods of suppressing line transients.

vides additional protection on the secondary side of the transformer. It should be 0.01 μf. for transformer voltages of 100 or less, and 0.001 μf. for high-voltage transformers.

Fig. 12-29B shows another transient-suppression method using selenium suppressor diodes. The diodes do not conduct unless the peak voltage becomes abnormally high. Then they clip the transient peaks. General Electric sells protective diodes under the trade name, "Thyrector." Sarkes-Tarzian uses the descriptive name, "Klipvolt."

Transient voltages can go as high as twice the normal line voltage before the suppressor diodes clip the peaks. Capacitors cannot give perfect suppression either. Thus, it is a good idea to use power-supply rectifiers rated at about twice the expected p.i.v.

Diodes in Series

Where the p.i.v. rating of a single diode is not sufficient for the application, similar diodes may be used in series. (Two 500-p.i.v. diodes in series will withstand 1000 p.i.v., and so on.) When this is done, a resistor and a capacitor should be placed across each diode in the string. Fig. 12-30 illustrates the reason. In Fig. 12-30A, we have a half-wave rectifier operating from a 70-volt transformer. The output voltage with light loading is 100 volts (1.4 E_{RMS}). So is the peak transformer voltage. The p.i.v. required in this half-wave circuit is 200 volts (2.8 E_{RMS}). We might consider using two 100-p.i.v. rectifiers. In Fig. 12-30B, we see what might happen. Even though the diodes are of the same type, same p.i.v. and all, when they are cut off they may have widely-different back resistances. In this example, one diode has a back resistance of 1 megohm and the other, 3 megohms. The inverse voltage divides according to Ohm's Law. The better diode, the one with 3-megohm back resistance, gets 150 volts. The other diode gets 50 volts. The better diode will break down.

If we put a swamping resistor across each diode, as shown in Fig. 12-30C, the resultant resistance across each diode will be almost the same, and the back voltage will divide almost equally. A good rule of thumb for resistor size is this: Multiply the p.i.v. rating of the diode by 500 ohms. For example, a 50-p.i.v. diode should be shunted by 50 × 500, or 25,000 ohms.

The shift from forward conduction to high back resistance does not take place instantly in a silicon diode. Some diodes take longer than others to develop high back resistance. To protect the "fast" diodes in a series string until all the diodes are properly cut off, a capacitor should be placed across each diode.

Fig. 12-30D shows the complete series diode circuit. The capacitors should be noninductive, ceramic disk, for example, and should be well matched. Use 10-percent-tolerance capacitors if possible.

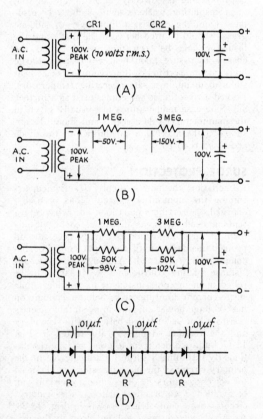

Fig. 12-30—A—Half-wave rectifier circuit with two diodes in series. B—Equivalent circuit when diodes are not conducting. The inverse voltage does not divide equally. C—Voltages are equalized by shunting the diodes with equal resistances of value low compared to the diode back resistances. D—Capacitors are added across each diode to distribute transient voltages equally.

Diodes in Parallel

Diodes can be placed in parallel to increase current-handling capability. Equalizing resistors should be added as shown in Fig. 12-31. Without the resistors, one diode may take most of the current. The resistors should be selected to have about a 1-volt drop at the expected peak repetitive current.

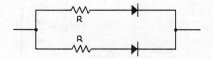

Fig. 12-31—Diodes in parallel should have equalizing resistors. See text for appropriate value.

POWER-LINE CONSIDERATIONS

POWER LINE CONNECTIONS

If the transmitter is rated at much more than 100 watts, special consideration should be given to the a.c. line running into the station. In some residential systems, three wires are brought in from the outside to the distribution board, while in other systems there are only two wires. In the three-wire system, the third wire is the **neutral** which is grounded. The voltage between the other two wires normally is 230, while half of this voltage (115) appears between each of these wires and neutral, as indicated in Fig. 12-32A. In systems of this type, usually it will be found that the 115-volt household load is divided as evenly as possible between the two sides of the circuit, half of the load being connected between one wire and the neutral, while the other half of the load is connected between the other wire and neutral. Heavy appliances, such as electric stoves and heaters, normally are designed for 230-volt operation and therefore are connected across the wires should be fused, a fuse should never be used in the wire to the neutral, nor should a switch be used in this side of the line. The reason for this is that opening the neutral wire does not disconnect the equipment. It simply leaves the equipment on one side of the 230-volt circuit in series with whatever load may be across the other side of the circuit, as shown in Fig. 12-32B. Furthermore, with the neutral open, the voltage will then be divided between the two sides

in inverse proportion to the load resistance, the voltage on one side dropping below normal, while it soars on the other side, unless the loads happen to be equal.

The usual line running to baseboard outlets is rated at 15 amperes. Considering the power consumed by filaments, lamps, transmitter, receiver and other auxiliary equipment, it is not unusual to find this 15-ampere rating exceeded by the requirements of a station of only moderate power. It must also be kept in mind that the same branch may be in use for other household purposes through another outlet. For this reason, and to minimize light blinking when keying or modulating the transmitter, a separate heavier line should be run from the distribution board to the station whenever possible. (A three-volt drop in line voltage will cause noticeable light blinking.)

If the system is of the three-wire type, the three wires should be brought into the station so that the load can be distributed to keep the line balanced. The voltage across a fixed load on one side of the circuit will increase as the load current on the other side is increased. The rate of increase will depend upon the resistance introduced by the neutral wire. If the resistance of the neutral is low, the increase will be correspondingly small. When the currents in the two circuits are balanced, no current flows in the neutral wire and the system is operating at maximum efficiency.

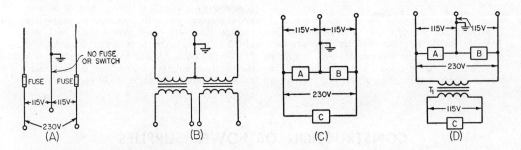

Fig. 12-32—Three-wire power-line circuits. A—normal 3-wire-line termination. No fuse should be used in the grounded (neutral) line. B—Showing that a switch in the neutral does not remove voltage from either side of the line. C—Connections for both 115- and 230-volt transformers. D—Operating a 115-volt plate transformer from the 230-volt line to avoid light blinking. T_1 is a 2-to-1 step-down transformer.

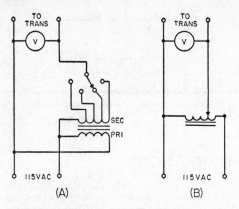

Fig. 12-33—Two methods of transformer primary control. At A is a tapped toy transformer which may be connected so as to boost or buck the line voltage as required. At B is indicated a variable transformer or autotransformer (Variac) which feeds the transformer primaries.

Light blinking can be minimized by using transformers with 230-volt primaries in the power supplies for the keyed or intermittent part of the load, connecting them across the two ungrounded wires with no connection to the neutral, as shown in Fig. 12-32C. The same can be accomplished by the insertion of a step-down transformer whose primary operates at 230 volts and whose secondary delivers 115 volts. Conventional 115-volt transformers may be operated from the secondary of the step-down transformer (see Fig. 12-32D).

When a special heavy-duty line is to be installed, the local power company should be consulted as to local requirements. In some localities it is necessary to have such a job done by a licensed electrician, and there may be special requirements to be met. Some amateurs terminate the special line to the station at a switch box, while others may use electric-stove receptacles as the termination. The power is then distributed around the station by means of conventional outlets at convenient points. All circuits should be properly fused.

Fusing

All transformer primary circuits should be properly fused. To determine the approximate current rating of the fuse to be used, multiply each current being drawn from the supply in amperes by the voltage at which the current is being drawn. Include the current taken by bleeder resistances and voltage dividers. In the case of series resistors, use the source voltage, not the voltage at the equipment end of the resistor. Include filament power if the transformer is supplying filaments. After multiplying the various voltages and currents, add the individual products. Then divide by the line voltage and add 10 or 20 per cent. Use a fuse with the nearest larger current rating.

LINE-VOLTAGE ADJUSTMENT

In certain communities trouble is sometimes experienced from fluctuations in line voltage. Usually these fluctuations are caused by a variation in the load on the line and, since most of the variation comes at certain fixed times of the day or night, such as the times when lights are turned on at evening, they may be taken care of by the use of a manually operated compensating device. A simple arrangement is shown in Fig. 12-33A. A toy transformer is used to boost or buck the line voltage as required. The transformer should have a tapped secondary varying between 6 and 20 volts in steps of 2 or 3 volts and its secondary should be capable of carrying the full load current.

The secondary is connected in series with the line voltage and, if the phasing of the windings is correct, the voltage applied to the primaries of the transmitter transformers can be brought up to the rated 115 volts by setting the toy-transformer tap switch on the right tap. If the phasing of the two windings of the toy transformer happens to be reversed, the voltage will be reduced instead of increased. This connection may be used in cases where the line voltage may be above 115 volts. This method is preferable to using a resistor in the primary of a power transformer since it does not affect the voltage regulation as seriously. The circuit of 12-33B illustrates the use of a variable autotransformer (Variac) for adjusting line voltage.

Constant-Voltage Transformers

Although comparatively expensive, special transformers called **constant-voltage transformers** are available for use in cases where it is necessary to hold line voltage and/or filament voltage constant with fluctuating supply-line voltage. They are rated over a range of 17 v.a. at 6.3 volts output up to several thousand v.a. at 115 or 230 volts. On the average they will hold their output voltages within one percent under an input-voltage variation of 30 percent.

CONSTRUCTION OF POWER SUPPLIES

The length of most leads in a power supply is unimportant, so that the arrangement of components from this consideration is not a factor. More important are the points of good high-voltage insulation, adequate conductor size for filament wiring — important of all — safety to the operator. Exposed high-voltage terminals or wiring which might be bumped into accidentally should not be permitted to exist. They should be covered with adequate insulation or placed in-

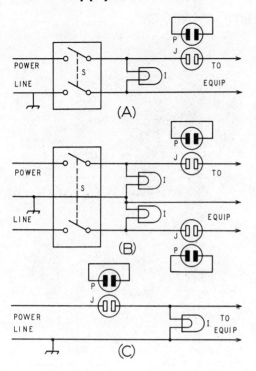

Fig. 12-34—Reliable arrangements for cutting off all power to the transmitter. S is an enclosed double-pole power switch, J a standard a.c. outlet. P a shorted plug to fit the outlet and I a red lamp.

A is for a two-wire 115-volt line, B for a three-wire 230-volt system, and C a simplified arrangement for low-power stations.

accessible to contact during normal operation and adjustment of the transmitter. Power-supply units should be fused individually. All negative terminals of plate supplies and positive terminals of bias supplies should be securely grounded to the chassis, and the chassis connected to a waterpipe or radiator ground. All transformer, choke, and capacitor cases should also be grounded to the chassis. A.c. power cords and chassis connectors should be arranged so that exposed contacts are never "live." Starting at the conventional a.c. wall outlet which is female, one end of the cord should be fitted with a male plug. The other end of the cord should have a female receptacle. The input connector of the power supply should have a male receptacle to fit the female receptacle of the cord. The power-output connector on the power supply should be a female socket. A male plug to fit this socket should be connected to the cable going to the equipment. The opposite end of the cable should be fitted with a female connector, and the series should terminate with a male con-

nector on the equipment. There should be no "live" exposed contacts at any point, regardless of where a disconnection may be made.

Rectifier filament leads should be kept short to assure proper voltage at the rectifier socket. Through a metal chassis, grommet-lined clearance holes will serve for voltages up to 500 or 750, but ceramic feed-through insulators should be used for higher voltages. Bleeder and voltage-dropping resistors should be placed where they are open to air circulation. Placing them in confined space reduces the rating.

SAFETY PRECAUTIONS

All power supplies in an installation should be fed through a single main power-line switch so that all power may be cut off quickly, either before working on the equipment, or in case of an accident. Spring-operated switches or relays are not sufficiently reliable for this important service. Foolproof devices for cutting off all power to the transmitter and other equipment are shown in Fig. 12-34. The arrangements shown in Fig. 12-34A and B are similar circuits for two-wire (115-volt) and three-wire (230-volt) systems. S is an enclosed double-throw switch of the sort usually used as the entrance switch in house installations. J is a standard a.c. outlet and P a shorted plug to fit the outlet. The switch should be located prominently in plain sight and members of the household should be instructed in its location and use. I is a red lamp located alongside the switch. Its purpose is not so much to serve as a warning that the power is on as it is to help in identifying and quickly locating the switch should it become necessary for someone else to cut the power off in an emergency.

The outlet J should be placed in some corner out of sight where it will not be a temptation for children or others to play with. The shorting plug can be removed to open the power circuit if there are others around who might inadvertently throw the switch while the operator is working on the rig. If the operator takes the plug with him, it will prevent someone from turning on the power in his absence and either injuring themselves or the equipment or perhaps starting a fire. Of utmost importance is the fact that the outlet J *must* be placed in the *ungrounded* side of the line.

Those who are operating low power and feel that the expense or complication of the switch isn't warranted can use the shorted-plug idea as the main power switch. In this case, the outlet should be located prominently and identified by a signal light, as shown in Fig 12-34C.

The test bench ought to be fed through the main power switch, or a similar arrangement at the bench, if the bench is located remote from the transmitter.

A bleeder resistor with a power rating giving a considerable margin of safety should be used across the output of all transmitter power supplies so that the filter capacitors will be discharged when the high-voltage transformer is turned off.

12-VOLT BATTERY CHARGER

This a.c.-operated 12-volt 2-ampere battery-charger circuit was developed by RCA. It is a useful piece of equipment for any ham shack because it can be used to keep a workshop storage battery fully charged, to assure that the automobile's battery is fully charged for the following day's mobile activity, or to keep field-day or emergency batteries at full charge. The charging rate is 2 amperes until a preset battery voltage is reached. Then, the battery receives a "trickle" charge to keep it ready for use.

How It Works

Refering to Fig. 12-36, T_1 provides a secondary output of 21 volts at 2 amperes. This voltage is rectified by CR_1 through CR_4. The d.c. from the bridge rectifier charges C_1, which in turn permits CR_5 to conduct. This action supplies gate current to Q_1 and allows it to fire. When this happens the SCR, Q_1, and the battery being charged, represent a full load for the bridge rectifier. A charging current which is proportional to the difference between the battery voltage and the rectifier output then flows through the battery. R_1 limits the current to a safe value to protect the bridge rectifier diodes in the event that the battery is completely depleted. C_1 stays charged to enable Q_1 to continue conducting, thus assuring that charging current flows for practically the full 180 degrees of each successive half cycle of input until the battery is fully charged.

Once the battery is charged, a regenerative switch (Q_2 and Q_3) is triggered into operation at a preset point which is established by the setting of R_3, the cutout control. When the switch conducts, the transistors provide a discharge path for C_1, causing the SCR to be nonconductive

Fig. 12-35—This battery charger is built on a 4 x 5 x 6-inch aluminum chassis and has a home-made panel. The power transformer is enclosed (left side of the chassis) to lessen shock hazard. The small parts are mounted on perforated board and the assembly is located under the chassis. R_1 is visible at the far right.

on the succeeding half cycle of the input. During this period the 12-volt pilot lamp, I_1, illuminates and indicates that a full charge has been reached. The current in the lamp circuit (R_1, I_1, and the regenerative switch) establishes a trickle charge of roughly 150 milliamperes.

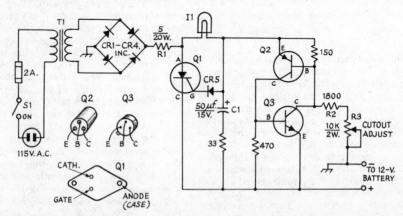

Fig. 12-36—Schematic of the battery charger. Resistance is in ohms. Fixed-value resistors are ½-watt composition unless otherwise indicated. C_1 is electrolytic.

CR₁–CR₄, inc.—1-ampere, 200-p.r.v. diode (RCA 1N2860).
CR₅—125-ma. 100-p.r.v. silicon diode (RCA 1N3754).
I₁—No. 1488 (150-ma., 12-volt) pilot lamp.
Q₁—RCA 2N3228 SCR.
Q₂—RCA 2N2614.   Q₃—RCA 2N3241A.

R₁, R₂—For reference purposes.
R₃—10,000-ohm linear-taper 2-watt control.
S₁—S.p.s.t. switch.
T₁—Allied/Knight Catalog No. 54E2332 or Stancor RT-202, or equivalent (21 volts total secondary at 2 amperes).

Depending upon the actual beta of the transistor used at Q_2, the value of bias resistor R_2 may have to be determined experimentally. If the bias is wrong, R_3 will not have any effect on the circuit. Ordinarily, a value somewhere between 1000 and 10,000 ohms will be required. The value shown on the diagram is recommended by RCA.

Operation

The charger should be connected to the battery, observing correct polarity, then turned on. R_1 should be set for the full-charge voltage required. A midrange setting results is approximately 12.5 volts at full charge with the model described here. Clockwise rotation increases the charge level. If a battery is nearly charged when this unit is connected to it, it may be necessary to advance R_3 until I_1 extinguishes, indicating that a full charge is taking place.

This model is built on a $4 \times 5 \times 6$-inch aluminum chassis and has a home-made 5×6-inch aluminum panel. The transformer is enclosed in a perforated aluminum shield to prevent accidental contact with the primary terminals. Most of the small parts are installed on a piece of perforated insulating board. The board is mounted on standoff posts under the chassis. R_1 is mounted on top of the chassis, out in the clear, to allow adequate circulation of air around it. It runs quite warm during full-charge periods.

12-VOLT REGULATED POWER SUPPLY

This general-purpose regulated power supply has electronic filtering which provides very clean output voltage. The ripple was measured with a 1-ampere load connected across the output terminals; it was too low to be measured accurately with a standard oscilloscope. A 1-ampere transformer is used, therefore the output current should be limited to approximately 500 milliamperes. Momentary loads of up to one ampere will not damage the supply, however.

The Circuit

In the circuit of Fig. 12-37, output from T_1 is fed to a full-wave bridge rectifier to provide 25 volts d.c. This voltage is fed to the collector of Q_1, the series regulator. Q_1 is mounted on a home-made heat sink which is attached to the main chassis. CR_1, a 14-volt Zener diode, provides a reference voltage for the regulator transistor, Q_1. Current to CR_1 is supplied by means of R_1. C_3 is the input filter capacitor. C_4 filters whatever ripple may appear across CR_1. The output of the supply is equal to the Zener voltage minus the emitter-to-base voltage of Q_1—approximately 0.7 volts. This results in an output voltage of 13.3 volts, but will depend on the actual Zener voltage. Most low-cost Zener diodes have a 10- or 20-percent tolerance, hence, it is

impossible to predict the absolute final output voltage. Whatever it is, it will be close enough to 12 volts to work alright with any of the *Handbook* circuits calling for 12 volts at up to 0.5 ampere.

R_2 is a bleeder, and C_5 is an r.f. bypass. C_1 and C_2 bypass the a.c. line and offer some protection against transients.

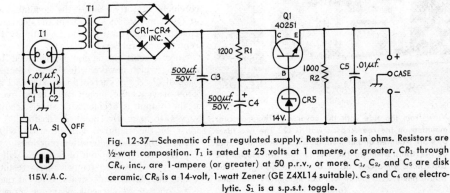

Fig. 12-37—Schematic of the regulated supply. Resistance is in ohms. Resistors are ½-watt composition. T_1 is rated at 25 volts at 1 ampere, or greater. CR_1 through CR_4, inc., are 1-ampere (or greater) at 50 p.r.v., or more. C_1, C_2, and C_5 are disk ceramic. CR_5 is a 14-volt, 1-watt Zener (GE Z4XL14 suitable). C_3 and C_4 are electrolytic. S_1 is a s.p.s.t. toggle.

Construction

The model shown here is built in a $3 \times 4 \times 5$-inch Minibox. The size of the cabinet will depend upon the physical dimensions of the transformer used at T_1. An etched-circuit board holds most of the components. (A scale template showing the placement of all of the parts is available from the ARRL for 25 cents and a SASE.) Point-to-point wiring can be used if the constructor does not wish to use a circuit board.

The heat sink for Q_1 is an aluminum L bracket made from $\frac{1}{8}$-inch thick stock. Each side of the sink is 2 inches wide and $1\frac{1}{2}$ inch high. Q_1 is insulated from the sink by means of its mica washer and two nylon shoulder washers. The insulating materials come with the transistor. Silicone grease is applied on both sides of the mica insulator to enhance heat transfer.

Three output terminals are used. One is common to the B-plus line, one connects to the minus bus, and the third terminal is common to the case. Depending upon the polarity required, the case can be connected to either side of the output by means of a shorting strap. The etched-circuit board is mounted inside the case by means of two metal spacers.

ADJUSTABLE REGULATED TRANSISTOR POWER SUPPLY

This power supply will develop from 1 to 15 volts at currents up to 1 ampere, which should be adequate to power most transistorized devices. Short-circuit protection is also provided.

How It Works

The maximum required reference voltage is set by Zener diode CR_1. The desired reference voltage is taken from R_1, the voltage-control potentiometer. This reference voltage is applied to the base of Q_1, a d.c. amplifier, which in turn establishes a stiff reference voltage at the emitter of Q_2, the heart of the regulator.

Transistors Q_3 and Q_4 form a two-stage emitter-follower d.c. amplifier. Thus the voltage applied to the base of Q_3 will determine the the voltage at the emitter of Q_4, and also the output voltage. Suppose a voltage is applied to the emitter of Q_2 from Q_1, the reference-voltage amplifier. The output voltage is also applied to the base of Q_2 via R_5. If the output voltage is greater than Q_2's emitter voltage, base current will flow, causing Q_2 to conduct. This reduces the voltage at the collector of Q_2, and

The regulated power supply is housed in a homemade two-piece metal box. Pin jacks are used for the d.c. output, neither side of which is grounded. The third jack is a ground connected to the case. On-off and meter switches are along the right side; the knob in the middle is on the voltage-control potentiometer. Originally described in May 1967 QST by A. Baker, KOPSG.

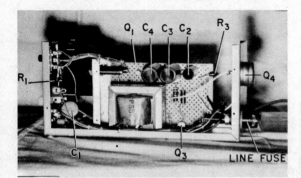

View from the side with the cover off. The transistor mounted on the rear chassis wall is Q_4. The two fuses also are mounted on this wall. Q_1 is just above the center of the transformer to the left of the two electrolytic capacitors, while Q_3 is at the bottom to the right of the transformer. Q_2 is below Q_1, but hidden by the transformer.

the output voltage accordingly, since the output voltage is a result of Q_2's collector voltage. In the opposite case, suppose that feedback current doesn't flow: then Q_2 won't conduct, thus the collector voltage rises to a point where Q_2 again conducts slightly. Since the available current at Q_2 is many times less than the desired output current, transistors Q_3 and Q_4 amplify the current to a useful level.

Short-circuit protection is provided by CR_6 and R_3, which develop a feedback voltage at the base of Q_3 if the current load exceeds 1 ampere. This prevents the supply from being overloaded if the output is accidentally short-circuited. R_3 serves to trim the point of feedback current; most of the required voltage drop will occur between the base and emitter junctions of Q_3 and Q_4. Obviously, the point of feedback will depend upon the junction temperature, resulting in what could be an undersirable effect if the supply is to operate at currents near one ampere. Re-

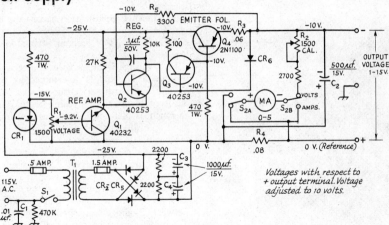

Fig. 12-38—Circuit of the transistor power supply. Resistances are in ohms; resistors are ½-watt, 20-percent tolerance, unless otherwise specified. Capacitors with polarity indicated are electrolytic; others are ceramic. Voltages shown are with respect to positive output terminal with R_1 adjusted for 10 volts output. Components not listed below are numbered for reference.

C_1—A.c.-type ceramic.
CR_1—Zener diode, 15 volts, 1 watt.
CR_2-CR_6, incl.—Silicon, 50 volts p.i.v., 1 amp.
M_1—0-5 ma. d.c., 20 ohms internal resistance.
R_1, R_2—Linear control.
R_3—0.06 ohm 5 percent tolerance (see text).

R_4—0.08 ohm, 5 percent tolerance (see text).
R_5—For text reference.
S_1—S.p.s.t. slide switch.
S_2—D.p.d.t. slide switch.
T_1—Power, 18 volts, 1 amp.

moving CR_6 and shorting out R_3 will result in better regulation at currents near one ampere, so it might be useful to many to delete these parts.

Circuit Notes

A d.c. input to the regulator of 25 volts is used to permit the supply to be useful at low a.c. power-line voltages. Good regulation can still be obtained with a primary a.c. supply of only 90 volts.

The transistors used RCA types and are not very expensive. However, the types are not critical should substitution become necessary.

The meter is calibrated to read full scale at 15 volts when in the voltage position, and one ampere when the meter switch is in the current position. The voltmeter calibration can be adjusted to a know standard with R_2.

R_3 and R_4 are homemade from lengths of No. 30 copper wire wound over a 1-megohm ½-watt resistor. The wire for R_3 is 7 inches long. R_4

requires 9.3 inches. The length of wire used for R_3 can be adjusted for the resistance required to limit the maximum-current protection to any desired value. R_4 should be adjusted to calibrate the ammeter to a known standard.

Construction

The power supply is built in a two-piece cabinet assembly. The bottom piece serves as the main chassis, front panel, and rear panel. The top piece serves also as the sides.

Circuit components are mounted on a slab of perforated board. The board is secured to the meter bracket and a lug on the chassis. Q_4 is mounted on the rear panel, on mica insulation, for good heat transfer to the cabinet. This is very important if Q_4 is to dissipate 25 watts without overheating. Note that Q_3 is mounted to the chassis with a metal clamp, for good heat transfer. The case of Q_3 must not be internally connected to any of the leads, so keep this in mind if a substitution is made.

A 700-VOLT GENERAL-PURPOSE SUPPLY FOR TRANSCEIVERS

This power supply is designed to be used with many of the medium-power s.s.b. transceivers that are commercially available. It has variable bias and low-voltage lines, making it adaptable to most equipment needs. The high voltage is approximately the value that most sweep-tube and 6146 p.a. stages require. In this model a discarded TV set transformer provided the heart of the supply. The filament circuit can be hooked up for 6.3- or 12.6-volt output.

Circuit Information

Referring to Fig. 12-39, the primary circuit of T_1 has a diode-protection relay, K_1, and a 25-ohm surge resistor, R_1, in one side of the line. When the supply is first turned on, R_1 drops the primary voltage to T_1 until the capacitor bank at the output of the bridge rectifier is charged. Then, the voltage drop across R_1 lessens and enables K_1 to pull in, thus shorting out the limiting resistor until the next time the supply is

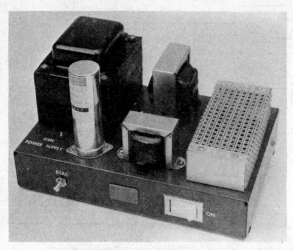

A top-chassis view of the general-purpose power supply. T_1 is at the far left, and is a transformer from a junked TV set. The high-wattage resistors are housed in the perforated shield at the far right. The bottom of the chassis is enclosed and has four rubber feet attached to the cover plate.

used. This form of protection prevents high surge currents from harming the diode bridge, CR_1 through CR_4, inclusive.

A standard bridge-rectifier string changes the secondary voltage of T_1 to d.c. Three 200-μf. capacitors are series-connected to filter the d.c., thus providing a 1350-volt 66-uf. rating for the filter. Voltage equalization across the capacitors is effected by the three 50,000-ohm 5-watt resistors shown. The resistor string doubles as a bleeder.

Low voltage is taken from the secondary center tap of T_1, and is determined by the setting of R_1. With ordinary transceivers, R_1 can be adjusted to provide anything from 200 volts to as much as 300 volts. Its actual setting will depend upon the current drawn by the low-voltage circuit of the equipment.

T_2 supplies 6.3 volts for powering the filaments of the transceiver. Alternatively, the 6.3-volt winding of T_2 can be used. If the equipment is wired for 12-volt filament operation, points X and Y can be joined and the output taken between Z and chassis ground. The phasing of T_1 and T_2 must be correct if the two voltages are to add, rather than cancel. If 12 volts does not appear with the filament string connected, merely reverse the primary leads of *one* of the two transformers.

Bias is taken from T_3, a 6.3-volt 1-ampere filament transformer which is connected back-to-back with T_2. CR_5 is a half-wave rectifier, and its output is filtered by a 100-μf. capacitor. The required amount of bias is obtained by adjustment of R_2.

The supply is built on an 11 $\times$ 10 $\times$ 2½-inch aluminum chassis. R_1 and the 150-ohm 10-watt resistor connected to it are mounted atop the chasis for cooling purposes. They are enclosed in a perforated shield to prevent accidental shock to the operator.

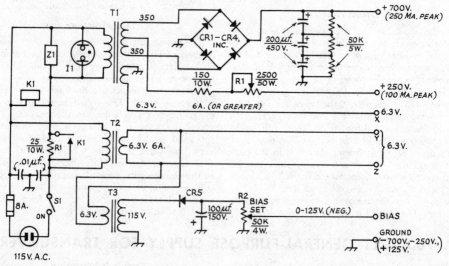

Fig. 12-39—Schematic of the power supply. Capacitors are disk ceramic, 1000 volts, except those with polarity marking, which are electrolytic. Resistance is in ohms. K-1000.

CR₁-C₄, incl.—1000 p.r.v., 1-ampere silicon diode.
CR₅—200 p.r.v., 500 ma. silicon diode.
I₁—115-v.a.c. panel lamp assembly.
K₁—115-v.a.c. relay with s.p.s.t. 10-ampere contacts.
R₁—2500-ohm, 50-watt adjustable resistor.
S₁—S.p.s.t. toggle switch with 10-ampere contacts.
T₁—TV-set transformer, 350 or 375 volts each side of

center tap, with 6.3 volt winding. (5-volt winding not used.) Use Stancor P-6315 as alternate.
T₂—6.3-volt, 6-ampere filament transformer.
T₃—6.3-volt, 1-ampere filament transformer.
Z₁—Thyrector assembly (for transient suppression). G. E. No. 20SP8B8 suitable.

MOBILE POWER SUPPLY FOR TRANSCEIVERS

This power supply operates from the 12-volt automotive storage battery and delivers 800 volts d.c. at 300 milliamperes, 250 volts d.c. at 200 milliamperes, and 0 to 150 volts negative (bias) at 40 milliamperes. Most commercially-built mobile transceivers can be operated from this power supply. Its wattage rating is 300 with a 100-percent duty cycle. The ICAS rating is 500 watts. This circuit was designed by Bob Karl, W8QFH, and was built by W1NPG. (Assistance was also given by W8WXK of Midway Electronics, W9IWJ of Delco Radio Corp., and W8ZM of Osborne Transformer Co.)

The Circuit

A two-transformer hookup is used in the circuit of Fig. 12-40, offering better efficiency because the load transformer, T_2, does not have

to saturate during switching. T_1, a small toroidal-wound transformer, handles the switching, which takes place at approximately 1000 Hz. Q_1 and Q_2 are the switching transistors and have a 50-ampere maximum rating. Substitute types are not recommended as they may lead to faulty operation of the supply.

Hash filtering is provided by L_1 and its associated bypass capacitors in the primary lead. Transient suppression is assured CR_{13}, CR_{14}, and CR_{15}. Bleeder resistors are used on each supply leg to provide a constant minimum load for the circuit. This supply can be operated without being connected to its load without fear of damaging the diodes or transistors.

Input and output terminals for the power supply can be selected to meet the operator's requirements. In this model a large terminal board

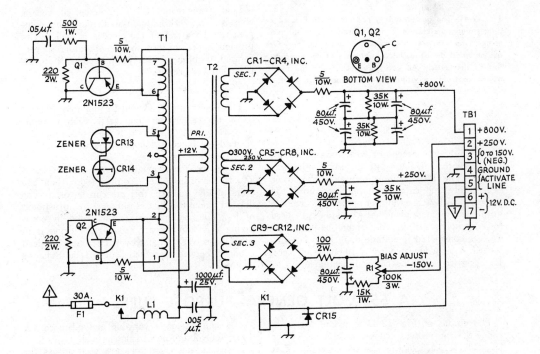

Fig. 12-40—Schematic diagram of the power supply. Polarized capacitors are electrolytic, others are paper or mica. Resistance is in ohms. K = 1000.

CR₁-CR₄, incl.—1000 p.r.v., 1-ampere silicon diode (1N5054 suitable).

CR₅-CR₈, incl.—600 p.r.v., 500 ma. silicon diode (1N2071 suitable).

CR₉-CR₁₂, incl.—400 p.r.v., 200 ma. silicon diode (1N2070 suitable).

CR₁₃, CR₁₄—12-volt Zener diode, 1 watt (G.E. Z4XL12 suitable).

CR₁₅—200 p.r.v., 500 ma. silicon diode (1N2069 suitable).

F₁—30-amp., 250-volt cartridge-type fuse and holder.

K₁—S.p.s.t. 12-volt d.c. relay with 60-amp. contacts

(Potter-Brumfield Type MB3D-SPST No. DB).

L₁—Hash choke, 20 turns No. 10 enameled wire on ½ diameter form.

Q₁, Q₂—Delco 2N1523 transistor (substitutions not recommended).

R₁—100,000-ohm, 3-watt linear-taper control.

T₁—Feedback transformer, 1000 Hz. (Osborne Transformer Co. No. 2709)*.

T₂—500/2000 Hz. power transformer, 12-volt primary. (Osborne Transformer Co. 21555.)*

* Osborne Transformer Co., 3834 Mitchell Ave., Detroit, Michigan 48207.

Heat sinks are Delco Radio No. 7281366, available from all Delco distributors. Write W91WJ for distributor list.

Fig. 12-41—The power supply is built on an 8 x 12 x 3-inch aluminum chassis. T_2 is enclosed in a ventilated compartment to prevent accidental shock. Q_1 and Q_2 are mounted on large Delco heat sinks at the opposite end of the chassis. An accessory socket and the bias-adjust control are visible on the front edge of the chassis.

Construction

The designer recommends that all leads in the noise-filtering circuit be returned to a common point. Current should not be permitted to flow through the heat sinks or the chassis. Use separate No. 8 or No. 6 bus wire for all connections, returning them to a common point on their respective bus terminals. If wire of this gauge is not available, strips of flashing copper, ¼ inch in width, can be used. Alternatively, paralleled sections of No. 10 bus wire can be used.

The heat sinks are bolted to the 8 × 12 × 3-inch aluminum chassis. A thin coating of silicone grease should be added between the heat sinks and the chassis to aid in heat transfer. Q_1 and Q_2 are insulated electrically from the heat sinks by means of their mica washers. Silicone grease should be spread over both sides of the mica insulators to provide good thermal coupling to the sinks.

Load transformer T_2 is mounted above the chassis along with L_1 and the other filtering components. That end of the chassis is enclosed to prevent shock hazard to the operator. A perforated aluminum cover plate permits the compartment to "breathe."

Operation

The power supply should be mounted as close to the car battery terminals as possible to minimize voltage drop. If it is to be trunk mounted, ¼-inch (or larger) copper conductors should be used to connect it to the car battery.

A 300-volt tap is available on Secondary 2 of T_2. If the transceiver requires more than 250 volts of low voltage, this tap can be used. The desired amount of bias is obtained by adjustment of R_1. The power supply is activated by energizing K_1 from a spare set of relay contacts in the transceiver's changeover circuit. This lead connects between terminal 5 of TB_1 and chassis ground.

was used, and an accessory socket was wired in parallel with it in the event an extra outlet was needed. The 12-volt input terminals should be heavy duty and capable of handling up to 35 amperes without heating or causing a voltage drop. Heavy-gauge insulated wire should be used for all primary wiring. No. 8 should be the smallest size considered if voltage drop is to be minimized. L_1 is wound from No. 10 enameled wire. Larger wire would be better if available.

A 650-VOLT GENERAL-PURPOSE SUPPLY

The circuit of Fig. 12-42 is useful for s.s.b. and c.w. transmitters whose peak input power level to the p.a. stage is less than 200 watts. It will handle a peak current of up to 300 ma. during a s.s.b. duty cycle. If used with a.m. transmitters, under ICAS conditions, the maximum current taken should be limited to 100 ma. or less.

The Circuit

Referring to Fig. 12-42, a full-wave bridge rectifier is connected to the secondary of T_1 to provide the 650-volt bus. Output is taken from the center tap of the same winding to establish a low-voltage bus. The latter is split by means of two 10-watt resistors at the output side of L_1, thus providing two values of low voltage. The actual values of the resistors will depend upon the current requirements of the equipment which is powered by the supply. The two re-

sistors can be made variable and adjusted for the exact voltage needed under load.

Resistors and capacitors are used across the rectifier diodes to protect them from unequal currents, and from transients. The high- and low-voltage lines are filtered by two series-connected 100-μf., 450-volt electrolytic capacitors. Equalizing resistors are bridged across them, also serving as a bleeder.

Voltage for operating a 12-volt d.c. control relay(s) is obtained by placing the 6.3 and 5-volt filament windings of T_1 in series and rectifying the output. The windings must be phased correctly to have the voltages add rather than cancel. If proper output is not obtained under load, simply reverse the leads of one of the windings.

A bias transformer, T_2, supplies up to 130 volts (negative) to the equipment. If less bias is needed, the 100,000-ohm bleeder resistor can

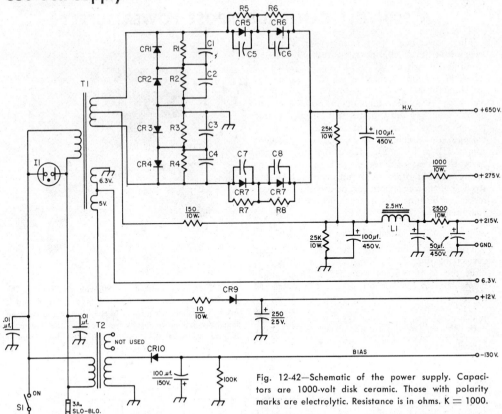

Fig. 12-42—Schematic of the power supply. Capacitors are 1000-volt disk ceramic. Those with polarity marks are electrolytic. Resistance is in ohms. K = 1000.

R₁-R₈, incl.—390,000 ohm resistor, ½-watt.
R_1-R_8, incl.—390,000 ohm resistor, ½-watt.
S₁—S.p.s.t. toggle.
S_1—S.p.s.t. toggle.
T₁-650-volt c.t. at 150 ma., 5 volts at 3 A., 6.3 volts at 5A. (Allied-Knight 6-K-45 HB, or equiv.)
T_1-650-volt c.t. at 150 ma., 5 volts at 3 A., 6.3 volts at 5A. (Allied-Knight 6-K-45 HB, or equiv.)
T₂—Bias transformer, 125 volts at 50 ma. (Allied-Knight 54-1411, or equiv.).
T_2—Bias transformer, 125 volts at 50 ma. (Allied-Knight 54-1411, or equiv.).

C¹-C⁸, incl.—.01-μf. 1000-volt disk ceramic.
CR₁-CR₈, incl.—RCA 1N3195, or equiv.
CR₉—RCA 1N2860A, or equiv.
CR₁₀—RCA 1N3194, or equiv.
I₁—115-volt neon lamp assembly.
L₁—2.5 hy. 130 ma. filter choke. (Allied-Knight 6-X-24 HF, or equiv.)

be replaced by a 2-watt variable resistor. The output can then be set to the desired value by taking the bias voltage from the movable contact of the resistor.

Construction

The supply is built on a 7 × 9 × 2-inch aluminum chassis. The high-voltage rectifier diodes and their associated resistors and capacitors are installed on a piece of insulating board and mounted beneath the chassis. All high-wattage resistors are mounted above the chassis and are enclosed by a perforated-aluminum cover to lessen shock hazard. If mounted under the chassis, they would cause damage to the other components because of excessive heating.

Fig. 12-43—View of the 650-volt power supply showing the screened-in section of the chassis (lower right) which contains the power resistors. Holes (⅜ inch in dia.) are drilled along each side of the chassis to permit heat to escape from inside the chassis. A perforated cover (and 4 rubber feet) is mounted on the bottom of the chassis to prevent accidental contact with the voltages within.

A 900-VOLT GENERAL-PURPOSE POWER SUPPLY

This power supply is suitable for use with sweep-tube linear amplifiers, medium-power v.h.f. amplifiers which use 4CX150A or 4CX250 type tubes, or for any equipment which requires approximately 900 volts at up to 900 ma., s.s.b. or c.w. duty cycle. For a.m. operation, the equipment should not draw more than 200 ma. if this power supply is to be used. Bias and relay voltage is available, as is 25.2 volts of filament supply. T_2 and T_3, Fig. 12-45, can be replaced by transformers of different voltage and current ratings should other operating voltages be desired. This power supply can be used as the basis for other designs which are tailored to specific equipment needs.

Circuit Data

The primary side of T_1 has a neon indicator across the line, I_1, to serve as an on-off panel indicator. I_1 is a Solico type SS/L lamp which has a built-in resistor for use at 115 v.a.c.[1] I_2

[1] The pilot lamps and the three rocker switches used here are available from Carling Electric, Inc., 505 New Park Avenue, West Hartford, Conn. 06110. Order direct if not locally available. Catalog available if requested.

Fig. 12-44—Top view of the 900-volt d.c. supply. The 60-watt lamp is screwed into a standard socket and is used during initial charging of the filter capacitors (see text). A satin finish results from soaking the chassis in a mild lye bath, then spraying it with clear lacquer after drying.

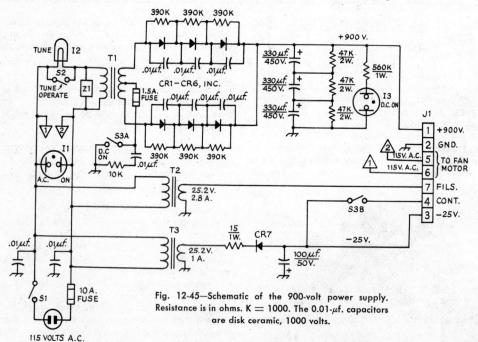

Fig. 12-45—Schematic of the 900-volt power supply. Resistance is in ohms. K = 1000. The 0.01-μf. capacitors are disk ceramic, 1000 volts.

CR$_1$-CR$_6$, inc.—1000 p.r.v., 1-ampere silicon diodes.
CR$_7$—50 p.r.v., 2-ampere silicon diode.
I$_1$, I$_3$—115-v.a.c. neon panel indicator (see footnote 1).
I$_2$—60-watt, 115 v.a.c. bulb.
J$_1$—7-pin female chassis socket (Amphenol 77MIP7S or equal).
S$_1$, S$_2$—S.p.s.t. rocker switch (see footnote 1).
S$_3$—D.p.s.t. rocker switch (see footnote 1).

T$_1$—1540 volts c.t. at 375 I.C.A.S. ma., or greater. (Stancor P-8042 suitable. Available from Arrow Electronics, Inc., 900 Route 110, Farmingdale, N.Y. 11735.)
T$_2$—25.2 volts at 2.8 amperes (Stancor P-8388). T$_2$ chosen for actual filament requirements.
T$_3$—25.2 volts at 1 ampere (Stancor P-6469). T$_3$ chosen for actual bias and relay voltage requirements.
Z$_1$—Thyrector module (G.E. 20SP8B8).

is a standard 60-watt incandescent lamp which screws into a receptacle on the top of the chassis. This lamp is used when the supply is first turned on (S_2 open) to provide protection to CR_1 through CR_6, inclusive, while the filter capacitor bank charges. The bulb will glow brightly for a few seconds, gradually diminishing as the capacitors become charged. Once this happens, S_2 is closed, shorting out the lamp and placing the power supply in the ready position. S_3 must be in the D.C. ON position during the foregoing operation.[2] Z_1, a G.E. Thyrector assembly, is bridged across the primary of T_1 to knock down any transients above the normal primary level, thus offering protection to the diode string in the secondary circuit.

Six diodes are used in a full-wave rectifier circuit at the secondary of T_1. Each diode has a resistor and a capacitor across it to offer protection in the event the voltage division across the diodes is unequal. A 1.5-ampere fuse is connected in the center-tap of the secondary winding to offer protection should a short in the 900-volt line occur. Frequently the primary fuse will not blow quick enough to save the rectifiers and the transformer. $S3_A$ is the OPERATE switch and has a transient suppressor across it to prevent damage to the switch when it is cycled.

---

[2] An alternate protection circuit for capacitor charging is shown in *QST*, October 1967, page 18. Also, see the 700-V. general-purpose transceiver supply in this chapter.

Three computer-grade capacitors are series-connected at the output of the rectifier to provide 110-μf. at 1350 volts. Each capacitor has a 47,000-ohm resistor across it to assure equal voltage drop. I_3 is the high-voltage ON indicator. Output from T_2 is for filament supply. The output from T_3 is rectified and split for use as a low-voltage bias supply, and as relay supply voltage for the mating equipment. Other voltages can be had by using different transformers at T_2 and T_3.

Construction Notes

Fig. 12-44 shows that open-chassis construction has been used. No voltage points are exposed, and the bottom of the chassis is enclosed to prevent shock hazard. The supply is built on a $17 \times 10 \times 3$-inch aluminum chassis. Modern rocker-type switches are used (Carling Electric, Inc.) to impart a professional appearance.

The three filter capacitors are mounted on a sheet of $\frac{1}{4}$-inch thick plexiglas and are held in place by their terminal screws. Each screw has a solder lug and lock washer under it for making circuit connections. Three holes, each $1\frac{1}{2}$ inch in diameter, are bored in the chassis to match up with the bottoms of the capacitors, thus making their terminals accessible for wiring.

The rectifier diodes and their related resistors and capacitors are mounted under the chassis on a home-made circuit board. The board is supported inside the chassis on standoff posts.

Chapter 13

Transmission Lines

The place where r.f. power is generated is very frequently not the place where it is to be utilized. A transmitter and its antenna are a good example: The antenna, to radiate well, should be high above the ground and should be kept clear of trees, buildings and other objects that might absorb energy, but the transmitter itself is most conveniently installed indoors where it is readily accessible.

The means by which power is transported from point to point is the r.f. transmission line.

At radio frequencies a transmission line exhibits entirely different characteristics than it does at commercial power frequencies. This is because the speed at which electrical energy travels, while tremendously high as compared with mechanical motion, is not infinite. The peculiarities of r.f. transmission lines result from the fact that a time interval comparable with an r.f. cycle must elapse before energy leaving one point in the circuit can reach another just a short distance away.

OPERATING PRINCIPLES

If a source of e.m.f.—a battery, for example—is connected to the ends of a pair of insulated parallel wires that extend outward for an infinite distance, electric currents will immediately become detectable in the wires near the battery terminals. The electric field of the battery will cause free electrons in the wire connected to the positive terminal to be attracted to the battery, and an equal number of free electrons in the wire connected to the negative terminal will be repelled from the battery. These currents do not flow instantaneously throughout the length of the wires; the electric field that causes the electron movement cannot travel faster than the speed of light, so a measurable interval of time elapses before the currents become evident even a relatively short distance away.

For example, the currents would not become detectable 300 meters (nearly 1000 feet) from the battery until at least a microsecond (one millionth of a second) after the connection was made. By ordinary standards this is a very short length of time, but in terms of radio frequency it represents the time of one

complete cycle of a 1000-kilocycle current — a frequency considerably lower than those with which amateurs communicate.

The current flows to charge the capacitance

between the two wires. However, the conductors of this "linear" capacitor also have appreciable inductance. The line may be thought of as being composed of a whole series of small inductances and capacitances connected as shown in Fig. 13-1, where each coil is the inductance of a very short section of one wire and each capacitor is the capacitance between two such short sections.

Characteristic Impedance

An infinitely long chain of coils and capacitors connected as in Fig. 13-1, where the small inductances and capacitances all have the same values, respectively, has an important property. To an electrical impulse applied at one end, the combination appears to have an impedance — called the **characteristic impedance** or **surge impedance** — approximately equal to $\sqrt{L/C}$ where L and C are the inductance and capacitance per unit length. This impedance is purely resistive.

In defining the characteristic impedance as $\sqrt{L/C}$, it is assumed that the conductors have no inherent resistance — that is, there is no I^2R loss in them — and that there is no power loss in the dielectric surrounding the conductors. There is thus no power loss in or from the line no matter how great its length. This may not seem consistent with calling the characteristic impedance a pure resistance, which implies that the power supplied is all dissipated in the line. But in an infinitely long line the effect, so far as the source of power is concerned, is exactly the same as though the power were dissipated in a resistance, because the power leaves the source and travels outward forever along the line.

The characteristic impedance determines the amount of current that can flow when a

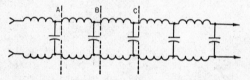

Fig. 13-1—Equivalent of a transmission line in lumped circuit constants.

given voltage is applied to an infinitely long line, in exactly the same way that a definite value of actual resistance limits current flow when a voltage is applied.

The inductance and capacitance per unit length of line depend upon the size of the conductors and the spacing between them. The closer the two conductors and the greater their diameter, the higher the capacitance and the lower the inductance. A line with large conductors closely spaced will have low impedance, while one with small conductors widely spaced will have relatively high impedance.

"Matched" Lines

Actual transmission lines do not extend to infinity but have a definite length and are connected to, or **terminate** in, a load at the "output" end, or end to which the power is delivered. If the load is a pure resistance of a value equal to the characteristic impedance of the line, the line is said to be **matched**. To current traveling along the line such a load just looks like still more transmission line of the same characteristic impedance.

In other words, a short line terminated in a purely resistive load equal to the characteristic impedance of the line acts just as though it were infinitely long. In a matched transmission line, power travels outward along the line from the source until it reaches the load, where it is completely absorbed.

R.F. on Lines

The principles discussed above, although based on direct-current flow from a battery, also hold when an r.f. voltage is applied to the line. The difference is that the alternating voltage causes the amplitude of the current at the input terminals of the line to vary with the voltage, and the direction of current flow also periodically reverses when the polarity of the applied voltage reverses. The current at a given instant at any point along the line is the result of a voltage that was applied at some *earlier* instant at the input terminals. Since the distance traveled by the electromagnetic fields in the time of one cycle is equal to one wavelength (Chapter 2), the instantaneous amplitude of the current is different at all points in a one-wavelength section of line. In fact, the current flows in opposite directions in the same wire in successive half-wavelength sections. However, at any given point along the line the current goes through similar variations with time that the current at the input terminals did.

Thus the current (and voltage) travels along the wire as a series of waves having a length equal to the speed of travel divided by the frequency of the a.c. voltage. On an infinitely long line, or one properly matched by its load, an ammeter inserted anywhere in the line will show the same current, because the ammeter averages out the variations in current during a cycle. It is only when the line is not properly matched that the wave motion becomes apparent through observations made with ordinary instruments.

STANDING WAVES

In the infinitely long line (or its matched counterpart) the impedance is the same at any point on the line because the ratio of voltage to current is always the same. However, the impedance at the end of the line in Fig. 13-2 is zero — or at least extremely small — because the line is short-circuited at the end. The outgoing power, on meeting the short-circuit, reverses its direction of flow and goes back along the transmission line toward the input end. There is a large current in the short-circuit, but substantially no voltage across the line at this point. We now have a voltage and current representing the power going outward **(incident power)** toward the short-circuit, and a second voltage and current representing the **reflected power** traveling back toward the source.

The reflected current travels at the same speed as the outgoing current, so its instantaneous value will be different at every point along the line, in the distance represented by the time of one cycle. At some points along

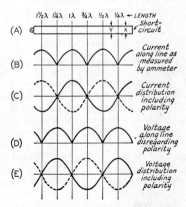

Fig. 13-2—Standing waves of voltage and current along short-circuited transmission line.

the line the phase of the incident and reflected currents will be such that the currents cancel each other while at others the amplitude will be doubled. At in-between points the amplitude is between these two extremes. The points at which the currents are in and out of phase depend only on the *time* required for them to travel and so depend only on the *distance* along the line from the point of reflection.

In the short-circuit at the end of the line the two current components are in phase and the total current is large. At a distance of one-half wavelength back along the line from the short-circuit the outgoing and reflected components will again be in phase and the resultant current will again have its maximum value. This is also true at any point that is a multiple of a half wavelength from the short-circuited end of the line.

The outgoing and reflected currents will cancel at a point one-quarter wavelength, along the line, from the short-circuit. At this point, then, the current will be zero. It will also be zero at all points that are an *odd* multiple of one-quarter wavelength from the short-circuit.

If the current along the line is measured at successive points with an ammeter, it will be found to vary about as shown in Fig. 13-2B. The same result would be obtained by measuring the current in either wire, since the ammeter cannot measure phase. However, if the phase could be checked, it would be found that in each successive half-wavelength section of the line the currents at any given instant are flowing in opposite directions, as indicated by the solid line in Fig. 13-2C. Furthermore, the current in the second wire is flowing in the opposite direction to the current in the adjacent section of the first wire. This is indicated by the broken curve in Fig. 13-2C. The variations in current intensity along the transmission line are referred to as **standing waves.** The point of maximum line current is called a **current loop** or **current antinode** and the point of minimum line current is called a **current node.**

Voltage Relationships

Since the end of the line is short-circuited, the voltage at that point has to be zero. This can only be so if the voltage in the outgoing wave is met, at the end of the line, by a reflected voltage of equal amplitude and opposite polarity. In other words, the phase of the voltage wave is *reversed* when reflection takes place from the short-circuit. This reversal is equivalent to an extra half cycle or half wavelength of travel. As a result, the outgoing and returning voltages are in phase a quarter wavelength from the end of the line, and again out of phase a half wavelength from the end. The standing waves of voltage, shown at D in Fig. 13-2, are therefore displaced by one-quarter wavelength from the standing waves of current. The drawing at E shows the voltages on both wires when phase is taken into account. The polarity of the voltage on each wire reverses in each half wavelength section of transmission line. A voltage maximum is called a **voltage loop** or **antinode** and a voltage minimum is called a **voltage node.**

Open-Circuited Line

If the end of the line is open-circuited instead of short-circuited, there can be no current at the end of the line but a large voltage can exist. Again the incident power is reflected back toward the source. The incident and reflected components of current must be equal and opposite in phase at the open circuit in

order for the total current at the end of the line to be zero. The incident and reflected components of voltage are in phase and add together. The result is again that there are standing waves, but the conditions are reversed as compared with a short-circuited line. Fig. 13-3 shows the open-circuited line case.

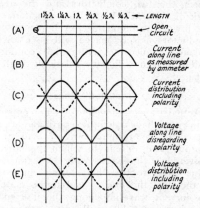

Fig. 13-3—Standing waves of current and voltage along an open-circuited transmission line.

Lines Terminated in Resistive Load

Fig. 13-4 shows a line terminated in a resistive load. In this case at least part of the incident power is absorbed in the load, and so is not available to be reflected back toward the source. Because only part of the power is reflected, the reflected components of voltage and current do not have the same magnitude as the incident components. Therefore neither voltage nor current cancel completely at any point along the line. However, the *speed* at which the incident and reflected components travel is not affected by their amplitude, so the phase relationships are similar to those in open- or short-circuited lines.

It was pointed out earlier that if the load resistance, Z_R, is equal to the characteristic impedance, Z_0, of the line all the power is absorbed in the load. In such a case there is no reflected power and therefore no standing waves of current and voltage. This is a special case that represents the change-over point

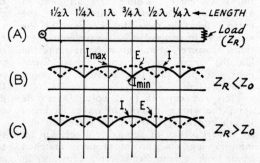

Fig. 13-4—Standing waves on a transmission line terminated in a resistive load.

between "short-circuited" and "open-circuited" lines. If Z_R is less than Z_0, the current is largest at the load, while if Z_R is greater than Z_0 the voltage is largest at the load. The two conditions are shown at B and C, respectively, in Fig. 13-4.

The resistive termination is an important practical case. The termination is seldom an actual resistor, the most common terminations being resonant circuits or resonant antenna systems, both of which have essentially resistive impedances. If the load is reactive as well as resistive, the operation of the line resembles that shown in Fig. 13-4, but the presence of reactance in the load causes two modifications: The loops and nulls are shifted toward or away from the load; and the amount of power reflected back toward the source is increased, as compared with the amount reflected by a purely resistive load of the same total impedance. Both effects become more pronounced as the ratio of reactance to resistance in the load is made larger.

Standing-Wave Ratio

The ratio of maximum current to minimum current along a line, Fig. 13-5, is called the **standing-wave ratio.** The same ratio holds for maximum voltage and minimum voltage. It is a measure of the mismatch between the load and the line, and is equal to 1 when the line is perfectly matched. (In that case the "maximum" and "minimum" are the same, since the current and voltage do not vary along the line.) When the line is terminated in a purely resistive load, the standing-wave ratio is

$$S.W.R. = \frac{Z_R}{Z_0} \text{ or } \frac{Z_0}{Z_R} \qquad \text{(13-A)}$$

Where $S.W.R.$ = Standing-wave ratio

Z_R = Impedance of load (must be pure resistance)

Z_0 = Characteristic impedance of line

Example: A line having a characteristic impedance of 300 ohms is terminated in a resistive load of 25 ohms. The s.w.r. is

$$S.W.R. = \frac{Z_0}{Z_R} = \frac{300}{25} = 12 \text{ to } 1$$

It is customary to put the larger of the two quantities, Z_R or Z_0, in the numerator of the

fraction so that the s.w.r. will be expressed by a number larger than 1.

It is easier to measure the standing-wave ratio than some of the other quantities (such as the impedance of an antenna) that enter into transmission-line computations. Consequently, the s.w.r. is a convenient basis for work with lines. The higher the s.w.r., the greater the mismatch between line and load. In practical lines, the power loss in the line itself increases with the s.w.r., as shown later.

INPUT IMPEDANCE

The input impedance of a transmission line is the impedance seen looking into the sending-end or input terminals; it is the impedance into which the source of power must work when the line is connected. If the load is perfectly matched to the line the line appears to be infinitely long, as stated earlier, and the input impedance is simply the characteristic impedance of the line itself. However, if there are standing waves this is no longer true; the input impedance may have a wide range of values.

This can be understood by referring to Figs. 13-2, 13-3, or 13-4. If the line length is such that standing waves cause the voltage at the input terminals to be high and the current low, then the input impedance is higher than the Z_0 of the line, since impedance is simply the ratio of voltage to current. Conversely, low voltage and high current at the input terminals mean that the input impedance is lower than the line Z_0. Comparison of the three drawings also shows that the range of input impedance values that may be encountered is greater when the far end of the line is open- or short-circuited than it is when the line has a resistive load. In other words, the higher the s.w.r. the greater the range of input impedance values when the line length is varied.

In addition to the variation in the absolute value of the input impedance with line length, the presence of standing waves also causes the input impedance to contain both reactance and resistance, even though the load itself may be a pure resistance. The only exceptions to this occur at the exact current loops or nodes, at which points the input impedance is a pure resistance. These are the only points at which the outgoing and reflected voltages and currents are exactly in phase: At all other distances along the line the current either leads or lags the voltage and the effect is exactly the same as though a capacitance or inductance were part of the input impedance.

The input impedance can be represented either by a resistance and a capacitance or by a resistance and an inductance. Whether the impedance is inductive or capacitive depends on the characteristics of the load and the length of the line. It is possible to represent the input impedance by an equivalent circuit having resistance and reactance either in ser-

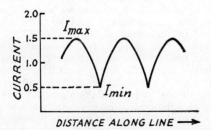

Fig. 13-5—Measurement of standing-wave ratio. In this drawing, I_{max} is 1.5 and I_{min} is 0.5, so the s.w.r. = I_{max} I_{min} = 1.5/0.5 = 3 to 1.

ies or parallel, so long as the total impedance and phase angle are the same in either case.

The magnitude and character of the input impedance is quite important, since it determines the method by which the power source must be coupled to the line. The calculation of input impedance is rather complicated and its measurement is not feasible without special equipment. Fortunately, in amateur work it is unnecessary either to calculate or measure it. The proper coupling can be achieved by relatively simple methods described later in this chapter.

Lines Without Load

The input impedance of a short-circuited or open-circuited line not an exact multiple of one-quarter wavelength long is practically a pure reactance. This is because there is very little power lost in the line. Such lines are frequently used as "linear" inductances and capacitances.

If a shorted line is less than a quarter-wave long, as at X in Fig. 13-2, it will have inductive reactance. The reactance increases with the line length up to the quarter-wave point. Beyond that, as at Y, the reactance is capacitive, high near the quarter-wave point and becoming lower as the half-wave point is approached. It then alternates between inductive and capacitive in successive quarter-wave sections. Just the reverse is true of the open-circuited line.

At exact multiples of a quarter wavelength the impedance is purely resistive. It is apparent, from examination of B and D in Fig. 13-2, that at points that are a multiple of a half wavelength—i.e., $\frac{1}{2}$, 1, $1\frac{1}{2}$ wavelengths, etc. —from the short-circuited end of the line the current and voltage have the same values that they do at the short circuit. In other words, if the line were an exact multiple of a half wavelength long the generator or source of power would "look into" a short circuit. On the other hand, at points that are an odd multiple of a quarter wavelength—i.e., $\frac{1}{4}$, $\frac{3}{4}$, $1\frac{1}{4}$, etc.— from the short circuit the voltage is maximum and the current is zero. Since $Z = E/I$, the impedance at these points is theoretically infinite. (Actually it is very high, but not infinite. This is because the current does not actually go to zero when there are losses in the line. Losses are always present, but usually are small.)

Impedance Transformation

The fact that the input impedance of a line depends on the s.w.r. and line length can be used to advantage when it is necessary to transform a given impedance into another value.

Study of Fig. 13-4 will show that, just as in the open- and short-circuited cases, if the line is one-half wavelength long the voltage and current are exactly the same at the input terminals as they are at the load. This is also true of lengths that are integral multiples of a half wavelength. It is also true for all values of s.w.r. Hence the input impedance of any line, no matter what its Z_0, that is a multiple of a half wavelength long is exactly the same as the load impedance. Such a line can be used to transfer the impedance to a new location without changing its value.

When the line is a quarter wavelength long, or an odd multiple of a quarter wavelength, the load impedance is "inverted." That is, if the current is low and the voltage is high at the load, the input impedance will be such as to require high current and low voltage. The relationship between the load impedance and input impedance is given by

$$Z_S = \frac{Z_0{}^2}{Z_R} \qquad \text{(13-B)}$$

where Z_S = Impedance looking into line (line length an odd multiple of one-quarter wavelength)

Z_R = Impedance of load (must be pure resistance)

Z_0 = Characteristic impedance of line

Example: A quarter-wavelength line having a characteristic impedance of 500 ohms is terminated in a resistive load of 75 ohms. The impedance looking into the input or sending end of the line is

$$Z_S = \frac{Z_0{}^2}{Z_R} = \frac{(500)^2}{75} = \frac{250,000}{75} = 3333 \text{ ohms}$$

If the formula above is rearranged, we have

$$Z_0 = \sqrt{Z_S Z_R} \qquad \text{(13-C)}$$

This means that if we have two values of impedance that we wish to "match," we can do so if we connect them together by a quarter-wave transmission line having a characteristic impedance equal to the square root of their product. A quarter-wave line, in other words, has the characteristics of a transformer.

Resonant and Nonresonant Lines

The input impedance of a line operating with a high s.w.r. is critically dependent on the line length, and resistive only when the length is some integral multiple of one-quarter wavelength. Lines cut to such a length and operated with a high s.w.r. are called "tuned" or "resonant" lines. On the other hand, if the s.w.r. is low the input impedance is close to the Z_0 of the line and does not vary a great deal with the line length. Such lines are called "flat," or "untuned," or "nonresonant."

There is no sharp line of demarcation between tuned and untuned lines. If the s.w.r. is below 1.5 to 1 the line is essentially flat, and the same input coupling method will work with all line lengths. If the s.w.r. is above 3 or 4 to 1 the type of coupling system, and its adjustment, will depend on the line length and such lines fall into the "tuned" category.

It is usually advantageous to make the s.w.r. as low as possible. A resonant line becomes necessary only when a considerable mismatch between the load and the line has to be tolerated. The most important practical example of this is when a single antenna is operated on several harmonically related frequencies, in which case the antenna impedance will have widely different values on different harmonics.

RADIATION

Whenever a wire carries alternating current the electromagnetic fields travel away into space with the velocity of light. At power-line frequencies the field that "grows" when the current is increasing has plenty of time to return or "collapse" about the conductor when the current is decreasing, because the alternations are so slow. But at radio frequencies fields that travel only a relatively short distance do not have time to get back to the conductor before the next cycle commences. The consequence is that some of the electromagnetic energy is prevented from being restored to the conductor; in other words, energy is radiated into space in the form of electromagnetic waves.

The lines previously considered have consisted of two parallel conductors of the same diameter. Provided there is nothing in the system to destroy symmetry, at every point along the line the current in one conductor has the same intensity as the current in the other conductor at that point, but the currents flow in opposite directions. This was shown in Figs. 13-2C and 13-3C. It means that the fields set up about the two wires have the same intensity, but *opposite directions*. The consequence is that the total field set up about such a transmission line is zero; the two fields "cancel out." Hence no energy is radiated.

Practically, the fields do not quite cancel out because for them to do so the two conductors would have to occupy the same space, whereas they are actually slightly separated. However, the cancellation is substantially complete if the distance between the conductors is very small compared to the wavelength. Transmission line radiation will be negligible if the distance between the conductors is 0.01 wavelength or less, provided the currents in the two wires are balanced.

The amount of radiation also is proportional to the current flowing in the line. Because of the way in which the current varies along the line when there are standing waves, the effective current, for purposes of radiation, becomes greater as the s.w.r. is increased. For this reason the radiation is least when the line is flat. However, if the conductor spacing is small and the currents are balanced, the radiation from a line with even a high s.w.r. is inconsequential. A small unbalance in the line currents is far more serious — and is just as serious when the line is flat as when the s.w.r. is high.

PRACTICAL LINE CHARACTERISTICS

The foregoing discussion of transmission lines has been based on a line consisting of two parallel conductors. The **parallel-conductor** line is but one of two general types, the other being the **coaxial** or **concentric** line. The coaxial line consists of a conductor placed in the center of a tube. The inside surface of the tube and the outside surface of the smaller inner conductor form the two conducting surfaces of the line.

In the coaxial line the fields are entirely inside the tube, because the tube acts as a shield to prevent them from appearing outside. This reduces radiation to the vanishing point. So far as the electrical behavior of coaxial lines is concerned, all that has previously been said about the operation of parallel-conductor lines applies. There are, however, practical differences in the construction and use of parallel and coaxial lines.

PARALLEL-CONDUCTOR LINES

A type of parallel-conductor line sometimes used in amateur installations is one in which two wires (ordinarily No. 12 or No. 14) are supported a fixed distance apart by means of insulating rods called "spacers." The spacings used vary from two to six inches, the smaller spacings being necessary at frequencies of the order of 28 Mc. and higher so that radiation will be minimized. The construction is shown in Fig. 13-6. Such a line is said to be **air-insulated**. The characteristic impedance of such "open-wire" lines is between 400 and 600 ohms, depending on the wire size and spacing.

Parallel-conductor lines also are occasionally constructed of metal tubing of a diameter of ¼ to ½ inch. This reduces the characteristic impedance of the line. Such lines are mostly used as quarter-wave transformers, when different values of impedance are to be matched.

Prefabricated parallel-conductor line with

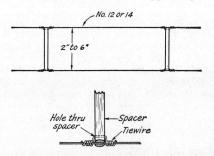

Fig. 13-6—Typical construction of open-wire line. The line conductor fits in a groove in the end of the spacer, and is held in place by a tie-wire anchored in a hole near the groove.

air insulation, developed for television reception, can be used in transmitting applications. This line consists of two conductors separated one-half to one inch by molded-on spacers. The characteristic impedance is 300 to 450 ohms, depending on the wire size and spacing.

A convenient type of manufactured line is one in which the parallel conductors are imbedded in low-loss insulating material (polyethylene). It is commonly used as a TV lead-in and has a characteristic impedance of about 300 ohms. It is sold under various names, the most common of which is "Twin-Lead." This type of line has the advantages of light weight, close and uniform conductor spacing, flexibility and neat appearance. However, the losses in the solid dielectric are higher than in air, and dirt or moisture on the line tends to change the characteristic impedance. Moisture effects can be reduced by coating the line with silicone grease. A special form of 300-ohm Twin-Lead for transmitting uses a polyethylene tube with the conductors molded diametrically opposite; the longer dielectric path in such line reduces moisture troubles.

In addition to 300-ohm line, Twin-Lead is obtainable with a characteristic impedance of 75 ohms for transmitting purposes. Lightweight 75-and 150-ohm Twin-Lead also is available.

Characteristic Impedance

The characteristic impedance of an air-insulated parallel-conductor line is given by:

$$Z_0 = 276 \log \frac{b}{a} \qquad (13\text{-}D)$$

where Z_0 = Characteristic impedance
　　　b = Center-to-center distance between conductors
　　　a = Radius of conductor (in same units as b)

It does not matter what units are used for a and b so long as they are the *same* units. Both quantities may be measured in centimeters, inches, etc. Since it is necessary to have a table of common logarithms to solve practical problems, the solution is given in graphical form in Fig. 13-7 for a number of common conductor sizes.

In solid-dielectric parallel-conductor lines such as Twin-Lead the characteristic impedance cannot be calculated readily, because part of the electric field is in air as well as in the dielectric.

Unbalance in Parallel-Conductor Lines

When installing parallel-conductor lines care should be taken to avoid introducing electrical unbalance into the system. If for some reason the current in one conductor is higher than in the other, or if the currents in the two wires are not exactly out of phase with each other, the electromagnetic fields will not cancel completely and a considerable amount of power may be radiated by the line.

Maintaining good line balance requires, first of all, a balanced load at its end. For this reason the antenna should be fed, whenever possible, at a point where each conductor "sees" exactly the same thing. Usually this means that the antenna system should be fed at its electrical center. However, even though the antenna appears to be symmetrical physically, it can be unbalanced electrically if the part connected to one of the line conductors is coupled to something (such as house wiring or a metal pole or roof) that is not duplicated on the other part of the antenna. Every effort should be made to keep the antenna as far as possible from other wiring or sizable metallic objects. The transmission line itself will cause some unbalance if it is not brought away from the antenna at right angles to it for a distance of at least a quarter wavelength.

In installing the line conductors take care to see that they are kept away from metal. The minimum separation between either con-

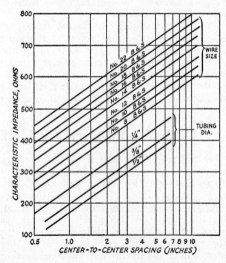

Fig. 13-7—Chart showing the characteristic impedance of spaced-conductor parallel transmission lines with air dielectric. Tubing sizes given are for outside diameters.

ductor and all other wiring should be at least four or five times the conductor spacing. The shunt capacitance introduced by close proximity to metallic objects can drain off enough current (to ground) to unbalance the line currents, resulting in increased radiation. A shunt capacitance of this sort also constitutes a reactive load on the line, causing an impedance "bump" that will prevent making the line actually flat.

COAXIAL LINES

The most common form of coaxial line consists of either a solid or stranded-wire inner conductor surrounded by polyethylene dielectric. Copper braid is woven over the dielectric to form the outer conductor, and a waterproof vinyl covering is placed on top of the braid. This cable is made in a number of different diameters. It is moderately flexible, and so is convenient to install. This solid coaxial cable is commonly available in impedances approximating 50 and 70 ohms.

Air-insulated coaxial lines have lower losses than the solid-dielectric type, but are rarely used in amateur work because they are expensive and difficult to install as compared with the flexible cable. The common type of air-insulated coaxial line uses a solid-wire conductor inside a copper tube, with the wire held in the center of the tube by means of insulating "beads" placed at regular intervals.

TABLE 13-I

Transmission-Line Data

Type	Description or Type Number	Characteristic Imped-ance	Velocity Factor	Capacitance per foot pf.	Power Rating[1] Watts at 30 Mc.
Coaxial	RG-8A/U	53	0.66	29.5	1700
	RG-58A/U	53	0.66	28.5	430
	RG-17A/U	50	0.66	30	5600
	621-111[1]	50	—	26.0	3500[2]
	RG-11A/U	75	0.66	20.5	1700
	RG-59A/U	73	0.66	21.0	680
	621-100[1]	75	—	16.5	3000[2]
Parallel Conductor	Air-insulated	200-600	0.975[3]	—	—
	214-023[1]	75	0.71	20.0	1000
	214-056[1]	300	0.82	5.8	—
	214-076[1]	300	0.84	3.9	1000
	214-022[1]	300	0.85	3.0	—

[1]Amphenol type numbers and data. Similar lines may be made by other manufacturers but losses and maximum ratings may differ. Type 214–056 is standard receiving "Twin-Lead"; 214–022 has No. 16 Copperweld conductors for extra strength.
[2]Maximum operating volts, r.m.s.
[3]Average figure for lines insulated with ceramic spacers at intervals of a few feet.

Characteristic Impedance

The characteristic impedance of an air-insulated coaxial line is given by the formula

$$Z_0 = 138 \log \frac{b}{a} \qquad \text{(13-E)}$$

where Z_0 = Characteristic impedance
b = Inside diameter of outer conductor
a = Outside diameter of inner conductor (in same units as b)

The formula for coaxial lines is approximately correct for lines in which bead spacers are used, provided the beads are not too closely spaced. When the line is filled with a solid dielectric, the characteristic impedance as given by the formula should be multiplied by $1/\sqrt{K}$, where K is the dielectric constant of the material.

ELECTRICAL LENGTH

In the discussion of line operation earlier in this chapter it was assumed that currents traveled along the conductors at the speed of light. Actually, the velocity is somewhat less, the reason being that electromagnetic fields

travel more slowly in material dielectrics than they do in free space. In air the velocity is practically the same as in empty space, but a practical line always has to be supported in some fashion by solid insulating materials. The result is that the fields are slowed down; the currents travel a shorter distance in the time of one cycle than they do in space, and so the wavelength along the line is less than the wavelength would be in free space at the same frequency.

Whenever reference is made to a line as being so many wavelengths (such as a "half wavelength" or "quarter wavelength") long, it is to be understood that the *electrical* length of the line is meant. Its actual physical length as measured by a tape always will be somewhat less. The physical length corresponding to an electrical wavelength is given by

$$Length\ in\ feet = \frac{984V}{f} \qquad \text{(13-F)}$$

where f = Frequency in megacycles
V = Velocity factor

The **velocity factor** is the ratio of the actual velocity along the line to the velocity in free space. Values of V for several common types of lines are given in Table 13-I.

Example: A 75-foot length of 300-ohm Twin-Lead is used to carry power at a frequency of 7150 kc. From Table 13-I, V is 0.82. At this frequency (7.15 Mc.) a wavelength is

$$Length\ (feet) = \frac{984V}{f} = \frac{984}{7.15} \times 0.82$$

$$= 137.6 \times 0.82 = 112.8\ \text{ft.}$$

The line length is therefore $75/112.8 = 0.665$ wavelength.

Because a quarter-wavelength line is frequently used as a linear transformer, it is convenient to calculate the length of a quarter-wave line directly. The formula is

$$Length\ (feet) = \frac{246V}{f} \qquad \text{(13-G)}$$

where the symbols have the same meaning as above.

LOSSES IN TRANSMISSION LINES

There are three ways by which power may be lost in a transmission line: by radiation, by heating of the conductors (I^2R loss), and by heating of the dielectric, if any. Radiation losses are in general the result of "antenna currents" on the line, resulting from undesired coupling to the radiating antenna. They cannot readily be estimated or measured, so the following discussion is based only on conductor and dielectric losses.

Heat losses in both the conductor and the dielectric increase with frequency. Conductor losses also are greater the lower the charac-

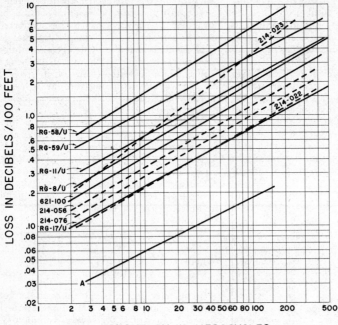

Fig. 13-8—Attenuation data for common types of transmission lines. Curve A is the nominal attenuation of 600-ohm open-wire line with No. 12 conductors, not including dielectric loss in spacers nor possible radiation losses. Additional line data are given in Table 13-I.

teristic impedance of the line, because a higher current flows in a low-impedance line for a given power input. The converse is true of dielectric losses because these increase with the voltage, which is greater on high-impedance lines. The dielectric loss in air-insulated lines is negligible (the only loss is in the insulating spacers) and such lines operate at high efficiency when radiation losses are low.

It is convenient to express the loss in a transmission line in decibels per unit length, since the loss in db. is directly proportional to the line length. Losses in various types of lines operated without standing waves (that is, terminated in a resistive load equal to the characteristic impedance of the line) are given in graphical form in Fig. 13-8. In these curves the radiation loss is assumed to be negligible.

When there are standing waves on the line the power loss increases as shown in Fig. 13-9. Whether or not the increase in loss is serious depends on what the original loss would have been if the line were perfectly matched. If the loss with perfect matching is very low, a large s.w.r. will not greatly affect the *efficiency* of the line — i.e., the ratio of the power delivered to the load to the power put into the line.

Example: A 150-foot length of RG-11/U cable is operating at 7 Mc. with a 5-to-1 s.w.r. If perfectly matched, the loss from Fig. 13-8 would be 1.5 × 0.55 = 0.825 db. From Fig. 13-9 the additional loss because of the s.w.r. is 0.73 db. The total loss is therefore 0.825 + 0.95 = 1.775 db.

An appreciable s.w.r. on a solid-dielectric line may result in excessive loss of power at the higher frequencies. Such lines, whether of the parallel-conductor or coaxial type, should be operated as nearly flat as possible, particularly when the line length is more than 50 feet.

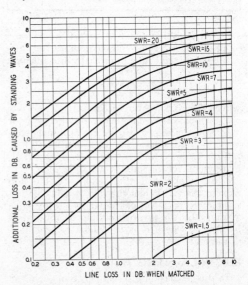

Fig. 13-9—Effect of standing-wave radio on line loss. The ordinates give the *additional* loss in decibels for the loss, under perfectly matched conditions, shown on horizontal scale.

TESTING OLD COAXIAL CABLE

Unknown coaxial cable or cable that has been exposed to the weather may have losses above the published figures for the cable type. If one has access to a sensitive s.w.r. bridge, the cable can be checked for losses at the frequency to be used. Connect the cable to the bridge and a low-powered source of r.f., and short circuit the far end of the cable. The s.w.r. measurement can then be transformed to the line loss (when perfectly terminated) by referring to Fig. 13-10.

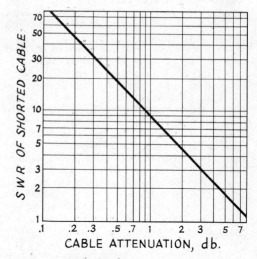

Fig. 13-10—By short-circuiting the far end of a length of transmission line and measuring the s.w.r. at the transmitter end, the loss in the line (when perfectly terminated) can be found from this chart. (Cholewski, QST, January, 1960)

LOADS AND BALANCING DEVICES

The most important practical load for a transmission line is an antenna which, in most cases, will be "balanced"—that is, symmetrically constructed with respect to the feed point. Aside from considerations of matching the actual impedance of the antenna at the feed point to the characteristic impedance of the line (if such matching is attempted) a balanced antenna should be fed through a balanced transmission line in order to preserve symmetry with respect to ground and thus avoid difficulties with unbalanced currents on the line and consequent undesirable radiation from the transmission line itself.

If, as is often the case, the antenna is to be fed through coaxial line (which is inherently unbalanced) some method should be used for connecting the line to the antenna without upsetting the symmetry of the antenna itself. This requires a circuit that will isolate the balanced load from the unbalanced line while providing efficient power transfer. Devices for doing this are called **baluns**. The types used between the antenna and transmission line are generally "linear," consisting of transmission-line sections as described in Chapter 14.

The need for baluns also arises in coupling a transmitter to a balanced transmission line, since the output circuits of most transmitters have one side grounded. (This type of output circuit is desirable for a number of reasons, including TVI reduction.) The most flexible type of balun for this purpose is the inductively coupled matching network described in a subsequent section in this chapter. This combines impedance matching with balanced-to-unbalanced operation, but has the disadvantage that it uses resonant circuits and thus can work over only a limited band of frequencies without readjustment. However, if a fixed impedance ratio in the balun can be tolerated, the coil balun described below can be

used without adjustment over a frequency range of about 10 to 1 — 3 to 30 Mc., for example. Alternatively, a similarly wide band can be covered by a properly designed transformer (with the same impedance limitation) but the design principles and materials used in such transformers are quite specialized. Their

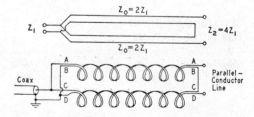

Fig. 13-11—Baluns for matching between push-pull and single-ended circuits. The impedance ratio is 4 to 1 from the push-pull side to the unbalanced side. Coiling the lines (lower drawing) increases the frequency range over which satisfactory operation is obtained.

construction is beyond the scope of this *Handbook.*

Coil Baluns

The type of balun known as the "coil balun" is based on the principles of a linear transmission-line balun as shown in the upper drawing of Fig. 13-11. Two transmission lines of equal length having a characteristic impedance Z_0 are connected in series at one end and in parallel at the other. At the series-connected end the lines are balanced to ground and will match an impedance equal to $2Z_0$. At the parallel-connected end the lines will be matched by an impedance equal to $Z_0/2$. One side may be connected to ground at the parallel-connected end, provided the two lines have a length such that, considering each line as a single wire, the balanced end is effectively decoupled from the parallel-connected end. This requires a length that is an odd multiple of ¼ wavelength.

A definite line length is required only for decoupling purposes, and so long as there is adequate decoupling the system will act as a 4-to-1 impedance transformer regardless of line length. If each line is wound into a coil, as in the lower drawing, the inductances so formed will act as choke coils and will tend to isolate the series-connected end from any ground connection that may be placed on the parallel-connected end. Balun coils made in this way will operate over a wide frequency range, since the choke inductance is not critical. The lower frequency limit is where the coils are no longer effective in isolating one end from the other; the length of line in each coil should be about equal to a quarter wavelength at the lowest frequency to be used.

The principal application of such coils is in going from a 300-ohm balanced line to a 75-ohm coaxial line. This requires that the Z_0 of the lines forming the coils be 150 ohms.

A balun of this type is simply a fixed-ratio transformer, when matched. It cannot compensate for inaccurate matching elsewhere in the system. With a "300-ohm" line on the balanced end, for example, a 75-ohm coax cable will not be matched unless the 300-ohm line actually is terminated in a 300-ohm load.

TWO BROAD-BAND TOROIDAL BALUNS

Air-wound balun transformers are somewhat bulky when designed for operation in the 1.8- to 30-Mc. range. A more compact broad-band trans-

Fig. 13-11D—Layout of a kilowatt 4:1 toroidal balun transformer. Phenolic insulating board is mounted between the transformer and the Minibox wall to prevent short-circuiting. The board is held in place with epoxy cement. Cement is also used to secure the transformer to the board. For outdoor use, the Minibox cover can be installed, then sealed against the weather by applying epoxy cement along the seams of the box.

former can be realized by using toroidal ferrite core material as the foundation for bifilar-wound coil balun transformers. Two such baluns are described here.

In Fig. 13-13C at A, a 1:1 ratio balanced-to-unbalanced-line transformer is shown. This transformer is useful in converting a 50-ohm balanced line condition to one that is 50 ohms, unbalanced.

Fig. 13-11C—Schematic and pictorial representations of the balun transformers. T_1 and T_2 are wound on CF-123 toroid cores (see footnote 1, and the text). J_1 and J_4 are SO-239-type coax connectors, or similar. J_2, J_3, J_5, and J_6 are steatite feedthrough bushings. The windings are labeled a, b, and c to show the relationship between the pictorial and schematic illustrations.

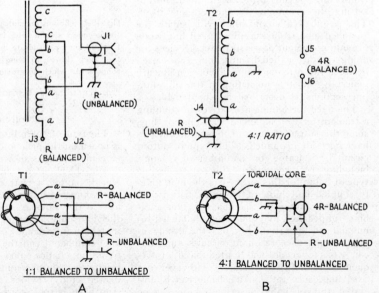

Similarly, the transformer will work between balanced and an unbalanced 75-ohm impedances. A 4:1 ratio transformer is illustrated in Fig. 13-11C at B. This balun is useful for converting a 200-ohm balanced condition to one that is 50 ohms, unbalanced. In a like manner, the transformer can be used between a balanced 300-ohm point and a 75-ohm unbalanced line. Both balun transformers will handle 1000 watts of r.f. power and are designed to operate from 1.8 through 60 Mc.

Low-loss high-frequency ferrite core material is used for T_1 and T_2.[1,3] The cores are made from Q-2 material and cost approximately $5.50 in single-lot quantity. They are 0.5 inches thick, have an O.D. of 2.4 inches, and the I.D. is 1.4 inches. The permeability rating of the cores is 40. A packaged one-kilowatt balun kit, with winding instructions for 1:1 or 4:1 impedance transformation ratios, is available, but uses a core of slightly different dimensions.[2]

Winding Information

The transformer shown in Fig. 13-11C at A has a trifilar winding consisting of 10 turns of No. 14 formvar-insulated wire. A 10-turn bifilar winding of the same type of wire is used for the balun of Fig. 13-11C at B. If the cores have rough edges, they should be carefully sanded until smooth enough to prevent damage to the wire's formvar insulation. The windings should be spaced around the entire core as shown in Fig. 13-11D. Insulating tape need not be used between the core material and the windings because the ferrite material is essentially nonconductive.

Using the Baluns

For indoor applications, the transformers can be assembled open-style, without benefit of a protective enclosure. For outdoor installations, such as at the antenna feed point, the balun should be encapsulated in epoxy resin or mounted in a suitable weather-proof enclosure. A Minibox, sealed against moisture, works nicely for the latter.

NONRADIATING LOADS

Typical examples of nonradiating loads for a transmission line are the grid circuit of a power amplifier (considered in the chapter on transmitters), the input circuit of a receiver, and another transmission line. This last case includes the "antenna tuner" — a misnomer because it is actually a device for coupling a transmission line to the transmitter. Because of its importance in amateur installations, the antenna coupler is considered separately in a later part of this chapter.

[1] Available in single-lot quantity from Permag Corp., 88-06 Van Wyck Expy., Jamaica, N.Y. 11418.

[2] Ami-Don Associates, 12033 Otsego Street, North Hollywood, California

[3] Toroid cores are also available from Ferroxcube Corp. of America, Saugerties, New York.

Coupling to a Receiver

A good match between an antenna and its transmission line does not guarantee a low standing-wave ratio on the line when the antenna system is used for receiving. The s.w.r. is determined wholly by what the line "sees" at the receiver's antenna-input terminals. For minimum s.w.r. the receiver input circuit must be matched to the line. The rated input impedance of a receiver is a nominal value that varies over a considerable range with frequency. Methods for bringing about a proper match are discussed in the chapter on receivers.

The most desirable condition is that in which the receiver is matched to the line Z_0 and the line in turn is matched to the antenna. This transfers maximum power from the antenna to the receiver with the least loss in the transmission line.

COUPLING TO RANDOM-LENGTH ANTENNAS

Several impedance-matching schemes are shown in Fig. 13-11E, permitting random-length wires to be matched to normal lo-Z transmitter outputs. The circuit used will depend upon the length of the antenna wire and its impedance at the desired operating frequency. Ordinarily, one of the four methods shown will provide a suitable impedance match to an end-fed random wire, but the configuration will have to be determined experimentally. For operation between 3.5 and 30 Mc., C_1 can be a 200-pf. type with suitable plate spacing for the power level in use. C_2 and C_3 should be 500-pf. units to allow for flexibility in matching. L_1, L_4, and L_5 should be tapped or rotary inductors with sufficient L for the operating frequency. L_3 can be a tapped Miniductor coil with ample turns for the band being used. An s.w.r. bridge should be used as a match indicator.

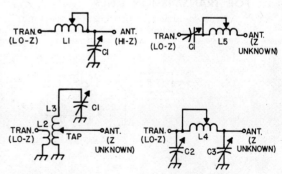

Fig. 13-11E—Networks for matching a lo-Z transmitter output to random-length end-fed wire antennas.

COUPLING THE TRANSMITTER TO THE LINE

The type of coupling system that will be needed to transfer power adequately from the final r.f. amplifier to the transmission line depends almost entirely on the input impedance of the line. As shown earlier in this chapter, the input impedance is determined by the standing-wave ratio and the line length. The simplest case is that where the line is terminated in its characteristic impedance so that the s.w.r. is 1 to 1 and the input impedance is equal to the Z_0 of the line, regardless of line length.

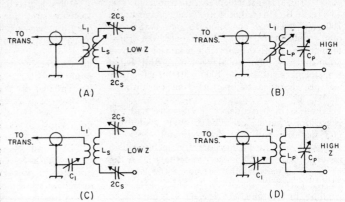

Fig. 13-12—Simple circuits for coupling a transmitter to a balanced line that presents a load different than the transmitter design output impedance. (A) and (B) are respectively series- and parallel-tuned circuits using variable inductive coupling between coils, and (C) and (D) are similar but use fixed inductive coupling and a variable series capacitor, C_1. A series-tuned circuit works well with a low-impedance load; the parallel circuit is better with high-impedance loads (several hundred ohms or more).

Coupling systems that will deliver power into a flat line are readily designed. For all practical purposes the line can be considered to be flat if the s.w.r. is no greater than about 1.5 to 1. That is, a coupling system designed to work into a pure resistance equal to the line Z_0 will have enough leeway to take care of the small variations in input impedance that will occur when the line length is changed, if the s.w.r. is higher than 1 to 1 but no greater than 1.5 to 1.

Current practice in transmitter design is to provide an output circuit that will work into such a line, usually a coaxial line of 50 to 75 ohms characteristic impedance. The design of such output circuits is discussed in the chapter on high-frequency transmitters. If the input impedance of the transmission line that is to be connected to the transmitter differs appreciably from the value of impedance into which the transmitter output circuit is designed to operate, an impedance-matching network must be inserted between the transmitter and the line input terminals.

IMPEDANCE-MATCHING CIRCUITS FOR TRANSMISSION LINES

As shown earlier in this chapter, the input impedance of a line that is operating with a high standing-wave ratio can vary over quite wide limits. The simplest type of circuit that will match such a range of impedances to 50 to 75 ohms is a simple series- or parallel-tuned circuit, approximately resonant at the operating frequency. If the load presented by the line at the operating frequency is low (below a few hundred ohms), a series-tuned circuit should be used. When the load is higher than this, the parallel-tuned circuit is easier to use.

Typical simple circuits for coupling between the transmitter with 50- to 75-ohm coaxial-line output and a balanced transmission line are shown in Fig. 13-12. The inductor L_1 should have a reactance of about 60 ohms (see Fig. 2-44) when adjustable inductive coupling is used (Figs. 13-12A and 13-12B). When a

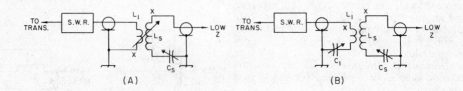

Fig. 13-13—Coupling from a transmitter designed for 50- to 75-ohm output to a coaxial line with a 3- or 4-to-1 s.w.r. is readily accomplished with these circuits. Essential difference between the circuits is (A) adjustable inductive coupling and (B) fixed inductive coupling with variable series capacitor.

In either case the circuit can be adjusted to give a 1-to-1 s.w.r. on the meter in the line to the transmitter.

The coil ends marked "x" should be adjacent, for minimum capacitive coupling.

variable series capacitor is used, L_1 should have a reactance of about 120 ohms. The variable capacitor, C_1, should have a reactance at maximum capacitance of about 100 ohms.

On the secondary side, L_s and C_s should be capable of being tuned to resonance at about 80 percent of the operating frequency. In the series-tuned circuits, for a given low-impedance load looser coupling can be used between L_1 and L_s as the L_s-to-C_s ratio is increased. In the parallel-tuned circuits, for a given high-impedance load looser coupling can be used between L_1 and L_p as the C_p-to-L_p ratio is increased. The constants are not critical; the rules of thumb are mentioned to assist in correcting a marginal condition where sufficient transmitter loading cannot be obtained.

Coupling to coaxial lines that have a high s.w.r., and consequently may present a transmitter with a load it cannot couple to, is done with an unbalanced version of the series-tuned circuit, as shown in Fig. 13-13. The rule given above for coupling ease and L_s-to-C_s ratio applies to these circuits as well.

The most satisfactory way to set up initially any of the circuits of Figs. 13-12 or 13-13 is to connect a coaxial s.w.r. bridge in the line to the transmitter, as shown in Fig. 13-13. The "Monimatch" type of bridge, which can handle the full transmitter power and may be left in the line for continuous monitoring, is excellent for this purpose. However, a simple resistance bridge such as is described in the chapter on measurements is perfectly adequate, requiring only that the transmitter output be reduced to a very low value so that the bridge will not be overloaded. To adjust the circuit, make a trial setting of the coupling (coil spacing in Figs. 13-12A and B and 13-13A, C_1 setting in others) and adjust C_s or C_p for minimum s.w.r. as indicated by the bridge. If the s.w.r. is not close to 1 to 1, readjust the coupling and retune C_s or C_p, continuing this procedure until the s.w.r. is practically 1 to 1. The settings may then be logged for future reference.

In the series-tuned circuits of Figs. 13-12A and 13-12C, the two capacitors should be set at similar settings. The "$2C_s$" indicates that a balanced series-tuned coupler requires twice the capacitance in each of two capacitors as does an unbalanced series-tuned circuit, all other things being equal.

It is possible to use circuits of this type without initially setting them up with an s.w.r. bridge. In such a case it is a matter of cut-and-try until adequate power transfer between the amplifier and main transmission line is secured. However, this method frequently results in a high s.w.r. in the link, with consequent power loss, "hot spots" in the coaxial cable, and tuning that is critical with frequency. The bridge method is simple and gives the optimum operating conditions quickly and with certainty.

A WIDE-RANGE COUPLER FOR BALANCED TRANSMISSION LINES

Matching networks or "Transmatches" for unbalanced (coaxial) lines are normally satisfied by the circuits shown in Fig. 13-13. The limitations of coaxial line with high standing-wave ratios automatically put a limit on the power ratings of the components in the network.

It is different with open-wire (balanced) line. They can operate with much higher standing-wave ratios than coaxial lines can, for the same loss or without failure. As a result, couplers designed for use with open-wire lines may be called upon to withstand higher voltages and currents at any given power level than would a coupler used with coaxial line. For this reason, couplers designed to be used with open-wire lines often seem to require components out of proportion to the power being handled. However, the antenna system with the open-wire line and the "large" coupler may be an efficient system on three or four amateur bands, while the "convenient" system may be a compromise with efficiency on two or three bands.

A wire antenna, fed at the center with open-wire line, is the most efficient multiband antenna devised to date. A transmission-line coupler of the type to be described is required, because the transmission line is "tuned" (it always has a high s.w.r.). The coupler permits the antenna system to present a proper load to the transmitter, with maximum overall efficiency. Regardless of the s.w.r. on the open-wire line, the coupler transforms the load to a non-reactive 50 ohms. A built-in "Monimatch" s.w.r. indicator shows when the correct tuning has been obtained.

Since low-impedance loads require series tuning, and high-impedance loads require parallel tuning, provision is included for both types of circuits. Tapped coils tend to be lossy at the higher frequencies and suitable switches are expensive, so the coupler uses plug-in coils for efficiency and clip leads for simplicity.

The choice of series or parallel tuning is obtained by using a split-stator capacitor (C_3 in Fig. 13-18) and an inductor, L_2, that may or may not be split in the center. When the inductor is not opened, the transmission line is connected across the entire coil, to provide parallel tuning. Series tuning is obtained by opening the coil and connecting the transmission line to the break. The several combinations are shown in Fig. 13-18.

A good idea of the construction can be obtained from Figs. 13-17 and 13-19. All construction is straightforward and conventional, with the possible exception of the Monimatch. The jack bar for the inductors (Millen 41305) is mounted above a hole through which the coaxial line (inner conductor) from P_1 passes, as well as the return back to the stator of C_1 and, on the 80-meter unit, the jumper to the stator of C_2. C_1 is supported by a small aluminum bracket, to bring its shaft to the same height as that of C_3. A Millen 39106 shaft coupling is

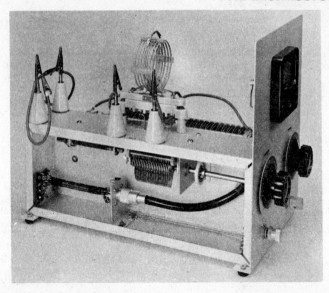

Fig. 13-17—Wide-range transmission-line coupler has provision for high- or low-C series or parallel tuning. A built-in Monimatch simplifies the tuning and insures offering the proper load to the transmitter.

The Monimatch section is at the lower left. Coaxial line running from it loops around and outer conductor is grounded at C_1 rotor. On front panel, left-hand dial tunes C_1 and right-hand dial turns split-stator C_3.

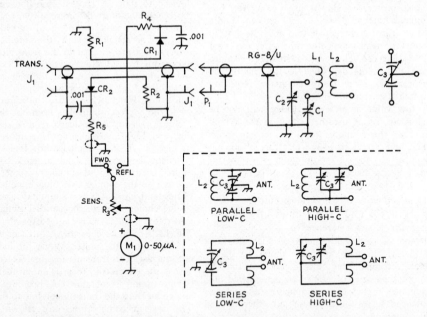

Fig. 13-18—Circuit diagram of the wide-range coupler. Capacitor C_3 connects to L_2 in several ways through use of clip leads. Similarly, the transmission line may be connected either to the outside of the inductor L_2 (parallel tuning) or to the inside (series tuning).

C_1—325-pf. variable (Hammarlund (MC-325)
C_2—Same as C_1; used on 80 meters only. Jumper on L_2 plug bar connects C_2 in circuit.
C_3—Dual 100-pf. transmitting variable (Johnson 154-510)
CR_1, CR_2—1N34A or similar diode
J_1, J_2—Coaxial chassis receptacle, SO-239
L_1, L_2—See coil table.

M_1—0-50 microammeter (Lafayette 99G5042)
P_1—Coaxial plug, PL-259
R_1, R_2—68-ohm ½-watt composition. See text.
R_3—30,000-ohm ½-watt potentiometer, linear taper.
S_1—Single-pole 5-position (two used) rotary switch (Mallory 3215J)
R_4, R_5—1000 ohm, ½ watt. For use below 50 watts, substitute 1 mh. r.f. choke. (Miller 70F103A)

Fig. 13-19—The coupler is built on a 13 X 5 X 3-inch aluminum chassis. The front panel is 8 X 10½ inches. Split-stator C_3 is supported on 1-inch ceramic cone insulators, and the four alligator clips that take the transmission line are mounted on 1½-inch cone insulators. Note clip lead connected to split-stator capacitor rotor connection: this can be connected to lug on chassis or to one side of L_2.

used to C_1; a Hammarlund FC-46-S is used at C_3. Alligator clips used to take the transmission line are forced on to decapitated brass screws and soldered in place. The pair of clips at the rear of the chassis are used with series tuning; those on the side with parallel. This preserves the symmetry, provided the transmission line is brought down vertically to the coupler.

The Monimatch is made from a 6-inch length of RG-8/U. The vinyl outer covering is removed and the outside braid slipped off. One inch of polyethylene insulation is removed at each end, revealing 1-inch lengths of inner conductor and leaving 4 inches of polyethylene. Two 4½-inch lengths of No. 14 wire are taped to opposite sides of the polyethylene. Tin the ends of the wires before fastening them in place with the tape. Slip the outer braid back over the assembly and tape it tightly in place. The 1-inch excess outer conductor at each end is unbraided and twisted together to form *four* leads at each end. These leads are to be connected to soldering lugs under each corner of J_1 and J_2, while the inner conductor is soldered to the inner connection of J_1 and J_2.

If a 50-ohm dummy load is available, it can be used to test the Monimatch. Starting with the value of 68 ohms at R_1 and R_2, check the reflected indication when the transmitter is connected to J_1 and the dummy load is connected to J_2. Then try resistors a few ohms either side of this value, until a good null is obtained. Reverse the connections to J_1 and J_2 and check the value of R_2 in the same manner. It is not absolutely essential that a perfect null be obtained; it is more a matter of pride, since it won't make much difference to the transmitter if it is offered 48 or 52 ohms instead of the magic 50.

It is possible to make an educated guess on what kind of load (high- or low-impedance) the line presents in the shack, based on the electrical length of the line. However, it is more likely that a little "cut and try" is in order. The coil table shows some values and the ranges of impedances they will handle. It is suggested that initial experiments be carried on at low power (50 to 100 watts). Try parallel tuning first. If a match cannot be obtained with any settings of C_1 and C_3 (C_2 in circuit if on 80 meters), leave the coil connected for parallel tuning but tap the transmission line in towards the center of the coil. If this is the condition that will permit a "reflected" reading of zero, series tuning is indicated and the coil should be opened at the center and the series connection used on that band. The wire is clipped at the center of the coil and bent out and upwards; the two clip leads from the rear of the chassis are used to make the connection. The temporary tests on individual turns can be made with clips that have been flattened at the tips.

When constructing the coils, the leads from L_1 must be "snaked" between the turns of L_2. To insulate the leads, use a couple of the ceramic bushings furnished with Centralab index heads for ceramic switch sections (Centralab PA-301).

Antenna Coupler Coil Table						
Band	Range—ohms		L1		L2	
	Parallel	Series	Turns	Material	Turns	Material
3.5 Mc.	800-4000	80-700	12	A	39	B
7	600-5000	25-600	6	A	13	C
14	600-5000	25-700	3	A	7	C
21	500-5000	50-500	3	A	5	C
21	1500-5000	20-100	4	A	5	C

Material A: No. 16, 2 inch diam., 10 t.p.i. (B&W 3907-1)

B: No. 14, 2½ inch diam., 8 t.p.i. (B&W 3906-1)

C: No. 12, 2½ inch diam., 6 t.p.i. (B&W 3905-1)

AN L-NETWORK COUPLER FOR END-FED WIRES

The coupler shown schematically in Fig. 13-21 is suitable for feeding an end-fed antenna on all bands from 3.5 MHz. to 30 MHz. It permits matching the low-impedance transmitter output to the relatively high-impedance end-fed antenna. An overall antenna length of 125 to 135 feet is suitable for use with this tuner. No feeders are used, and the end of the antenna connects directly to the input terminal of the tuner. Coaxial cable can be used between the tuner and the transmitter, and it can be any convenient length. An antenna and tuner combination of this type is handy for portable operation, or where the end of the antenna can be brought directly into the window of the operating room. Good earth grounding is essential to minimize r.f. pickup on the equipment and microphone. If convenient, the tuner should be situated a distance away from the operating position to minimize r.f. feedback.

An s.w.r. indicator, Z_1, is shown in Fig. 13-21 and can be any of the various models of the Monimatch which have been described in *QST*.[1] Suitable dimensions for the pickup unit are given in Chapter 21 in the section which describes an s.w.r. bridge for low-power transmitters. The transistorized amplifier is not used with this tuner.

A short length of insulated wire with an alligator clip is used to short out the unneeded section of the coil, L_1. For any band of operation, the inductance of L_1 and the capacitance of C_1 are experimentally adjusted until a 1:1 s.w.r. is obtained. The lower the operating frequency, the greater will be the number of turns used at L_1. A band switch can be installed, if desired, once the proper tap point for each band (with a given antenna) is located.

This tuner is built on an aluminum base which is 8 inches deep, 10 inches wide, and 6 inches high. If an s.w.r. bridge is already available, there is no need to include the one shown. The regular station s.w.r. indicator can be used "outboard" by installing it between the transmitter and the antenna tuner. This tuner will also work with random-length wires provided the feed end of the antenna does not present a current node at the tuner.

[1] Monimatch Mark II, *QST*, February 1957.

Fig. 13-22—Inside view of the tuner. A short clip lead is used to adjust the inductor for the required number of turns. The s.w.r. pickup assembly, Z_1, is located under L_1 and is at right angles to it (far left). A steatite feed-through bushing is used as an antenna connector. A stud for connecting an earth ground is visible to the right of the steatite bushing. This coupler will handle 2000 watts p.e.p. without arcing or overheating.

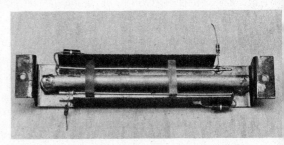

Fig. 13-23—Inside view of the s.w.r. element, Z_1, used in the tuner. It was formed from $\frac{1}{32}$-inch thick brass stock and is 4 inches long. The inner dimension of the channel is 1 X 1 inch. The inner line is a piece of $\frac{1}{4}$-inch diameter copper tubing, 3-$\frac{3}{4}$ inches long. The pickup lines are made of No. 16 bus wire and are 3 inches long. They are spaced $\frac{1}{8}$ inch from the copper tubing by means of plastic blocks (see text). Feedthrough bushings are used as connectors for Z_1. They protrude from the top of the brass channel.

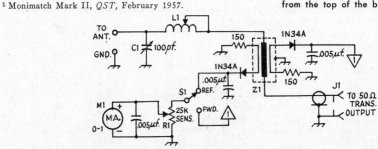

Fig. 13-21—Schematic of the tuner. C_1 is an E. F. Johnson 154-14 variable. L_1 is an Air Dux (Illumitronics) 2007A inductor consisting of 24 turns of No.-12 wire. It is 2½ inches in diameter and is 3¼ inches long. S_1 is a s.p.d.t. wafer switch. R_1 is a 25,000-ohm linear-taper carbon control. Z_1 is a Monimatch-type s.w.r. bridge (see text). J_1 is an SO-239-type coax connector.

Chapter 14

Antennas

An *antenna system* can be considered to include the antenna proper (the portion that radiates the r.f. energy), the feed line, and any coupling devices used for transferring power from the transmitter to the line and from the line to the antenna. Some simple systems may omit the transmission line or one or both of the coupling devices. This chapter will describe the antenna proper, and in many cases will show popular types of lines, as well as line-to-antenna couplings where they are required. However, it should be kept in mind that *any* antenna proper can be used with *any* type of feedline if a suitable coupling is used between the antenna and the line. Changing the line does not change the type of antenna.

Selecting an Antenna

In selecting the type of antenna to use, the majority of amateurs are somewhat limited through space and structural limitations to simple antenna systems, except for v.h.f. operation where the small space requirements make the use of multielement beams readily possible. This chapter will consider antennas for frequencies as high as 30 Mc.—a later chapter will describe the popular types of v.h.f. antennas. However, even though the available space may be limited, it is well to consider the propagation characteristics of the frequency band or bands to be used, to insure that best possible use is made of the available facilities. The propagation characteristics of the amateur-band frequencies are described in Chapter Fifteen. In general, antenna construction and location become more critical and important on the higher frequencies. On the lower frequencies (3.5 and 7 Mc.) the vertical angle of radiation and the plane of polarization may be of relatively little importance; at 28 Mc. they may be all-important.

Definitions

The **polarization** of a straight-wire antenna is determined by its position with respect to the earth. Thus a vertical antenna radiates vertically polarized waves, while a horizontal antenna radiates horizontally polarized waves in a direction broadside to the wire and vertically polarized waves at high vertical angles off the ends of the wire. The wave from an antenna in a slanting position, or from the horizontal antenna in directions other than mentioned above, contains components of both horizontal and vertical polarization.

The **vertical angle of maximum radiation** of an antenna is determined by the free-space pattern of the antenna, its height above ground, and the nature of the ground. The angle is measured in a vertical plane with respect to a tangent to the earth at that point, and it will usually vary with the horizontal angle, except in the case of a simple vertical antenna. The **horizontal angle of maximum radiation** of an antenna is determined by the free-space pattern of the antenna.

The **impedance** of the antenna at any point is the ratio of the voltage to the current at that point. It is important in connection with feeding power to the antenna, since it constitutes the load to the line offered by the antenna. It can be either resistive or complex, depending upon whether or not the antenna is resonant.

The **field strength** produced by an antenna is proportional to the current flowing in it. When there are standing waves on an antenna, the parts of the wire carrying the higher current have the greater radiating effect. All resonant antennas have standing waves—only terminated types, like the terminated rhombic and terminated "V," have substantially uniform current along their lengths.

The ratio of power required to produce a given field strength with a "comparison" antenna to the power required to produce the same field strength with a specified type of antenna is called the **power gain** of the latter antenna. The field is measured in the optimum direction of the antenna under test. The comparison antenna is generally a half-wave antenna at the same height and having the same polarization as the antenna under consideration. Gain usually is expressed in decibels.

In unidirectional beams (antennas with most of the radiation in only one direction) the **front-to-back** ratio is the ratio of power radiated in the maximum direction to power radiated in the opposite direction. It is also a measure of the reduction in received signal when the beam direction is changed from that for maximum response to the opposite direction. Front-to-back ratio is usually expressed in decibels.

The **bandwidth** of an antenna refers to the frequency range over which a property falls within acceptable limits. The **gain bandwidth,** the **front-to-back-ratio bandwidth** and the **standing-wave-ratio bandwidth** are of prime interest in amateur work. The gain bandwidth is of interest because, generally, the higher the antenna gain is the narrower the gain bandwidth will be. The s.w.r. bandwidth is of interest because it is an indication of the transmission-line efficiency over the useful frequency range of the antenna.

GROUND EFFECTS

The radiation pattern of any antenna that is many wavelengths distant from the ground and all others objects is called the **free-space pattern** of that antenna. The free-space pattern of an antenna is almost impossible to obtain in practice, except in the v.h.f. and u.h.f. ranges. Below 30 Mc., the height of the antenna above ground is a major factor in determining the radiation pattern of the antenna.

When any antenna is near the ground the free-space pattern is modified by reflection of radiated waves from the ground, so that the actual pattern is the resultant of the free-space pattern and ground reflections. This resultant is dependent upon the height of the antenna, its position or orientation with respect to the surface of the ground, and the electrical characteristics of the ground. The effect of a perfectly reflecting

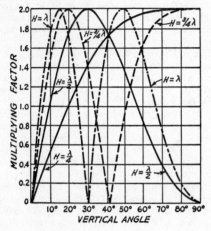

Fig. 14-1—Effect of ground on radiation of horizontal antennas at vertical angles for four antenna heights. This chart is based on perfectly conducting ground.

ground is such that the original free-space field strength may be multiplied by a factor which has a maximum value of 2, for complete reinforcement, and having all intermediate values to zero, for complete cancellation. These reflections only affect the radiation pattern in the vertical plane—that is, in directions upward from the earth's surface—and not in the horizontal plane, or the usual geographical directions.

Fig. 14-1 shows how the multiplying factor varies with the vertical angle for several representative heights for horizontal antennas. As the height is increased the angle at which complete reinforcement takes place is lowered, until for a height equal to one wavelength it occurs at a vertical angle of 15 degrees. At still greater heights, not shown on the chart, the first maximum will occur at still smaller angles.

Radiation Angle

The vertical angle of maximum radiation is of primary importance, expecially at the higher

frequencies. It is advantageous, therefore, to erect the antenna at a height that will take advantage of ground reflection in such a way as to reinforce the space radiation at the most desirable angle. Since low angles usually are most effective, this generally means that the antenna should be high—at least one-half wavelength at 14 Mc., and preferably three-quarters or one wavelength, and at least one wavelength, and preferably higher, at 28 Mc. The physical height required for a given height in wavelengths decreases as the frequency is increased, so that good heights are not impracticable; a half wavelength at 14 Mc. is only 35 feet, approximately, while the same height represents a full wavelength at 28 Mc. At 7 Mc. and lower frequencies the higher radiation angles are effective, so that again a useful antenna height in not difficult of attainment. Heights between 35 and 70 feet are suitable for all bands, the higher figures being preferable.

Imperfect Ground

Fig. 14-1 is based on ground having perfect conductivity, whereas the actual earth is not a perfect conductor. The principal effect of actual ground is to make the curves inaccurate at the lowest angles; appreciable high-frequency radiation at angles smaller than a few degrees is practically impossible to obtain over horizontal ground. Above 15 degrees, however, the curves are accurate enough for all practical purposes, and may be taken as indicative of the result to be expected at angles between 5 and 15 degrees.

The effective ground plane—that is, the plane from which ground reflections can be considered to take place—seldom is the actual surface of the ground but is a few feet below it, depending upon the character of the soil.

Impedance

Waves that are reflected directly upward from the ground induce a current in the antenna in

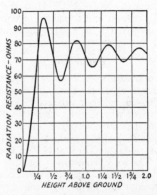

Fig. 14-2—Theoretical curve of variation of radiation resistance for a very thin half-wave horizontal antenna as a function of height in wavelength above perfectly reflecting ground.

passing, and, depending on the antenna height, the phase relationship of this induced current to the original current may be such as either to increase or decrease the total current in the antenna. For the same power input to the antenna, an increase in current is equivalent to a decrease in impedance, and vice versa. Hence, the impedance of the antenna varies with height. The theoretical curve of variation of radiation resistance for a very thin half-wave antenna above perfectly reflecting ground is shown in Fig. 14-2. The impedance approaches the free-space value as the height becomes large, but at low heights may differ considerably from it.

Choice of Polarization

Polarization of the transmitting antenna is generally unimportant on frequencies between 3.5 and 30 Mc. However, the question of whether the antenna should be installed in a horizontal or vertical position deserves consideration for other reasons. A vertical half-wave or quarter-wave antenna will radiate equally well in all *horizontal* directions, so that it is substantially nondirectional, in the usual sense of the word. If installed horizontally, however, the antenna will tend to show directional effects, and will radiate best in the direction at right angles, or broadside, to the wire. The radiation in such a case will be least in the direction toward which the wire points.

The vertical angle of radiation also will be affected by the position of the antenna. If it were not for ground losses at high frequencies, the vertical half-wave antenna would be preferred because it would concentrate the radiation horizontally, and this low-angle radiation is preferable for practically all work.

THE HALF-WAVE ANTENNA

A fundamental form of antenna is a single wire whose length is approximately equal to half the transmitting wavelength. It is the unit from which many more-complex forms of antennas are constructed. It is known as a **dipole antenna.**

The length of a half-wave in space is:

$$Length \text{ (feet)} = \frac{492}{Freq. \text{ (Mc.)}} \qquad (14\text{-}A)$$

The actual length of a half-wave antenna will not be exactly equal to the half-wave in space, but depends upon the thickness of the conductor in relation to the wavelength as shown in Fig. 14-3, where K is a factor that must be multiplied by the half wavelength in free space to obtain the resonant antenna length. An additional shortening effect occurs with wire antennas supported by insulators at the ends because of the capacitance added to the system by the insulators **(end effect).** The following formula is sufficiently accurate for wire antennas at frequencies up to 30 Mc.:

$$Length \text{ of half-wave antenna (feet)} =$$
$$\frac{492 \times 0.95}{Freq. \text{ (Mc.)}} = \frac{468}{Freq. \text{ (Mc.)}} \qquad (14\text{-}B)$$

Example: A half-wave antenna for 7150 kc.
(7.15 Mc.) is $\frac{468}{7.15}$ = 65.45 feet, or 65 feet 5 inches.

Above 30 Mc. the following formulas should be used, particularly for antennas constructed from rod or tubing. K is taken from Fig. 14-3.

$$Length \text{ of half-wave antenna (feet)} =$$
$$\frac{492 \times K}{Freq. \text{ (Mc.)}} \qquad (14\text{-}C)$$

$$or \text{ length (inches)} = \frac{5905 \times K}{Freq. \text{ (Mc.)}} \qquad (14\text{-}D)$$

Example: Find the length of a half wavelength antenna at 28.7 Mc., if the antenna is made of ½-inch diameter tubing. At 28.7 Mc., a half wavelength in space is $\frac{492}{28.7}$ = 17.14 feet, from Eq. 14-A. Ratio of half wavelength to conductor diameter (changing wavelength to inches) is $\frac{(17.14 \times 12)}{0.5}$ = 411. From Fig. 14-3, K = 0.97 for this ratio. The length of the antenna, from Eq. 14-C, is $\frac{(492 \times 0.97)}{28.7}$ = 16.63 feet, or 16 feet 7½ inches. The answer is obtained directly in inches by substitution in Eq. 14-D: $\frac{(5905 \times 0.97)}{28.7}$ = 199.6 inches.

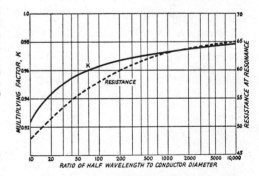

Fig. 14-3—Effect of antenna diameter on length for half-wave resonance, shown as a multiplying factor, K, to be applied to the free-space half wavelength (Equation 14-A). The effect of conductor diameter on the center impedance also is shown.

Current and Voltage Distribution

When power is fed to an antenna, the current and voltage vary along its length. The current is maximum **(loop)** at the center and nearly zero **(node)** at the ends, while the opposite is true of the r.f. voltage. The current does not actually reach zero at the current nodes, because of the end effect; similarly, the voltage is not

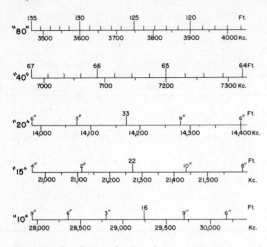

Fig. 14-4—The above scales, based on Eq. 14-B, can be used to determine the length of a half-wave antenna of wire.

zero at its node because of the resistance of the antenna, which consists of both the r.f. resistance of the wire (*ohmic resistance*) and the **radiation resistance.** The radiation resistance is an *equivalent* resistance, a convenient conception to indicate the radiation properties of an antenna. The radiation resistance is the equivalent resistance that would dissipate the power the antenna radiates, with a current flowing in it equal to the antenna current at a current loop (maximum). The ohmic resistance of a half wavelength antenna is ordinarily small enough, compared with the radiation resistance, to be neglected for all practical purposes.

Impedance

The radiation resistance of an infinitely-thin half-wave antenna in free space is about 73 ohms. The value under practical conditions is commonly taken to be in the neighborhood of 60 to 70 ohms, although it varies with height in the manner of Fig. 14-2. It increases toward the ends. The actual value at the ends will depend on a number of factors, such as the height, the physical construction, the insulators at the ends, and the position with respect to ground.

Conductor Size

The impedance of the antenna also depends upon the diameter of the conductor in relation to the wavelength, as indicated in Fig. 14-3. If the diameter of the conductor is increased the capacitance per unit length increases and the inductance per unit length decreases. Since the radiation resistance is affected relatively little, the decreased L/C ratio causes the Q of the antenna to decrease, so that the resonance curve becomes less sharp. Hence, the antenna is capable of working over a wide frequency range. This effect is greater as the diameter is increased, and is a property of some importance at the very-high frequencies where the wavelength is small.

Radiation Characteristics

The radiation from a dipole antenna is not uniform in all directions but varies with the angle with respect to the axis of the wire. It is most intense in directions perpendicular to the wire and zero along the direction of the wire,

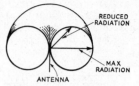

Fig. 14-5—The free-space radiation pattern of a half-wave antenna. The antenna is shown in the vertical position, and the actual "doughnut" pattern is cut in half to show how the line from the center of the antenna to the surface of the pattern varies. In practice this pattern is modified by the height above ground and if the antenna is vertical or horizontal. Fig. 14-1 shows some of the effects of height on the vertical angle of radiation.

with intermediate values at intermediate angles. This is shown by the sketch of Fig. 14-5, which represents the radiation pattern in free space. The relative intensity of radiation is proportional to the length of a line drawn from the center of the figure to the perimeter. If the antenna is vertical, as shown, then the field strength will be uniform in all horizontal directions; if the antenna is hori-

Fig. 14-6—Illustrating the importance of vertical angle of radiation in determining antenna directional effects. Off the end, the radiation is greater at higher angles. Ground reflection is neglected in this drawing of the free-space pattern of a horizontal antenna.

zontal, the relative field strength will depend upon the direction of the receiving point with respect to the direction of the antenna wire. The variation in radiation at various vertical angles from a half wavelength horizontal antenna is indicated in Figs. 14-6 and 14-7.

FEEDING A DIPOLE ANTENNA

Since the impedance at the center of a dipole is in the vicinity of 70 ohms, it offers a good match for 75-ohm two-wire transmission lines. Several types are available on the market, with different power-handling capabilities. They can be connected in the center of the antenna, across a small strain insulator to provide a convenient connection point. Coaxial line of 75 ohms impedance can also be used, but should be used with a 1:1 balun transformer to assure symmetry. In either case, the transmission line should be run away at right angles to the antenna for at least one-quarter wavelength, if possible, to avoid current unbalance in the line caused by pick-up

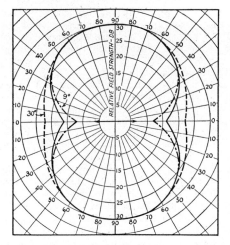

Fig. 14-7—Horizontal pattern of a horizontal half-wave antenna at three vertical radiation angles. The solid line is relative radiation at 15 degrees. Dotted lines show deviation from the 15-degree pattern for angles of 9 and 30 degrees. The patterns are useful for shape only, since the amplitude will depend upon the height of the antenna above ground and the vertical angle considered. The patterns for all three angles have been proportioned to the same scale, but this does not mean that the maximum amplitudes necessarily will be the same. The arrow indicates the direction of the horizontal antenna wire.

from the antenna. The antenna length is calculated from Equation **14-B**, for a half wavelength antenna. When No. 12 or No. 14 enameled wire is used for the antenna, as is generally the case, the length of the wire is the overall length measured from the loop through the insulator at each end. This is illustrated in Fig. 14-8.

The use of 75-ohm line results in a "flat" line over most of any amateur band. However, by making the half-wave antenna in a special manner, called the **two-wire** or **folded dipole**, a good match is offered for a 300-ohm line. Such an antenna is shown in Fig. 14-9. The open-wire line shown in Fig. 14-9 is made of No. 12 or No. 14 enameled wire, separated by lightweight spacers of Lucite or other material (it doesn't have to be a *low-loss* insulating material), and the spacing can be on the order of from 4 to 8 inches, depending upon what is convenient and what the operating frequency is. At 14 Mc., 4-inch separation is satisfactory, and 8-inch spacing can be used at 3.5 Mc.

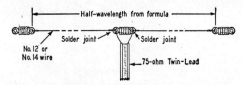

Fig. 14-8—Construction of a dipole fed with 75-ohm line. The length of the antenna is calculated from Equation 14-B or Fig. 14-4.

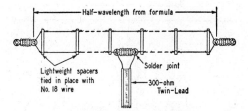

Fig. 14-9—The construction of an open-wire folded dipole fed with 300-ohm line. The length of the antenna is calculated from Equation 14-B or Fig. 14-4.

The half wavelength antenna can also be made from the proper length of 300-ohm line, opened on one side in the center and connected to the feedline. After the wires have been soldered together, the joint can be strengthened by molding some of the excess insulating material (polyethylene) around the joint with a hot iron, or a suitable lightweight clamp of two pieces of Lucite can be devised.

Similar in some respects to the two-wire folded dipole, the three-wire folded dipole of Fig. 14-10 offers a good match for a 600-ohm line. It is favored by amateurs who prefer to use an open-wire line instead of the 300-ohm insulated line.

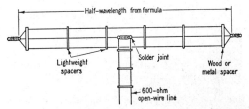

Fig. 14-10—The construction of a 3-wire folded dipole is similar to that of the 2-wire folded dipole. The end spacers may have to be slightly stronger than the others because of the greater compression force on them. The length of the antenna is obtained from Equation 14-B or Fig. 14-4. A suitable line can be made from No. 14 wire spaced 5 inches, or from No. 12 wire spaced 6 inches.

The three wires of the antenna proper should all be of the same diameter.

Another method for offering a match to a 600-ohm open-wire line with a half wavelength antenna is shown in Fig. 14-11. The system is called a **delta match**. The line is "fanned" as it approaches the antenna, to have a gradually increasing impedance that equals the antenna impedance at the point of connection. The dimensions are fairly critical, but careful measurement before installing the antenna and matching section is generally all that is necessary. The length of the antenna, L, is calculated from Equation **14-B** or Fig. 14-4. The length of section C is computed from:

$$C \text{ (feet)} = \frac{118}{Freq. \text{ (Mc.)}} \qquad (14\text{-E})$$

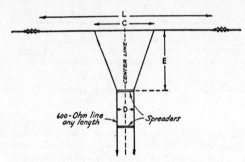

Fig. 14-11—Delta-matched antenna systems. The dimensions *C, D,* and *E* are found by formulas given in the text. It is important that the matching section, *E,* come straight away from the antenna.

The feeder clearance, *E,* is found from

$$E \text{ (feet)} = \frac{148}{\text{Freq. (Mc.)}} \qquad (14\text{-}F)$$

Example: For a frequency of 7.1 Mc., the length

$$L = \frac{468}{7.1} = 65.91 \text{ feet, or } 65 \text{ feet } 11 \text{ inches}$$

$$C = \frac{118}{7.1} = 16.62 \text{ feet, or } 16 \text{ feet } 7 \text{ inches.}$$

$$E = \frac{148}{7.1} = 20.84 \text{ feet, or } 20 \text{ feet } 10 \text{ inches.}$$

Since the equations hold only for 600-ohm line, it is important that the line be close to this value. This requires 5-inch spaced No. 14 wire, 6-inch spaced No. 12 wire, or 3¾-inch spaced No. 16 wire.

If a half wavelength antenna is fed at the center with other than 75-ohm line, or if a two-wire dipole is fed with other than 300-ohm line, standing waves will appear on the line and coupling to the transmitter may become awkward for some line lengths, as described in Chapter 13. How-

ever, in many cases it is not convenient to feed the half-wave antenna with the correct line (as is the case where multiband operation of the same antenna is desired), and sometimes it is not convenient to feed the antenna at the center. Where multiband operation is desired (to be discussed later) or when the antenna must be fed at one end by a transmission line, an open-wire line of from 450 to 600 ohms impedance is generally used. The impedance at the end of a half wavelength antenna is in the vicinity of several thousand ohms, and hence a standing-wave ratio of 4 or 5 is not unusual when the line is connected to the end of the antenna. It is advisable, therefore, to keep the losses in the line as low as possible. This requires the use of ceramic or Micalex feeder spacers, if any appreciable power is used. For low-power installations in dry climates, dry wood spacers boiled in paraffin are satisfactory. Mechanical details of half wavelength antennas fed with open-wire lines are given in Fig. 14-12. Regardless of the power level, solid-dielectric Twin-Lead is not recommended for this use.

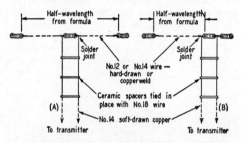

Fig. 14-12—The half-wave antenna can be fed at the center or at the end with an open-wire line. The antenna length is obtained from Equation 14-B or Fig. 14-4.

THE "INVERTED V" ANTENNA

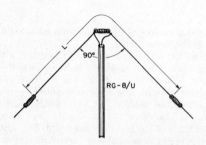

Fig. 14-13—The inverted V antenna is a dipole with the ends lower than the center. It is convenient to use because it requires only one high support, which also supports the weight of the coaxial transmission line. Shown here in its simplest form, with a glass insulator in the center, a deluxe version can be made with a waterproof fitting.

A popular and effective antenna on 40 and 80 meters is the so-called "inverted V" antenna. Actually it is a half-wave dipole with the ends lower than the center; a true "V" antenna is usually several wavelengths long. However, the convenience of installation of the antenna (only one high support is required) makes it a useful low-frequency antenna.

Referring to Fig. 14-13, an inverted V antenna with the wires at 45 degrees to the vertical will require a support about 60 feet high for an 80-meter antenna and about 35 feet for a 40-meter version, if the ends are to be no closer than 10 feet from the ground. As with any antenna, additional height is an advantage.

When its ends are near the ground, the length of the wire in an inverted V antenna is slightly shorter than when the dipole is strung in a straight line, and the overall length can be approximated by

$$Length \text{ (feet)} = \frac{464}{Freq. \text{ (Mc.)}}$$

Example: For a frequency of 3.9 Mc., the length equals 464 ÷ 3.9 = 119 feet.

The impedance of the inverted V antenna is lower than that of a linear dipole, and 50-ohm coaxial cable is recommended for the transmission line. Since the exact angle of the wires, the presence of nearby objects and the height above ground will all affect the impedance and the frequency of resonance, it is desirable to cut the antenna a little long at first and check for resonance by finding the frequency of minimum s.w.r. If the minimum s.w.r. occurs at a frequency well below the desired operating frequency, trim small equal amounts off of each end of the inverted V and repeat the test.

LONG-WIRE ANTENNAS

An antenna will be resonant so long as an integral number of standing waves of current and voltage can exist along its length; in other words, so long as its length is some integral multiple of a half wavelength. When the antenna is more than a half-wave long it usually is called a long-wire antenna, or a harmonic antenna.

Current and Voltage Distribution

Fig. 14-14 shows the current and voltage distribution along a wire operating at its fundamental frequency (where its length is equal to a

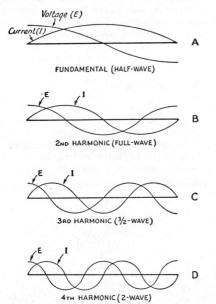

Fig. 14-14—Standing-wave current and voltage distribution along an antenna when it is operated at various harmonics of its fundamental resonant frequency.

half wavelength) and at its second, third and fourth harmonics. For example, if the fundamental frequency of the antenna is 7 Mc., the current and voltage distribution will be as shown at A. The same antenna excited at 14 Mc. would have current and voltage distribution as shown at B. At 21 Mc., the third harmonic of 7 Mc., the current and voltage distribution would be as in C; and at 28 Mc., the fourth harmonic, as in D. The number of the harmonic is the number of half waves contained in the antenna at the particular operating frequency.

The polarity of current or voltage in each standing wave is opposite to that in the adjacent standing waves. This is shown in the figure by drawing the current and voltage curves successively above and below the antenna (taken as a zero reference line), to indicate that the polarity reverses when the current or voltage goes through zero. Currents flowing in the same direction are *in phase;* in opposite directions, *out of phase.*

It is evident that one antenna may be used for harmonically-related frequencies, such as the various amateur bands. The long-wire or harmonic antenna is the basis of multiband operation with one antenna.

Physical Lengths

The length of a long-wire antenna is not an exact multiple of that of a half-wave antenna because the end effects operate only on the end sections of the antenna; in other parts of the wire these effects are absent, and the wire length is approximately that of an equivalent portion of the wave in space. The formula for the length of a long-wire antenna, therefore, is

$$Length \text{ (feet)} = \frac{492 \ (N - 0.05)}{Freq. \text{ (Mc.)}} \quad (14\text{-G})$$

where N is the number of *half*-waves on the antenna.

Example: An antenna 4 half-waves long at 14.2 Mc. would be $\dfrac{492 \ (4 - 0.05)}{14.2} = \dfrac{492 \times 3.95}{14.2}$ = 136.7 feet, or 136 feet 8 inches.

It is apparent that an antenna cut as a half-wave for a given frequency will be slightly off resonance at exactly twice that frequency (the second harmonic), because of the decreased influence of the end effects when the antenna is more than one-half wavelength long. The effect is not very important, except for a possible unbalance in the feeder system and consequent radiation from the feedline. If the antenna is fed in the exact center, no unbalance will occur at any frequency, but end-fed systems will show an unbalance on all but one frequency in each harmonic range.

Impedance and Power Gain

The radiation resistance as measured at a current loop becomes higher as the antenna length is increased. Also, a long-wire antenna radiates more power in its most favorable direction than does a half-wave antenna in its most favorable

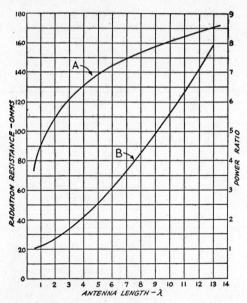

Fig. 14-15—Curve A shows variation in radiation resistance with antenna length. Curve B shows power in lobes of maximum radiation for long-wire antennas as a ratio to the maximum radiation for a half-wave antenna.

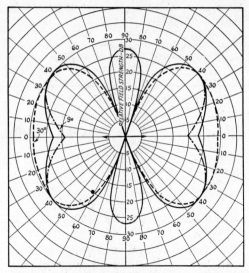

Fig. 14-17—Horizontal patterns of radiation from an antenna three half-waves long. The solid line shows the pattern for a vertical angle of 15 degrees; dotted lines show deviation from the 15-degree pattern at 9 and 30 degrees. Minor lobes coincide for all three angles.

direction. This power gain is secured at the expense of radiation in other directions. Fig. 14-15 shows how the radiation resistance and the power in the lobe of maximum radiation vary with the antenna length.

Directional Characteristics

As the wire is made longer in terms of the number of half wavelengths, the directional effects change. Instead of the "doughnut" pattern of the half-wave antenna, the directional characteristic splits up into "lobes" which make various angles with the wire. In general, as the length of the wire is increased the direction in which maximum radiation occurs tends to approach the line of the antenna itself.

Directional characteristics for antennas one wavelength, three half-wavelengths, and two wavelengths long are given in Figs. 14-16,

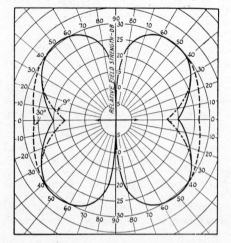

Fig. 14-16—Horizontal patterns of radiation from a full-wave antenna. The solid line shows the pattern for a vertical angle of 15 degrees; dotted lines show deviation from the 15-degree pattern at 9 and 30 degrees. All three patterns are drawn to the same relative scale; actual amplitudes will depend upon the height of the antenna.

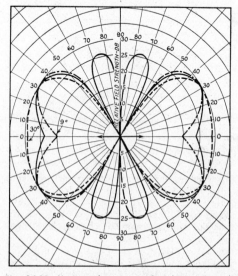

Fig. 14-18—Horizontal patterns of radiation from an antenna two wavelengths long. The solid line shows the pattern for a vertical angle of 15 degrees; dotted lines show deviation from the 15-degree pattern at 9 and 30 degrees. The minor lobes coincide for all three angles.

14-17 and 14-18, for three vertical angles of radiation. Note that, as the wire length increases, the radiation along the line of the antenna becomes more pronounced. Still longer antennas can be considered to have practically "end-on" directional characteristics, even at the lower radiation angles.

Methods of Feeding

In a long-wire antenna, the currents in adjacent half-wave sections must be out of phase, as shown in Fig. 14-14. The feeder system must not upset this phase relationship. This is satisfied by feeding the antenna at either end or at any current loop. A two-wire feeder cannot be inserted at a current node, however, because this invariably brings the currents in two adjacent half-wave sections in phase. A long wire antenna is usually made a half wavelength at the lowest frequency and fed at the end.

MULTIBAND ANTENNAS

As suggested in the preceding section, the same antenna may be used for several bands by operating it on harmonics. When this is done it is necessary to use tuned feeders, since the impedance matching for nonresonant feeder operation can be accomplished only at one frequency unless means are provided for changing the length of a matching section and shifting the point at which the feeder is attached to it.

A dipole antenna that is center-fed by a solid-dielectric line is useless for even harmonic operation; on all even harmonics there is a voltage maximum occurring right at the feed point, and the resultant impedance mismatch causes a large standing-wave ratio and consequently high losses arise in the solid dielectric. It is wise not to attempt to use on its even harmonics a half-wave antenna center-fed with coaxial cable. On odd harmonics, as between 7 and 21 Mc., a current loop will appear in the center of the antenna and a fair match can be obtained. High-impedance solid-dielectric lines such as 300-ohm Twin-Lead may be used in an emergency, provided the power does not exceed a few hundred watts, but it is an inefficient feed method.

When the same antenna is used for work in several bands, the directional characteristics will vary with the band in use.

Simple Systems

The most practical simple multiband antenna is one that is a half wavelength long at the lowest frequency and is fed either at the center or one end with an open-wire line. Although the standing wave ratio on the feedline will not approach 1.0 on any band, if the losses in the line are low the system will be efficient. From the standpoint of reduced feedline radiation, a center-fed system is superior to one that is end-fed, but the end-fed arrangement is often more convenient and should not be ignored as a possibility. The center-fed antenna will not have the same radiation pattern as an end-fed one of the same length, except on frequencies where the length of the antenna is a half wavelength. The end-fed antenna acts like a long-wire antenna on all bands (for which it is longer than a half wavelength), but the center-fed one acts like two antennas of half that length fed in phase. For example, if a full-wavelength antenna is fed at one end, it will have a radiation pattern as shown in Fig. 14-16, but if it is fed in the center the pattern will be somewhat similar to Fig. 14-7, with the maximum radiation broadside to the wire. Either antenna is a good radiator, but if the radiation pattern is a factor, the point of feed must be considered.

Since multiband operation of an antenna does not permit matching of the feedline, some attention should be paid to the length of the feedline if convenient transmitter-coupling arrangements are to be obtained. Table 14-I gives some suggested antenna and feeder length for multiband operation. In general, the length of the feedline can be other than that indicated, but the type of coupling circuit may change.

Open-wire line feed is recommended for an antenna of this type, since the losses will run too high in solid-dielectric line. For low-power applications up to a few hundred watts, open-wire TV line is convenient and satisfactory to use. However, for high-power installations up to the kilowatt limit, an open-wire line with No. 14 or No.

TABLE 14-I

Multiband Tuned-Line-Fed Antennas

Antenna Length (Ft.)	Feeder Length (Ft.)	Band	Type of Coupling Circuit
With end feed:			
135	45	3.5 – 21 28	Series Parallel
67	45	7 – 21 28	Series Parallel
With center feed:			
135	42	3.5 – 21 28	Parallel Series
135	77½	3.5 – 28	Parallel
67	42½	3.5 7 – 28	Series Parallel
67	65½	3.5, 14, 28 7, 21	Parallel Series

Antenna lengths for end-fed antennas are approximate and should be cut to formula length at favorite operating frequency.

Where parallel tuning is specified, it will be necessary in some cases to tap in from the ends of the coil for proper loading — see Chapter 13 for examples of antenna couplers.

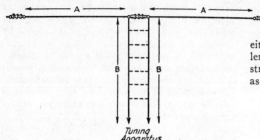

Fig. 14-19—Practical arrangement of a shortened antenna. When the total length, A + B + B + A, is the same as the antenna length plus twice the feeder length of the center-fed antennas of Table 14-I, the same type of coupling circuit will be used. When the feeder length or antenna length, or both, makes the sum different, the type of coupling circuit may be different but the effectiveness of the antenna is not changed, unless A + A is less than a quarter wavelength.

12 conductors should be used. This can be built from soft-drawn wire and ceramic or other suitable spacers, or it can be bought ready-made.

Antennas for Restricted Space

If the space available for the antenna is not large enough to accommodate the length necessary for a half wave at the lowest frequency to be used, quite satisfactory operation can be secured by using a short antenna and making up the missing length in the feeder system. The antenna itself may be as short as a quarter wavelength and will radiate fairly well, although of course it will not be as effective as one a half wave long. Nevertheless such a system is useful where operation on the desired band otherwise would be impossible.

Tuned feeders are a practical necessity with such an antenna system, and a center-fed antenna will give best all-around performance. With end feed the feeder currents become badly unbalanced.

With center feed, practically any convenient length of antenna can be used. If the total length of antenna plus twice feedline is the same as in Table 14-I, the type of tuning will be the same as stated. This is illustrated in Fig. 14-19. If the total length is not the same, different tuning conditions can be expected on some bands. This should not be interpreted as a fault in the antenna, and any tuning system (series or parallel) that works well without any trace of heating is quite satisfactory. Heating may result when the taps with parallel tuning are made too close to the center of the coil—it can often be corrected by using less total inductance and more capacitance.

Bent Antennas

Since the field strength at a distance is proportional to the current in the antenna, the high-current part of a dipole antenna (the center quarter wave, approximately) does most of the radiating. Advantage can be taken of this

fact when the space available does not permit building an antenna a half-wave long. In this case the ends may be bent, either horizontally or vertically, so that the total length equals a half wave, even though the straightaway horizontal length may be as short as a quarter wave. The operation is illustrated

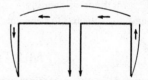

Fig. 14-20—Folded arrangement for shortened antennas. The total length is a half-wave, not including the feeders. The horizontal part is made as long as convenient and the ends dropped down to make up the required length. The ends may be bent back on themselves like feeders to cancel radiation partially. The horizontal section should be at least a quarter wave long.

in Fig. 14-20. Such an antenna will be a somewhat better radiator than a quarter wavelength antenna on the lowest frequency, but is not so desirable for multiband operation because the ends play an increasingly important part as the frequency is raised. The performance of the system in such a case is difficult to predict, especially if the ends are vertical (the most convenient arrangement) because of the complex combination of horizontal and vertical polarization which results as well as the dissimilar directional characteristics. However, the fact that the radiation pattern is incapable of prediction does not detract from the general usefulness of the antenna. For one-band operation with a "flat" line, end-loading with coils (5 feet or so in from each end) is practical and efficient.

"Windom" or Off-Center-Fed Antenna

A multiband antenna that enjoyed considerable popularity in the 1930s is the "off-center feed" of "Windom," named after the amateur who wrote a comprehensive article about it. Shown in Fig. 14-21A, it consists of a half wavelength antenna on the lowest-frequency band to be used, with a *single-wire* feeder connected 14% off center. The antenna will operate satisfactorily on the even-harmonic frequencies, and thus a single antenna can be made to serve on the 80-, 40-, 20-, and 10-meter bands. The single-wire feeder shows an impedance of approximately 600 ohms to ground, and consequently the antenna coupling system must be capable of matching this value to the transmitter. A tapped parallel-tuned circuit or a properly-proportioned pi-network coupler is generally used. Where TVI is a problem, the antenna coupler is required, so that a low-pass filter can be used in the connecting link of coaxial line.

Although theoretically the feed line can be of any length, some lengths will tend to give trouble with "too much r.f. in the shack," with the consequence that r.f. sparks can be drawn from

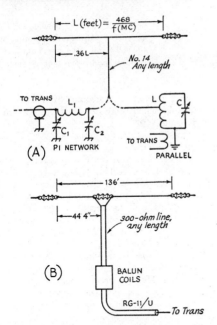

Fig. 14-21—Two versions of the off-center-fed antenna.

(A) Single-wire feed shows approximately 600 ohms impedance to ground and is most conveniently coupled to the transmitter as shown. The pi-network coupling will require more capacity at C_1 than at C_2. L_1 is best found by experiment—an inductance of about the same size as that used in the output stage is a good starting point. The parallel-tuned circuit will be a tuned circuit that resonates at the operating frequency with L and C close to those used in the output stage. The tap is found by experiment, and it should be as near the top of L as it can and still give good loading of the transmitter.

(B) Two-wire off-center feed uses 300-ohm TV line. Although the 300-ohm line can be coupled directly to some transmitters, it is common practice to step down the impedance level to 75 ohms through a pair of "balun" coils.

the transmitter's metal cabinet and/or v.f.o. notes will develop serious modulation. If such is found to be the case, the feeder length should be changed.

A newer version of the off-center-feed antenna uses 300-ohm TV Twin-Lead to feed the antenna, as shown in Fig. 14-21B. It is claimed that the antenna offers a good match for the 300-ohm line on four bands and, although this is more wishful thinking than actual truth, the system is widely used and does work satisfactorily. It is subject to the same feed line length and "r.f.-in-the-shack" troubles that the single-wire version enjoys. However, in this case a pair of "balun" coils can be used to step down the impedance level to 75 ohms and at the same time alleviate some of the feedline troubles. This antenna system is popular among amateurs using multiband transmitters with pi-network-tuned output stages.

With either of the off-center-fed antenna systems, the feedline should run away from the an-

tenna at right angles for as great a distance as possible before bending. No sharp bends should be allowed anywhere in the line.

Multiband Operation with Coaxial Line Feed

The proper use of coaxial line requires that the standing-wave ratio be held to a low value, preferably below 2 :1. Since the impedance of an ordinary antenna changes widely from band to band, it is not possible to feed a simple antenna with coaxial line and use it on a number of bands without tricks of some kind. The single exception to this is the use of 75-ohm coaxial line to feed a 7-Mc. half-wave antenna, as in Fig. 14-19; this antenna can also be used on 21 Mc. and the s.w.r. in the line will not run too high.

One multiband antenna system that can be used by anyone without much trouble is shown in Fig. 14-22. Here separate dipoles are connected to one feedline. The 7-Mc. dipole also serves on 21 Mc. A low s.w.r. will appear on the feedline in each band if the dipoles are of the proper length. The antenna system can be built by suspending one set of elements from the one above, using insulator-terminated wood spreaders about one foot long. An alternative is to let one antenna droop several feet under the other, bring ropes attached to the insulators back to a common support point. It has been found that a separation of only an inch or two between dipoles is satisfactory. By using a length of the Twin-Lead used for folded dipoles (one Copperweld conductor and one soft-drawn) the strong wire can be used for the low-frequency dipole. The soft-drawn wire is then used on a higher band, supported by the solid dielectric.

A vertical antenna can be operated on several bands and fed with a single length of coaxial line provided the antenna is no longer than 0.6 wavelength at the highest frequency and that a suitable matching network for each band is used at the base. A good radial or ground system is required. The matching sections can be housed in a

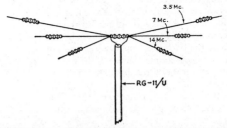

Fig. 14-22—An effective "all-band" antenna fed with a single length of coaxial line can be constructed by joining several half wavelength antennas at their centers and feeding them at the common point. In the example above, a low s.w.r. will be obtained on 80, 40, 20 and 15 meters. (The 7-Mc. antenna also works on 21 Mc.) If a 28-Mc. antenna were added, 10-meter operation could also be included. The antenna lengths can be computed from formula 14-B. The shorter antennas can be suspended a foot or two below the longest one or fanned out in the same horizontal plane.

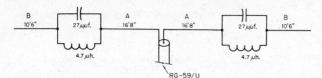

weatherproof box and changed manually or by stepping relays; their form will vary from parallel-tuned circuits to L sections. (See McCoy, *QST*, December, 1955, for description of L-section coupler.)

Multiband "Trap" Antennas

Another approach to the problem of multiband operation with a single untuned feedline is the use of parallel-tuned circuits installed in the antenna at the right points to "divorce" the remainder of the antenna from the center section (part fed by coaxial line) as the transmitter is changed to a higher-frequency band. This principle of the divorcing circuits is utilized in a commercial "all-band" vertical antenna, and a 5-band kit for horizontal antennas is also available commercially. The divorcing circuits are also used in several commercial multiband beams for the 14-, 21- and 28-Mc. bands.

The multiband antenna system shown in Fig. 14-23 may be of interest to the ham who wishes to work on several bands but doesn't have sufficient space for an 80-meter antenna and consequently is limited to 40 meters and below. (A five-band antenna requires more than a 100-foot span; see Greenberg, *QST*, October, 1956.)

On 40 meters the traps serve as inductors to load the system to 7 Mc. On 20, the traps (resonant to 14.1 Mc.) divorce the B sections from the antenna proper. On 28 Mc. the entire antenna becomes approximately a 5/2-wavelength radiator.

As shown in Fig. 14-24, each trap is literally built around an "egg" or "strain" insulator. In this type of insulator, the hole at one end is at right angles to the hole at the other end, and the wires are fastened as in Fig. 14-25. These insulators have greater compressive strength than tensile strength and will not permit the antenna to fall should the insulator break, since the two interlooped wires prevent it. There is ample space within the inductor for both the insulator and capacitor. The plastic covers are not essential but are considered desirable because they provide mechanical pro-

tection and prevent the accumulation of ice or soot and tars which may not wash off the traps when it rains.

Electrically, each trap consists of a $25\text{-}\mu\mu f.$ capacitor shunted by 4.7 $\mu h.$ of inductance. A Centralab ceramic transmitting capacitor 857-25Z, rated at 15,000 volts d.c., is shown and will safely handle a kilowatt. Other ceramic capacitors rated at approximately 6000 volts would be satisfactory, as well as cheaper. The inductors are made of No. 12 wire, 2½ inches in diameter, 6 turns per inch (B & W 3905-1 coil stock).

One may wish to choose a different frequency in the 20-meter band for which optimum results are desired; for example, 14.05 Mc. for c.w. operation, 14.25 Mc. for phone operation, or perhaps 14.175 Mc. for general coverage. In any case, the number of inductor turns is adjusted accordingly.

Trap Adjustment

As a preliminary step, loops of No. 12 wire are fitted to one of the egg insulators in the normal manner (see Fig. 14-25), except that after the wraps are made, the end leads are snipped off close to the wraps. A capacitor is then placed in position and bridged with short leads across the insulator and soldered sufficiently to provide temporary support. The combination is then slipped inside about 10 turns of the inductor, one end of which should be soldered to an insulator-capacitor lead.

Adjustment to the resonant frequency can now proceed, using a grid-dip meter.

Coupling between the g.d.o. and the trap should be very loose. To insure accuracy, the station receiver should be used to check the g.d.o. frequency. The inductance should be reduced ¼ turn at a time. If one is careful, the resonant fre-

Fig. 14-24—The 14-Mc. trap is enclosed in a weatherproof cover made of plastic sheet. The ceramic capacitor and strain insulator are inside the coil.

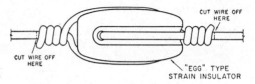

CUT WIRE OFF HERE

CUT WIRE OFF HERE

"EGG" TYPE STRAIN INSULATOR

quency can easily be set to within a few kilocycles of the chosen figure.

The reason for snipping the end leads close to the wraps and the inclusion of the loops through the egg insulator soon becomes apparent. The resonant frequency of the capacitor and inductor alone is reduced about 20 kc. per inch of end lead length and about 350 kc. by the insulator loops. The latter add approximately 2 $\mu\mu$f. to the fixed capacitor value and account for the total of 27 $\mu\mu$f. shown in Fig. 14-23.

Assembly

Having determined the exact number of inductor turns, the trap is taken apart and reassembled with leads of any convenient length. One may, of course, connect the entire lengths of sections A and B to the trap at this time, if desired. But, if more convenient, a foot or two of wire can be fastened and the remaining lengths soldered on just before the antenna is raised.

The protective covers are most readily formed by wrapping two turns (plus an overlap of ½ inch) of 0.020-inch polystyrene or lucite sheeting around a 3-inch plastic disk held at the center of the cylinder so formed. The length of the cover should be about 4 inches. A very small amount of plastic solvent (a cohesive cement that actually softens the plastic surfaces) should then be applied under the edge of the overlap and the joint held firmly for about two minutes to insure a strong, tight seal. The disk is pushed out and the inner seam of the sheeting sealed.

The trap is then placed in the plastic cylinder and the end disks marked where the antenna wires are to pass through. After drilling these holes, the disks are slipped over the leads, pressed into the ends of the cylinder and a small amount of solvent applied to the periphery to obtain a good seal.

Some air can flow in and out of the trap through the antenna-wire holes, and this will prevent the accumulation of condensation.

Length Adjustment

Standing-wave ratios are not uniform throughout the band or bands for which an antenna is designed. In a trap antenna, the choice of frequencies for best performance is a compromise. After making the traps resonant at 14.1 Mc., sections A are adjusted for resonance. Sections B are then adjusted for resonance at approximately 7.2 Mc. For the dimensions shown, with the antenna about 250 ft. above street level and 35 ft. above electrical ground, an s.w.r. of virtually 1 to 1 was obtained at 7.2 Mc., with maximums of 1.3 and 1.1 at 7.0 and 7.3 Mc., respectively. In the 20-meter band, the s.w.r. was also 1 to 1 at 14.1 Mc., 1.1 at 14.0 Mc. and 1.3 at 14.3 Mc. In the 10-meter band, the s.w.r. was 1.3 to 1 at 28.0 Mc., 1.1 at 28.4 Mc., 1.5 at 29 Mc., and only 2.4 at the upper extreme of the band. The s.w.r. on 21 Mc. will be high because the antenna is not resonant in that band.

RG-59/U cable forms the transmission line and is connected to the antenna. After connecting the cable and antenna wires, the connection should be coated with several layers of insulating varnish to make certain that the junction is watertight.

VERTICAL ANTENNAS

A vertical quarter-wavelength antenna is often used in the low-frequency amateur bands to obtain low-angle radiation. It is also used when there isn't enough room for the supports for a horizontal antenna. For maximum effectiveness is should be located clear of nearby objects and it should be operated in conjunction with a good ground system, but it is still worth trying where these ideal conditions cannot be obtained.

Four typical examples and suggested methods for feeding a vertical antenna are shown in Fig. 14-26. The antenna may be wire or tubing supported by wood or insulated guy wires. When tubing is used for the antenna, or when guy wires (broken up by insulators) are used to reinforce the structure, the length given by the formula is likely to be long by a few per cent. A check of the standing-wave ratio on the line will indicate the frequency at which the s.w.r. is minimum,

and the antenna length can be adjusted accordingly.

A good ground connection is necessary for the most effective operation of a vertical antenna (other than the ground-plane type). In some cases a short connection to the cold-water system of the house will be adequate. But maximum performance usually demands a separate ground system. A single 4- to 6-foot ground rod driven into the earth at the base of the antenna is usually not sufficient, unless the soil has exceptional conductivity. A minimum ground system that can be depended upon is 6 to 12 quarter wavelength radials laid out as the spokes of a wheel from the base of the antenna. These radials can be made of heavy aluminum wire, of the type used for grounding TV antennas, buried at least 6 inches in the ground. This is normally done by slitting the earth with a spade and pushing the

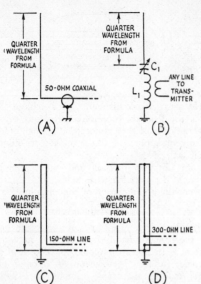

Fig. 14-26—A quarter-wavelength antenna can be fed directly with 50-ohm coaxial line (A) with a low standing-wave ratio, or a coupling network can be used (B) that will permit a line of any impedance to be used. In (B), L_1 and C_1 should resonate to the operating frequency, and L_1 should be larger than is normally used in a plate tank circuit at the same frequency. By using multiwire antennas, the quarter-wave vertical can be fed with (C) 150-or (D) 300-ohm line.

wire into the slot, after which the earth can be tamped down.

The examples shown in Fig. 14-26 all require an antenna insulated from the ground, to provide for the feed point. A *grounded* tower or pipe can be used as a radiator by employing "shunt feed," which consists of tapping the inner conductor of the coaxial-line feed up on the tower until the best match is obtained, in much the same manner as the "gamma match" (described later) is used on a horizontal element. If the antenna is not an electrical quarter wavelength long, it is necessary to tune out the reactance by adding capacity or inductance between the coaxial line and the shunting conductor. A metal tower supporting a TV antenna or rotary beam can be shunt-fed only if all of the wires and leads from the supported antenna run down the center of the tower and underground away from the tower.

THE GROUND-PLANE ANTENNA

A ground-plane antenna is a vertical quarter-wavelength antenna using an artificial metallic ground, usually consisting of four rods or wires perpendicular to the antenna and extending radially from its base. Unlike the quarter-wavelength vertical antennas without an artificial ground, the ground-plane antenna will give low-angle radiation regardless of the height above actual ground. However, to be a true ground-plane antenna, the plane of the radials should be at least

a quarter wavelength above ground. Despite this one limitation, the antenna is useful for DX work in any band below 30 Mc.

The vertical portion of the ground-plane antenna can be made of self-supported aluminum tubing, or a top-supported wire depending upon the necessary length and the available supports. The radials are also made of tubing or heavy wire depending upon the available supports and necessary lengths. They need not be exactly symmetrical about the base of the vertical portion.

The radiation resistance of a ground-plane antenna varies with the diameter of the vertical element. The radiation resistance is usually in the vicinity of 30 ohms, and the antenna can be fed with 75-ohm coaxial line with a quarter-wavelength section of 50-ohm line between line and antenna. For multiband operation, a ground-plane antenna can be fed with tuned open-wire

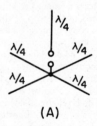

(A)

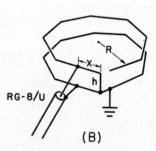

(B)

Fig. 14-27—(A) Basic ground-plane antenna. The practical antenna usually is fed by coaxial line; the vertical section is tubing or wire, and the radials are also tubing or wire. Radials may slope down (and be actual guy wires for support).

(B) The unusual DDRR vertically-polarized antenna. Length around top (open) wire or bottom (closed) wire, in feet, $= 252/f$ (Mc.). (E.g., 64.7 feet for 3.9 Mc.). Height $h = 8.5/f$ (Mc.) (E.g., 2.2 feet at 3.9 Mc.) The feedpoint distance, x, is given approximately by $x = 28/f$ (Mc.). (E.g., 7.2 feet at 3.9 Mc.)

line, or the vertical section can be quarter-wavelength pieces for each band. The radials should be a quarter wavelength at the lowest frequency.

The DDRR Antenna

A new (and controversial) vertically-polarized antenna is the DDRR (directional-discontinuity ring radiator) shown in Fig. 14-27B. (See *Elec-tronics,* January, 1963). If an excellent ground is available, the bottom wire would not be required, otherwise it should be laid on the ground or the roof or whatever flat plane the DDRR is placed over. The antenna shown is the version tried by WØMOX, which is simpler to construct than the original circular configuration. This is an antenna that merits further investigation by experimentally-inclined amateurs.

ANTENNAS FOR 160 METERS

Results on 1.8 Mc. will depend to a large extent on the antenna system and the time of day or night. Almost any random long wire that can be tuned to resonance will work during the night but it will generally be found very ineffective during the day. A vertical antenna—or rather an antenna from which the radiation is predominantly vertically polarized—is probably the best for 1.8-Mc. operation. A horizontal antenna (horizontally-polarized radiation) will give better results during the night than the day. The vertically-polarized radiator gives a strong ground wave that is effective day or night, and it is to be preferred on 1.8 Mc.

The low-angle radiation from a horizontal antenna $\frac{1}{8}$ or $\frac{1}{4}$ wavelength above ground is almost insignificant. Any reasonable height is small in terms of wavelength, so that a horizontal antenna on 160 meters is a poor radiator at angles useful for long distances ("long," that is, for this band). Its chief usefulness is over relatively short distances at night.

Bent Antennas

Since ideal vertical antennas are generally out of the question for practical amateur work, the best compromise is to bend the antenna in such a way that the high-current portions of the antenna run vertically. It is advisable to place the antenna so that the highest currents in the antenna occur at the highest points above actual ground. Two antenna systems designed along these lines are shown in Fig. 14-28. The antenna of Fig. 14-28B uses a full half wavelength of wire but is bent so that the high-current portion runs vertically. The horizontal portion running to L_1C_1 should run 8 or 10 feet above ground.

Grounds

A good ground connection is generally important on 160 meters. The ideal system is a number of wire radials buried a foot or two underground and extending 50 to 100 feet from the central connection point. The use of any less than six or eight radials is inadvisable.

If the soil is good (not rocky or sandy) and generally moist, a low-resistance connection to the cold-water pipe system in the house will often serve as an adequate ground system. The connection should be made close to where the pipe enters the ground, and the surface of the pipe should be scraped shiny before tightening the clean ground clamp around the cold-water pipe.

A 6- or 8-foot length of 1-inch water pipe, driven into the soil at a point where there is considerable natural moisture, can be used for the ground connection. Three or four pipes driven into the ground 8 or 10 feet apart and all joined

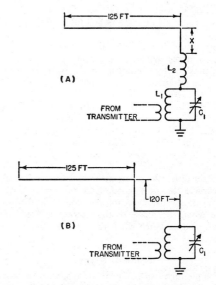

Fig. 14-28—Bent antenna for the 160-meter band. In the system at A, the vertical portion (length X) should be made as long as possible. In either antenna system, L_1C_1 should resonate at 1900 kc., roughly. To adjust L_2 in antenna A, resonate L_1C_1 alone to the operating frequency, then connect it to the antenna system and adjust L_2 for maximum loading. Furthur loading can be obtained by increasing the coupling between L_1 and the link.

together at the top with heavy wire are more effective than the single pipe.

The use of a counterpoise is recommended where a buried system is not practicable or where a pipe ground cannot be made to have low resistance because of poor soil conditions. A counterpoise consists of a number of wires supported from 6 to 10 feet above the surface of the ground. Generally the wires are spaced 10 to 15 feet apart and located to form a square or polygonal configuration under the vertical portion of the antenna.

LONG-WIRE DIRECTIVE ARRAYS

As the length (in wavelengths) of an antenna is increased, the lobes of maximum radiation make a more acute angle with the wire. Two long wires can be combined in the form of a horizontal "V", in the form of a horizontal rhombus, or in parallel, to provide a long-wire directive array. In the "V" and rhombic antennas the main lobes reinforce along a line bisecting the acute angle between the wires; in the parallel antenna the reinforcement is along the line of the lobe. This reinforcement provides both gain and directivity along the line, since the lobes in other directions tend to cancel. When the proper configuration for a given length and height above ground is used, the power gain depends upon the length (in wavelengths) of the wires.

Rhombic and "V" antennas are normally bi-directional along the bisector line mentioned above. They can be made unidirectional by terminating the ends of the wires away from the feed point in the proper value of resistance. When properly terminated, "V" and rhombic antennas of sufficient length work well over a three-to-one or four-to-one frequency range and hence are useful for multiband operation.

Antenna gains of the order of 10 to 15 db. can be obtained with properly-constructed long-wire arrays. However, the pattern is rather sharp with gains of this order, and rhombic and "V" beams are not used by amateurs as commonly as they were, having been displaced by the rotatable multi-element Yagi beam. Further information on these antennas can be found in *The ARRL Antenna Book*.

BEAMS WITH DRIVEN ELEMENTS

By combining individual half-wave antennas into an **array** with suitable spacing between the antennas (called **elements**) and feeding power to them simultaneously, it is possible to make the radiation from the elements add up along a single direction and form a beam. In other directions the radiation tends to cancel, so a power gain is obtained in one direction at the expense of radiation in other directions. There are several methods of arranging the elements. If they are strung end to end, so that all lie on the same straight line, the elements are said to be **collinear**. If they are parallel and all lying in the same plane, the elements are said to be **broadside** when the phase of the current is the same in all, and **end-fire** when the currents are not in phase.

Collinear Arrays

Simple forms of collinear arrays, with the current distribution, are shown in Fig. 14-29. The shown will result in an "X"-shaped pattern that no longer has the maximum radiation at right angles to the wire.

Collinear arrays may be mounted either horizontally or vertically. Horizontal mounting gives increased horizontal directivity, while the vertical directivity remains the same as for a single element at the same height. Vertical mounting gives the same horizontal pattern as a single element, but improves the low-angle radiation.

Broadside Arrays

Parallel antenna elements with currents in phase may be combined as shown in Fig. 14-30 to form a **broadside** array, so named because the direction of maximum radiation is broadside to the plane containing the antennas. Again the gain and directivity depend upon the spacing of the elements.

Broadside arrays may be suspended either with the elements all vertical or with them horizontal

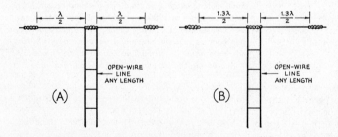

Fig. 14-29—Collinear antennas in phase. The system at A is known as "two half waves in phase" and has a gain of 1.8 db. over a half-wave antenna. By lengthening the antenna slightly, as in B, the gain can be increased to 3 db. Maximum radiation is at right angles to the antenna. The antenna at A is sometimes called a "double Zepp" antenna, and that at B is known as an "extended double Zepp."

two-element array at A is popularly known as "two half-waves in phase" or a **double Zepp** antenna. It will be recognized as simply a center-fed dipole operated at its second harmonic.

By extending the antenna, as at B, the additional gain of an **extended double Zepp** antenna can be obtained. Carrying the length beyond that and one above the other (**stacked**). In the former case the horizontal pattern becomes quite sharp, while the vertical pattern is the same as that of one element alone. If the array is suspended horizontally, the horizontal pattern is equivalent to that of one element while the vertical pattern is sharpened, giving low-angle radiation.

Driven Elements

Fig. 14-30—Simple broadside array using horizontal elements. By making the spacing S equal to ⅜ wavelength, the antenna at A can be used at the corresponding frequency and up to twice that frequency. Thus when designed for 14 Mc. it can also be used on 21 and 28 Mc. The antenna at B can be used on only the design band. This array is bidirectional, with maximum radiation "broadside" or perpendicular to the antenna plane (perpendicularly through this page). Gain varies with the spacing S, running from 2½ to almost 5 db. (See Fig. 14-32).

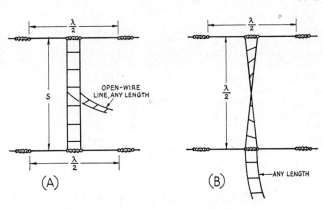

Broadside arrays may be fed either by tuned open-wire lines or through quarter-wave matching sections and flat lines. In Fig. 14-30B, note the "crossing over" of the phasing section, which is necessary to bring the elements into proper phase relationship.

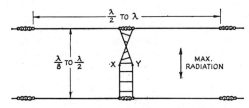

Fig. 14-31—Top view of a horizontal end-fire array. The system is fed with an open-wire line at x and y; the line can be of any length. Feed points x and y are equidistant from the two insulators, and the feed line should drop down vertically from the antenna. The gain of the system will vary with the spacing, as shown in Fig. 14-32, and is a maximum at ⅛ wavelength. By using a length of 33 feet and a spacing of 8 feet, the antenna will work on 20, 15 and 10 meters.

End-Fire Arrays

Fig. 14-31 shows a pair of parallel half-wave elements with currents out of phase. This is

known as an **end-fire** array because it radiates best along the plane of the antennas, as shown.

The end-fire array may be used either vertically or horizontally (elements at the same height), and is well adapted to amateur work because it gives maximum gain with relatively close element spacing. Fig. 14-32 shows how the gain varies with spacing. End-fire elements may be combined with additional collinear and broadside elements to give a further increase in gain and directivity.

Either tuned or untuned lines may be used with this type of array. Untuned lines preferably are matched to the antenna through a quarter-wave matching section or phasing stub.

Combined Arrays

Broadside, collinear and end-fire arrays may be combined to give both horizontal and vertical directivity, as well as additional gain. The lower angle of radiation resulting from stacking elements in the vertical plane is desirable at the higher frequencies. In general, doubling the number of elements in an array by stacking will raise the gain from 2 to 4 db.

Although arrays can be fed at one end as in Fig. 14-30B, it is not especially desirable in the case of large arrays. Better distribution of energy between elements, and hence better overall performance will result when the feeders are attached as nearly as possible to the center of the array.

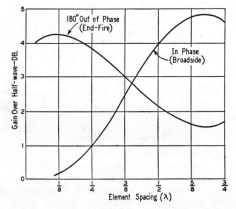

Fig. 14-32—Gain vs. spacing for two parallel half-wave elements combined as either broadside or end-fire arrays.

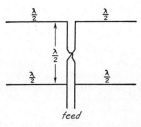

Fig. 14-33—A four-element combination broadside-collinear array, popularly known as the "lazy-H" antenna. A closed quarter-wave stub may be used at the feed point to match into an untuned transmission line, or tuned feeders may be attached at the point indicated. The gain over a half-wave antenna is 5 to 6 db.

A four-element array, known as the **"lazy-H"** antenna, has been quite frequently used. This arrangement is shown, with the feed point indicated, in Fig. 14-33. (Compare with Fig. 14-30B). For best results, the bottom section should be at least a half wavelength above ground.

It will usually suffice to make the length of each element that given by Equations **14-B** or **14-C**. The phasing line between the parallel elements should be of open-wire construction, and its length can be calculated from:

Length of half-wave line (feet) =

$$\frac{480}{Freq. \text{ (Mc.)}} \qquad \text{(14-H)}$$

Example: A half-wavelength phasing line for 28.8 Mc. would be $\frac{480}{28.8} = 16.66$ feet $= 16$ feet 8 inches.

The spacing between elements can be made equal to the length of the phasing line. No special adjustments of line or element length or spacing are needed, provided the formulas are followed closely.

DIRECTIVE ARRAYS WITH PARASITIC ELEMENTS

Parasitic Excitation

The antenna arrays previously described are bidirectional; that is, they will radiate in directions both to the "front" and to the "back" of the antenna system. If radiation is wanted in only one direction, it is necessary to use different element arrangements. In most of these arrangements the additional elements receive power by induction or radiation from the driven element generally called the "antenna," and reradiate it in the proper phase relationship to achieve the desired effect. These elements are called *parasitic* elements, as contrasted to the driven elements which receive power directly from the transmitter through the transmission line.

The parasitic element is called a **director** when

it reinforces radiation on a line pointing to it from the antenna, and a **reflector** when the reverse is the case. Whether the parasitic element is a director or reflector depends upon the parasitic-element tuning, which usually is adjusted by changing its length.

Gain vs. Spacing

The gain of an antenna with parasitic elements varies with the spacing and tuning of the elements and thus for any given spacing there is a tuning condition that will give maximum gain at this spacing. The maximum front-to-back ratio seldom if ever, occurs at the same condition that gives maximum forward gain. The impedance of the driven element also varies with the tuning and spacing, and thus the antenna system must be tuned to its final condition before the match between the line and the antenna can be completed. However, the tuning and matching may interlock to some extent, and it is usually necessary to run through the adjustments several times to insure that the best possible tuning has been obtained.

Two-Element Beams

A 2-element beam is useful where space or other considerations prevent the use of the larger structure required for a 3-element beam. The general practice is to tune the parasitic element as a reflector and space it about 0.15 wavelength from the driven element, although some successful antennas have been built with 0.1-wavelength spacing and director tuning. Gain vs. element spacing for a 2-element antenna is given in Fig. 14-34, for the special case where the parasitic element is resonant. It is indicative of the performance to be expected under maximum-gain tuning conditions.

Three-Element Beams

A theoretical investigation of the 3-element case (director, driven element and reflector) has indicated a maximum gain of slightly more than 7 db. A number of experimental investigations have shown that the optimum spacing between the driven element and reflector is in the region of 0.15 to 0.25 wavelength, with 0.2 wavelength representing probably the best over-all choice.

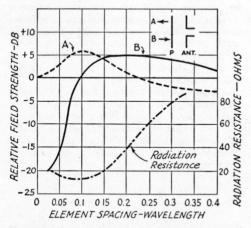

Fig. 14-34—Gain vs. element spacing for an antenna and one parasitic element. The reference point, 0 db., is the field strength from a half-wave antenna alone. The greatest gain is in direction A at spacings of less than 0.14 wavelength, and in direction B at greater spacings. The front-to-back ratio is the difference in db. between curves A and B. Variation in radiation resistance of the driven element also is shown. These curves are for a self-resonant parasitic element. At most spacings the gain as a reflector can be increased by slight lengthening of the parasitic element: the gain as a director can be increased by shortening. This also improves the front-to-back ratio.

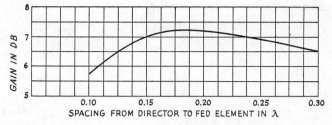

Fig. 14-35—Gain of 3-element Yagi versus director spacing, the reflector spacing being fixed at 0.2 wavelength.

With 0.2 wavelength reflector spacing, Fig. 14-35 shows the gain variation with director spacing. It is obvious that the director spacing is not especially critical, and that the over-all length of the array (boom length in the case of a rotatable antenna) can be anywhere between 0.35 and 0.45 wavelength with no appreciable difference in gain.

Wide spacing of both elements is desirable not only because it results in high gain but also because adjustment of tuning or element length is less critical and the input resistance of the driven element is higher than with close spacing. The latter feature improves the efficiency of the antenna and makes a greater band width possible. However, a total antenna length, director to reflector, of more than 0.3 wavelength at frequencies of the order of 14 Mc. introduces considerable difficulty from a constructional standpoint, so lengths of 0.25 to 0.3 wavelength are frequently used for this band, even though they are less than optimum.

In general, the gain of the antenna drops off less rapidly when the reflector length is increased beyond the optimum value than it does for a corresponding decrease below the optimum value. The opposite is true of a director. It is therefore advisable to err, if necessary, on the long side for a reflector and on the short side for a director. This also tends to make the antenna performance less dependent on the exact frequency at which it is operated, because an increase above the design frequency has the same effect as increasing the length of both parasitic elements, while a decrease in frequency has the same effect as shortening both elements. By making the director slightly short and the reflector slightly long, there will be a greater spread between the upper and lower frequencies at which the gain starts to show a rapid decrease.

When the over-all length has been decided upon, the element lengths can be found by referring to Fig. 14-36. The lengths determined by these charts will vary slightly in actual practice with the element diameter and the method of supporting the elements, and the tuning of a beam should always be checked after installation. However, the lengths obtained by the use of the charts will be close to correct in practically all cases, and they can be used without checking if the beam is difficult of access.

The preferable method for checking the beam is by means of a field-strength meter or the S-meter of a communications receiver, used in conjunction with a dipole antenna located at least 10 wavelengths away and as high as or higher than the beam that is being checked. A few watts of power fed into the antenna will give a useful signal at the observation point, and the power input to the transmitter (and hence the antenna) should be held constant for all of the readings. Beams tuned on the ground and then lifted into place are subject to tuning errors and cannot be depended upon. The impedance of the driven element will vary with the height above ground, and good practice dictates that all final matching between antenna and line be done with the antenna in place at its normal height above ground.

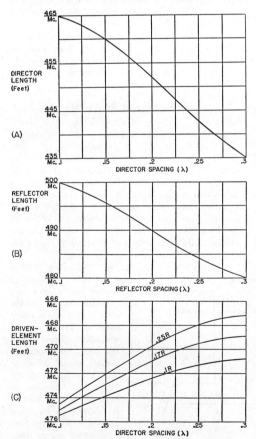

Fig. 14-36—Element lengths for a 3-element beam. These lengths will hold closely for tubing elements supported at or near the center.

Simple Systems: the Rotary Beam

Two- and 3-element systems are popular for rotary-beam antennas, where the entire antenna

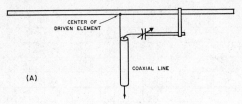

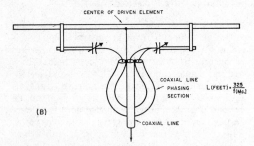

$$L(FEET) = \frac{325}{f(Mc.)}$$

Fig. 14-37—The most popular methods of feeding the driven element of a beam antenna are (A) the gamma match and (B) the T match. The aluminum tubing or rod used for the matching section is usually of smaller diameter than the antenna element; its length will vary somewhat with the spacing and number of elements in the beam. The coaxial line in the phasing section can be coiled in a 2- or 3-foot diameter coil instead of hanging as shown.

system is rotated, to permit its gain and directivity to be utilized for any compass direction. They may be mounted either horizontally (with the plane containing the elements parallel to the earth) or vertically.

A 4-element beam will give still more gain than a 3-element one, provided the support is sufficient for about 0.2 wavelength spacing between elements. The tuning for maximum gain involves many variables, and complete gain and tuning data are not available.

The elements in close-spaced (less than one-quarter wavelength element spacing) arrays preferably should be made of tubing of one-half to one-inch diameter. A conductor of large diameter not only has less ohmic resistance but also

has lower Q; both these factors are important in close-spaced arrays because the impedance of the driven element usually is quite low compared to that of a simple dipole antenna. With 3- and 4-element close-spaced arrays the radiation resistance of the driven element may be so low that ohmic losses in the conductor can consume an appreciable fraction of the power.

Feeding the Rotary Beam

Any of the usual methods of feed (described later under "Matching the Antenna to the Line") can be applied to the driven element of a rotary beam. Tuned feeders are not recommended for lengths greater than a half wavelength unless open lines of copper-tubing conductors are used. The popular choices for feeding a beam are the gamma match with series capacitor and the T match with series capacitors and a half-wavelength phasing section, as shown in Fig. 14-37. These methods are preferred over any others because they permit adjustment of the matching and the use of coaxial line feed. The variable capacitors can be housed in small plastic cups for weatherproofing; receiving types with close spacing can be used at powers up to a few hundred watts. Maximum capacity required is usually 140 $\mu\mu$f. at 14 Mc. and proportionately less at the higher frequencies.

If physically possible, it is better to adjust the matching device after the antenna has been installed at its ultimate height, since a match made with the antenna near the ground may not hold for the same antenna in the air.

Sharpness of Resonance

Peak performance of a multielement parasitic array depends upon proper phasing or tuning of the elements, which can be exact for one frequency only. In the case of close-spaced arrays, which because of the low radiation resistance usually are quite sharp-tuning, the frequency range over which optimum results can be secured is only of the order of 1 or 2 per cent of the resonant frequency, or up to about 500 kc. at 28 Mc. However, the antenna can be made to work satisfactorily over a wider frequency range by

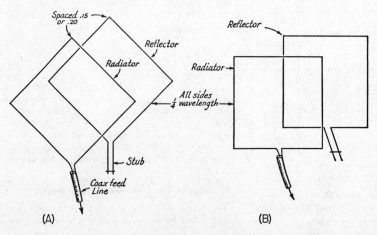

Fig. 14-38—The cubical quad antenna, consisting of two square loops one of which is driven and the other is used as a parasitic reflector. The planes of the loops are parallel, and the loops are coaxial although shown offset in these drawings for clarity. Note the difference in feed points in A and B; the shift in feed point is necessary if both loop orientations are to transmit signals of the same polarization (horizontal in both cases shown here).

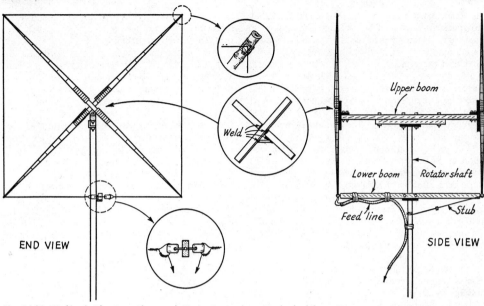

END VIEW   SIDE VIEW

Fig. 14-39—End and side views of a quad. Upper insert shows method of fastening antenna wire to support arms. Center insert shows construction of support-arm mounting bracket. Lower insert shows method of attaching feed line and stub to the center insulators. Two small egg insulators are used, fastened to end of lower boom as shown with a small nail.

$$\text{The length of one side is found from } L \text{ (feet)} = \frac{251}{f(\text{Mc.})}$$

adjusting the director or directors to give maximum gain at the *highest* frequency to be covered, and by adjusting the reflector to give optimum gain at the *lowest* frequency. This sacrifices some gain at all frequencies, but maintains more uniform gain over a wider frequency range.

The use of large-diameter conductors will broaden the response curve of an array because the larger diameter lowers the Q. This causes the reactances of the elements to change rather slowly with frequency, with the result that the tuning stays near the optimum over a considerably wider frequency range than is the case with wire conductors.

Combination Arrays

It is possible to combine parasitic elements with driven elements to form arrays composed of collinear driven and parasitic elements and combination broadside-collinear-parasitic elements. Thus two or more collinear elements might be provided with a collinear reflector or director set, one parasitic element to each driven element. Or both directors and reflectors might be used. A broadside-collinear array can be treated in the same fashion.

THE "QUAD" ANTENNA

The "cubical quad" or, simply, "quad" antenna

consists of a pair of square loops, one-quarter wavelength on a side or one-wavelength around the periphery, one loop being driven and the other used as a parasitic reflector. The separation between the two is usually of the order of 0.15 to 0.2 wavelength, with the planes of the loops parallel.

Fig. 14-38 shows typical quad arrangements, that at B being the more frequently used. The reflector is tuned by means of a stub to a lower frequency than the one at which the fed loop is driven, just as is done with the conventional straight elements in a driven element-reflector array of the parasitic type. With the reflector in place and properly tuned the impedance of the driven element at the feed point is of the same order as the characteristic impedance of coaxial cable, so ordinarily the standing-wave ratio on

Fig. 14-40—A 15/10-meter quad. Tuning stubs for the reflectors are looped back along the tie bars. Total weight of this assembly, not including the mast, is 13 pounds.

the transmission line will be low enough so that no special means need be included for matching.

A few measurements on the quad have indicated that its gain is roughly comparable with that of a three-element Yagi of ordinary design. Early quads consisted only of driven element and parasitic reflector; recent designs have included two parasitic directors, with consequent improved gain. (See Bergren, *QST,* May, 1963.). The two-element quad is, however, the one most commonly in use.

The quad is a more cumbersome structure than an ordinary parasitic beam, but is light in weight and relatively inexpensive. Diagonal spreaders, usually of bamboo (fiberglas poles are also available) are used to support the corners of the loop, the loop itself being made of ordinary antenna wire. The spreaders usually are mounted on a boom which in general is similar to the booms used with Yagi antennas and is also similarly mounted on the mast or tower and rotated. The light weight permits rotation by a TV rotator. Constructional details of a typical quad are given in Fig. 14-39.

If the fishing poles are well treated with a weatherproofing compound they will last several years. Weatherproofing compounds are available at all lumber dealers. Get straight poles with no splits in them. No insulators are necessary, the poles themselves acting as long insulators. The easiest way to mount the antenna wire on the arms is to lay a long length of wire on the ground and mark it at the approximate quarter-wave intervals, and use these marks to indicate where the wire fastens to the pole.

Dual and triple quads can be built for the bands 20 through 10 meters. One such antenna is shown in Fig. 14-40, a dual quad for 15 and 10 meters. The same supporting structure is used for the two antennas, making the boom length equal to 0.15 to 0.2 wavelengths at the lower-frequency band. Separate coaxial cable feed lines are brought down from the two driven elements. In a two-band quad (20/15 or 15/10) the length of one side is obtained from

$$L \text{ (feet)} = 250 \div \text{ (Mc.)}$$

In the case of any quad or combination of quads, each quad should be tuned up separately for maximum forward gain by adjusting the stub length on the reflector element and checking the field strength with a nearby ham. If accessible, the reflector element can be resonated with a grid-dip meter to a frequency just below the lowest to be used; this is a good starting place for further adjustment. The resonance of the antenna system can be checked by finding the frequency that gives the lowest s.w.r. on the feed line; this lowest s.w.r is not necessarily 1.0. If the resonant frequency is higher than the desired frequency, lengthen the driven element; shorten the element if the resonant frequency is too low. In the dual antennas that have been constructed, there has been little or no evidence of interaction of tuning.

MATCHING THE ANTENNA TO THE LINE

The load for a transmission line may be any device capable of dissipating r.f. power. When lines are used for transmitting applications the most common type of load is an antenna. When a transmission line is connected between an antenna and a receiver, the receiver input circuit (not the antenna) is the load, because the power taken from a passing wave is delivered to the receiver.

Whatever the application, the conditions existing at the load, and *only* the load, determine the standing-wave ratio on the line. If the load is purely resistive and equal in value to the characteristic impedance of the line, there will be no standing waves. If the load is not purely resistive, and/or is not equal to the line Z_0, there will be standing waves. No adjustments that can be made at the input end of the line can change the s.w.r., nor is it affected by changing the line length.

Only in a few special cases is the load inherently of the proper value to match a practicable transmission line. In all other cases it is necessary either to operate with a mismatch and accept the s.w.r. that results, or else to take steps to bring about a proper match between the line and load by means of transformers or similar devices. Impedance-matching transformers may take a variety of physical forms, depending on the circumstances.

Note that it is essential, if the s.w.r. is to be made as low as possible, that the load at the point of connection to the transmission line be purely resistive. In general, this requires that the load be tuned to resonance. If the load itself is not resonant at the operating frequency the tuning sometimes can be accomplished in the matching system.

THE ANTENNA AS A LOAD

Every antenna system, no matter what its physical form, will have a definite value of impedance at the point where the line is to be connected. The problem is to transform this **antenna input impedance** to the proper value to match the line. In this respect there is no one "best" type of line for a particular antenna system, because it is possible to transform impedances in any desired ratio. Consequently, any type of line may be used with any type of antenna. There are frequently reasons other than impedance matching that dictate the use of one type of line in preference to another, such as ease of installation, inherent loss in the line, and so on, but these are not considered in this section.

Although the input impedance of an antenna system is seldom known very accurately, it is often possible to make a reasonably close estimate of its value. The information earlier in this chapter can be used as a guide.

Matching circuits may be constructed using ordinary coils and capacitors, but are not used very extensively because they must be supported at the antenna and must be weatherproofed. The systems to be described use **linear transfomers.**

The Quarter-Wave Transformer or "Q" Section

As mentioned previously (Chapter 13), a quarter-wave transmission line may be used as an impedance transformer. Knowing the antenna impedance and the characteristic impedance of the

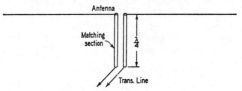

Fig. 14-41—"Q" matching section, a quarter-wave impedance transformer.

transmission line to be matched, the required characteristic impedance of a matching section such as is shown in Fig. 14-41 is

$$Z = \sqrt{Z_1 Z_0} \qquad (14\text{-}I)$$

where Z_1 is the antenna impedance and Z_0 is the characteristic impedance of the line to which it is to be matched.

> Example: To match a 600-ohm line to an antenna presenting a 72-ohm load, the quarter-wave matching section would require a characteristic impedance of $\sqrt{72 \times 600} = \sqrt{43,200}$ = 208 ohms.

The spacings between conductors of various sizes of tubing and wire for different surge impedances are given in graphical form in the chapter on "Transmission Lines." (With ½-inch tubing, the spacing in the example above should be 1.5 inches for an impedance of 208 ohms.)

The length of the quarter-wave matching section may be calculated from

$$Length \text{ (feet)} = \frac{246\,V}{f} \qquad (14\text{-}J$$

where V = Velocity factor
f = Frequency in Mc.

> Example: A quarter-wave transformer of RG-11/U is to be used at 28.7 Mc. From the table in Chapter Thirteen, $V = 0.66$.
> $$Length = \frac{246 \times 0.66}{28.7} = 5.67 \text{ feet}$$
> $$= 5 \text{ feet } 8 \text{ inches}$$

The antenna must be resonant at the operating frequency. Setting the antenna length by formula is amply accurate with single-wire antennas, but in other systems, particularly close-spaced arrays, the antenna should be adjusted to resonance before the matching section is connected.

When the antenna input impedance is not known accurately, it is advisable to construct the matching section so that the spacing between conductors can be changed. The spacing then may be adjusted to give the lowest possible s.w.r. on the transmission line.

Folded Dipoles

A half-wave antenna element can be made to match various line impedances if it is split into two or more parallel conductors with the transmission line attached at the center of only one of them. Various forms of such "folded dipoles" are shown in Fig. 14-42. Currents in all conductors are in phase in a folded dipole, and since the conductor spacing is small the folded dipole is equivalent in radiating properties to an ordinary single-conductor dipole. However, the current flowing into the input terminals of the antenna from the line is the current in one conductor only, and the entire power from the line is delivered at this value of current. This is equivalent to saying that the input impedance of the antenna has been raised by splitting it up into two or more conductors.

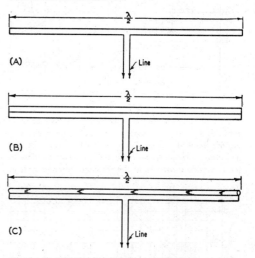

Fig. 14-42—The folded dipole, a method for using the antenna element itself to provide an impedance transformation.

The ratio by which the input impedance of the antenna is stepped up depends not only on the number of conductors in the folded dipole but also on their relative diameters, since the distribution of current between conductors is a function of their diameters. (When one conductor is larger than the other, as in Fig. 14-42C, the larger one carries the greater current.) The ratio also depends, in general, on the spacing between the conductors, as shown by the graphs of Figs. 14-43 and 14-44. An important special case is the 2-conductor dipole with conductors of equal diameter; as a simple antenna, not a part of a directive array, it has an input resistance close enough to 300 ohms to afford a good match to 300-ohm Twin-Lead.

The required ratio of conductor diameters to give a desired impedance ratio using two conductors may be obtained from Fig. 14-43. Similar information for a 3-conductor dipole is given

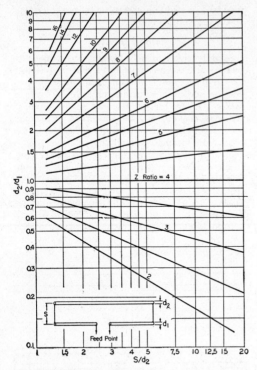

Fig. 14-43—Impedance transformation ratio, two-conductor folded dipole. The dimensions d_1, d_2 and s are shown on the inset drawing. Curves show the ratio of the impedance (resistive) seen by the transmission line to the radiation resistance of the resonant antenna system.

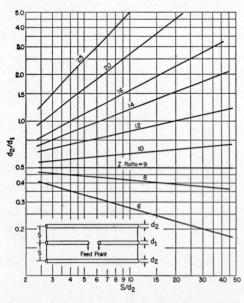

Fig. 14-44—Impedance transformation ratio, three-conductor folded dipole. The dimensions d_1, d_2 and s are shown on the inset drawing. Curves show the ratio of the impedance (resistive) seen by the transmission line to the radiation resistance of the resonant antenna system.

in Fig. 14-44. This graph applies where all three conductors are in the same plane. The two conductors not connected to the transmission line must be equally spaced from the fed conductor, and must have equal diameters. The fed conductor may have a different diameter, however. The unequal-conductor method has been found particularly useful in matching to low-impedance antennas such as directive arrays using close-spaced parasitic elements.

The length of the antenna element should be such as to be approximately self-resonant at the median operating frequency. The length is usually not highly critical, because a folded dipole tends to have the characteristics of a "thick" antenna and thus has a relatively broad frequency-response curve.

"T" and "Gamma" Matching Sections

The method of matching shown in Fig. 14-45A is based on the fact that the impedance between any two points along a resonant antenna is resistive, and has a value which depends on the spacing between the two points. It is therefore possible to choose a pair of points between which the impedance will have the right value to match a transmission line. In practice, the line cannot be connected directly at these points because the distance between them is much greater than the conductor spacing of a practicable transmission line. The "T" arrangement in Fig. 14-45A overcomes this difficulty by using a second conductor paralleling the antenna to form a matching section to which the line may be connected.

The "T" is particularly suited to use with a parallel-conductor line, in which case the two points along the antenna should be equidistant from the center so that electrical balance is maintained.

The operation of this system is somewhat complex. Each "T" conductor (y in the drawing) forms with the antenna conductor opposite it a short section of transmission line. Each of these transmission-line sections can be considered to be terminated in the impedance that exists at the point of connection to the antenna. Thus the part of the antenna between the two points carries a transmission-line current in addition to the normal antenna current. The two transmission-line

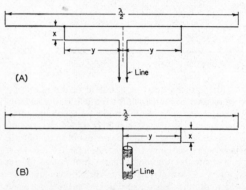

Fig. 14-45—The "T" match and "gamma" match.

matching sections are in series, as seen by the main transmission line.

If the antenna by itself is resonant at the operating frequency its impedance will be purely resistive, and in such case the matching-section lines are terminated in a resistive load. However, since these sections are shorter than a quarter wavelength their input impedance—i.e., the impedance seen by the main transmission line looking into the matching-section terminals—will be reactive as well as resistive. This prevents a perfect match to the main transmission line, since its load must be a pure resistance for perfect matching. The reactive component of the input impedance must be tuned out before a proper match can be secured.

One way to do this is to detune the antenna just enough, by changing its length, to cause reactance of the opposite kind to be reflected to the input terminals of the matching section, thus cancelling the reactance introduced by the latter. Another method, which is considerably easier to adjust, is to insert a variable capacitor in series with the matching section where it connects to the transmission line, as shown in Fig. 14-37. The capacitor must be protected from the weather.

The method of adjustment commonly used is to cut the antenna for approximate resonance and then make the spacing x some value that is convenient constructionally. The distance y is then adjusted, while maintaining symmetry with respect to the center, until the s.w.r. on the transmission line is as low as possible. If the s.w.r. is not below 2 to 1 after this adjustment, the antenna length should be changed slightly and the matching-section taps adjusted again. This process may be continued until the s.w.r. is as close to 1 to 1 as possible.

When the series-capacitor method of reactance compensation is used (Fig. 14-37), the antenna should be the proper length to be resonant at the operating frequency. Trial positions of the matching-section taps are taken, each time adjusting the capacitor for minimum s.w.r., until the standing waves on the transmission line are brought down to the lowest possible value.

The unbalanced ("gamma") arrangement in Fig. 14-45B is similar in principle to the "T," but is adapted for use with single coax line. The method of adjustment is the same.

BALANCING DEVICES

An antenna with open ends, of which the half-wave type is an example, is inherently a balanced radiator. When opened at the center and fed with a parallel-conductor line this balance is maintained throughout the system, so long as the causes of unbalance discussed in the transmission-line chapter are avoided.

If the antenna is fed at the center through a coaxial line, as indicated in Fig. 14-46A, this balance is upset because one side of the radiator is connected to the shield while the other is connected to the inner conductor. On the side connected to the shield, a current can flow down

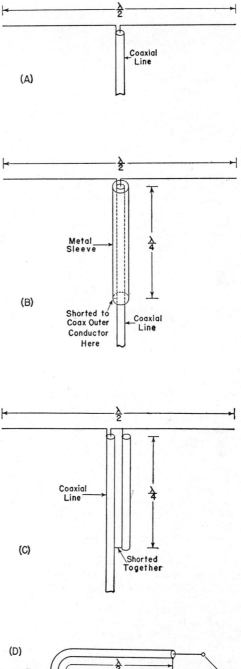

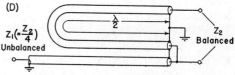

Fig. 14-46—Radiator with coaxial feed (A) and methods of preventing unbalance currents from flowing on the outside of the transmission line (B and C). The half-wave phasing section shown at D is used for coupling between an unbalanced and a balanced circuit when a 4-to-1 impedance ratio is desired or can be accepted.

over the *outside* of the coaxial line, and the fields thus set up cannot be canceled by the fields from the inner conductor because the fields *inside* the line cannot escape through the shielding afforded by the outer conductor. Hence these "antenna" currents flowing on the outside of the line will be responsible for radiation.

Linear Baluns

Line radiation can be prevented by a number of devices whose purpose is to detune or decouple the line for "antenna" currents and thus greatly reduce their amplitude. Such devices generally are known as **baluns** (a contraction for "balanced to unbalanced"). Fig. 14-46B shows one such arrangement, known as a **bazooka**, which uses a sleeve over the transmission line to form, with the outside of the outer line conductor, a shorted quarter-wave line section. As described earlier in this chapter, the impedance looking into the open end of such a section is very high, so that the end of the outer conductor of the coaxial line is effectively insulated from the part of the line below the sleeve. The length is an *electrical* quarter wave, and may be physically shorter if the insulation between the sleeve and the line is other than air. The bazooka has no effect on the impedance relationships between the antenna and the coaxial line.

Another method that gives an equivalent effect is shown at C. Since the voltages at the antenna terminals are equal and opposite (with reference to ground), equal and opposite currents flow on the surfaces of the line and second conductor. Beyond the shorting point, in the direction of the transmitter, these currents combine to cancel out. The balancing section "looks like" an open circuit to the antenna, since it is a quarter-wave parallel-conductor line shorted at the far end, and thus has no effect on the normal antenna operation. However, this is not essential to the line-balancing function of the device, and baluns of this type are sometimes made shorter than a quarter wavelength in order to provide the shunt inductive reactance required in certain types of matching systems.

Fig. 14-46D shows a third balun, in which equal and opposite voltages, balanced to ground, are taken from the inner conductors of the main transmission line and half-wave phasing section. Since the voltages at the balanced end are in series while the voltages at the unbalanced end are in parallel, there is a 4-to-1 step-down in impedance from the balanced to the unbalanced side. This arrangement is useful for coupling between a balanced 300-ohm line and a 75-ohm coaxial line, for example.

RECEIVING ANTENNAS

Nearly all of the properties possessed by an antenna as a radiator also apply when it is used for reception. Current and voltage distribution, impedance, resistance and directional characteristics are the same in a receiving antenna as if it were used as a transmitting antenna. This reciprocal behavior makes possible the design of a

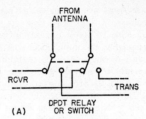

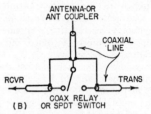

Fig. 14-47—Antenna changeover for receiving and transmitting in two-wire (A) and coaxial line (B). The low-pass filter for TVI reduction should be connected between switch or relay and the transmitter.

receiving antenna of optimum performance based on the same considerations that have been discussed for transmitting antennas.

The simplest receiving antenna is a wire of random length. The longer and higher the wire, the more energy it abstracts from the wave. Because of the high sensitivity of modern receivers, sometimes only a short length of wire strung around the room is used for a receiving antenna, but such an antenna cannot be expected to give good performance, although it is adequate for loud signals on the 3.5- and 7-Mc. bands. It will serve in emergencies, but a longer wire outdoors is always better.

The use of a tuned antenna improves the operation of the receiver, because the signal strength is greater than with a wire of random length. Where local electrical noise is a problem, as from an electrical appliance, a measure of relief can often be obtained by locating the antenna as high above and as far as possible from the noise source and power lines. The lead-in wire, from the center of the antenna, should be a coaxial line or shielded twin-conductor cable (RG-62/U). If the twin-conductor cable is used, the conductors connect to the antenna binding posts and the shield to the ground binding post of the receiver.

Antenna Switching

Switching of the antenna from receiver to transmitter is commonly done with a changeover relay, connected in the antenna leads or the coupling link from the antenna tuner. If the relay is one with a 115-volt a.c. coil, the switch or relay that controls the transmitter plate power will also control the antenna relay. If the convenience of a relay is not desired, porcelain knife switches can be used and thrown by hand.

Typical arrangements are shown in Fig. 14-47. If coaxial line is used, a coaxial relay is recommended, although on the lower-frequency bands a regular switch or change-over relay will work almost as well. The relay or switch contacts should be rated to handle at least the maximum power of the transmitter.

An additional refinement is the use of an electronic transmit-receive switch, which permits full break-in operation even when using the transmitting antenna for receiving. For details and circuitry on t.r. switches, see Chapter Eight.

ANTENNA CONSTRUCTION

The use of good materials in the antenna system is important, since the antenna is exposed to wind and weather. To keep electrical losses low, the wires in the antenna and feeder system must have good conductivity and the insulators must have low dielectric loss and surface leakage, particularly when wet.

For short antennas, No. 14 gauge hard-drawn enameled copper wire is a satisfactory conductor. For long antennas and directive arrays, No. 14 or No. 12 enameled copper-clad steel wire should be used. It is best to make feeders and matching stubs of ordinary soft-drawn No. 14 or No. 12 enameled copper wire, since hard-drawn or copper-clad steel wire is difficult to handle unless is is under considerable tension at all times. The wires should be all in one piece; where a joint cannot be avoided, it should be carefully soldered. Open-wire TV line is excellent up to several hundred watts.

In building a two-wire open line, the spacer insulation should be of as good quality as in the antenna insulators proper. For this reason, good ceramic spacers are advisable. Wooden dowels boiled in paraffin may be used with untuned lines, but their use is not recommended for tuned lines. The wooden dowels can be attached to the feeder wires by drilling small holes and binding them to the feeders.

At points of maximum voltage, insulation is most important, and Pyrex glass or ceramic insulators with long leakage paths are recommended for the antenna. Insulators should be cleaned once or twice a year, especially if they are subjected to much smoke and soot.

In most cases poles or masts are desirable to lift the antenna clear of surrounding buildings, although in some locations the antenna will be sufficiently in the clear when strung from one chimney to another or from a housetop to a tree. Small trees usually are not satisfactory as points of suspension for the antenna because of their movement in windy weather. If the antenna is strung from a point near the center of the trunk of a large tree, this difficulty is not so serious. Where the antenna wire must be strung from one of the smaller branches, it is best to tie a pulley firmly to the branch and run a rope through the pulley to the antenna, with the other end of the rope attached to a counterweight near the ground. The counterweight will keep the tension on the antenna wire reasonably constant even when the branches sway or the rope tightens and stretches with varying climatic conditions.

Telephone poles, if they can be purchased and installed economically, make excellent supports because they do not ordinarily require guying

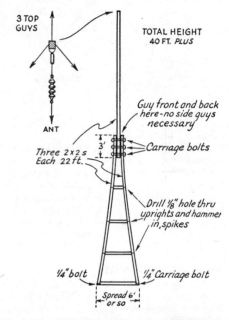

Fig. 14-48—Details of a simple 40-foot "A"-frame mast suitable for erection in locations where space is limited.

in heights up to 40 feet or so. Many low-cost television-antenna supports are now available, and they should not be overlooked as possible antenna aids.

"A"-FRAME MAST

The simple and inexpensive mast shown in Fig. 14-48 is satisfactory for heights up to 35 or 40 feet. Clear, sound lumber should be selected. The completed mast may be protected by two or three coats of house paint.

If the mast is to be erected on the ground, a couple of stakes should be driven to keep the bottom from slipping and it may then be "walked up" by a pair of helpers. If it is to go on a roof, first stand it up against the side of the building and then hoist it from the roof, keeping it vertical. The whole assembly is light enough for two men to perform the complete operation—lifting the mast, carrying it to its permanent berth, and fastening the guys—with the mast vertical all the while. It is entirely practicable, therefore, to erect this type of mast on any small, flat area of roof.

By using 2 × 3s or 2 × 4s, the height may be extended up to about 50 feet. The 2 × 2 is too flexible to be satisfactory at such heights.

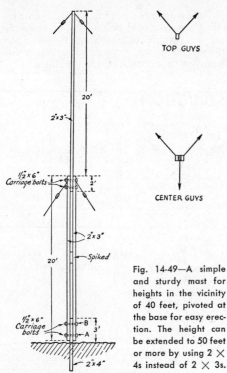

TOP GUYS

CENTER GUYS

Fig. 14-49—A simple and sturdy mast for heights in the vicinity of 40 feet, pivoted at the base for easy erection. The height can be extended to 50 feet or more by using 2 × 4s instead of 2 × 3s.

SIMPLE 40-FOOT MAST

The mast shown in Fig. 14-49 is relatively strong, easy to construct, readily dismantled, and costs very little. Like the "A"-frame, it is suitable for heights of the order of 40 feet.

The top section is a single 2 × 3, bolted at the bottom between a pair of 2 × 3s with an overlap of about two feet. The lower section thus has two legs spaced the width of the narrow side of a 2 × 3. At the bottom the two legs are bolted to a length of 2 × 4 which is set in the ground. A short length of 2 × 3 is placed between the two legs about halfway up the bottom section, to maintain the spacing.

The two back guys at the top pull against the antenna, while the three lower guys prevent buckling at the center of the pole.

The 2 × 4 section should be set in the ground so that it faces the proper direction, and then made vertical by lining it up with a plumb bob. The holes for the bolts should be drilled beforehand. With the lower section laid on the ground, bolt *A* should be slipped in place through the three pieces of wood and tightened just enough so that the section can turn freely on the bolt. Then the top section may be bolted in place and the mast pushed up, using a ladder or another 20-foot 2 × 3 for the job. As the mast goes up, the slack in the guys can be taken up so that the whole structure is in some measure continually supported. When the mast is vertical, bolt *B* should be slipped in place and both *A* and *B* tightened. The lower guys can then be given a final tightening, leaving those at the top a little slack until the antenna is pulled up, when they

should be adjusted to pull the top section into line.

GUYS AND GUY ANCHORS

For masts or poles up to about 50 feet, No. 12 iron wire is a satisfactory guy-wire material. Heavier wire or stranded cable may be used for taller poles or poles installed in locations where the wind velocity is likely to be high.

More than three guy wires in any one set usually are unnecessary. If a horizontal antenna is to be supported, two guy wires in the top set will be sufficient in most cases. These should run to the rear of the mast about 100 degrees apart to offset the pull of the antenna. Intermediate guys should be used in sets of three, one running in a direction opposite to that of the antenna, while the other two are spaced 120 degrees either side. This leaves a clear space under the antenna. The guy wires should be adjusted to pull the pole slightly back from vertical before the antenna is hoisted so that when the antenna is pulled up tight the mast will be straight.

When raising a mast that is big enough to tax the available facilities, it is some advantage to know nearly exactly the length of the guys. Those on the side on which the pole is lying can then be fastened temporarily to the anchors beforehand, which assures that when the pole is raised, those holding opposite guys will be able to pull it into nearly vertical position with no danger of its getting out of control. The guy lengths can be figured by the right-angled-triangle rule that "the sum of the squares of the two sides is equal to the square of the hypotenuse." In other words, the distance from the base of the pole to the anchor should be measured and squared. To this should be added the square of the pole length to the point where the guy is fastened. The square root of this sum will be the length of the guy.

Guy wires should be broken up by strain insulators, to avoid the possibility of resonance at the transmitting frequency. Common practice is to insert an insulator near the top of each guy, within a few feet of the pole, and then cut each section of wire between the insulators to a length which will not be resonant either on the fundamental or harmonics. An insulator every 25 feet will be satisfactory for frequencies up to 30 Mc. The insulators should be of the "egg" type with the insulating material under compression, so that the guy will not part if the insulator breaks.

Twisting guy wires onto "egg" insulators may be a tedious job if the guy wires are long and of large gauge. A simple time- and finger-saving device (piece of heavy iron or steel) can be made by drilling a hole about twice the diameter of the guy wire about a half inch from one end of the piece. The wire is passed through the insulator, given a single turn by hand, and then held with a pair of pliers at the point shown in Fig. 14-50. By passing the wire through the hole in the iron and rotating the iron as shown, the wire may be quickly and neatly twisted.

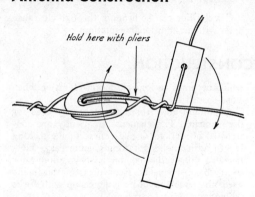

Fig. 14-50—Using a lever for twisting heavy guy wires.

Guy wires may be anchored to a tree or building when they happen to be in convenient spots. For small poles, a 6-foot length of 1-inch pipe driven into the ground at an angle will suffice.

HALYARDS AND PULLEYS

Halyards or ropes and pulleys are important items in the antenna-supporting system. Particular attention should be directed toward the choice of a pulley and halyards for a high mast since replacement, once the mast is in position, may be a major undertaking if not entirely impossible.

Galvanized-iron pulleys will have a life of only a year or so. Especially for coastal-area installations, marine-type pulleys with hardwood blocks and bronze wheels and bearings should be used.

For short antennas and temporary installations, heavy clothesline or window-sash cord may be used. However, for more permanent jobs, ⅜-inch or ½-inch waterproof hemp rope should be used. Even this should be replaced about once a year to insure against breakage.

It is advisable to carry the pulley rope back up to the top in "endless" fashion in the manner of a flag hoist so that if the antenna breaks close to the pole, there will be a means for pulling the hoisting rope back down.

BRINGING THE ANTENNA OR FEED LINE INTO THE STATION

The antenna or transmission line should be anchored to the outside wall of the building, as shown in Fig. 14-52, to remove strain from the lead-in insulators. Holes cut through the walls of the building and fitted with feed-through insulators are undoubtedly the best means of bringing the line into the station. The holes should have plenty of air clearance about the conducting rod, especially when using tuned lines that develop high voltages. Probably the best place to go through the walls is the trimming board at the top or bottom of a window frame which provides flat surfaces for lead-in insulators. Cement or rubber gaskets may be used to waterproof the exposed joints.

Where such a procedure is not permissible,

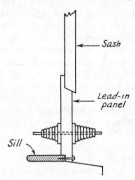

Fig. 14-51—An antenna lead-in panel may be placed over the top sash or under the lower sash of a window. Substituting a smaller height sash in half the window will simplify the weatherproofing problem where the sash overlaps.

the window itself usually offers the best opportunity. One satisfactory method is to drill holes in the glass near the top of the upper sash. If the glass is replaced by plate glass, a stronger job will result. Plate glass may be obtained from automobile junk yards and drilled before placing in the frame. The glass itself provides insulation and the transmission line may be fastened to bolts fitting the holes. Rubber gaskets will render the holes waterproof. The lower sash should be provided with stops to prevent damage when it is raised. If the window has a full-length screen, the scheme shown in Fig. 14-52B may be used.

As a less permanent method, the window may be raised from the bottom or lowered from the top to permit insertion of a board which carries the feed-through insulators. This lead-in arrangement can be made weatherproof by making an overlapping joint between the board and win-

Fig. 14-52—A—Anchoring feeders takes the strain from feedthrough insulators or window glass. B—Going through a full-length screen, a cleat is fastened to the frame of the screen on the inside. Clearance holes are cut in the cleat and also in the screen.

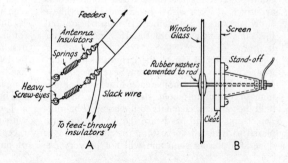

dow sash, as shown in Fig. 14-51, or by using weatherstrip material where necessary.

Coaxial line can be brought through clearance holes without additional insulation.

ROTARY-BEAM CONSTRUCTION

It is a distinct advantage to be able to shift the direction of a beam antenna at will, thus securing the benefits of power gain and directivity in any desired compass direction. A favorite method of doing this is to construct the antenna so that it can be rotated in the horizontal plane. The use of such rotatable antennas is usually limited to the higher frequencies—14 Mc. and above—and to the simpler antenna-element combinations if the structure size is to be kept within practicable bounds. For the 14-, 21- and 28-Mc. bands such antennas usually consist of two to four elements and are of the parasitic-array type described earlier in this chapter. At 50 Mc. and higher it becomes possible to use more elaborate arrays because of the shorter wavelength and thus obtain still higher gain. Antennas for these bands are described in another chapter.

The problems in rotary-beam construction are those of providing a suitable mechanical support for the antenna elements, furnishing a means of rotation, and attaching the transmission line so that it does not interfere with the rotation of the system.

Elements

The antenna elements usually are made of metal tubing so that they will be at least partially self-supporting, thus simplifying the sup-

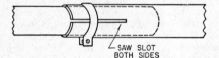

SAW SLOT
BOTH SIDES

Fig. 14-53—Details of telescoping tubing for beam elements.

porting structure. The large diameter of the conductor is beneficial also in reducing resistance, which becomes an important consideration when close-spaced elements are used.

Aluminum alloy tubes are generally used for the elements. The elements frequently are constructed of sections of telescoping tubing making length adjustments for tuning quite easy. Electrician's thin-walled conduit also is suitable for rotary-beam elements. Regardless of the tubing used, the ends should be plugged up with corks sealed with glyptal varnish.

The element lengths are made adjustable by sawing a 6- to 12-inch slot in the ends of the larger-diameter tubing and clamping the smaller tubing inside. Homemade clamps of aluminum can be built, or hose clamps of suitable size can be used. An example of this construction is shown in Fig. 14-53. If steel clamps are used, they should be cadmium- or zinc-plated before installation.

Supports

Metal is commonly used to support the elements of the rotary beam. For 28 Mc., a piece of 2-inch diameter duraluminum tubing makes a good "boom" for supporting the elements. The elements can be made to slide through suitable holes in the boom, or special clamps and brackets can be fashioned to support the elements. Fittings for TV antennas can often be used on 21- and 28-Mc. beams. "Irrigation pipe" is a good source of aluminum tubing up to diameters of 6 inches and lengths of 20 feet. Muffler clamps can be used to hold beam elements to a boom.

Most of the TV antenna rotators are satisfactory for turning the smaller beams.

With all-metal construction, delta, "gamma" or "T"-match are the only practical matching methods to use to the line, since anything else requires opening the driven element at the center, and this complicates the support problem for that element.

"PLUMBER'S-DELIGHT" CONSTRUCTION

The lightest beam to build is the so-called "plumber's delight", an array constructed entirely of metal, with no insulating members between the elements and the supporting structure. Some suggestions for the constructional details are given in Figs. 14-54, 14-55 and 14-56. These show portions of a 4-element 10-meter beam, but the same principles hold for 15- and 20-meter beams.

Boom material can be the irrigation pipe suggested earlier (available from Sears Roebuck). Muffler clamps and homemade brackets (aluminum or cadmium-plated steel) can be used to hold the parasitic elements to the boom. The muffler clamps and all hardware should be cadmium-plated to forestall corrosion; the plating can be done at a plating shop and will not be very ex-

pensive if it is all done at the same time.

Muffler clamps and a steel plate can be used to hold the boom to the supporting mast, as shown in Fig. 14-55. For maximum strength, the mast section should be a length of galvanized iron pipe. The plate thickness should run from $\frac{3}{16}$ inch for a 10-meter beam to $\frac{1}{2}$ inch or more for a 20-meter beam. Steel plates of this thickness are best cut in a welding shop, where it can be done quickly for a nominal fee. After the plate has been cut and the muffler-clamp holes drilled, the plate, clamps and hardware should be plated.

The photograph in Fig. 14-56 shows one way a T-matched driven element can be assembled with its half-wave balun. Three coaxial chassis receptacles are fastened to a $\frac{1}{4}$-inch thick sheet of phenolic that is supported below the driven

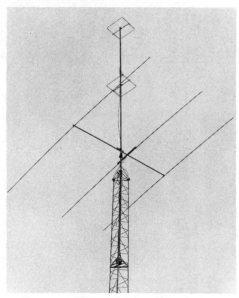

Fig. 14-54—A three-element plumber's-delight beam for 10-meter operation. The dimensions were taken from the chart in Fig. 14-36. The mast is recessed a considerable distance into the tower to lessen the strain imposed upon the rotator by wind loading. A pair of 2-meter "Squalos" are mounted above the 10-meter beam but do not interfere with its operation.

element by three aluminum straps. The two T rods are also supported by the phenolic sheet at the inner ends and by suitable straps at the outer ends where they make up to the driven element.

Rotation

It is common practice to use a motor to rotate the beam. There are several complete motor driven rotators on the market, and they are easy to mount, convenient to use, and require little or no maintenance. Generally speaking, light-weight units are better because they reduce the tower load.

The speed of rotation should not be too great—one or 1½ r.p.m. is about right. This re-

quires a considerable gear reduction from the usual 1750-r.p.m. speed of small induction motors; a large reduction is advantageous because the gear train will prevent the beam from turning in weather-vane fashion in a wind. The usual beam does not require a great deal of power for rotation at slow speed, and a ⅛-hp. motor will be ample. A reversible motor should be used. War-surplus "prop pitch" motors have found wide application for rotating 14-Mc. beams, while TV rotators can be used with many 28-Mc. lightweight beams.

Driving motors and gear housings will stand the weather better if given a coat of aluminum paint followed by two coats of enamel and a coat of glyptal varnish. Even commerical units will last longer if treated with glyptal varnish. Be sure that the surfaces are clean and free from grease before painting. Grease can be removed by brushing with kerosene and then squirting the surface with a solid stream of water. The work can then be wiped dry with a rag.

The power and control leads to the rotator should be run in electrical conduit or in lead covering, and the metal should be grounded.

Fig. 14-55—The boom can be tied to the mast with muffler clamps and a steel plate. The coaxial line from the driven element is taped to the boom and mast.

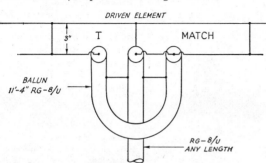

DRIVEN ELEMENT

T   MATCH

3"

BALUN
11'-4" RG-8/U

RG-8/U
ANY LENGTH

Fig. 14-56—(Diagram, above) Details of a coaxial-line termination board and T-match support for a 10-meter beam. The balun of a half-wavelength of coaxial line is coiled and then fastened to the boom with tape (right).

A WINDOWSILL ANTENNA

This antenna (originally described in June 1967 *QST*) is capable of providing the apartment dweller with a system that can be used over the range from 3.5 to 29.7 MHz. It consists of a 12-foot aluminum-tubing radiator, an impedance-matching network, and a wooden base mount. The system can be installed on a windowsill or back porch and will not occupy very much space. Though not nearly as efficient a radiating system as a full-size vertical or horizontal wire in free space, it will do a creditable job as compared to any similar antenna system used inside the building. This is especially true if the operator lives inside an apartment building which has a steel framework.

Materials

An 8-foot length of 8A and a 6-foot length of type 185 (both Reynolds aluminum tubing) are combined to make the radiator, a semivertical element. The sections telescope together and are made secure at their common point by means of a small hose clamp. The larger tube is slotted at this point by means of a hack saw to enable the clamp to compress it around the smaller tubing (Fig. 14-53).

The wooden base can be sized to suit the installation. It should be large enough to permit the antenna to be out of doors while the tuning network is inside the window. The photo of Fig. 14-57 shows the details for mounting the various parts. If convenient, the wooden base can be bolted to the windowsill, or the window can be closed on it to hold it in place.

A 100-pf. tuning capacitor with 0.125-inch spacing should be used for power levels up to a few hundred watts. Somewhat greater spacing may be needed for the 1000-watt level. An E. F. Johnson 154-14 is shown here. The coil is adjusted by means of a clip lead which shorts out the unused portion of the inductor. Another clip

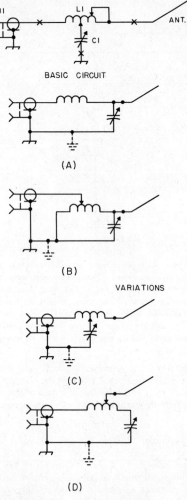

BASIC CIRCUIT

(A)

(B)

VARIATIONS

(C)

(D)

Fig. 14-58—The basic circuit is shown first. L_1 consists of 36 turns of No. 14 wire, is 2½ inches in diameter, and has 8 turns per inch. It can be a Polycoils 1775, a B&W 3906-1, or an Air-Dux 2008T. Drawings A through D show four possible ways to use the tuning network, any one of which may be required for a particular operating frequency.

Fig. 14-57—Photo of the tuning system and the base of the radiator. A home-made aluminum mount holds the radiator to the wood base. U bolts are used to secure the tubing to its mount. The coax connector is mounted on a small aluminum bracket near the coil.

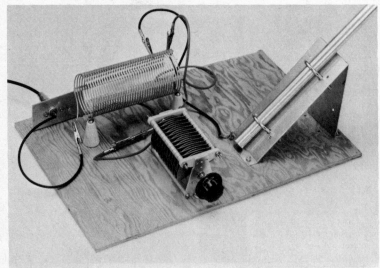

lead taps the tuning capacitor along the coil stock until the desired impedance match is obtained.

Adjustment

An s.w.r. indicator is connected between the transmitter and the input jack of the antenna system, J_1. A small amount of power is applied to the antenna and the coil and capacitor are experimentally adjusted until a 1:1 s.w.r. is obtained. The final setting of C_1, and the tap points on L_1, can be jotted down for each band, making future band changing less involved. A random length of wire can be substituted for the vertical element if desired. The longer the radiator, the more effective will be the results.

A ground connection is important. A water pipe or a radiator will suffice, but the better the ground system the better will be the results from this antenna. The ground should be attached to the bracket that holds J_1. Four possible ways to connect the tuning network are shown. One of them will provide the 1:1 match needed.

HELICALLY-WOUND SHORT VERTICAL ANTENNAS

An effective physically-short radiator can be built by helically-winding a length of wire on a long insulating rod or pole as shown in the sketch. Supporting poles such as bamboo rods, fiber glass tubing, or treated dowel rod, serve as practical foundation material for such an antenna. This type of antenna is most often used as a vertical radiator and is worked against ground as a quarter-wavelength system. The voltage and current distribution is more linear than when a lumped-inductance (loading coil and whip) is employed, a possible reason for its effective performance.

This type of antenna is particularly useful for limited-space applications in the lower part of the h.f. spectrum—1.8, 3.5, and 7.0 MHz. It can be used for 14 MHz. and higher, but is desirable only if an antenna shorter than a natural quarter wavelength is required.

Construction

The length of the supporting pole can be anything between 4 feet and 20 feet in length. The longer the rod, the better the performance. Fiber glass spreader poles for cubical-quad antennas are ideal for this application. Alternatively, bamboo fishing poles, covered with fiber glass, work well. Some lumber yards carry 16-foot long hand-rail stock (wooden) which can be coated with fiber glass or several coats of exterior spar varnish and used as a coil form. The main consideration is that the antenna pole be of good dielectric properties and that it be weatherproofed.

So that the antenna will be approximately ¼-wavelength long *electrically,* a ½ wavelength piece of insulated wire is needed for the radiating element. When helically-wound as shown, the antenna becomes approximately a one-quarter wavelength long, electrically. No. 14 or No. 12 Formvar-insulated copper wire is recommended for the antenna winding. It should be spacewound in as linear a manner as possible. The far end of the vertical should have a 6-inch diameter metal disk, or 12-inch spike, to add sufficient capacitance to lower the impedance at the far end of the radiator sufficiently to prevent corona effects which can burn the far end of the element during medium- and high-power operation. An aluminum base-mounting plate and two U clamps can serve as a support for the antenna.

Operation

To build the antenna for use on 160 meters, for example, wind approximately 248 feet of wire on the pole as shown. Since this will fall just short of natural resonance at one quarter wavelength, some type of variable inductor will be needed at the base of the antenna. A rotary inductor from an old Command Set transmitter will do the

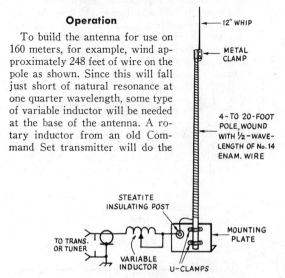

job. It should be enclosed in a weatherproof box of plastic or metal. The inductor is adjusted by means of an s.w.r. indicator for the best match obtainable at the operating frequency. An earth ground is required for proper operation, and a buried radial system is recommended. Alternatively, several ground rods can be driven into the earth near the base of the antenna and bonded together with heavy wire.

It may not be possible to secure a 1:1 s.w.r. without using some form of impedance-matching system. After the antenna is made resonant at the operating frequency, a tuning network such as that of Fig. 14-58 can be employed to provide the desired 1:1 s.w.r. Since antennas of this type are relatively "frequency conscious," it will be necessary to "retune the matching network when moving from one part of the band to another. The completed antenna should be given a coating of fiber glass or spar varnish to seal it against the weather, and to secure the coil turns. It has been observed that this antenna has exceptional immunity to man-made electrical noises. It also cuts down the response to broadcast-band signals which sometimes tend to overload the station receiver. The foregoing attributes result from the fact that it is a narrow-band antenna.

Chapter 15

Wave Propagation

Much of the appeal of amateur communication lies in the fact that the results are not always predictable. Transmission conditions on the same frequency vary with the year, season and with the time of day. Although these variations usually follow certain established patterns, many peculiar effects can be observed from time to time. Every radio amateur should have some understanding of the known facts about radio wave propagation so that he will stand some chance of interpreting the unusual conditions when they occur. The observant amateur is in an excellent position to make worthwhile contributions to the science, provided he has sufficient background to understand his results. He may discover new facts about propagation at the very-high frequencies or in the microwave region, as amateurs have in the past. In fact, it is through amateur efforts that most of the extended-range possibilities of various radio frequencies have been discovered, both by accident and by long and careful investigation.

CHARACTERISTICS OF RADIO WAVES

Radio waves, like other forms of electromagnetic radiation such as light, travel at a speed of 300,000,000 meters per second in free space, and can be reflected, refracted, and diffracted.

An electromagnetic wave is composed of moving fields of electric and magnetic force. The lines of force in the electric and magnetic fields are at right angles, and are mutually per-

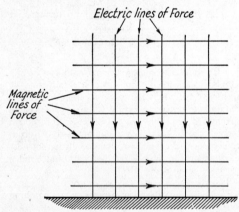

Electric lines of Force

Magnetic lines of Force

Fig. 15-1—Representation of electric and magnetic lines of force in a radio wave. Arrows indicate instantaneous directions of the fields for a wave traveling toward the reader. Reversing the direction of one set of lines would reverse the direction of travel.

pendicular to the direction of travel. A simple representation of a wave is shown in Fig. 15-1. In this drawing the electric lines are perpendicular to the earth and the magnetic lines are horizontal. They could, however, have any position with respect to earth so long as they remain perpendicular to each other.

The plane containing the continuous lines of electric and magnetic force shown by the grid-or mesh-like drawing in Fig. 15-1 is called the wave **front**.

The **medium** in which electromagnetic waves travel has a marked influence on the speed with which they move. When the medium is empty space the speed, as stated above, is 300,000,000 meters per second. It is almost, but not quite, that great in air, and is much less in some other substances. In dielectrics, for example, the speed is inversely proportional to the square root of the dielectric constant of the material.

When a wave meets a good conductor it cannot penetrate it to any extent (although it will travel through a dielectric with ease) because the electric lines of force are practically short-circuited.

Polarization

The **polarization** of a radio wave is taken as the direction of the lines of force in the electric field. If the electric lines are perpendicular to the earth, the wave is said to be **vertically polarized**; if parallel with the earth, the wave is **horizontally polarized**. The longer waves, when traveling along the ground, usually maintain their polarization in the same plane as was generated at the antenna. The polarization of shorter waves may be altered during travel, however, and sometimes will vary quite rapidly.

Spreading

The field intensity of a wave is inversely proportional to the distance from the source. Thus if in a uniform medium one receiving point is twice as far from the transmitter as another, the field strength at the more distant point will be just half the field strength at the nearer point. This results from the fact that the energy in the wave front must be distributed over a greater area as the wave moves away from the source. This **inverse-distance law** is based on the assumption that there is nothing in the medium to absorb energy from the wave as it travels. This is not the case in practical communication along the ground and through the atmosphere.

Types of Propagation

According to the altitudes of the paths along which they are propagated, radio waves may be classified as **ionospheric waves, tropospheric waves** or **ground waves.**

The ionospheric or **sky wave** is that part of the total radiation that is directed toward the ionosphere. Depending upon variable conditions in that region, as well as upon transmitting wave length, the ionospheric wave may or may not be returned to earth by the effects of refraction and reflection.

The tropospheric wave is that part of the total radiation that undergoes refraction and reflection in regions of abrupt change of dielectric constant in the troposphere, such as may occur at the boundaries between air masses of differing temperature and moisture content.

The ground wave is that part of the total ra-

Fig. 15-2—Showing how both direct and reflected waves may be received simultaneously.

diation that is directly affected by the presence of the earth and its surface features. The ground wave has two components. One is the **surface wave,** which is an earth-guided wave, and the other is the **space wave** (not to be confused with the ionospheric or sky wave). The space wave is itself the resultant of two components — the **direct wave** and the **ground-reflected wave,** as shown in Fig. 15-2.

IONOSPHERIC PROPAGATION

PROPERTIES OF THE IONOSPHERE

Except for distances of a few miles, nearly all amateur communication on frequencies below 30 Mc. is by means of the sky wave. Upon leaving the transmitting antenna, this wave travels upward from the earth's surface at such an angle that it would continue out into space were its path not bent sufficiently to bring it back to earth. The medium that causes such bending is the **ionosphere,** a region in the upper atmosphere, above a height of about 60 miles, where free ions and electrons exist in sufficient quantity to have an appreciable effect on wave travel.

The ionization in the upper atmosphere is believed to be caused by ultraviolet radiation from the sun. The ionosphere is not a single region but is composed of a series of layers of varying densities of ionization occurring at different heights. Each layer consists of a central region of relatively dense ionization that tapers off in intensity both above and below.

Refraction

The greater the intensity of ionization in a layer, the more the path of the wave is bent. The bending, or refraction (often also called reflection), also depends on the wavelength; the longer the wave, the more the path is bent for a given degree of ionization. Thus low-frequency waves are more readily bent than those of high frequency. For this reason the lower frequencies — 3.5 and 7 Mc. — are more "reliable" than the higher frequencies — 14 to 28 Mc.; there are times when the ionization is of such low value that waves of the latter frequency range are not bent enough to return to earth.

Absorption

In traveling through the ionosphere the wave gives up some of its energy by setting the ionized particles into motion. When the moving ionized particles collide with others this energy is lost. The **absorption** from this cause is greater at lower frequencies. It also increases with the intensity of ionization, and with the density of the atmosphere in the ionized region.

Virtual Height

Although an ionospheric layer is a region of considerable depth it is convenient to assign to it a definite height, called the **virtual height.** This is the height from which a simple reflection would give the same effect as the gradual

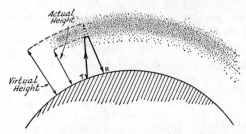

Fig. 15-3—Bending in the ionosphere, and the echo or reflection method of determining virtual height.

bending that actually takes place, as illustrated in Fig. 15-3. The wave traveling upward is bent back over a path having an appreciable radius of turning, and a measurable interval of time is consumed in the turning process. The virtual height is the height of a triangle having equal sides of a total length proportional to the time taken for the wave to travel from T to R.

Normal Structure of the Ionosphere

The lowest useful ionized layer is called the E layer. The average height of the region of maximum ionization is about 70 miles. The air at this height is sufficiently dense so that the ions and electrons set free by the sun's radiation do not travel far before they meet and recombine to form neutral particles, so the layer can maintain its normal intensity of ionization only in the presence of continuing radiation from the sun. Hence the ionization is greatest around local noon and practically disappears after sundown.

In the daytime there is a still lower ionized area, the *D* **region.** *D*-region ionization is proportional to the height of the sun and is greatest at noon. The lower amateur-band frequencies (1.8 and 3.5 Mc.) are almost completely absorbed by this layer, and only the high-angle radiation is reflected by the *E* layer. (Lower-angle radiation travels farther through the *D* region and is absorbed.)

The second principal layer is the *F* **layer,** which has a height of about 175 miles at night. At this altitude the air is so thin that recombination of ions and electrons takes place very slowly. The ionization decreases after sundown, reaching a minimum just before sunrise. In the daytime the *F* layer splits into two parts, the F_1 and F_2 **layers,** with average virtual heights of, respectively, 140 miles and 200 miles. These layers are most highly ionized at about local noon, and merge again at sunset into the *F* layer.

SKY-WAVE PROPAGATION

Wave Angle

The smaller the angle at which a wave leaves the earth, the less the bending required in the ionosphere to bring it back. Also, the smaller the angle the greater the distance between the point where the wave leaves the earth and that at which it returns. This is shown in Fig. 15-4. The vertical angle that the wave makes with a tangent to the earth is called the **wave angle** or **angle of radiation.**

Skip Distance

More bending is required to return the wave to earth when the wave angle is high, and at times the bending will not be sufficient unless the wave angle is smaller than some critical value. This is illustrated in Fig. 15-4, where *A* and smaller angles give useful signals while waves sent at higher angles penetrate the layer and are not returned. The distance between *T* and R_1 is, therefore, the shortest possible distance, at that particular frequency, over which communication by ionospheric refraction can be accomplished.

The area between the end of the useful ground wave and the beginning of ionospheric-wave reception is called the **skip zone,** and the distance from the transmitter to the nearest point where the sky wave returns to earth is called the **skip distance.** The extent of the skip zone depends upon the frequency and the state of the ionosphere, and also upon the height of the layer in which the refraction takes place. The

higher layers give longer skip distances for the same wave angle. Wave angles at the transmitting and receiving points are usually, although not always, approximately the same for any given wave path.

Critical and Maximum Usable Frequencies

If the frequency is low enough, a wave sent vertically to the ionosphere will be reflected back down to the transmitting point. If the frequency is then gradually increased, eventually a frequency will be reached where this vertical reflection just fails to occur. This is the **critical frequency** for the layer under consideration. When the operating frequency is below the critical value there is no skip zone.

The critical frequency is a useful index to the highest frequency that can be used to transmit over a specified distance—the **maximum usable frequency (m.u.f.).** If the wave leaving the transmitting point at angle *A* in Fig. 15-4 is, for example, at a frequency of 14 Mc., and if a higher frequency would skip over the receiving point R_1, then 14 Mc. is the m.u.f. for the distance from *T* to R_1.

The greatest possible distance is covered when the wave leaves along the tangent to the earth; that is, at zero wave angle. Under average conditions this distance is about 4000 kilometers or 2500 miles for the F_2 layer, and 2000 km. or 1250 miles for the *E* layer. The distances vary with the layer height. Frequencies above these limiting m.u.f.'s will not be returned to earth at any distance. The 4000-km. m.u.f. for the F_2 layer is approximately 3 times the critical frequency for that layer, and for the *E* layer the 2000-km. m.u.f. is about 5 times the critical frequency.

Absorption in the ionosphere is least at the maximum usable frequency, and increases very rapidly as the frequency is lowered below the m.u.f. Consequently, best results with low power always are secured when the frequency is as close to the m.u.f. as possible.

It is readily possible for the ionospheric wave to pass through the *E* layer and be refracted back to earth from the *F*, F_1 or F_2 layers. This

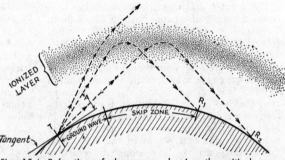

Fig. 15-4—Refraction of sky waves, showing the critical wave angle and the skip zone. Waves leaving the transmitter at angles above the critical (greater than A) are not bent enough to be returned to earth. As the angle is decreased, the waves return to earth at increasingly greater distances.

is because the critical frequencies are higher in the latter layers, so that a signal too high in frequency to be returned by the E layer can still come back from one of the others, depending upon the time of day and the existing conditions.

Multihop Transmission

On returning to the earth the wave can be reflected upward and travel again to the ionosphere. There it may once more be refracted, and again bent back to earth. This process may be repeated several times. **Multihop** propagation of this nature is necessary for transmission over great distances because of the limited heights of the layers and the curvature of the earth, which restrict the maximum one-hop distance to the values mentioned in the preceding section. However, ground losses absorb some of the energy from the wave on each reflection (the amount of the loss varying with the type of ground and being least for reflection from sea water), and there is also absorption in the ionosphere at each reflection. Hence the smaller the number of hops the greater the signal strength at the receiver, other things being equal.

Fading

Two or more parts of the wave may follow slightly different paths in traveling to the receiving point, in which case the difference in path lengths will cause a phase difference to exist between the wave components at the receiving antenna. The total field strength will be the sum of the components and may be larger or smaller than one component alone, since the phases may be such as either to aid or oppose. Since the paths change from time to time, this causes a variation in signal strength called **fading**. Fading can also result from the combination of single-hop and multihop waves, or the combination of a ground wave with an ionospheric or tropospheric wave.

Fading may be either rapid or slow, the former type usually resulting from rapidly-changing conditions in the ionosphere, the latter occurring when transmission conditions are relatively stable. Severe changes in signal strength of 10 to 20 db. or more are called "deep" fades, in contrast to the more normal "shallow" fades of a few db.

It frequently happens that transmission conditions are different for waves of slightly different frequencies, so that in the case of voice-modulated transmission, involving sidebands differing slightly from the carrier in frequency, the carrier and various sideband components may not be propagated in the same relative amplitudes and phases they had at the transmitter. This effect, known as **selective fading**, causes severe distortion of the signal. The distortion is most marked on amplitude-modulated signals and at high percentages of modulation; it is possible to reduce the effects considerably by using "exalted-carrier reception" and "single-sideband" techniques that, in effect, reduce the modulation percentage at the receiver.

Back Scatter

Even though the operating frequency is above the m.u.f. for a given distance, it is usually possible to hear signals from within the skip zone. This phenomenon, called **back scatter**, is caused by reflections from distances beyond the skip zone. Such reflections can occur when the transmitted energy strikes the earth at a distance and some of it is reflected back into the skip zone to the receiver. Such scatter signals are weaker than those normally propagated, and also have a rapid fade or "flutter" that makes them easily recognizable.

A certain amount of scattering of the wave also takes place in the ionosphere because the ionized region is not completely uniform. Scattering in the normal propagation direction is called **forward scatter**, and is responsible for extending the range of transmission beyond the distance of a regular hop, and for making communication possible on frequencies greater than the actual m.u.f.

OTHER FEATURES OF IONOSPHERIC PROPAGATION

Cyclic Variations in the Ionosphere

Since ionization depends upon ultraviolet radiation, conditions in the ionosphere vary with changes in the sun's radiation. In addition to the daily variation, seasonal changes result in higher critical frequencies in the E layer in summer, averaging about 4 Mc. as against a winter average of 3 Mc. The F layer critical frequency is of the order of 4 to 5 Mc. in the evening. The F_1 layer, which has a critical frequency near 5 Mc. in summer, usually disappears entirely in winer. The daytime maximum critical frequencies for the F_2 are highest in winter (10 to 12 Mc.) and lowest in summer (around 7 Mc.). The virtual height of the F_2 layer, which is about 185 miles in winter, averages 250 miles in summer. These values are representative of latitude 40 deg. North in the Western hemisphere, and are subject to considerable variation in other parts of the world.

Very marked changes in ionization also occur in step with the **11-year sunspot cycle**. Although there is no apparent direct correlation between sunspot activity and critical frequencies on a given day, there is a definite correlation between *average* sunspot activity and critical frequencies. The critical frequencies are highest during sunspot maxima and lowest during sunspot minima. During the period of minimum sunspot activity, the lower frequencies — 7 and 3.5 Mc. — frequently are the only usable bands at night. At such times the 28-Mc. band is seldom useful for long-distance work, while the 14-Mc. band performs well in the daytime but is not ordinarily useful at night.

Ionosphere Storms

Certain types of sunspot activity cause considerable disturbances in the ionosphere (ionosphere storms) and are accompanied by disturbances in the earth's magnetic field (magnetic storms). Ionosphere storms are characterized by a marked increase in absorption, so that radio conditions become poor. The critical frequencies also drop to relatively low values during a storm, so that only the lower frequencies are useful for communication. Ionosphere storms may last from a few hours to several days. Since the sun rotates on its axis once every 28 days, disturbances tend to recur at such intervals, if the sunspots responsible do not become inactive in the meantime. Absorption is usually low, and radio conditions good, just preceding a storm.

Sporadic-E Ionization

Scattered patches or clouds of relatively dense ionization occasionally appear at heights approximately the same as that of the E layer, for reasons not yet known. This sporadic-E ionization is most prevalent in the equatorial regions, where it is substantially continuous. In northern latitudes it is most frequent in the spring and early summer, but is present in some degree a fair percentage of the time the year 'round. It accounts for much of the night-time short distance work on the lower frequencies (3.5 and 7 Mc.) and, when more intense, for similar work on 14 to 28 Mc. Exceptionally intense sporadic-E ionization permits work over distances exceeding 400 or 500 miles on the 50-Mc. band.

There are indications of a relationship between sporadic-E ionization and average sunspot activity, but it does not appear to be directly related to daylight and darkness since it may occur at any time of the day. However, there is an apparent tendency for the ionization to peak at mid-morning and in the early evening.

Tropospheric Propagation

Changes in temperature and humidity of air masses in the lower atmosphere often permit work over greater than normal ground-wave distances on 28 Mc. and higher frequencies. The effect can be observed on 28 Mc., but it is generally more marked on 50 and 144 Mc. The subject is treated in detail later.

PREDICTION CHARTS

The Institute for Telecommunication Sciences and Aeronomy (formerly CRPL) offers ionospheric prediction charts with which it is possible to predict with considerable accuracy the maximum usable frequency that will hold over any path on the earth during a monthly period. The charts can be obtained from the Superintendent of Documents, U. S. Government Printing Office, Washington, D.C. 20402, for 25 cents per copy or $2.50 per year. They are called "ITSA Ionospheric Predictions." The use of the charts is explained in Handbook 90, "Handbook for CRPL Ionospheric Predictions," available for 40 cents from the same address.

Predictions on E-layer propagation may be obtained from information included in Handbook 90.

PROPAGATION IN THE BANDS BELOW 30 MC.

The 1.8-Mc., or "160-meter," band offers reliable working over ranges up to 25 miles or so during daylight. On winter nights, ranges up to several thousand miles are not impossible. Only small sections of the band are currently available to amateurs, because of the loran (navigation) service in that part of the spectrum.

The 3.5-Mc., or "80-meter," band is a more useful band during the night than during the daylight hours. In the daytime, one can seldom hear signals from a distance of greater than 200 miles or so, but during the darkness hours distances up to several thousand miles are not unusual, and transoceanic contacts are regularly made during the winter months. During the summer, the static level is high.

The 7-Mc., or "40-meter," band has many of the same characteristics as 3.5, except that the distances that can be covered during the day and night hours are increased. During daylight, distances up to a thousand miles can be covered under good conditions, and during the dawn and dusk periods in winter it is possible to work stations as far as the other side of the world, the signals following the darkness path. The winter months are somewhat better than the summer ones. In general, summer static is much less of a problem than on 80 meters, although it can be serious in the semitropical zones.

The 14-Mc., or "20-meter," band is probably the best one for long-distance work. During the high portion of the sunspot cycle it is open to some part of the world during practically all of the 24 hours, while during a sunspot minimum it is generally useful only during daylight hours and the dawn and dusk periods. There is practically always a skip zone on this band.

The 21-Mc., or "15-meter," band shows highly variable characteristics depending on the sunspot cycle. During sunspot maxima it is useful for long-distance work during a large part of the 24 hours, but in years of low sunspot activity it is almost wholly a daytime band, and sometimes unusable even in daytime. However, it is often possible to maintain communication over distances up to 1500 miles or more by sporadic-E ionization which may occur either day or night at any time in the sunspot cycle.

The 28-Mc. ("10-meter) band is generally considered to be a DX band during the daylight hours (except in summer) and good for local work during the hours of darkness, for about half the sunspot cycle. At the very peak of the sunspot cycle, it may be "open" into the late evening hours for DX communication. At the sunspot minimum the band is usually "dead" for long-distance communication, by means of the F_2 layer, in the northern latitudes. Nevertheless, sporadic-E propagation is likely to occur at any time, just as in the case of the 21-Mc. band.

There will often be exceptions to the general conditions described above, and their observation is a very interesting facet of amateur radio.

PROPAGATION ABOVE 50 MC.

The importance to the amateur of having some knowledge of wave propagation was stressed at the beginning of this chapter. An understanding of the means by which his signals reach their destination is an even greater aid to the v.h.f. worker. Each of his bands shows different characteristics, and knowledge of their peculiarities is as yet far from complete. The observant user of the amateur v.h.f. assignments has a good opportunity to contribute to that knowledge, and his enjoyment of his work will be greatly enhanced if he knows when to expect unusual propagation conditions.

CHARACTERISTICS OF THE V.H.F. BANDS

An outstanding feature of our bands from 50 Mc. up is their ability to provide consistent and interference-free communication within a limited range. All lower frequencies are subject to varying conditions that impair their effectiveness for work over distances of 100 miles or less at least part of the time, and the heavy occupancy they support results in severe interference problems in areas of dense population. The v.h.f. bands, being much wider, can handle many times the amateur population without crowding, and their characteristics for local work are more stable. It is thus to the advantage of amateur radio as a whole to make use of 50 Mc. and higher bands for short-range communication wherever possible.

In addition to reliable local coverage, the v.h.f. bands also exhibit several forms of long-distance propagation at times, and use of 50 and 144 Mc. has been taken up in recent years by many isolated amateurs who must depend on these propagation peculiarities for all or most of their contacts. It is particularly important to these operators that they understand common propagation phenomena. The material to follow supplements information presented earlier in this chapter, but deals with wave propagation only as it affects the occupants of the world above 50 Mc. First let us consider each band.

50 to 54 Mc.: This band is borderline territory between the DX frequencies and those normally employed for local work. Thus just about every form of wave propagation found throughout the radio spectrum appears, on occasion, in the 50-Mc. region. This has contributed greatly to the popularity of the 50-Mc. band.

During the peak years of a sunspot cycle it is occasionally possible to work 50-Mc. DX of world-wide proportions, by reflection of signals from the F_2 layer. Sporadic-E skip provides contacts over distances from 400 to 2500 miles or so during the early summer months, regardless of the solar cycle. Reflection from the aurora regions allows 100- to 1000-mile work during pronounced ionospheric disturbances. The ever-changing weather pattern offers extension of the normal coverage to as much as 300 to 500 miles.

This develops most often during the warmer months, but may occur at any season. In the absence of any favorable propagation, the average well-equipped 50-Mc. station should be able to work a radius of 75 to 100 miles or more, depending on local terrain.

144 to 148 Mc.: Ionospheric effects are greatly reduced at 144 Mc. F_2-layer reflection is unlikely, and sporadic-E skip is rare. Aurora DX is fairly common, but signals are generally weaker than on 50 Mc. Tropospheric effects are more pronounced than on 50 Mc., and distances covered during favorable weather conditions are greater than on lower bands. Air-mass boundary bending has been responsible for communication on 144 Mc. over distances in excess of 2500 miles, and 500-mile work is fairly common in the warmer months. The reliable range under normal conditions is slightly less than on 50 Mc., with comparable equipment.

220 Mc. and Higher: Ionospheric propagation is unlikely at 220 Mc. and up, but tropospheric bending is more prevalent than on lower bands. Amateur experience on 220 and 420 Mc. is showing that they can be as useful as 144 Mc., when comparable equipment is used. Under minimum conditions the range may be slightly shorter, but when signals are good on 144 Mc., they may be better on 220 or 420. Even above 1000 Mc. there is evidence of tropospheric DX.

PROPAGATION PHENOMENA

The various known means by which v.h.f. signals may be propagated over unusual distances are discussed below.

F_2-Layer Reflection: Most contacts made on 28 Mc. and lower frequencies are the result of reflection of the wave by the F_2 layer, the ionization density of which varies with solar activity, the highest frequencies being reflected at the peak of the 11-year solar cycle. The maximum usable frequency (m.u.f.) for F_2 reflection also follows other well-defined cycles, daily, monthly, and seasonal, all related to conditions on the sun and its position with respect to the earth.

At the low point of the 11-year cycle, such as in the early '50s, the m.u.f. may reach 28 Mc. only during a short period each spring and fall, whereas it may go to 60 Mc. or higher at the peak of the cycle. The fall of 1946 saw the first authentic instances of long-distance work on 50 Mc. by F_2-layer reflection, and as late as 1950 contacts were made in the more favorable areas of the world by this medium. The rising curve of the current solar cycle again made F_2 DX on 50 Mc. possible in the low latitudes in the winter of 1955-6. DX was worked over much of the earth in the years 1956 through 1959, falling off in 1960. Loss of the 50-Mc. band to television in some countries will limit the scope of 50-Mc. DX in years to come.

The F_2 m.u.f. is readily determined by observation, and it may be estimated quite accur-

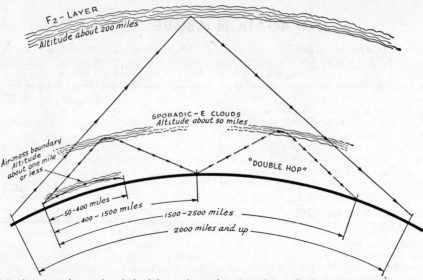

Fig 15-5—The principal means by which v.h.f. signals may be returned to earth, showing the approximate distances over which they are effective. The F_2 layer, highest of the reflecting layers, may provide 50-Mc. DX at the peak of the 11-year sunspot cycle. Such communication may be world-wide in scope. Sporadic ionization of the E region produces the familiar "short skip" on 28 and 50 Mc. It is most common in early summer and in late December, but may occur at any time, regardless of the sunspot cycle. Refraction of v.h.f. waves also takes place at air-mass boundaries, making possible communication over distances of several hundred miles on all v.h.f. bands. Normally it exhibits no skip zone.

ately for any path at any time. It is predictable for months in advance, enabling the v.h.f. worker to arrange test schedules with distant stations at propitious times. As there are numerous commercial signals, both harmonics and fundamental transmissions, on the air in the range between 28 and 50 Mc., it is possible to determine the approximate m.u.f. by careful listening in this range. Daily observations will show if the m.u.f. is rising or falling, and once the peak for a given month is determined it can be assumed that another will occur about 27 days later, this cycle coinciding with the turning of the sun on its axis. The working range, via F_2 skip, is roughly comparable to that on 28 Mc., though the *minimum* distance is somewhat longer. Two-way work on 50 Mc. by reflection from the F_2 layer has been accomplished over distances from 2200 to 12,000 miles. The maximum frequency for F_2 reflection is believed to be about 70 Mc.

Sporadic-E Skip: Patchy concentrations of ionization in the E-layer region are often responsible for reflection of signals on 28 and 50 Mc. This is the popular "short skip" that provides fine contacts on both bands in the range between 400 and 1300 miles. It is most common in May, June and July, during morning and early evening hours, but it may occur at any time or season. Multiple-hop effects may appear, making possible work over more than 2500 miles.

The upper limit of frequency for sporadic-E skip is not positively known, but scattered instances of 144-Mc. propagation over distances in excess of 1000 miles indicate that E-layer reflection, possibly aided by tropospheric effects, may be responsible.

Aurora Effect: Low-frequency communication is occasionally wiped out by absorption in the ionosphere, when ionospheric storms, associated with variations in the earth's magnetic field, occur. During such disturbances, however, v.h.f. signals may be reflected back to earth, making communication possible over distances not normally workable in the v.h.f. range. Magnetic storms may be accompanied by an aurora-borealis display, if the disturbance occurs at night and visibility is good. Aiming a beam at the auroral curtain will bring in signals strongest, regardless of the direction to the transmitter.

Aurora-reflected signals are characterized by a rapid flutter, which lends a "dribbling" sound to 28-Mc. carriers and may render modulation on 50- and 144-Mc. signals completely unreadable. The only satisfactory means of communication then becomes straight c.w. The effect may be noticeable on signals from any distance other than purely local, and stations up to about 1000 miles in any direction may be worked at the peak of the disturbance. Unlike the two methods of propagation previously described, aurora effect exhibits no skip zone. It is observed frequently on 50 and 144 Mc. in northeastern U. S. A., usually in the early evening hours or after midnight. The highest frequency for auroral reflection is not yet known, but pronounced disturbances have permitted work by this medium in the 220-Mc. band.

Tropospheric Bending: The most common form of v.h.f. DX is the extension of the normal operating range associated with easily observed weather phenomena. It is the result of the change in refractive index of the atmosphere at the boundary between air masses of differing temperature and humidity characteristics. Such boundaries usually lie along the western or southern edges of a stable slow-moving area of high barometric pressure (fair, calm weather) in the period prior to the arrival of a storm.

A typical upper-air sounding showing temperature and water-vapor gradients favorable to v.h.f. DX is shown in Fig. 15-6. An increase in temperature and a sharp drop in water-vapor content are seen at about 4000 feet.

Such a favorable condition develops most often in the late summer or early fall, along the junction between air masses that may have come together from such widely separated points as the Gulf of Mexico and Northern Canada. Under

quencies are relatively inactive. It is probable that this tendency continues on up through the microwave range, and there is good evidence to indicate that our assignments in the u.h.f. and s.h.f. portions of the frequency spectrum may someday support communication over distances far in excess of the optical range.

Scatter: Forward scatter, both ionospheric and tropospheric, may be used for marginal communication in the v.h.f. bands. Both provide very weak but consistent signals over distances that were once thought impossible on frequencies higher than about 30 Mc.

Tropospheric scatter is prevalent all through the v.h.f. and microwave regions, and is usable

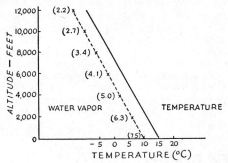

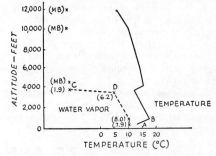

Fig. 15-6—Upper-air conditions that produce extended-range communication on the v.h.f. bands. At the left is shown the U. S. Standard Atmosphere temperature curve. The humidity curve (dotted) is that which would result if the relative humidity were 70 per cent from the ground level to 12,000 feet elevation. There is only slight refraction under this standard condition. At the right is shown a sounding that is typical of marked refraction of v.h.f. waves. Figures in parentheses are the "mixing ratio"—grams of water vapor per kilogram of dry air. Note the sharp break in both curves at about 4000 feet. (From Collier, "Upper-Air Conditions for 2-Meter DX," QST, September, 1955.)

stable weather conditions the two air masses may retain their original character for several days at a time, usually moving slowly eastward across the country. When the path between two v.h.f. stations separated by fifty to several hundred miles lies along such a boundary, signal levels run far above the average value.

Many factors other than air-mass movement of a continental character provide increased v.h.f. operating range. The convection along coastal areas in warm weather is a good example. The rapid cooling of the earth after a hot day, with the air aloft cooling more slowly, is another, producing a rise in signal strength in the period starting just after sundown. The early morning hours just after midnight may be the best time of the day for extended v.h.f. range.

The v.h.f. enthusiast soon learns to correlate various weather manifestations with radio-propagation phenomena. By watching temperature, barometric pressure, changing cloud formations, wind direction, visibility, and other easily-observed weather signs, he can tell with a reasonable degree of accuracy what is in prospect on the v.h.f. bands.

The responsiveness of radio waves to varying weather conditions increases with frequency. The 50-Mc. band is more sensitive to weather variations than is the 28-Mc. band, and the 144-Mc. band may show strong signals from far beyond visual distances when lower fre-

over distances up to about 400 miles. Ionospheric scatter, augmented by meteor bursts, usually brings in signals over 600 to 1300 miles, on frequencies up to about 100 Mc. Either form of scatter requires high power, large antennas and c.w. technique to provide useful communication.

Back scatter, of the type heard on the lower-frequency bands, is also heard occasionally on 50 Mc., when F_2 or sporadic-E skip is present.

Reflections from Meteor Trails: Probably the least-known means of v.h.f. wave propagation is that resulting from the passage of meteors across the signal path. Reflections from the ionized meteor trails may be noted as a Doppler-effect whistle on the carrier of a signal already being received, or they may cause bursts of reception from stations not normally receivable. Ordinarily such reflections are of little value in communication, since the increases in signal strength are of short duration, but meteor showers of considerable magnitude and duration may provide fluttery signals from distances up to 1500 miles on both 50 and 144 Mc.

As meteor-burst signals are relatively weak, their detection is greatly aided if high power and high-gain antennas are used. Two-way communication of sorts has been carried on by this medium on 50 and 144 Mc. over distances of 600 to 1300 miles.

Chapter 16

V.H.F. and U.H.F. Receiving

Good receiving equipment is essential in v.h.f. and u.h.f. work. The important considerations are good signal-to-noise ratio, high sensitivity, and excellent stability. These attributes are generally secured by using crystal-controlled converters ahead of a well-engineered communications receiver, the latter serving as a tunable i.f. at some frequency in the 1.8 to 30-Mc. range. Although there are many commercially-built v.h.f. and u.h.f. converters on the market, the amateur can frequently meet his particular receiving needs better by custom-designing his own equipment—often at reduced cost.

The greatest practical degree of selectivity should be used in v.h.f./u.h.f. reception and is an important factor in improving the signal-to-noise ratio of the system. It is not uncommon to employ bandwidths of 100 or 200 c.p.s. in the reception of weak c.w. signals such as those encountered in scatter and "moonbounce" communications. Good receiving selectivity also lessens the problem of QRM in areas of high v.h.f. activity. Broadband receiving equipment of the war-surplus variety finds but limited application in this period of improved techniques. The possible exception is the use of simple superregenerative receivers whose broad response characteristics are acceptable for short-range applications involving hand-held or battery-operated portable/emergency equipment. The basic design of superregenerative detectors is treated later in this chapter.

R.F. AMPLIFIER DESIGN

The noise generated within the receiver plays a vital role in the reception of weak signals. From 50 Mc. and down, external noise is a limiting factor. At 144 Mc. and higher the tube or semiconductor choice, plus the application of good design techniques, determines how good the signal-to-noise ratio will be. Noise figure in the "front end" of the v.h.f. receiver is more important a consideration than is the matter of gain.

Modern-day techniques have provided the industry with planar-triode tubes that offer good v.h.f. and u.h.f. performance. Similarly, state-of-the-art advances have resulted in the availability of low-noise, high-gain bipolar and field-effect transistors for effective use above 50 Mc. The remaining considerations in r.f. amplifier design are the matters of front-end overload, cross-talk, and the susceptibility of the tube or semiconductor to damage. The latter is frequently caused by high r.f. levels or transients which reach the control element of the tube or transistor. Front-end protection is discussed later in this chapter.

Stabilization

Neutralization is usually necessary when triode tubes are used as amplifiers, the possible exception being when the tube is used as a grounded-grid amplifier. The same rules apply in the use of transistors. Some form of neutralization is ordinarily required unless the bipolar transistor is operated in common-base configuration, or if an FET is used, in common-gate arrangement. The grounded-grid, common-base, or common-gate amplifiers do not offer as much selectivity through the r.f. stages of the

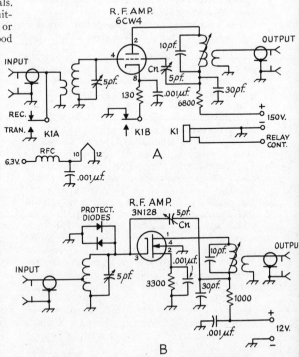

Fig. 16-1—At A, schematic of a neutralized Nuvistor r.f. amplifier showing a relay in a protection circuit. At B, an insulated-gate FET r.f. amplifier which is protected from strong-signal damage by a pair of diodes. Cn is the neutralizing capacitor in both circuits.

receiver as can be expected with the more common grounded-cathode, common-emitter, or common-source hookups.

A single-ended neutralized triode is shown in Fig. 16-1A. This method is sometimes referred to as "sloppy-capacitor" neutralization. A similar circuit featuring an insulated-gate FET is illustrated at B. Typical values for operation at 144 Mc. are given in the schematic. In these circuits it is important that the B-plus end of the output coil be "above ground" at r.f., providing a tap point for opposite-phase neutralization voltage. This voltage is supplied to the input circuit through Cn. The 6800-ohm resistor at A, and the 1000-ohm resistor at B, serve to keep that part of the circuit above r.f. ground. It is important that the 1000-ohm resistor be of that value, or greater, if good isolation is to be had. The setting of Cn will depend upon the circuit, its layout, and the tube or transistor type employed. A shield plate should be mounted across the socket between the input and output halves of the tube or transistor circuit. The shield should be grounded securely to the chassis.

The cascode r.f. amplifier stages shown in Fig. 16-2 have a good noise figure and provide excellent broadband characteristics. It has been said that this configuration is extremely stable and requires very little attention as far as stability is concerned. Not so, because modern-day v.h.f. tubes have high transconductance, as do most v.h.f. and u.h.f. transistors. Because of the high gain with such tubes or transistors, instability can be a serious problem. For this reason the use of neutralization is mandatory if good stability is to be realized. Also, the neutralization circuit, when carefully adjusted, will enhance the noise figure of the stage. Metal shields, grounded to the chassis, should be installed between the tuned circuits as illustrated in Fig. 16-2. By dividing the input and output tuned circuits in this manner, stray coupling is reduced and there is less chance for instability.

In Fig. 16-2, at A, separate Nuvistor tubes are used in a cascode arrangement. Ln is the neutralizing inductor and resonates with the grid-plate capacitance of the first tube. At B, a twin-triode tube—especially designed for cascode service—is neutralized by capacitive divider consisting of Cn and a 30-pf. fixed capacitor. L is self-resonant at the signal frequency by virtue of the tube capacitances, and this combination forms somewhat of an impedance-matching network for coupling V_{1A} to V_{1B}. In both circuits the neutralizing component is adjusted for the best noise figure. The initial adjustment can best be made by temporarily disconnecting the filament voltage from the amplifier and adjusting Ln or Cn for minimum signal feed through to the output of the amplifier. A number of twin triodes have been designed especially for v.h.f. cascode service. Among them are the 6BS8, 6BZ7, 6BQ7A, and

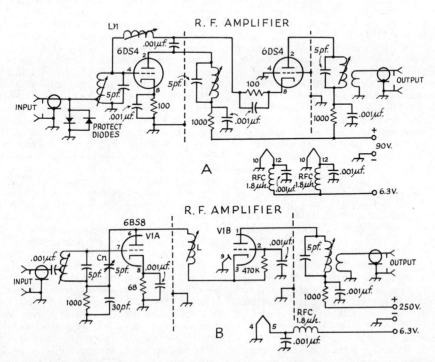

Fig. 16-2—A schematic diagram of a two-tube cascode r.f. amplifier stage using Nuvistors. Protective diodes are used at the input terminals and the amplifier is neutralized by inductor Ln. The filament circuit is decoupled by means of r.f. chokes. The chokes must be able to handle the filament current of the 6DS4s. At B, an example of a typical cascode amplifier which utilizes a dual-triode tube designed specifically for that application. Cn serves as a neutralizing capacitor. The component values given at A and B are typical for 144-Mc. operation.

Fig. 16-3—Schematic diagrams of
a two-stage grounded-grid amplifier, at A, and a single-stage
common-gate r.f. amplifier, at B.
The tube heaters in the circuit at
A are kept above r.f. ground by
means of r.f. chokes which present a high impedance at the
operating frequency. The chokes
must be able to carry the heater
current of the tubes. C is used as
an impedance-matching capacitor. The input tap on L also plays
a role in the impedance matching
procedure. L is self-resonant with
the circuit capacitance, at the
operating frequency. Protective
diodes are bridged between the
high-Z end of L and ground. In
the circuit at B, a JFET serves in a
typical v.h.f. r.f. stage with its
gate grounded. Protective diodes
are shown between the source
element and ground. Component
values shown for both circuits are
typical for 144-Mc. operation.

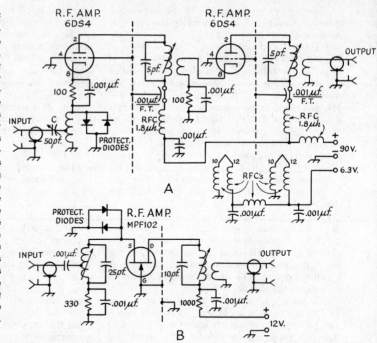

Fig. 16-3—Schematic diagrams of
a two-stage grounded-grid amplifier, at A, and a single-stage
common-gate r.f. amplifier, at B.
The tube heaters in the circuit at
A are kept above r.f. ground by
means of r.f. chokes which present a high impedance at the
operating frequency. The chokes
must be able to carry the heater
current of the tubes. C is used as
an impedance-matching capacitor. The input tap on L also plays
a role in the impedance matching
procedure. L is self-resonant with
the circuit capacitance, at the
operating frequency. Protective
diodes are bridged between the
high-Z end of L and ground. In
the circuit at B, a JFET serves in a
typical v.h.f. r.f. stage with its
gate grounded. Protective diodes
are shown between the source
element and ground. Component
values shown for both circuits are
typical for 144-Mc. operation.

6ES8. Pin 9 of these tubes connects to an internal
shield which, when grounded, aids in isolating
V_{1A} from V_{1B}.

Grounded-grid amplifier techniques are shown
in Fig. 16-3. The grid, base, or gate is grounded,
depending upon the device employed. The signal
is fed into the cathode, emitter, or source element
of the stage—a low-impedance point in the circuit. Output is taken from the plate, collector, or
drain element which exhibits a much higher impedance than does the input circuit of the stage.
This configuration, if properly constructed, has
excellent stability characteristics and should not
require neutralization. Effective bypassing and
input-output isolation are the prime factors in
keeping the grounded-grid amplifiers "tame."
These amplifiers are easily adjusted and are useful in broadband applications. Because stage gain
may be low with grounded-grid amplifiers, two
or more stages—isolated physically and decoupled in the filament and B-plus lines—are
sometimes connected in cascade. Tubes that are
well-suited to grounded-grid service include the
6CW4, 6DS4, 5842 (417A), 416B, 7588, 7768,
and 7784. Disk-seal and "pencil-tube" types are
commonly used at frequencies above 500 Mc.
There are a variety of bipolar and field-effect
transistors that lend themselves well to common-
gate or common-base r.f. amplifier service. It
would be impractical to list specific types here
because of rapid advances which are being made
in semiconductor state of the art. Improved types
are constantly being introduced, only to make
previous types obsolete.

Protective Measures

Most v.h.f. and u.h.f. tubes and transistors are
easily damaged by excessive voltage or current

levels. Generally, the control element—grid, gate,
or base—is subjected to abnormal values of voltage from time to time, a condition which can lead
to the immediate or ultimate destruction of the
tube or transistor. Such voltages can come from
static buildup on the antenna system, or from excessive r.f. levels from a nearby transmitter. An
r.f. stage that is exposed to such conditions can
be destroyed at once, or may show a gradual de-
cline in gain and noise figure until its inferior
performance is noted. In the case of a tube-type
amplifier, the grid element may draw excessive
current which in turn causes the element to warp
and short out to the plate or cathode, or both.
With insulated-gate FET amplifiers, high transient voltages can perforate the gate insulation
and cause a short between the gate and the remaining elements. With junction FETs and
bipolar transistors, excessive input voltages can
cause too much current to flow in the gate or base
circuit. This in turn heats the semiconductor
junction and destroys the gate-source, or base-
emitter junctions. Tubes can usually survive these
excesses somewhat better than transistors can.

The first rule for front-end protection is to use
a good-quality antenna-transfer relay—preferably one that has a shorting contact across the
receiver port during the transmit cycle. Only
first-quality coaxial relays should be used. When
vacuum-tube r.f. amplifiers are used, a small relay
is sometimes employed to open the cathode circuit
of the tube during the transmit period, or to apply
cut-off bias to the grid of the tube. These techniques are useful in preventing tube destruction
from high levels of r.f. leakage. A spare set of
contacts on the same relay might be used to short
out the low-Z input terminal to the r.f. stage during transmit (Fig. 16-1A).

It is common practice in the protection of transistorized r.f. stages to install a pair of small-signal diodes across the input tuned circuit as shown in Fig. 16-1B. Each diode is connected in opposite polarity to its mate and will conduct when the input voltage reaches approximately 0.2 volts for germanium types, or 0.6 volts for silicon diodes. The back-to-back feature enables the diodes to protect the transistor during both the positive and negative halves of the incoming r.f. cycle. Attention should be paid to the quality of the diodes used, lest the Q of the tuned circuit be lowered. Only high-back-resistance diodes should be employed. Most microwave diodes, or diodes designed for very high-speed switching, are suitable.

Reducing Spurious Responses

In areas where a high level of v.h.f. or u.h.f. activity prevails in the amateur radio bands, or where strong commercial v.h.f. or u.h.f. stations operate near the amateur bands, front-end overload or cross-talk is often a serious problem in the receiving converter.

Although many types of bipolar transistors are capable of operating at v.h.f. and u.h.f. with very low noise figures, they exhibit poor dynamic range and linearity. For this reason they are less satisfactory than are tubes or FETs for use in r.f. and mixer circuits designed for good immunity against cross-talk and overloading. Furthermore, if a.g.c. is applied to them in an effort to provide a greater practical range of signal-handling capability, the a.g.c. circuitry becomes somewhat complex in design. Alternatively, FETs are now available for low-noise use in the v.h.f. and u.h.f. ranges and offer even better dynamic range and linearity than do most vacuum tubes. By employing the latter much can be done to resolve the problems of overload and cross-talk. Protection against out-of-band signals can be enhanced by the use of highly-selective tuned circuits in the r.f. and mixer stages of the receiver, or by installing high-Q coaxial filters (of the type described in Chapter 23) between the input of the converter and the transmission line.

A common problem with some converters is the appearance of spurious responses, sometimes called "birdies." Harmonics from the converter's oscillator chain appear in the tuning range of the receiver and manifest themselves as *unmodulated carriers*. Additional responses can at times result from beat notes between these harmonics and the main receiver's local oscillator. Much can be done to prevent "birdies" by using a high oscillator frequency in the converter, thus reducing the required number of multiplier stages. Harmonics from the oscillator chain can also reach the mixer stage of the converter and permit unwanted signals to be received. These conditions can be reduced, or eliminated, by isolating the oscillator chain from the rest of the converter—physically *and* electrically. A shield compartment should be used to contain the oscillator section of the converter, and all power leads that enter and leave the compartment should be well filtered. Series- or parallel-tuned harmonic traps can be used between the last stage of the chain and the injection point in the mixer stage, helping to prevent unwanted energy from reaching the mixer. A high-pass filter, designed to attenuate those frequencies that lie below the desired injection frequency, can be installed between the mixer and the oscillator chain to reduce spurious responses. Similarly, a low-pass filter can be used between the converter output and the input of the main receiver to isolate the two oscillator chains, thus reducing the chance of additional spurious responses.

MIXER CIRCUITS

The most simple v.h.f. or u.h.f. mixer is a silicon diode. This device finds frequent application in the upper u.h.f. region, and at microwave frequencies. Although diode mixers are simple and inexpensive, they have certain characteristics that make them less desirable than thermionic mixers at frequencies below 1000 Mc. The main disadvantages of crystal mixers are high noise figure—generally from 8 to 15 decibels—and their susceptibility to r.f. burnout. Diode mixers generally require about 0.5 ma. of crystal current for optimum performance. About 0.5 mw. of oscillator injection is needed to provide this amount of crystal current. At least 10 times that amount of injection should be available from the oscillator chain to permit light coupling and to allow for losses in the circuit.

At frequencies below 1215 Mc., transistor or vacuum-tube mixers of the type illustrated in Fig. 16-4 can be used for the amateur radio frequencies—432 Mc., and down. Pentode mixers generally give higher output and may require less oscillator injection than triodes do. Also, specially-developed mixer-type pentodes can handle larger signals than triodes, lessening the chance of overload and cross-talk. Unfortunately, most tubes of this type are too noisy for practical use above the 6-meter band. MOS and junction-type field-effect transistors are excellent performers in mixer applications and are fast becoming the choice of the circuit designers.

In Fig. 16-4A a Nuvistor is used as a mixer in a typical v.h.f. circuit. The input circuit is of the bandpass variety, providing good selectivity—an aid in the rejection of unwanted signals. A 100-ohm cathode resistor is used to prevent the Nuvistor from exceeding its plate-dissipation ratings. A 10-pf. capacitor is connected from the plate pin of the tube socket to ground, aiding in the prevention of oscillation which sometimes occurs near the signal frequency because of stray inductance. At B, a bipolar transistor is used as a mixer and is connected in a common-base manner. Again, the bandpass technique is used at the input of the stage (emitter circuit) to provide needed selectivity. Oscillator injection is fed into the emitter leg of the circuit through a 0.001-μf. blocking capacitor. The injection voltage can be

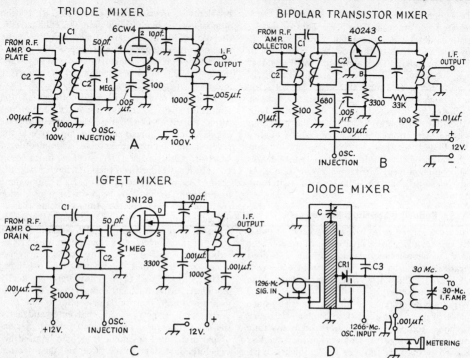

Fig. 16-4—Schematic diagrams of typical v.h.f. or u.h.f. mixers. Bandpass circuits are employed at the input of the mixers at A, B, and C. The actual value of C_1 and C_2 will depend upon the impedance of the circuits, and on the desired bandwidth. Design data for bandpass circuits are given in Chapter 2. At D, a typical diode-mixer configuration is shown. L and C form a resonant circuit at the signal frequency. CR_1, a 1N21C or similar, serves as the mixer and is mounted inside the cavity assembly. C_3 is the capacitance that exists between the case of the diode and the wall of the cavity, usually about 5 pf. A metering jack is available for reading the diode current, generally about 0.5 ma. with normal oscillator injection.

taken from the emitter circuit of the oscillator stage, or from some other low-impedance point. At 16-4C an insulated-gate FET is used as a mixer. Bandpass coupling is employed for the same reasons as previously stated. This circuit is similar to that of A, except for operating voltages. A typical diode mixer is illustrated at D. A reso-nant cavity is the heart of this circuit and is tuned to the signal frequency. Input and output circuits are low impedance and are effected by means of links or taps near the cold end of the cavity. Or-dinarily, the mixer diode is mounted inside the cavity as shown. Diode mixers are seldom used below 420 Mc.

OSCILLATORS

Modern-day v.h.f. and u.h.f. receiving equip-ment has a high order of selectivity. For this reason the oscillator chain of the receiving con-verter should be electrically and mechanically as stable as is practical.

A suitable approach to this problem is the use of crystal-controlled oscillators, with frequency multipliers when needed, to obtain the required mixer injection-signal voltage. Examples of two crystal-controlled 3rd-overtone oscillators are given in Fig. 16-5 at A and B. To enhance the frequency stability of the oscillator at A, the plate voltage is regulated at 150 volts by a VR tube. The filaments are supplied with regulated d.c. voltage (using a 6.3-volt Zener-diode regulator) to further assure stability. The latter technique is not always necessary and is more likely to be ap-plied to tunable oscillators in standard communi-cation receivers, especially in those units that are used as tunable i.f. receivers for v.h.f. or u.h.f. converters. The circuit at B is a standard bipolar-transistor overtone oscillator and uses a Zener-regulated 9.1-volt d.c. supply. For best long-term stability, crystal ovens can be used to maintain the crystal temperature. Also, the oscillator stage can be left running day and night for added long-term stability.

A typical transistorized tunable v.h.f. oscillator is illustrated at D. Again, the supply voltage is regulated by a Zener diode. To reduce oscillator pulling, a buffer stage should be used between the tunable oscillator and the mixer stage of the receiver or converter. Tunable oscillators are seldom used at the v.h.f. and u.h.f. levels because they lack sufficient stability to be practical by today's standards. They do find limited application in broad-band receivers and in portable equipment.

At C, in Fig. 16-5, an illustration is given of how a semiconductor diode can be used as a frequency multiplier. In this circuit the desired out-

put frequency for the mixer is 130 Mc. A series-tuned 86.67-Mc. trap is used to attenuate the second-harmonic of the oscillator output frequency. The 130-Mc. tuned circuit should have a high Q to provide good selectivity.

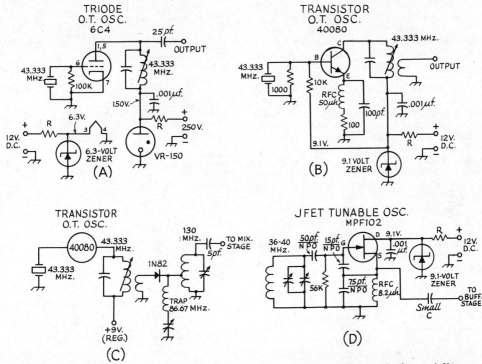

Fig. 16-5—Typical v.h.f./u.h.f. converter oscillator circuits. At A, an overtone oscillator with plate and filament voltage regulation. At B, a similar circuit using a bipolar n-p-n transistor. The circuit at C illustrates a typical diode multiplier arrangement which is driven by a transistorized overtone oscillator. A JFET tunable oscillator is shown at D. Its tuning range is typical for receiving 50- to 54-Mc. signals with a 14-Mc. i.f. The value of R depends upon the current drawn by the circuit.

SUPERREGENERATIVE DETECTORS

One of the simplest types of v.h.f. receiver is the superregenerator. It employs the superregenerative detector, a device which is useful from the upper h.f. region well into the microwave spectrum. This detector offers circuit simplicity and good sensitivity. It is particularly useful and practical in lightweight equipment, and offers a low-cost approach to receiver design. Superregenerators lend themselves handily to use in simple, light-weight transceiver circuits. This is especially true where low-drain, hand-held units are concerned. These advantages are counterbalanced to some extent by the poor selectivity characteristics of the superregenerator, its inability to demodulate other than a.m. and wide-band f.m. signals, and its high noise level. Reradiation is also a problem with this type of detector, requiring some form of isolation between it and the antenna system—usually an r.f. amplifier stage. Where simple equipment is required, the advantages outweigh the bad features, however.

The superregenerative principle can be applied to any type of oscillator. Representative circuits are given in Fig. 16-6.

The sensitivity of this type of detector results from the use of an alternating quench voltage, usually in the range between 20 and 350 kc. A good rule of thumb in selecting the quench frequency is to maintain a ratio of approximately 100 between the signal and quench frequency. The detector is set so that it goes into oscillation on each positive peak of the quench voltage. On each negative swing of the quench voltage, the oscillating detector is cut off. The operating point is controlled by the regeneration control, R_3, at A, B, and C of Fig. 16-6. At D, a fixed level of bias is established by adjusting R_1, permitting the positive half of the quench cycle to send V_1 into an oscillating condition when it overrides the fixed-bias level. During the negative-going portion of the cycle, V_1 is cut off. This principle permits the regeneration to be increased far beyond the amount usable in a straight regenerative detector, hence excellent sensitivity results.

The quench frequency is above the audible range, therefore it is not heard in the output of the receiver. It is necessary, however, to filter out any quench voltage that may appear at the detector output, preventing it from reaching subsequent audio stages. At A, B, and D of Fig. 16-6, RFC_2, C_3, and C_4 form a quench filter. At C, R_4 and C_3 serve as the quench filter. The plate, collector, or drain circuit—depending upon the device used as a detector—will have pulses of current at the quench frequency. During no-signal periods, this action establishes a certain average current in that part of the circuit. During signal periods, and depending upon the amplitude of the incoming signal, the character of these pulses changes. Because of this action, the average plate, collector, or drain current varies in amplitude at an audio rate, bringing about the demodulation of the incoming signal.

The selectivity of a superregenerative receiver can be made comparable to that of some of the less selective superheterodynes—300 to 400 kc.—by utilizing a strip-line or cavity-type tuned circuit in the detector. The Q of this type of circuit is superior to that obtainable with lumped-inductance tuned circuits. The selectivity of a superregenerator is determined by the response curve of this single tuned circuit, and not by a series of tuned circuits in cascade as would be the case in a t.r.f. or superheterodyne receiver. Therefore, it is desirable to use high-Q circuits. Also, the lower the quench frequency, the better the selectivity will be. This results from a marked reduction in multiple resonance effects.

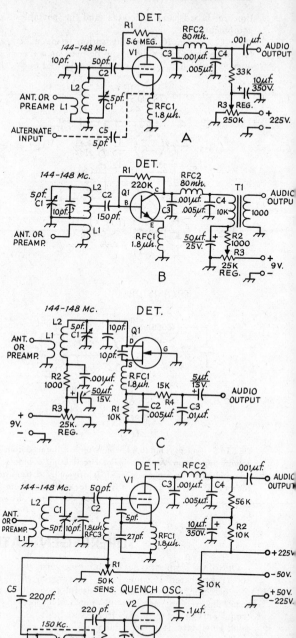

Fig. 16-6—Representative circuits of superregenerators. At A, a self-quenching vacuum-tube detector. At B, an equivalent circuit using a bipolar n-p-n transistor. The circuit at C uses a JFET in a standard self-quenching arrangement. At D, a superregenerative detector which uses an outboard quench oscillator to provide the interruption frequency for the detector. At A, B, and C, R_1 and C_2 determine the quench rate. R_3 is used as a regeneration control, and RFC_1 keeps the cathode, emitter, or source circuits above ground at the signal frequency. R_1 also establishes the operating bias for the detectors. At A, B, and D, C_3, RFC_2, and C_4 form a filter network for removing the quench frequency from the detector's output. R_4 and C_3 serve in the same manner at C. In all four circuits, R_2 and the associated electrolytic capacitor form an audio decoupling circuit, preventing motorboating when the audio amplifier section of the receiver is added. In all cases, L_2 and C_1 are tuned to the signal frequency. The fixed capacitor in parallel with C_1 providing a minimum capacitance for the tuned circuit, helping to maintain the Q of the tank across the entire tuning range—a requisite for smooth superregeneration. V_1 should be a high-mu v.h.f. triode such as a 6CW4. V_2 could be a 6C4 or similar triode. Q_1, at B, should be a medium- or high-beta v.h.f.

transistor such as a 2N3932. Q_1 at C should be a high-transconductance junction FET designed for v.h.f. use. The sensitivity of these detectors, at the frequency indicated, is such that a 30-percent modulated 0.5-uv. signal should be perfectly discernible when the output from the detectors is fed into a conventional audio channel. Capacitance is in pf. except decimal-value capacitances which are in μf. Polarized capacitors are electrolytic. Resistance is in ohms. K = 1000.

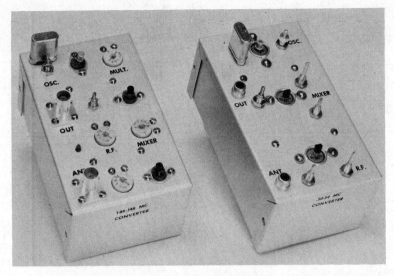

Fig. 16-7—Top view of the 6- and 2-meter FET converters. Both units are built in standard-size Miniboxes. The 6-meter model is at the right.

SIMPLE FET CONVERTERS FOR 6 AND 2 METERS

The converters shown in Fig. 16-7 employ JFET (junction field-effect transistors) in the r.f. and mixer stages, and offer good immunity to front-end overload and cross-talk—features not easy to realize in similar circuits that use bipolar transistors. (Originally described in *QST*, May 1967.) The Motorola MPF102 FETs are inexpensive and offer good performance on 6 and 2 meters.

For applications where a simple, inexpensive, crystal-controlled converter is desired, either of these units should be satisfactory. Because they operate from 9 or 12 volts, d.c., they can be put to good use in mobile or portable work.

The 6-Meter Circuit

A 7 to 11-Mc. i.f. is used for the 6-meter converter of Fig. 16-8. Any communications receiver that tunes from 7 to 11 Mc. can be used as an i.f. Alternatively, this converter can be used with a 6- to 9-Mc. Command receiver, provided a high order of selectivity is not desired.

Diodes CR_1 and CR_2 are bridged between J_1 and ground to limit the level of r.f. or transient voltages at the converter input. This measure was taken for the protection of the r.f. amplifier, Q_1. Since Q_1 is operated as a common-gate amplifier, no neutralization circuit is necessary. A shield plate is needed, however, between bandpass circuits L_1L_2 and L_3L_4 to prevent stray coupling. The bandpass circuits provide better input selectivity than single-tuned circuits, hence reduce image response. Q_2, the mixer, operates in a common-source circuit with its oscillator injection fed into the source by means of L_8. The oscillator, a 2N706A, uses a standard overtone crystal circuit operating at 43 Mc.

The converter can be operated from 9 volts, drawing approximately 7 milliamperes, or from 12 volts with a current drain of about 12 ma.

2-Meter Converter

Referring to Fig. 16-10, CR_3 and CR_4 are used as protective diodes as in the 6-meter version. Q_4 works as a neutralized r.f. amplifier, with L_{10} serving as the neutralizing inductor. L_9 is shielded from the $L_{11}L_{12}$ bandpass circuit as shown in the photographs.

Mixer stage Q_5 is common-source connected and combines the incoming 2-meter signal with a 130-Mc. oscillator signal to provide an i.f. of 14 to 18 Mc. This i.f. range was chosen to allow for dial-calibration convenience—14.0 Mc. equals 144.0 Mc., and so on. Oscillator injection is by means of a 5-pf. capacitor at the gate of Q_5.

An overtone oscillator is used at Q_6, producing output at 43.333 Mc. This frequency is multiplied to 130 Mc. by means of diode CR_5 which is connected between L_{16} and L_{17}. The tuned circuit, $L_{17}C_4$, provides selectivity and peaks the 130-Mc. output from CR_5.

The converter draws 6 milliamperes when operated from 9 volts. With a 12-volt supply, the drain is 8 ma.

Construction

Each unit is assembled in a $3 \times 5\frac{1}{4} \times 2\frac{1}{4}$-inch Minibox. Shield partitions are placed across the inside of each chassis as shown in the photos. The shields are made from pieces of 16-gauge aluminum and the dimensions are not critical. The main idea here is to break up the stray-coupling paths between the tuned circuits of the various stages.

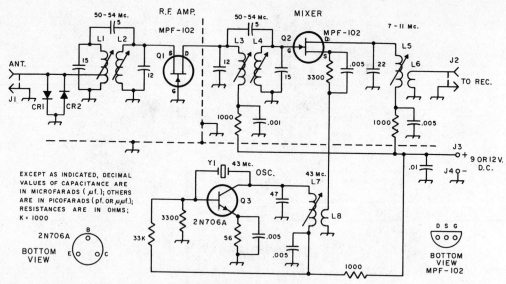

Fig. 16-8—Schematic of the 6-meter FET converter. All resistors are ½-watt composition. All capacitors are disk or tubular ceramic.

CR₁, CR₂—Small-signal germanium diode (1N34A suitable).

J₁, J₂—Phono connector.

J₃, J₄—Insulated banana jack, one red, one black.

L₁, L₄, inc.—0.68 μh., slug-tuned (Millen 69054-0.68*).
   L₁ has tap added at 2nd turn from ground end.

L₅—11 to 24 μh. slug-tuned (Miller 4507).

L₆—5 turns small-gauge insulated wire over cold end of L₅.

L₇—0.33 μh., slug-tuned (Millen 69054-0.33*).

L₈—1 turn small-gauge insulated wire over cold end of L₇.

Y₁—43.0-Mc. third-overtone crystal (International Crystal Co.).

* Available directly from James Millen Mfg. Co. 150 Exchange Street, Malden, Mass.

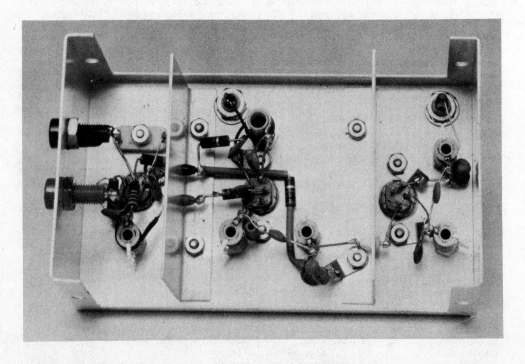

Fig. 16-9—Looking into the under side of the 6-meter converter the oscillator stage is at the left, the mixer is in the center, and the r.f. stage is at the far right. Shield partitions divide the sections.

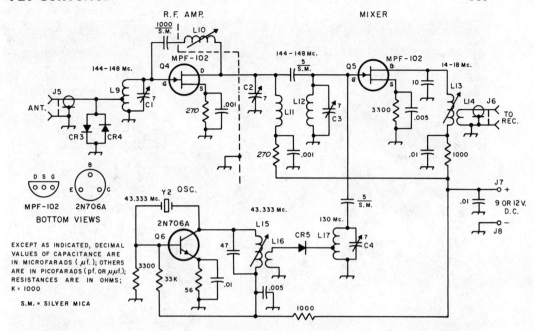

Fig. 16-10—Schematic of the 2-meter FET converter. Resistors are ½-watt composition. Fixed capacitors are tubular or disk ceramic unless otherwise noted.

C_1–C_4, inc.—1.5 to 7-pf. ceramic trimmer.

CR_3, CR_4—Small-signal germanium diode (1N34A).

CR_5—Small-signal crystal diode for v.h.f. use (IN82A suitable).

J_5, J_6—BNC chassis fitting.

J_7, J_8—Insulated banana jack, one red and one black.

L_9—4 turns No. 20 tinned copper wire, 5/16 in dia., ½ inch long. Tap one turn from ground end.

L_{10}—10 turns No. 24 enam. wire, close-wound on ¼-inch dia. ceramic slug-tuned form (Miller 4500-4).

L_{11}—5 turns No. 20 tinned-copper wire, 5/16 inch dia., ¾ inch long.

L_{12}—4 turns No. 20 tinned copper wire 5/16 inch dia., ½ inch long.

L_{13}—5 to 9 μh., slug-tuned (Miller 4505).

L_{14}—5 turns small-gauge insulated wire over cold end of L_{13}.

L_{15}—5 turns No. 24 enam. close-wound on ¼-inch dia. ceramic slug-tuned form (Miller 4500-4).

L_{16}—2 turns small-gauge insulated wire over cold end of L_{15}.

L_{17}—6 turns No. 20 tinned-copper wire, 5/16 dia., ½ inch long. Diode tap ½ turn from ground end.

Y_2—43.333-Mc. third-overtone crystal (International Crystal Co.).

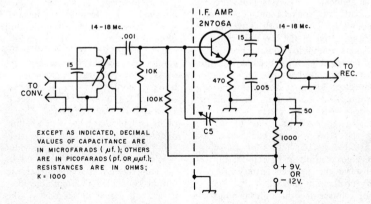

Fig. 16-11—Typical i.f. amplifier circuit for use between the 2-meter converter and the tunable i.f. receiver. Resistors are ½ watt composition. Capacitors are disk ceramic. C_5 can be a 1.5 to 7-pf. ceramic trimmer. Input and output tuned-circuit coils can be wound on Miller 4500-2 slug-tuned ceramic forms or equal. The amplifier could be built on a small Minibox, or could be incorporated in the 2-meter converter. C_5 is a neutralizing capacitor and should be adjusted for best circuit stability.

Fig. 16-12—Bottom view of the 2-meter converter. The oscillator chain is at the left end of the chassis, the mixer is in the center and the r.f. stage is at the right. The neutralizing inductor is in the mixer compartment, adjacent to the shield partition.

Transistor sockets, per se, were not used in these converters. The 6-meter model uses standard Nuvistor sockets. The 2-meter version uses 8-pin subminiature tube sockets, all of which happened to be available in the junk drawer. The latter are too expensive to buy as "new" items, at least for this application, so it is recommended that either Nuvistor sockets or good-quality transistor sockets be used in both converters. A word of caution: Most of the low-cost imported transistor sockets found in bargain houses are too flimsy to be reliable. They become intermittent, even during nonrigorous use.

Phono connectors are used for the input and output jacks on the 6-meter unit. BNC fittings are used in the 2-meter converter.

Banana jacks, one red and one black, are mounted on the rear wall of each converter chassis and are used as connectors for the supply voltage. The color coding helps remind the operator to observe the correct battery polarity when hooking up the equipment.

Small E. F. Johnson feedthrough bushings are used between the sections of the converters. The bushings are mounted on the shield partitions and are used to route the signal leads from one stage to another. In the 2-meter model, neutralizing inductor L_{10} is supported by its coil terminals between two of the feedthrough bushings by

soldering it in place with short lengths of stiff wire.

Converter Adjustment

The completed converters should be given a thorough visual inspection before applying power to them. Make sure that there are no physical short circuits, and inspect the work to see that no joints have been left unsoldered. An ohmmeter can be used to make a superficial check for d.c. shorts in the B+ line. The semiconductors should not be removed from their sockets for this test. A normal reading for the 6-meter converter will be approximately 1000 ohms with the ohmmeter connected between the B+ and B— minus jacks. A reading of 2000 ohms is typical for the 2-meter unit. If the ohmmeter leads are reversed, the readings will be about 500 ohms less than these values.

With the converter connected to the antenna system (or v.h.f. signal generator), and with its output connected to a suitable i.f. receiver, tune in a weak signal in the part of the band where you expect to operate. Peak all of the tuned circuits for maximum signal strength. If the signal cannot be found, chances are that the oscillator stage is not operating. Carefully adjust the oscillator collector tuned circuit, L_7 or L_{15}, until an increase in receiver noise is noted. This should indicate that the oscillator "kicked" in. Once the point is found where the oscillator starts working, unscrew the coil slug two or three more turns (this will assure quick starting of the oscillator each time the converter is turned on). Then tune in a weak signal and peak the stages as described in the foregoing.

It should be possible to stagger-tune the two bandpass circuits of the 6-meter converter so that near-uniform response across approximately 500 kc. of the band can be achieved.[1] A little experimenting should be all that is required to accomplish this. The 2-meter converter, when stagger-tuned, will not provide uniform response across a spread of more than about 700 kc. without a sacrifice in converter gain. If wider coverage is required, an i.f. amplifier of the type illustrated in Fig. 16-11 should be used between the converter and the i.f. receiver.[2] Some may wish to include the i.f. amplifier as a permanent part of the 2-meter converter. A slightly larger chassis could be used and the added stage could be contained in a separate compartment. Converter gain is adequate in the 6-meter model.

---

[1] The actual bandwidth of the converters will be determined to a greater extent by the characteristics of the i.f. output tuned circuits. By lowering the Q of the i.f. output circuits, greater band-width will be possible, but at the cost of reduced converter gain.

[2] The overall converter gain of the 2-meter model is rather low. For this reason, the tunable i.f. receiver should have good sensitivity in the 14- to 18-Mc. range. If not, the i.f. amplifier circuit shown in Fig. 16-11 can be built as an outboard assembly—or as a part of the converter—and used between the output of the converter and the input of the i.f. receiver.

Performance

Both converters were tested at 9 and 12 volts. The performance showed little difference when going from 9 to 12 volts, making them useful as mobile converters or as portable units operated from a self-contained 9-volt battery. A small transistor radio battery will give many hours of operation. A Burgess D6, or equivalent, is a bit huskier and should last almost as long as its normal shelf life.

Although the noise figures of these converters were not measured, it should be on the order of 2.5 db.

Stability is good with either unit and "birdies" were not evident when tuning across either i.f. range. If the r.f. stage is unstable in the 2-meter unit—evidenced by "blurps" and squeals when L_9 or L_{11} are adjusted—simply adjust L_{10} a turn at a time until the condition disappears.

For those who have noise generators and wish to set the converters up for the best noise figure, the taps on the input coils can be adjusted for optimum performance. The neutralization circuit in the 2-meter model should also be adjusted for the lowest noise figure.

There is no reason why these converters cannot be modified to work into i.f.s other than those specified. It will be necessary to select the appropriate oscillator crystals if this is done, and to make modifications to the tuned circuits in the oscillator chain. The i.f. output coil will have to be altered for resonance at the chosen intermediate frequency.

SERIES-RESONANT BYPASSING

It is well-known that the inexpensive disk-ceramic and "dog-bone" types of capacitors are relatively ineffective for bypassing above about 100 Mc. or so. This is due mainly to their considerable lead inductance, even when they are connected as close to the elements to be bypassed as possible. Actually this lead inductance can be used to advantage, by selecting lead lengths that make the capacitor series-resonant at the frequency to be bypassed.

This approach is recommended by WA2-KYF, who supplied the information in Table 13-I, showing capacitor and lead-length combinations for effective bypassing of r.f. energy at frequencies commonly encountered in v.h.f. work. The values are not particularly critical, as a series-resonant circuit is broad by nature. The impedance of a series-resonant bypass is very close to zero ohms at the frequency of resonance, and it will be lower than most conventional capacitors for a considerable range of frequency.

A high-capacitance short-lead combination is preferable to a lower value with longer leads, because the former will be less likely to allow

TABLE 16-I

Values of capacitance in pf. required for resonance of frequencies commonly encountered in amateur-band v.h.f. work, for leads of ¼, ½ and 1 inch in length.

Frequency Mc.	¼-Inch Leads	½-Inch Leads	1-Inch Leads
48-50	800	400	200
72	390	180	91
96	220	100	56
144	100	47	25
220	39	20	10

unwanted coupling to other circuits. For example, a 100-pf. capacitor with ¼-inch leads is a better bet than a 25-pf. with 1-inch leads, for bypassing at 144 Mc. The series-resonant bypass is worth a try in any circuit where instability is troublesome, and conventional bypassing has been shown to be ineffective. Screen, heater and cathode circuits are usually good candidates.

Fig. 16-13—A look at the completed 2-meter etched-circuit FET/IC converter and its 12-volt a.c.-operated power supply. The converter is at the right, mounted in a Vector case. The power supply is at the left and is housed in a 4 x 5 x 2-inch aluminum chassis. It has a bottom plate to which four rubber feet have been attached.

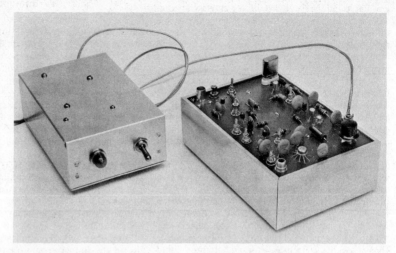

A LOW-NOISE 144-Mc. CONVERTER

A noise figure of approximately 2.5 db. is possible with this circuit.[1] It uses solid-state devices throughout, a feature which contributes to its compactness. An integrated-circuit i.f. amplifier boosts the overall gain of the converter to a suitable preset level for the station receiver with which it is used. Total cost of the converter should not exceed 30 dollars if all components are purchased as new items. By garnering the small parts—resistors, capacitors, hardware, and the like—from an old TV chassis, or from the workshop junk box, a considerable savings can be realized.

The Circuit

A standard cascode configuration makes up the r.f. amplifier section of the converter, Fig. 16-14. Two junction-type FETs, Q_1 and Q_2, comprise that part of the circuit. Although the circuit was quite stable without neutralization, L_{14} was included in the interest of securing a low noise figure. Q_1 and Q_2 have separate d.c. feed, making it unnecessary to select transistors with similar characteristics as might be required were they series-connected. A bandpass circuit, $L_3 C_1 L_4$, couples Q_2 to the mixer, Q_3.

The oscillator chain consists of three bipolar transistors, Q_4, Q_5, and Q_6. Q_4 operates in a third-overtone circuit and provides output at 58 Mc. The high frequency of Y_1 was chosen to reduce the number of multiplier stages required, and to cut down on harmonic frequencies which might cause spurious responses and "birdies" in the output of the converter. R_2, a 22-ohm resistor, was added because a parasitic condition was noted while tuning L_{10}. Adding the resistor cured the problem. Link L_{11} couples the oscillator output to the base of Q_6, which serves as a doubler to 116 Mc. A two-turn link, L_{13}, connects

to another two-turn link, L_5, on the mixer coil (L_4) to provide 116-Mc. injection to the mixer. Transistor Q_5 acts as a Zener diode, regulating the oscillator's d.c. supply at approximately 9 volts. The collector and base leads of Q_5 are grounded in this application.

Output from the mixer, Q_3, is at 28 Mc. The i.f. amplifier stage uses an integrated-circuit device, AR_1. Stage gain is controlled by applying a positive bias to terminal 5 of the integrated circuit by means of R_1. As the movable arm of R_1 is brought closer to ground the gain of the i.f. amplifier increases. R_1 varies the gain from zero to roughly 30 db.

Diode CR_1, an ordinary top-hat type rectifier, is used in series with the d.c. feed to the converter. When connected as shown — anode toward the power supply — the transistors cannot be damaged if the polarity of the power supply is wrong. CR_1 acts like an open circuit when the negative terminal of the power supply is connected to its anode.

Overall r.f. stability is enhanced by the use of decoupling networks between stages, and through the use of flashing-copper shields between some of the tuned circuits. An aluminum shield divides the etched-circuit board down the center and helps to isolate the r.f. and mixer stages from the oscillator chain.

The Etched-Circuit Board

A $4\frac{1}{2}$ x $6\frac{1}{2}$ x $\frac{1}{16}$-inch copper-clad phenolic circuit board (Vector CU65/45-1) is used as a chassis for the unit.[2]

Etch-resistant material, such as paint or Vectoresist rub-on transfers can be used to protect the portions of the board that aren't to be removed.[3]

[1] Circuit originally described by W1CER, *QST*, Sept. 1967.

[2] Scale-size template of circuit-board pattern is available from ARRL for 25 cents plus s.a.s.e.

[3] Complete information on circuit-board etching is given in Chap. 20.

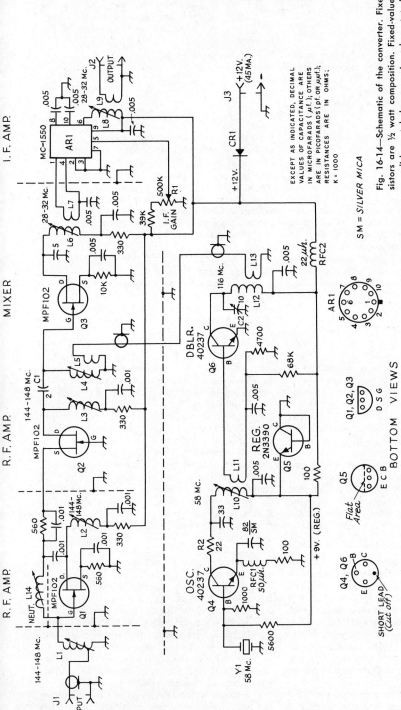

Fig. 16-14—Schematic of the converter. Fixed-value resistors are ½ watt composition. Fixed-value capacitors are disk or tubular ceramic unless stated otherwise.

L_{11}—2-turn link of small-dia. wire over cold end of L_{10}.

L_{12}—5 turns No. 20 tinned copper wire (or enam.), 5/16-inch diameter, ⅜ inch long.

L_{13}—2 turns small-dia. insulated hookup wire inserted in cold end of L_{12}, ¼-inch dia.

L_{14}—9 turns No. 24 enam. wire, close-wound on same style form as L_{10}.

Q_1-Q_6, inc.—For text reference purposes.

R_1—500,000-ohm control, linear taper.

RFC_1—50-μh. r.f. choke (Millen J-300-50).

RFC_2—22-μh. r.f. choke (Millen J-300-22).

Y_1—58-Mc. third-overtone crystal (International Crystal type FA-5).

EXCEPT AS INDICATED, DECIMAL VALUES OF CAPACITANCE ARE IN MICROFARADS (μf.); OTHERS ARE IN PICOFARADS (pf. or μμf.); RESISTANCES ARE IN OHMS;

K = 1000

SM = SILVER MICA

BOTTOM VIEWS

AR_1—Motorola MC-1550 integrated circuit (see text and Fig. 2).

C_1—Gimmick capacitor: two 1-inch lengths of insulated hookup wire, twisted 6 times. A 2-pf. fixed-value ceramic capacitor can be substituted.

C_2—10-pf. piston-type trimmer (Centralab 829-10).

CR_1—Silicon diode, 50 p.r.v. or greater, at 200 ma.

J_1—BNC-style chassis connector.

J_2, J_3—Phono jack.

L_1—6 turns No. 24 enam. wire to occupy ⅜ inch on slug-tuned form, ¼ in. dia.; (Miller 4500-4) tap 1¼ turns above ground end.

L_2—4 turns No. 24 enam. wire to occupy ⅜ inch on same type form as L_1.

L_3—5 turns No. 24 enam. to occupy ⅜ inch on same type form as L_1.

L_4—4 turns No. 24 enam. to occupy ⅜ inch on same style form as L_1.

L_5—2 turns insulated hookup wire over ground end of L_4.

L_6, L_8—Slug-tuned, 1.6 to 2.8 μh. (Miller No. 4503).

L_7, L_9—Three-turn link over cold ends of L_6 and L_8. Use small-diameter insulated hookup wire.

L_{10}—5 turns No. 24 enam. wire to occupy ⅜ inch on Miller 4500-4 slug-tuned form.

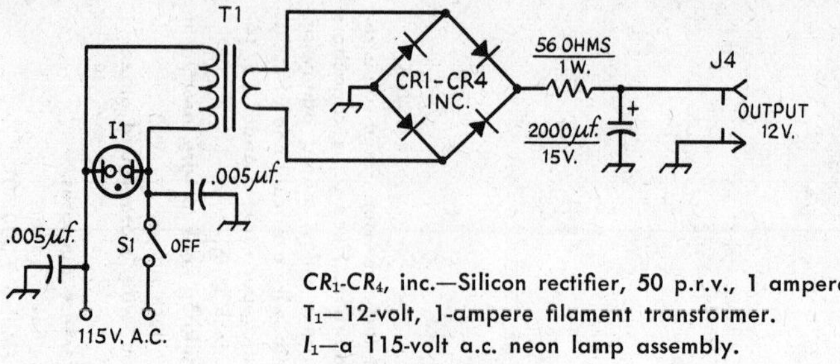

Fig. 16-15—Schematic of the converter's power supply. The 2000-μf. capacitor is electrolytic, others are disk ceramic, 1000-volt units. The 56-ohm resistor was selected to give the proper power-supply voltage when used with the circuit of Fig. 16-14 (12 volts d.c.)

CR$_1$-CR$_4$, inc.—Silicon rectifier, 50 p.r.v., 1 ampere.
T$_1$—12-volt, 1-ampere filament transformer.
I$_1$—a 115-volt a.c. neon lamp assembly.
J$_4$—Phono jack.
S$_1$—S.p.s.t. toggle.

Once the board is etched and cleaned, the holes can be drilled. A 100-watt soldering iron will be required when soldering the copper shields to the circuit board. It will be necessary to cut away those portions of the shields which might come in contact with ungrounded sections of the etched circuit. A nibbling tool is useful for this. Since patterns are not available for the shields, some cut-and-try effort will be necessary. Ordinary plumber's-style flashing copper was used for the shields in this model. Light-gauge brass could also be used. The center shield is made from aluminum stock and is bolted to the circuit board with 4-40 hardware. All shields are 1¼ inches high.

Assembling the Converter

Fig. 16-17 shows the layout of the under side of the circuit board (copper-clad side). Key components are labeled on the template to show their placement.[2] The positions of the various semiconductors are given to show where the individual leads of each are connected. Once the key parts are installed, it should become apparent where the rest of the parts will be placed. The text photos will also help the builder to determine where the small parts go.

Miniature coax cable is used between L_5 and L_{13}. A tightly-twisted pair of insulated hookup wires would no doubt serve as well in that part of the circuit. The 22-ohm resistor in the collector circuit of Q_4 is mounted between the coil terminal of L_{10} and the collector strip of that stage.

Power Supply

A 12-volt d.c. power source is required to operate this converter. Because the circuit draws approximately 45 ma., battery power does not appear to be the most practical answer to the power supply problem. An a.c. operated 12-volt supply is recommended for fixed-station use. A recommended circuit is given in Fig. 16-15. The complete assembly is housed in a 4 × 5 × 2-inch aluminum chassis which is enclosed by an aluminum bottom plate. Rubber feet prevent damage to table tops.

If portable operation is anticipated, the converter can be powered by eight D-size flashlight cells, series-connected, to provide several hours of intermittent use. Needless to say, a 12-volt auto battery could assure many more hours of

portable or mobile operation. If mobile operation is planned, it would be prudent to connect an 18-volt Zener diode between the positive terminal of J_3 and ground, thus protecting the transistors from transient peaks which commonly occur in the automotive electrical system. Such voltage spikes often exceed the safe maximum-voltage ratings of the transistors being used. Under normal conditions, the Zener will not conduct.

Checkout and Testing

Before applying the operating voltage at J_3, a thorough check for short circuits between sections of the etched circuit should be instituted. Make certain that pigtails or small blobs of solder do not form bridges between the copper strips.

If available, a v.h.f. signal generator should be connected to J_1 for initial testing and alignment. The output of the converter, taken from J_2, should be fed into a communications receiver that is capable of being tuned from 28 to approximately 30 Mc. With power applied to the converter, tune in a signal at approximately 145 Mc. (29 Mc. on the main receiver dial). Adjust L_1, L_2, L_3, L_4, L_6, and L_8 for maximum output from the converter. If the signal cannot be found, chances are that the oscillator, Q_4, has not started. If this is the case, adjust L_{10} until a slight increase in noise is evident, indicating that Q_3 is receiving injection voltage. The slug in L_{10} should be set approximately three turns toward minimum inductance from the setting at which the crystal "kicks" in. This will assure reliable starting of the oscillator each time the converter is turned on. C_2 should be adjusted for maximum converter output.

L_4 should be adjusted with the aid of a noise generator. It should be set for the best n.f. possible. Adjustment of the input tap on L_1 will also have a marked effect on the noise figure. The tap point given for L_1 proved to be optimum for this model and will be satisfactory in most instances. There will be some interaction between L_1 and L_{14}, requiring two or three adjustments before optimum results are secured.

A reasonably flat response from the converter can be realized over a two-megacycle range. It is necessary to stagger-tune the r.f. and mixer coils, as well as those in the i.f. channel. L_1 was tuned for best noise figure at 144 Mc. L_2 was

Fig. 16-16—A head-on view of the top surface of the etched-circuit board. The i.f. gain-control knob is at the upper right. The input jack for the 12-volt supply is just to the left of the gain control. The i.f. output jack is at the lower right, and the r.f. input jack is at the lower left on the board. The IC is located at the far right, just above the i.f. output connector.

peaked at 144.5 Mc., L_3 was tuned for a peak at 145 Mc., and L_4 was optimized at 145.5 Mc. Those wishing to operate in other parts of the 2-meter band can use a similar tuning procedure. L_6 was tuned for maximum response at 28.5 Mc. The i.f. output coil, L_8, was peaked at 29.9 Mc. The converter response is flat within 3 decibels from 144 to 146 Mc. when tuned in this way.

After the tuneup is completed, adjust R_1 through its range. If AR_1 is functioning correctly, the converter gain should vary markedly from one end of the control's range to the other.

Some Final Comments

Cross-talk and overload immunity are good with this circuit. A 100,000-μv. signal failed to swamp the front-end of this converter. On-the-air tests when the band was heavily occupied with strong local signals — some very strong signals that were within two or three blocks of the test location — proved the converter to be free of the aforementioned problems. No "birdies" or other spurious responses could be found when tuning across the lower two megacycles of the 2-meter band. The converter was being used with a Collins 75A-1. When the unit was fed into a Collins 51S-1, no spurious signals could be found when the entire 144- to 148-Mc. range

was tuned. The oscillator stability was good, permitting the converter to return to the same receiving frequency each time it was cycled. Line voltage changes had no noticeable effect on the oscillator stability.

A modern-style Vector printed-circuit chassis base is used to house this converter. These units are supplied in sections, enabling the user to fabricate a variety box sizes and shapes. The side channels are grooved to accommodate printed-circuit boards. This box was made up from one pair of Fram-Loc rails which measure $2 \times 6\frac{5}{8}$ inches (Vector SR2-6.6/062) and one pair of rails which are 2 inches high and $4\frac{1}{2}$ inches long (Vector SR2- 4.6/062).

An aluminum cover panel (Vector PL4566) serves as a bottom plate. Four rubber feet were attached to the bottom cover in this model. This box cost approximately $2.40, minus the circuit board. There is no reason why a standard chassis or Minibox could not be used as a base. The circuit board could then be mounted over a cut-out area just slightly smaller in area than the board.

The photos show that large 0.005-μf. disk capacitors were used. The smaller 0.005-μf. 50-volt disk capacitors that are available from most supply houses would have resulted in a neater-appearing layout. Either type is satisfactory, however.

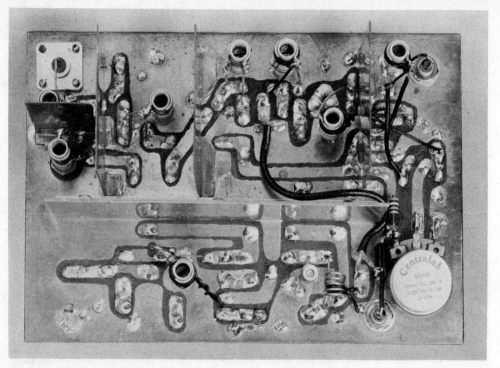

Fig. 16-17A—Bottom view of the etched-circuit board. Wiring has been completed and the general layout is apparent. The i.f. gain control and 12-volt power jack are at the lower right. The input circuit and r.f. stages are at the upper left. The mixer is at the upper center, and the IC i.f. amplifier is at the upper right. The oscillator chain extends along the lower portion of the board. The interstage shields are in place, but are difficult to see in this photo.

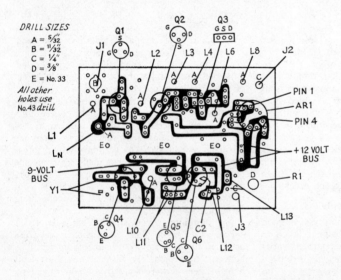

Fig. 16-17B—Layout of the etched circuit board. The lines show where the key components are mounted and indicate the way the semiconductor leads are indexed. This is a bottom view of the board (copper side). The inked-in areas represent the sections of the board that have been etched away. The white areas are the copper strips that remain.

A 220-MHZ. CONVERTER

The superiority of transistors over tubes becomes more marked as the upper frequency limit of the tubes concerned is approached. Thus a well-designed 220-MHz. converter using the better transistors may outperform one using anything but the most expensive and hard-to-get vacuum tubes. The 220-MHz. converter of Fig. 16-18 is almost a duplicate of the 144-MHz. model shown earlier in this chapter. Its weak-signal sensitivity should be better than has been possible heretofore at this frequency, for anything of comparable simplicity and moderate cost.

It was built by Tom McMullen, W1QVF.

To save space and avoid duplication, only those portions of the converter that are different from the 144-MHz. version are discussed here. An identical circuit board is used. The circuit, Fig. 16-18, is similar, but not identical to that of the 144-MHz. converter. The same parts designations are used insofar as possible. Self-supporting coils and cylindrical ceramic trimmers are used in the r.f. circuits. The first r.f. stage has capacitive neutralization. Injection at 192 MHz. (for 28-MHz. i.f.) is provided by a 48-MHz. crystal oscillator and a quadrupler. Oscillator voltage is Zener-diode regulated at 9 volts.

Almost any silicon v.h.f. transistor will work in the oscillator and quadrupler stages. The r.f. and mixer are FETs. A noise figure of 3 db. or better should be obtainable with several different types, in addition to the Motorola MPF series shown here. The 28-MHz. i.f. amplifier stage is not shown, as it is identical to that in the 144-MHz. converter. It is definitely recommended, not only to assure adequate gain for some of the less-effective communications receivers, but also to permit setting the desired converter output level to match the particular receiver in use.

One difference between this converter and the one for 144 MHz. might not be readily apparent, but it is important. Note the resistor, R_2, in the line to the mixer drain circuit. This is not in the 2-meter version. It was put into the 220-MHz. model when a signal-frequency resonance developed in the circuit board, causing an oscillation problem. Looking at the layout drawing of the circuit board, Fig. 16-17B, pick out the 12-volt bus that runs from near the middle of the board horizontally to the right, before dropping vertically into the lower half. This should be severed below the letter "A" on the sketch. The 100-ohm R_2 is bridged across the gap.

Other minor mechanical differences resulting from the slightly-modified circuitry in the r.f. portion are apparent from the photographs. The small shield between L_1 and L_{14} in the 2-meter model is not needed here. The neutralizing capacitor, C_4, appears about where L_{14} was. The cylindrical trimmers, C_3, C_5, C_6 and C_7, are mounted where the slug coils are seen in the 144-MHz. model. Note the mounting positions of the r.f. coils. L_1, L_3 and L_4 are similar, i.e., their axes parallel to the chassis. L_2 is perpendicular to it.

Adjustment

The first step should be to get the oscillator and multiplier running. It may be advisable to keep voltage off the stages other than the ones being checked, at this point. Make sure that the oscillator is on 48 MHz., and no other frequency. (In this type of circuit it is possible to get oscil-

Fig. 16-19—Interior of the 220-MHz. FET converter. Minor differences from the 144-MHz. model, Fig. 4-16-14, are discussed in the text. The r.f., mixer and i.f. amplifier circuits, left to right, occupy the upper half of the circuit board. Board layout is identical to that of Fig. 16-17B.

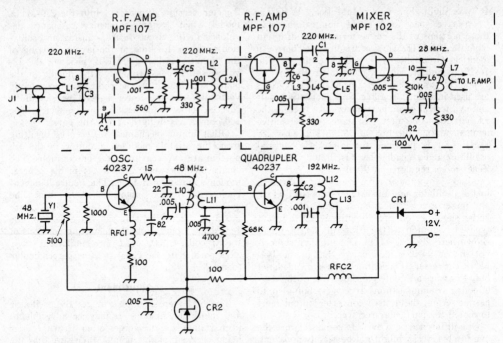

Fig. 16-18—Schematic diagram and parts information for the 220-MHz. converter. Only those portions wherein there are differences from the 144-MHz. circuit, Fig. 16-14, are shown. Parts are labelled similar to those of the 144-MHz. converter, wherever possible.

C_1—2pf., or 2 1-inch lengths of insulated wire, twisted six times.

C_2, C_3, C_5, C_6, C_7—8-pf. cylindrical ceramic trimmer (Centralab 829-7).

C_4—9-pf. subminiature trimmer (Johnson 189-503-4).

CR_1—Silicon diode, 50 p.r.v. or greater, 200 ma. or more.

CR_2—9-volt Zener diode.

J_1—BNC coaxial fitting.

L_1, L_3, L_4, L_{12}—3 turns No. 22, ¼-inch diam., ¼ inch long. Tap L_1 at one turn from ground end.

L_3—6½ turns No. 22, ¼-inch diam., ½ inch long. Tap at 2 turns from top end.

L_{2A}—3 turns insulated wire between turns of L_2.

L_5—1 turn insulated wire between bottom turns of L_4.

L_6, L_7—Same as in 144-MHz. model.

L_{10}—7 turns No. 22 5/16 inch long, on ¼-inch iron-slug form (Miller 4500-4 form).

L_{11}—2 turns insulated wire over bottom turns of L_{10}.

L_{13}—1 turn insulated wire between first two turns of L_{12}.

R_2—See text.

RFC_1, RFC_2—25-uh. r.f. choke (Millen J-300-25).

Y_1—48-MHz. third-overtone crystal.

lation on the crystal fundamental, in this case 16 MHz., if the collector circuit does not resonate at 48 MHz.) Now fire up the quadrupler and peak C_2 for maximum energy at 192 MHz.

With the converter connected to the receiver, there should be a marked increase in noise when voltage is applied to the r.f., mixer and i.f. amplifier stages. The i.f. can be peaked for maximum noise at 28 MHz. It is helpful at this point to have a signal on 220. A dipper signal will do. It is also desirable to have a properly-matched antenna connected to J_1, unless a good signal generator with 50-ohm termination is available for alignment purposes. If a random antenna must be used, put a 50-ohm resistor across J_1 to simulate the eventual load, for neutralization purposes.

There may be no oscillation in the r.f. stages, regardless of tuning, if the converter is operated with a proper load. If this is the case it is merely necessary to adjust the neutralizing capacitor, C_4, and the tuning of the input circuit, L_1C_3, for best signal-to-noise ratio on a weak signal. All other circuits affect only the gain and frequency response characteristics, so they can be adjusted for flat response across the desired frequency range, and there will be no sacrifice in the ability of the system to respond to weak signals.

Most realistic operation of the receiver's S-meter will be obtained if the meter adjustment is set so that there is an appreciable reading on noise only, with no signal. The converter i.f. gain control is then set so that the meter reads S-0 or S-1, with the antenna on. In this way the relative strength of signals will be indicated on the meter, within the usual variations encountered. The receiver's antenna trimmer, if there is one, can also be used as an auxilliary gain control, and it will have no effect whatever on the sensitivity of the system.

Fig. 16-20—Transistor preamplifiers for 50, 144 and 220 MHz., left to right. Appearance is similar, except for the type of tuned circuit used.

FET PREAMPLIFIERS FOR 50, 144 AND 220 MHZ.

Where a v.h.f. receiver lacks gain, or has a poor noise figure, an external preamplifier can improve its ability to detect weak signals. Some multiband receivers that include the 50-MHz. band are not as good as they might be on 6. Converters for 144 MHz. having pentode r.f. stages, or using some of the earlier dual triodes, may also need some help. Most 220-MHz. converters are marginal performers, at best. The field-effect transistor preamplifiers of Fig. 16-20 should improve results with these, and with any other receivers for these bands that may not be in optimum working condition.

The circuits of the amplifiers are similar, though iron-core coils are used in the 50-MHz. model, and air-found coils in the other two. The common-source circuit requires neutralization. This is done with a capacitive feedback adjustment, rather than with the inductive circuit commonly used. A tapped input circuit is used in the 50-MHz. amplifier, and capacitive input is shown for the other two, though this was done mainly to show alternative circuits. The output circuit is matched to the receiver input by means of C_2.

Fig. 16-21—Circuit diagrams and parts information for the FET preamplifiers. Values of capacitors not described are in picofarads (pf. or $\mu\mu$f.).

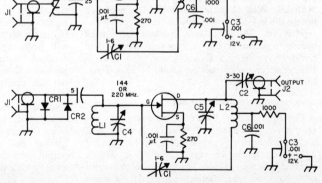

C_1—1.3 to 6.7-pf. subminiature variable (Johnson 189-502-5).

C_2—3 to 30-pf. miniature mica trimmer.

C_3—0.001-μf. feedthrough (Centralab MFT-1000; FT-1000 in 220-MHz. amplifier).

C_4, C_5—3 to 12-pf. ceramic trimmer in 144-MHz. amplifier; 1 to 6-pf. cylindrical ceramic in 220.

C_6—0.001-μf. 50-volt mylar. Omitted in 220-MHz. model.

CR_1, CR_2—1N34A or similar germanium diode.

J_1, J_2—Coaxial fitting. BNC type shown.

L_1—50 MHz.; 7 turns No. 24 enamel in ¼-inch iron-slug ceramic form, tapped at 3 turns from ground end (Form is Miller 4500-4. 144 MHz.: 3 turns No. 22, ¼-inch diam., ⅜ inch long. 220 MHz.: same, but with 2 turns ⅛ inch long.

L_2—50 MHz.: 10 turns like L_1, but center-tapped. 144 MHz.: 5 turns No. 22, ¼-inch diam., ½ inch long, center-tapped. 220 MHz.: Same but 4 turns.

Fig. 16-22—Interiors of the FET preamplifiers, in the same order as in Fig. 16-20. The input end is toward the left in each unit.

Many inexpensive transistors will work well in these amplifiers. Motorola MPF-102, 104 and 106, all low-priced molded-plastic units and the more expensive metal-case 2N4416 were tried, and all were more than adequate. The MPF-102 is the least expensive, and, surprisingly, it was as good as any, even on 220 MHz. Careful readjustment is required when changing transistors, so the builder should not jump to conclusions about the relative merit of different types.

Construction

The amplifiers are built in small handmade boxes, aluminum for the 50- and 144-MHz. models, and flashing copper for the 220-MHz. one, but any small metal box should do. Those shown are $1\frac{1}{2}$ by 2 by 3 inches in size. The transistor socket is in the middle of the top surface, and the BNC input and output fittings are centered on the ends. The tuned circuits are roughly $\frac{3}{4}$ inch either side of the transistor socket, but this should be adjusted for good layout with the parts available. Flat ceramic trimmers are used for tuning the 144-MHz. amplifier, and the cylindrical type in the 220-MHz. one. Sockets were used mainly to permit trying various transistors; they could be wired directly in place equally well. Printed-circuit construction would be fine, if you like this method.

Adjustment

The preamplifier should be connected to the receiver or converter with which it is to be used, with any length of coaxial cable, or by hooking J_2 directly to the converter input jack with a suitable adaptor. If you have a noise generator or signal generator, connect it to J_1. If not, use a test signal from a grid-dip oscillator, or some other signal source known to be in the band for which the amplifier was designed. Preferably a matched antenna for the band in question should be hooked to J_1, if a signal generator is not used. A 50-ohm resistor across J_1 may be helpful if a random antenna is used for the adjustment work.

Set the neutralizing capacitor near half capacitance; then, with no voltage yet applied, tune the input and output circuits roughly for maxi-

mum signal. (The level may be only slightly lower than it would be with the converter or receiver alone.) Now apply voltage, and check current drain. It should be 4 to 7 ma., depending on the voltage. Probably there will be an increase in noise and signal when voltage is turned on. If not, the stage may be oscillating. This will be evident from erratic tuning and bursts of noise when adjustments are attempted.

If there is oscillation (and it is likely) move C_1 in small increments, returning the input and output circuits each time, until a setting of C_1 is found where oscillation ceases, and the signal is amplified. All adjustments interlock, so this is a see-saw procedure at first. Increasing the capacitance of C_2 tends to stabilize the amplifier through increased loading, but if carried too far will have an adverse effect on gain. The best setting is one where the input and output circuits do not tune too critically, but the gain is adequate.

The input circuit is first peaked for maximum signal, but final adjustment should be for best signal-to-noise ratio. This process is very similar to that with tube amplifiers, and the best point will probably be found with the input circuit detuned on the low-frequency side of the gain peak. In listening to a weak modulated signal, the fact that the noise drops off faster than the signal with a slight detuning is quite obvious. Typically the meter reading may drop about one full S-unit, while the noise level drops two S-units. The exact setting depends on the neutralization, and on the loading, both input and output, and can only be determined by experiment, with a noise generator or a weak signal.

Results

Because external noise is more of a limiting factor in 50-MHz. reception than on the higher bands, tuning for best reception is not critical on this band. Very likely you can set the neutralization to prevent oscillation, peak the input and output circuits roughly, and you'll be all set. On 144 the job is fussier if the amplifier is to effect a real improvement, particularly if your receiver is a fairly good one. This preamplifier should get you down to the point where external noise limits your reception, for sure, if you were not there before. On 220 the preamp is almost certain to help, unless you already have an exceptional receiving setup, and optimum performance is worth the trouble you take to get it. With all three, you should be certain that, if a given signal can be heard in your location, on your antenna, you will now be able to hear it.

Warning: if the preamp is to be used with a transceiver, be sure to connect it in the line to the receiver only, not in the main line from the transceiver to the antenna. It is best to do this before any work is done on the amplifier; otherwise you're sure to throw the send-receive switch inadvertently, and destroy the transistor.

If you're in doubt about the possibility of r.f. coming down the antenna line, connect protective diodes across the input, as shown with CR_1 and CR_2 in one of the circuits. Install these after the preamplifier tuneup, and check weak-signal reception with and without them, to be sure that they are not causing signal loss. Junction-type field-effect transistors are capable of withstanding much more r.f. voltage than bipolar transistors, so this kind of protection may not be needed in situations where it would have been mandatory with earlier types of transistor front ends.

A TWO-STAGE TRANSISTOR PREAMPLIFIER FOR 1296 MHZ.

Transistor preamplifiers[1] have been instrumental in extending the reliable coverage of several 1296-MHz. stations. A single r.f. stage will work very well with a crystal-mixer converter for this frequency range, if the mixer and its following i.f. amplifier stage are already fairly low-noise devices. If they are not close to optimum in design, more r.f. gain than one transistor stage is capable of delivering may be needed to effectively mask the mixer and i.f. amplifier noise.

This and the availability of improved u.h.f. transistors suggests the use of a two-stage amplifier. The gain with two stages is around 19 db, which is adequate to override the noise of all but the worst of mixers. With this much gain, and the low noise figure of the new transistors, the mixer and i.f. amplifier are no longer critical factors in the overall performance of the 1296-MHz. receiving system.

The two stages are built in separate units, though they could be combined in one, if desired. Separation has the advantage of permitting the builder to start with one stage, and then progress to two if the additional gain is needed. The transistors may be either the 5200 or 5500 series. The latter has more gain, and is probably better for the second stage.

[1] "A 1296-MHz. Preamplifier—That Works!"—Katz, Nov., 1967, *QST*, page 32.

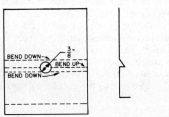

Fig. 16-24—Details of the thin brass shield plate used to support the transistor in the first r.f. amplifier stage. Dimensions will depend on the case size and height of the tuning capacitors used. The emitter leads are soldered to the horizontal "shelf" made by bending the plate as seen in the end view. (Designed and built by D. Vilardi, WA2VTR.)

Fig. 16-23—The two-stage preamplifier for 1296 MHz. is built in separate units. The first stage is at the right. A jack for plugging in a small 9-volt transistor radio battery is shown in the foreground.

Construction

Transistors used in early work with 1296-MHz. amplifiers had wire leads. The KMC KC5200 and K5500[2] used here have flat ribbon leads, making possible a mounting having substantially no lead inductance. The "accordion-pleated" shield plate shown in Fig. 1 suspends the transistor on its emitter leads, with the base lead on one side and the collector lead on the other. These two leads are soldered to their respective strip lines, L_1 and L_2, with the minimum possible length.

The input and output coupling capacitors are no-lead disks, though conventional disk ceramics may be used if the minimum possible lead length is assured. Their value is not particularly critical. The tuning capacitors, C_1 through C_6, should be high-quality short piston or coaxial capacitors, $3/4$ inch center to center.

In the two photographs the first stage is shown at the right side. The boxes are handmade of thin sheet brass. Standard aluminum Miniboxes could be used, though brass or copper facilitates soldering direct to the case. The shield in the first

[2] The KMC transistors used in these stages are expensive if obtained through the usual channels. Units entirely satisfactory for amateur service may be obtained at reduced prices from Samuel G. Nelson, W2MHK, Reaville Associates, RFD 1, Box 200, Flemington, N.J. 08822.

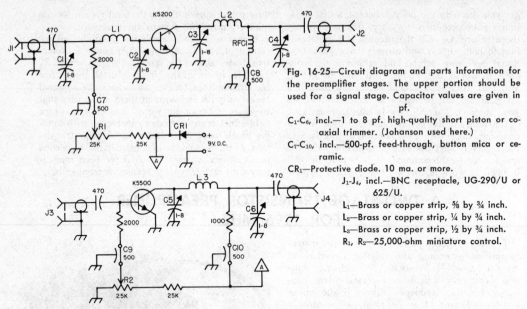

Fig. 16-25—Circuit diagram and parts information for the preamplifier stages. The upper portion should be used for a signal stage. Capacitor values are given in pf.

C_1-C_6, incl.—1 to 8 pf. high-quality short piston or co-axial trimmer. (Johanson used here.)

C_7-C_{10}, incl.—500-pf. feed-through, button mica or ceramic.

CR_1—Protective diode. 10 ma. or more.

J_1-J_4, incl.—BNC receptacle, UG-290/U or 625/U.

L_1—Brass or copper strip, ⅝ by ¾ inch.

L_2—Brass or copper strip, ¼ by ¾ inch.

L_3—Brass or copper strip, ½ by ¾ inch.

R_1, R_2—25,000-ohm miniature control.

stage should extend nearly the full width and height of the box. This is not so important in the second stage, which has a tuned circuit only on the output side. The bent brass mounting plate in the second stage is primarily to insure minimum emitter lead inductance.

The interior views show the input sides at the bottom. It will be seen that the strip for the input circuit, L_1, is wider than that for the output, L_2. The transistor has higher input than output capacitance, requiring less inductance in the input circuit. All strip inductors are brass and are ¾ inch long. They are soldered directly to the tops of the tuning capacitors and are pi-networks.

Fig. 16-26—Interior views of the two preamplifier stages, again with the first stage at the right. The input ends are toward the bottom of the picture.

Adjustment

A signal source is necessary in tuning up the preamplifier. Most small two-meter transmitters put out enough energy on the 9th harmonic to be plainly audible at 1296 MHz. Transistorized "beacons" commonly used by amateur u.h.f. experimenters are fine. Anything strong enough to be heard on the converter, without the preamplifier, will serve. Just be sure that, if you are listening to harmonic, it is the *right* one.

Initial peaking can be done with no voltage on the preamp. If a 50-ohm antenna is used the tuned circuits will be close to optimum adjustment if peaked first in this way. The same is true if one is fortunate enough to have a 1296-MHz. signal generator with 50-ohm termination.

Now apply about 5 to 6 volts, and check the current on each transistor. Adjust the bias controls, R_1 and R_2, for 1 to 2 ma. on the 5200 and 2 to 15 ma. on the 5500. Now reduce the strength maximum response. Readjust the bias, for minimum noise on the first stage and maximum gain on the second. *Do not exceed 4 ma. on 5200.*

The preamplifier as shown has a socket for plugging in a small 9-volt transistor radio battery. This may now be used, and a final peaking and bias adjustment made for best results. Bear in mind that optimum signal-to-noise ratio is the objective. This can be achieved by careful adjustment of the first stage, and it is not likely to be the same as for maximum signal level. The second stage can be used as a gain control, to some extent, though this is best done in the first i.f. amplifier. The gain of the two stages is about 19 db, when the system is adjusted for best noise figure. Not many amateurs will be able to measure noise figure accurately at this frequency, but it should be under 5 db. A system noise figure of 3 db. is possible with these transistors at 1000 MHz., but at 1296 MHz. it may be slightly higher.

A TRANSISTORIZED PREAMPLIFIER FOR 432 MC.

This preamplifier uses two RCA 2N3478 transistors in cascade to produce a noise figure of less than 5 decibels. The 2N3478 is a low-cost TV-type semiconductor that sells for less than $2.00 and performs nearly as well in this circuit as did some higher-priced units that were tried.

Trough-line construction is used to provide tuned circuits with high Q characteristics, a valuable feature in the reduction of unwanted signals in the u.h.f. spectrum. The entire preamplifier can be fashioned with ordinary workbench tools if the layout of Fig. 16-30 is followed.

Construction

Lines L_1, L_2 and L_3 are ¼-inch copper tubing, fitted tightly into holes in one end of the box, and soldered directly to the fixed elements of the ceramic trimmers at the other. No need to use expensive glass trimmers—the Centralab 829 series are low cost and will do the job nicely. The end of the tubing is countersunk slightly with a ¼-inch drill, to fit over the silvered end of the trimmer. This is better mechanically and electrically than using the flexible wire lead on the trimmer for making this connection.

Dimensions of the box are shown in Fig. 16-30. Although 1/32-inch thick brass is used in this model, flashing copper would be good enough, and should be easier for the kitchen-table worker to handle.

Although the box, partitions, and lines are silver-plated in this unit, it is not essential to the performance. Without silver plating, copper is better than brass, electrically. Brass is easier to work with hand tools and is easily silver plated.[1] The partitions are held in place with two spade bolts each.

The transistors are in the left and center compartments, about 1¾ inches up from the bottom, as seen in Fig. 16-29. They hang by their leads, which are kept as short as possible. The base leads go directly to feed-through capacitors, C_4 and C_6. The bias networks, R_1–R_2 and R_3–R_4, are connected externally.

The emitter leads are connected to the junctions of the blocking capacitors and 1000-ohm resistors, without support other than that afforded by these parts. The collector leads run through ¼-inch holes in the two partitions. As indicated in Fig. 16-30, the collector circuits are in the center and right-hand compartments. Collector voltage is fed in through C_5 and C_7, from the top of the box.

Adjustment

Tuning of the preamplifier is very simple. The circuits are first peaked for maximum gain, and the input circuit is adjusted for best signal-to-noise ratio. No attempt was made to adjust the

---

[1] Three methods for doing silver plating at home are described in Chapter 13 of *The Radio Amateur's V.H.F. Manual.*

Fig. 16-27—The two-stage preamplifier for 432 Mc. The box is silver-plated brass, but flashing copper could be used with equally good results. Connections to the bases and collectors are brought out on feed-through bypass capacitors, to permit changing the operating conditions. (Described in *QST*, Feb. 1966.)

tap positions, as the amplifier seemed to work up to the specifications for the transistors, just as assembled. The value of R_1 in the bias network of the first stage is the principal critical factor, and it will vary with different types of transistors. We used a 5000-ohm control at this point, with a 10-ma. meter connected in the negative lead to monitor the total current drain. The optimum value for R_1 was about 2800 ohms, and the current to the first stage was about 2 ma. Higher current drain causes noise to rise faster than signal level, and much lower current costs some gain. About 200 ohms either way is enough to make a noticeable difference in noise figure or gain.

The value of R_3 can be juggled to suit requirements. It is not often necessary to run this stage at maximum gain, since noise figure is controlled mainly by the first stage. With about 1000 ohms at R_3 there is ample gain, with complete stability. More gain is available, with higher resistor values (more current drain) but instability may develop with some transistors. There should be no problem in getting adequate gain with the 2N3478s, and holding gain down by means of R_3 need not "cost you" in noise figure.

Total drain at 9 volts is about 4 ma. Higher or lower voltages may be used if R_1 and R_3 are adjusted in the manner outlined above, using the lowest current drain that gives optimum noise figure (R_1) and gain (R_3). A gain in excess of 19 decibels should be possible if the preamplifier is functioning properly.

The same precautions outlined in the section on 50, 144, and 220-Mc. solid-state preamplifiers should be followed when taking steps to prevent burnout of the transistors.

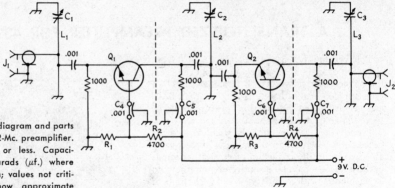

Fig. 16-28—Schematic diagram and parts information for the 432-Mc. preamplifier. Resistors are ½-watt or less. Capacitances are in microfarads (μf.) where shown on the diagram; values not critical. Broken lines show approximate positions of shield partitions.

C_1, C_2, C_3—1 to 7.5-pf. cylindrical trimmer (Centralab 829-7).

C_4, C_5, C_6, C_7—0.001-μf. feedthrough bypass; 500-pf. also usable (Centralab FT-500 or 1000).

J_1, J_2—Coaxial connector, BNC type.

L_1—¼-inch copper tubing 3½ inches long. Drill out end slightly to fit over capacitor body. Tap L_1 at 2 inches and 1¾ inches, L_2 at 1 inch and 2 inches, L_3 at 2 inches and ½ inch, all up from grounded end. See Fig. 16-00.

Q_1, Q_2—2N3478. (Other types suitable).

R_1—Adjust for maximum gain and best signal-to-noise ratio. (See text).

R_3—Adjust value for maximum gain, if necessary. (See text.)

R_2, R_4—Labeled for text reference.

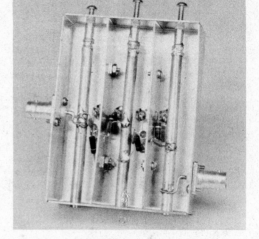

Fig. 16-29—Interior of the 432-Mc. amplifier, with the input circuit at the left. Partitions are held in place with spade bolts and no heavy soldering is required.

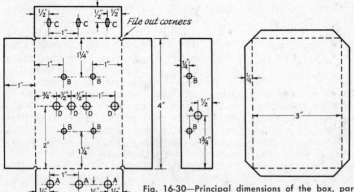

Fig. 16-30—Principal dimensions of the box, partitions and cover for the 432-Mc. amplifier. Material is 1/32-inch sheet brass, silver plated. Flat plates should be cut as shown then bent up along broken lines. Where precise bending cannot be done it is recommended that the cover be bent up to fit after the box is made. Hole sizes should be checked with available parts. Those shown are as follows: A—¼ inch, B—No. 28 drill, C—No. 28 drill, with 3/32 by 1/32 notches, D—3/16 inch. The three "A" holes in the bottom lip of the case should be a press fit for the tubing used for L_1, L_2 and L_3.

432-Mc. CONVERTER

Circuit design and mechanical construction can be very simple with transistors. The methods employed in this converter for 432 Mc. evolved from the need to match the transistors effectively. The trough lines make adjustment of matching easy, and their high Q provides better selectivity than would be obtainable with coils. Selectivity is important with transistors, which are susceptible to mixing effects from strong signals outside the desired passband, and because image rejection in a receiver for the 420-Mc. band would normally be relatively poor with an intermediate frequency as low as 14 Mc. Image rejection with this converter is about 40 db., and gain ahead of the mixer is as much as 40 db., if need be.

Bias networks for the grounded-base r.f. stages are mounted externally, to permit easy variation of operating conditions. Either n.p.n. or p.n.p. transistors may be used in either r.f. stage, merely by reversing the battery polarity on the stage in question.

Circuit and Layout

The converter uses four transistors and two diodes, with trough-line circuits in all u.h.f. stages. The best available u.h.f. transistor should be used in the first r.f. amplifier, but less expensive ones do very well in all other stages. A wide choice of transistors is available, and many different types can be used if the polarity of voltages applied is corrected for the transistors substituted for those shown. The Motorola 2N3280 used here for Q_1, and 3284 used for Q_2 and Q_4, are p.n.p.; the 2N706 oscillator, Q_3, is n.p.n. Inexpensive substitutes are 2N3478s and Amperex 2N3399s for Q_1 and Q_2, and a 40235 for the oscillator. A Motorola 2N3284 was found to be best for the multiplier. The silicon n.p.n. types require polarity reversal from that shown.

As may be seen from the interior photograph, Fig. 16-32, the r.f. circuits are in three troughs, at the left. These are high-Q lines, tuned at the top end and grounded at the lower. The transistors and input and output coupling leads are tapped at various points along these lines. Adjustment of loading is thus made continuously variable, an advantage over coils, wherein taps must be changed a turn at a time, or the builder runs into inconvenient arrangements.

The mixer diode may be seen projecting into the output compartment, lower right. The larger compartment above this houses the oscillator-multiplier chain, with the diode multiplier circuit, a line similar to those used in the r.f. stages.

Construction

Copper flashing or brass of similar thickness, or heavier, can be used to make the chassis and partitions. Dimensions of the box and hole locations are given in Fig. 4. No attempt is made to give hole sizes, as parts used by builders are likely to vary somewhat from those used by the writer. Hole centers should work out the same, but mounting hole sizes required may be different, so check your parts before drilling the metalwork. Holes are identified in Fig. 4 as follows: tuning capacitors—A, crystal socket—B, feedthrough capacitors—C, coaxial connectors—D.

Next, bend the chassis beginning with the long sides, then the bottom tabs, and last the short end sides. All joints should preferably be silver-soldered together. If ordinary solder is used, the bond between overlapping surfaces can be strengthened with small screws or rivets. Mount I_1, L_2, L_3, and L_8 by inserting the end of the wire through the hole provided, and then solder from the outside of the chassis. The chassis and lines can be silver plated at this point, if you have facilities for doing the job. This should not be considered a necessity, as converters have been built without plating and they work very well.

The button-type feedthrough capacitors specified may be hard to find, and rather expensive, but are preferred. Other types will work, and

Fig. 16-31—The complete 432-Mc. semiconductor converter is hardly larger than a man's hand. In this model, ordinary insulating feedthrough bushings were used, and bypassing was done on the top side of the case, instead of doing the whole job with feedthrough capacitors, as indicated in Fig. 16-33 Tuning screws for the three r.f. circuits are at left-front portion of the chassis.

(Designed and built by John Clark, K2AOP.)

Fig. 16-32—Interior of the 432-Mc. converter. R.f. circuits are at the left, in separate troughs. Large compartment at the upper right contains the crystal oscillator and multiplier circuits. Section at the lower right has the mixer diode projecting into its left end, and the injection coupled through the top. The mixer output circuit, L_4C_6, is the principal occupant of this compartment.

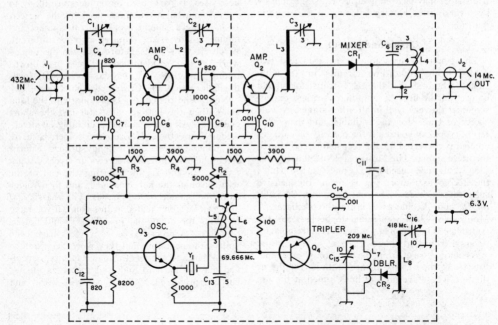

Fig. 16-33—Schematic diagram and parts information for the 432-Mc. solid-state converter.

C_1, C_2, C_3—0.5- to 3-pf. ceramic or glass trimmer (Centralab 829-3).

C_4, C_5, C_{12}—820-pf. disk ceramic (0.001-μf. also suitable).

C_7, C_8, C_9, C_{10}, C_{14}—0.001-μf. feedthrough capacitor (Erie 654-017102K. Centralab FT-1000 also suitable).

C_6—27-pf. dipped mica.

C_{11}, C_{13}—5-pf. dipped mica.

C_{15}, C_{16}—1- to 10-pf. ceramic or glass trimmer (Centralab 829-10).

CR_1—U.h.f. mixer diode (Sylvania 1N82A).

CR_2—Silicon signal diode (GE 1N4009).

J_1, J_2—Coaxial fitting.

L_1, L_2, L_3, L_8—No. 12 wire, 2½ inches long. Tap L_1 at 1

and 1½ inches, L_2 at ½ and 1 inch, L_3 at ¾ and 1¼ inches, L_8 at ½ and 1¼ inches.

L_4—No. 26 enamel wound as per text on ⅜-inch iron-slug form (CTC 1534-2-2, slug coded red).

L_5, L_6—No. 26 enamel wound as per text on ⅜-inch iron-slug form (CTC 1534-4-2, slug coded white).

L_7—4½ turns No. 16 enamel, ⅜-inch diam., ⅝ inch long. Tap at 1 and 2 turns.

Q_1, Q_2, Q_3, Q_4—See text.

R_1, R_2—5000-ohm miniature control. All other resistors ½ watt or less, values as marked.

R_3, R_4—for text reference.

Y_1—5th-overtone crystal, 69.666 Mc. (International Crystal Co.).

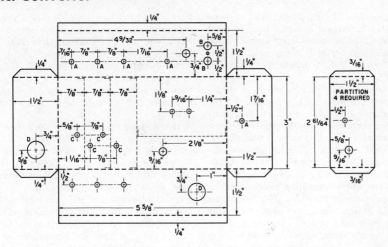

Fig. 16-34—Principal dimensions of the chassis and partitions. Hole dimensions are not given, as they will vary with components used. Locations should be similar to those shown, if parts generally similar to the original are employed. Lettered holes are as follows: A—ceramic trimmers, B—crystal socket, C—feedthroughs, D—coaxial fittings.

ordinary feed through bushings can be used if by-passed effectively.

Before any connections are made, tin all transistor and diode leads to aid in solder. Do this, and all other soldering to semiconductors, with no more heat than necessary. Hold the lead in long-nose pliers, close to the device, making the pliers serve as a heat sink to prevent overheating.

The only areas that may present problems are the r.f. amplifier emitter leads and the connections to L_7. Mount the 1000-ohm resistor to C_7 first, then C_4 between it and L_1 close to the hole in the partition. The transistor emitter lead, with insulated sleeving over it, will then connect to C_4 through the hole. Assembly of the second stage follows the same procedure as the first.

Connections to L_7 must be done carefully to prevent shorting out turns. The diode is mounted first, one turn up from ground, then the transistor connects to the second turn. A thin-tipped iron must be used to be successful. The rest of the wiring is point-to-point with the shortest possible leads on all components.

The mixer output coil, L_4, may be wound as follows: Set the collars on the form so that Terminal 1 is at 12 o'clock, as you look down on the form, Terminals 2 and 3 at 3 o'clock, and Terminal 4 at 6 o'clock. Starting at Terminal 2, the grounded end, wind No. 26 enameled wire counterclockwise $5\frac{1}{4}$ turns, and solder to Terminal 1. Continue $5\frac{1}{2}$ turns in the same direction, solder to Terminal 4, and then $11\frac{1}{4}$ turns to Terminal 3. When C_6 is connected across the coil, leave a half-inch lead at the top for grounding.

The oscillator coil form is prepared for winding by putting Terminal 1 at 12 o'clock, 2 at 3 o'clock, 3 at 6 o'clock and the tap at 9 o'clock. Start L_5 at the top, Terminal 1, winding clockwise $7\frac{1}{2}$ turns, tapped at $\frac{3}{4}$ turn, ending at Terminal 3. L_6 is $1\frac{3}{4}$ turns between Terminals 1 and 2, also clockwise. In making the tap on L_5, clean the

enamel off about 3 inches of the wire, double this back on itself, and twist the loop tightly. Tin it throughout its length, to make the lead to the crystal socket.

Adjustment

With an absorption wavemeter (or grid-dip meter not oscillating) adjusted to 70 Mc. and coupled into L_5, screw the slug in slowly from full out. The oscillator should start abruptly at about half in, and decrease gradually as the slug continues into the coil. The proper setting for the slug is $\frac{1}{4}$ turn further in than the point where oscillations start. Improper operation is indicated if the oscillator does not follow this pattern or if birdies are heard near 14 Mc. when the receiver is connected to the converter. These indicate oscillation in Q_4, in which case the value of the 1000-ohm resistor must be decreased. No oscillation means it must be increased in value, or removed.

Assemble an r.f. probe by attaching a wire to the cathode of a 1N82 diode, and taping the diode onto a pencil. A high-impedance meter is then used to measure rectified current between the probe and circuit ground. Touching the probe to the L_7 side or CR_2 should produce some meter movement which then can be peaked with C_{15}. Determine the frequency by sweeping 140 to 209 Mc. with the absorption wavemeter, while watching the meter on the probe. You will find that there will be a very noticeable dip on the probe meter. An r.f. indication on the grid-dip meter is unlikely, because of its lack of sensitivity. Move the probe to the L_8 side of CR_2. The 418-Mc. tank circuit (L_8C_{16}) should tune from about 250 to 550 Mc. Starting with the screw full in, the second peak should fall at 418 Mc. It can be checked with Lecher wires, but the converter will work as long as the tank is tuned to one of the peaks.

The alignment of the r.f. stages will be very simple if a 432-Mc. signal is available. The third harmonic of a strong two-meter signal below 144.1 Mc. will also serve. Without a signal, one may have a great deal of difficulty peaking the three high-Q r.f. tanks.

Using a strong signal, with R_1 and R_2 at maximum resistance, adjust C_1, C_2, C_3 and L_4 for maximum signal at 14 Mc. in a receiver connected to the converter. When the signal has been peaked up, recheck C_{16}. The various peaks noted previously will produce differing conversion gains. The peak that produces the greatest output will be the one at 418 Mc. Now set R_1 to just below the point where oscillation develops in the first r.f. stage, then decrease R_2. The first stage should be run at near maximum gain or the signal-to-noise ratio may suffer. The second stage is relatively unimportant when the first stage is working properly. There will be no measurable drop in performance with any transistor having a noise figure of 6 db. or so.

The positions of the taps on the lines will provide adequate performance for most builders. If you want to optimize the noise figure, use a signal generator through a cable properly terminated or very long, to reduce s.w.r. A high s.w.r. into the converter, indicated by a high degree of instability, will make improvements in noise performance impossible. With a proper load, the first stage should begin to oscillate with about 5 volts at the junction of R_3 and R_1. If the stage will not oscillate, either move C_4 further from the ground end of the line, or move the input tap closer to the ground.

If the stage oscillates with less than 4.5 volts at the R_1-R_3 junction, either couple the antenna tighter by moving the input tap higher on the line, L_1, or move C_4 lower. Keep in mind the procedure outlined above for achieving maximum gain while the signal-to-noise ratio is optimized. Careful adjustment of the first stage will provide a very good noise figure and a first-stage gain of at least 20 db. When the first stage is near optimum gain the front end bandwidth between the 3-db. points will be less than 300 kc.

The use of a noise generator for optimizing the r.f. stages at 432 Mc., or for comparisons with other front ends, is not recommended. A signal generator or weak-signal source will be far more likely to produce a correct alignment than a noise generator.

TABLE 16-I

Crystal frequencies recommended for use with popular v.h.f. and u.h.f. converter i.f.s.

Band Mc.	Crystal frequency for i.f. range from			
	7 Mc.	14 Mc.	28 Mc.	30.5 Mc.
50	43.0 Mc.	36 Mc.	22.0 Mc.	19.5 Mc.
144	45.667 Mc.	43.333 Mc.	38.667 Mc.	37.833 Mc.
220	53.25 Mc.	51.5 Mc.	48.0 Mc.	47.375 Mc.
432	———	46.44 Mc.	44.9 Mc.	44.611 Mc.

Other i.f. tuning ranges can be used, but will require different crystal frequencies and suitable L-C combinations in the multiplier chain to effect proper resonance.

TABLE 16-II

Required mixer injection frequencies from the oscillator chain when using the tunable i.f. ranges listed in Table 16-I. Ordinarily, the crystal frequency is multiplied 3 times in 144-Mc. converters, 4 times for 220 Mc., and 9 times for 432.

Band Mc.	Injection frequencies for i.f.s. of			
	7 Mc.	14 Mc.	28 Mc.	30.5 Mc.
50	43 Mc.	36 Mc.	22 Mc.	19.5 Mc.
144	137 Mc.	130 Mc.	116 Mc.	113.5 Mc.
220	213 Mc.	206 Mc.	192 Mc.	189.5 Mc.
432	———	418 Mc.	404 Mc.	401.5 Mc.

Chapter 17

V.H.F. and U.H.F. Transmitting

Through the hard work of radio amateurs the world over, v.h.f., u.h.f., and microwave techniques have advanced tremendously in the past decade. Because new communication modes have been explored, then subsequently refined, such media as E.M.E. ("moonbounce"), scatter, meteor shower, and satellite communications have become practical for amateur radio work. With these state-of-the-art advances has come the need for better equipment than was heretofore necessary. Because high orders of receiving selectivity are employed, then the frequency stability of the v.h.f. or u.h.f. transmitter must be excellent. Noise-cancelling devices have made possible the reception of very weak signals, further extending the usable communications path of some modes. As the technology has advanced, higher levels of transmitter power have become possible—even in the upper u.h.f. region—bringing the maximum legal power level within the financial and technical reach of most radio amateurs. Reliability, frequency stability, and purity of emissions have become the watchwords of dedicated v.h.f./u.h.f. experimenters. No longer is war surplus equipment the "standard" in v.h.f. work. Most modern-day v.h.f. or u.h.f. operators employ home-built transmitting and receiving equipment, or at least use composite stations made up from high-quality commercial and home-built gear.

For the reasons outlined in the foregoing paragraph, and so the state-of-the-art will continue to advance in amateur radio, today's v.h.f./u.h.f. enthusiast should strive to build and operate equipment that reflects the technical concepts of the times. The success or failure of any v.h.f. or u.h.f. operation is dependent not only upon the skill of the operator, but also on the quality of the equipment being used.

Crystal Oscillators

Fundamental- or harmonic-type crystal-controlled oscillators of the type described in Chapter 6 can be used for v.h.f. and u.h.f. transmitters. If variable-frequency control is desired, some form of VXO or v.f.o. can be employed. Alternatively, overtone crystal oscillators of the type illustrated in Chapter 16 can be used in the exciter. The choice of frequency-controlling element is usually influenced by the overall efficiency desired (the higher the oscillator frequency, the fewer multiplier stages required), the transmit mode (low-frequency oscillators being better for wide-band f.m.), and the desire to lessen the chances of harmonic radiation—the higher oscillator frequencies being better in this respect.

Overtone crystals oscillate on some approximate odd multiple of their fundamental cut. That is to say, for example, a 24-Mc. third-overtone crystal is actually ground for 8 Mc. but its third

overtone may not be an *exact* multiple of 8 Mc. The same is true of crystals designed for 5th-overtone use. The manufacturers of overtone crystals provide recommended circuits for transistor or vacuum-tube use so that they can guarantee, within a certain tolerance, the overtone frequency of their crystals. Generally, any significant departure from the prescribed circuit values will cause a shift in crystal frequency. Although fundamental-cut crystals of the war surplus variety can often be made to oscillate on their 3rd or 5th overtones, it is impossible to predict the frequency at which the overtone will occur. Generally, the overtone frequency will fall several kilocycles or more away from what would be the exact harmonic frequency of the crystal.

It is important that some form of voltage regulation be used on the crystal oscillator stage of the exciter if good frequency stability if to be had. The techniques shown in the first part of Chapter 16 are applicable to v.h.f. and u.h.f. exciters and should be considered in the design. Further, for best overall stability, the oscillator stage should not be required to deliver power. It is best to operate the oscillator at a very low power level and build up the output from the oscillator by means of a buffer stage.

Frequency Multipliers

Information on frequency multipliers is given in Chapter 6 of this book. Frequency multipliers, though for v.h.f., u.h.f., or for the h.f. bands, operate in the same manner. It is important to provide for ample driving power from the preceding stage of the exciter if the frequency multiplier stage is to be properly excited. All too often, the final amplifier stage in a v.h.f. or u.h.f. transmitter lacks sufficient grid drive to operate efficiently. The cause of low grid drive can usually be attributed to skimpy design in the exciter, or to poor design of the interstage coupling circuits.

To assure adequate grid drive, each stage of the exciter should be checked to make certain that it is being driven hard enough to develop its rated grid current and grid voltage. Also, for safety reasons, this is particularly important in circuits that do not use some form of protective bias. A tube that depends solely upon the bias developed across a grid resistor can exceed its rated plate dissipation and become damaged if not driven adequately from the preceding stage of the exciter. For this reason it is wise to provide at least enough protective bias, by means of a cathode resistor or fixed-bias supply, to limit the plate dissipation of the exciter tubes to somewhat less than their maximum ratings during the absence of grid drive.

The amount of grid bias and grid current required by an exciter stage is dependent upon the task performed by the tube. The requirements are different for a buffer stage than for a doubler or a tripler. Frequency multipliers require a value of bias that is several times cutoff. For doublers and triplers, the grid circuit operates with about the same amount of current as does a buffer stage, but requires a grid resistor of from twice to several times the ohmic value used for a buffer. Therefore, the developed grid bias is considerably higher than for straight-through buffer operation. A fair rule of thumb in designing frequency multipliers is to consult the tube tables for the proper grid-current and grid-resistor values for the tube used (for use as a straight amplifier), then double the grid resistor's ohmic value for doublers, and triple it for triplers. Maintaining the same amount of grid current will provide the higher bias required, enabling the tube to operate with a suitable angle of plate-current flow for its particular order of multiplication. (The efficiency of a frequency multiplier stage is dependent upon the angle of plate-current flow.) Multipliers provide efficiencies that are approximate reciprocals of the harmonics at which the stages operate: A doubler will be about 50 percent efficient; a tripler 33 percent; a quadrupler 25 percent. It is important to realize that the driving power requirements that manufacturers specify for a given tube type are apt to be somewhat misleading, especially for v.h.f. and u.h.f. service. If a tube chart calls for 0.5 watt of driving power for a class C amplifier operating at, say, 50 Mc., this means that this amount of power must reach the grid element of the tube. In practice, and particularly at v.h.f. and u.h.f., it could take as much as 5 or 6 watts of driving power from the preceding stage to provide the required 0.5-watt level at the control grid of the driven stage. A good rule in designing v.h.f. and u.h.f. exciters is to plan on having approximately 10 times the required driving power available, thus providing sufficient leeway in available drive. It is also a good idea to select a driver or multiplier tube that is not required to operate at, or near, its maximum safe power level when supplying the drive required by the following stage. If 10 watts of driving power are needed, one should select a tube that can provide 15 or 20 watts of power output without being operated at its maximum ratings. This practice will assure longer tube life and offer greater transmitter reliability.

Amplifiers

Most v.h.f. and u.h.f. amplifier stages are operated class C or class AB_1. The AB_1 mode is useful for amplifying s.s.b., c.w., or low-level a.m. signals. An AB_1-type amplifier requires but little power from the driver stage, and is frequently the choice of v.h.f. operators. A.m. operators who use low-power commercial transceivers can conveniently increase their transmitted power level from five or 10 watts to as much as 300 watts (output) by means of an AB_1 linear amplifier. External-anode tubes such as the 4CX250 series are often used in these amplifiers. Class-C operation is frequently the choice of the operator who

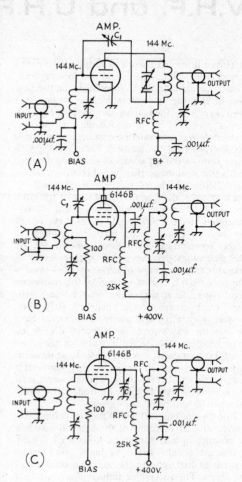

Fig. 17-1—Representative circuits for neutralizing v.h.f. single-ended amplifiers. The same techniques are applicable to stages that operate in push-pull. At A, C_1 is connected in the manner that is common to most v.h.f. or u.h.f. amplifiers. The circuits at B and C are required when the tube is operated above its natural self-neutralizing frequency. At B, C_1 is connected between the grid and plate of the amplifier. Ordinarily, a short length of stiff wire can be soldered to the grid pin of the tube socket, then routed through the chassis and placed adjacent to the tube envelope, and parallel to the anode element. Neutralization is effected by varying the placement of the wire with respect to the anode of the tube, thus providing variable capacitance at C_1. The circuit at C is a variation of the one shown at B. It too is useful when a tube is operated above its self-neutralizing frequency. In this instance, C_1 provides a low-Z screen-to-ground path at the operating frequency. RFC in all circuits shown are v.h.f. types and should be selected for the operating frequency of the amplifier.

desires good efficiency when operating c.w., f.m., or a.m., the latter with high-level modulation.

Where space conservation is not a prime consideration, lumped-inductance plate tanks are generally avoided. The strip-line, coaxial, parallel-line, or resonant-cavity tank circuits offer better efficiency, higher Q, and good thermal stability in comparison to coil/capacitor-style tank circuits. Lumped inductance tank circuits are useful in portable and mobile equipment, or in other compact assemblies.

Stabilization

Neutralization of v.h.f. and u.h.f. amplifiers is required if good stability is desired. Unfortunately, the stray inductance and capacitance introduced by most neutralizing circuits may be excessive for operation at 220 Mc. and higher. In such instances grounded-grid amplifiers can be used. The latter seldom require neutralization, but because part of the driving power appears in the output, both the driver and the amplifier must be modulated when a.m. is used—provided 100 percent modulation is desired. Grounded-grid amplifiers are ideal, however, for the amplification of f.m., s.s.b., and c.w. signals. Conventional neutralization techniques are discussed in Chapter 6 and are applicable to most v.h.f. amplifiers. If, however, certain tubes are used in the upper v.h.f. region, but were designed for use in the h.f. and lower v.h.f. regions (such as 6146s, 4-125As, and similar types), it may be necessary to employ the type of neutralization circuit illustrated in Fig. 17-1 at B. The more common type of neutralization circuit is shown at A. The circuit at B is useful when the tube is operated *above* its self-neutralizing frequency. This circuit is necessary when the screen-lead inductance of the tube is too high to permit the proper division of voltage between the internal capacitances of the tube when conventional neutralization is attempted. Another technique for neutralizing such a tube is shown in Fig. 17-1 at C. This method reduces the voltage developed across the screen-lead inductance by series-tuning the screen lead to ground, thus providing a low-impedance screen-to-ground path at the operating frequency. When this type of neutralization is employed, retuning of the neutralizing capacitor, C_1, is necessary when major changes in the operating frequency are carried out. A panel-controlled variable capacitor can be used for C_1 if greater operating convenience is desired. The screen-lead r.f. choke and its associated bypass capacitor serve as a decoupling network. Neutralization of transistorized v.h.f. amplifiers is not practical except in the case of single-frequency amplifiers that are looking into a constant load impedance. Frequently, the addition of neutralization circuits to transistorized r.f. amplifiers contributes to, rather than cures, the instability problem.

Another problem faced by the v.h.f./u.h.f. operator is that of parasitic oscillation in one or more stages of the transmitter. Such oscillations usually occur above the self-neutralizing frequency of the tube being used, and in some instances the neutralizing circuit can contribute to the parasitic condition by increasing the level of the r.f. feedback at the parasitic frequency. A common cure for this form of instability is the addition of a parasitic choke to the plate circuit of the unstable stage. The circuits of Fig. 17-2 A and B are commonly used in 6-meter transmitters. However, the circuit at A will absorb sufficient fundamental energy to burn up in all but the lowest-power transmitters. A better approach is to use the parasitic choke illustrated at B. In this circuit the choke is coupled to the plate circuit and tuned to the parasitic frequency. Since a minimum amount of the fundamental energy will be absorbed by the trap, heating should no longer be a problem.

At 144 Mc. and higher, it is difficult to construct a parasitic choke that will not be resonant at or near the operating frequency. Should u.h.f. parasitics occur, an effective cure can often be realized by shunting a 56-ohm 1-watt resistor across a small section of the plate end of the tuned circuit as shown in Fig. 17-2, at C. The resistor should be attached as near the plate connector as is practical. Such a trap can often be constructed by bridging the resistor across a portion of the flexible strap-connector that is used in some transmitters to join the anode fitting to the plate-tank inductor.

Instability in solid-state v.h.f. and u.h.f. amplifiers can often be traced to oscillations in the l.f. and h.f. regions. Because the gain of the transistors is very high at the lower frequencies, instability is almost certain to occur unless proper bypassing and decoupling of stages is carried out. Low-frequency oscillation can usually be cured by selecting a bypass-capacitor value that is effective at the frequency of oscillation and connecting it in parallel with the v.h.f. bypass capacitor in the same part of the circuit. It is not unusual, for example, to employ a 0.1-uf. disk ceramic in parallel with a 0.001-uf. disk capacitor in such circuits as the emitter, base, or collector return. The actual values used will depend upon the frequencies involved. This technique is shown in Fig. 17-2D.

Other methods for transmitter stabilization, such as interstage shielding, are discussed in Chapter 6 and are applicable to v.h.f. and u.h.f. construction.

V.H.F. TVI PREVENTION AND CURE

The principal causes of TVI from v.h.f. transmitters are as follows:

1) Adjacent-channel interference in Channels 2 and 3 from 50 Mc.

2) Fourth harmonic of 50 Mc. in Channels 11, 12 or 13, depending on the operating frequency.

3) Radiation of unused harmonics of the oscillator or multiplier stages. Examples are 9th harmonic of 6 Mc., and 7th harmonic of 8 Mc. in Channel 2; 10th harmonic of 8 Mc. in Channel 6; 7th harmonic of 25-Mc. stages in Channel 7; 4th harmonic of 48-Mc. stages in Channel 9 or 10; and many other combinations. This may include i.f. pickup, as in the cases of 24-Mc. inter-

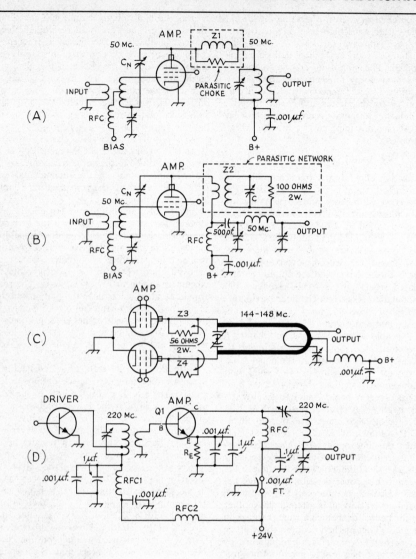

Fig. 17-2—Representative circuits for v.h.f. parasitic suppression are shown at A, B, and C. At A, Z_1 (for 6-meter operation) would typically consist of 3 or 4 turns of No. 14 wire wound on a 100-ohm 2-watt non-inductive resistor. Z_1 overheats in all but very low power circuits. The circuit at B, also for 6-meter use, is more practical where heating is concerned. Z_2 is tuned to resonance at the parasitic frequency by C. Each winding of Z_2 consists of two or more turns of No. 14 wire—determined experimentally—wound over the body of a 100-ohm 2-watt (or larger) noninductive resistor. At C, an illustration of u.h.f. parasitic suppression as applied to a 2-meter amplifier. Noninductive 56-ohm 2-watt resistors are bridged across a short length of the connecting lead between the tube anode and the main element of the tank inductor, thus forming Z_3 and Z_4.

The circuit at D illustrates how bypassing for both the operating frequency and lower frequencies is accomplished. Low-frequency oscillation is discouraged by the addition of the 0.1-uf. disk ceramic capacitors. RFC_1 and RFC_2 are part of the decoupling network used to isolate the two stages. This technique is not required in vacuum-tube circuits.

ference in receivers having 21-Mc. i.f. systems, and 48-Mc. trouble in 45-Mc. i.f.'s.

4) Fundamental blocking effects, including modulation bars, usually found only in the lower channels, from 50-Mc. equipment.

5) Image interference in Channel 2 from 144 Mc., in receivers having a 45-Mc. i.f.

6) Sound interference (picture clear in some cases) resulting from r.f. pickup by the audio circuits of the TV receiver.

There are many other possibilities, and u.h.f. TV in general use will add to the list, but nearly all can be corrected completely, and the rest can be substantially reduced.

Items 1, 4 and 5 are receiver faults, and nothing can be done at the transmitter to reduce them, except to lower the power or increase separation between the transmitting and TV antenna systems. Item 6 is also a receiver fault, but it can be alleviated at the transmitter by using f.m. or c.w. instead of a.m. phone.

Treatment of the various harmonic troubles, Items 2 and 3, follows the standard methods detailed elsewhere in this *Handbook*. It is suggested that the prospective builder of new v.h.f. equipment familiarize himself with TVI prevention techniques, and incorporate them in new construction projects.

Use as high a starting frequency as possible, to reduce the number of harmonics that might cause trouble. Select crystal frequencies that do not have harmonics in TV channels in use locally. Example: The 10th harmonic of 8-Mc. crystals used for operation in the low part of the 50-Mc. band falls in Channel 6, but 6-Mc. crystals for the same band have no harmonic in that channel.

If TVI is a serious problem, use the lowest transmitter power that will do the job at hand.

Keep the power in the multiplier and driver stages at the lowest practical level, and use link coupling in preference to capacitive coupling.

Plan for complete shielding and filtering of the r.f. sections of the transmitter, should these steps become necessary.

Use coaxial line to feed the antenna system, and locate the radiating portion as far as possible from TV receivers and their antenna systems.

TIPS ON LINEAR V.H.F. AMPLIFIERS

If you must use an a.m. linear, don't expect 70 per cent efficiency from it. Don't expect 50. Expect and see that you *get,* no more than 35 per cent from a Class AB$_1$ linear, or no more than about half the rated plate dissipation for the tubes used. This means 350 watts out of the 50-Mc. amplifier, Fig. 17-23, with a kilowatt in, even though you can get 750 watts out of it in Class C. For the 144-Mc. amplifier, Fig. 17-26, 200 watts out with 700 in is about the safe maximum for a.m. linear service. These are optimum figures; you may get less, but you can't get more and be *linear*.

About Driver Stages

Obviously the driver stage is important in the linear picture. If we are going to amplify it in exactly its original form, the signal had better be good to start with. A distorted splattering signal fed to a linear results in more of the same; lots more! The exciter should be stable and its output stage as perfectly modulated as we can make it. Since the driver operates at very low level, this is not hard to do. If an exciter is being built especially to drive a linear, it might be well to go with a neutralized-triode output stage, with no more than about 5 watts input. A Class-A modulator employing inverse feedback and some form of output limiting would be good. Peak limiting is important, to keep the average modulation percentage high and prevent overmodulation.

Most v.h.f. transmitters will have a lot more output than is needed, so the drive applied to the amplifier must be reduced in some way. Detuning the driver output circuit or the amplifier grid circuit will not do, as it may leave the driver without a proper load, and impair its modulation quality. A simple solution is to connect a 50-ohm dummy load parallel with the driver output. A coaxial T fitting is connected to the driver output receptacle. The dummy load is connected to one side of the T, and the amplifier grid input to the other. The amplifier grid circuit still may have to be detuned slightly, if the exciter output is more than 2 or 3 watts, but this will not be harmful for only a small reduction in drive. Driver output may also be reduced by lowering its plate or plate-and-screen voltage, though it is well to check the quality to be sure that linear modulation characteristics are being obtained in the driver.

Checking Signal Quality

The Heath Monitor Scope, Model SB-610, is ideal for use with a v.h.f. linear, as it may be left connected to the transmission line for continuous monitoring. Some modification may be necessary for effective use of this scope on 144 Mc., though it works nicely on 50 Mc. and lower bands as is. Two coaxial receptacles of the SO-239 type are mounted on the back of the scope, with their inner terminals joined by a wire about 1½ inches long. The transmitter is connected to one receptacle and the antenna coax to the other. The unshielded wire inside the scope causs an appreciable impedance bump in a 144-Mc. line. This may be corrected by connecting a coaxial T fitting to one of the terminals, and using its two arms to make the above connections from transmitter to antenna line. Internal scope connections and functions remain intact, and the impedance bump is held to manageable proportions.

The scope, milliammeters in the grid, screen and plate circuits of the amplifier, and a power-indicating device in the coaxial line are useful in setting up the linear for maximum effectiveness. The power meter will tell you if you are getting all you should from the amplifier. If you're getting too much, the scope will tell you. The meters are necessary to assure operation at both safe and optimum conditions.

The tube manufacturers' data sheets give

typical operating conditions for various classes of service, usually including a.m. linear. These are the best guides available and you'll do well to follow them closely, especially when just learning your way around with a linear. They do not tell the whole story, however. They are merely "typical"; there may be other combinations that will work well, if you know how to read the indications your meters and scope provide. Conversely, it may be possible to radiate a less-than-admirable signal, when meter indications alone seem to be in order. You'll need that scope!

In using the high-powered 6- and 2-meter linears the plate voltage can be almost anything, provided that the amplifier is adjusted carefully whenever the plate voltage is changed. From 800 to 2000 volts has been used on 4CX250Rs and Bs. Screen voltage should be what the sheet calls for; in this case 250 volts for Class C and 350 volts for Class AB_1. Bias should be variable and adjusted so that the tube or tubes will draw the recommended no-drive plate current. In this instance it's about 100 ma. per tube. It is well to start with bias on the high side (no-drive plate current low) to be on the safe side until set up correctly.

With the amplifier running in this fashion, feed in enough drive to make the plate current rise and output start to appear. Tune the final plate circuit and adjust the loading control for maximum output, as indicated by the height of the scope pattern or by the power-indicating meter in the transmission line. Disregard the final plate current, so long as it is at a safe value (Do not tune for dip; tune for maximum output.) Run up the drive now to the point where grid current just starts to show, and then back it off slightly. Readjust the plate and loading controls for maximum output. Be sure that you're putting every watt you can into the transmission line for this amount of grid drive. Maximum loading is a must for linear operation.

Try modulating the driver, while watching the scope pattern. Using a single tone should produce the usual pattern. At 100 per cent modulation, the peaks and valleys should be sharp and the valleys (negative peaks) just reach the zero line. Positive peaks are just twice the total height of the unmodulated envelope. If you don't have some form of negative-peak limiting, watch out for excessive modulation in that direction. That's where the splatter comes from first if audio and r.f. operation is clean otherwise. In watching your voice modulation beware of the bright flashes at the zero line of the modulation pattern that indicate over-modulation on negative voice peaks.

Practice the adjustment routine with a dummy load connected to the transmitter, and you'll soon get the hang of it. Deliberately over-drive the amplifier and see how quickly you can detect the results on the scope pattern. Observe the meter action, too. You'll see that you can't draw *any* grid current without spoiling the picture. You'll also see that when the scope picture is

right the plate current stands still on all modulation peaks. The screen current will probably be just a bit negative. Output will absolutely not exceed 35 per cent of the input. If it does, you've got some meter inaccuracies, or you're cheating on the interpretation of the scope pattern. The scope is the final authority; you *have* to believe it.

Now, once over lightly again. Loading is all-important. Keep it at the maximum output you can get for a given value of grid drive. Recheck it for every frequency change or change in plate voltage. Grid current will *always* be zero. Grid drive can be lower than optimum as regards output, but never more than optimum. (You can read grid *voltage* for a reference on amount of grid drive, if you like.) The scope will tell you very clearly the minute you go too high. So will the sound of the signal, but this may be hard to determine, if your receiver overloads on your own signal. Most receivers will. Final plate current will rise with increasing grid drive, but it must stand still during modulation. If it kicks on modulation peaks, you've got distortion, and very likely splatter.

All adjustments react on one another to some extent, and each time you change any operating condition you have to go through the routine completely again. This sounds as if you'd spend the rest of your life tuning the rig, but once you get the hang of it you can make the necessary corrections in seconds.

Using Other Modes

Since a.m. linear is the most critical of all, it is in order to switch to any other mode without making any adjustments, if you want to switch instantly. A good linear is more versatile than this, however. It's possible to do a lot better than the a.m. conditions on sideband, and still stay in the AB_1 mode. Efficiency on c.w. will shoot up markedly with just a slight increase in grid drive, with no other changes. Same for f.m., which is identical to c.w., as far as the tubes in the final are concerned. If you want the ultimate in c.w. or f.m. output, switch to 250 volts on the screen, and run up the grid drive some more. Drive level is very uncritical, so about all you have to watch for is to keep the final input below the kilowatt level, and avoid swinging the plate current on f.m. Readjustment of the plate tuning and loading will be needed for top efficiency. Plate-modulated voice service is quite similar to the c.w. conditions, except that the maximum plate voltage permissible is lower with most tubes. The grid drive requirements are usually slightly higher for good plate modulation conditions than they are for c.w. or f.m., and the bias should be juggled for best modulation characteristics.

An in-depth discussion about the tuneup and operation of linear amplifiers is given in Chapters 9 and 11 of this book. Oscilloscope patterns are also given and are applicable to v.h.f. and u.h.f. operation as well as to the h.f. bands.

50-WATT TRANSMITTERS FOR 6 AND 2

The two transmitters (Figs. 17-1 and 17-4) have several features in common. They were designed with the cost-conscious amateur in mind, they represent the simplest *good* construction techniques available, they share a common modulator design, and they include provision for *good* c.w. operation. (Many transmitters in this frequency range have poor code performance or ignore the problem altogether.) Although shown for crystal control, a jack is included in the circuit for external v.f.o. control when desired.

The 50-Mc. Transmitter

Referring to the circuit diagram, Fig. 17-3, the crystal oscillator circuit uses a 25-Mc. overtone crystal. V.f.o. input through J_1 should be at a level of 10 volts or better, to obtain adequate frequency multiplication in V_{1A}. The doubler section of V_1 drives the neutralized output amplifier, a 6146B. Two tuned circuits between driver and amplifier are used to improve the selectivity and minimize the chances for out-of-band signals. The output amplifier is neutralized to improve both the code and the a.m. performance. The TUNE-OPERATE switch, S_1, enables the operator to adjust the final-stage grid current without running full power.

A $5 \times 9\frac{1}{2} \times 2$-inch chassis is used. The area around the 6146B output amplifier is enclosed by a perforated-aluminum box (Fig. 17-1) that is 5-⅝ inches wide, 5-inches deep, and 4-inches high. Edges of the shielded compartment are made of ⅜-inch angle material, which can be bent in a vise from sheet aluminum. Standard angle stock can of course be substituted. Sheet-metal screws hold the perforated aluminum to the corner stock. The aluminum front panel is 10-inches wide and 6½-inches high.

The neutralizing capacitor, C_3, is a 2½-inch piece of No. 14 wire mounted alongside the 6146B. The plate of the tube serves as one plate of the

Figure 17-1—Top view of the 6-meter r.f. deck. The VR tubes are at the upper left, V_1 is to the right of them, and the tuning knob for C_1 is just above V_1. The 6146B p.a. and its plate tank are enclosed in the shielded area at the right.

capacitor and the wire is the other plate. The wire is supported by a small feedthrough bushing.

A critical part of the wiring is the r.f. grounding of the 6146B cathode. To this end a small "Y" of sheet copper (see Fig. 17-7) was used to bond the three cathode pins together, and each pin has its own 0.005-uf. ceramic bypass to ground. A shielded wire runs to the key jack, J_5.

The 144-Mc. Transmitter

The construction of the 144-Mc. transmitter is similar to that of the 50-Mc unit. Chassis and power-amplifier shield cage dimensions are the same.

Referring to the circuit diagram, Fig. 17-7, the oscillator is designed to use 8-Mc. crystals. It can also be controlled by an external v.f.o. that has 8-, 12- or 24-Mc. output. When a v.f.o. is used, S_2 should be closed, to short out the cathode choke.

The output amplifier, a 6146B, is neutralized in the same way that the 50-Mc. amplifier was. However, the output circuit is series-tuned, in contrast to the pi network of the 50-Mc. unit. Series tuning is used to obtain the best possible L-to-C ratio at 144 Mc.; it requires inductive coupling to the antenna transmission line.

The 6146B socket is mounted on a 2-inch square brass plate, so that the cathode bypass capacitor leads can be soldered to the plate. An alternative would be to solder to the aluminum chassis using aluminum solder. The same copper "Y" treatment of the cathode pins is used.

Modulator and Power Supply

The modulator and power supply are built on a $10 \times 12 \times 3$-inch aluminum chassis. The modulator circuit is conventional, although r.f. filtering of the microphone input is included, as protection against r.f. feedback. The modulator uses a pair of 7868 tetrodes, inexpensive tubes used primarily in hi-fi amplifiers. As used here, they deliver 30 watts of audio power.

Fig. 17-2—A look at the underside of the 6-meter chassis. V_1 is at the right and the p.a., V_2 is on the left. Banana jacks for metering the grid and plate current are located on the rear apron of the chassis.

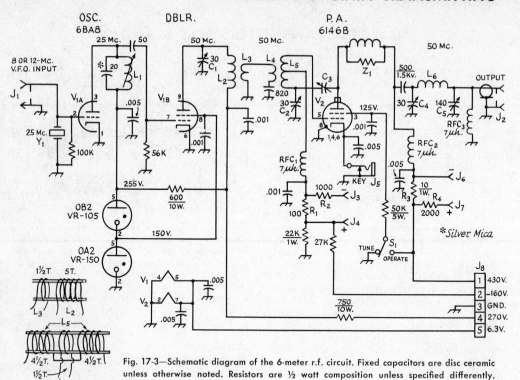

Fig. 17-3—Schematic diagram of the 6-meter r.f. circuit. Fixed capacitors are disc ceramic unless otherwise noted. Resistors are ½ watt composition unless specified differently.

C_1, C_2—30-pf. miniature variable (Millen 20025).

C_3—Neutralizing stub (see text).

C_4—30-pf. double-spaced miniature variable (Hammarlund HF-30X).

C_5—140-pf. miniature variable (Millen 19140).

J_1—Phono connector.

J_2—SO-239 coax fitting.

J_3, J_4, J_6, J_7—Insulated banana jacks.

J_5—Closed-circuit jack.

J_8—5-pin male connector (Amphenol 86CP5 suitable).

L_1—8 turns No. 22 enam. close-wound on ⅜-inch dia. ceramic slug-tuned form. (Miller 4400 form.)

L_2—5 turns No. 20, space-wound, ⅝-inch dia. (5 turns of Polycoils 1736 or B&W 3007 stock. See L_3 data before preparing.)

L_3—1½ turns No. 20, space-wound, ⅝-inch dia. (Part of L_2 Miniductor stock at cold end of L_2 See inset.)

L_4—1½ turns No. 20, space-wound, ⅝-inch dia. (1½ turns of same type Miniductor stock as used for L_2. See inset.)

L_5—9 turns No. 20, space-wound, ⅝-inch dia., center tapped. (Length of same type Miniductor stock used for L_2. See inset.)

L_6—6 turns No. 14 enam., ⅝-inch dia., 9/16 inch long.

R_1-R_4—5 per cent tolerance, or better.

RFC_1-RFC_3—7-μh. r.f. choke. (Millen 300-8.2 suitable).

S_1—S.p.d.t. toggle.

Y_1—25-Mc. overtone crystal.

Z_1—6 turns No. 14 enam., wound on 56-ohm, 1-watt resistor. Solder ends of coil to resistor pigtails.

Silicon diodes are used throughout the power supply. A relay is included in the power supply, and it is used to control receiver muting and the antenna changeover relay. The relay is controlled by the send-receive switch, S_5, which also controls the plate power supply. Another switch, S_6, turns off the modulator and bypasses the modulation transformer for c.w. operation.

The main consideration in the wiring of the modulator is to avoid hum. To this end the 12AX7 wiring should be done carefully, keeping the "hot" heater lead (to Pin 9) away from Pins 1 and 2.

Testing

A three-foot-long power cable is used between the modulator/power-supply chassis and the r.f. strip in use. The cable should have a male con-

nector to mate with J_{18} and a female connector for connection J_8 or J_{16}.

Plug the power cable into J_8 of the 50-Mc. assembly. Attach a 0-1 milliammeter to J_3 and J_4. Place S_1 in the TUNE position and connect a 50- or 75-ohm dummy load to J_2. Apply power and adjust L_1, C_1 and C_2 for maximum grid current as indicated on the meter. (Full-scale deflection is 10 ma. in the grid circuit.) It may be necessary to detune L_1 slightly from the peak setting in order to insure quick starting of the oscillator each time the transmitter is turned on. Use C_2 to adjust the grid current to approximately 3 ma.

Turn off the transmitter and plug the milliammeter into J_6 and J_7. (Full-scale deflection now represents 200 ma.) Place S_1 in the OPERATE position and turn the transmitter on. With C_5 set at maximum capacitance, quickly tune C_4 for

Fig. 17-4—Top-chassis view of the 2-meter r.f. assembly. The p.a. compartment is at the right. Copper strap is used to connect the 6146B plate cap to the plate coil. The neutralizing stub is adjacent to the 6146B tube envelope. The oscillator stage is at the lower left of the photo, the VR tube is directly above it, and the buffer and doubler are at the center of the chassis.

Fig. 17-6—The underside of the 2-meter r.f. unit. The oscillator/tripler is at the lower right of the photo and the buffer is just to the left of it. Doubler stage V_5 is at the upper-center. A brass ring surrounds the socket of V_5 and is used as a ground buss. The 6146B p.a. is at the left of the chassis.

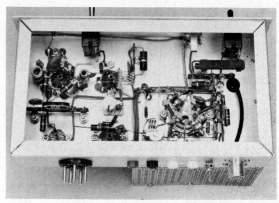

Fig. 17-5—Top-chassis view of the modulator/power supply. The audio section is at the right side of the chassis and the power supply is at the left.

a dip in plate current. Adjust C_5 toward minimum capacitance until the meter indicates 100 ma. (0.5 on meter) at resonance. It will be necessary to readjust C_4 for a dip in plate current as C_5 is tuned. The off-resonance plate current should go as high as 150 ma. if the amplifier is working properly.

To neutralize the amplifier, first set the grid and plate currents to their normal values with a dummy load, as previously described. Then switch S_1 to TUNE and rotate C_4 while watching the grid-current reading. If the grid current drops when the plate tank is tuned to resonance, try another position of the neutralizing wire (closer to or farther from tube plate). Position the wire so that tuning C_4 under these conditions has little or no effect on the grid current. An alternative method of neutralizing is to connect a sensitive wavemeter to J_2 and adjust the neutralizing for minimum output with S_1 in the TUNE position. *Caution:* When adjusting the neutralization wire,

be careful to avoid contact with the 6146B plate voltage. Turn off the transmitter each time the wire is adjusted.

The tune-up procedure for the 2-meter assembly is similar to that of the 50-Mc. unit. With the meter plugged in at J_{10} and J_{11}, and with S_3 in the TUNE position, apply power to the transmitter and peak L_7, L_8, C_7 and C_8 for maximum grid current. Should it be impossible to get a reading on the meter, the circuits will have to be "rough tuned" by using a sensitive wavemeter or a grid-dip meter. If the grid-dip meter is used, the transmitter should be turned off. Once aligned, the transmitter will be able to run the rated 3 ma. of grid current; C_8 can be used as a drive control to set the grid current to the desired value.

With a dummy load connected to J_{12}, place S_3 in the operate position and quickly adjust C_{10} for a dip in plate current, as indicated by the milliammeter plugged in at J_{13} and J_{14}. C_{11} will serve as a loading control to bring the plate current to the desired value.

Neutralization is carried out in exactly the same way as it was on 50 Mc.

Operation

Because the 6146Bs are operated well below their maximum ratings, tube life should be excellent. Both units can be run at 50 watts input on phone and 60 watts input on c.w. A plate current of 120 ma. is recommended for voice operation and 140 ma. plate current is satisfactory for c.w.

When the transmitters are placed in operation, the lid should be screwed in place on the amplifier shield cages. Bottom plates, preferably with rubber feet attached, should be installed.

The shaping network, Fig. 17-8A, can be housed in a small Minibox and used with either transmitter. The electrolytic capacitor and the 33-ohm resistor shape the keying; the other resistor and capacitor serve as an arc suppressor for the key contacts.

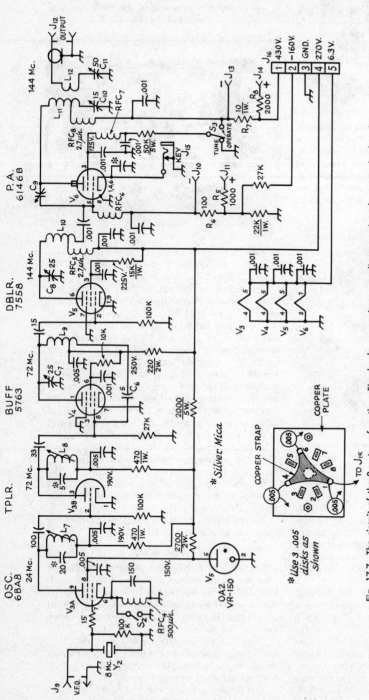

Fig. 17-7—The circuit of the 2-meter r.f. section. Fixed-value capacitors are disc ceramic unless stated otherwise. Resistors are ½ watt composition unless noted differently.

C_7, C_8—25-pf. miniature variable (Millen 25025 E).

C_9—Neutralizing stub. See text.

C_{10}—15-pf. double-spaced variable (Millen 22910 suitable).

C_{11}—50-pf. miniature variable (Millen 22050).

J_9—Phono connector.

J_{10}, J_{11}, J_{13}, J_{14}—Insulated banana jack.

J_{12}—SO-239 type chassis connector.

J_{15}—Closed-circuit jack.

J_{16}—5-pin male connector (Amphenol 86CP5).

L_7—10 turns No. 22 enam., close-wound on ⅜-inch dia.

ceramic slug-tuned form. (Millen 4400 form)

L_8—7 turns No. 22 enam., close-wound on ¼-inch dia. ceramic slug-tuned form. (Millen 4500-Z)

L_9—4 turns No. 20, ⅝-inch dia., ⅝ inch long. Tap 1 turn from cold end. (4 turns from 10-turns-per-inch Miniductor stock, ⅝-inch dia. (Airdux 510T or Polycoils 1735 suitable.)

L_{10}—4 turns No. 20, 5/16-inch dia., ½ inch long. Tap 1 turn from grid end.

L_{11}—4 turns No. 10, ⅝-inch dia., 1 inch long. Tap 1 turn from C_{10} end.

L_{12}—2 turns No. 20, ⅝-inch dia. Space approximately ¼ inch away from C_{10} end of L_{11}. (See text.)

R_5–R_8—5 per cent tolerance, or better.

$RFC_{4,5}$—500-μh. choke (Millen 34300-500).

RFC_5–RFC_6—7-μh. choke (Millen J300-8.2 suitable).

RFC_7—0.82-μh. choke (Millen 34300-0.82).

RFC_8—2.7-μh. choke (Millen 34300-2.7).

S_2—S.p.s.t. toggle.

S_3—S.p.d.t. toggle.

Y_1—8-Mc. fundamental type crystal.

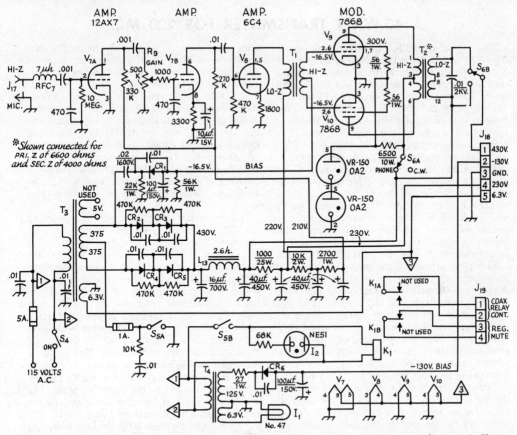

Fig. 17-8—Schematic diagram of the power supply and 30-watt modulator. Capacitors are disc ceramic. Those bearing polarity marking are electrolytic. Resistors are ½ watt composition unless noted otherwise.

CR₁-CR₅—1000 p.o.v., 750-ma. silicon diode.

CR₆—600 p.o.v., 250-ma. silicon diode.

I₁—No. 47 lamp or equal.

I₂—NE-51 neon.

J₁₇—Single-terminal microphone connector.

J₁₈—5-pin female connector (Amphenol 77MIP5).

J₁₉—4-terminal barrier strip (Millen E-304).

K₁—D.p.d.t. 115-volt a.c. relay. Two contacts not used. (Guardian IR-1220-2C-115A.)

L₁₃—2.6-h., 300-ma. filter choke (Stancor C-2706).

R₉—500,000-ohm control, audio taper.

RFC₇—8.5-μh. choke (Millen J300-8.2).

S₄—S.p.s.t. toggle.

S₅—D.p.s.t. toggle.

S₆—Ceramic rotary, 1 section, 2 poles, 5 positions. 2 positions used. (Centralab 2505).

T₁—Interstage transformer, 1:3 step-up ratio. (Stancor A-63-C.)

T₂—Varimatch modulation transformer, 30 watts. (UTC-S19.)

T₃—Power tranformer. 370 volts at 275 ma., 6.3 volts at 7 amperes, 5 volts at 3 amperes (not used). Stancor P-6315 or equivalent type from old TV set.

T₄—Power transformer (bias). 125 volts at 25 ma. (Stancor PS-8415).

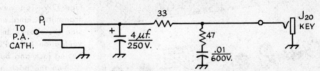

Fig. 17-8A—Schematic diagram of the key-shaping network. The unit is housed in a small-size Minibox and is installed between the key and the key jack of the r.f. deck in use during c.w. operation. The shaper is removed from the circuit during phone operation. P₁ is a PL-55 style plug and J₂₀ is an open-circuit jack. The 4-μf. capacitor is electrolytic. Resistors are ½ watt composition.

A 40-WATT TRANSMITTER FOR 220 MC.

The crystal-controlled transmitter shown in Figs. 17-9 and 17-11 will run 30 to 40 watts at 220 Mc. Referring to Fig. 17-10, a simple overtone oscillator circuit uses one section of a 12AT7 dual triode. The crystal may be between 8.15 and 8.33 Mc. or 24.45 and 25.0 Mc. In either case, the frequency of oscillation is in the latter range, as the crystal works on the third overtone. The second section of the 12AT7 is a tripler to 73 to 75 Mc. This stage has a balanced plate circuit, so that its output may be capacitively coupled to the grids of a second 12AT7, working as a push-pull tripler to 220 Mc.

Though the oscillator-tripler circuit works well as shown, slightly better oscillator stability and second tripler grid drive may be obtained with the 6CX8 circuit shown as an alternative. The circuit remains the same from the plate of V_{1B} on.

The plate circuit of the push-pull tripler is inductively coupled to the grid circuit of an Amperex 6360 dual tetrode amplifier that runs straight through on 220 Mc. Similar inductive coupling transfers the drive to the grid circuit of the final amplifier stage, an Amperex 6252 dual tetrode. This tube is a somewhat more efficient outgrowth of the 832A, which may also be used, though with lower efficiency and output. Base connections are the same for both tubes.

The grid return of the 6252 is brought out to the terminal strip on the back of the unit, to allow for connection of a grid meter. Both this point and the tip jack in the 6360 grid circuit have 1000-ohm resistors completing the grid returns to ground, so that operation of the stages is unaffected if the meters are removed.

Instability in tetrode amplifiers for v.h.f. service may develop as a result of the ineffective bypassing of the screen. In the case of the 6360 stage stable operation was obtained with no bypassing at all, while on the 6252 a mica trimmer is connected from the screen terminal to ground. It is operated near the minimum setting.

Construction

The transmitter is built on an aluminum plate 6 by 17 inches in size. This screws to a standard chassis of the same dimensions, which serves as both shield and case. Cut-outs about three inches square are made in the chassis and base plate, above and below the tube, to allow for ventilation. These openings are fitted with perforated alumi-num or screening to preserve shielding. The case should be equipped with rubber feet, to avoid marring the surface it rests on, and to allow air circulation around the tube.

The tube sockets and all the controls except the tuning capacitor of the oscillator are mounted along the center line of the cover plate. The 220-Mc. stages are inductively coupled, using hairpin loop tank circuits the dimensions of which are given in Fig. 17-10. The tuning range of these circuits is affected by the widths and lengths of the loops, so some variation can be had by squeezing the sides together or spreading them apart.

It is important that the method of mounting the 6252 socket be followed closely. An aluminum bracket about $2\frac{7}{8}$ inches high and 4 inches wide supports the socket. Note that the socket and tube are on the *same* side of the plate. Holes are drilled in the plate in line with the control grid terminals to pass the grid leads. These holes are $\frac{3}{8}$-inch diameter, and are equipped with rubber grommets to prevent accidental shorting of the grid leads to ground. The shape of the grid inductance should be such that its leads pass through the centers of the holes. The socket is supported on $\frac{5}{16}$-inch metal pillars. It may be necessary to bend the socket lugs slightly to keep them from shorting to the mounting plate. The heater lead comes to the top of the plate, and the cathode lead bends around the bottom of it.

Power leads are made with shielded wire, and are brought out to a terminal strip on the back of the chassis. These leads and the coax to the output connector should be long enough so that the plate on which the transmitter is built can be lifted off the chassis and inverted.

Adjustment

Initial test should be made with a power supply that delivers no more than 250 volts, and as little as 150 to 200 volts can be used. If the voltage is more than 250, insert a 5000-ohm 10-watt resistor in series with the power lead temporarily. Plate voltage should be applied to the various stages separately, starting with the oscillator, making sure that each stage is working.

A milliammeter of 50- to 100-ma. range should be connected temporarily in series with the 1000-ohm resistor in the oscillator plate lead. When power is applied the current should be

Fig. 17-9—Top view of the 220-Mc. transmitter. Final amplifier tube is inside the chassis, below the screened ventilation hole. Power connections, keying jack and output terminal are on the back of the chassis

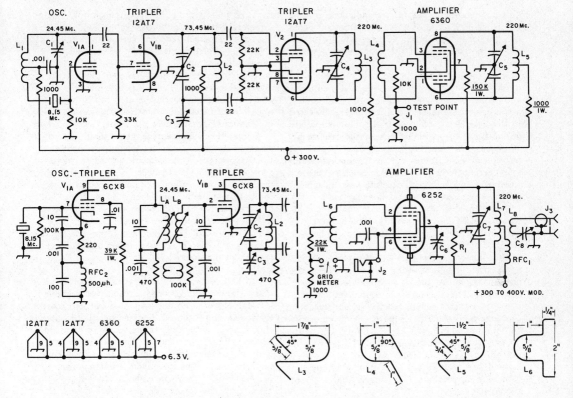

Fig. 17-10—Schematic diagram and parts information for the 220-Mc. transmitter. Capacitor values below 0.001 μf. are in pf. Resistors ½ watt unless specified. The 6CX8 oscillator-tripler may be substituted for slightly improved stability and drive.

C₁—50-pf. miniature variable (Hammarlund MAPC-50-B).

C₂ C₄, C₅—8-pf. miniature butterfly variable (Johnson 160-208).

C₃, C₆—3-30-pf. mica trimmer.

C₇—Butterfly variable, 1 stator and 1 rotor (Johnson 167-21, with plates removed).

C₈—15-pf. miniature variable (Hammarlund MAPC-15-B).

J₁—Tip jack, insulated.

J₂—Closed-circuit phone jack.

J₃—Coaxial chassis fitting, SO-239.

L₁—15 t. No. 20 tinned, ½-inch diam., 1 inch long (B & W Miniductor No. 3003). Tap at 4 turns from crystal end; see text.

L₂—12 t. No. 18 tinned, ½-inch diam., 1 inch long, center-tapped.

L₃, L₄, L₅, L₆—U-shaped loops No. 18 enam., center-tapped. Dimensions given on drawing.

L₇—2 t. No. 14 enam., 1-inch, 1-inch diam., leads ⅝ inch long. Center-tapped, space turns ½ inch apart.

L₈—1 t. No. 18 enam., inserted between turns of L₇. Cover with insulating sleeving.

L_A, L_B—3-μh. (approx.) iron-slug coil (Miller 4404). Link L₁ and L₂ with 1-turn loops of insulated hookup wire.

R₁—23,500 ohms, 2 watts. (Two 47,000-ohm 1-watt resistors in parallel.)

RFC₁—25 t. No. 28 enam. on 1-watt high-value resistor.

not more than about 10 ma. Rotate C_1 and note if an upward kick occurs, probably near the middle of the range of C_1. At this point the stage is oscillating. Lack of oscillation indicates too low feedback, or a defective crystal. Listen for the note on a communications receiver tuned near 24 Mc., if one is available. There should be no more than a slight change in frequency when a metallic tool is held near the tuned circuit, or when the circuit is tuned through its range. The note should be of pure crystal quality. If it has a rough sound, or changes with vibration, the oscillator is not controlled by the crystal. This indicates too much feedback, and the tap on the

coil, L_1, should be moved near the crystal end.

The proper amount of feedback is the lowest tap position that allows the oscillator to start readily under load. If 24-Mc. crystals are used, the tap, can be lower on the coil than with 8-Mc. crystals. When 8-Mc. crystals are operated on the third overtone, as in this case, the frequency of oscillation may not be exactly three times that marked on the crystal holder.

Now apply plate voltage to the second half of the 12AT7, again using a temporary plate meter connected in series with the 100-ohm decoupling resistor that feeds plate power to L_2. Current will be about 10 ma., as with the oscillator. Tune

C_2 for maximum output, as indicated by the brilliance of a 2-volt 60-ma. pilot lamp connected to a 1-turn loop of insulated wire coupled to L_2. Check the frequency of this stage with a wavemeter.

Now connect a low-range milliammeter (not more than 10 ma.) between the test point, J_1, and ground. Apply power to the push-pull tripler, again using a temporary milliammeter connected in the lead to the plate coil, L_3. Tune the plate circuit for maximum indication on the grid meter. Plate current will be about 20 ma. Adjust the position of L_3 with respect to L_4 for maximum grid current. Now go back over all previous adjustments and set them carefully for maximum grid current. Adjust the balancing padder, C_3, retuning C_2 each time this is done, until the combination of C_2 and C_3 that gives the highest grid current is found. Check the frequency to be sure that the stage is tripling to 220 Mc.

Now apply power to the 6360 plate circuit, again using the temporary meter to check the current. Connect the low-range milliammeter between the grid-metering terminal on the connector strip and ground. Set the screen trimmer, C_6, near minimum, and tune the 6360 plate circuit for maximum grid current. With 300 volts on the preceding stages, it should be possible to get at least 4 ma. Adjust the spacing between L_5 and L_6 carefully for maximum grid current, retuning C_5 each time this is done. Plate current should not exceed 55 ma.

Check for neutralization of the final amplifier by tuning C_7 through resonance while watching the grid-current meter. If there is no change, or only a slight rise as the circuit goes through resonance, the stage is near enough to neutralization to apply plate power. The 6252 has built-in cross-over capacitance, intended to provide neutralization in the v.h.f. range, so it is likely to be stable at this frequency. If there is a downward kick in the grid current at resonance, adjust the screen trimmer until it disappears. If best neutralization shows at minimum setting of the screen trimmer, eliminate the trimmer.

With an antenna or dummy load connected at J_3, final plate voltage can be applied. Tune the final plate circuit for maximum output, with a meter of 100 ma. or higher range connected to read the combined plate and screen current. This meter may be connected in the power lead, or it can be plugged into the cathode jack. In the latter position it will read the combined plate, screen and grid currents. Tune for maximum output and note the plate current. If it is much over 100 ma., loosen the coupling between L_7 and L_8. The input should not be over 50 watts.

A final check for neutralization should now be made. Pull out the crystal or otherwise disable the early stages of the transmitter. The grid current and output should drop to zero. If they do not, adjust the screen trimmer until they do. Make this test only very briefly, as the tubes will draw excessive current when drive is removed. When perfect neutralization is achieved, maximum output will be found at a setting of C_7 at which plate current is at a minimum and grid current at maximum.

Operation

All stages should be run as lightly as possible, for stable operation and long tube life. No more than 300 volts should be run on the exciter stages, and if sufficient grid drive can be obtained, lower voltage is desirable. The 6360 stage runs with rather low drive, and its efficiency is consequently poor, but it delivers enough power to drive the 6252, even when run at 250 volts.

Observe the plates of the tubes when the transmitter is operated in a darkened room. There should be no reddening of the plates. If one side of any of the last three stages shows red and the other does not it is evidence of unbalance. This can usually be corrected by adjustment of the balancing trimmer, C_3, in the first tripler plate circuit. Lack of symmetry in lead lengths or unbalanced capacitance to ground in any of the r.f. circuits may also lead to lopsided operation.

Though the 6252 is rated for up to 600 volts on the plates, it is recommended that no more than 400 be used in this application, particularly if the stage is to be modulated for voice work. In the latter case, the plate-screen current of the 6252 is run through the secondary of the output transformer on the modulator having an output of 20 watts or so.

Fig. 17-11—Interior view of the 220-Mc. transmitter. All r.f. components are mounted on an aluminum plate, which is screwed to the top of a standard 6 x 17-inch chassis.

The crystal oscillator is at the far right. Next to the left is the first tripler plate coil, mounted over its trimmer, with the mica balancing padder, C_3, above. The 12AT7 tripler, the test point, J_1, the tuning capacitor C_4, the tripler plate and amplifier grid loops, L_3 and L_4, the 6360 socket, the 6360 plate and amplifier grid loops, the 6252, and its tuned circuits follow in that order.

A.M./C.W. EXCITER FOR 144 MHz.

This transmitter can be used by itself as a low-power phone and c.w. rig, or it can be used as a high-quality exciter for an AB1 linear amplifier which uses a 4X150 or 4CX250-type tube. Since the amplified signal is only as good as the signal from the exciter, the emphasis is on quality in this unit.

Referring to Fig. 17-14, the r.f. section uses two 6BA8 triode-pentode miniature tubes. V_{1A} operates as a crystal-controlled oscillator, but has provisions for shorting out RFC_1 so that a v.f.o. can be connected at J_1. It is necessary to short out RFC_1 to prevent V_{1A} from oscillating during v.f.o. operation. Y_1 is removed from its socket when the v.f.o. is connected. The v.f.o. should be capable of supplying between 25 and 50 volts of r.f. (peak) at 8, 12, or 24 MHz.

V_{1B} triples the 24-MHz. output from the oscillator to 72 MHz. The 72-MHz. signal is fed to V_{2A}, where it is doubled to 144 MHz. Amplification of the 144-MHz. energy is provided by the p.a. stage, V_{2B}. A series-tuned plate tank is used at V_{2B}. Output to the antenna is taken by means of a tuned link, L_5. Some of the r.f. voltage is sampled by CR_1 and is routed to E_1, a metering test point. The doubler and the p.a. are keyed for c.w. operation and shaping is provided by means of a 1000-ohm resistor and a 0.47-uf. capacitor in the keying line. I_1 serves as a visual indicator for the cathode currents of the doubler and final amplifier stages. It need not be included since it is not essential to the operation of the equipment.

A high-impedance crystal, ceramic, or dynamic microphone is connected to the modulator at J_4. The microphone output is amplified by V_{3A}. R.f. filtering of the input is accomplished by a 33,000-ohm resistor in series with the grid lead of V_{3A}, and a 470-pf. grid bypass capacitor. A similar r.f.

Fig. 17-12—Top-chassis view of the exciter and its power supply. The equipment is finished in dark gray enamel. The controls and jacks are identified by means of decal labels.

filter is used at the grid of the second stage, V_{3B}. Additional amplification is provided by V_{4A}, assuring ample speech gain even with microphones that are low in output. Modulation of the p.a. stage is provided by V_{4B} which is coupled to V_{2B} by means of T_1, an audio output transformer with a center-tapped primary. The voice-coil winding is not used. Switch S_2 removes the B-plus voltage from the speech and modulator stages and shorts out the modulation transformer secondary winding during c.w. operation.

Construction

This transmitter is built open-chassis style to keep the cost at a minimum, and to simplify the construction job. A Bud AC-406 aluminum chassis is used. It measures $7 \times 9 \times 2$ inches. An aluminum bottom plate helps to keep the r.f. confined in the chassis, thus reducing the chance for TVI-causing radiation from the multiplier stages.

An aluminum divider isolates the audio section of the unit from the rest of the circuit. Another shield plate is used to isolate the output tuned circuit of V_{2B} from the rest of the r.f. stages. It is mounted so that it divides the bottom of the tube socket at V_{2B} into two halves, as shown in the accompanying photo.

Two crystal sockets are used. They are parallel-connected. This was done to provide for

Fig. 17-13—Looking into the bottom of the transmitter, the audio section is in the right-hand compartment. A 4-pin power plug is mounted on the rear wall of the audio compartment and is used as a connector for the power supply cable. The oscillator, tripler, and doubler stages are located in the center compartment. In the compartment at the far left are the components for the p.a. output tuned circuit. C_4 is mounted on the front wall of the chassis.

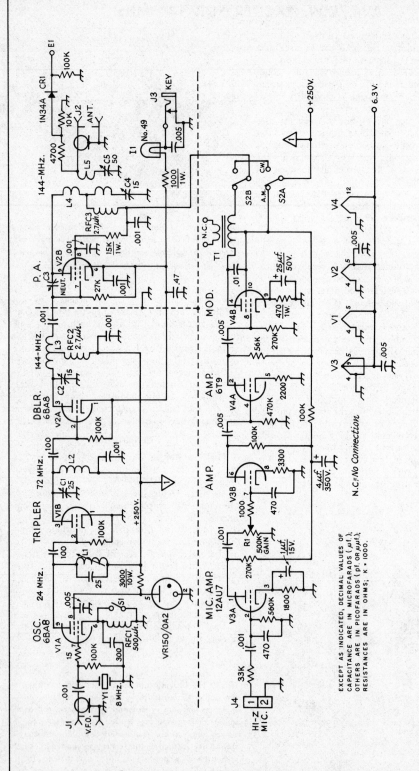

Fig. 17-14—Schematic diagram of the 144-Mc. equipment. Fixed-value capacitors are disk ceramic unless noted differently. Capacitors with polarity marking are electrolytic. Fixed-value resistors are ½-watt composition unless otherwise indicated.

C₁—25-pf. miniature variable (Millen 25025-E used here).

C₂—15-pf. miniature variable (Millen 25015-E used here).

C₃—1-inch length of insulated hookup wire soldered to pin 7 of V_{2B}. Place free end near pin 9 of same tube. Adjust spacing to pin 9 for best neutralization of p.a.

C₄—15-pf. miniature variable (Hammarlund HF-15X used here).

C₅—50-pf. miniature variable (Millen 26050E used here).

CR₁—1N34A germanium diode.

E₁—Insulated pin jack.

I₁—No. 49 pilot lamp.

J₁—Chassis-mount BNC connector.

J₂—SO-239 style coax fitting.

J₃—Closed-circuit phone jack.

J₄—Two-circuit audio connector.

L₁—11 turns No. 24-enam. wire, close-wound on 3/8-inch diameter slug-tuned form (Miller 4400-2 form wound).

L₂—7 turns No. 20 enam. wire, close-wound, 1/4-inch diametner by 3/8 inch long.

L₃—5 turns No. 20 enam. wire, 3/8-inch dia. by 3/8 inch long. Tap 3 turns from end which connects to C₂.

L₄—6 turns No. 20 copper wire, 1/2-inch dia. by 1 1/4 inches long, center-tapped.

L₅—1 turn of insulated hookup wire, 1/2-inch dia., inserted in center of L₄.

R₁—500,000-ohm, audio-taper carbon control.

S₁—S.p.s.t. slide switch.

S₂—D.p.d.t. slide switch.

T₁—8-watt push-pull output transformer (Stancor A-3850 suitable).

Y₁—8-MHz. fundamental-type crystal (International Crystal Co. or JAN Crystals).

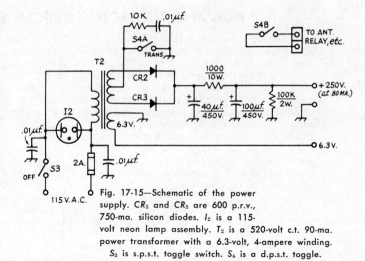

Fig. 17-15—Schematic of the power supply. CR_2 and CR_3 are 600 p.r.v., 750-ma. silicon diodes. I_2 is a 115-volt neon lamp assembly. T_2 is a 520-volt c.t. 90-ma. power transformer with a 6.3-volt, 4-ampere winding. S_3 is s.p.s.t. toggle switch. S_4 is a d.p.s.t. toggle.

crystals with the two popular pin sizes. One socket is for crystals with 0.093-inch diameter pins. The other socket accomodates crystals with 0.125-inch diameter pins.

I_1 is inserted into a 3/8-inch diameter rubber grommet for mounting purposes. It has a snug fit, and the connecting wires are soldered directly to the base of the bulb. The completed chassis can be sprayed with a coating of zinc-chromate base paint, then finished off with spray enamel of the builder's color choice. This method was used by K1MET who built this model. Decals were used to identify the various jacks and controls.

Tuning Up

Before applying operating voltages to the exciter, adjust each of the tuned circuits for resonance at their respective operating frequencies by means of a grid-dip oscillator. The tubes should be installed when this is done. Next, connect a dummy load (a No. 47 pilot lamp will suffice) to J_2. Place S_2 in the c.w. position. With power applied, connect a v.t.v.m. to E_1, using the 10-volt scale. Tune all of the stages for maximum meter deflection. The dummy load should be illuminated to near maximum normal brilliance, and the v.t.v.m. should read between 3 and 7 volts. If the tripler, doubler, or p.a. tanks do not peak within the tuning range of their variable capacitors, it may be necessary to spread or compress the coils slightly until the desired condition is met.

The next step is to place S_2 in the phone position and modulate the rig. The dummy load should brighten noticably on voice peaks if all is as it should be. The audio should sound crisp and clean when copied on the station receiver.

Power Supply

A schematic diagram is given in Fig. 17-15 for a suitable power supply for this transmitter. Since there is nothing complicated about its assembly, an in-depth treatment will not be given. It is assembled on a 4 × 6 × 2-inch aluminum chassis, but could be a part of the r.f. and audio chassis if a larger foundation were used.

A SIMPLE VARACTOR TRIPLER FOR 432 MC.

As pointed out in the chapter on semiconductors, a varactor tripler circuit requires the presence of an "idler" circuit tuned to the second harmonic of the fundamental frequency. The fundamental frequency and the second harmonic beat together to give the third harmonic output. This conversion action (rather than distortion action as in a vacuum-tube frequency multiplier) means that an a.m. signal can be used to excite a varactor tripler, and the a.m. will be maintained in the output at the third harmonic. Thus a 144-Mc. a.m. signal can be used to drive a varactor tripler to obtain an a.m. signal at 432 Mc.

The tripler shown in Fig. 17-17 will deliver about 14 watts at 432 Mc. when driven with 20 watts at 144 Mc. It features a "strip line" output circuit for good selectivity and efficiency. Referring to the circuit diagram, Fig. 17-18, C_1C_2 form a capacitive-divider input circuit to provide a 50-ohm load for the transmitter driving the tripler. These tune with L_1 to 144 Mc. The varactor is an Amperex H4A (1N4885). L_2 and C_3 tune to 288 Mc. to form the idler circuit, and L_3C_4 provides coupling adjustment to the strip-line circuit tuned to 432 Mc. L_5 and C_6 provide output coupling.

The tripler is built in a $5 \times 7 \times 2$-inch chassis. A shield is formed to fit the length of the chassis 2 inches from one wall, forming a 2-inch square trough inside the chassis. A National TPB polystyrene feedthrough connects the varactor to L_3.

Details of the strip-line circuit construction are shown in Fig. 17-20. The line is a 5-inch brass strip $\frac{1}{2}$ inch wide, having a $\frac{1}{2}$-inch "foot" at the bottom for bolting the strip to the chassis. The input and output links are tuned with TV-type ceramic trimmers. The low-potential ends of L_3 and L_5 are soldered directly to the tops of these trimmers. C_5 is made by cutting two 1-inch disks from sheet brass. One disk is soldered to the end of L_4, and a mount for the other disk is fashioned from a Miller 4400 coil form. The ceramic form itself is broken off the mount, and the slug removed from the end of the threaded rod. The disk is then soldered to the end of the rod. The coil-form base is mounted on the chassis so that the two disks are opposite each other. For better mechanical stability of the tuning shaft, a 6-32 lock nut can be placed on the shaft.

Tuning Up

A varactor multiplier is simple to tune, provided one has the proper test equipment. But test equipment for 432 Mc. is not easy to come by. Most constructors will find they have to spend more time making test gear to check the varactor than in building the multiplier itself. Fig. 17-21 shows two possible test setups for checking a multiplier unit. The first requires a nonreactive 50-ohm dummy load, and the second uses a transmatch with a 300-ohm load. Most of the dummy loads available to amateurs are too reactive at 432 to be any good. The constructor may make his own 50-ohm load from 100 feet of RG-58/U coax. This length of coax, terminated with a 50-

ohm, 2-watt composition resistor, will provide a nonreactive load that will handle the power from the varactor multiplier—and give the builder a good lesson in the losses of coax lines!

Another approach is to make a dummy load from carbon resistors and use a transmatch to tune out any reactance in the load. This resonant load, when used with an s.w.r. indicator, will give a check on the harmonic content of the varactor's output. (More about this later.) When the varactor multiplier is working, the transmatch can be used in the station to match Twin-Lead feeders.

The 432-Mc. transmatch circuit is shown in Fig. 17-19. It is constructed from a $4\frac{1}{2} \times 7\frac{3}{4}$-inch piece of sheet copper, with a $1\frac{1}{2}$-inch lip bent on either end. Two hairpin loops are used for L_1 and L_2. L_2 is supported by a $\frac{3}{4}$-inch standoff insulator. A crystal socket is used as an output connector as it has the proper pin size and spacing for the popular Twin-Lead connectors. The taps given in Fig. 17-19 for L_2 should be good for any low-reactance 300-ohm load. Other impedances will require changing the position of the taps.

In either test setup, a filter is used to insure that the output you are measuring is 432-Mc. energy and not some other harmonic. A simple strip-line filter like the unit described in the chapter on Interference with other Services will do the job. A power indicator is the hardest item of all to come up with. Bird wattmeters are very expensive; it may, however, be possible to borrow one from a local business-radio repairman. Several models of Micromatch-type bridges that work on 432 are available on the surplus market.* One of these units is a good investment for anyone seriously interested in 432 work. If you are not able to get a wattmeter, a simple relative indicator such as a wavemeter can be used at the load.

The s.w.r. bridge between the 144-Mc. exciter and the varactor multiplier indicates when the varactor input circuit is properly tuned. The input circuit of any of the varactor multipliers should be adjusted for a minimum s.w.r. reading. Then adjust the idler and output circuits for maximum output on 432 Mc. As the second-harmonic frequency is approached, the idler adjustment will make the output jump up.

The tuning adjustments will vary with changes in the drive level. First adjustments should be made with 10 or 15 watts from the exciter. After all the tuned circuits are adjusted correctly at this power level, the drive may be increased to about 30 watts for the H4A. With higher-power varactors, higher drive levels can be used. For any drive level, the varactor circuits should be tuned for best power output.

If you are using the 432-Mc. transmatch, you can get a check on the harmonic output by adjusting the transmatch for a 1:1 s.w.r. between the multiplier and transmatch. Then remove the strip-line filter and recheck the s.w.r. If the s.w.r.

---

* Try E. C. Hayden, Bay Saint Louis, Mississippi.

has gone up, you can be sure some harmonic energy is getting out. Often these harmonics will not cause any trouble even when the multiplier is used directly into the antenna, but remember that if they are there you will never see a 1:1 match to your antenna.

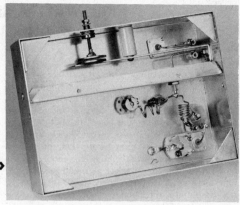

Fig. 17-17—The 432-Mc. varactor tripler. The input circuit is at the lower right and the varactor with its biasing resistor is at the center. The strip-line tank circuit in the trough is tuned by a homemade capacitor described in the text. »

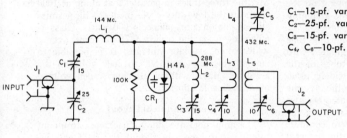

C₁—15-pf. variable (Hammarlund MAPC-15).
C₂—25-pf. variable (Hammarlund MAPC-25).
C₃—15-pf. variable (Johnson 160-107).
C₄, C₆—10-pf. ceramic trimmer (Centralab 829-10).
C₅—See text.
J₁, J₂—BNC coaxial receptacle, chassis-mounting.
L₁—6 turns No. 16, 3/16-inch diam., 1/2 inch long.
L₂—3 turns No. 12, 3/16-inch diam., 3/4 inch long.

Fig. 17-18—Circuit diagram of the 432-Mc. varactor tripler. A strip-line output circuit is used for better attenuation of unwanted harmonics than is possible with lumped-constant circuits.

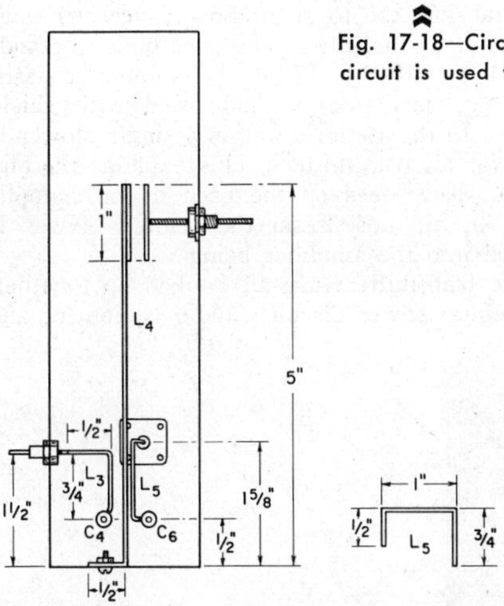

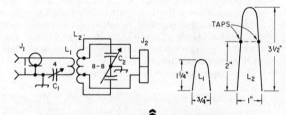

Fig. 17-20—432-Mc. tank-circuit details for the varactor tripler. L₃ and L₅ are coupling loops made from No. 14 wire, and L₄ is a 1/2-inch wide brass strip.

Fig. 17-19—432-Mc. transmatch diagram.
C₁—15-pf. variable (Johnson 160-107).
C₂—8-8-pf. dual-section variable (Johnson 160-208).
J₁—BNC coaxial receptacle, chassis mounting.
J₂—Crystal socket.
L₁—Hairpin loop No. 14 wire; see above.
L₂—Hairpin loop No. 10, wire; see above; tap as shown.

Fig. 17-21—Test setups for checking varactor multipliers.

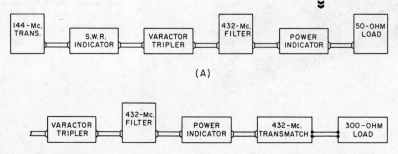

(A)

(B)

KILOWATT AMPLIFIERS FOR 50 AND 144 MC.

The amplifiers shown in Fig. 17-22 were designed for versatility. Though capable of running at the maximum legal power for amateur stations, they operate efficiently at much lower levels. They work well as linears, for use with a.m. or s.s.b., or they can be modulated or keyed in high-efficiency Class-C service. Though the tube type shown is expensive when purchased new, an effective substitute is commonly available on the surplus market at much lower cost. Operated as a rack-mounted pair, as pictured, the amplifiers offer convenient band-changing from 50 to 144 Mc., merely by snapping on the appropriate heater voltage switch, and changing the air connection from one to the other.

The external-anode type of transmitting tube has many variations. The family originated with the 4X150A many years ago, and tubes of the early type are still available, and widely used. A later version, with improved cooling, is the 4X250B, capable of higher power but otherwise very similar to the 4X150A. More recently the insulation was changed from glass to ceramic, and the prefix became 4CX. All the general types thus far mentioned were made with variations in basing and heater voltage that will be apparent to any reader of tube catalogs. The 4CX250R used here is a special rugged version, otherwise very similar to the 4CX250B, and interchangeable with it for amateur purposes. Similar types are supplied by other makers as the 7034/4X150A 7203/4CX250B and 7580. There is another version for linear-amplifier service only, called the 4CX350A.

If one then goes to other basing arrangements similar power capabilities may be found in the 4CX300A, 8122 and others, but differences in tube capacitance might require modification of the circuit elements described here. The air-system sockets (required for all external-anode tubes mentioned) may be the same for all types in the second paragraph, but those just above require different sockets.

Both amplifiers take a kilowatt on c.w. or s.s.b. with ease. The 144-Mc. model must be held to 600 watts input for plate-modulated service to stay within the manufacturer's ratings. On 50 Mc. the three tubes in parallel loaf along at 1000 watts in the low-duty-cycle modes. The permissible input on a.m. phone is 900 watts. Class C efficiency is on the order of 75 per cent, over a wide range of plate voltages. It is possible to run all the way from 800 to 2000 volts on the amplifier plates without altering screen voltage or drive levels appreciably.

Mechanical Layout

The amplifiers are similar packages, to mount together harmoniously, though this is of only incidental interest to the fellow concerned with one band or the other. They are built in standard 4 by 10 by 17-inch aluminum chassis, mounted open side up and fitted with shield covers. In the author's station a single blower is used for all transmitters. This explains the air-intake sleeve seen on the back of each amplifier. An air hose from the remote blower is pushed into the amplifier being used.

The transmitters are all hooked up together, to meters, power circuits, audio equipment and

Fig. 17-22—The kilowatt amplifiers for 50 and 144 Mc. in a rack made from aluminum angle stock. At the bottom is a meter panel with controls for meter and mode switching.

power supplies common to all. Changing bands involves mainly the switching on of the desired heater circuits, and the insertion of the air hose in the proper intake sleeve. Separate antenna relays are provided for each final stage, and power switching and plugging and unplugging are largely eliminated.

Tube sockets are the air-system type, mounted on 4-inch high partitions with folded-over edges that are drawn up tightly to the top, bottom, front and back of the chassis with self-tapping screws. Air is fed into the grid compartments at the left side, as viewed from the front. Its only path is through the sockets and tube anodes, and out through screened holes in the right side of the chassis. Panels are standard 5½-inch aluminum. Controls for the amplifiers are similar, though their locations are slightly different. No attempt was made to achieve symmetry through mechanical gadgetry, since the unbalance of the front panels is not unpleasing. The rack shown

in Fig. 17-22 was made up from aluminum angle stock to fit the job. Several screen and bias control arrangements were tried before the circuit shown in Fig. 17-27 was settled upon. Meters read driver plate current, and amplifier grid, screen and plate currents. Switches enable the operator to check the grid and screen currents to each tube in the 144-Mc. amplifier separately, and the screen currents in the 50-Mc. amplifier likewise. A mode switch provides proper screen operating conditions for a.m., linear or c.w. service.

The 50-Mc. Amplifier

The use of three tubes in parallel in the 50-Mc. amplifier was an experiment, tried with the expectation that parasitics, unbalance, excessive tank circuit heating and all manner of troubles would develop. These problems never materialized; use of paralleled tubes seemed to introduce no problems on its own, and extensive

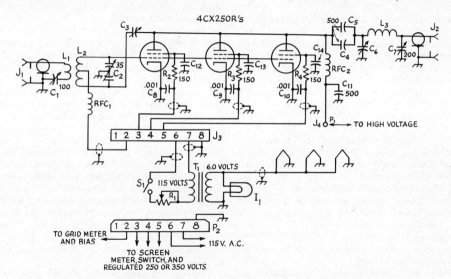

Fig. 17-23—Schematic diagram and parts information for the 50-Mc. amplifier.

C_7—200-pf. variable, .03-inch spacing (Johnson 167-12 or 200L15).

C_8, C_9, C_{10}—.001-μf. disk ceramic.

C_{12}, C_{13}, C_{14}—Bypass built into special air-system socket.

I_1—Green-jewel pilot lamp holder.

J_1, J_2—Coaxial chassis receptacle.

J_3—8-pin male power fitting.

J_4—H.v. power connector female (half of Millen 37501).

L_1—1 turn insulated wire about 1-inch diam. Make from inner conductor of coax running to J_1. Strip jacket and braid back about 4 inches. Insert

C_1—100-pf. miniature trimmer (Hammarlund MAPC-100).

C_2—35-pf. per section split-stator (Hammarlund HFD-35X).

C_3—Neutralizing capacitance—see text.

C_4, C_5, C_{11}—500-pf. 5000-volt transmitting capacitor (Centralab 858S-500).

C_6—Tuning capacitor made from 3-inch aluminum disks —see text and Fig. 3.

between center turns of L_2.

L_2—8 turns No. 14, ⅝-inch diam., 1¼-inches long, center-tapped.

L_3—3 turns 2 inches diam., 3 inches long, ¼-inch copper tubing.

P_1—High-voltage power connector, male (half of Millen 37501).

P_2—8-pin cable connector to match J_3, female.

R_1—20-ohm 10-watt slider-type resistor. Set so that heater voltage is 6.0 at socket.

R_2, R_3, R_4—150-ohm ½-watt resistor. Connect at socket screen terminal.

RFC_1—No. 32 enamel wire, close-wound full length of 1-watt resistor, 10,000 ohms or higher.

RFC_2—No. 28 d.s.c. or enamel-wound 1¾ inch on ½-inch Teflon rod. Space turns 1 wire diam. 8.3 μh. For winding information see QST, Nov. 1963, p. 43.

S_1—S.p.s.t. toggle.

T_1—6.3-volt 8-amp. Adjust R_1 to give 6.0 volts.

experience with the amplifier has confirmed the worth of the idea. This happy state of affairs involves a few basic considerations that should be stated here.

1) Paralleling straps in the grid and plate circuits were made "three of a kind." The two going to the outer grids were bent identically, and then the one for the middle tube was bent back on itself as necessary to use the same total length of strap. The same was done in the plate circuit.

2) The grid circuit was split-stator tuned, to get a reasonably-sized grid coil, even with the combined input capacitance of the three tubes plus circuit capacitance—some 60 pf. or more. This also provided a means for easy neutralization.

3) The pi-network plate circuit is tuned with a handmade disk capacitor. This has a far lower minimum C than the more conventional tuning capacitor, and it is devoid of the side bars and multiple ground paths that are so often the cause of parasitics in v.h.f. amplifiers. No parasitic resonances were found in this amplifier, other than one around 100 Mc. introduced apparently by the r.f. choke. This caused a blowup when grid-plate feedback developed with a similar choke in the grid circuit. The problem was solved easily by use of a low-Q choke of different inductance in the grid circuit. Do *not* use a high-quality r.f. choke for RFC_1!

4) All power leads except the high-voltage one are in the grid compartment, and made with shielded wire. Where the high voltage comes into the plate compartment it is bypassed at the feed-through fitting.

5) The plate circuit is made entirely of copper strap and tubing, for highest possible Q and low resistance losses. It may be of interest that the entire tank circuit was silver-plated after the photographs were made. Efficiency measurements made carefully before and after plating showed identical results.

Looking at the interior view, Fig. 17-24, we see the grid compartment at the left. The coaxial input fitting, J_1 in Fig. 17-24, is in the upper left corner of the picture. Coax runs from this, out of sight on the left wall, terminating in a loop, L_1, made from its inner conductor. This is inserted between turns at the center of the grid coil, L_2. The series capacitor, C_1, is just visible on the left chassis wall. It is not particularly critical in adjustment, so no inconvenience results from its location away from the front panel.

Screen voltage, bias, and 115 volts a.c. come through an 8-pin fitting, J_3, mounted between the air intake and the heater transformer, T_1. On the front panel are the heater switch, S_1, and the pilot-lamp holder.

The three air-system sockets (Eimac SK-600 or Johnson 124-111-1 with chimneys) are centered on the partition, spaced so that there is about ¼ inch between their flanges. The small angle brackets that come with the sockets should be tightened down with their inner ends bearing against the ceramic chimneys, to hold them in place. Note that the 150-ohm isolating resistors R_2, R_3, and R_4 are connected right at the screen terminals.

Both grid and plate straps are cut from flashing copper ⅝-inch wide. Lengths are not critical, except that all grid straps should be the same length, and all plate straps identical. The plate straps are made in two pieces soldered together in T shape, to wrap around the anode and join at the coupling capacitors, C_4 and C_5. These T-shaped connections could be cut from a sheet of copper in one piece, with a little planning.

The copper-tubing plate coil, L_3, is mounted on stand-off insulators not visible in the picture. Connections to the coupling capacitors the tuning capacitor, C_6, and the loading capacitor, C_7, are made with copper strap. It will be seen that these various pieces are bolted together, but they were also soldered. The connection from C_7 to the output fitting, J_2, is a single strap of copper, bolted and soldered to L_3.

The disk tuning capacitor can be made in several ways. Flashing copper is easy to work, and the 144-Mc. capacitor was made of this material. A more sturdy disk can be made from ⅛-inch aluminum. Those shown in Fig. 17-24 were 3-inch meter cutouts from an aluminum panel. Disk-type neutralizing capacitors (if you can find them; they're not common catalog items these days) provide ready-made disks and lead screws for tuning. For the latter we used 3-inch ¼-20 brass screws from the neighborhood hardware store. A panel bushing with brass nuts soldered to it provided the lead-screw sleeve. The stationary disk is supported on ½-inch-diameter Teflon rod, a material also used for the r.f. choke form. Teflon works easily and is unexcelled for insulating applications where high temperatures are encountered. We found it reasonably priced, in various diameters, at a local plastics house.

The plate r.f. choke, RFC_2, is important. You'll probably have to make it to get one of sufficiently good quality. For more on this see information under Fig. 17-23. Two coupling capacitors were paralleled because we've experienced trouble with exploding capacitors in pi-network plate circuits in the past. Maybe one would have handled the job, but two do for sure.

Some Possible Variations

It is always risky to suggest variations on a design unless they have been checked out in use, as bugs may develop in unforeseen ways. The following are ideas only, to be used at the builder's risk, since they have not been tested by the designer.

You might not care for three tubes in parallel. Two should work equally well, handling a kilowatt except in a.m. linear or plate-modulated service.

For those who can afford it, a vacuum variable

Fig. 17-24—Interior of the 50-Mc. amplifier. Note method of paralleling grid and plate connections. Cylinder at lower right is for detachable air hose.

capacitor should be ideal for C_6. One with about 10 pf. maximum capacitance should do nicely.

For lower tube cost, 4X150As from surplus should work without mechanical changes. Use plenty of air, if you intend to push the ratings of the 150As. A 100-c.f.m. blower is not too much. The ability of the anode structure to withstand heat is the main difference between the 150A and later versions of this tube, and some people have gotten away with 250 ratings with 150-type tubes. In this connection, the 50-Mc. amplifier will take a kilowatt at 1200 to 1500 volts, if your power supply will handle the current. This approach, plus plenty of air, is preferable to using plate voltages much in excess of the 4X150A ratings.

The 144-Mc. Plumber's Special

Use of $1\frac{5}{8}$-inch copper tubing for a 2-meter tank circuit is by no means new.* We simply went one step further and made the entire circuit from standard plumbing components. All the heavy metal you see in the plate compartment of Fig. 17-25 came from the plumbing counter of the local Sears store. The picture and Fig. 17-26 should be largely self-explanatory.

At the tube end of the plate line, L_4 in Fig. 17-26, we have brass castings normally used to join sections of the copper pipe. They make a nice sliding fit over the tube anodes. For tighter fit, cut thin brass shim stock and insert as much as needed between the anode and the sleeve. The end of the fitting can be slotted and then clamped firm on the anode with a hose clamp, as an alternative. The short at the B-plus end of the

---

*"High-Efficiency 2-Meter Kilowatt," *QST*, Feb. 1960, p. 30. "Top Efficiency at 144 Mc. with 4X250Bs," Breyfogle, *QST*, Dec. 1961, p. 44.

line is made with two T fittings, with their flanges cut down to $\frac{1}{2}$ inch and slipped over a short section of the pipe that is not visible. Joints throughout the assembly were silver-soldered with a torch, but conventional soldering should do equally well. The flanges at the open ends of the T fittings are cut down to about $\frac{1}{4}$-inch in length.

The last instruction and the information about the plate line given under Fig. 17-26 apply only if the fittings are identical to those obtained by the builder. Since there are several types of fittings available from plumbing supply houses, the following overall dimensions should be heeded: tube end of the plate line to center-line of short—$10\frac{3}{8}$ inches; spacing of pipes center to center—$3\frac{1}{2}$ inches.

In using tube types other than those specified, it may be that some change in plate circuit inductance will be needed. A simple check will show if this is needed. Slip the castings and pipe together without soldering, and assemble the plate circuit temporarily. Check the tuning range by means of a grid-dip meter. No plate or heater voltage is needed for this rough check, but it is well to have the coupling loop in place, and a 50-ohm resistor connected across J_2.

The coupling loop, L_5, is cut from a single piece of flashing copper $\frac{1}{2}$ inch wide. This delivered slightly more output to the load than was obtained with loops of wire of various lengths tried. The loop should be positioned so that the bottom edge is approximately flush with the bottom of the pipes. Optimum coupling to a 50-ohm load is achieved when the closed end of the "U" is about $\frac{1}{4}$ inch lower than the open end. Looking down at the plate-line assembly, the coupling loop is centered between the pipes.

The loop and plate line are supported on

Teflon rod insulators. The r.f. choke is also wound on Teflon. Note its position *outside* the U of the plate line. First mounted inside the loop, it went up in a furious burst of smoke when high power was applied to the amplifier.

Our tuning disks are 3-inch sheets of flashing copper. For nicer appearance and better mechanical stability, use ⅛-inch aluminum as in the 50-Mc. model. Three-inch brass ¼-20 screws are threaded through the pipe fittings. The rear one is held in place with a lock nut, and the other is rotated by the tuning knob, a bakelite shaft coupling, and a length of ¼-inch Teflon rod running in a panel bushing.

A third disk is mounted adjacent to the rear portion of the tank circuit. Its position is adjusted to achieve perfect balance in the tank circuit, but in practice this turned out to have no measurable effect. It is felt that a really good choke at RFC_1, and careful adjustment of C_1, can practically eliminate the effect of any slight unbalance if the point of connection of RFC_1 to the tank circuit is not bypassed to ground.

The 144-Mc. grid circuit, L_1L_2, looks like two coils, but actually is a coiled-up half-wave line. This is somewhat more compact than a half-wave line with its conductors out straight, and it seems equally effective. The grids are connected to the outer ends and the tuning capacitor to the inner. The point of connection of the bias-feed resistors should be determined in the same way as with the usual half-wave line: by coupling in 144-Mc. energy and touching a pencil lead along the inductance while watching the grid current. The correct point for final connection of the resistors is that at which no reaction on grid current is observed. Isolating resistors here, and for feeding screen voltage to the sockets, are preferable to r.f. chokes. The inner conductor of the coaxial line is used to make the coupling loop, L_3, which is placed between the inner ends of the grid circuit.

Balanced drive is maintained by adjustment of the differential capacitor, C_1, connected in parallel with C_2, and mounted on the side of the chassis adjacent to it. The series capacitor, C_3, is out of sight under the tuning capacitor, which is mounted on standoff insulators. It is adjusted by inserting a small screwdriver in a hole in the side of the chassis, but if we were doing it again we'd mount C_3 on the side wall, just under C_1, to make it more readily adjustable. Note that the rotor of C_2 is ungrounded.

About Neutralization

These amplifiers were tested without neutralization and we almost got away with it, but use of all modes, particularly a.m. linear and s.s.b., imposes strict requirements on stability. Conventional cross-over neutralization employed in the 144-Mc. amplifier is omitted from Fig. 17-24 in the interests of clarity. The schematic representation, C_3 in Fig. 17-23, is not very informative either.

In the 50-Mc. amplifier the lead visible in Fig. 17-24, attached to the rear stator terminal of C_2, runs to a polystyrene feedthrough bushing (National TPB) mounted in the partition between the rear and middle sockets. Even this bushing's wire stub projecting into the plate compartment turned out to be too much "C_3" and it was trimmed off 1/16th inch at a time, until minimum feedthrough was indicated on a wavemeter coupled to L_3 and tuned to the driving frequency.

Similar feedthrough bushings are used in the 144-Mc. amplifier, but here a small wire had to be added to each one. The wire connected to the grid of the front tube is aimed toward the anode of the rear tube, and vice versa. Small sheets of thin brass or copper should be fastened under the adjacent edges of the sockets, and bent up at right angles to the partition. These ¾-inch high barriers act to shield the

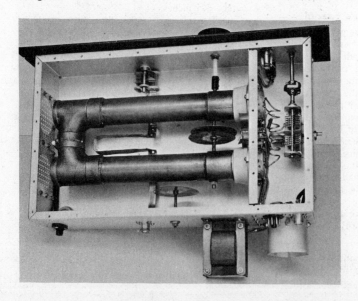

Fig. 17-25—Interior of the 144-Mc. amplifier, showing the plate circuit made from standard plumbing components. Brass pipe junctions make connection to the anodes, and T fittings are modified to form the short at the end of the line.

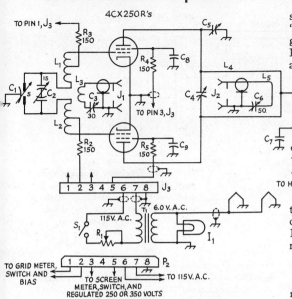

Fig. 17-26—Schematic diagram and parts information for the 144-Mc. amplifier.

C_1—5-pf. differential trimmer (Johnson 160-303 or 6MA11).

C_2—15-pf. per section split-stator (Hammarlund HFD-15X). Leave rotor ungrounded.

C_3—30-pf. miniature trimmer (Hammarlund MAC-30).

C_4—Tuning capacitor made with 3-inch disks. See text.

C_5—3-inch disk movable with respect to L_4. See text.

C_6—50-pf. variable (Hammarlund MC-50).

C_7—500-pf. 5000-volt (Centralab 858S-500).

C_8, C_9—Bypass capacitor built into air-system socket.

I_1—Green-jewel pilot lamp holder.

J_1, J_2—Coaxial chassis receptacle.

J_3—8-pin male chassis connector.

J_4—High-voltage power connector, female (half of Millen 37501).

L_1, L_2—3½ turns No. 14, ⅝-inch diam., turns spaced ½-inch. R_2 and R_3 tap on about 1 turn in from grid end. See text.

L_3—1-turn inner conductor of coax from J_1, about ¾ inch diam. Remove jacket and braid about 3 inches. Adjust position with respect to L_1, L_2 for maximum grid current.

L_4—Plate line 1⅜-inch copper pipe, with junctions and T fittings. Exposed portion of pipe is 8 inches long. Cut right end of T fittings to ¼-inch shoulder, and joined ends to ⅜-inch shoulders.

L_5—½-inch strap of flashing copper, U portion 4 inches long and 1¼ inch wide. Make loop and connections from single piece. Support L_4 and L_5 on standoffs of ceramic or Teflon.

P_1—High-voltage connector, male (half of Millen 37501).

P_2—8-pin female cable connector to match J_3.

R_1—20-ohm 10-watt slider-type. Adj. for 6.0 v. at socket.

R_2, R_3, R_4, R_5—150-ohm ½-watt resistor.

S_1—S.p.s.t. toggle.

T_1—6.3 volt 8-amp. Adjust R_1 for 6.0 volts.

RFC_1—2.15 μh. r.f. choke. No. 22 enamel closewound 1⅜⁄₁₆ inch on ¼-inch Teflon rod.

screen rings of the tubes from the feedback "capacitors" and assure that the coupling is from grid to opposite plate, and not to the screen.* Length and position of the feedback wires are adjusted for minimum feedthrough of driver energy to the plate circuit, as described above. About a half inch of wire was needed in addition to the terminal stub in this case.

When used as linear amplifiers the tubes must be biased to permit them to draw considerable plate current with no drive, so perfect neutralization is a "must." Properly neutralized, the amplifiers will be stable when run at or near maximum safe plate dissipation with no drive, even when the grid and plate circuits are swung through their entire ranges. If they will not pass this test the amplifiers are not ready to be used for linear service.

Controls and Metering

Almost everyone who builds his own equipment has a favored way of controlling it, so the system shown schematically in Fig. 17-27 may not suit everyone. It is for use in a station where power supplies are actuated by closing the primary circuits to all that the operator wants to have come on for transmitting purposes. They are mounted away from the transmitting position, and a cable carries the various voltages to the r.f. position. At the left, J_1, J_3, J_4 and J_5 are terminals carrying all voltages from the power-supply position. These are distributed through meters, controls and output fittings, J_6, J_7 and J_8, to various transmitters. Circuit breakers at the supply position are used to turn everything off when the station is closed down.

Adjustable bias, 50 to 90 volts negative, is brought in through Pin 2 to a 50-ma. meter and appropriate shunts that keep the circuit that is not being metered closed. The switch S_1 enables the operator to read the grid currents separately in the 144-Mc. amplifier. Grid voltage may be read when required, at J_2.

Similarly, a 500-volt positive source is connected through Pin 3, a voltage-regulating system, an audio choke, a 100-ma. meter and a 3-position switch, S_2, to the screens. Currents can be read separately here, too, and this facility is important in determining that all tubes are running within ratings. The VR system is switched by S_{3A} to provide regulated 250 or 350 volts to the screens. Ganged to it is S_{3B}, which shorts the audio choke for all modes except plate-modulated a.m. This must be done, as the choke will cause trouble on the other modes. The series-parallel VR-tube bank is by no means an ideal regulating system, but it prevents soaring of the screen voltage under conditions of low or negative screen current. These occur

---

*An air-system socket is now available that has built-in shielding of the screen ring. The Eimac number is SK-620.

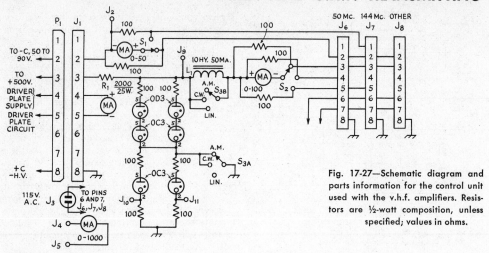

Fig. 17-27—Schematic diagram and parts information for the control unit used with the v.h.f. amplifiers. Resistors are ½-watt composition, unless specified; values in ohms.

J_1—8-pin male power connector.

J_2, J_9, J_{10}, J_{11}—Tip jack.

J_3—A.c. connector, male.

J_4, J_5—High-voltage feedthrough connector (Millen 37501).

J_6, J_7, J_8—8-pin female power connector.

L_1—10 hy. 50-ma. choke. Must be shorted out for other than plate-modulated service.

P_1—8-pin female cable plug.

R_1—2000-ohm 25-watt resistor. Value may be reduced to as low as 1000 ohms if regulation a high values of screen current is desired, provided current measured in J_{10} and J_{11} does not exceed 40 ma. under low-screen-current conditions.

S_1—Single pole 2-position switch.

S_2—Single-pole 3-position switch.

S_3—Double-pole 3-position switch.

only in linear operation, and on c.w. when the key is up. It is not particularly important that screen voltage be held constant for high screen current, as in plate-modulated a.m. and key-down c.w. conditions with low plate voltage. The screen voltage will be kept down by the heavy load on the supply at such times. Actually a single string of three regulator tubes will do the job quite well, and both amplifiers have been worked successfully with this simpler screen arrangement. Current through the regulator tube strings can be measured between J_{10} or J_{11} and ground.

Operation

Because a variety of tubes may be used, with a wide range of conditions as to plate voltage and drive, we're not going to be too specific here. If you follow the tube manufacturer's recommendations for the plate voltage you intend to use you won't be far wrong. All tubes of this class are quite versatile as to drive level and plate voltage; unless you are running close to the maximum plate-input ratings the principal factor to watch is screen dissipation, as far as safety of the tubes is concerned. Set up your amplifier with a dummy load and then try the various conditions given in tube data sheets, observing the operation on all meters. In this way you'll soon learn your way around. A few words of preliminary advice may, however, be in order.

First, don't feel that you have to run a kilowatt right off the bat. Put a Variac in your final plate supply primary and run the voltage down for initial testing, or use a lower-voltage supply

until you become familiar with the way the rig works. Watch the screen current closely, particularly at low plate voltage or with high grid drive or light loading. The provision for checking individual screen currents is important, otherwise you may learn too late that one tube has been taking all or most of what you have seen on a meter that reads total screen current only. In the push-pull amplifier it may be advantageous to balance screen currents by C_1, rather than grid currents, if balance of both screen and grid currents does not occur at one setting.

Tune up for Class C and get the feel of the amplifiers before trying linear operation. Use a scope; there is no sure way to set up and operate a linear without one. The Heath Monitor Scope, HO-10, is ideal for this job because of its built-in tone oscillator and in-the-transmission-line features. Running a linear, either sideband or a.m., without a scope check is inviting trouble.

For higher plate efficiencies go to s.s.b., c.w. or plate-modulated a.m. In any of these modes these amplifiers will give you the biggest legal signal around, if that's what you want. Or they'll throttle down nicely to 300 watts input or less, merely by lowering the plate voltage. They'll work efficiently at much lower inputs if the screen voltage is dropped appropriately. Chances are that you'll still have a signal that will stand out in most neighborhoods, on either 6 or 2.

Additional information on the construction and operation of v.h.f. and u.h.f. linear amplifiers is given in *The Radio Amateur's V.H.F. Manual*, 1st Edition, Chapter 6. Several circuits are described therein.

A RESONANT-CAVITY AMPLIFIER FOR 432 MHZ.

This highly-efficient 4CX250 amplifier operates at approximately 63-percent efficiency when used with a plate supply of 1750 volts and a screen supply of 255 volts. It can be operated with higher voltage on its plate, but at reduced efficiency. It provides power levels up to 500 watts input on c.w. and f.m.

The grid circuit of the amplifier is as shown in Fig. 17-30 and is pretty much a duplication of the one shown in the 2nd Edition of *The Radio Amateur's V.H.F. Manual* (ARRL), page 257. The plate side of the circuit is a resonant cavity and is shown in representative form in Fig. 17-30. Detailed information on how the plate circuit is built is given in Fig. 17-31.

Construction

Much of the information concerning the way the amplifier is built can be taken from the photos. The dimensions of the plate cavity are given in Fig. 17-31. The cavity is constructed, cylindrical fashion, from $\frac{1}{8}$-inch thick copper or brass stock and has an inside diameter of $6\frac{1}{4}$ inches. The wall height of the cylinder is $1\frac{1}{2}$ inches. Both end plates are fashioned from $\frac{1}{8}$-inch thick copper or brass stock. A firm bond is essential between the end plates and the cylinder to assure maximum efficiency. It would be wise to have the cylinder milled flat on each end to assure a good fit, then use a liberal amount of machine screws to hold the end plates in place. Mechanical rigidity is imperative with this type of structure, thus assuring good continuity at the high-current points of the cavity, and to enhance the tuning stability of the plate circuit.

The tube and socket are mounted $\frac{5}{8}$ inch off center from the center of the cavity. The hole in the top plate of the cavity should be large enough in diameter to assure a 3/16-inch clearance all around the anode of the tube. Care should be taken to smooth the edges of the hole lest arcing occur during operation. The home-built capacitor,

Fig. 17-28—View of the top of the assembled amplifier. Teflon bushings hold the square capacitor plate in place on the wall of the cavity. One bushing is not shown. The high voltage and r.f. choke connect to that bushing's screw when it is in place. Plate-tuning adjustments are made from the bottom of the cavity. The shaft for C_3 is accessible on the bottom wall of the cavity. This amplifier was designed and built by H. E. Holshouser, Jr., K4QIF.

C_6, is formed by making a 3-$\frac{7}{8}$-inch square copper or brass plate of $\frac{1}{8}$-inch thick stock and placing a sheet of 10-mil teflon insulation between it and the cavity top plate. The plate has a clearance hole for the anode of the 4CX250 and is ringed with finger stock so that it contacts the tube's anode. Insulating bushings of teflon are used at each corner of the capacitor plate to secure it to the wall of the cavity, Fig. 17-28.

An Eimac SK-600 tube socket is used, and no chimney is needed. The socket has built-in bypass capacitors on the screen and filament terminals. These are not shown on the schematic diagram. The bottom of the tube socket projects into the main chassis where the grid circuit is located. The output link, L_3, is a straight piece of 1/16-inch thick brass or copper, $\frac{1}{8}$ inch wide, shaped as shown in Fig. 17-31.

Two fixed capacitors are shown in the schematic diagram, C_2 and C_4. These capacitors are not indicated on the mechanical drawing of Fig. 17-31 as they were added as a modification when some models of this amplifier showed a tendency toward arcing between the disk of C_3 and the cavity wall. C_2 and C_4 are disks of copper which are $1\frac{1}{4}$ inches in diameter. They are spaced approximately $\frac{1}{8}$ inch from the top wall of the cavity. They are supported from the bottom wall of the cavity by means of $\frac{3}{8}$-inch diameter brass posts and are positioned generally as shown in Fig. 17-32. *A word of caution:* The tuning shaft of C_3 should not pass through the grid compartment of the amplifier. The cavity as-

Fig. 17-29—Inside view of the amplifier. The grid circuit and filament transformer are inside the chassis. Plate and output-tuning adjustments are made from the bottom of the cavity (far right).

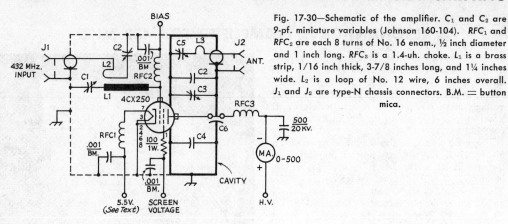

Fig. 17-30—Schematic of the amplifier. C_1 and C_2 are 9-pf. miniature variables (Johnson 160-104). RFC_1 and RFC_2 are each 8 turns of No. 16 enam., ½ inch diameter and 1 inch long. RFC_3 is a 1.4-uh. choke. L_1 is a brass strip, 1/16 inch thick, 3-7/8 inches long, and 1¼ inches wide. L_2 is a loop of No. 12 wire, 6 inches overall. J_1 and J_2 are type-N chassis connectors. B.M. = button mica.

sembly is offset on the main chassis so that the shaft is accessible outside the grid compartment.

The output tuning capacitor, C_5, is a glass piston trimmer with a maximum capacitance of 10 pf. Do not try to use a plastic piston trimmer here as it will be destroyed because of its poor dielectric properties. Neutralization of this amplifier was not found to be necessary as no tendency toward instability was noted.

Operation

It is suggested that a 0.5-ampere fuse be used in series with the high-voltage lead to protect the plate meter should an arc or short circuit occur. The screen current should be metered so that at no time an excessive amount of current will be permitted to flow. Heed the manufacturer's ratings at all times.

The amplifier must always look into a nonreactive load if damage is not to occur. It is de-

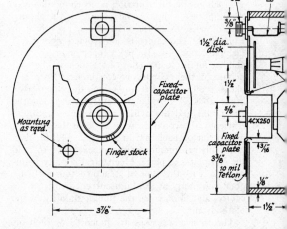

Fig. 17-31—Mechanical layout of the plate cavity and its dimensions.

signed to work into a 50-ohm load, but a 75-ohm load will be acceptable if the s.w.r. is kept low. *Warning:* The anode of the 4CX250 should be covered with a perforated box of some type to prevent accidental contact with the high voltage. It should allow the free passage of air from the forced-air cooling system, which is piped into the grid compartment. The grid compartment should be made as air-tight as possible to assure a heavy flow of air through the socket and the anode fins of the tube.

The heater voltage for this type of tube is 6.0 and not 6.3. It is satisfactory to use the 6-volt figure at the lower frequencies, but at 432-MHz. the voltage should be reduced to 5.5 to compensate for the back-bombardment that the cathode is subjected to. The latter causes overheating, which in turn causes drifting of operating conditions and shortened tube life. Other operating voltages and currents for this amplifier must be chosen for the class of operation desired. It is best to consult the manufacturer's ratings for this information.

Fig. 17-32—Inside view of the K4QIF amplifier cavity. The stationary capacitors, C_2 and C_4, are located on either side of the 4CX250 socket.

GROUNDED-GRID AMPLIFIER FOR 1296 MC.

There are few tubes available that will provide the radio amateur with low-cost construction while at the same time delivering moderate power output in the 1215-Mc. region. One popular low-cost tube is the 2C39. Also available are its newer brothers the 2C39A, 2C39B, 3CX100A5, and 7289. All look pretty much alike, but only the early versions have appeared on the surplus market. This amplifier uses 2C39As in a cavity assembly and is capable of delivering 100 watts or more as a linear amplifier, with a gain of 6 to 10 decibels.[1] It can be built with simple hand tools.

Amplifier Details

U.h.f. circuits, particularly those involving cavities, do not lend themselves well to conventional schematic presentation, but the circuit diagram, Fig. 17-34, may aid the reader in identifying the components and understanding their functions. The structural features of the amplifier are not all apparent from the photographs, so are described in some detail, using component designations of Fig. 17-36 in referring to the various parts.

This is a grounded-grid amplifier. The large square box visible in the pictures houses the cathode input circuit. The whole assembly is shown from the top in Fig. 17-33, and from the bottom in Fig. 17-35. Details of the principal metal parts are given in Fig. 17-36. It will be seen that the bottom cover of the cathode compartment (part D in Fig. 17-36) is cut diagonally to permit access to the cathode circuit for adjustment purposes. The tuned circuit, L_1–C_2, is effectively a halfwave line, tuned at the end opposite to the tubes. The inductance, part E in Fig. 17-36, is tuned by means of a beryllium copper spring finger, visible in the lower left corner of Fig. 17-35. It is actuated by an adjustment screw running through a shoulder nut mounted in the removable cover plate. Input coupling is capacitive, through C_1, a small glass trimmer at the center of the line, between the tubes. An approximate input match is established by adjustment of this capacitor.

The plate circuit, L_2–C_3, is a square tuned cavity not visible in the pictures. It is made by bending part G into a square, and soldering it to the top of part C and to the bottom of part B, with all lined up on a common center. The *Outside* of the cavity is at r.f. ground potential. The tubes are mounted on a diagonal, at equal distances from the center. The plate tuning capacitor, C_3, is coaxial. Its movable element is a 6-32 screw, running through a shoulder nut in the top plate of the bypass capacitor, C_4, soon to be described. The fixed portion is a metal sleeve $\frac{5}{16}$ inch inside diameter and $\frac{5}{8}$ inch high, soldered to the top side of part C. It is centered on a 6-32 binder-head screw, threaded into the center hole in part C. This screw also holds a $\frac{3}{8}$-inch insulat-

Fig. 17-33—The 2-tube 1296-Mc. amplifier. Two 2C39As are used in this grounded-grid setup. The large square base unit houses the cathode input circuit. The plate cavity is not visible, as it is obscured by the plate bypass assembly seen here. *(Built by WB6IOM)*

ing spacer that supports the cathode inductor, part E. Output coupling is by means of a fixed loop, L_3, on a BNC or TNC coaxial fitting mounted in the $\frac{3}{8}$-inch hole in part G, the cavity wall.

The bypass capacitor, C_4, consists of the top cover of the plate cavity, part B, a layer of 0.02-inch Teflon sheet, and the top plate, part A. This combination does not act as a pure capacitance, because of the large size of the plates in terms of wavelength at 1296 Mc. It is important not to make substitutions here, as variations in size of the plates or thickness of the insulation may cause the capacitor to become resonant. The plates are held together with nylon screws. Metal screws with insulating sleeving, and insulating shoulder washers, may also be used. Nylon screws and other insulation, other than Teflon, may melt if the bypass capacitor becomes resonant. Nylon is very lossy at 1296 Mc.

Construction

Major sheet-metal parts are cut from 0.04 or 0.05-inch sheet brass. The cutting, bending and soldering can be done with hand tools. The soldering is done readily over a kitchen stove, or with a 300-watt or larger soldering iron. Silver plating is recommended, to assure good r.f. contact throughout. Several methods usable in the home are outlined in *The Radio Amateur's V.H.F. Manual*. All sheet brass parts are shown in Fig. 17-36, with dimensions and hole locations. Note that the bottom plate of the cathode assembly, part D, is cut diagonally, and fitted with spring finger stock to assure good electrical continuity when the assembly is closed.

On the smaller part of D is a 6-32 screw that runs through a shoulder nut soldered into the sheet, with the head of the screw on the outside when the cover is in place. The end of the screw

---

[1] Described in Jan. 1968 QST.

bears on the beryllium copper spring finger, ⅝ inch wide, bent so that its position with respect to the cathode circuit varies with the position of the screw. Its position and approximate size should be evident from Fig. 17-35. The bottom end is soldered to the inside of part C. The free end should be wrapped with smooth insulating tape, so that the cathode bias will not be shorted out if the capacitor is closed down too far.

Spring finger stock is used to provide flexible low-inductance contact with the plate, grid and cathode elements of the tubes. Finger stock numbers are given for stock obtained from Instrument Specialty Co., Little Falls, N. J. The material used for tube contact purposes is No. 97-380. That on the triangular cover plate is 97-134. If tubes with recessed grid rings are used (example: the 7289) it is necessary to solder a small piece of brass against the bottom of the grid finger stock, to prevent the tube from being pushed in too far. Otherwise it is impossible to remove the tube without damage to either the finger stock or the tube. The finger stock used in the grid, plate and cathode holes should be preformed to fit, and then soldered in with a 200-watt or larger iron. That on part D is soldered to the outside of the plate. It may be necessary to strengthen the cover plate with a strip of brass soldered to the inside, opposite to the finger stock, to prevent bulging. This should protrude about 1/16 inch from the edge of the cover plate. Any intermittent contact here will detune the input circuit severely.

The finger stock in the plate bypass should be flush with the sheet metal on the side facing the cavity. With the grid and cathode connections the stock may protrude somewhat. The soldering of the cavity parts should be done first. The parts should be lined up carefully, clamped together, and then soldered in place over a gas flame for preheating, doing the actual soldering with a small iron. Check alignment prior to final cool-down. The output BNC fitting can be soldered in at this time, adding the coupling loop

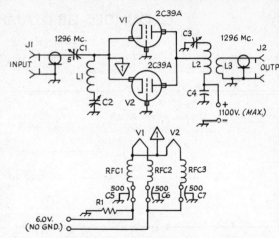

Fig. 17-34—Representative circuit of the 1296-Mc. cavity amplifier. The plate cavity and tuning device are indicated by L_2C_3, the cathode inductance and tuning capacitor by L_1C_2. Note that the heater supply must not be grounded.

C_1—5-pf. glass trimmer.

C_2—Beryllium-copper spring finger; see text and Fig. 17-35.

C_3—Coaxial plate capacitor (see text).

C_4—Plate bypass capacitor, composed of parts A and B, Fig. 17-36 separated by 0.02-inch Teflon sheet. See text.

C_5, C_6, C_7—Feed-through bypass, 500 pf.

J_1, J_2—Coaxial jack, BNC or TNC type.

L_1—Cathode inductor, part E, Fig. 17-36. See text and Fig. 17-35.

L_2—Plate cavity, composed of parts C, B, and G of Fig. 17-36. See text.

L_3—Copper strap ⅜ inch wide, from pin of J_2 to top side of part C.

RFC_1, RFC_2, RFD_3—10 turns No. 22 enamel, ⅛-inch diam., 1 inch long.

R_1—50 to 100 ohms, 2 watts (see text).

later. It is merely a strip of copper or brass, ⅜ inch wide, soldered between the center pin of J_2 and the cavity bottom. The strip should rest against the teflon shoulder of the fitting, and extend ¼ inch beyond the center pin before being bent 90 degrees down to the cavity bottom. Solder solidly to part A, and to the full length of the pin on J_2. Now put in the finger stock. If a small iron is used, preheating with the gas flame, the heavy brass parts will not come loose. The top cover of the plate cavity, part B, is then soldered in place, using a clamp as before.

In cutting the Teflon insulation for the plate bypass, make tube holes only just large enough

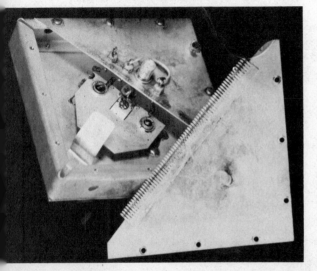

Fig. 17-35—Bottom (or back) view of the cathode circuit and housing, showing the divided cover plate, part D in Fig. 17-36. Inside are the cathode inductance, part E, and the spring-finger tuning capacitor plate, C_2. The heater and cathode feed-through bypasses and the input coaxial fitting are on the cover plate, near the center. The outside surface of the removable cover plate is shown.

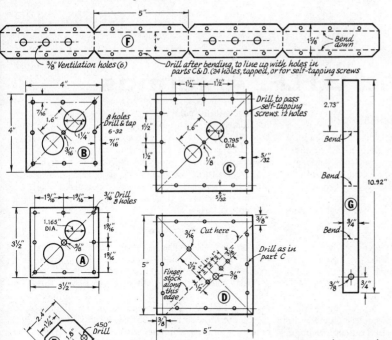

Fig. 17-36—Principal sheet-metal parts of the 1296-Mc. amplifier: top plate of the by-pass capacitor, A; its bottom plate and top cover of the plate cavity, B; top plate of the cathode assembly, C; and two-piece bottom cover, D. The long strip, F, is the side walls of the cathode assembly, and G is the side walls of the plate cavity, both before bending into their square shape.

to clear the tube. There should also be some area of insulation around the outer edges of the top plate. These precautions are helpful in preventing arc-over.

Connection to the tube heaters is made by bending a U-shaped piece of beryllium copper or spring bronze to make a snug fit in the heater cup at the end of the tube. The air-wound r.f. choke is connected directly to this, with the other end running to the feed-through bypasses. The heaters being brought out separately permits a check on condition of tubes, by turning off the heaters one at a time. Leaving the tube in place, but cold, does not detune the system, and a comparison of the tubes may be made in this way. Note that neither side of the heater circuit can be grounded.

Tuning and Operation

When construction is completed and checked out, apply heater power to the tubes. Connect a milliammeter in series with the cathode resistor. Set the input glass trimmer at the middle of its range, and place the cover plate in position, but without putting in the screws as yet. Keep some pressure on it by hand to insure uniform contact. Apply 10 to 20 watts of driving power, tune C_2, and observe the cathode current. Open the cathode compartment, move the input trimmer, replace the cover, and observe the current again. Repeat until highest current is achieved, but do not go over 120 ma. Reduce driving power, if necessary, to keep below this level. Fasten the cover plate in place, and re-check cathode current.

Supply cooling air, if this has not already been done. Be sure that adequate air flow is provided, especially if the plate input is to be

near maximum ratings. If there is to be no cowling around the tube fins an air stream of some 150 c.f.m. from a low-pressure blower across the area of the tube fins is required. With an enclosure confining the air flow to a path through the fins a 30 c.f.m. high pressure blower should suffice. In either case it does no harm to have more. If you have a quiet blower it probably is not enough!

Connect a 50-ohm termination to J_2 and apply plate power, preferably at a lower voltage than the maximum that will be used eventually. Apply drive, and tune the input circuit for maximum plate current, and the output circuit for maximum output. A suitable indicator is an incandescent lamp connected at the end of a 50-foot length of RG-58 cable. This will be so lossy that it will look like 50 ohms, regardless of the termination, and the lamp will show relative output. Maximum output may not coincide with minimum plate current.

Once the amplifier appears to be working normally, plate voltage may be increased, re-checking the tuning adjustments for each change in plate voltage. Use a value of cathode resistor that will result in about 50 ma. plate current with no drive. With 1000 volts on the plates do not operate the amplifier for more than a few seconds at a time under key-down conditions. With a normal c.w. keying duty cycle you can run up to 400 ma. plate current. With s.s.b. you may run up to 600 ma. peak current, or a 300-ma. indicated meter reading during normal voice operation. With the expected 100 watts output, with 300 to 400 in, the RG-58 cable should melt in a few minutes. This is not a very satisfactory method of measuring output, and some reliable power-indicating meter should be used for at least an intermittent check, if at all possible.

Chapter 18

V.H.F. And U.H.F. Antennas

DESIGN CONSIDERATIONS

At 50 Mc. and higher it is usually important to have the antenna work well over all or most of the band in question, and as the bands are wider than at lower frequencies the attention of the designer must be focused on broad frequency response. This may be attained in some instances through sacrificing other qualities such as high front-to-back ratio.

The loss in a given length of transmission line rises with frequency. V.h.f. feedlines, therefore, should be kept as short as possible. Matching of the impedances of the antenna and transmission line should be done with care, and in open locations a high-gain antenna at relatively low height may be preferable to a low-gain system at great height. Wherever possible, however, the v.h.f. array should be well above heavy foliage, buildings, power lines or other obstructions.

The physical size of a v.h.f. array is usually more important than the number of elements. A 4-element array for 432 Mc. may have as much gain over a dipole as a similarly designed array for 144 Mc., but it will intercept only one-third as much energy in receiving. Thus to be equal in communication, the 432-Mc. array must equal the 144-Mc. antenna in *capture area,* requiring three times as many elements, if similar element configurations are used in both.

Polarization

Tests made over long paths have indicated that there is little difference in results obtained from vertically- or horizontally-polarized antennas. The choice of polarization is usually based upon which polarity is in vogue in a given geographical area. Unfortunately, standardization has not occurred in this regard despite the fact that most v.h.f. and u.h.f. stations in the U.S.A. are equipped for horizontal polarization.

Horizontal arrays are generally more effective than vertical systems are when it comes to discriminating against man-made noise pulses. Simple 3- or 4-element arrays are more effective when horizontal than when vertical, as their radiation patterns are broad in the plane of the elements and are sharp in the plane perpendicular to them.

Vertical antennas are beneficial for base-station and mobile use where non-directional coverage is desired. Similarly, such antennas are useful for net operation. Vertical antennas can be designed to provide gain while still radiating an omnidirectional pattern. Vertical polarization, because it is of the opposite sense to that of home TV antennas, helps to lessen TVI from v.h.f. ham transmitters.

Horizontally-polarized mobile antennas—halos, turnstiles, and the like—provide a signal with considerably less flutter than do vertical antennas. The latter transmit and receive less effectively because trees, power poles, and most man-made structures have a vertical format, hence momentarily obstruct a vertically-polarized signal more seriously than were the antenna horizontally polarized.

Feed-Line Choice

Line losses increase with frequency. For this reason it is particularly important that a good grade of transmission line be used, and that it be properly matched to the antenna. Open-wire line offers the least amount of loss and is commercially available in 300- and 450-ohm impedances. It is more difficult to install than is coaxial cable, hence is not as popular with most operators. U.h.f. foam-filled 300-ohm TV ribbon is satisfactory for use as a low-loss line in regions where the air is dry most of the time and where the atmosphere has a low salt or chemical content.

Coaxial cables of good dielectric quality are fast becoming preferred by loss-conscious amateurs. Some of the more common lines are listed in Fig. 18-1. War surplus coax should be avoided at all cost because much of that type of line is old and no longer has good dielectric properties. In time, the polyethylene material becomes "poisoned" and acts as a high-resistance conductor. Similarly, the shield braid deteriorates from corrosion and becomes ineffective. Small-diameter coax lines of the RG-58 and RG-59 variety are very lossy in the v.h.f. and u.h.f. regions and should be avoided except when used as short interconnecting cables. Low-cost flat TV ribbon should also be avoided because some of it is extremely lossy in the v.h.f. region.

Impedance Matching

The impedance-matching techniques employed in v.h.f. and u.h.f. work are the same as those used in h.f. antenna design. The more common methods are described in detail in Chapter 14. Most v.h.f. antennas employ Gamma-Match, "T"-Match, or "Q"-section impedance-matching devices. Also, folded dipoles can be designed to provide a terminal impedance that allows them to work with balanced lines of standard ohmic values. Where an unbalanced (coax) line is connected to a balanced feed point on a driven element, some form of balancing device should be used to prevent skewing of the antenna pattern and to prevent line radiation. Examples of balancing devices are given in Fig. 14-46. The types shown at B and D are preferred at 50 Mc. and higher.

FEED LINE CHARACTERISTICS

Type of Line	Impedance (Ohms) (nominal)	Velocity Factor	Pf. Per Ft.	DB. Atten. Per 100 Ft.			Dia. (inches)
				100 Mc.	300 Mc.	1000 Mc.	
RG-58A	52	0.66	28.5	4.2	7.9	16	0.195
RG-59A	73	0.66	21	3.8	7.0	14	0.242
RG-8A	52	0.66	29.5	2.1	4.2	9	0.4
RG-11A	75	0.66	20.5	2.1	3.8	7.8	0.4
RG-17A	52	0.66	29.5	0.85	1.8	4.2	0.87
*AM-5012P	50	0.81	25	0.75	1.6	3.1	0.5
*AM-7512P	75	0.81	16.7	0.75	1.6	3.1	0.5
*AM-5078P	50	0.81	25	0.5	1.0	2.2	0.875
*AM-7578P	75	0.81	16.7	0.5	1.0	2.2	0.875
Open Wire	300-450	0.97	—	0.18	0.6	1.0	—
Flat Ribbon (8225)	300	0.8	4.4	1.1	2.2	5.0	—
Foam-Filled Ribbon (8275)	300	0.8	4.6	1.05	2.12	4.8	—

* Semiflexible aluminum-jacketed foam-filled line. Times Wire and Cable, Wallingford, Conn.
** Belden type. Loss figures are for dry, clean line. Losses increase rapidly when line is wet.

Fig. 18-1—Modern v.h.f./u.h.f. feed lines and some of their characteristics. RG-58A and RG-59A types are not recommended for long runs at 50 Mc. and higher.

When the impedance of a particular antenna is unknown—frequently the case with multi-element Yagis—the universal stub of Fig. 18-2 can be used. This adjustable transformer will match the transmission line to the antenna and will tune out reactance in the driven element. The stub can be made from copper or aluminum tubing and equipped with sliding clips, or it can be a section of 300- or 450-ohm open-wire line with some form of adjustable shorting bar. The transmission line can be open wire or twin lead. If a coaxial line is used, a balun transformer should be connected between the line and the stub.

To adjust the stub, insert an s.w.r. indicator in the main feed line and short out the end of the stub farthest from the antenna. Using low transmitter power, slide the feeders up and down on the stub until a point is found where the s.w.r. is the lowest. Then turn the transmitter off and move the shorting strap a short distance up on the stub and readjust the line connection for the lowest s.w.r. reading. Repeat the foregoing procedure until the s.w.r. is as close to 1:1 as possible. Once the correct tap and short points are found, permanent connections can be made and the portion of the matching stub below the shorting strap can be cut off and discarded. Complete information on the use of matching stubs is given in *The A.R.R.L. Antenna Book*, Chapter 3.

Elements, Lengths, And Spacings

When designing a v.h.f. or u.h.f. array, attention must be given to both the physical and elec-

trical properties of the system. The electrical features will be dictated for the most part by the type of performance required. Mechanical design offers a myriad of possibilities, however, and the exact approach taken will depend upon the builder's budget, the availability of materials, and his engineering skill.

Because v.h.f. and u.h.f. arrays are relatively small and lightweight compared to directive arrays for the h.f. spectrum, TV antennas offer an excellent source of tubing and boom stock. Many TV antennas can be modified for use in the ham bands by merely pruning the elements to length and relocating them on the boom for the desired spacing. Brass and aluminum brazing and welding rods—available from most welding supply houses—make good element material. Aluminum

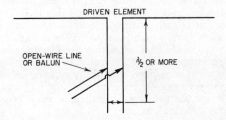

Fig. 18-2—Combination tuning and matching stub for feeding v.h.f. and u.h.f. antennas. The sliding short is used to tune out reactance of the driven element or phasing system. Transmission line, balanced or coaxial balun, is attached at the point of lowest s.w.r.

clothesline wire is rigid enough to be used for element stock on 220- and 432-Mc. beams. No. 10 copperweld wire is excellent material for 432-Mc. beams. Coat hangers can be straightened and cut to length for indoor attic antennas. Most hardware stores sell do-it-yourself aluminum tubing, angle stock, and sheeting. TV antenna masting can be used for boom material. Thin-wall electrical conduit, though not recommended for antenna elements, can be used as boom and mast stock.

Dimensions for Yagi or collinear arrays and their matching devices can be taken from Table 18-I. The driven element is usually cut to the formula:

$$Length \text{ (in inches)} = \frac{5540}{Freq. \text{ (Mc.)}}$$

This is the basis of the lengths in Table 18-I, which are suitable for the tubing or rod sizes commonly used. Arrays for 50 Mc. usually have $\frac{1}{2}$ to 1-inch elements. For 144 Mc. $\frac{1}{4}$ to $\frac{1}{2}$-inch stock is common. Rod or tubing $\frac{1}{8}$ to $\frac{3}{8}$ inch in diameter is suitable for 220 and 420 Mc. Note that the element lengths in the table are for the middle of the band concerned. For peaked performance at other frequencies the element lengths should be altered according to the figures in the third line of the table.

Reflector elements are usually about 5 percent longer than the driven element. The director nearest the driven element is 5 percent shorter, and others are progressively shorter, as shown in the table. Parasitic elements should also be adjusted according to Line 3 of the table, if peak performance is desired at some frequency other than midband.

Parasitic element lengths of Table 18-I are based on element spacings of 0.2 wavelength. This is most often used in v.h.f. arrays, and is suitable for up to 4 or 5 elements. Other spacings can be used, however. If the element lengths are adjusted properly there is little difference in gain with reflector spacings of 0.15 to 0.25 wavelength. The closer the reflector is to the driven element, the shorter it must be for optimum forward gain, and the greater will be its effect on the driven element impedance.

Directors may also be spaced over a similar range. Closer spacing than 0.2 wavelength for arrays of two or three elements will require a longer director than shown in Table 18-I. Thus it can be seen that close-spaced arrays tend to work over a narrower frequency range than wide-spaced ones, when they are tuned for best performance. They also result in lower driven-element impedance, making them more difficult to feed properly. Spacings less than 0.15 wavelength are not commonly used in v.h.f. arrays for these reasons.

PRACTICAL V.H.F. AND U.H.F. ARRAYS

The antenna systems pictured and described herewith are examples of ways in which the information in Table 18-I can be used in arrays of proven performance. Dimensions can be taken

TABLE 18-I
Dimensions for V.H.F. Arrays in Inches

Freq. (Mc.)	52*	146*	222.5*	435*
Driven Element	106.5	38	24⅞	12¾
Change per Mc.*	2	0.25	0.12	0.03
Reflector	111½	40	26⅛	13⅜
1st Director	101½	36	23⅝	12⅛
2nd Director	99½	35¾	23⅜	12
3rd Director	97½	35	23	11⅞
1.0 Wavelength	234	81	53	27
0.625 Wavelength	147	50½	33⅛	16¾
0.5 Wavelength	117	40½	26½	13.5
0.25 Wavelength	58½	20¼	13¼	6¾
0.2 Wavelength	47	16	10⅝	5⅜
0.15 Wavelength	35	12	8	4
Balun loop (coax)	76	26.5	17¼	8¾

*Dimensions given for element lengths are for the middle of each band. For other frequencies adjust lengths as shown in the third line of table. Example: A dipole for 50.0 Mc. would be 106.5 + 4 = 110.5 inches.

Apply change figure to parasitic elements as well. For phasing lines or matching sections, and for spacing between elements, the midband figures are sufficiently accurate. They apply only to open-wire lines.

Parasitic-element lengths are optimum for 0.2 wavelength spacing.

from the table, except where otherwise noted. If the builder wishes to experiment with element lengths, it may be possible in some instances to increase the forward gain of the system by making the directors the same length—at a sacrifice in bandwidth. Similarly, the element lengths can be experimented with—staggering their dimensions—to secure greater bandwidth, but at the cost of reduced gain. Normally, the dimensions given in Table 18-1 will provide good all-around performance for average use.

PARASITIC ARRAYS

Single-bay arrays of 2 or more elements are widely used in 50-Mc. work. These may be built in many different ways, using the dimensions given in the table. Probably the strongest and lightest structure results from use of aluminum or dural tubing (usually 1¼ to 1½ inches in diameter) for the boom, though wood is also usable. If the elements are mounted at their midpoints there is no need to use insulating supports. Usually the elements are run through the boom and clamped in place in a manner similar to that shown in Fig. 18-6. Where a metal boom is used the joints between it and the elements must be tight, as any movement at this point will result in noisy reception.

Popular Matching Devices

Most common of the balanced-feed impedance-matching devices are the Delta or "Y" match, the so-called "hairpin" match—a modified version of the "Y" match, and the T Match. The Gamma Match is the favored device for direct connection to coax lines in unbalanced feed systems.

T-Match

The type of matching system used depends upon the type of feed line or phasing harness employed in the array. The T Match is the least difficult to adjust of the balanced systems and lends itself readily to providing the popular feedpoint impedances of 200 and 300 ohms. The latter impedance is useful when 300-ohm balanced feeders are used, or, a 4:1 balun can be connected to the T Match to convert the 300-ohm balanced terminal of the antenna to a 75-ohm unbalanced condition, suitable for use with 75-ohm coaxial feed line. If the T Match is adjusted for 200 ohms, a 4:1 balun permits the use of 50-ohm coaxial feed line. Whatever the arrangement, unbalanced feed-

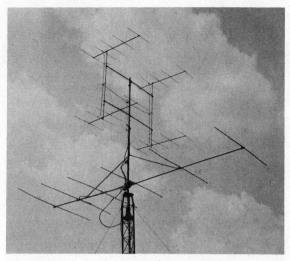

Fig. 18-4—The 6-element 50-Mc. array mounted and ready for use. A quad configuration of 5-element 144-Mc. Yagis is shown above the 6-meter beam.

ers should not be used with a balanced-feed driven element without the use a balanced-to-unbalanced transformer, for the reasons outlined earlier in this chapter.

A thorough discussion of T-Match design and adjustment is given in *The A.R.R.L. Antenna Book,* Chapter 3. Typical dimensions for an adjustable T Match are given in Fig. 18-3, at A.

Delta Match

The delta is the simplest of matching devices to be described here. It is particularly useful for feeding antennas with balanced transmission line. Baluns, however, can be used between the delta and a coaxial feeder to convert from a balanced to an unbalanced condition while at the same time transforming the antenna's feedpoint impedance to that of the coax line.

The less desireable features of the delta are its mechanical instability, particularly below 220 Mc., and its tendency to radiate, which may interfere with the effectiveness of a multi-element array. It is more critical to adjust than is the T Match. Information on deltas is given in Fig. 18-3, at B.

Gamma Match

Gamma-match feed is well suited to unbalanced transmission lines, permitting direct connection to the driven element of the antenna. The shield braid of the coax line connects to the center of the driven element and the center conductor is fed through a variable capacitor which connects to a metal arm which is tapped out on one half of the driven element. The tap point and the setting of the variable capacitor are juggled until a 1:1 s.w.r. is obtained. The gamma can be considered as one half of a T Match. With both systems, small mica compression trimmers can be used for the variable capacitors when the transmitter

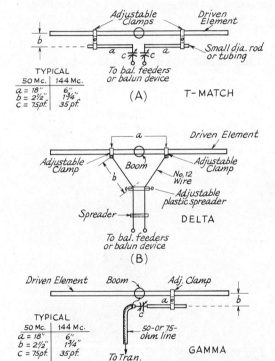

Fig. 18-3—Popular matching techniques for use with v.h.f. arrays. At A, adjustable clamps and capacitance, C, provide the required variables to secure an impedance match. At B, dimensions a and b are varied until a 1:1 s.w.r. is secured. Plastic spreader nearest the Delta section can be made to permit adjustment of dimension b. Dimension a is varied by means of adjustable clamps. Typical 144-Mc. dimensions are: a = 10 inches, b = 8 inches. Gamma match at C is used when coaxial feed line is connected directly to the driven element. Adjustable clamp and C are adjusted until a 1:1 s.w.r. is obtained. Typical values are given for 50- and 144-Mc.

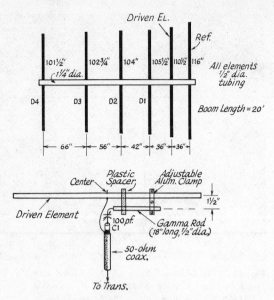

Fig. 18-5—Dimensions for the 50-Mc. array. C₁ should be mounted in a weatherproof box, as near to the gamma rod as possible. The shield braid of the coax cable is grounded to the center of the driven element.

at its center of gravity, rather than at its physical center. The boom is braced to prevent drooping, at points about 5 feet out from the mounting point. Braces are aluminum tubing, flattened at the ends, and clamped to the boom and the vertical member. Suspension bracing, as shown in Fig. 18-4, provides strength with lightweight supports.

Adjustment

Matching requires an s.w.r. bridge. It can be done properly in no other way. Mount the beam at least a half wavelength above ground and clear of trees and wires by at least the same distance. Set the transmitter at a frequency in the middle of the range you want to work (50.3 is a good spot for low-end operation) and adjust the position of the clip and the variable capacitor, $C1$, for minimum s.w.r. Move first one variable and then the other until zero reflected power is indicated. Tighten the clip solidly, then seal the variable capacitor's enclosure against the weather. Dow Corning Silastic RTV-732 sealant is available in 2-ounce tubes and is ideal for sealing antenna connections and coax fittings that are used out of doors.

13-ELEMENT YAGI FOR 144 MC.

A low-cost high-gain array for 2-meter operation is shown in Fig. 18-8. If properly constructed and adjusted, it should be capable of at least 15 db. of forward gain. Such an antenna is excellent for DX work. Two such antennas, stacked $1\frac{1}{2}$ wavelengths apart, should not be overlooked as a possibility for stringent DXing such as "scatter" communications.

power does not exceed approximately 100 watts input. Miniature receiving-type variable capacitors are suitable for powers up to 500 watts, provided a low s.w.r. is maintained. Double-spaced receiving-type variable capacitors are satisfactory for transmitters running between 500 and 1000 watts. The gamma- or T-match capacitors should be enclosed in a weatherproof plastic box and mounted as near to their related matching devices as possible. Gamma-match information is given in Fig. 18-3, at C. In-depth treatment of the subject is presented in *The A.R.R.L. Antenna Book,* Chapter 3.

6-ELEMENT 50-MC. ARRAY

The high-performance Yagi of Figs. 18-4 and 18-5 is built on a 20-foot boom, and features "plumber's-delight" construction. The $1\frac{1}{4}$" diameter boom is made from two 10-foot lengths of aluminum TV masting which have been fitted together and locked in place with sheet-metal screws. Support braces are used to prevent the boom from sagging and are visible in the photo. A gamma match is employed to permit the use of 50-ohm transmission line. The long boom and wide-spaced elements result in a sharp horizontal radiation pattern. This antenna is designed to work well over the low end of the band, 50 to 51 Mc.

Construction

The elements are attached to the boom as shown in Fig. 18-6. Details for fabricating the mounting hardware are given in Fig. 18-7. A detailed description of this antenna was published in *QST,* October 1966, p. 33. The array is mounted

Fig. 18-6—Mechanical details of the clamps used for attaching the elements to the boom of the 50-Mc. array.

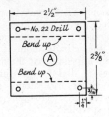

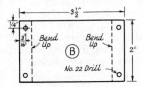

Fig. 18-7—Layout information for the home-made element mounts used on the 50-Mc. Yagi. Aluminum sheet, 1/16 inch thick or greater, should be used.

The boom length is 24 feet, requiring that three sections of aluminum TV masting be spliced together and braced with support arms (such as used in the 6-element 50-Mc. array) to prevent the boom from drooping. If 10-foot mast sections are used, it will be necessary to remove about six feet of stock from one of the sections.

Details for the folded-dipole driven element are given in Fig. 18-8. When used as shown, the s.w.r. will be less than 2:1, a tolerable level. If precise matching is desired, the universal matching stub, described earlier in this chapter, can be used between the 200-ohm feedpoint and the balun.

A 220-MC. BEAM ANTENNA

An effective easy-to-build Yagi for 220-Mc. use is shown in Fig. 18-9. This optimum-spaced 11 element array, if carefully constructed and adjusted, should be capable of at least 13 decibels of forward gain. A stacked array consisting of two or four of these beams should be excellent for DX applications.

A folded-dipole driven element is employed and is designed to provide a feedpoint impedance of approximately 200 ohms. A 4:1 balun is used to step the impedance down to 50 ohms, unbalanced, so that coaxial feed line can be used. A 1:1 match can be secured by using a universal matching stub in the same fashion as described for the 2-meter Yagi.

The boom is a 2 × 2-inch piece of lumber, 12 feet long. There is no reason why a metal boom could not be used, but if such is the case, the element lengths may have to be changed to assure optimum performance. This Yagi is cut for the low end of the band and works nicely from 220 to 221 Mc.

11-ELEMENT YAGI FOR 432 MC.

The high-performance array shown in Fig. 18-10 was described in *QST*, April 1966, page 19. The illustration shows one bay of the 4-bay array originally described. Used by itself, it will perform well and is capable of providing moderate coverage on 432 Mc. with a few watts of transmitter power.

The boom is fashioned from a piece of 1 × 1-inch lumber, 6 feet in length. A delta match is employed and its dimensions are given in Fig. 18-10. The gain of this antenna should be similar to that of the 220-Mc. array described in the foregoing text.

STACKED YAGI ARRAYS

The gain (in power) obtainable from a single Yagi array can be approximately doubled by stacking two or more of them vertically and feeding them in phase.[1] This refers to horizontal systems, of course. Vertically-polarized bays are usually stacked side by side. The principles to follow apply in either case.

The spacing between bays should be at least one-half wavelength, and more is desirable. For dipoles or Yagis of up to five elements optimum spacing between bays is about 5/8 wavelength, but with longer Yagis the spacing can

[1] Brown—"The Wide-Spread Twin-Five" *CQ*, March, 1950.

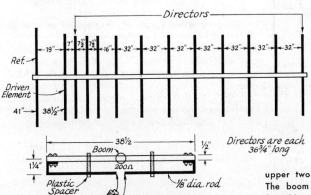

Fig. 18-8—Dimensions for the high-performance 144-Mc. long Yagi. Performance above 145 Mc. deteriorates considerably. Element lengths should be scaled down if operation in the upper two megacycles of the band is contemplated. The boom length of this array approaches 24 feet. Parasitic elements are made from hard-drawn aluminum rod such as is available from welding supply houses. (Original design data by W2NLY and W6QKI, QST, Jan. 1956.)

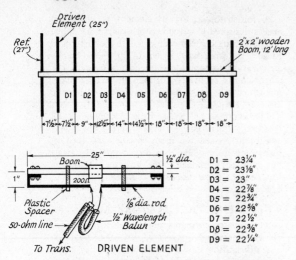

D1 = 23¼"
D2 = 23⅛"
D3 = 23"
D4 = 22⅞"
D5 = 22¾"
D6 = 22⅝"
D7 = 22½"
D8 = 22⅜"
D9 = 22¼"

Fig. 18-9—Construction data for a high-performance 220-Mc. Yagi. Parasitic elements are made from ⅛-inch diameter aluminum rod. Balun precautions of Fig. 18-8 should be followed.

be increased to one wavelength or more. Bays of 6 elements or more, spaced one wavelength, are commonly used in antennas for 144 Mc. and higher frequencies. Optimum spacing for long Yagis is about two wavelengths.

Where half-wave stacking is to be employed, the phasing line between bays can be treated as a double "Q" section. If two bays, each designed for 300-ohm feed, are to be stacked a half wavelength apart and fed at the midpoint between them, the phasing line should have an impedance of about 380 ohms. No. 12 wire spaced one inch will do for this purpose. The midpoint then can be fed either with 300-ohm line, or with 72-ohm coax and a balun.

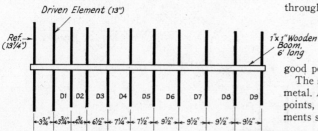

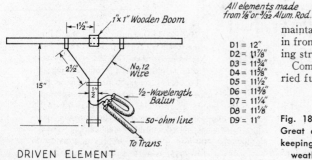

D1 = 12"
D2 = 11⅞"
D3 = 11¾"
D4 = 11⅝"
D5 = 11½"
D6 = 11⅜"
D7 = 11¼"
D8 = 11⅛"
D9 = 11"

When a spacing of ⅝ wavelength between bays is employed, the phasing lines can be coax. (The velocity factor of coax makes a full wavelength of line actually about ⅝ wavelength physically.) The impedance at the midpoint between two bays is slightly less than half the impedance of either bay alone, due to the coupling between bays. This effect decreases with increased spacing.

When two bays are spaced a full wavelength the coupling is relatively slight. The phasing line can be any open-wire line, and the impedance at the midpoint will be approximately half that of the individual bays. Predicting what it will be with a given set of dimensions is difficult, as many factors come into play. It will usually be of a value that can be fed through the combination of a "Q" section and a transmission line of 300 to 450 ohms impedance. An adjustable "Q" section, or an adjustable stub like to one shown in Fig. 18-2, may be used when the antenna impedance is not known.

LARGE COLLINEAR ARRAYS FOR 144 MC. AND HIGHER

High gain and very broad frequency response are desirable characteristics found in curtains of half-wave elements fed in phase and backed up by reflectors. The reflector can be made up of parasitic elements, or it can be a screen extending approximately a quarter wavelength beyond the ends of the driven elements. There is not a large difference between the two types of reflectors, except that higher front-to-back ratio and somewhat broader frequency response are achieved with the plane reflector.

16-Element Arrays

A collinear system that may be used on 144, 220 or 420 Mc. is shown in Fig. 18-12. It may be fed directly with 300-ohm transmission line, or through coaxial line and a balun. The 16-element array, Figs. 18-11 and 18-12, uses 0.2 wavelength spacing. Dimensions may be taken from Table 18-I, and figures for the middle of the band will give good performance across either band.

The supporting frame may be made of wood or metal. All elements can be mounted at their midpoints, and no insulators need be used. The elements should be mounted in front of the supporting frame, to keep metal out of the field of the array. This method is preferable to that wherein mechanical balance is maintained through mounting the driven elements in front and the reflectors in back of the supporting structure.

Combination of collinear arrays may be carried further. Pairs of 16-element systems fed in

Fig. 18-10—Dimensions for the 432-Mc. Yagi array. Great care should be given to the balun assembly, keeping leads as short as possible. Balun should be weatherproofed after being attached to the boom.

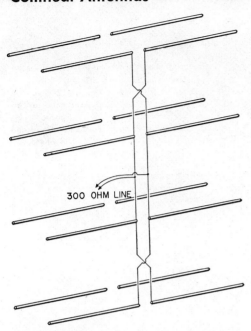

Fig. 18-11—Schematic of a 16-element collinear array. An adjustable matching stub, Fig. 18-2, can be attached at the feed point if precise matching is desired. Reflector-to-director spacing is 0.2 wavelength.

300 OHM LINE

phase are common, and even 64-element arrays (four 16-element beams fed in phase) are used in some stations on 144 Mc. Configurations of 32 to 64 elements are not difficult to build and support at 220 or 420 Mc. An example of two 16-element beams mounted on the same support is pictured in Fig. 18-12.

ARRAYS FOR 220 AND 420 MC.

The use of high-gain antenna systems is almost a necessity if work is to be done over any great distance on 220 and 420 Mc. Experimentation with antenna arrays for these frequencies is fascinating indeed, as their small size permits trying various element arrangements and feed systems with ease. Arrays for 420 Mc., particularly, are convenient for study and demonstration of antenna principles, as even high-gain systems may be of table-top proportions.

In some instances a good arrangement is obtained by mounting beams "back to back" on a single rotator. For example, a 16-element 220-Mc. array might be mounted with a 24-element 420-Mc. array (two 12-element assemblies mounted one above the other) and fed with separate transmission lines.

(For an example of stacking several commercial 220-Mc. beams, see "A 66-Element Stacked-Yagi Array for 220 Mc.," *QST*, January, 1959.)

Parabolic Reflectors

A plane sheet may be formed into the shape of a parabolic curve and used with a driven

radiator situated at its focus, to provide a highly directive antenna system. If the parabolic reflector is sufficiently large so that the distance to the focal point is a number of wavelengths, optical conditions are approached and the wave across the mouth of the reflector is a plane wave. However, if the reflector is of the same order of dimensions as the operating wavelength, or less, the driven radiator is appreciably coupled to the reflecting sheet and minor lobes occur in the pattern. With an aperture of 10 to 20 wavelengths, a practical size for microwave work, a beam width of approximately 5 degrees may be achieved.

A reflecting paraboloid must be carefully designed and constructed to obtain ideal performance. The antenna must be located at the focal point. The most desirable focal length of the parabola is that which places the radiator along the plane of the mouth; this length is equal to one-half the mouth radius.

CIRCULAR POLARIZATION

The need for circular antenna polarization—either left- or right-hand circularity—arises when a v.h.f. or u.h.f. station is employed for space communications. Such antennas are commonly used for E.M.E. (earth-moon-earth), frequently called "moonbounce," communications, and for Satellite work. Generally, such a station is equipped for both right- and left-hand circularity. Some stations use crossed dipoles, directors, and reflectors to provide the equivalent of one vertical and one horizontal Yagi on a single boom. A switchable phasing harness is used to

A stacked array for 144 Mc. (W1AW) which uses ⅝-wavelength spacing. The phasing lines and the ½-wavelength balun are joined in a weatherproof box. Element lengths for such an array can be taken from table 18-1. Element spacing is 0.2 wavelength.

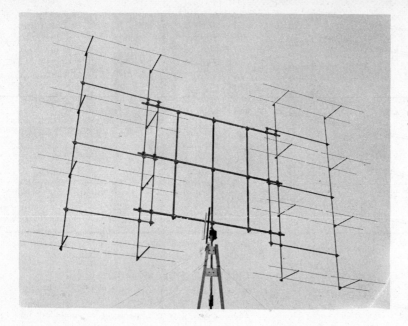

Fig. 18-12—Two 16-element collinear arrays spaced 1⅝ wavelength apart and fed in phase.

provide either right- or left-hand circularity at the operator's discretion. Parabolic antennas can be used in a similar fashion. The need for circular polarization and sense switching results from a condition known as "Faraday rotation."[2]

HELICAL BEAM ANTENNAS

A simple, yet practical approach to circular polarization is seen in the use of helical antennas.[3] Either right- or left-hand circular polarization can be had by winding the helix spiral with a right- or left-hand thread. The 8-turn helix of Fig. 18-13 is cut for 432-Mc. and has left-hand circularity. It is made up from a 213-inch length of aluminum clothesline wire. This length includes an extra 6 inches of wire, most of which is snipped away when the beam is pruned for a 1:1 s.w.r. after completion. Each turn of the helix is one wavelength long, resulting in a turn diameter of 0.31 wavelength. The distance between each turn is 0.25 wavelength. The turns are stapled to wooden support arms. The latter should be coated with liquid fibreglass or exterior spar varnish to make them weatherproof. The screen reflector is one wavelength (25 inches) square. A type-N coax fitting is soldered in place at the exact center of the screen to provide a connector for the quarter-wavelength matching section which converts the antenna's nominal 140-ohm impedance to that of the 50-ohm transmission line. The transformer should have an impedance of 83.7 ohms. Once the antenna is completed, and after its matching transformer is attached, an s.w.r. bridge can be connected in the line, power applied to the system, and the far end

of the helix trimmed (¼ inch at a time) for the lowest s.w.r. possible.

The support arms are made from sections of 1 × 1 wood and are each 60 inches long. The spacing between them is 8.25 inches, outer dimension. The screen of the antenna in Fig. 18-13 is tacked to the support arms for temporary use. A wooden framework for the screen would provide a more rugged antenna structure.[3] The theoretical gain of an 8-turn helical is approximately 14 decibels. Where both right- and left-hand circularity is desired, two antennas can be mounted on a common framework, a few wavelengths apart, and each antenna can be wound for the opposite sense.

OTHER ANTENNA TYPES

This section describes a few antenna systems that have not received wide-spread attention, mainly because little has been written about their use in the v.h.f. spectrum. These arrays, as well as many other "old standards," can provide excellent performance when used for the purposes outlined here.

The antennas of Figs. 18-15 through 18-17 provide moderate power gains over a dipole and are, for the most part, bidirectional. They can be used as portable antennas, eliminating the need for carrying a beam-type array to remote operating locations. All that is needed to support these systems are a couple of trees or similar mounts. They can be positioned for maximum effectiveness in the desired direction. Because they are bidirectional, it is possible to obtain good coverage in two directions—often an advantage. Some of these antennas are small enough to be used indoors, either in the attic or in a bedroom ham shack. The smaller arrays can be pinned to the wall with thumb tacks, or suspended from

[2] Kelso, *Radio Ray Propagation in the Ionosphere,* McGraw-Hill, p. 45, 137.

[3] DeMaw, "The Basic Helical Beam," *QST,* Nov. 1965.

the rafters in the attic. Although the latter approach is a compromise condition as far as erecting a highly-effective antenna is concerned, it is often the only choice for a city dweller.

The 3-element collinear array of Fig. 18-16, and the 10-wavelength long wire of Fig. 18-17 are natural candidates for backyard erection and will fit into even the smallest of city lots. Although not recommended as substitutes for the high-performance arrays described earlier in this chapter, these simple systems will do a creditable job for the operator that is not able to erect a tower, or mast-supported multi-element rotary array. Long-wire and collinear antennas are described in detail in *The A.R.R.L. Antenna Book*.

The four-bay "cubical-quad" antenna system described here, Fig. 18-18, is highly effective as a DX antenna and is comparable in performance to some of the Yagi antennas described earlier. Since it is inexpensive to build, and can be made

Fig. 18-14—An example of a 4-bay helical array cut for 1296-Mc. use. This stacked system offers approximately 6 db. more gain than a single bay is capable of providing. (Described in detail, QST, August 1963, by K6UQH.)

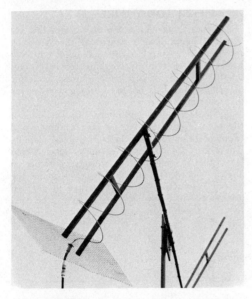

Fig. 18-13—An 8-turn 432-Mc. helical array. The helix is made from aluminum clothesline wire, but copper tubing could be used as well. The screen reflector is fashioned from galvanized hardware cloth. This beam is wound for left-hand circular polarization.

erators. It consists of four half-wavelength elements which are fed with a transposed phasing line, and matched to the transmission line by means of a quarter-wavelength adjustable stub, T_1. Although a 300-ohm (twinlead) feeder is shown in the illustration, there is no reason why a $\frac{1}{2}$-wavelength balun (4:1) could not be tapped to the appropriate points to T_1 to enable the user to employ 75-ohm coax as a feed line.

Construction

A 10-foot length of a.c. zip cord can be used for making up the elements and the phasing line for the 2-meter array. The cord can be split at one end and the two conductors (each with its insulation remaining) pulled apart, making two 10-foot sections of wire. Each wire should be pruned to a length of 115.5 inches and arranged in the configuration shown in Fig. 18-15. The center sections, B-B, are crossed, and use a plastic insulator, $3\frac{1}{2}$ inches square, to maintain uniform spacing between the two wires of the phasing line. The insulator should be located at the

from readily-available materials, it is worthy of consideration by those who are building their first 2-meter beam.

2-Meter Lazy H

This antenna is handy for the apartment dweller in that it can be built in a few minutes and is readily adaptable to wall mounting by means of Scotch tape or thumb tacks. It has a theoretical gain of 5.9 db. over a dipole, bidirectional—the equivalent of doubling the transmitter power two times.

Originally described in *QST*, December 1966, this array is a scaled-down version the Lazy H which has been popular with some low-band op-

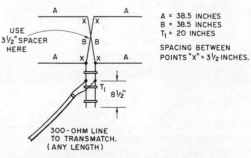

Fig. 18-15—Dimensions for the 144-Mc. Lazy H. This array is useful for the apartment dweller who cannot have an outdoor antenna.

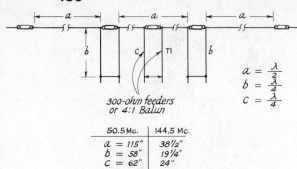

$$a = \frac{\lambda}{2}$$
$$b = \frac{\lambda}{4}$$
$$c = \frac{\lambda}{4}$$

	50.5 Mc.	144.5 Mc.
$a =$	115"	38½"
$b =$	58"	19¼"
$c =$	62"	24"

Fig. 18-16—A 3-element collinear for use indoors, in the back yard, or for portable operation.

exact center of the line. The insulation will have to be stripped from the wires at the point marked X so that the matching transformer, T_1, can be soldered in place. T_1 can be a 20-inch section of 450-ohm open-wire line, or a home-made transformer consisting of two 20-inch lengths of No. 12 bare wire, spaced approximately one inch apart.

Adjustment

If 300-ohm feeders are used, they can be tapped up on T_1 to a point about 8½ inches from the bottom of the transformer. This should provide a close match. If precise matching is desired, a 4:1 coax balun can be connected to the 300-ohm feed line and an s.w.r. bridge inserted in the 75-ohm feeder below the balun. The tap points on T_1 should then be adjusted for a 1:1 s.w.r. By making suitable changes in the dimensions of A, B, and T_1, the Lazy H can be built for 6-meter operation. Maximum radiation occurs at right angles to the plane of the antenna. The array, when mounted as shown, radiates a horizontally-polarized beam.

3-ELEMENT COLLINEAR

This array has a theoretical gain of 3.2 db., bidirectional. It radiates a horizontally-polarized signal and is small enough to be used indoors if need be. The 2-meter version is short enough to be pinned to a wall in the ham shack, provided approximately 10 feet of wall space is available. The 6-meter version requires about 29 feet of space and will fit into most attics. Either version could be used more effectively if erected out of doors, as high as possible. Three-element collinears of this kind are handy for "hill topping" and other portable work.

Construction

Dimensions for 6- or 2-meter operation are given in Fig. 18-16. The phrasing stubs, b, can be made from lengths of 300-ohm twinlead, or from suitable lengths of open-wire line. Each stub is shorted at the end opposite the antenna. The center stub, T_1, is made slightly longer than ¼ wavelength to permit some latitude of adjustment. It can be composed of two lengths of No. 12 bare wire, spaced 1 inch center to center.

Plastic spacers should be used to maintain even spacing. If some 450-ohm open-wire line is handy, it can be used for T_1. The half-wave elements, a, can be made from No. 14 or No. 12 copper wire, stranded or solid.

Adjustment

A 4:1 coax balun can be tapped on T_1 and 75-ohm coax line can be used for a feeder. If this is done, an s.w.r. bridge should be connected in the line and the taps on T_1, plus the short on the bottom end of T_1, adjusted for a 1:1 s.w.r. Once the proper adjustments are made, the balun can be replaced by 300-ohm twinlead and the transmitter connected to the line through a Transmatch of the type described at the end of this chapter. The Transmatch will permit greater changes in operating frequency before the s.w.r. "seen" by the transmitter is too high for satisfactory operation.

A 2-METER LONG WIRE

Although long-wire antennas (Chap. 14) are usually thought of as h.f. antennas, they are very useful in the v.h.f. region. An antenna is not truly a "long wire" until it contains several wavelengths of wire. A long piece of wire, in terms of inches or feet, is not a true long wire as far as proper antenna terminology is concerned. The long, single wire described here, Fig. 18-17, has a theoretical gain of 7.4 db. over a dipole and radiates its major lobes in bidirectional fashion. There are also a number of minor lobes which leave the antenna at many different radiation angles. The aforementioned features make the antenna useful for general coverage in a given area, but with two major lobes that can be used to favor specific areas.

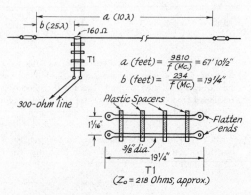

$$a \text{ (feet)} = \frac{9810}{f \text{ (Mc.)}} = 67'10\tfrac{1}{2}''$$
$$b \text{ (feet)} = \frac{234}{f \text{ (Mc.)}} = 19\tfrac{1}{4}''$$

Fig. 18-17—A 144-Mc. 10-wavelength long-wire antenna. This system is suitable for portable operation, or it can be erected in the back yard for local and medium-distance work. The matching section T_1, can be eliminated and tuned feeders can be attached directly to the feed point. A v.h.f. Transmatch, described later in this chapter, can be used to tune the line. If 300-ohm u.h.f. ribbon line is employed, the mismatch will be on the order of 2:1 and will not seriously impair operation.

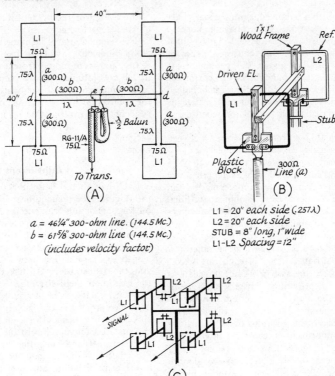

$a = 46\tfrac{1}{4}''\ 300\text{-}ohm\ line.\ (144.5\,Mc.)$
$b = 61\tfrac{5}{8}''\ 300\text{-}ohm\ line\ (144.5\,Mc.)$
(includes velocity factor)

L1 = 20″ each side (.257λ)
L2 = 20″ each side
STUB = 8″ long, 1″ wide
L1–L2 Spacing = 12″

Fig. 18-18—A four-bay cubical-quad array for 144-Mc. At A, the harnessing details. The 0.75 wavelength sections of 300-ohm ribbon line step the impedance up from 75 ohms to 1200 ohms at d. Paralleling the line sections at d halves the impedance which results in a 600-ohm condition. Two 1-wavelength line sections of 300-ohm line repeat the 600-ohm impedances at e-f, placing them in parallel to give a resultant impedance of 300 ohms. The line sections should be dressed along the wooden support structure, and taped in place in a symmetrical fashion. At B, details for one bay of the array. The sketch at C shows a perspective view of the assembled array.

The antenna is 10 wavelengths long and is fed at a current loop, one-quarter wavelength in from one end. The approximate impedance of the antenna is 160 ohms, requiring that a quarter-wave transformer, T_1, approximately 218 ohms, be used to step the impedance up to 300 ohms. The latter impedance is convenient for connection to standard 300-ohm twinlead, or to a 4:1 balun for use with 75-ohm coaxial cable. The values given in Fig. 18-17 are approximate and may not provide a 1:1 s.w.r. ratio. However, conditions will be good enough to permit satisfactory operation. If precise matching is desired, the universal stub of Fig. 18-2 can be connected to the 160-ohm feed point of the antenna.

Maximum radiation is off the *ends* of the antenna—not off the broad side. A radiation angle of roughly 18 degrees is typical for this antenna when mounted a few wavelengths above flat ground.

This antenna, if cut to 10 wavelengths on 50 Mc., would be quite long—nearly 200 feet. For this reason, it might not be too practical for 6-meter use. It could, however, be cut down to five or six wavelengths and still be useful, but at reduced gain. The feed impedance is differ-

ent for each number of wavelengths used, requiring that T_1 be tailored accordingly. A universal adjustable stub could be used if other than 10 wavelengths are used. This antenna is handy for portable operation and can be rolled up and carried in the trunk of the car. When in use, it can be strung between a couple of trees, or similar supports.

4-BAY QUAD FOR 144 MC.

The approximate gain of a single 2-element cubical quad is 5.7 db. over that of a dipole. The front-to-back ratio is on the order of 25 decibels, with a front-to-side ratio that is extremely high. The antenna of Fig. 18-18, by virtue of its additional bays, has a theoretical gain of 11.7 decibels. By arranging four quads as shown, greater aperture results and the array becomes useful for long-range communications. A single bay, Fig. 18-18B, can be gainfully employed as a medium-range antenna and performs well for local work also. Interlaced quads, cut for 6- and 2-meter operation, have been used successfully by some.

The driven element of a cubical quad has a balanced feed point. Therefore, the array of Fig.

18-18A is fed with a balanced, symmetrical phasing harness. A coaxial-cable phasing harness could be employed (DeMaw, "A Quad-Quad Array," *73,* May 1964) but causes a skew of approximately 10 degrees in the radiated pattern. Also, it is not uncommon to encounter feeder radiation when connecting unbalanced feeders to balanced antenna terminals. Feeder radiation is particularly troublesome when using stacked arrays.

A spacing of 0.12 wavelength is used between the driven elements, L_1, and the reflectors, L_2, to provide a feed impedance of approximately 75 ohms. The bays are spaced ½ wavelength away from one another. Line sections *a* are made from ¾-wavelength sections of 300-ohm foam-filled TV ribbon and serve as matching transformers to convert the 75-ohm feed impedance of each bay to 1200 ohms, at *d*. By joining sections *a*, at *d*, the impedance is halved and becomes 600 ohms. Two additional lines, *b*, each one wavelength long, place the two 600-ohm impedances in parallel at *e-f*, providing a feed impedance of 300 ohms for the array. The system can be fed directly with 300-ohm line and a transmatch, or a balun (4:1) can be used at *e-f* and 75-ohm line (RG-11/A) can be used between the antenna and the equipment. Line sections *a* were cut to ¾ wavelength because standard ¼-wavelength transformers would have been too short, physically, to reach between the driven elements. Care must be taken to connect the various lines as shown in Fig. 18-18A, thus assuring the correct phase relationship between the bays.

Construction

An in-depth description of the supporting frame for this array will not be given here. Details for the framework of one bay are given in Fig. 18-18B. Support arms for the composite array can be cut from 2 × 2 or 1 × 2-inch lumber. If a metal framework is used, both elements (L_1 and L_2) should be mounted in front of the framework to prevent interference with the antenna's performance.

The elements are fashioned from aluminum clothesline wire, available from Sears, Roebuck & Co., and from most hardware stores. The ends of L1 are flattened with a hammer, then drilled to accommodate 4-40 hardware and solder lugs for connection to line sections *a*. The stub on the reflector is a continuation of L2. Plastic blocks, ⅛ inch thick, attach to the frame as shown, serving as insulators and tie points for the elements.

Adjustment

Each bay should be adjusted separately, prior to attaching the phasing harness. Mount all bays on the supporting frame and raise the system to a height of at least two wavelengths above ground. Place a field-strength meter several wavelengths in front of the array and attach a length of 75-ohm line between one of the bays and the transmitter. Adjust the reflector stub for maximum field-strength. Repeat the foregoing with each of the 4 bays. The harness can now be attached and no further adjustment should be necessary. If the operator wishes, he can install a universal adjustable stub, Fig. 18-2, at points *e-f* and tune the stub to give a 1:1 s.w.r. between the line and the antenna. By using a 4:1 coaxial balun, and tapping it on the universal stub, a 200-ohm point can be found, thus permitting the use of 50-ohm coaxial transmission line.

The bandwidth of this array is such that operation from 144 to 145.5 Mc. can be carried out without a significant increase in s.w.r. The antenna has provided excellent performance over long paths, resulting in a marked reduction in signal fading over that which was possible with Yagis and collinear arrays. Some operators have experimented with this basic design and have used as many as 5 elements per bay (3 directors), reporting an apparent increase in overall gain of as much as one S unit.

V BEAMS AND RHOMBICS

By combining long-wire antennas it is possible to realize excellent gain and directivity in v.h.f. and u.h.f. operation. Long-wire antennas can be combined to form V beams or rhombics. When made several wavelengths long on each leg, such antennas perform in an excellent manner for long-haul point-to-point communications.

Information concerning leg lengths and other important dimensions is given in *The Radio Amateur's V.H.F. Manual,* 1st Edition, Chapter 8. Additional design information is available in *The ARRL Antenna Book,* all editions.

V beams and rhombics, when not terminated by a non-inductive resistor whose value matches their characteristic impedance, are bidirectional as far as the radiated signal is concerned. When the termination is added at the end of the antenna opposite the feed point, either type becomes unidirectional with maximum radiation off the terminated end.

It is practical to stack one or more v.h.f. rhombic or V-beam antennas for added gain and increased aperature. Either antenna type can be fed with open-wire line and used with a Transmatch of the type described in Chapter 17.

Rhombic antennas have been used successfully for 144-Mc. e.m.e. (moonbounce) communications. Their dimensions are such that is is often practical to erect them on ordinary-size city lots. Their usefullness should not be overlooked for point-to-point and DX work.

A TRANSMATCH FOR 50 AND 144 MC. WITH S.W.R. BRIDGE

The antenna coupler (Transmatch) shown in Fig. 18-19 will permit unbalanced transmitter output lines (50-75 ohms) to be matched to balanced feeders in the 300 to 450-ohm impedance range. Also, "coax-to-coax" matching is possible with this circuit, permitting 50-ohm lines to be matched to 75-ohm lines, or vice versa. In situations where a high s.w.r. condition exists—where an antenna is being used in a part of the band to which it has not been tuned—this coupler will enable the transmitter to look into a flat load, thus permitting maximum loading for better efficiency. The Transmatch will of course permit matching between unbalanced lines of like impedance as well—50-ohm to 50-ohm, or 75-ohm to 75-ohm lines.

Couplers of this type are beneficial in the reduction of harmonic energy from the transmitter, an aid to TVI reduction. It should be possible to realize a 30-db.-or-greater decrease in harmonic level by using this Transmatch between the transmitter and the feed line. When connected ahead of the receiver as well—a common arrangement—the added selectivity of the coupler's tuned circuits will help to reduce images and other undesired receiver responses from out-of-band signals. The built-in Monimatch-type s.w.r. indicator [1] enables the operator to tune the Transmatch for minimum reflected power, assuring a good match between the transmitter and the feed line. It is wise to remember that the use of devices of this kind *will not* correct for any mismatch that exists at the antenna end of the line. Although it assures a good match between the transmitter and the line, it can only disguise the fact that a mismatch exists at the antenna.

The Circuit

Balanced circuits are used for both bands, Fig. 18-20. Butterfly capacitors are employed to aid in securing good circuit symmetry. The links of each tuned circuit, L_2 and L_3, are series-tuned by single-ended capacitors to help tune out reactance in the line. Switch S_1 transfers the s.w.r. bridge element from one tuned circuit to the other, providing visual indication of the matching adjustments. A section of S_1 (S_{1B}) shorts out the unused tuned circuit to prevent interaction between the circuits. Switch S_2 selects either the forward- or reflected-power sampling circuits from the bridge and supplies their rectified d.c. voltages to R_1, the meter sensitivity control. R_1 is used to adjust M_1 to full scale when S_2 is set to read forward power.

Construction

A home-made $12 \times 5 \times 5$-inch aluminum cabinet is used to contain the circuit.[2] If a similar layout is followed, keeping all leads as short as practical, there is no reason why the complete

Fig. 18-19—This 6- and 2-meter antenna coupler has a built-in s.w.r. bridge and permits power levels up to 500 watts. This unit will work with balanced or unbalanced feeders.

unit cannot be housed in a commercially-available chassis or cabinet. The r.f. tuning controls are mounted in a straight line across the front of the cabinet. The s.w.r. bridge element, Fig. 18-20 B, is bolted to the bottom of the case (inside) between the input jack, J_7, and the band-change switch, S_1. Shielded audio cable is used to connect the output of the bridge to the lugs on S_2. Short lengths of RG-58/U coax cable connect L_2 and L_3 to S_{1A}. The shield braids of both cables should be grounded to the chassis at each end.

A 2-lug terminal strip is bolted to the chassis directly under the center of L_1. Similarly, a second terminal strip with two lugs is mounted under the midpoint of L_4. These strips serve as mounting points for links L_2 and L_3. No. 12 buss wire (bare) connects the rotors of all four tuning capacitors in to one another. The ground buss is also connected to the main chassis at one point. This procedure assures a better ground return for the capacitors than might be possible by relying upon the physical contact provided by the shaft bushings.

The coil taps are effected by bending standard No. 6 solder lugs around the coil wire at the proper spots, then soldering the lugs in place. No. 20 buss wire is used to connect the taps of L_1 to jacks J_1 and J_2. A short piece of 300-ohm twin line connects the taps of L_4 to J_4 and J_5. A No. 6 solder lug is bolted to the outside (back) of the cabinet as near to J_1 as possible. Another such lug is placed adjacent to J_4. When operating coax-to-coax style, a short jumper wire connects J_1 to its ground lug, or J_4 to its ground lug, depending on the band being operated. *The jumper must be removed for balanced-feeder operation.*

The cabinet is finished in two-tone gray. Masking tape was used to facilitate the division between the two colors. Standard aerosol-type spray-can paints were used. Decals were added to identify the controls and to give the unit a professional look.

[1] McCoy, "Monimatch Mark II", Feb. 1957, *QST*.
[2] DeMaw, "The Easy Box", September 1966, *QST*.

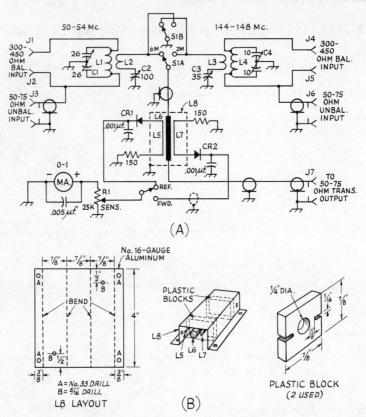

Fig. 18-20—At A, the schematic diagram of the v.h.f. Transmatch. Capacitance is in pf. unless otherwise noted. Resistance is in ohms, K = 1000. At B, physical layout of the bridge element and the plastic insulating blocks.

C_1—26-pf. per section butterfly (E. F. Johnson 167-22).

C_2—100-pf. miniature variable (Millen 20100).

C_3—35-pf. miniature variable (Millen 20035).

C_4—10-pf. per section butterfly (E. F. Johnson 167-21).

CR_1, CR_2—Germanium diode, 1N34A or equal.

J_1, J_2, J_3, J_4—Insulated binding post.

J_5, J_6, J_7—SO-239-style chassis connector.

L_1—7 turns No. 10 copper wire, 1½-inch dia., spaced one wire thickness between turns. Tap 2½ turns from each end.

L_2—Two turns No. 14 enam. or spaghetti-covered bare wire, 2½-inch dia., over center of L_1.

L_3—Two turns No. 14 enam. or spaghetti-covered bare wire, 1½-inch dia., over center of L_4.

L_4—5 turns No. 10 copper wire, 1-inch dia., spaced one wire thickness between turns. Tap 1½ turns from each end.

L_5—3-inch length of No. 16 solid wire.

L_6—4-inch length of ¼-inch dia. copper tubing.

L_7—Same as L_5.

L_8—See drawing.

R_1—25,000-ohm control, linear taper.

S_1—2-pole 2-position rotary, single section, phenolic switch (Centralab 1462).

S_2—S.p.s.t. rotary, single section, phenolic switch (Centralab 1460).

The Bridge Element

The s.w.r. element is of the Monimatch variety, popularized in QST in the 1950s.[1] The circuit is given in Fig. 18-20A, with its physical layout shown in Fig. 18-20 at B. The inner line, L_6, is a 4-inch length of ¼-inch o.d. copper tubing. One end of L_6 is soldered directly to the center lug of J_7, the remaining end supported by a small standoff insulator. The line is mounted in plastic blocks for additional support, making sure that it is centered within the walls of L_8, the aluminum outer channel. J_7 should be mounted on the back wall of the box so as to be centered on the axis of L_6 when it is in position. The pickup lines, L_5 and L_7, are made from No. 16 wire, each 3 inches in length, and are spaced ⅛ inch away from L_6, being supported by the plastic blocks. Once they are in place, a drop of Duco cement should be added at each point where they pass through the plastic blocks, thus securing them. The 150-ohm terminating resistors (½-watt units) are mounted inside the channel, L_8, and are soldered to ground lugs. Diodes CR_1 and CR_2 attach to the remaining ends of wires and are

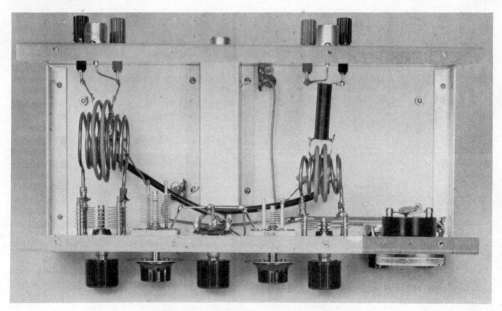

Fig. 18-21—Inside view of the Transmatch. The 6-meter circuit is at the left, the s.w.r. bridge element is at the center, and the 2-meter circuit is to the right of the bridge element. The meter, S_2, and R_1 are at the far right.

routed out through small holes in the walls of L_8. It is important that the physical placement of the diodes, the resistors, and the pickup wires be executed in symmetrical fashion. The better the symmetry, the better will be the balance of the bridge, electrically. The diodes are their related 0.001-uf. bypass capacitors are attached to small terminal strips that are mounted near the holes in L_8. If matched resistors and matched diodes are used in the bridge circuit, electrical balance will be even better than is possible with random-selected components. Since the bridge is but a relative-reading instrument, the latter condition is not vital, however.

Operation

Attach the v.h.f. transmitter to J_7 with a short length of coax cable. Connect a balanced feeder to J_1 and J_2 (for 50-Mc. operation), or to J_4 and J_5 (for 144-Mc. operation). Set S_1 to the desired band position and switch S_2 to read forward power. Initially, R_1 should be set for minimum meter sensitivity. Apply power from the transmitter—low power until initial tuning is completed—and adjust R_1 for full-scale meter reading. Next, set S_2 to the reflected-power position. Adjust C_1 and C_2, alternately (for 50-Mc. operation) for minimum meter reading. For

144-Mc. operation, tune C_3 and C_4 in the same manner. Repeat the tuning until no further reduction in reflected power is possible. The meter should fall to zero, indicating a 1:1 match. Switch S_2 back to the forward position and set R_1 for a full-scale meter reading. No further adjustments will be needed until the transmitter frequency is moved 50 kc. or more. The tuning procedure is identical for matching coax to coax. In doing so, however, the antenna feed line (coax) is connected to either J_3 or J_6 and the shorting strap (discussed earlier) must be connected to J_1 or J_4. In some situations, it may be possible to get a better match by leaving the shorting strap off.

After the coupler is tuned up, the transmitter power can be increased to its normal level. This unit will handle power levels up to 500 watts (transmitter output power) provided the coupler is tuned for a matched condition at all times. Reduced power (less than 50 watts) should be used during initial tuneup, thus preventing parts from being damaged by heating or arcing. The coupler should *never* be operated without a load connected to its output terminals. Such operation will usually destroy the 150-ohm resistors and the diodes, CR_1 and CR_2, in additon to causing arcs in the Transmatch.

Chapter 19

Mobile and Portable-Emergency Equipment

Amateur mobile operation provides many opportunities for exercising one's individuality and for developing original ideas in equipment. Each installation has its own special problems.

Simple a.m. mobile receiving systems are based on the use of an h.f. converter working into a standard car broadcast receiver tuned to 1500 kc., which serves as the i.f. and audio amplifiers. The car receiver is modified to take a noise limiter and to provide power for the converter.

While a few mobile a.m. transmitters may run final-amplifier powed inputs of 100 watts or more, an input of 30 to 50 watts is a more usual figure, unless the car is equipped with a special battery-charging system. Transistor amplifiers for modulator stages (instead of vacuum tubes) reduce the power-supply requirements.

S.s.b. *transceivers* offer the most effective use of the total available power.

Mobile c.w. operation has been accomplished by a few hardy driver-operators, but never with the best wishes of highway safety agencies. "Portable" c.w. operation (from a *parked* car), or mobile operation by a passenger, are worthy considerations for emergency work.

If the mobile station is a single package, such as an s.s.b. transceiver, it will usually be mounted under the dashboard over the transmission tunnel.

The power supply is best mounted in the engine compartment or in the trunk. If the station consists of several units (exclusive of power supply), tuning dials requiring observation should be mounted where they can be seen by the operator with a minimum of acrobatics. Power-control switches, which can be operated without direct observation, are not subject to this restriction. Common spots for the location of tunable converters or receivers are on top or bottom of the instrument panel, or attached to the steering post.

The send-receive switch, which usually controls a heavy-duty relay (to avoid having to carry heavy current), can be incorporated in the unit mounted closest to the driver-operator.

Frequency within any of the phone bands sometimes is changed remotely by means of a stepping-switch system that switches crystals. In most cases, however, extensive frequency excursions within a band, and band-changing, require stopping the car to make the necessary transmitter and antenna changes.

When a mobile a.m. transmitter is used, only the frequency-control unit (v.f.o. or crystal-selector switch) need be readily available to the operator. The transmitter proper can be mounted anywhere if small, and in the trunk if large.

Most mobile antennas consist of a vertical whip with some system of adjustable loading for the lower frequencies. Power supplies are of the vibrator, motor-generator, or transistor type operating from the car storage battery.

Units intended for use in mobile installations should be assembled with greater than ordinary care, since they will be subject to considerable vibration. Soldered joints should be well made and wire wrap-arounds should be used to avoid dependence upon the solder for mechanical strength. Self-tapping screws should be used wherever feasible, otherwise lock-washers should be provided. Any shafts that are normally operated at a permanent or semi-permanent setting should be provided with shaft locks so they cannot jar out of adjustment. Where wires pass through metal, the holes should be fitted with rubber grommets to prevent chafing. Any cabling or wiring between units should be securely clamped in place where it cannot work loose to interfere with the operation of the car.

NOISE ELIMINATION

Electrical-noise interference to reception in a car arise from several different sources. Trouble may be experienced with ignition noise, generator and voltage-regulator hash, or wheel static.

A noise limiter added to the car broadcast receiver will go far in reducing some types, especially ignition noise from passing cars as well as your own. But for the satisfactory reception of weaker signals, some treatment of the car's electrical system will be necessary.

Tire Static

The traditional cure for tire static is to inject "antistatic powder" into the tire tubes. However, few garages or other suppliers stock such a powder these days, and the injector (for getting the antistatic powder into the tubes) is even harder to find.

"Antistatic powder" is nothing more than the graphite powder used for lubricating locks. The dry graphite powder is packaged in a small plastic tube similar to a small toothpaste tube. To use it for eliminating tire static, deflate the tires, squeeze the graphite into the tubes and re-inflate the tires. Tire men state that the powder has no adverse effect on the tube.

Ignition Interference

Fig. 19-1 indicates the measures that may be taken to suppress ignition interference. The capacitor at the primary of the ignition coil should be of the coaxial type; ordinary types are not effective. It should be placed as close to the coil terminal as possible. In stubborn cases, two of these capacitors with an r.f. choke between them may provide additional suppression. The size of the choke must be determined experimentally. The winding should be made with wire heavy enough to carry the coil primary current. A 10,000-ohm suppressor resistor should be inserted at the center tower of the distributor, a 5000-ohm suppressor at each spark-plug tower on the distributor, and a 10,000 ohm suppressor

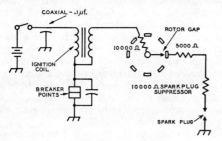

Fig. 19-1—Ignition system with recommended suppression methods.

at each spark plug. The latter may be built-in or external. A good suppressor element should be molded of material having low capacitance. Several concerns manufacture satisfactory suppressors. In extreme cases, it may be necessary to use shielded ignition wire. Suppressor ignition wire kits having the resistance distributed throughout the length of the wire are available from some automobile supply dealers. Distributed resistance of this type is somewhat superior to lumped resistance and may be used if the lead lengths are right to fit your car. They should not be cut, but used as they are sold.

D.C. Generator Noise

Generator hash is caused by sparking at the commutator. The pitch of the noise varies with the speed of the motor. This type of noise may be eliminated by using a 0.1- to 0.25 μf. coaxial capacitor in the generator armature circuit. This capacitor should be mounted as near the armature terminal as possible and directly on the frame of the generator.

To reduce the noise at 28 Mc., it may be necessary to insert a parallel trap, tuned to the middle of the band, in series with the generator output lead. The coil should have about 8 turns of No. 10 wire, space-wound on a 1-inch diameter and should be shunted with a 30-p.f. mica trimmer. It can be pretuned by putting it in the antenna lead to the home-station receiver tuned to the middle of the band, and adjusting the trap to the point of minimum noise. The tuning may need to be peaked up after installing in the car, since it is fairly critical.

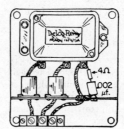

Fig. 19-2—Bypasses installed to reduce regulator interference. A capacitor should never be connected across the generator field lead without the small series resistor indicated.

Practically all of the newer cars use alternators (generators of a.c.) in conjunction with silicon-diode rectifiers for battery charging. The system provides better battery charging and less headlight-intensity variation at low engine speeds. However, normal care and maintenance is required for minimum radio noise. Alternator noise will be caused by dirty collector rings, and the rings and brushes should be cleaned every 10,000 miles for best radio performance.

Voltage-Regulator Interference

In eliminating voltage-regulator noise, the use of two coaxial capacitors, and a resistor-mica-capacitor combination, as shown in Fig. 19-2, are effective. A 0.1- to 0.25-μf. coaxial capacitor should be placed between the battery terminal of the regulator and the battery, with its case well grounded. Another capacitor of the same size and type should be placed between the generator terminal of the regulator and the generator. A 0.002-μf. mica capacitor with a 4-ohm carbon resistor in series should be connected between the field terminal of the regulator and ground. Never use a capacitor across the field contacts or between field and ground without the resistor in series, since this greatly reduces the life of the regulator. In some cases, it may be necessary to pull double-braid shielding over the leads between the generator and regulator. It will be advisable to run new wires, grounding the shielding well at both ends. If regulator noise persists, it may be necessary to insulate the regulator from the car body. The wire shielding is then connected to the regulator case at one end and the generator frame at the other.

Wheel Static

Wheel static shows up as a steady popping in the receiver at speeds over about 15 m.p.h. on smooth dry streets. Front-wheel static collectors are available on the market to eliminate this variety of interference. They fit inside the dust cap and bear on the end of the axle, effectively grounding the wheel at all times. Those designated particularly for your car are preferable, since the universal type does not always fit well. They are designed to operate without lubrication and the end of the axle and dust cap should be cleaned of grease before the installation is made. These collectors require replacement about every 10,000 miles.

Rear-wheel collectors have a brush that bears against the inside of the brake drum. It may be necessary to order these from the factory through your dealer.

Tracing Noise

To determine if the receiving antenna is picking up all of the noise, the shielded lead-in should be disconnected at the point where it connects to the antenna. The motor should be started with the receiver gain control wide open. If no noise is heard, all noise is being picked up via the antenna. If the noise is still heard with the antenna disconnected, even though it may be reduced in strength, it indicates that some signal from the ignition system is being picked up by the antenna transmission line. The

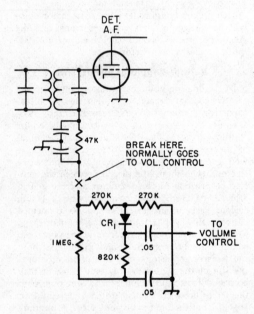

Fig. 19-3—Diagram showing addition (heavy lines) of series noise limiter to car radio receiver. A high back-resistance silicon diode is required (see text) but a vacuum-tube diode may be substituted if there is sufficient room in the receiver. A switch across the diode will remove the noise-limiting action, but leads to the switch must be short and shielded.

lead-in may not be sufficiently-well shielded, or the shield not properly grounded. Noise may also be picked up through the battery circuit, although this does not normally happen if the receiver is provided with the usual r.f.-choke-and-bypass capacitor filter.

In case of noise from this source, a direct wire from the "hot" battery terminal to the receiver is recommended.

Ignition noise varies in repetition rate with engine speed and usually can be recognized by that characteristic in the early stages. Later, however, it may resolve itself into a popping noise that does not always correspond with

engine speed. In such a case, it is a good idea to remove all leads from the generator so that the only source left is the ignition system.

Regulator and generator noise may be detected by racing the engine and cutting the ignition switch. This eliminates the ignition noise. Generator noise is characterized by its musical whine contrasted with the ragged raspy irregular noise from the regulator.

With the motor running at idling speed, or slightly faster, checks should be made to try to determine what is bringing the noise into the field of the antenna. It should be assumed that any control rod, metal tube, steering post, etc., passing from the motor compartment through an insulated bushing in the firewall will carry noise to a point where it can be radiated to the antenna. All of these should be bonded to the firewall with heavy wire or braid. Insulated wires can be stripped of r.f. by bypassing them to ground with $0.5-\mu$f. metal-case capacitors. The following should not be overlooked: battery lead at the ammeter, gasoline gauge, ignition switch, headlight, backup and taillight leads and the wiring of any accessories running from the motor compartment to the instrument panel or outside the car.

The firewall should be bonded to the frame of the car and also to the motor block with heavy braid. If the exhaust pipe and muffler are insulated from the frame by rubber mountings, they should likewise be grounded to the frame with flexible copper braid.

Noise Limiting

Fig. 19-3 shows the alterations that may be made in the existing car-receiver circuit to provide for a noise limiter. The dark lines show the additional circuitry for a self-adjusting series limiter. It is important that the diode CR_1 be silicon and of the high back-resistance type. Some silicon diodes will give only fair results and germanium diodes will not work at all. The 1N658 computer diode works well in this application and its performance can be compared to that of a vacuum tube. The limiter can be switched out of the circuit by shorting the diode CR_1, but the leads to the switch should be as short as possible and must be shielded.

The switch that cuts the limiter in and out of the circuit may be located for convenience on or near the converter panel. Regardless of its placement, however, the leads to the switch should be shielded to prevent hum pick-up.

Several other noise limiter circuits are described in ARRL's publication, *The Mobile Manual For Radio Amateurs*. The *Mobile Manual* also describes a combination noise limiter and audio squelch circuit. Squelch circuits are designed to suppress receiver background noise in the absence of signals (see Chapter 5); their chief use is in fixed-frequency (net) operation.

At least one manufacturer produces a complete noise limiter unit. The unit is mounted external to the main chassis and takes operating voltages from the receiver.

160-Meter FET Mobile Converter

This simple converter has good immunity to cross-talk and overload from strong signals. It operates from a 12-volt supply, but can also be used for portable work while using a 9-volt battery.

The circuit is shown in Fig. 19-4. Signals arriving from the antenna are routed through FL_1, a band-rejection filter which is designed to attenuate signals in the range of 500 to 1600 kc., thus helping to reduce broadcast-station response in the tunable i.f. range of this converter. The JFET r.f. amplifier, Q_1, has a tuned circuit in its gate lead, and another in the drain circuit. C_1 is operated from the front panel, permitting the operator to peak the input circuit when moving from one part of the band to another. A bandpass coupler, consisting of L_7 and L_8 (and some fixed-value capacitors), is used between the r.f. and mixer stages to provide added selectivity. Once tuned as described later, this circuit requires no further attention.

For high Q, thus good selectivity, the input tuned circuit, C_1-L_6, uses a toroid core. Windings L_4 and L_5 use heavy wire—No. 14 gauge—so that the pigtails are stiff enough to be used as supports for the inductor. Other mounting methods can be used, thus eliminating the need for heavy wire in those windings. The main winding, L_6, uses small-diameter wire.

A second JFET, Q_2, is used as a mixer. A Pierce oscillator, Q_3, employs a bipolar transistor and supplies injection voltage to the mixer through a small coupling capacitor. An untuned output circuit is used at Q_2 to eliminate the need for special tuning controls or impedance-matching circuits between the converter and the input of the car radio.

Switch S_1 permits the operator to turn the converter off when not operating in the 160-meter band. The same switch routes the antenna around the converter (OUT position) so that re-ception of standard broadcast stations is possible. In some instances it may be necessary to insert a small trimmer capacitor in series with the converter bypass lead of S_1 (3-30 pf. or similar) to compensate for the reactance presented to the input circuit of the car radio by the 160-meter mobile antenna. The trimmer will also help to reduce the added capacitance of the longer coax line section. Some radios will not peak up when their input trimmers are adjusted, unless this capacitor is added to the circuit.

A d.c. chassis ground is not used in this circuit to allow the converter to be used with either a positive or negative ground system. R.f. grounding to the chassis is provided by C_3. If a negative ground vehicle is used, C_3 can be omitted and a solid connection made between this point and the chassis.

Construction

The converter may be assembled in any convenient form provided the leads are kept short and in-line layout is followed. A sample layout is suggested by the photograph. All of the components are housed in a $5\frac{1}{4} \times 3 \times 2$-inch Minibox (CU-2106-A) that can be mounted on or near the car's dashboard. Tie strips mounted in the box give good support to the components.

Miniature 50-ohm coax cable is used where long runs of r.f. wiring are required, such as between J_1, J_2, and S_1.

Tuneup and Use

Determine if the oscillator, Q_3, is performing properly by monitoring its signal on a general-coverage receiver, or by coupling a wavemeter to L_9. Next, connect a signal generator to J_1, or tune in a 160-meter signal, and tune C_1 for a peak. The response should be quite pronounced because of the high-Q inductor, L_6. When adjusting the bandpass circuit, tune L_7 for a peak at

View of the 160-meter converter. Input, output, and battery connectors are on the panel, at the left. The in-out switch and peaking control are on the right side of the panel. FL_1 components are soldered to tie strips (not visible) just below the in-out switch, S_1. The L_4,L_5,L_6 toroid assembly is visible between S_1 and tuning capacitor C_1. The two slug-tuned coils at the center are L_7 and L_8. The oscillator section is at the left. The other half of the Minibox (not shown here) is attached to the car's dashboard. When mounting the converter, simply snap it into place in the cover.

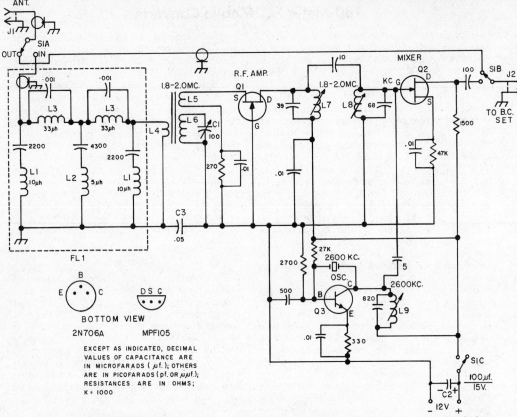

Fig. 19-4—Circuit of the 160-meter FET converter. Fixed-value capacitors are disk ceramic, except C_2 which is electrolytic. Resistors are ½-watt composition units.

C_1—100-pf. midget variable.
C_2—Electrolytic capacitor.
C_3—For text reference.
FL_1—For text reference.
J_1, J_2—Phono jack or similar.
L_1—10-uh. inductor (Millen 34300-10).
L_2—5-uh. inductor (Millen 34300-5).
L_3—33-uh. inductor (Millen J300-33).
L_4—6 turns No. 14 enam. over L_6 winding.
L_5—Same as L_4.

L_6—55 turns No. 30 enam. wire evenly wound over CF-111-Q2 toroid core (Indiana General Corp.) see footnote 1.
L_7, L_8—Variable inductor, 92 through 187 uh. (J. W. Miller 21A154RBI).
L_9—6.8-uh. inductor (J. W. Miller 21A686RBI).
Q_1, Q_2—MPF104 or MPF105 (Motorola JFET type).
Q_3—2N706A or similar.
S_1—3-p.d.t. slide switch (Cont.-Wirt G369 or equal).

1900 kc., then adjust L_8 for resonance at 1800 kc. In areas where the 1900- and 2000-kc. band segments are used, the bandpass circuit can be peaked for those parts of the band. The converter should now be ready for use.

With the oscillator frequency shown, 2600 kc., the 1800-kc. end of 160 meters will tune in at 800 kc. on the car radio dial. The other end of the band, 2000 kc., will appear at 600 kc. on the car radio dial. Other crystal frequencies can be used, but should be selected to give an i.f. tuning range that does not include strong local broadcast stations.

Filter FL_1 may not be required in areas where local broadcast stations do not exist. Or, the filter can be built outboard and used as an accessory when operating in metropolitan areas. If the filter is not used, the antenna lead from S_1 should connect directly to L_4. There will be some

insertion loss through FL_1, but not enough to impair reception in the 160-meter band.

A suitable length of Miniductor stock, or similar, can be substituted for L_6. If this is done, approximately 75 uh. of inductance will be required. The Q will be somewhat less, but good results can be expected. Links L_4 and L_5 will still use 6 turns of insulated wire, but they will be wound over the ground (cold) end of L_6.

JFETs can withstand a considerable amount of gate voltage, peak-to-peak value, therefore no input-protection diodes are included in the circuit. No difficulties should be observed provided a good-quality coaxial relay is used for antenna switching between the converter and the 160-meter mobile transmitter.

---

[1] Available from Indiana General Corp., through Termag Corp., 88-06 Van Wyck Expressway, Jamaica, N. Y. 11418.

A SIMPLE TRANSISTORIZED RECEIVER FOR 50 MC.

The transistorized 6-meter receiver uses two FETs and three bipolar transistors in a sensitive super-regenerative lineup. The main-tuning control does not need a vernier drive because of the broad-tuning effect of this type of detector. A vernier drive can be added, however, if the operator wishes.

The receiver shown in the photographs is useful for a.m. reception, and offers fair reception of wide-band f.m. signals. Because it is completely transistorized, it can be used advantageously in portable and mobile work. The receiver operates from a 12-volt d.c. supply and draws approximately 400 milliamperes.

Q_1 is used as a common-gate r.f. amplifier and because it is an FET (field-effect transistor) it offers good immunity to cross-modulation and overload. Q_2 performs as a common-gate super-regenerative detector and is also an FET. C_3 is used to provide feedback. C_1 is a trimmer capacitor and C_2 is the main-tuning control. R_1 controls the superregeneration of the detector. R_2, C_4, and C_5 make up the quench-frequency network, providing an interruption frequency that is just above the audible range—desireable for best selectivity. R_3 and C_6 filter out the quench frequency from the audio output of the detector, keeping that energy from reaching Q_3, the first audio stage. R_4 is the audio gain control.

A three-stage audio amplifier consisting of Q_3, Q_4, and Q_5 is used to provide up to 2 watts of output. Negative d.c. feedback is used in the audio channel to assure stable operation despite changes in temperature and supply voltage. T_1 matches the 24-ohm collector impedance of Q_5 to an 8-ohm speaker.

Construction

A 4 × 5 × 6-inch utility cabinet is used to enclose the receiver. A hand-formed chassis is made from 16-gauge aluminum and measures 4 × 5 inches with a 1½-inch high lip at the rear. The front and side lips are ⅜ of an inch wide. A bench vise was used in forming the chassis shown.

Transistor sockets are used to mount Q_1 through Q_4. Q_5 is mounted on the chassis, permitting the chassis to serve as a heat sink. Q_5 is insulated from the chassis by means of the hardware that is supplied with it. Silicone grease should be used between the transistor and the mica spacer, and between the mica spacer and the chassis. This will assure better heat transfer.

Perforated aluminum of the hardware store variety is used for the speaker grille. It is held in place between the speaker and panel by means of the speaker's mounting screws.

To provide proper grounding of C_2's rotor, a lead is connected to the rotor terminal and is passed through a small hole in the chassis where the free end is soldered to a ground lug. Keep this lead as short as possible and use large-diameter wire.

Operation

The bandwidth of the receiver is similar to that of most "supergennys." A 1000-μv. signal, 100 percent modulated, occupies approximately 400 kilocycles of the tuning range. Weaker signals are narrower, stronger signals are broader. Nevertheless, there are many benefits to be realized from the use of this receiver. It has excellent a.g.c.-type action, good sensitivity, and has an inherent noise-limiting action that is useful for mobile applications, or in noisy areas. A 0.3-μv., 30 percent modulated signal at J_1 will produce a plainly audible signal at the speaker. A well-modulated phone signal of 2 or 3 microvolts intensity should be perfectly readable under normal conditions.

With an antenna connected to J_1, and with R_4 set at mid range, adjust R_1 until a rushing sound

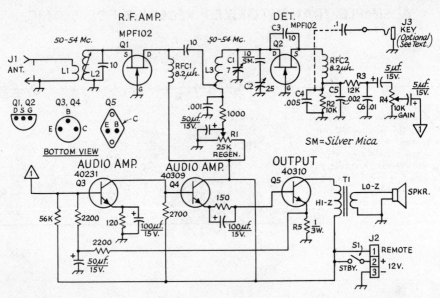

Fig. 19-5—Schematic diagram of the receiver. Unless otherwise noted, all resistors are ½ watt. Resistance is in ohms. K = 1000. Capacitors are disk ceramic unless otherwise indicated. Capacitors with polarity marks are electrolytic. Capacitance is in pf. Dashed lines indicate an optional circuit which is discussed in the text.

C_1—1.5 to 7-pf. ceramic trimmer.

C_2—25-pf. miniature variable (Hammarlund MAPC-25-B shown).

C_3-C_6, inc.—For text reference purposes.

J_1—Phono jack.

J_2—3-terminal connector (Millen E-303).

J_3—Open-circuit key jack (if used).

L_1—2 turns small dia. insulated wire over ground end of L_2.

L_2—9 turns No. 24 enam. wire, close-wound on ¼-inch dia. iron-slug form. (Miller 4500-4 form used.)

L_3—10 turns No. 20 tinned copper wire, air-wound to ½-inch dia. Space one wire thickness between turns.

Q_1-Q_5, inc.—For text reference.

R_1—25,000-ohm linear-taper control.

R_2, R_3—For text reference.

R_4—10,000-ohm audio-taper control.

R_5—1-ohm 3-watt resistor, or 6 feet of No. 32 enam. wire scramble-wound over the body of a 100,000-ohm 1-watt resistor. (A 1-ohm length of nichrome wire is also suitable.)

RFC_1, RFC_2—8.2-uh. choke (Millen J300-8.2 suitable).

S_1—S.p.s.t. slide switch.

T_1—Output transformer, 24 ohms to 8 ohms. (Lafayette 33R7501, or equivalent.) 2 watts or more in power rating.

Top view of the receiver chassis. The output transformer, T_1, is at the left. Q_3, Q_4, and Q_5 are along the rear edge of the chassis. Q_1 and Q_2 are at the right-front of the chassis. A Millen E-303 terminal is at the left of the chassis apron and is used for connecting the receiver to the 12-volt power source. The regeneration control is to the right of the power supply terminal. The antenna jack is at the far right on the rear apron.

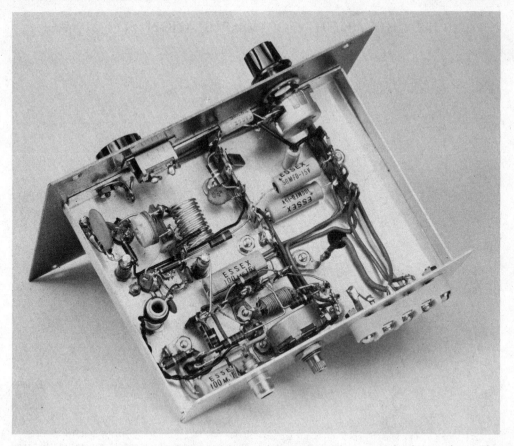

The r.f. and detector stages are at the upper left. L_3 and C_1 are mounted on an insulated terminal strip. The ground lug for C_2's rotor is just to the left of the slide switch.

is heard from the speaker. R_1 should be set just slightly beyond the point where the rushing sound is first heard. There should be no "dead" spots when C_2 is tuned through its range—approximately 50 to 55 Mc. If there are any so-called dead spots, advance R_1 slightly and again tune the receiver through its range, repeating the procedure until smooth superregeneration results across the entire 5-Mc. range. Maximum sensitivity occurs when R_1 is set just above the point where the rushing noise begins. Next, adjust L_2 for peak response while listening to a weak signal. The response will be rather broad, making readjustment unnecessary once L_2 is peaked for the middle of the 6-meter band. C_1 should be adjusted to set the tuning range of C_2 within the limits of the band.

Code-Practice Option

An optional circuit, to permit code practice, is shown in the diagram of Fig. 19-5 and is represented by dashed lines connected to the junction of RFC_2, C_4, and R_2. Two components are required if the addition is made—a 0.1-μf. capacitor and an open-circuit key jack. When the key is closed, at J_3, the 0.1-μf. capacitor is placed in parallel with C_4 and C_5, lowering the quench frequency into the audible range. The larger the value of the paralleled capacitance, the lower the pitch of the note will be. If the option is desired, J_3 can be mounted either on the front panel, or on the rear apron of the chassis. R_1 can be adjusted so that super-regeneration ceases, preventing the hiss noise from being heard during code practice.

Concerning the Transistors

All of the semiconductors used in this receiver are of the low-cost variety. The MPF102s are manufactured by Motorola for use up to 100 Mc. They are available at $1.00 each from any Motorola distributor. The bi-polar transistors, Q_3, Q_4, and Q_5, are made by RCA and are available from most mail-order houses by ordering them by their part numbers.

Care should be taken to prevent damage to the transistors. Do not use the receiver in the immediate vicinity of a 6-meter transmitter unless the antenna is disconnected from $J1$ during transmit. A coax relay that shorts out the receiver input during transmit periods is recommended. Do not pull the transistors from their sockets while the receiver is turned on.

A FEATHERWEIGHT PORTABLE STATION FOR 50 MC.

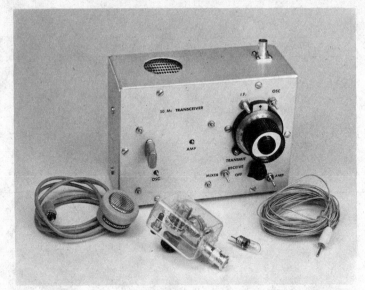

Fig. 19-6—The 50-Mc. transistor station, complete with microphone, battery and antenna system, weighs in at under 3 pounds. The antenna coupler built in a small plastic parts box is used with random "long wires." Coaxfed antennas connect directly to the BNC fitting on the top of the case.

The transceiver shown in Figs. 19-6 through 19-12 [1] is an effective portable station for normal v.h.f. hamming as well; light enough to be carried to the most inaccessible spots, and easy on battery power.

How It Works

In receiving, a simple two-transistor converter works into an inexpensive pocket broadcast receiver. With this scheme, sensitivity is good.

The transmitter r.f. section also uses two transistors. It is modulated by a ready-made audio unit that requires only minor modification to adapt it to this purpose. This transmitter delivers no more than 100 milliwatts output, which is about the limit that is practical for very lightweight batteries. It does well on a small 9-volt battery, and provision is made for connection to the car's 12-volt system through the lighter socket, if long hours of use are intended.

The Receiver Section

The front end of the receiving system is made tunable. Leaving the receiver set on 1600 kc. gives uniform image rejection across the band, and prevents interference from strong broadcast signals. A tunable oscillator works at half the desired injection frequency, tuning 24.1 to just above 25 Mc. The second harmonic beats with signals from just below 50 Mc. to about 52, to give an i.f. of 1600 k.c. One transistor serves as both mixer and oscillator. An R.F. amplifier stage, Q_1, gives some gain and helps the front-end selectivity. Layout is not critical, and only two precautions seem necessary. First, if one of the small imported dials is used, be sure that the mounting arrangement does not introduce drag. The torque capability of these

Japanese imports is rather low, but if the capacitor turns freely they do the tuning job nicely. They are available under many names; this one was an Argonne (Lafayette) AR-105, 2-inch model. Its small knob was replaced by a larger unit, for easier tuning. Second, be sure that the i.f. output coil, L_5 in Fig. 19-8 is in position to couple to the loopstick antenna of the broadcast receiver. This is not critical, but there are so many different receiver arrangements that we cannot be too specific about where to mount the receiver and the mixer output coil. Variations of a half inch either way make no great difference, so long as there is inductive coupling between the two.

In the unit pictured the broadcast receiver is mounted in the top left portion of the case, speaker facing up. The combination volume control and switch is accessible through a rectangular hole cut in the back wall of the case. The earphone jack also is reached through a hole in the back wall. Two small aluminum brackets hold the receiver in place, against the top of the case.

Looking at the front panel, Fig. 19-6, we see the send-receive switch just below the vernier dial. In the lower right corner of the panel is the slug adjustment of the r.f. coil, L_2. At the left is the interstage coil adjustment, L_3. At the upper right is the oscillator coil, L_6. To the upper left of the main dial is the mixer output coil, L_5. This is tuned to 1600 kc. by the 470-pf. capacitor across it, which looks like an r.f. bypass to the 24-Mc. energy from the oscillator circuit.

The back-of-panel view, Fig. 19-7, shows that most of the converter parts (left side) are mounted on tie-point strips. There are three of these: one running vertically at the edge, one horizontally between the tuning capacitor and

---

[1] "Featherweight Portable Station for 50 Mc.," *QST*, Nov. 1964, p. 24.

the send-receive switch, and a third vertically at the right, adjacent to the transmitter assembly.

The transistors are soldered into the circuit without using sockets. The r.f. amplifier, Q_1, is at the lower left, the mixer-oscillator, Q_2, is near the upper center of the rear view. The heavy grey leads are small-size coax, connecting the output fitting to the send-receive switch and transmitter output.

The Transmitter

Of many transistors tried for transmitting service, three types, all n-p-n, gave outstanding results. Since the opposite polarity, p-n-p, worked best for receiving we have some circuit differences between the transmitting and receiving portions of Fig. 19-8. The whole station is wired for positive ground, which is more-or-less standard procedure in transistor work. (The packaged audio unit and the broadcast receiver are wired that way.) If the station is to be operated from the battery in an American or other negative-ground car, the case should be isolated from ground.

The 2N706 is the one that was found satisfactory for transmitting. With the biasing shown, input to the oscillator is about 50 milliwatts and the amplifier 200 milliwatts, with a new 9-volt battery.

The transmitter is assembled on perforated insulating material known as *Vectorbord*, $2\frac{1}{8}$ by $2\frac{1}{4}$ inches in size, using push-in terminals for mounting and wiring the small components. Mounting screws at each corner are joined with No. 18 wire, which acts as a ground bus. The side of the transmitter toward the panel is set away from it by $\frac{3}{16}$-inch metal pillars and 4-40 nuts at each corner.

Little trouble should be encountered in duplicating results. Note the polarity of the crystal oscillator feedback loop, L_8, and the amplifier coupling, L_9, with respect to the oscillator collector coil.

Installing the Modulator

The modulator is a 5-transistor audio amplifier available ready-made from Lafayette Radio Elec-

tronic Corp., Model PK-544. The PK-544 is intended for use with a speaker, so its output transformer has an 8-ohm secondary. For modulator service this transformer should be replaced with one having 500-ohm center-tapped primary and secondary windings. Lafayette supplies an Argonne AR-162 for this purpose. If a high-impedance crystal or ceramic microphone (latter preferred) is used, an input transformer with a 200,000-ohm primary and 1000-ohm secondary is required. Lafayette's TR-120 is suitable.

No gain control is included with the PK-544, and none is really needed. A fixed resistor, R_1, is connected across the gain control terminals, the value selected to suit the user's preference as to voice level and microphone. We found 470 to 820 ohms suitable for various microphones tried.

The modulator is mounted on the inside back wall of the case, in back of the converter. The microphone connector is also on the back wall, near the modulator input terminals. The modulator is shown in outline form at the lower left of Fig. 19-6, with the various terminals at the approximate positions of the original.

Battery Options

Provision is made for use of the internal battery, BT_1, an external battery of larger size, BT_2, or a 12-volt car battery. The car battery may be either positive or negative ground, but if it is the latter be sure that the case of the rig is isolated from the car ground. With the simple plug-in arrangements shown, no switching is required to change the power source.

The broadcast receiver is operated from its own battery and is turned on and off with its own volume control and switch. When operating from

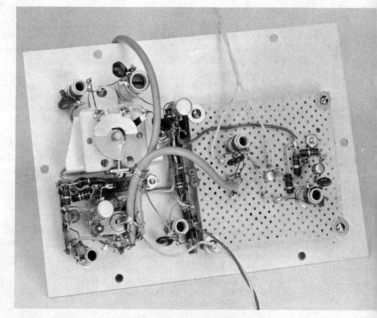

Fig. 19-7—Interior view of the transistor rig. The converter portion is at the left. The coil above and to the right of the tuning capacitor is the i.f. output coil, L_5, which couples to a small broadcast receiver visible in the upper part of the case in Fig. 19-9.

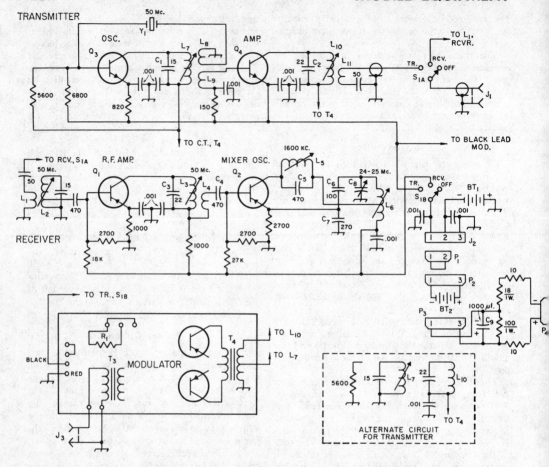

Fig. 19-8—Schematic diagram and parts information for the complete 50-Mc. station. Resistors are composition, ½-watt or less unless specified. Capacitors C_1 through C_7 are dipped silver-mica. Others are ceramic unless indicated. Decimal values are in μf.; others in p.f. unless indicated.

BT$_1$—9-volt battery. (Eveready No. 246, Burgess 2N6 are largest usable size).

BT$_2$—9-volt battery. Can be 6 flashlight cells in series or any 9-volt unit.

C$_8$—15-pf. miniature variable (Hammarlund HF-15, modified for desired bandspread; see text).

C$_9$—1000-μf. 12-volt electrolytic.

J$_1$—Coaxial chassis fitting, BNC type.

J$_2$—3-pin male power connector.

J$_3$—Phono jack or other microphone connector.

L$_1$—2 turns No. 22 enamel wound over bottom turns of L$_2$.

L$_2$—10 turns No. 22 enamel closewound on ¼-inch iron-slug ceramic form (Miller 4500). Tap at 4 turns.

L$_3$—8 turns like L$_2$; no tap.

L$_4$—2 turns No 22 enamel over bottom turns of L$_3$.

L$_5$—14.8 to 31-μh. adjustable coil (Miller 4407).

L$_6$—8 turns No. 22 enamel, ⅜ inch long on ¼-inch iron-slug ceramic form (Miller 4500). Tap at center.

L$_7$, L$_{10}$—7 turns like L$_3$.

L$_8$—2 turns No. 22 enamel wound near middle of L$_7$. Connect top of winding to ground, but wind in same direction as L$_7$.

L$_9$—3 turns No. 22 enamel over bottom of L$_7$, in same direction.

L$_{11}$—2 turns No. 22 enamel at bottom of L$_{10}$.

P$_1$, P$_2$, P$_3$—3-pin female plug.

P$_4$—Plug for automotive cigar lighter socket.

Q$_1$, Q$_2$—Germanium v.h.f. transistor. 2N1177 preferred.

Q$_3$, Q$_4$—Silicon u.h.f. transistor, n.p.n. type, 2N706.

R$_1$—Resistor substituted for gain control, value to suit microphone and desired voice level, 470 to 820 ohms.

S$_1$—2-pole 3-position wafer switch, subminiature type.

T$_1$, T$_2$—Integral parts of the Lafayette PK-544 audio amplifier, not shown in above diagram.

T$_3$—Miniature microphone transformer, 200,000-ohm primary, 1000-ohm secondary (Lafayette TR-120).

T$_4$—Miniature modulation transformer, both windings 500 ohms, center-tapped (Lafayette AR-162). Substitute for T$_2$.

Y$_1$—50-Mc. crystal for desired transmitting frequency (International Crystal Mfg. Co. Type FA-5 or FA-9. FA-5 has small pins.

Fig. 19-9—Panel side of the transmitter assembly. Holes are drilled in the front panel for mounting the pegboard chassis, and to permit the crystal socket and coil slug screws to project through. Note grounding bus around edges.

draw 8 to 10 ma. with the audio turned down. Room-filling audio takes up to 40 ma. on audio peaks. Levels sufficient for use within 3 feet or so of the speaker require very little current, and that will give a good many hours of listening, even on a small 9-volt battery.

Transmitter adjustment is simple. You merely tune first for maximum output from the oscillator and amplifier. Current drain of the amplifier increases with drive, so it is a good indication of oscillator peaking. Fiddling with coupling may be needed, both as to number of turns and position of the coupling windings, particularly if transistors other than those specified are used. Once you have obtained satisfactory output it is well to listen to the signal with a selective receiver with the b.f.o. on. Tune the oscillator for best stability and freedom from frequency modulation, even if it means a slight reduction in output.

A 2-volt 60-ma. (No 48) pilot lamp makes a good load. With everything working well there is a good glow in the lamp, and this will brighten markedly on modulation peaks.

the car battery use the arrangement shown in the schematic diagram. The plug P_3 connects to the rig in the same manner as P_2. A bleeder across the battery helps regulation and C_9, a low-voltage high-capacitance electrolytic, helps too. The 10-ohm ½-watt series resistors connected in the line to a cigar-lighter plug, P_4, act as fuses, in case you inadvertently ground the case when working with a car having negative ground.

Adjustment and Use

Putting the receiver to work is mainly a matter of tuning for maximum noise and signal strength. Set the broadcast receiver at the high end of its range and apply voltage to the converter. The noise level will rise markedly if the oscillator is working. Adjust the slug in L_5 for maximum noise, and you should be able to hear any strong 50-Mc. signals if the oscillator tuning range is right. Set the band where you want it by means of the slug in L_6. Peak L_2 and L_3 for maximum response on a 50-Mc. signal, and you're in business.

Bandspread and tuning range can be adjusted to suit one's preference by modifying the tuning capacitor, C_8, or the capacitive feedback network, C_6-C_7. To make for easy tuning, we cut C_8 to one rotor and two stator plates, which provides about two megacycles tuning range. You can get a rough check on the oscillator tuning range with an absorption wavemeter.

There may be a slight tendency toward acoustic feedback between the speaker and the oscillator circuit components, but this is not troublesome if the audio volume is set a bit down from the maximum position. Most receivers

Fig. 19-10—Back of the transmitter section, showing the two transistors and tuned circuits. The crystal oscillator is at the left.

Fig. 19-11—Looking into the case we see the small broadcast receiver, upper left, the ready-made modulator, right, and the built-in 9-volt battery, lower left.

Antenna Ideas

With low power a good antenna is a must. (Remember, 70 milliwatts is 30 db. down from the average 50-Mc station output!)

Whip antennas are ineffective for anything but purely local work, so the "long-wire" idea was tried. Long wires have gain and directivity. They respond to various polarizations and are extremely light. The antenna coupler system of Figs. 19-12 and 13 was worked out to cut down spurious receiver responses, as well as to facilitate transmitter loading.

Various wire lengths can be plugged into the jacks connected to taps on L_1. A balanced line, or even a V or rhombic, can be plugged into J_1 and J_2. Anything will work, but usually the longer the better. Tune in a signal on the receiver and peak the coupler for maximum signal strength.

The coupler can be connected directly to the BNC fitting on the transceiver, or a length of coax can be used. The support for the far end of the wire can be a tree, building, or whatever happens to be handy. If there is room to maneuver, walk around (maypole fashion) until maximum signal is found. Contacts have been made at distances up to 125 miles on several occasions employing this approach.

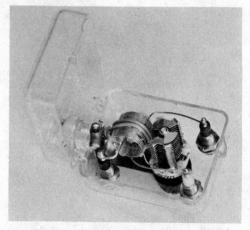

Fig. 19-12—The miniature antenna coupler is built in a hinged plastic parts box 1¾ by 2¼ by 1¼ inches in size. End-fed long wires or balanced-line antenna systems can be accomodated, through use of the appropriate taps on the tuned circuit.

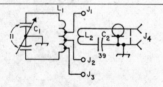

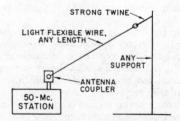

Fig. 19-13—Circuit of the antenna coupler and its application in feeding a long wire in portable work. Tip jacks J_1 and J_2 may be used for a balanced-line system. Any of the three jacks may be used for random-length long wires, merely by checking for best reception. Peak C_1 for maximum signal on receiving. Gain and directivity of the long wire will depend on length and slope.

C_1—11-pf. per section butterfly variable (Johnson 160—211 or 11MB11).

C_2—Fixed ceramic capacitor, 39 to 68 pf. Check with variable temporarily, if possible.

L_1—18 turns No. 24, ½ inch diameter, 32 t.p.i. Tap at 5 turns from each end and 1½ turns from one end (B&W No. 3004).

L_3—2 turns insulated hookup wire around center of L_1.

J_1, J_2, J_3—Tip jack.

J_4—BNC cable fitting. Connect J_4 and rotor of C_1 with copper strip.

A TRANSISTOR PHONE RIG FOR 1.8 MHz.

There are many applications in which a low-power 160-meter phone rig can be used to advantage. The transmitter to be described operates from 12 volts d.c., making it useful for mobile, portable, or fixed-station work. Although the input power to the final stage is only 8 watts, and it won't make you the 160-meter DX czar of your call area, some mighty respectable distances can be spanned if a good antenna is used. (Described in *QST*, Sept. 1968.)

The R.F. Circuit

For oscillator use, it is a good idea to select a transistor whose f_T (the frequency at which the common-emitter current gain drops to unity) is well above the operating frequency. For this reason, an RCA 2N2102 was chosen for the crystal oscillator, Q_1, Fig. 19-16. It has an f_T of 100 MHz., costs less than $1.50, and has a 5-watt dissipation rating. It is used in a Pierce arrangement with C_1 helping to regulate the feedback. In order to assure quick starting it may be necessary to experiment with the value of C_1, which should be between 100 pf. and 0.001 μf. depending on the crystal activity and the h_{FE} (forward current-transfer ratio) of the particular transistor. The setting of the slug in L_1 also affects the operation of the oscillator. A high-C collector tank is used in order to get the high operating Q needed to reduce the harmonic output from Q_1.

Driver stage Q_2 operates more or less in Class C (actually somewhere between Class B and Class C because it is just beyond cutoff) and gets its drive from Q_1 by means of L_2, a five-turn link over the cold end of L_1. Q_2 is also a 2N2102, used as a driver because of its power rating and f_T. In r.f. amplifier service, it is desirable to pick a transistor whose f_T is at least 10 times higher than the desired operating frequency; this assures that the stage will have

Fig. 19-14—Front view of the 12-volt 160-meter transmitter. The oscillator transistor is under the chassis near the crystal socket. The driver stage is just to the right of the crystal, mounted in its heat sink. All of the modulator components are located above and below the chassis at the right; Q_7 and Q_8 are mounted on a heat sink on the right-side apron of the chassis. The meter jacks and jumper cable are visible at the top center.

a useful power gain. If f_T is near the operating frequency or only slightly higher, there will be no gain—and possibly even a loss—through the transistor. On the other hand, if f_T is a great deal *more* than 10 times the operating frequency —say, 500 MHz. for use at 2 MHz.—the low-frequency gain would be extremely high and could cause incurable low-frequency oscillations. Altogether, it is best to stick pretty close to the 10-times-f_T rule. A heat sink is used on Q_2 to keep the transistor temperature within its safe range.

A high-C tank is used for the collector of Q_2 to get rid of some of the harmonic energy developed there. A toroidal tank is used at L_3 because the self-shielding property of toroidal tuned circuits practically eliminates stray inter-stage coupling, a common cause of instability.[1] An air-wound or Miniductor coil of suitable inductance (approximately 10 μh.) can be used in place of the toroid if desired, but some inter-stage shielding may be required.

Several types of transistors were tried as power amplifiers (Q_3). A few bargain-house mesa-type power transistors[2] gave good results; some were 40-watt 40-MHz.-f_T n-p-n units, others were 85-watt 25-MHz.-f_T mesa transistors, and some were 85-watt 10-MHz.-f_T types. All performed satisfactorily, but the 40-MHz. types exhibited a tendency toward instability when C_4 was not tuned for the best match to the 50-ohm load. A swamping resistor, 15 to 56 ohms, can usually be connected between the base and ground (across L_4 in this instance) to help correct this type of instability. It will, however, result in some loss

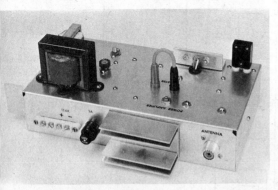

Fig. 19-15—A look at the rear side of the transmitter. Power connections are made at the terminal block at the far left. A homemade heat sink consisting of two aluminum channels is used for the p.a. transistor, Q_3. It is insulated from the chassis by means of meat-wrapping paper and silicone grease.

[1] "Toroidal-Wound Inductors," *QST*, January, 1968.
[2] Poly Paks, Box 942M, Lynnfield, Mass. 01940. Send 10 cents for catalog.

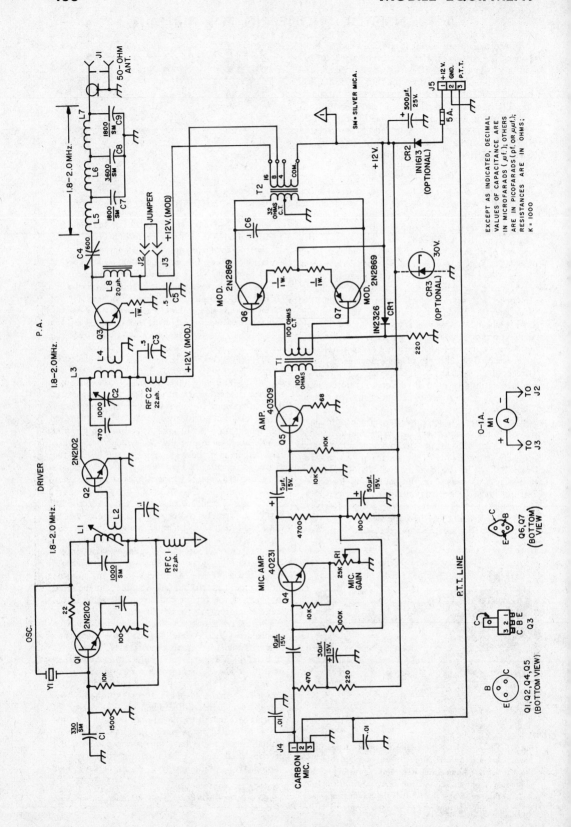

Fig. 19-16—Schematic of the 160-meter transmitter. Fixed capacitors are disk ceramic unless otherwise indicated; capacitors with polarity marking are electrolytic. Fixed-value resistors not otherwise specified are ½-watt composition.

C_1—For text reference.

C_2—1000-pf. compression padder (J. W. Miller * 160-A or equivalent).

C_3, C_5—0.5-μf. 200-volt tubular.

C_4—200-600-pf. compression padder (J. W. Miller 160-C).

C_6-C_9, incl.—For text reference.

CR_1—1N2326 (RCA) diode.

CR_2—Silicon diode, 5 amp. 100 p.r.v. rating (see text).

CR_3—30-volt 1-watt Zener diode (1N3031B or similar); see text.

J_1—SO-239 coax connector.

J_2, J_3—Insulated banana jacks (E. F. Johnson 108-902, red, 108-903, black).

J_4—3-terminal microphone connector (Mallory SCA-2B or equivalent).

J_5—4-terminal connection strip (Millen E-304); one terminal reserved as spare.

L_1—3.6 to 8.5-μh., slug tuned (J. W. Miller 21A686RBI).

L_2—5 turns small-diameter insulated hookup wire wound over bypassed end of L_1.

L_3—10 μh.; 20 turns No. 28 enam. wire space-wound on Indiana General ** CF-111 (Q_2) toroid core.

L_4—8 turns insulated hookup wire spaced over entire L_3 winding on toroid core.

L_5—25 μh.; 55 turns No. 24 enam. wire close-wound over 2-inch length of ¼-inch diam. ferrite rod (see text).

L_6, L_7—4 μh.; 10 turns No. 16 enam. wire, close-wound

on 1-inch length of ½-inch diam. ferrite rod (see text).

L_8—20 μh.; 50 turns No. 24 enam. wire, close-wound over 2-inch length of same type material used for L_5 (see text).

M_1—0-1 ampere d.c.

Q_1-Q_7, incl.—For text reference. Q_3 can be any type specified in the text, but Texas Instrument TIP-14 may be easiest to locate (Allied Radio Corp., $1.50 ea.).

R_1—25,000-ohm linear-taper carbon control.

RFC_1, RFC_2—22-μh. r.f. choke (Millen 34300-22).

T_1—Transistor driver transformer, 100-ohm primary to 100-ohm c.t. secondary (Stancor TA-58).

T_2—10-watt transistor output (Triad TY-64X).

Y_1—1.8-MHz. fundamental crystal. (JAN Crystal Co.)

* J. W. Miller Co., 5917 S. Main St., Los Angeles, Calif. 90003.

** Indiana General Corp., Electronics Div., Keasbey, N. J. 08832. Att.: Product Mgr. Ask for Bulletin 101 and price list. Order core from Permag Corp., 8806 Van Wyck Expy., Jamaica, N. Y. 11418.

of driving power. A low-cost regularly available transistor—Texas Instruments TIP-14—was also tried at Q_3 and performed well. The TIP-14 has an f_T of 40 MHz., is rated at 10 watts collector dissipation, and has a V_{CEO} of 70 volts. It costs $1.50. Some of the bargain types mentioned are available at two for $1.

The 1-ohm 1-watt resistor in the emitter of Q_3 serves as a protective device should thermal runaway occur. It also biases Q_3 farther into the Class C region for better efficiency.

L_8 must carry the 600-ma. collector current, so fairly heavy wire must be used. To keep the size down L_8 was wound on a piece of ¼-inch diameter ferrite rod taken from an old transistor broadcast-radio antenna. This provides the required 20 μh. of inductance with considerably fewer turns of wire than would be needed for an air-wound inductor. The same general technique is used for L_5, L_6, and L_7.

Transistorized amplifiers tend to generate considerably more harmonic output than vacuum-tube amplifiers, because of nonlinearity in the transfer characteristics of the transistor, including a nonlinear variation in interelement capacitances with changes in element voltages. The harmonic currents approach the fundamental current in amplitude, so a highly-selective collector tank circuit is an absolute essential. The combination of C_4, C_7, L_5 and L_8 is a simple tank circuit which meets this requirement to a degree, but the second and third harmonics are down only some 20 decibels without additional selectivity. If the transmitter is intended primarily for mobile operation, no real problem exists because the selectivity of the mobile antenna is high. However, since the transmitter is designed for fixed-station use as well as for mobiling, a "Harmonicker-type" filter network, composed of C_7, L_6, C_8, L_7, and C_9, has been added. With this filter in the circuit the second and third harmonics dropped to more than 50 db. below the fundamental.

Banana jacks, J_2 and J_3, permit inserting a 1-ampere meter, M_1, in the collector lead during tuneup. A jumper shorts the jacks out in normal operation.

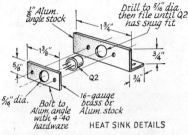

Fig. 19-17—Details of the homemade heat sink for Q_2. The assembly is mounted on insulating washers or rubber grommets to prevent a short circuit from collector to chassis. The hole in the angle stock is just large enough to permit Q_2 to fit snugly. A thin layer of silicone grease will help transfer heat from case of Q_2 to the heat sink.

Fig. 19-18—Looking into the underside of the transmitter, the audio section is in the compartment at the left. The oscillator stage is at the lower right. Driver stage Q_2 is at the lower center (obscured by the chassis wall), and the p.a. circuit is along the upper half of the right-hand compartment. The four amplifier tank inductors are mounted at right angles to one another to minimize coupling effects. The p.a. transistor (Q_3) protruding into the r.f. compartment at top center is an 85-watt, 10-MHz. bargain-house mesa type. The polarity-guarding diode, CR_1, is mounted on the divider strip at the center of the chassis. The shield serves as a heat sink for the diode, which is electrically insulated from it by a mica washer.

Stage decoupling in the transmitter is effected by RFC_1, RFC_2, and their associated bypass capacitors.

Audio Circuit

The audio circuit is conventional in most respects and needs little explanation. A carbon microphone is used at Q_4, Fig. 19-16. A decoupling network consisting of a 220-ohm resistor and a 30-μf. capacitor is used in the microphone-voltage supply line to prevent motor-boating. The 30-μf. capacitor also helps to filter the d.c. to the mike. Q_4 is RG-coupled to Q_5, the second audio amplifier stage. A driver transformer, T_1, connects Q_5 to the Class B modulator stage, Q_6Q_7. To prevent crossover distortion in the modulator a small amount of forward bias is applied to the bases of Q_6 and Q_7. The required amount of bias is obtained from the voltage drop across a 220-ohm resistor in the center-tap lead. The resistor is connected to the positive end of the supply through CR_1, a special temperature-sensitive diode. CR_1 should be clamped to the chassis between Q_6 and Q_7. As the temperature of the two output transistors rises their collector current increases, in turn increasing the temperature still more and leading to "thermal runaway" if not controlled. Because CR_1 is close to Q_6 and Q_7, its temperature also rises, causing the junction resistance of the diode to decrease. The resulting increase in current through CR_1 causes a larger voltage drop across the 220-ohm bias resistor, lowering the forward bias on Q_6 and Q_7.

This reduces the collector current, thereby protecting the transistors from damage. It should be noted that CR_1, by virtue of its normal conduction characteristic, establishes a fairly constant level of forward bias for the modulator stage despite supply-voltage variations. It is this bias voltage that determines what the no-signal idling current of Q_6 and Q_7 will be. Additional overload protection is offered by the 1-ohm resistors in the emitter leads of the output transistors.

CR_2 is intended solely as a polarity-guarding diode to prevent transistor damage if the transmitter is incorrectly connected to its power source. It must be able to handle the total current drawn by the transmitter. It will conduct only if a positive voltage is applied. CR_3 is a 10-watt Zener diode which will conduct when transients of 30 volts or more occur on the supply line; transients of this kind are not uncommon in automotive systems. The Zener diode will protect the transmitter from such peaks, but is shown only as an option.

Construction Data

The accompanying photos quite likely tell a better story about the assembly techniques than can be told with words. A $5 \times 9\frac{1}{2} \times 2$-inch aluminum chassis is used.

A homemade heat sink is used on Q_2; the details are given in Fig. 19-17. Similar sinks were made for the modulator transistors, Q_7 and Q_8, and for the p.a. transistor, Q_3. (See Chap. 20). The details are reasonably clear in the photographs. Their dimensions are not critical.

L_6 and L_7 are wound on $\frac{3}{4}$-inch lengths of $\frac{1}{2}$-inch-diameter ferrite rod. The rod was obtained from Lafayette Radio Electronics and was supplied in a $7\frac{1}{2}$-inch length for $0.65.

Testing and Operation

Without the microphone being plugged in at J_4, apply power (dummy load attached to J_1) and peak all r.f. stages for maximum transmitter output. This can be done by observing forward power on an s.w.r. meter, or by observing the S meter on a communications receiver. Cycle the transmitter a few times to make sure Q_1 starts rapidly. If it does not, adjust the slug in L_1 for a setting that assures quick starting of the oscillator. With M_1 plugged in at J_2-J_3, the reading should be approximately 600 ma. The collector current will vary somewhat, depending upon the transistor type used at Q_3. A low reading indicates low base drive or a particularly low-beta transistor at Q_3. Because of nonuniform production, several transistors of the same manufacture and type number may give different results, and for this reason it is impossible to specify an exact value of collector current.

In checking out the modulator, make absolutely certain that the dummy load is connected to J_1. If the transmitter has an improper load the p.a. transistor can be destroyed the moment you speak into the mike. *Always make sure that the transmitter has a proper load!*

A PORTABLE TRANSCEIVER FOR 144 MHz.

Here's a v.h.f. transceiver that's truly portable, is easy to build, and is capable of spanning many miles when used with a good antenna. It can be operated from its internal 12-volt flashlight-cell pack, from the cigar lighter of any 12-volt negative-ground car, or from an a.c.-operated 12-volt d.c. pack. The transmitter and the two-stage FET superregenerative receiver are assembled on etched-circuit boards to simplify construction. The audio section is a prewired "import"—also on a circuit board. (From *QST*, Aug. 1968.)

Receiver-Section Circuit

Two FETs are used in the simple receiver circuit of Fig. 19-21. A JFET (junction field-effect transistor), Q_4, operates as a common-gate r.f. amplifier and offers a fair amount of detector isolation while providing a few decibels of gain. Its output is coupled to the detector, Q_5, through C_{19}, which is a "gimmick" capacitor. The latter consists of three turns of insulated hookup wire wrapped around the ground end of L_8. The opposite end of the wire is soldered to the drain end of L_7. A junction-type FET is used at Q_4 to make it less subject to r.f. burnout than would be the case if an IGFET (insulated-gate FET) were used.

An IGFET is used as the detector, Q_5. Since it is isolated from the antenna circuit there is little chance of its being harmed by strong r.f. fields.

Quench-frequency voltage is provided by R_{14} and C_{26} in the source lead of Q_5. Feedback for the detector is between gate and source, making it necessary to keep the source above r.f. ground by means of RFC_4.

A.f. output from the the detector is taken from the drain through a quench-frequency filter consisting of C_{24}, C_{25}, RFC_5, and C_{27}. The filter prevents the quench voltage from reaching the

Fig. 19-19—The 2-meter transceiver is housed in a legal-bond box. A home-made dial-calibration chart for the receiver is pasted on the inside of the lid. Two plastic cable clamps serve as holders for the two-section ¼-wavelength whip antenna (inside lid) when the unit is not in use. The antenna is held together at the center by a home-made ¼-inch diameter threaded coupling.

audio amplifier. L_9 isolates the a.f. signal from the B-plus line, and R_{15} varies the drain supply voltage to control supperregeneration. R_{16} is the a.f. gain control.

A word of caution at this point: When soldering the IGFET, Q_5, into the circuit, be sure to connect a clip lead between the tip of the soldering iron and a good earth ground. This will help prevent damage to the gate of the 3N128 should static charges be present. Also, *do not handle* the leads of Q_5. The leads should be removed

Fig. 19-20—Top-chassis layout of the transceiver. The receiver section is at the left. Controls for regeneration and modulation are in the foreground near the center of the chassis. The audio module is at the lower right, and the transmitter board is near the panel, directly under the loudspeaker. The homemade heat sinks are visible at the left end of the audio board.

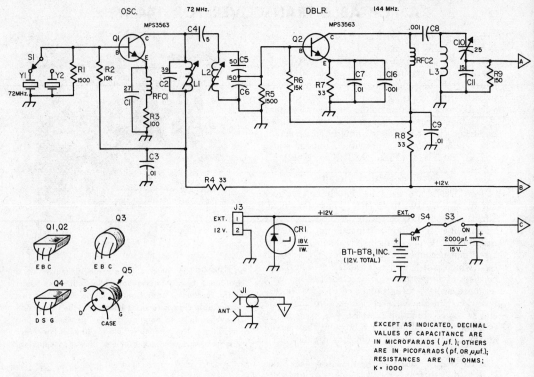

EXCEPT AS INDICATED, DECIMAL
VALUES OF CAPACITANCE ARE
IN MICROFARADS (μf.); OTHERS
ARE IN PICOFARADS (pf. OR μμf.);
RESISTANCES ARE IN OHMS;
K = 1000

Fig. 19-21—Schematic of the 2-meter transceiver. Fixed-value capacitors are disk ceramic except those with polarity marking, which are electrolytic. Resistors are ½-watt composition. Component numbering is for identification
of parts on the circuit-board templates. Significant parts are listed below in the usual manner.

AR₁—200-milliwatt audio module (Round Hill Associates
Model AA-100*).

BT₁, BT₈, Inc.—Eight 1.5-volt size-D flashlight cells,
series-connected and mounted inside box by means
of four Keystone No. 176 dual-battery clips.

C₁₀, C₁₂—5 to 25-pf. ceramic trimmer, Erie 822-CN or
equiv. (Midget 3 to 30-pf. mica trimmer also suitable.)

C₁₅—8 to 50-pf. ceramic trimmer, Erie 822-AN or equiv.
(midget 8 to 60-pf. mica trimmer also suitable.)

C₁₉—Gimmick-type capacitor. See text.

C₂₀—15-pf. subminiature variable (E. F. Johnson 160-
107).

C₂₂—5-pf. min. variable (Hammarlund MAPC-15B all but
one rotor and one stator plate removed).

CR₁—18-volt 1-watt Zener diode (used for transient protection during mobile operation).

J₁—SO-239 coax fitting (chassis mount).

J₂, J₃—Two-terminal single-contact audio connector (Amphenol 75PC1M or similar).

L₁, L₂—3 turns No. 22 enam. wire spaced to occupy ½
inch on ¼-inch dia. ceramic slug-tuned form (J. W.
Miller 4500-4*).

L₃—4 turns No. 20 bare wire, ½ inch long, 5/16-inch inside diameter.

L₄—6 turns No. 20 bare wire, ½ inch long, 5/16-inch
i.d.

L₅—Same as L₃.

L₆—8 turns No. 20 bare wire, 1 inch long, 5/16-inch i.d.
Tap 5 turns from source lead of Q₄.

from their shorting collar by means of a non-
plastic or nonmetallic tool. A wooden toothpick
is recommended for this, and for spreading the
leads apart. Once Q_5 is soldered in place, it
should be quite safe from static-charge damage.

Transmitter Circuit

Referring again to Fig. 19-21, the transmitter
section starts out with a Colpitts oscillator, Q_1,
which uses 72-MHz overtone crystals. C_1 and the
internal base-emitter capacitance of Q_1 control
the feedback. RFC_1 keeps the emitter above r.f.
ground. Bandpass coupling is used between Q_1
and Q_2 to reduce harmonics in the driving signal
to Q_2. A capacitive divider, C_5 and C_6, is used

to match the collector of Q_1 to the low base impedance of Q_2. The high value of capacitance
between the base of Q_2 (C_6) and ground helps
to further reduce harmonic energy in that part
of the circuit. Both Q_1 and Q_2 are low-cost
Motorola transistors designed for amplifier or
oscillator use at frequencies up to 500 MHz.
They have a beta spread of 20 to 200, and have
a collector dissipation rating of 500 milliwatts.
Other transistors can be substituted provided
they have similar specifications. It is quite likely
that 2N706As would work satisfactorily in
these two stages. Resistors R_5 and R_6 establish
Class A bias for Q_2, making it easier to drive
with the low output of Q_1.

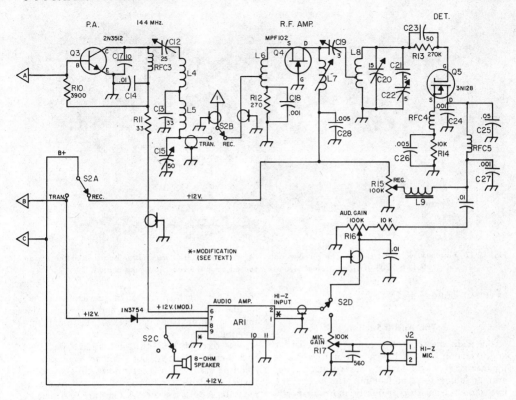

L_7—5 turns No. 22 enam. wire, close-wound on ¼-inch dia. ceramic slug-tuned form (J. W. Miller 4500-4).

L_8—4 turns No. 10 bare copper wire, 1 inch long, ⅜-inch i.d. (The tap shown is not a physical one; see text discussion of C_{19}.)

L_9—Total primary winding of 500-ohm c.t. transistor output transformer. 8-ohm secondary winding not used. (Argonne AR-164 or similar.)

R_{15}, R_{17}, inc.—100,000-ohm audio-taper carbon control.

RFC_1—Miniature 50-μh. choke (Millen 34300-50*).

RFC_2-RFC_4, inc.—Miniature 2.7-μh. r.f. choke (Millen 34300-2.7).

RFC_5—Subminiature 10-mh. r.f. choke (J. W. Miller 73F102AF).

S_1, S_4—S.p.d.t. slide switch.

S_2—4-pole 2-pos. phenolic single-section rotary wafer switch. (Mallory 3142J).

S_3—S.p.s.t. slide switch.

Y_1, Y_2—72-MHz. overtone crystal (International Crystal Co. in HC-6/U holder.*).

---

* Round Hill Assoc., Inc., 325 Hudson St., N. Y., N. Y. 10013.

* J. W. Miller Co., 5917 S. Main St., Los Angeles, Cal. 90003

* International Crystal Co., 10 N. Lee St., Okla. City, Okla. 73102

* James Millen Mfg. Co., 150 Exchange St., Malden, Mass. 148

An RCA 2N3512 is used in the power amplifier, Q_3. It was selected because of its low cost ($1.82) and high maximum dissipation rating of 4 watts. It is designed for high-speed switching applications and has an f_T of 375 MHz. Its h_{FE} rating is approximately 10. The low h_{FE} makes it easier to stabilize than would be the case if a high-beta transistor were used. Other transistors can also be used at Q_3; a 40280 and a 2N3553 were tried and performed as well as the 2N3512, but are more costly. To assure good heat dissipation at Q_3, a heat sink is clipped to the transistor body. A Wakefield Engineering NF205 costs 27 cents and is ideal.

A capacitive divider, C_{10} and C_{11}, matches the output of Q_2 to the base of Q_3. C_{10} tunes L_3 to resonance. Forward bias is used on the base of Q_3 to establish Class AB conditions. This provided greater output from Q_3 than resulted with Class C operation, as is usually the case when the driver stage has low output. The collector tank of Q_3 is a combination L and pi network. The L network, C_{12} and L_4, matches the load to the collector. The pi network is used for harmonic reduction, a necessary provision when clean output is desired from transistorized transmitters. C_{12} tunes the p.a. tank to resonance; C_{15} serves as a loading control.

In order to assure suitable stability, the power leads of the stages are decoupled by means of C_3, C_9, and C_{14} in combination with R_4, R_8, and R_{11}. The three resistors also serve

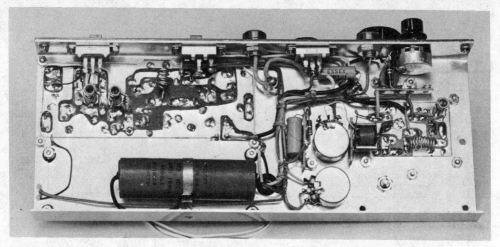

Fig. 19-22—Bottom view of the chassis. The receiver board is at the right. The transmitter board is at the upper left. A 2000-μf. 15-volt electrolytic is mounted near the rear lip of the chassis.

as current-limiting devices to protect Q_1, Q_2, and Q_3.

The Audio Section

The audio channel, AR_1, can be purchased for approximately $8. It has a 200-milliwatt output rating at 9 volts, but by increasing the operating voltage to 12, and adding heat sinks to the two output transistors, slightly more than 300 milliwatts of output is available. This was done in the circuit of Fig. 19-21.

AR_1 has two input impedances—50 ohms and 100,000 ohms. Two output impedances are available, providing a 500-ohm transformer winding for modulator service, and an 8-ohm winding for driving a loudspeaker. The high-impedance input connects to the microphone gain control, R_{17}, during transmit, and is switched to the receiver gain control, R_{16}, during receive. The 50-ohm tap is not used.

Because the module is designed for a positive-ground bus (p-n-p transistors are used), it is necessary to "float" the entire assembly above chassis ground to prevent short-circuiting the power supply. Information on the mounting techniques and some modifications to the board is given later.

Building the Transceiver

The packaging of this circuit can be up to the builder. In this instance a standard legal-bond box was chosen. It measures $5 \times 6 \times 11\frac{1}{2}$ inches.

The chassis and panel are made from 16-gauge aluminum sheeting. An aluminum cookie tin from a hardware store can be the source of the panel and chassis stock. Many are made of heavy-gauge material and are large enough to assure that there will be excess stock. The chassis measures $11\frac{1}{4} \times 4 \times 1$ inch. The panel is $11\frac{1}{4}$ inches by $4\frac{3}{4}$ inches. After the panel holes are drilled, a coating of zinc chromate should be sprayed on it. Then, after thorough drying, a

coat of spray-can enamel or lacquer can be added for the final touch. The zinc chromate helps the finish coat of paint adhere to the aluminum sheeting.

The receiver and transmitter are built on etched-circuit boards, but point-to-point wiring could be used if done neatly and with short connections. Etched-circuit templates are available from the ARRL if desired.[1] They are to scale and show where the various parts are mounted.

AR_1 is insulated from the main chassis to prevent short-circuiting the power supply. It has a plus-ground bus; the rest of the transceiver circuit uses a negative ground. A piece of cardboard is mounted between the circuit board and the chassis to prevent accidental contact between AR_1 and the chassis. AR_1 is bolted to the chassis at four points. The four mounting holes in the main chassis contain small rubber grommets, each serving as an insulator. Terminals 1 and 9 of the audio board are common to its plus-ground bus. These terminals must be disconnected from the ground bus by removing the thin copper connecting strip which joins the cir-

---

[1] Scale templates with parts layout for the boards are available for 25 cents from ARRL. Send s.a.s.e.

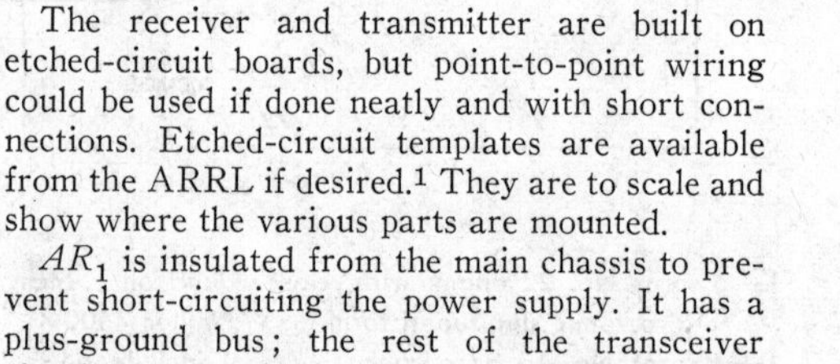

Fig. 19-23—Hookup that will permit other types of audio boards to be used. S_1 is used to switch in an outboard modulation transformer, a transformer connected back-to-back with the one supplied with the module. T_1 is an outboard transformer which matches the low-impedance input of the audio amplifier to the high-impedance microphone, and to the output of the detector during receive.

cuits. A pocket knife works nicely for this job; the copper can then be peeled off.

To operate AR_1 at 12 volts it is necessary to add heat sinks to the two transistors nearest the output transformer. The sinks can be fashioned from pieces of thin brass, copper, or aluminum. They are $1\frac{1}{2}$ inches long and each is formed by warping the stock around a drill bit which is slightly smaller in diameter than the body of the transistor.

Fig. 19-24—Details of the home-made heat sinks for AR_1.

All interconnecting r.f. leads are made with subminiature coax cable, RG-174/U (Belden 8216). Shielded audio cable should be used for all a.f. wiring which is more than a couple of inches in length. A bargain-house import is used for the receiver tuning dial. No slippage was noted with the 2-inch-diameter model used here. The next smaller model is not recommended because it will not handle the torque of the tuning capacitor specified in Fig. 1.

A $2\frac{1}{2}$-inch-diameter loudspeaker is used. Its protective grille can be made from perforated aluminum.

Two 3-inch-long brass angle brackets, each with $\frac{3}{4}$-inch sides, are used as mounts for the panel-chassis assembly inside the box. Two 6-32 hex nuts are soldered to the bottom side of each bracket, directly under No. 10 access holes. Four 6-32 $\times$ $\frac{3}{8}$-inch screws hold the transceiver in place. The brackets are attached to the sides of the box with 4-40 hardware.

Tune-Up and Use

The receiver should be tested first. With an antenna connected to J_1, apply operating voltage and adjust R_{15} until a rushing noise is heard in the speaker. Do not advance R_{15} beyond this point as the sensitivity of the receiver will decrease. Next, tune in a weak signal from another ham station (or from a signal generator) and tune L_7 for a peak response. Chances are that when the peak is reached, the detector will stop oscillating. If this happens, advance R_{15} until the hiss returns. If it does not, detune L_7 slightly until a compromise is reached (L_7 usually loads the detector somewhat when it is tuned to the operating frequency). Alternatively, a 1000-ohm swamping resistor can be connected across L_7 to reduce its effect on the detector. Trimmer C_{20} is used to set the tuning range of C_{22}. The turns of L_8 can be spread or compressed for additional frequency adjustment. The receiver should tune the entire 4-MHz. of the 2-meter band, or nearly so.

A No. 49 pilot lamp makes a suitable dummy load for visual tune-up of the transmitter, though somewhat reactive at 144 MHz. First, determine that the oscillator, Q_1, is operating by coupling a wavemeter (or grid-dip meter in the diode-detector position) to L_1 and look for an indication of output. Adjust the slug in L_1 for maximum output, then turn the transmitter on and off a few times to make sure the crystal always kicks in. If not, detune L_1 slightly toward the high-frequency side of resonance until the oscillator does start each time. Next, peak L_2, C_{10}, C_{12}, and C_{15} for maximum indication on the bulb. There will be some interaction between the circuits, so the foregoing steps should be repeated a few times to assure maximum output. Final adjustments should be made with the antenna connected, and with an s.w.r. indicator in the line.[2]

---

[2] A highly sensitive s.w.r. indicator is needed at this power level. One of the Monimatch indicators with a 4-inch-or-longer line (air-dielectric element type) can provide full-scale readings if a 100-µa. meter is installed. Alternatively, see *QST*, August 1967 for a low-power bridge. Also, see the "Monimatch Mark II," *QST*, Feb. 1957.

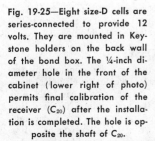

Fig. 19-25—Eight size-D cells are series-connected to provide 12 volts. They are mounted in Keystone holders on the back wall of the bond box. The $\frac{1}{4}$-inch diameter hole in the front of the cabinet (lower right of photo) permits final calibration of the receiver (C_{20}) after the installation is completed. The hole is opposite the shaft of C_{20}.

THE MOBILE ANTENNA

For mobile operation in the range between 1.8 and 30 Mc., the vertical whip antenna is almost universally used. Since longer whips present mechanical difficulties, the length is usually limited to a dimension that will resonate as a quarter-wave antenna in the 10-meter band. The car body serves as the ground connection. This antenna length is approximately 8 feet.

With the whip length adjusted to resonance in the 10-meter band, the impedance at the feed point, X, Fig. 19-29, will appear as a pure resistance at the resonant frequency. This resistance will be composed almost entirely of radiation resistance (see index), and the efficiency will be high. However, at frequencies lower than the resonant frequency, the antenna will show an increasingly large capacitive reactance and a decreasingly small radiation resistance.

The equivalent circuit is shown in Fig. 19-30. For the average 8-ft. whip, the reactance of the

Fig. 19-29—The quarterwave whip at resonance will show a pure resistance at the feed point X.

capacitance, C_A, may range from about 150 ohms at 21 Mc. to as high as 8000 ohms at 1.8 Mc., while the radiation resistance, R_R, varies from about 15 ohms at 21 Mc. to as low as 0.1 ohm at 1.8 Mc. Since the resistance is low, considerable current must flow in the circuit if any appreciable power is to be dissipated as radiation in the resistance. Yet it is apparent that little current can be made to flow in the circuit so long as the comparatively high series reactance remains.

Fig. 19-30—At frequencies below the resonant frequency, the whip antenna will show capacitive reactance as well as resistance. R_R is the radiation resistance, and C_A represents the capacitive reactance.

Eliminating Reactance

The capacitive reactance can be canceled out by connecting an equivalent inductive reactance, L_L, in series, as shown in Fig. 19-31, thus tuning the system to resonance.

Unfortunately, all coils have resistance, and this resistance will be added in series, as indicated at R_C in Fig. 19-32. While a large coil may

Fig. 19-31 — The capacitive reactance at frequencies lower than the resonant frequency of the whip can be canceled out by adding an equivalent inductive reactance in the form of a loading coil in series with the antenna.

radiate some energy, thus adding to the radiation resistance, the latter will usually be negligible compared to the loss resistance introduced. However, adding the coil makes it possible to feed power to the circuit.

Ground Loss

Another element in the circuit dissipating power is the ground-loss resistance. Fundamentally, this is related to the nature of the soil in the area under the antenna. Little information is available on the values of resistance to be expected in practice, but some measurements have shown that it may amount to as much as 10 or 12 ohms at 4 Mc. At the lower frequencies, it may constitute the major resistance in the circuit.

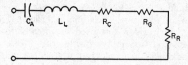

Fig. 19-32—Equivalent circuit of a loaded whip antenna. C_A represents the capacitive reactance of the antenna, L_L an equivalent inductive reactance. R_C is the loading-coil resistance, R_G the ground-loss resistance, and R_R the radiation resistance.

Fig. 19-32 shows the circuit including all of the elements mentioned above. Assuming C_A lossless and the loss resistance of the coil to be represented by R_C, it is seen that the power output of the transmitter is divided among three resistances—R_C, the coil resistance; R_G, the ground-loss resistance; and R_R, the radiation resistance. Only the power dissipated in R_R is radiated. The power developed in R_C and R_G is dissipated in heat. Therefore, it is important that the latter two resistances be minimized.

MINIMIZING LOSSES

There is little that can be done about the nature of the soil. However, poor electrical contact between large surfaces of the car body, and especially between the point where the feed line is grounded and the rest of the body, can add materially to the ground-loss resistance. For example, the feed line, which should be grounded as close to the base of the antenna as possible, may be connected to the bumper, while the bumper may have poor contact with the rest of the body because of rust or paint.

TABLE 19-I

Approximate Values for 8-ft. Mobile Whip						
Base Loading						
$f_{kc.}$	Loading $L\mu h.$	R_C (Q50) Ohms	R_C (Q300) Ohms	R_R Ohms	Feed R^* Ohms	Matching $L\mu h.$ *
1800	345	77	13	0.1	23	3
3800	77	37	6.1	0.35	16	1.2
7200	20	18	3	1.35	15	0.6
14,200	4.5	7.7	1.3	5.7	12	0.28
21,250	1.25	3.4	0.5	14.8	16	0.28
29,000	....	....	....	....	36	0.23
Center Loading						
1800	700	158	23	0.2	34	3.7
3800	150	72	12	0.8	22	1.4
7200	40	36	6	3	19	0.7
14,200	8.6	15	2.5	11	19	0.35
21,250	2.5	6.6	1.1	27	29	0.29

R_C = Loading-coil resistance; R_R = Radiation resistance.
* Assuming loading coil $Q = 300$, and including estimated ground-loss resistance.
Suggested coil dimensions for the required loading inductances are shown in a following table.

Loading Coils

The accompanying tables show the approximate loading-coil inductance required for the various bands. The graph of Fig. 19-33 shows the approximate capacitance of whip antennas of various average diameters and lengths. For 1.8, 4 and 7 Mc., the loading-coil inductance required (when the loading coil is at the base) will be approximately the inductance required to resonate in the desired band with the whip capacitance taken from the graph. For 14 and 21 Mc., this rough calculation will give more than the required inductance, but it will serve as a starting point for final experimental adjustment that must always be made.

Also shown in table 19-I are approximate values of radiation resistance to be expected with an 8-ft. whip, and the resistances of loading coils — one group having a Q of 50, the other a Q of 300. A comparison of radiation and coil resistances will show the importance of reducing the coil resistance to a minimum, especially on the three lower-frequency bands.

To minimize loading-coil loss, the coil should have a high ratio of reactance to resistance, i.e., high Q. A 4-Mc. loading coil wound with small wire on a small-diameter solid form of poor quality, and enclosed in a metal protector, may have a Q as low as 50, with a resistance of 50 ohms or more. High-Q coils require a large conductor, "air-wound" construction, turns spaced, the best insulating material available, a diameter not less than half the length of the coil (not always mechanically feasible), and a minimum of metal in the field. Such a coil for 4 Mc. may show a Q of 300 or more, with a resistance of 12 ohms or less. This reduction in loading-coil resistance may be equivalent to increasing the transmitter power by 3 times or more. Most low-loss transmitter plug-in coils of the 100-watt size or larger, commercially produced, show a Q of this order. Where larger inductance values are required, lengths of low-loss space-wound coils are available.

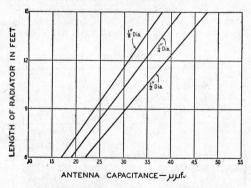

Fig. 19-33—Graph showing the approximate capacitance of short vertical antennas for various diameters and lengths, at 3.9 Mc. These values should be approximately halved for a center-loaded antenna.

Center Loading

The radiation resistance of the whip can be approximately doubled by placing the loading coil at the center of the whip, rather than at the base, as shown in Fig. 19-34. (The optimum position varies with ground resistance. The center is optimum for average ground resistance.) However, the inductance of the loading coil must be approximately doubled over the value required at the base to tune the system to resonance. For a coil of the same Q, the coil resistance will also be doubled. But, even if this

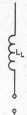

Fig. 19-34—Placing the loading coil at the center of the whip antenna, instead of at the base, increases the radiation resistance, although a larger coil must be used.

is the case, center loading represents a gain in antenna efficiency, especially at the lower frequencies. This is because the ground-loss resistance remains the same, and the increased radiation resistance becomes a larger portion of the total circuit resistance, even though the coil resistance also increases. However, as turns are added to a loading coil (other factors being equal) the inductance (and therefore the reactance) increases at a greater rate than the resistance, and the larger coil will usually have a higher Q.

Fig. 19-35—A field-strength meter is placed on the car roof and is used to indicate maximum output when tuning the antenna to resonance. In this installation, a telescoping antenna section is used above the loading coil. The length of the top section is varied until its capacitance provides resonance in combination with the fixed-inductance, weatherproof-loading coil. This photo shows a temporary mobile mount made from ⅛-inch thick steel plate which has been bent to catch on the top lip of the bumper. The lower portion attaches to the car body with two ¼-inch diameter bolts.

Fig. 19-36—K1MET prunes a capacity hat for antenna resonance at the low end of the 160-meter band. The Webster Big-K antenna is first tuned for the high segment of the band. The capacity hat is clipped on when operation on the "low end" is desired. Fine adjustments can be made by increasing or decreasing the spacing between the two No. 10 wires.

Top-Loading Capacitance

Because the coil resistance varies with the inductance of the loading coil, the resistance can be reduced, beneficially, by reducing the number of turns on the coil. This can be done by adding capacitance to that portion of the mobile antenna that is *above* the loading coil. To achieve resonance, the inductance of the coil is reduced proportionally. Capacity "hats," as they are often called, can consist of a single stiff wire, two wires or more (Fig. 19-36), or a disk made up from several wires, like the spokes in a wheel.

TABLE 19-II

Suggested Loading-Coil Dimensions					
Req'd L μh.	*Turns*	*Wire Size*	*Diam. In.*	*Length In.*	*Form or B & W Type*
700	190	22	3	10	Polystyrene
345	135	18	3	10	Polystyrene
150	100	16	2½	10	Polystyrene
77	75	14	2½	10	Polystyrene
77	29	12	5	4¼	160T
40	28	16	2½	2	80B less 7 t.
40	34	12	2½	4¼	80T
20	17	16	2½	1¼	80B less 18 t.
20	22	12	2½	2¾	80T less 12 t.
8.6	16	14	2	2	40B less 4 t.
8.6	15	12	2½	3	40T less 5 t.
4.5	10	14	2	1¼	40B less 10 t.
4.5	12	12	2½	4	40T
2.5	8	12	2	2	15B
2.5	8	6	2⅜	4½	15T
1.25	6	12	1¾	2	10B
1.25	6	6	2⅜	4½	10T

A solid metal disk can also be used. The larger the capacity hat, in terms of mass, the greater the capacitance. The greater the capacitance, the smaller the amount of inductance needed in the loading coil for a given resonant frequency.

Although there are two schools of thought concerning the attributes of center-loading and base-loading, it has not been established that one system is superior to the other, especially in the lower part of the h.f. spectrum. For this reason both the base- and center-loading schemes are popular. Capacity-hat loading is applicable to either system. Since more inductance is required for center-loaded whips to make them resonant at a given frequency, capacity hats should be particularly useful in improving their efficiency.

Tuning the Band

Especially at the lower frequencies, where the resistance in the circuit is low compared to the coil reactance, the antenna will present a very high-Q circuit, making it necessary to retune even for small changes in frequency. Though there are many ways to accomplish this, the capacity-hat system of Fig. 19-36 is one of the simplest. The hat is made from two pieces of No. 10 buss wire which have been soldered to a medium-size battery clamp. The clamp is attached just above the coil when it is desired to operate on a frequency which lies below the frequency to which the loading coil has been previously tuned. The capacity hat can be used with any loading coil, home-made or commercial style, and can be employed during initial adjustment of the system. The spacing between the wires can be varied to shift the antenna's resonance above or below a given frequency.

The antenna system of Fig. 19-35, a Webster Big-K, is set for 160-meter operation. The top whip section consists of two pieces of stock, one of which telescopes into the other. A machine screw locks the two sections together after antenna resonance has been effected. A field-strength meter can be used for adjusting the system, tuning the antenna (by varying the length of the top section) for maximum field-strength reading. Similarly, an s.w.r. bridge can be used, tuning the system for minimum reflected power at the operating frequency.

REMOTE ANTENNA RESONATING

Fig. 19-37 shows circuits of two remote-control resonating systems for mobile antennas. As shown, they make use of surplus d.c. motors driving a loading coil removed from a surplus ARC-5 transmitter. A standard coil and motor may be used in either installation at increased expense.

The control circuit shown in Fig. 19-37A is a three-wire system (the car frame is the fourth conductor) with a double-pole double-throw switch and a momentary (normally off) single-pole single-throw switch. S_2 is the motor reversing switch. The motor runs so long as S_1 is closed.

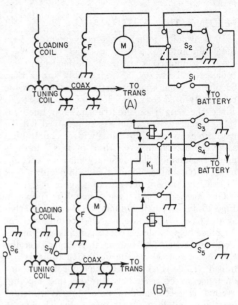

Fig. 19-37—Circuit of the remote mobile-whip tuning systems.

K_1—D.p.d.t. latching relay.

S_1, S_3, S_4, S_5—Momentary-contact s.p.s.t., normally open.

S_2—D.p.d.t. toggle.

S_6, S_7—S.p.s.t. momentary-contact microswitch, normally open.

The circuit shown in Fig. 19-37B uses a latching relay, in conjunction with microswitches, to automatically reverse the motor when the roller reaches the end of the coil. S_3 and S_5 operate the relay, K_1, which reverses the motor. S_4 is the motor on-off switch. When the tuning coil roller reaches one end or the other of the coil, it closes S_6 or S_7, as the case may be, operating the relay and reversing the motor.

The procedure in setting up the system is to prune the center loading coil to resonate the antenna on the highest frequency used without the base loading coil. Then, the base loading coil is used to resonate at the lower frequencies. When the circuit shown in Fig. 19-37A is used for control, S_1 is used to start and stop the motor, and S_2, set at the "up" or "down" position, will determine whether the resonant frequency is raised or lowered. In the circuit shown in Fig. 19-37B, S_4 is used to control the motor. S_3 or S_5 is momentarily closed (to activate the latching relay) for raising or lowering the resonant frequency. The broadcast antenna is used with a wavemeter to indicate resonance.

(Originally described in *QST*, Dec., 1953.)

Several companies offer motor tuning for getting optimum performance over a low-frequency band. (For a complete description of the commercially available remotely-tuned systems, see Goodman, "Frequency Changing and Mobile Antennas," *QST*, Dec., 1957.)

FEEDING THE ANTENNA

It is usually found most convenient to feed the whip antenna with coax line. Unless very low-Q loading coils are used, the feed-point impedance will always be appreciably lower than 52 ohms — the characteristic impedance of the commonly-used coax line, RG-8/U or RG-58/U. Since the length of the transmission line will seldom exceed 10 ft., the losses involved will be negligible, even at 29 Mc., with a fairly-high s.w.r. However, unless a line of this length is made reasonably flat, difficulty may be encountered in obtaining sufficient coupling with a link to load the transmitter output stage.

One method of obtaining a match is shown in Fig. 19-38. A small inductance, L_M, is inserted at the base of the antenna, the loading-coil inductance being reduced correspondingly to maintain resonance. The line is then tapped on the coil at a point where the desired loading is obtained. Table 19-I shows the approximate inductance to be used between the line tap and ground. It is advisable to make the experimental matching coil larger than the value shown, so that there will be provision for varying either side of the proper position. The matching coil can also be of the plug-in type for changing bands.

Fig. 19-38 — A method of matching the loaded whip to 52-ohm coax cable. L_L is the loading coil and L_M the matching coil.

Adjustment

For operation in the bands from 29 to 1.8 Mc., the whip should first be resonated at 29 Mc. with the matching coil inserted, but the line disconnected, using a grid-dip oscillator coupled to the matching coil. Then the line should be attached, and the tap varied to give proper loading, using a link at the transmitter end of the line whose reactance is approximately 52 ohms at the operating frequency, tightly coupled to the output tank circuit. After the proper position for the tap has been found, it may be necessary to readjust the antenna length slightly for resonance. This can be checked on a field-strength meter several feet away from the car.

The same procedure should be followed for each of the other bands, first resonating, with the g.d.o. coupled to the matching coil, by adjusting the loading coil.

After the position of the matching tap has been found, the size of the matching coil can be reduced to only that portion between the tap and ground, if desired. If turns are removed here, it will be necessary to reresonate with the loading coil.

If an entirely flat line is desired, a s.w.r. indicator should be used while adjusting the line tap. With a good match, it should not be necessary to readjust for resonance after the line tap has been set.

It should be emphasized that the figures shown in the table are only approximate and may be altered considerably depending on the type of car on which the antenna is mounted and the spot at which the antenna is placed.

ANTENNAS FOR 50 AND 144 MC.

A Simple Vertical Antenna

The most convenient type of antenna for mobile v.h.f. work is the quarter-wave vertical radiator, fed with 50-ohm coaxial line. The antenna, which may be a flexible telescoping "fish pole," can be mounted in any of several places on the car. An ideal mounting spot is on top of the car, though rear-deck mounting presents a better spot for esthetic reasons. Tests have shown that with the car in motion there is no observable difference in average performance of the antennas, regardless of their mounting positions. There may be more in the way of directional effects with the rear-deck mount, but the overall advantage of the roof mount is slight.

A good match may be obtained by feeding the simple vertical with 50-ohm line. However, it is well to provide some means for tuning the system, so that all variables can be taken care of. The simplest tuning arrangement consists of a variable capacitor connected between the low side of the transmitter coupling coil and ground, as shown in Fig. 19-39. This capacitor should

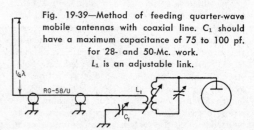

Fig. 19-39—Method of feeding quarter-wave mobile antennas with coaxial line. C_1 should have a maximum capacitance of 75 to 100 pf. for 28- and 50-Mc. work. L_1 is an adjustable link.

have a maximum capacitance of 75 to 100 $\mu\mu$f. for 50 Mc., and should be adjusted for maximum loading with the least coupling to the transmitter. Some method of varying the coupling to the transmitter should be provided.

Horizontal Polarization

Horizontally polarized antennas have a considerable advantage over the vertical whip under usual conditions of mobile operation. This is particularly true when horizontal polarization is used at both ends of a line-of-sight circuit, or on a longer circuit over reasonably flat terrain. An additional advantage, especially on 6 meters, is a marked reduction in ignition noise from neighboring cars as well as from the station car.

TWO-METER TURNSTILE

An effective omnidirectional 2-meter mobile or fixed-station antenna is the "turnstile," Fig. 19-41. This horizontally-polarized antenna provides somewhat better performance than does the "halo" antenna. It is decidedly better than a simple ¼-wave whip.

Two half-wave dipoles are crossed and fed 90 degrees out of phase by equal amounts of power. A *quarter*-wavelength stub assures the proper phase relationship of the second dipole. A quarter-wavelength Q-section, made from 50-ohm line, is used to match the 36-ohm antenna feed-point impedance to the 75-ohm transmission line. The Q-section can be omitted if a slight mismatch (less than 2:1) is tolerable. If this is done, the transmission line to the rig should be replaced by 50-ohm cable. The antenna pattern is nearly circular.

Mechanical details for the antenna are given in Fig. 19-40. The center insulator block can be made from a piece of Plexiglas, polystyrene, or similar substance of high dielectric quality. Phenolic material is the most rugged and is less likely to shatter in cold weather. The elements can be fashioned from ⅛-inch diameter aluminum rods, but brass is more durable and is better able to withstand stress. Brass brazing rod is available from most automotive parts houses, or from welding shops, and is excellent material for turnstile elements. No. 10 copperweld wire also works well and is virtually indestructible.

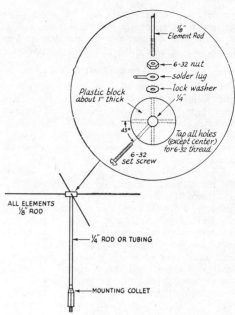

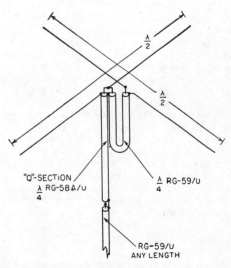

Fig. 19-40—Mechanical details of the turnstile.

Fig. 19-41—Schematic drawing of the turnstile antenna. Crossed dipoles are fed 90 degrees out of phase through a quarter-wave section of coax line. The quarter-wavelength Q-section matches the antenna's 36-ohm feed impedance to that of the 75-ohm feed line.

Two-meter turnstile antenna shown mounted on the front of an automobile. The miniature coax cable which feeds the antenna is taped to its ¼-inch diameter steel supporting rod. The ends of the antenna elements should be flattened, or rounded, to make them safer in the event of accidental contact with the human body.

A Horizontally Polarized Two-Band Antenna for V.H.F.

One type of horizontally-polarized antenna, called the "halo," is shown in Fig. 19-40. It is a dipole bent into a circle, with the ends capacitively loaded to reduce the circumference. Since the 50- and 144-Mc. bands are almost in third harmonic relationship, it is possible to build a single halo that will work on both bands. The antenna is changed from one band to another by changing the spacing between the end loading plates and adjusting the matching mechanism.

Mechanical Details

The halo is made of $\frac{7}{16}$-inch aluminum fuel-line tubing. This material is both strong and very light, but any tubing of about $\frac{1}{2}$-inch diameter could be used equally well. The loop is 67 inches in circumference and the capacitor plates are $2\frac{1}{4}$ inches square, with the corners rounded off.

To fasten the capacitor plates to the ends of the tubing, aluminum rod stock is turned down on a lathe to make a tight fit into the ends. This is tapped for 6–32 thread, and then forced into the tubing ends. Holes are drilled through tubing and inserts, at each end of the halo, and a screw run through each to keep the inserts from turning around or slipping out. The binding-head screws that hold the plates to the inserts are equipped with lock washers. The holes for mounting the ceramic cone spacer are drilled directly below the center, midway between the center and the edge of the capacitor plates.

The halo is set into a slot cut in the vertical support. This slot should be just big enough to permit the halo to be forced into it. The halo has to be stiffened, so cut it at the center and insert about 2 inches of aluminum rod, again turned down on a lathe to fit tightly inside the tubing. The two pieces of tubing are then pushed together, over the insert, and drilled each side of center to pass 6–32 screws. The halo and insert are also drilled at the midpoint, to pass the mounting screw. This is an 8–32 screw, $1\frac{1}{4}$ inches long. If lathe facilities are not available, the mounting of the capacitor plates and the securing of the halo to the vertical support can be handled with angle brackets.

Mechanical stability is important so straps of aluminum $\frac{1}{2}$ inch wide are wrapped around the halo either side of the mounting post. These are bent at right angles and the ends pulled together with a bolt.

The matching arm is $14\frac{1}{2}$ inches long, of the same material as the halo itself. It is mounted below the halo on two $\frac{3}{4}$-inch cone standoffs. For convenience in detaching the feed line a coaxial fitting is mounted on an L bracket bolted to the vertical support. The stator bar of the 25-pf. variable capacitor (Johnson 167-2) is soldered directly to the coaxial fitting. The rotor of the capacitor is connected to the gamma arm through a piece of stiff wire. For further stiffening an aluminum angle bracket is screwed to the lower mounting stud of the capacitor and the other end mounted under the screw that holds the first cone standoff in place. Contact between the arm and the halo proper is made through a strap of $\frac{1}{2}$-inch wide aluminum bent to form a sliding clip. Be sure that a clean tight contact is made between the tubing and the clip, as high current flows at this point. A poor or varying contact will ruin the effectiveness of the antenna.

Adjustment

The capacity-loaded halo is a high-Q device so it must be tuned on-the-nose, or it will not work properly. The only reliable method for adjusting a halo is to use a standing-wave bridge, making tuning and matching adjustments for minimum reflected power. Using a field-strength meter and attempting to adjust for maximum radiated power can give confusing indications, and is almost certain to result in something less than maximum effectiveness.

The adjustment process with this design can be simplified if the halo is first resonated approximately to the desired frequency ranges with the aid of a grid-dip meter. Set the clip at about one inch in from the end of the arm, and the series capacitor at the middle of its range. Check the resonant frequency of the loop with the grid-dip meter, with the $\frac{3}{4}$-inch spacer between the capacitor plates. It should be close to 50 Mc. If the frequency is too low, trimming the corners of the plates or putting shims under the ceramic spacer will raise it somewhat. If the frequency is too high already, make new and slightly larger capacitor plates.

Fig. 19-42—The 2-band halo as it appears when set up for 50-Mc. operation. Changing to 144 Mc. involves decreasing the plate spacing by swapping cone insulators, and resetting the gamma-matching clip and series capacitor.

Next, insert an s.w.r. bridge between the antenna and the transmission line. Apply power and swing the capacitor through its range, noting whether there is a dip in reflected power at any point. If the reflected power will not drop to zero, slide the clip along the gamma arm and retune the capacitor, until the lowest reading possible is obtained. If this is still not zero, the halo is not resonant. If the halo capacitance is on the low side, moving the hands near the plates will cause the reflected power to drop. Closer spacing of the plates, larger plates or a longer halo loop are possible solutions.

These adjustments should be made on a frequency near the middle of the range you expect to use. Adjusting for optimum at 50.25 Mc., for example, will result in usable operation over the first 500 kc. of the band, and a good match (below 1.5 to 1) from 50.1 to 50.4. The s.w.r. will rise rapidly either side of this range.

To tune up on 144 Mc., insert the ½-inch cone between the capacitor plates. Slide the clip back on the gamma arm about 3 to 4 inches and repeat the adjustment for minimum reflected power, using a frequency at the middle of a 2-Mc. range. Tuning up at 145 Mc., for example, will give quite satisfactory operation from the low end to 146 Mc., the halo being much broader in frequency response when it is operated on its third harmonic. In this model the series capacitor in the gamma arm was at about the middle of its range for 50 Mc., and near minimum for 144 Mc. Slight differences in mechanical construction may change the value of capacitance required, so these settings should not be taken as important.

The photograph, Fig. 19-40, shows a method used to avoid running the chance that the second ceramic cone would be missing when a band change was to be made. The head was cut from a 6–32 screw, leaving a threaded stud about ½ inch long. This is screwed into one of the ceramic cones. The other cone then serves as a nut, to tighten down the capacitor plate. In changing bands merely swap cones. (Original description appeared in *QST*, Sept., 1958.)

Commercial versions of the one- and two-band halo antennas are available.

Bibliography

Swafford, "Improved Coax Feed for Low-Frequency Mobile Antennas," *QST*, December, 1951.
Roberge McConnell, "Let's Go High Hat!," *QST*, January, 1952.
Belrose, "Short Antennas for Mobile Operation," *QST*, September, 1953.
Dinsmore, "The 'Hot-Rod' Mobile Antenna," *QST*, September, 1953.
Picken & Wambsganss, "Remote Mobile-Antenna Resonating," *QST*, December, 1953.
Webster, "Mobile Loop Antennas," *QST*, June, 1954.
Tilton, "Have you Tried V.H.F. Mobile?," *QST*, September, 1954.
Hargrave, "Automatic Mobile Antenna Tuning," *QST*, May, 1955.
Morgan, "Tuning the Mobile Antenna from the Driver's Seat," *QST*, October, 1955.
Braschwitz, "Directional Antenna for the Transmitter Hunter," *QST*, April, 1956.
Tilton, "Polarization Effects in V.H.F. Mobile," *QST*, December, 1956.
Breetz, "A Simple Halo for 2-Meter Mobile Use," *QST*, August, 1957.
Harris, "Continuously Loaded Whip Antennas," *QST*, May, 1958.
Mellen and Milner, "Big Wheel on Two," *QST*, Sept., 1961. Also "Big Wheel Performance Tests," *QST*, Oct., 1961.

A "MINI-WHEEL" ANTENNA FOR 432-MC. MOBILE

The "Mini-Wheel" antenna was created for mobile operation on 432.9 Mc. in the Detroit area, where there are about 35 stations active on this band. Since almost all 432-Mc. activity is horizontally polarized, the design was based on the 2-meter Big Wheel,[1] which is both horizontally polarized and omnidirectional. The antenna is only 15 inches in diameter, and can be constructed and tuned up in the workshop.[2] No power gain is claimed for it, and it won't compete with a good beam, but it is a practical mobile antenna and will give an excellent account of itself.

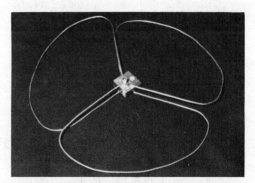

Fig. 19-43—The assembled Mini-Wheel viewed from the bottom. The matching stub is on the near corner of the block-and-plate assembly. In use, the antenna is mounted horizontally with the BNC fitting projecting downward. *(Built by G. Poland, W8FWF.)*

As shown in Fig. 19-44, the three antenna elements are each 26¾ inches long, including ¼ inch for soldering at each end. The material used here was No. 10 bare copper wire. The center mounting block is made of half-inch thick fiber—other insulating materials would do—and is sandwiched between two plates made from 1/32-inch copper. Brass could be used instead. One end of each element is soldered to the top plate, with the element overlapping the plate by ¼ inch. The other ends of the elements are soldered to the bottom plate, as shown in the drawing and photograph. A large soldering gun will handle the job with ease.

It is strongly advised that the elements be preshaped before attempting to mount and

[1] Mellen and Milner, "The Big Wheel on Two", *QST*, September, 1961.
[2] First described in *QST*, Oct. 1967.

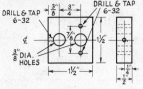

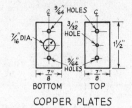

FIBER BLOCK   COPPER PLATES

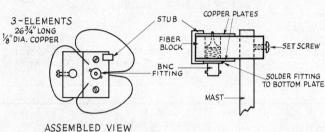

ASSEMBLED VIEW
Elements not to scale

Fig. 19-44—Construction details of the Mini-Wheel 432-Mc. antenna.

ment of the length may be needed when making final tuneup.

The BNC fitting (other types can be used) is soldered to the bottom plate by making a fillet of solder around the shoulder on the fitting. The center terminal is connected to the top plate.

solder them. Final shaping can be done after assembly. Each element should fill a 120-degree arc, so that when all three are assembled the rim will be approximately a complete circle. Working in a clockwise direction, the beginning radial portion of each element should be directly over the trailing radial portion of the preceding element.

A matching stub made of ¼-inch copper strap, 1 inch long, is soldered between the top and bottom plates, overlapping the plates ¼ inch at each end. About ½ inch of stub is all that is necessary for matching to a 50-ohm line. A slight adjust-

In the car installation the feed line can be a short (not over 5 or 6 feet) piece of RG-58/AU. RG-8/U is preferable, and an adapter (UG-255/U) can be used for making the connection to the BNC fitting.

In mobile operation, many contacts have been made over a distance of over 50 miles, as well as over shorter distances.

It should be possible to boost the signal by approximately 3 db. by using two stacked Mini-Wheels. The stacking distance would be about 15 inches.

MOBILE POWER SUPPLY

By far the majority of amateur mobile installations depend upon the car storage battery as the source of power. The tube types used in equipment are chosen so that the filaments or heaters may be operated directly from the battery. High voltage may be obtained from a supply of the vibrator-transformer-rectifier type, a small motor generator or a transistor-transformer-rectifier system operating from the car battery. Transistorized vibrator eliminators are available for modernizing old vibrator supplies.

Filaments

Because tubes with directly heated cathodes (filament-type tubes) have the advantage that they can be turned off during receiving periods and thereby reduce the average load on the battery, they are preferred by some for transmitter applications. However, the choice of types with direct heating is limited and the saving may not always be as great as anticipated, because directly heated tubes may require greater filament power than those of equivalent rating with indirectly heated cathodes. In most cases, the power required for transmitter filaments will be quite small compared to the total power consumed.

Plate Power

Transistor-transformer-rectifier plate supplies currently available operate with an efficiency of approximately 80 per cent. These compact, lightweight supplies use no moving parts (vibrator or armature) or vacuum tubes, and draw no starting surge current. Most transistorized supplies are designed to operate at 12 volts d.c. and some units deliver 125 watts or more.

"Inverter" units, both in the transistor, vibrator and rotating types, are also available. These operate at 6 or 12 volts d.c. and deliver 115 volts a.c. This permits operating standard a.c.-powered equipment in the car. Although these systems have the advantage of flexibility, they are less efficient than the previously mentioned systems because of the additional losses introduced by the transformers used in the equipment. Portable inverters that make connection to the car battery by plugging into the dash cigarette-lighter receptacle are available up to about 100 watts capacity. Where direct connection to the battery is used, inverters up to about 500 watts capacity are available.

Mobile Power Considerations

Since the car storage battery is a low-voltage source, this means that the current drawn from the battery for even a moderate amount of power will be large. Therefore, it is important that the resistance of the battery circuit be held to a minimum by the use of heavy conductors and good solid connections. A heavy-duty relay should be used in the line between the battery and the plate-power unit. An ordinary toggle switch, located in any convenient position, may then be used for the power control. A second relay may sometimes be advisable for switching the filaments. If the power unit must be located at some distance from the battery (in the trunk, for instance) the 6- or 12-volt cable should be of the heavy military type, to minimize the voltage drop.

A complete mobile installation may draw 30 to 40 amperes or more from the 6-volt battery or better than 20 amperes from a 12-volt battery. This requires a considerably increased demand from the car's battery-charging generator. The voltage-regulator systems on cars of recent years will take care of a moderate increase in demand if the car is driven fair distances regularly at a speed great enough to insure maximum charging rate. However, if much of the driving is in urban areas at slow speed, or at night, it may be necessary to modify the charging system. Special communications-type generators, such as those used in police-car installations, are designed to charge at a high rate at slow engine speeds. The charging rate of the standard system can be increased within limits by tightening up slightly on the voltage-regulator and current-regulator springs. This should be done with caution, however, checking for excessive generator temperature or abnormal sparking at the commutator.

The average 6-volt car generator has a rating of 35 amperes, but it may be possible to adjust the regulator so that the generator will at least hold even with the transmitter, receiver, lights, etc., all operating at the same time.

If higher transmitter power is used, it may be necessary to install an a.c. charging system. In this system, the generator delivers a.c. and works into a rectifier. A charging rate of 75 amperes is easily obtained. Commutator trouble often experienced with d.c. generators at high current is avoided, but the cost of such a system is rather high.

Some mobile operators prefer to use a separate battery for the radio equipment. Such a system can be arranged with a switch that cuts the auxiliary battery in parallel with the car battery for charging at times when the car battery is lightly loaded. The auxiliary battery can also be charged at home when not in use.

A tip: many mobile operators make a habit of carrying a pair of heavy cables five or six feet long, fitted with clips to make a connection to the battery of another car in case the operator's battery has been allowed to run too far down for starting.

THE AUTOMOBILE STORAGE BATTERY

The success of any mobile installation depends to a large extent upon intelligent use and maintenance of the car's battery.

The storage battery is made up of units consisting of a pair of coated lead plates immersed in a solution of sulphuric acid and water. Cells, each of which delivers about 2 volts, can be connected in series to obtain the desired battery voltage. A 6-volt battery therefore has three cells, and a 12-volt battery has 6 cells. The average stock car battery has a rated capacity of 600 to 800 watt-hours, regardless of whether it is a 6-volt or 12-volt battery.

Specific Gravity and the Hydrometer

As power is drawn from the battery, the acid content of the electrolyte is reduced. The acid content is restored to the electrolyte (meaning that the battery is recharged) by passing a current through the battery in a direction opposite to the direction of the discharge current.

Since the acid content of the electrolyte varies with the charge and discharge of the battery, it is possible to determine the state of charge by measuring the *specific gravity* of the electrolyte.

An inexpensive device for checking the s.g. is the hydrometer which can be obtained at any automobile supply store. In checking the s.g., enough electrolyte is drawn out of the cell and into the hydrometer so that the calibrated bulb floats freely without leaning against the wall of the glass tube.

While the readings will vary slightly with batteries of different manufacture, a reading of 1.275 should indicate full charge or nearly full charge, while a reading below 1.150 should indicate a battery that is close to the discharge point. More specific values can be obtained from the car or battery dealer.

Readings taken immediately after adding water, or shortly after a heavy discharge period will not be reliable, because the electrolyte will not be uniform throughout the cell. Charging will speed up the equalizing, and some mixing can be done by using the hydrometer to withdraw and return some of the electrolyte to the cell several times.

A battery should not be left in a discharged condition for any appreciable length of time. This is especially important in low temperatures when there is danger of the electrolyte freezing and ruining the battery. A battery discharged to an s.g. of 1.100 will start to freeze at about 20 degrees F., at about 5 degrees when the s.g. is 1.150 and at 16 below when the s.g. is 1.200.

If a battery has been run down to the point where it is nearly discharged, it can usually be fast-charged at a battery station. Fast-charging rates may be as high as 80 to 100 amperes for a 6-volt battery. Any 6-volt battery that will accept a charge of 75 amperes at 7.75 volts during the first 3 minutes of charging, or any 12-volt battery that will accept a charge of 40 to 45 amperes at 15.5 volts, may be safely fast-charged up to the point where the gassing becomes so excessive that electrolyte is lost or the temperature rises above 125 degrees.

A normal battery showing an s.g. of 1.150 or less may be fast-charged for 1 hour. One showing an s.g. of 1.150 to 1.175 may be fast-charged for 45 minutes. If the s.g. is 1.175 to 1.200, fast-charging should be limited to 30 minutes.

Care of the Battery

The battery terminals and mounting frame should be kept free from corrosion. Any corrosive accumulation may be removed by the use of water to which some household ammonia or baking soda has been added, and a stiff-bristle brush. Care should be taken to prevent any of the corrosive material from falling into the cells. Cell caps should be rinsed out in the same solution to keep the vent holes free from obstructing dirt. Battery terminals and their cable clamps should be polished bright with a wire brush, and coated with mineral grease.

Voltage Checks

Although the readings of s.g. are quite reliable as a measure of the state of charge of a normal battery, the necessity for frequent use of the hydrometer is an inconvenience and will not always serve as a conclusive check on a defective battery. Cells may show normal or almost normal s.g. and yet have high internal resistance that ruins the usefulness of the battery under load.

When all cells show satisfactory s.g. readings and yet the battery output is low, service stations check each cell by an instrument that measures the voltage of each cell under a heavy load. Under a heavy load the cell voltages should not differ by more than 0.15 volt.

A load-voltage test can also be made by measuring the voltage of each cell while closing the starter switch with the ignition turned off. In many cars it is necessary to pull the central distributor wire out to prevent the motor starting.

Electrolyte Level

Water is evaporated from the electrolyte, but the acid is not. Therefore water must be added to each cell from time to time so that the plates are always completely covered. The level should be checked at least once per week, especially during hot weather and constant operation.

Distilled water is preferred for replenishing, but clear drinking water is an acceptable substitute. Too much water should not be added, since the gassing that accompanies charging may force electrolyte out through the vent holes in the caps of the cells. The electrolyte expands with temperature.

EMERGENCY AND INDEPENDENT POWER SOURCES

Emergency power supply which operates independently of a.c. lines is available, or can be built in a number of different forms, depending upon the requirements of the service for which it is intended.

The most practical supply for the average individual amateur is one that operates from a car storage battery. Such a supply may take the form of a small motor generator (often called a dynamotor), a rotary converter, a vibrator-transformer-rectifier combination, or transistor supply.

Dynamotors

A dynamotor differs from a motor generator in that it is a single unit having a double armature winding. One winding serves for the driving motor, while the output voltage is taken from the other. Dynamotors usually are operated from 6-, 12-, 28- or 32-volt storage batteries and deliver from 300 to 1000 volts or more at various current ratings.

Successful operation of dynamotors requires heavy direct leads, mechanical isolation to reduce vibration, and thorough r.f. and ripple filtration. The shafts and bearings should be thoroughly "run in" before regular operation is attempted, and thereafter the tension of the bearings should be checked occasionally to make certain that no looseness has developed.

In mounting the dynamotor, the support should be in the form of rubber mounting blocks, or equivalent, to prevent the transmission of vibration mechanically. The frame of the dynamotor should be grounded through a heavy flexible connector. The brushes on the high-voltage end of the shaft should be by-passed with 0.002 μf. mica capacitors to a common point on the dynamotor frame, preferably to a point inside the end cover close to the brush holders. Short leads are essential. It may prove desirable to shield the entire unit, or even to remove the unit to a distance of three or four feet from the receiver and antenna lead.

When the dynamotor is used for receiving, a filter should be used similar to that described for vibrator supplies. A 0.01-μf. 600-volt (d.c.) paper capacitor should be connected in shunt across the output of the dynamotor, followed by a 2.5-mh. r.f. choke in the positive high-voltage lead. From this point the output should be run to the receiver power terminals through a smoothing filter using 4- to 8-μf. capacitors and a 15- or 30-henry choke having low d.c. resistance.

Vibrator Power Supplies

The vibrator type of power supply consists of a special step-up transformer combined with a vibrating interrupter (vibrator). When the unit is connected to a storage battery, plate power is obtained by passing current from the battery through the primary of the transformer. The circuit is made and reversed rapidly by the vibrator contacts, interrupting the current at regular intervals to give a changing magnetic field which induces a voltage in the secondary. The resulting square-wave d.c. pulses in the primary of the transformer cause an alternating voltage to be developed in the secondary. This high-voltage a.c. in turn is rectified, either by a vacuum-tube rectifier or by an additional synchronized pair of vibrator contacts. The rectified output is pulsating d.c., which may be filtered by ordinary means. The smoothing filter can be a single-section affair, but the output capacitance should be fairly large — 16 to 32 μf.

Fig. 19-44 shows the two types of circuits. At A is shown the **nonsynchronous** type of vibrator. When the battery is disconnected the reed is midway between the two contacts, touching neither. On closing the battery circuit the magnet coil pulls the reed into contact with one contact point, causing current to flow through the lower half of the transformer primary winding. Simultaneously, the magnet coil is short-circuited, de-energizing it, and the reed swings back. Inertia carries the reed into contact with the upper point, causing current to flow through the upper half of the transformer primary. The magnet coil again is energized, and the cycle repeats itself.

The synchronous circuit of Fig. 19-44B is provided with an extra pair of contacts which

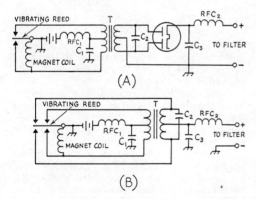

Fig. 19-45—Basic types of vibrator power-supply circuits. A—Nonsynchronous. B—Synchronous.

rectifies the secondary output of the transformer, thus eliminating the need for a separate rectifier tube. The secondary center-tap furnishes the positive output terminal when the relative polarities of primary and secondary windings are correct. The proper connections may be determined by experiment.

The buffer capacitor, C_2, across the transformer secondary, absorbs the surges that occur on breaking the current, when the magnetic field collapses practically instantaneously and hence causes very high voltages to be induced in the secondary. Without this capacitor excessive sparking occurs at the vibrator contacts, shortening the vibrator life. Correct values usually lie between 0.005 and 0.03 μf., and for 250-300-volt supplies the capacitor should be rated at 1500 to 2000 volts d.c. The exact capacitance is critical, and should be determined experimentally. The optimum value is that which results in least battery current for a given rectified d.c. output from the supply. In practice the value can be determined by observing the degree of vibrator sparking as the capacitance is changed. When the system is operating properly there should be practically no sparking at the vibrator contacts. A 5000-ohm resistor in series with C_2 will limit the secondary current to a safe value should the capacitor fail.

Vibrator-transformer units are available in a variety of power and voltage ratings. Representative units vary from one delivering 125 to 200 volts at 100 ma. to others with a 400-volt output rating at 150 ma. Most units come supplied with "hash" filters, but not all of them have built-in ripple filters. The requirements for ripple filters are similar to those for a.c. supplies. The usual efficiency of vibrator packs is in the vicinity of 70 per cent, so a 300-volt 200-ma. unit will draw approximately 15 amperes from a 6-volt storage battery. Special vibrator transformers are also available from transformer manufacturers so that the amateur may build his own supply if he so desires. These have d.c. output ratings varying from 150 volts at 40 ma. to 330 volts at 135 ma.

Vibrator-type supplies are also available for operating standard a.c. equipment from a 6- or 12-volt storage battery in power ratings up to 100 watts continuous or 125 watts intermittent.

"Hash" Elimination

Sparking at the vibrator contacts causes r.f. interference ("hash," which can be distinguished from hum by its harsh, sharper pitch) when used with a receiver. To minimize this, r.f. filters are incorporated, consisting of RFC_1 and C_1 in the battery circuit, and RFC_2 with C_3 in the d.c. output circuit.

Equally as important as the hash filter is thorough shielding of the power supply and its connecting leads, since even a small piece of wire or metal will radiate enough r.f. to cause interference in a sensitive amateur receiver.

The power supply should be built on a metal chassis, with all unshielded parts underneath. A bottom plate to complete the shielding is advisable. The transformer case, vibrator cover and the metal shell of the tube all should be grounded to the chassis. If a glass tube is used it should be enclosed in a tube shield. The battery leads should be evenly twisted, since these leads are more likely to radiate hash than any other part of a well-shielded supply. Experimenting with different values in the hash filters should come *after* radiation from the battery leads has been reduced to a minimum. Shielding the leads is not often found to be particularly helpful.

A 12-VOLT TO 250 VOLT D.C. CONVERTER

Small transceivers such as the Heath TWOer and Heath SIXer types require a separate power supply when operated from 12 volts d.c. Low-power home-built mobile and portable transmitters can also be powered from such a 12-volt source. The unit described here, when operated from 12-volts, will deliver approximately 250 volts d.c. at 100 ma., continuous-duty fashion. Transistorized d.c. to d.c. converters are quieter, more efficient, and less noisy (electrically) than are dynamotors or vibrator power supplies. For the foregoing reasons, this power unit is ideal for use with the type of equipment mentioned at the beginning of this discussion. It is designed to operate in a common-collector hookup (Fig. 19-48) so that it may be used with a negative-ground automotive electrical system. With positive-ground vehicles, the entire assembly should be mounted on a piece of bakelite, Masonite board, or similar insulating material to isolate it from the car frame. This will prevent short circuiting the car's battery.

The Circuit

Referring to Fig. 19-48, when the power is applied to the primary of T_1, one of the transistors —Q_1 or Q_2—will conduct heavily (dependent upon the slight d.c. imbalance which always exists among the passive and active elements of the primary circuit), while the remaining transistor is cut off. Assuming that Q_1 conducts first, for illustration purposes only, the voltage induced in the feedback windings (terminals 10 and 11, and 8 and 9) will level off as the transformer reaches saturation, causing Q_2 to conduct, while cutting off Q_1. This switching process continues to repeat, producing an alternating square

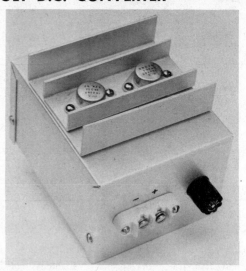

Fig. 19-46—Top view of the d.c. to d.c. converter. The input terminals and the fuse holder are on the front edge of the box. Switching transistors Q_1 and Q_2 are mounted on a home-made heat sink which is attached to the top of the box. The output jack, J_2, is on the rear wall of the box (not visible).

wave at the secondary of T_1. This square wave is rectified by diodes CR_1 through CR_4, and is filtered by C_2. C_1 is used to suppress transient spikes.

Construction

The power supply is built in a $3 \times 4 \times 5$-inch Minibox. The input terminals, a Millen E302 connector, and the fuse holder are mounted on one end of the top cover.

Transformer, T_1, and the 5-pin power-output socket, J_2, are mounted on the opposite end of the cover. The extra three terminals on J_2 are available for control-circuit wiring should the builder wish to mount a switching relay in the box.

The transistors, Q_1 and Q_2, are installed on home-made heat sinks and the complete assembly is attached to the top surface of the Minibox lid. Details of the heat sink are evident in Fig. 19-46. The larger channel is fashioned from a piece of aluminum stock that was four inches long and five inches wide. Its lips are one inch high. A second piece of aluminum, $2\frac{1}{4}$ inches wide and four inches long, is formed into a channel whose lips are $\frac{1}{2}$ inch high. These dimensions are not critical. It is important, however, that the inner-channel width of the smaller piece is large enough to permit the mounting of Q_1 and Q_2 inside it. Silicone grease, available from most electronics supply houses, should be spread thinly between the transistors and the heat sink, between the two heat-sink channels, and between the lower heat-sink channel and the Minibox. The grease contributes to better heat transfer between the various parts of the heat-sink assembly. After a

Fig. 19-47—Looking into the bottom of the power supply, T_1 is at the left, just below J_1. The fuse holder and the Millen E302 input connector are visible at the right of the assembly.

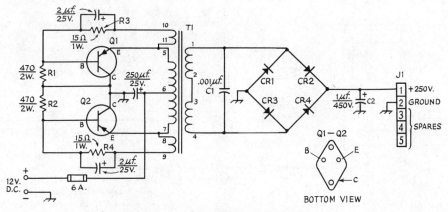

Fig. 19-48—Schematic diagram of the converter. Resistance is in ohms. Resistors are composition unit. Polarity-marked capacitors are electrolytic. C_1 is a 1000-volt disk ceramic. CR_1-CR_4, inc., are 600 p.r.v., 750-ma. top-hat rectifiers. Q_1 and Q_2 are 2N2869/2N301s. (2N376, 2N235A, or 2N1146 types are suitable). J_1 is a 5-pin female tube socket. T_1 is a Triad TY-78 transformer.

sustained 100-ma. load on the supply, the transistors and the heat sink should be just slightly warm to the touch.

The primary wiring of the converter should contain heavy-gauge insulated wire, No. 18 or larger. A 6-ampere fuse protects the supply from short-circuit or overload damage.

A Final Word

A recommended circuit is furnished with the Triad transformer and shows variable resistors for R_1 through R_4. Although the manufacturer states that the resistors can be adjusted for minimum spiking on the waveform, no significant changes were noted here when adjusting the resistors. For this reason, fixed-value resistors are

shown in Fig. 19-48. Also, Q_1 and Q_2 can be destroyed quickly if the resistors are set for too little resistance.

It was determined that the RCA 2N301s performed well and provided the output voltage and current characteristics stated by the manufacturer of the transformer. Other types were tried, resulting in a wide variety of output voltages. With some, the full-load voltage was as low as 85 volts. With others (high-beta, high-F_t ratings) the output voltage was as high as 395 volts under load. The transistor characteristics have a great deal to do with the performance of the converter, hence it is best to use the types specified by Triad (see Fig. 19-48), or the 2N301s used in this model.

12-VOLT D.C. TO 115-VOLT A.C. INVERTER

The 115-watt inverter shown in Fig. 19-49 can be used for portable/mobile operation to power small transceivers, receivers, test equipment, or accessories. It will also prove its worth in emergency situations where a small amount of a.c. power is needed for p.a. systems, portable lights, or similar.

The unit shown here provides 60 c.p.s. output, square wave, and has taps for 110, 115, or 125-volts. Because of the square-wave output, some hash noise may appear in the output of transmitters or receivers that are operated from the supply. If so, some form of filtering may be necessary at the output of the inverter.[1]

---

[1] A brute-force line filter is often helpful in reducing this type of hash. Commercial units of this kind are available from most wholesale houses (J. W. Miller Co. No. 7818). A home-made filter might consist of two scramble-wound inductors containing 10 feet (each) of No. 12 enameled copper wire. A coil would be placed in each leg of the a.c. output. Four 0.1-μf. 600-volt paper capacitors would be needed. They would be connected between the ends of each coil and ground. Such a filter could be built on the inverter chassis, or contained in its own case, outboard fashion.

Fig. 19-49—Top view of the d.c. to a.c. inverter. The transistors and their heat sink are at the right. Two a.c. outlets are used, offering greater convenience than would be possible with a single receptacle. A neon lamp lights when the unit is operating.

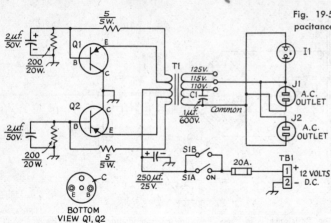

BOTTOM VIEW Q1, Q2

Fig. 19-50—Schematic diagram of the inverter. Capacitance is in $\mu f.$ Polarized capacitors are electrolytic. Resistance is in ohms.

C_1—1-$\mu f.$ 600 volt capacitor (paper type only).

I_1—Neon panel-lamp assembly with built-in dropping resistor.

J_1, J_2—Standard female-type a.c. outlet socket.

Q_1, Q_2—High-wattage power transistor. 2N278 used here. (2N678, 2N1146, 2N173 suitable.)

S_1—D.p.s.t. toggle switch with sections in parallel.

T_1—Inverter transformer, 12 volts d.c. to 115 volts a.c. (Triad TY-75A.)

TB_1—Two-terminal connector (Millen 37302 suitable).

Construction

The inverter is built on a home-made large-size Minibox-style base which measures $8 \times 6 \times 2$ inches. A Bud CU-3009-A Minibox can be used as a chassis. Rubber feet are attached to the bottom cover of the Minibox. The feet were added to help prevent the assembly from scratching the automobile's finish if it is to be placed on the hood or trunk of the car during portable use.

A large heat sink is used for cooling Q_1 and Q_2. The unit shown here is 4 inches long, is 3 inches wide, and is 2 inches high. It was manufactured by Delco Radio (part number 7281366). Any heat sink of similar dimensions will work satisfactorily. Because the circuit is operated in a common-collector configuration, the transistors need not be insulated from the heat sink, nor is it necessary to insulate the heat sink from the chassis. Silicone grease is used between the tran-

sistors and the heat sink, and between the heat sink and the chassis. This contributes to efficient heat transfer between the transistors and the thermal hardware.

All leads carrying primary current should be of large circular-mil size in order to prevent a voltage drop in that part of the circuit. Parallel sections of a.c. zip cord are used in this model. They are used between the input terminal block and the fuse holder, between the fuse holder and the toggle switch, and between the switch and the primary leads of T_1. A d.p.s.t. toggle switch is used at S_1 to permit both sections to be used in parallel, increasing the current-handling capacity.

Two a.c. outlets are located on the top-front of the chassis so that more than one piece of equipment can be plugged in at the same time.

Operation

In using the inverter, it is wise to have some kind of a load be connected across the output of the unit when it is turned on. Without a secondary load, transients can occur and cause the destruction of the switching transistors, Q_1 and Q_2. The best procedure is to attach the equipment to the inverter's outlet receptacle, turn the equipment on, then activate the inverter by turning it on with S_1. In turning the system off, this process should be reversed—turning the inverter off first, then the equipment.

Motor-operated equipment such as tape recorders and record players will not function satisfactorily from this inverter and should not be used with it. Also, make certain that the equipment which is to be operated from the inverter does not draw more than 100 watts if continuous-duty operation is planned. The inverter should safely handle intermittent loads of up to 175 watts.

For maximum efficiency, the inverter should be connected directly to the car battery terminals by means of large-diameter conductors. The shorter the conductor length, the less voltage drop there will be in the line.

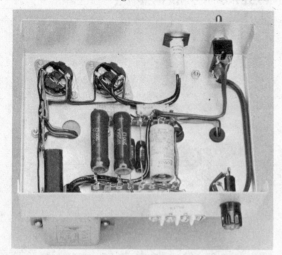

Fig. 19-51—A look at the underside of the chassis. The resistors and capacitors are mounted between insulated terminal strips. A.c. zip cord, paralleled, is used for the heavy-duty primary wiring.

GASOLINE-ENGINE DRIVEN GENERATORS

For higher-power installations, such as for communications control centers during emergencies, the most practical form of independent power supply is the gasoline-engine driven generator which provides standard 115-volt 60-cycle supply.

Such generators are ordinarily rated at a minimum of 250 or 300 watts. They are available up to ten kilowatts, or big enough to handle the highest-power amateur rig. Most are arranged to charge automatically an auxiliary 6- or 12-volt battery used in starting. Fitted with self-starters and adequate mufflers and filters,

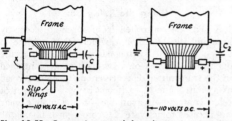

Fig. 19-52—Connections used for eliminating interference from gas-driven generator plants. C should be 1 µf., 300 volts, paper, while C_2 may be 1 µf. with a voltage rating of twice the d.c. output voltage delivered by the generator. X indicates an added connection between the slip ring on the grounded side of the line and the generator frame.

they represent a high order of performance and efficiency. Many of the larger models are liquid-cooled, and they will operate continuously at full load.

The output frequency of an engine-driven generator must fall between the relatively narrow limits of 50 to 60 cycles if standard 60-cycle transformers are to operate efficiently from this source. A 60-cycle electric clock provides a means of checking the output frequency with a fair degree of accuracy. The clock is connected across the output of the generator and the second hand is checked closely against the second hand of a watch. The speed of the engine is adjusted until the two second hands are in synchronism.

Output voltage should be checked with a voltmeter since a standard 115-volt lamp bulb, which is sometimes used for this purpose, is very inaccurate.

Noise Elimination

Electrical noise which may interfere with receivers operating from engine-driven a.c. generators may be reduced or eliminated by taking proper precautions. The most important point is that of grounding the frame of the generator *and* one side of the output. The ground lead should be short to be effective, otherwise grounding may actually increase the noise. A water pipe may be used if a short connection can be made near the point where the

pipe enters the ground, otherwise a good separate ground should be provided.

The next step is to loosen the brush-holder locks and slowly shift the position of the brushes while checking for noise with the receiver. Usually a point will be found (almost always different from the factory setting) where there is a marked decrease in noise.

From this point on, if necessary, bypass capacitors from various brush holders to the frame, as shown in Fig. 19-50, will bring the hash down to within 10 to 15 per cent of its original intensity, if not entirely eliminating it. Most of the remaining noise will be reduced still further if the high-power audio stages are cut out and a pair of headphones is connected into the second detector.

DRY CELL BATTERIES

Dry-cell batteries are a practical source of power for supplying portables or equipment which must be transported on foot.[1] A knowledge of the several kinds and their features will help in the selection of the most economical battery for a given application.

Zinc-carbon cells (1.5 volts) lose their power even when not in use, if allowed to stand idle for a year or more. This makes them uneconomical if not used more or less continuously. Their life depends also upon the discharge rate; the life is shorter under steady discharge than it is under intermittent discharge. (E.g., the AA penlite cell has a typical life to 1.0 volt of 14 hours at a steady 30-ma. discharge rate and a life of 33 hours at a 4-hours-per-day 20-ma. discharge. The No. 6 cell has a 43-hour life at a continuous 0.5-ampere discharge, but it jumps to 80 hours at a 4-hours-per-day 0.5-ampere drain.)

Alkaline-manganese cells (1.2 volts) find increasing application in portable radios, tape recorders, shavers and other portable devices. They are capable of high discharge rates over extended periods; heavy current can be drawn continuously without sacrificing ampere-hour capacity.

The mercury cell (1.35 volts) has a high ratio of ampere-hour capacity to volume at high current drains. The shelf life is excellent, and mercury batteries are well suited for emergency portable operation even after many months of storage. At relatively low current drain, the mercury cell will deliver substantially constant voltage during its life. (E.g., an AA penlite cell output voltage will drop to only 1.2 volts after 80 hours of service at 25 ma.)

The nickel-cadmium cell (1.25 volts) also shows little voltage change during its useful life. It is more expensive than any of the cells mentioned above, but it has the big advantage that it can be recharged. It finds widespread application anywhere a portable rechargeable power source is required. Typically, the AA penlite size has 0.5 ampere-hour capacity at a 5-hour discharge rate, while the D flashlight size has a 4-ampere-hour capacity at a 5-hour discharge rate.

[1] "Choosing Batteries," *QST*, Sept. 1967, p. 40.

A RELAY BOX FOR MOBILE GEAR

Some mobile equipment requires an external circuit control when changing over from the transmit to the receive mode. If separate transmitting and receiving units are contained in the system, an external relay box of the type shown in Fig. 19-26 can be used for antenna switching, receiver muting, and transmitter activation. Although K_1 is an open, leaf-type relay, it does not create an s.w.r. problem when used with equipment that operates between 1.8 and 30 Mc. For v.h.f. operation, a good quality coaxial relay should be used.

Construction

The control circuit is housed in a $5\frac{1}{4} \times 3 \times 2$-inch Minibox. The relay terminals are facing toward the SO-239 coax connectors so that the lead lengths between the relay and the connectors can be kept short. Number 12 tinned copper wire is used for the connections. Insulated number-24 hookup wire is used for making the connections between K_1 and TB_1, TB_2, and TB_3. The terminal blocks are ceramic units, but any satisfactory substitute can be used. It might be more convenient in some installations to use mating plugs and sockets for connection to the relay box, providing a quick-disconnect feature for those who frequently carry the equipment to and from the car.

The Relay

K_1 was chosen because of its low price and minimal interleaf capacitance. If 6-volt d.c. operation is desired, a

Fig. 19-26—Top view of the mobile relay box. The antenna connectors are in the foreground. TB_1, to which the 12-volt supply is connected, is on the rear wall of the box and is not visible. TB_2 and TB_3, the connectors for the remote lines, are located on the top-rear of the box.

KA14DY relay with a 6-volt coil can be substituted for the 12-volt model shown here. The relay contacts are rated at five amperes and have gold-flashed silver contacts, assuring low d.c. resistance between mating elements. Ten-ampere contacts are available in the KA14DG model relay, but at slightly higher cost.

Using the Relay Box

K_1 can be controlled from a remote point by breaking the 12-volt line which feeds it (line to TB_1). A toggle switch can be mounted at the operating position, or a switch already contained in the transmitter or receiver might be employed as a control for K_1. Alternatively, a spare set of relay contacts—if available—in the mobile gear can be used to activate K_1 from a push-to-talk or VOX circuit.

The relay box can be mounted anywhere in the car that is convenient for the particular installation.

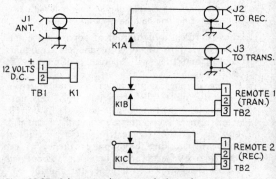

Fig. 19-27—Schematic diagram of the relay circuit. J_1, J_2, and J_3 are SO-239-style coax connectors. Relay K_1 is a 3-pole double-throw type (Potter and Brumfield KA14DY with 12-volt d.c. coil). TB_1 is a two-terminal connector (Millen E-302). TB_2 and TB_3 are three-terminal connectors (Millen E-303).

Fig. 19-28—Underside of the box showing the relay terminals facing toward the coaxial connectors. The wiring between the terminal blocks and K_1 is dressed neatly along the chassis. Twisting the wires together gives added rigidity.

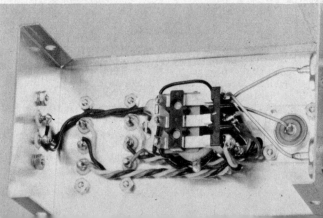

Chapter 20

Construction Practices

TOOLS AND MATERIALS

While an easier, and perhaps a better, job can be done with a greater variety of tools available, by taking a little thought and care it is possible to turn out a fine piece of equipment with only a few of the common hand tools. A list of tools which will be indispensable in the contruction of radio equipment will be found on this page. With these tools it should be possible to perform any of the required operations in preparing panels and metal chassis for assembly and wiring. It is an excellent idea for the amateur who does constructional work to add to his supply of tools from time to time as finances permit.

RECOMMENDED TOOLS

Long-nose pliers, 6-inch and 4-inch.
Diagonal cutters, 6-inch and 4-inch.
Combination pliers, 6-inch.
Screwdriver, 6- to 7-inch, ¼-inch blade.
Screwdriver, 4- to 5-inch, ⅛-inch blade.
Phillips screwdriver, 6- to 7-inch.
Phillips screwdriver, 3- to 4-inch.
Long-shank screwdriver with holding clip on blade.
Scratch awl or scriber for marking metal.
Combination square, 12-inch, for layout work.
Hand drill, ¼-inch chuck or larger.
Soldering pencil, 30-watt, ⅛-inch tip.
Soldering iron, 200-watt, ⅝-inch tip.
Hack saw and 12-inch blades.
Hand nibbling tool, for chassis-hole cutting.
Center punch, for hole marking.
Hammer, ball-peen, 1-lb. head.
Heavy-duty jack knife.
File set, flat, round, half-round, and triangular. Large and miniature types recommended.
High-speed drill bits, No. 60 through ⅜-inch diameter.
Set of "Spintite" socket wrenches for hex nuts.
Crescent wrench, 6-inch and 10-inch.
Machine-screw taps, 4-40 through 10-32 thread.
Socket punches, ½", ⅝", ¾", 1⅛", 1¼", and 1½".
Tapered reamer, T-handle, ½-inch maximum pitch.
Bench vise, 4-inch jaws or larger.
Medium-weight machine oil.
Tin shears, 10-inch size.
Motor-driven emery wheel for grinding.
Solder, *rosin core only.*
Contact cleaner, liquid or spray can.
Duco cement or equiv.
Electrical tape, vinyl plastic.

Radio-supply houses, mail-order retail stores and most hardware stores carry the various tools required when building or servicing amateur radio equipment. While power tools (electric drill or drill press, grinding wheel, etc.) are very useful and will save a lot of time, they are not essential.

Twist Drills

Twist drills are made of either high-speed steel or carbon steel. The latter type is more common and will usually be supplied unless specific request is made for high-speed drills. The carbon drill will suffice for most ordinary equipment construction work and costs less than the high-speed type.

While twist drills are available in a number of sizes, those listed in bold-faced type in Table 20-I will be most commonly used in construction of amateur equipment. It is usually desirable to purchase several of each of the commonly used sizes rather than a standard set, most of which will be used infrequently if at all.

Care of Tools

The proper care of tools is not alone a matter of pride to a good workman. He also realizes the energy which may be saved and the annoyance which may be avoided by the possession of a full kit of well-kept sharp-edged tools.

Drills should be sharpened at frequent intervals so that grinding is kept at a minimum each time. This makes it easier to maintain the rather critical surface angles required for best cutting with least wear. Occasional oilstoning of the cutting edges of a drill or reamer will extend the time between grindings.

The soldering iron can be kept in good condition by keeping the tip well tinned with solder and not allowing it to run at full voltage for long periods when it is not being used. After each period of use, the tip should be removed and cleaned of any scale which may have accumulated. An oxidized tip may be cleaned by dipping it in sal ammoniac while hot and then wiping it clean with a rag. If the tip becomes pitted it should be filed until smooth and bright, and then tinned immediately by dipping it in solder.

Useful Materials

Small stocks of various miscellaneous materials will be required in constructing radio apparatus, most of which are available from hardware or radio-supply stores. A representative list follows:

Sheet aluminum, solid and perforated, 16 or 18 gauge, for brackets and shielding.
½ × ½-inch aluminum angle stock.
¼-inch diameter round brass or aluminum rod for shaft extensions.
Machine screws: Round-head and flat-head, with nuts to fit. Most useful sizes: 4–40, 6–32 and 8–32, in lengths from ¼ inch to 1½ inches. (Nickel-plated iron will be found satisfactory except in strong r.f. fields, where brass should be used.)
Bakelite, lucite and polystyrene scraps.
Soldering lugs, panel bearings, rubber grommets, terminal-lug wiring strips, varnished-cambric insulating tubing.
Shielded and unshielded wire.
Tinned bare wire, Nos. 22, 14 and 12.

Machine screws, nuts, washers, soldering lugs, etc., are most reasonably purchased in quantities of a gross. Many of the radio-supply stores sell small quantities and assortments that come in handy.

SCR MOTOR-SPEED CONTROL

Most electric hand drills operate at a single high speed; however, from time to time, the need arises to utilize low or medium speeds. Low speeds are useful when drilling in tight spaces or on exposed surfaces where it is important that the drill bit doesn't slip, and when drilling bakelite, Plexiglas and similar materials. Medium

Fig. 20-B—Small enough to fit in the palm of your hand, the SCR motor-speed control is housed in a small Minibox.

speeds are useful for drilling non-ferrous metals such as aluminum and brass. One way to accomplish these ends with a single-speed electric drill is to use a silicon-controlled-rectifier (SCR) speed control.

The circuit of an SCR speed control is shown in Fig. 20-A. The SCR, CR_1, acts like an open circuit until it receives a positive trigger pulse between gate and cathode. If at this time the anode is negative with respect to the cathode, nothing will happen and the SCR will still appear to be an open circuit. If, however, the anode is positive with respect to the cathode when the positive trigger pulse arrives at the gate, the SCR will function like a normal diode and conduct. Once triggered, the SCR will continue to conduct until the voltage between the anode and the cathode returns to zero and reverses polarity. It will then cease to conduct and not conduct again, even when the correct forward polarity appears, until the gate receives another positive pulse. The timing of the gate pulse determines the instant at which conduction begins during a possible 180-degree conduction period for sine wave input.

The trigger circuit consists of C_1, R_1, R_2 and neon lamp I_1. When the voltage across C_1 reaches

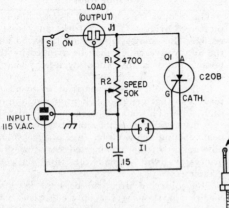

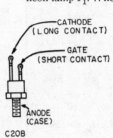

Fig. 20-A—Circuit diagram of the SCR motor-speed control.

C_1—0.15-uf. 200-v. paper tubular.
I_1—NE-2 neon lamp.
J_1—Chassis-mounting line socket (Amphenol 61-F1).
Q_1—C2OB SCR (General Electric).

R_1—4700-ohm ½-watt composition.
R_2—50,000-ohm linear-taper control.
S_1—S.p.s.t. toggle.

the ignition voltage of I_1, the neon lamp fires and sends a pulse to the gate of the SCR. The setting of R_2 determines the charging rate of C_1 and thus the conduction angle of the SCR. Decreasing R_2 increases the speed of an electric drill plugged in the output connector, J_1.

Construction

Because of the small complement of parts, the SCR speed control can be constructed inside a very small container. The model described was built in a $2\frac{3}{4} \times 2\frac{1}{8} \times 1\frac{5}{8}$-inch Minibox. Since the mounting stud and main body of the SCR are common with the anode, care should be used to mount the SCR clear from surrounding objects. In the unit shown, two soldering lugs were soldered together and the narrow ends connected to one side of the female output connector; the large ends were used as a fastening point for the SCR anode stud.

Operation

Although the circuit described is intended to be used to reduce the speed of electric hand drills that draw six amperes or less, it has many other applications. It can be used to regulate the temperature of a soldering iron, which is being used to wire a delicate circuit, or it may be used for dimming lamps or for controlling the cooking speed of a small hot plate. Note, however, if the circuit is used with a device drawing from three to six amperes for a continuous period of over ten minutes, it will be necessary to provide a heat sink (insulated from the chassis) for the SCR anode case.

CHASSIS WORKING

With a few essential tools and proper procedure, it will be found that building radio gear on a metal chassis is a relatively simple matter. Aluminum is to be preferred to steel, not only because it is a superior shielding material, but because it is much easier to work and to provide good chassis contacts.

The placing of components on the chassis is shown quite clearly in the photographs in this *Handbook*. Aside from certain essential dimensions, which usually are given in the text, exact duplication is not necessary.

| | | | TABLE 20-I | |
| | | | Numbered Drill Sizes | |
Number	Diameter (mils)	Will Clear Screw	Drilled for Tapping Iron, Steel or Brass*
1	228.0	—	—
2	221.0	12-24	—
3	213.0	—	14-24
4	209.0	12-20	—
5	205.0	—	—
6	204.0	—	—
7	201.0	—	—
8	199.0	—	—
9	196.0	—	—
10	193.5	10-32	—
11	191.0	10-24	—
12	189.0	—	—
13	185.0	—	—
14	182.0	—	—
15	180.0	—	—
16	177.0	—	12-24
17	173.0	—	—
18	169.5	8-32	—
19	166.0	—	12-20
20	161.0	—	—
21	159.0	—	10-32
22	157.0	—	—
23	154.0	—	—
24	152.0	—	—
25	149.5	—	10-24
26	147.0	—	—
27	144.0	—	—
28	140.0	6-32	—
29	136.0	—	8-32
30	128.5	—	—
31	120.0	—	—
32	116.0	—	—
33	113.0	4-40	—
34	111.0	—	—
35	110.0	—	6-32
36	106.5	—	—
37	104.0	—	—
38	101.5	—	—
39	099.5	3-48	—
40	098.0	—	—
41	096.0	—	—
42	093.5	—	4-40
43	089.0	2-56	—
44	086.0	—	—
45	082.0	—	3-48
46	081.0	—	—
47	078.5	—	—
48	076.0	—	—
49	073.0	—	2-56
50	070.0	—	—
51	067.0	—	—
52	063.5	—	—
53	059.5	—	—
54	055.0	—	—

*Use one size larger for tapping bakelite and phenolics.

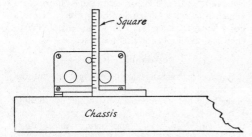

Fig. 20-1—Method of measuring the heights of capacitor shafts, etc. If the square is adjustable, the end of the scale should be set flush with the face of the head.

Much trouble and energy can be saved by spending sufficient time in planning the job. When all details are worked out beforehand the actual construction is greatly simplified.

Cover the top of the chassis with a piece of wrapping paper or, preferably, cross-section paper, folding the edges down over the sides of the chassis and fastening with adhesive tape. Then assemble the parts to be mounted on top of the chassis and move them about until a satisfactory arrangement has been found, keeping in mind any parts which are to be mounted underneath, so that interferences in mounting may be avoided. Place capacitors and other parts with shafts extending through the panel first, and arrange them so that the controls will form the desired pattern on the panel. Be sure to line up the shafts squarely with the chassis front. Locate any partition shields and panel brackets next, and then the tube sockets and any other parts, marking the mounting-hole centers of each accurately on the paper. Watch out for capacitors whose shafts are off center and do not line up with the mounting holes. Do not forget to mark the centers of socket holes and holes for leads under i.f. transformers, etc., as well as holes for wiring leads. The small holes for socket-mounting screws are best located and center-punched, using the socket itself as a template, after the main center hole has been cut.

By means of the square, lines indicating accurately the centers of shafts should be extended to the front of the chassis and marked on the panel at the chassis line, the panel being fastened on temporarily. The hole centers may then be punched in the chassis with the center punch. After drilling, the parts which require mounting underneath may be located and the mounting holes drilled, making sure by trial that no interferences exist with parts mounted on top. Mounting holes

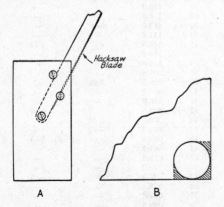

Fig. 20-2—To cut rectangular holes in a chassis corner, holes may be filed out as shown in the shaded portion of B, making it possible to start the hack-saw blade along the cutting line. A shows how a single-ended handle may be constructed for a hack-saw blade.

along the front edge of the chassis should be transferred to the panel, by once again fastening the panel to the chassis and marking it from the rear.

Next, mount on the chassis the capacitors and any other parts with shafts extending to the panel, and measure accurately the height of the center of each shaft above the chassis, as illustrated in Fig. 20-1. The horizontal displacement of shafts having already been marked on the chassis line on the panel, the vertical displacement can be measured from this line. The shaft centers may now be

marked on the back of the panel, and the holes drilled. Holes for any other panel equipment coming above the chassis line may then be marked and drilled, and the remainder of the apparatus mounted. Holes for terminals etc., in the rear edge of the chassis should be marked and drilled at the same time that they are done for the top.

Drilling and Cutting Holes

When drilling holes in metal with a hand drill it is important that the centers first be located with a center punch, so that the drill point will not "walk" away from the center when starting the hole. When the drill starts to break through, special care must be used. Often it is an advantage to shift a two-speed drill to low gear at this point. Holes more than $\frac{1}{4}$ inch in diameter should be started with a smaller drill and reamed out with the larger drill.

The chuck on the usual type of hand drill is limited to $\frac{1}{4}$-inch drills. Although it is rather tedious, the $\frac{1}{4}$-inch hole may be filed out to larger diameters with round files. Another method possible with limited tools is to drill a series of small holes with the hand-drill along the inside of the circumference of the large hole, placing the holes as close together as possible. The center may then be knocked out with a cold chisel and the edges smoothed up with a file. Taper reamers which fit into the carpenter's brace will make the job easier. A large rat-tail file clamped in the brace makes a very good reamer for holes up to the diameter of the file.

For socket holes and other large holes in an aluminum chassis, socket-hole punches should be used. They require first drilling a guide hole to pass the bolt that is turned to squeeze the punch through the chassis. The threads of the bolt should be oiled occasionally.

Large holes in steel panels or chassis are best cut with an adjustable circle cutter. Occasional application of machine oil in the cutting groove will help. The cutter first should be tried out on a block of wood, to make sure that it is set for the right diameter.

The burrs or rough edges which usually result after drilling or cutting holes may be removed with a file, or sometimes more conveniently with a sharp knife or chisel. It is a good idea to keep an old wood chisel sharpened and available for this purpose.

Rectangular Holes

Square or rectangular holes may be cut out by making a row of small holes as previously described, but is more easily done by drilling a $\frac{1}{2}$-inch hole inside each corner, as illustrated in Fig. 20-2, and using these holes for starting and turning the hack saw. The socket-hole punch and the square punches which are now available also may be of considerable assistance in cutting out large rectangular openings.

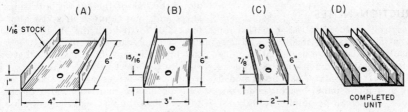

Fig. 20-C—Details for forming channel type heat sinks.

SEMICONDUCTOR HEAT SINKS

Homemade heat sinks can be fashioned from brass, copper or aluminum stock by employing ordinary workshop tools. The dimensions of the heat sink will depend upon the type of transistor used, and the amount of heat that must be conducted away from the body of the semiconductor.

Fig. 20-C shows the order of progression for forming a large heat sink from aluminum or brass channels of near-equal height and depth. The width is lessened in parts (B) and (C) so that each channel will fit into the preceding one as shown in the completed model at (D). The three pieces are bolted together with 8–32 screws and nuts. Dimensions given are for illustrative purposes only.

Heat sinks for smaller transistors can be fabricated as shown in Fig. 20-E. Select a drill bit that is one size smaller than the diameter of the transistor case and form the heat sink from 1/16 inch thick brass, copper or aluminum stock as shown in steps (A), (B), and (C). Form the stock around the drill bit by compressing it in a vise (A). The completed heat sink is press-fitted over the body of the semiconductor as illustrated at (D). The larger the area of the heat sink, the greater will be the amount of heat conducted away from the transistor body. In some applications, the heat sinks shown in Fig. 20-E may be two or three inches in height (power transistor stages).

Another technique for making heat sinks for TO-5 type transistors (1) and larger models

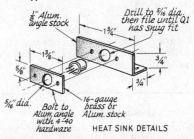

Fig. 20-D—Layout and assembly details of another homemade heat sink. The completed assembly can be insulated from the main chassis of the transmitter by using insulating washers.

(1) is shown in Fig. 20-D. This style of heat sink will dissipate considerably more heat than will the type shown in Fig. 20-E. The main body of the sink is fashioned from a piece of 1/8-inch thick aluminum angle bracket—available from most hardware stores. A hole is bored in the angle stock to allow the transistor case to fit *snugly* into it. The transistor is held in place by a small metal plate whose center hole is slightly smaller in diameter than the case of the transistor. Details are given in Fig. 20-D.

A thin coating of silicone grease, available from most electronics supply houses, can be applied between the case of the transistor and the part of the heat sink with which it comes in contact. The silicone grease will aid the transfer of heat from the transistor to the sink. This practice can be applied to all models shown here. In the example given in Fig. 20-C, the grease should be applied between the three channels before they are bolted together, as well as between the transistor and the channel it contacts.

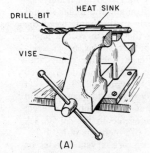

(A)

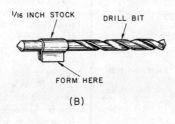

(B)

COMPLETED HEAT SINK

(C)

HEAT SINK INSTALLED ON TRANSISTOR

(D)

Fig. 20-E—Steps used in constructing heat sinks for small transistors.

CONSTRUCTION NOTES

If a control shaft must be extended or insulated, a flexible shaft coupling with adequate insulation should be used. Satisfactory support for the shaft extension, as well as electrical contact for safety, can be provided by means of a metal panel bearing made for the purpose. These can be obtained singly for use with existing shafts, or they can be bought with a captive extension shaft included. In either case the panel bearing gives a "solid" feel to the control.

The use of fiber washers between ceramic insulation and metal brackets, screws or nuts will prevent the ceramic parts from breaking.

STANDARD METAL GAUGES

Gauge No.	American or B. & S.[1]	U. S. Standard[2]	Birmingham or Stubs[3]
1	.2893	.28125	.300
2	.2576	.265625	.284
3	.2294	.25	.259
4	.2043	.234375	.238
5	.1819	.21875	.220
6	.1620	.203125	.203
7	.1443	.1875	.180
8	.1285	.171875	.165
9	.1144	.15625	.148
10	.1019	.140625	.134
11	.09074	.125	.120
12	.08081	.109375	.109
13	.07196	.09375	.095
14	.06408	.078125	.083
15	.05707	.0703125	.072
16	.05082	.0625	.065
17	.04526	.05625	.058
18	.04030	.05	.049
19	.03589	.04375	.042
20	.03196	.0375	.035
21	.02846	.034375	.032
22	.02535	.03125	.028
23	.02257	.028125	.025
24	.02010	.025	.022
25	.01790	.021875	.020
26	.01594	.01875	.018
27	.01420	.0171875	.016
28	.01264	.015625	.014
29	.01126	.0140625	.013
30	.01003	.0125	.012
31	.008928	.0109375	.010
32	.007950	.01015625	.009
33	.007080	.009375	.008
34	.006350	.00859375	.007
35	.005615	.0078125	.005
36	.005000	.00703125	.004
37	.004453	.006640626	....
38	.003965	.00625	....
39	.003531	....	....
40	.003145	....	....

[1] Used for aluminum, copper, brass and nonferrous alloy sheets, wire and rods.
[2] Used for iron, steel, nickel and ferrous alloy sheets, wire and rods.
[3] Used for seamless tubes; also by some manufacturers for copper and brass.

Cutting and Bending Sheet Metal

If a sheet of metal is too large to be cut conveniently with a hack saw, it may be marked with scratches as deep as possible along the line of the cut on both sides of the sheet and then clamped in a vise and worked back and forth until the sheet breaks at the line. Do not carry the bending too far until the break begins to weaken; otherwise the edge of the sheet may become bent. A pair of iron bars or pieces of heavy angle stock, as long or longer than the width of the sheet, to hold it in the vise will make the job easier. "C" clamps may be used to keep the bars from spreading at the ends. The rough edges may be smoothed with a file or by placing a large piece of emery cloth or sandpaper on a flat surface and running the edge of the metal back and forth over the sheet.

Bends may be made similarly.

Finishing Aluminum

Aluminum chassis, panels and parts may be given a sheen finish by treating them in a caustic bath. An enamelled or plastic container, such as a dishpan or infant's bathtub, should be used for the solution. Dissolve ordinary household lye in cold water in a proportion of 1/4 to 1/2 can of lye per gallon of water. The stronger solution will do the job more rapidly. Stir the solution with a stick of wood until the lye crystals are completely dissolved. Be very careful to avoid any skin contact with the solution. It is also harmful to clothing. Sufficient solution should be prepared to cover the piece completely. When the aluminum is immersed, a very pronounced bubbling takes place and ventilation should be provided to disperse the escaping gas. A half hour to two hours in the solution should be sufficient, depending upon the strength of the solution and the desired surface.

Remove the aluminum from the solution with sticks and rinse thoroughly in cold water while swabbing with a rag to remove the black deposit. When dry, finish by spraying on a light coat of clear lacquer.

Soldering

The secret of good soldering is to use the right amount of heat. Too little heat will produce a "cold-soldered joint"; too much may injure a component. The iron and the solder should be applied simultaneously to the joint. Keep the iron clean by brushing the hot tip with a paper towel. Always use rosin-core solder, never acid-core. Solders have different melting points, depending upon the ratio of tin to lead. A 50-50 solder melts at 425° F, while 60-40 melts at 371° F. When it is desirable to protect from excessive heat the components being soldered, the 60-40 solder is preferable to the 50-50. (A less-common solder, 63-37, melts at 361° F.)

When soldering transistors, crystal diodes or small resistors, the lead should be gripped with a pair of pliers up close to the unit so that the heat will be conducted away. Overheating of a transistor or diode while soldering can cause permanent damage. Also, mechanical stress will have a similar effect, so that a small unit should be mounted so that there is no appreciable mechanical strain on the leads.

Trouble is sometimes experienced in soldering to the pins of coil forms or male cable plugs. It helps if the pins are first cleaned on the inside

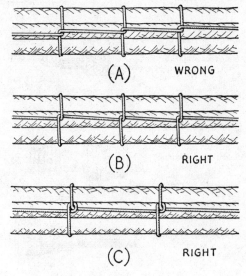

Fig. 20-3—Methods of lacing cables. The method shown at C is more secure, but takes more time than the method of B. The latter is usually adequate for most amateur requirements.

with a suitable twist drill and then tinned by flowing rosin-core solder into them. Immediately clear the surplus solder from each hot pin by a whipping motion or by blowing through the pin from the inside of the form or plug. Before inserting the wire in the pin, file the nickel plate from the tip. After soldering, round the solder tip off with a file.

When soldering to the pins of polystyrene coil forms, hold the pin to be soldered with a pair of heavy pliers, to form a "heat sink" and insure that the pin does not heat enough in the coil form to loosen and become misaligned.

Wiring

The wire used in connecting amateur equipment should be selected considering both the maximum current it will be called upon to handle and the voltage its insulation must stand without breakdown. Also, from the consideration to TVI, the power wiring of all transmitters should be done with wire that has a braided shielding cover. Receiver and audio circuits may also require the use of shielded wire at some points for stability, or the elimination of hum.

No. 20 stranded wire is commonly used for most receiver wiring (except for the high-frequency circuits) where the current does not exceed 2 or 3 amperes. For higher-current heater circuits, No. 18 is available. Wire with cellulose acetate insulation is good for volt-

ages up to about 500. For higher voltages, thermoplastic-insulated wire should be used. Inexpensive wire strippers that make the removal of insulation from hook-up wire an easy job are available on the market.

When power leads have several branches in the chassis, it is convenient to use fiber-insulated multiple tie points as anchorages or junction points. Strips of this type are also useful as insulated supports for resistors, r.f. chokes and capacitors. High-voltage wiring should have exposed points held to a minimum; those which cannot be avoided should be made as inaccessible as possible to accidental contact or short-circuit.

Where shielded wire is called for and capacitance to ground is not a factor, Belden type 8885 shielded grid wire may be used. If capacitance must be minimized, it may be necessary to use a piece of car-radio low-capacitance lead-in wire, or coaxial cable.

For wiring high-frequency circuits, rigid wire is often used. Bare soft-drawn tinned wire, sizes 22 to 12 (depending on mechanical requirements), is suitable. Kinks can be removed by stretching a piece 10 or 15 feet long and then cutting into short lengths that can be handled conveniently. R.f. wiring should be run directly from point to point with a minimum of sharp bends and the wire kept well spaced from the chassis or other grounded metal surfaces. Where the wiring must pass through the chassis or a partition, a clearance hole should be cut and lined with a rubber grommet. In case insulation becomes necessary, varnished cambric tubing (spaghetti) can be slipped over the wire.

In transmitters where the peak voltage does not exceed 2500 volts, the shielded grid wire mentioned above should be satisfactory for power circuits. For higher voltages, Belden type 8656, Birnbach type 1820, or shielded ignition cable can be used. In the case of filament circuits carrying heavy current, it may be necessary to use No. 10 or 12 bare or enameled wire, slipped through spaghetti, and then covered with copper braid pulled tightly over the spaghetti. The chapter on TVI shows the manner in which shielded wire should be applied. If the shielding is simply slid back over the insulation and solder flowed into the end of the braid, the braid usually will stay in place without the necessity for cutting it back or binding it in place. The braid should be cleaned first so that solder will take with a minimum of heat.

R.f. wiring in transmitters usually follows the method described above for receivers with due respect to the voltages involved.

Where power or control leads run together for more than a few inches, they will present a better appearance when bound together in a single cable. The correct technique is illustrated in Fig. 20-3; both plastic and waxed-linen lacing cords are available. Plastic cable clamps are available to hold the laced cable.

To give a "commercial look" to the wiring

BNC Connectors

1.—Cut end of cable even.

2.—Remove vinyl jacket ½"—*don't nick braid.*

3.—Push braid back and remove ⅛" of insulation and conductor.

4.—Taper braid.

5.—Slide sleeve over tapered braid. Fit inner shoulder or sleeve squarely against end of jacket.

6.—With sleeve in place, comb out braid, fold back smooth as shown, and trim ⁷⁄₃₂".

7.—Bare center conductor ⅛"—*don't nick conductor.*

8.—Tin center conductor of cable. Slip female contact in place and solder. Remove excess solder. *Be sure cable dielectric is not heated excessively and swollen so as to prevent dielectric entering body.*

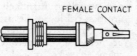

9.—Push into body as far as it will go. Slide nut into body and screw into place, with wrench, until it is moderately tight. Hold cable and shell rigidly and rotate nut.

10.—This assembly procedure applies to BNC jacks. The assembly for plugs is the same except for the use of male contacts and a plug body.

83-1SP Plug

1.—Cut end of cable even. Remove vinyl jacket 1⅛"—*don't nick braid.*

2.—Bare ¾" of center conductor—*don't nick conductor.* Trim braided shield 1⁄16" and tin. Slide coupling ring on cable.

3.—Screw the plug assembly on cable. Solder plug assembly to braid through solder holes. Solder conductor to contact sleeve.

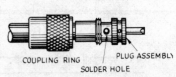

4.—Screw coupling ring on assembly.

83-1SP Plug with Adapters

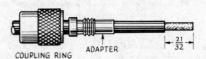

1.—Cut end of cable even. Remove vinyl jacket 21⁄32"—*don't nick braid.* Slide coupling ring and adapter on cable.

2.—Fan braid slightly and fold back over cable.

3.—Compress braid around cable. Position adapter to dimension shown. Press braid down over body of adapter to dimension shown. Press braid down over body of adapter and trim.

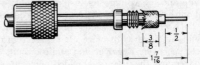

4.—Bare ½" of center conductor—*don't nick conductor.* Pre-tin exposed center conductor.

5, 6.—Same as 3 and 4 under 83-1SP Plug.

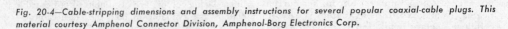

Fig. 20-4—Cable-stripping dimensions and assembly instructions for several popular coaxial-cable plugs. This material courtesy Amphenol Connector Division, Amphenol-Borg Electronics Corp.

of any unit, run any cabled leads along the edge of the chassis. If this isn't possible, the cabled leads should then run parallel to an edge of the chassis. Further, the generous use of tie points (mounted parallel to an edge of the chassis), for the support of one or both ends of a resistor or fixed capacitor, will add to the appearance of the finished unit. In a similar manner, "dress" the small components so that they are parallel to the panel or sides of the chassis.

Winding Coils

Close-wound coils are readily wound on the specified form by anchoring one end of a length of wire (in a vise or to a doorknob) and the other end to the coil form. Straighten any kinks in the wire and then pull to keep the wire under slight tension. Wind the coil to the required number of turns while walking toward the anchor, always maintaining a slight tension on the wire.

To space-wind the coil, wind the coil simultaneously with a suitable spacing medium (heavy thread, string or wire) in the manner described above. When the winding is complete, secure the end of the coil to the coil-form terminal and then carefully unwind the spacing material. If the coil is wound under suitable tension, the spacing material can be easily removed without disturbing the winding. Finish the space-wound coil by judicious applications of Duco cement, to hold the turns in place.

The "cold" end of a coil is the end at or close to chassis or ground potential. Coupling links should be wound on the cold end of a coil, to minimize capacitive coupling.

CIRCUIT-BOARD FABRICATION

Many modern-day builders prefer the neatness and miniaturization made possible by the use of etched or printed circuit boards. There are additional benefits to be realized from the use of circuit boards: Low lead inductances, excellent physical stability of the components and interconnecting leads, and good repeatability of the basic layout of a given project. The latter attribute makes the use of circuit boards ideal for group projects.

Methods

Perhaps the least complicated approach to circuit-board fabrication is the use of unclad perforated board into which a number of push-in terminals have been installed. The perforated board can be obtained with one of many hole patterns, dependent upon the needs of the builder. Perforated terminal boards are manufactured by such firms as Vector, Kepro, and Triad. Their products are available from the large mail-order houses.

Once the builder plots the layout of his circuit on paper, push-in terminals can be installed in the "perf" board to match the layout which was done on paper. The terminals serve as tie points and provide secure mounting-post anchors for the various components. Selected terminals can be wired together to provide ground and B-plus lines. Although this technique is the most basic of the methods, it is entirely practical.

An approach to etched-circuit board assembly can be realized by cutting strips of flashing copper, hobby copper, or brass shim stock into the desired shapes and lengths, then gluing them to a piece of unclad circuit board. Epoxy cement is useful for the latter. Alternatively, the strips can be held in place by means of brass eyelets which have been installed with a hand eyelet tool. If standard unclad circuit board is not handy, linolium or Formica sheeting can be made to serve as a base for the circuit board. If this technique is used, the metal strips should be soldered together at each point where they join, assuring good electrical contact.

Etched-circuit boards provide the most professional end result of the three systems described here. They are the most stable, physically and electrically, and can be easily repeated from a single template. Etched-circuits can be formed on copper-clad perforated board, or on unpunched copper-clad board. There is no advantage in using the perforated board as a base unless push-in terminals are to be used.

Planning and Layout

The constructor should first plan the physical layout of the circuit by sketching a pictorial diagram on paper, drawing it to scale. Once this has been done, the interconnecting leads can be inked in to represent the copper strips that will remain on the etched board. The Vector Company sells layout paper for this purpose. It is marked with the same patterns that are used on their perforated boards.

After the basic etched-circuit design has been completed the designer should go over the proposed layout several times to insure against errors. When the foregoing has been done, the pattern can be painted on the copper surface of the board to be etched. Etch-resistant solutions are available from commercial suppliers and can be selected from their catalogs. Some builders prefer to use India ink for this purpose. Perhaps the most readily-available material for use in etch-resist applications is ordinary exterior enamel paint. The portions of the board to be retained are covered with a layer of paint, applied with an artist's brush, duplicating the pattern that was drawn on the layout paper. The job can be made a bit easier by tracing over the original layout with a ballpoint pen and carbon paper while the pattern is taped to the copper side of the unetched circuit board. The carbon paper is placed between the pattern and the circuit board. After the paint has been applied, it should be allowed to dry for at least 24 hours prior to the etching process. The Vector Company produces a rub-on transfer material that can also be used as etch-resist when laying out circuit-board patterns. Thin strips of ordinary masking tape, cut to size and firmly applied, serve nicely as etch-resist material too.

Fig. 20-4—A home-made stand for processing etched-circuit boards. The heat lamp maintains the etchant-bath temperature between 90 and 115 degrees, F and is mounted on an adjustable arm. The tray for the bath is raised and lowered at one end by the action of a motor-driven eccentric disk, providing the necessary agitation of the chemical solution. A darkroom thermometer monitors the temperature of the bath.

The Etching Process

Almost any strong acid bath will serve as an etchant, but the two chemical preparations recommended here are the safest to use. A bath can be prepared by mixing 1 part ammonium persulphate crystals with 2 parts clear water. A normal quantity of working solution for most amateur radio applications is composed of 1 cup of crystals and 2 cups of water. To this mixture add ¼ teaspoon of mercuric chloride crystals. The latter serves as an activator for the bath. Ready-made etchant kits which use these chemicals are available from Vector. A two-bag kit is sold as item 2594 and costs just over $1. Complete kits which contain circuit boards, etchant powders, etch-resist transfers, layout paper, and plastic etchant bags are also available from Vector at moderate prices.

Another chemical bath that works satisfactorily for copper etching is made up from one part ferric chloride crystals and 2 parts water. No activator is required with this bath. Ready-made solutions (one-pint and one-gallon sizes) are available through some mail-order houses at low cost. They are manufactured by Kepro Co. and carry a stock number of E-1PT and E-1G, respectively. One pint costs less than a dollar.

Etchant solutions become exhausted after a certain amount of copper has been processed, therefore it is wise to keep a quantity of the bath on hand if frequent use is anticipated. With either chemical bath, the working solution should be maintained at a temperature between 90 and 115 degrees, *F*. A heat lamp can be directed toward the bath during the etching period, its distance set to maintain the required temperature. A darkroom thermometer is handy for monitoring the temperature of the bath.

While the circuit board is immersed in the solution, it should be agitated continuously to permit uniform reaction to the chemicals. This action will also speed up the etching process somewhat. Normally, the circuit board should be placed in the bath with the copper side facing down, toward the bottom of the tray. The tray should be non-metallic, preferably a Pyrex dish or a photographic darkroom tray.

The photograph, Fig. 20-4, shows a home-made etching stand made up from a heat lamp, some lumber, and an 8-r.p.m. motor. An eccentric disk has been mounted on the motor shaft and butts against the bottom of the etchant tray. As the motor turns, the eccentric disk raises and lowers one end of the tray, thus providing continuous agitation of the solution. The heat lamp is mounted on an adjustable, slotted wooden arm. Its height above the solution tray is adjusted to provide the desired bath temperature. Because the etching process takes between 15 minutes and one hour—dependent upon the strength and temperature of the bath—such an accessory is convenient.

After the etching process is completed, the board is removed from the tray and washed thoroughly with fresh, clear water. The etch-resist material can then be rubbed off by applying a few brisk strokes with medium-grade steel wool. *WARNING: Always use rubber gloves when working with etchant powders and solutions. Should the acid bath come in contact with the body, immediately wash the affected area with clear water. Protect the eyes when using these acid baths.*

COMPONENT VALUES

Values of composition resistors and small capacitors (mica and ceramic) are specified throughout this *Handbook* in terms of "preferred values." In the preferred-number system, all values represent (approximately) a constant-percentage increase over the next lower value. The base of the system is the number 10. Only two significant figures are used.

"Tolerance" means that a variation of plus or minus the percentage given is considered satisfactory. For example, the actual resistance of a "4700-ohm" 20-per-cent resistor can lie anywhere between 3700 and 5600 ohms, approximately. The permissible variation in the same resistance value with 5-per-cent tolerance would be in the range from 4500 to 4900 ohms, approximately.

TABLE 20-II

Approximate Series-Resonance Frequencies of
Disc Ceramic Bypass Capacitors

Capacitance	Freq.[1]	Freq.[2]
0.01 μf	13 Mc.	15 Mc.
0.0047	18	22
0.002	31	38
0.001	46	55
0.0005	65	80
0.0001	135	165

[1] Total lead lenth of 1 inch
[2] Total lead lenth of ½ inch

example, that a 5000-ohm resistor falls well
within the tolerance range of the 4700-ohm
20-per-cent resistor used in the example above.
It would not, however, be usable if the tolerance were specified as 5 per cent.

COLOR CODES

Standardized color codes are used to mark
values on small components such as composition resistors and mica capacitors, and to
identify leads from transformers, etc. The
resistor-capacitor number color code is given
in Table 20-II.

Fixed Capacitors

The methods of marking "postage-stamp"
mica capacitors, molded paper capacitors, and
tubular ceramic capacitors are shown in Fig.
20-5.

Capacitors made to American War Standards
or Joint Army-Navy specifications are marked
with the 6-dot code shown at the top. Practically
all surplus capacitors are in this category.

The 3-dot EIA code is used for capacitors having a rating of 500 volts and ±20% tolerance
only; other ratings and tolerances are covered
by the 6-dot EIA code.

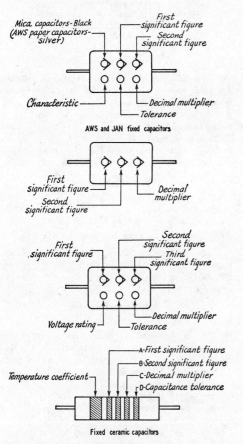

Fixed ceramic capacitors

Fig. 20-5—Color coding of fixed mica, molded paper
and tubular ceramic capacitors. The color code for mica
and molded paper capacitors is given in Table 20-III.
Table 20-IV gives the color code for tubular
ceramic capacitors.

> Examples: A capacitor with a 6-dot code has the
> following markings: Top row, left to right,
> black, yellow, violet; bottom row, right to left,
> brown, silver, red. Since the first color in the
> top row is black (significant figure zero) this is
> the AWS code and the capacitor has mica di-
> electric. The significant figures are 4 and 7, the
> decimal multiplier 10 (brown, at right of sec-
> ond row), so the capacitance is 470 μμf. The
> tolerance is ± 10%. The final color, the charac-
> teristic, deals with temperature coefficients and
> methods of testing (see Table 20-V on page
> 524)
> A capacitor with a 3-dot code has the follow-
> ing colors, left to right: brown, black, red.
> The significant figures are 1, 0 (10) and the
> multiplier is 100. The capacitance is therefore
> 1000 μμf.
> A capacitor with a 6-dot code has the follow-
> ing markings: Top row, left to right, brown,
> black, black; bottom row, right to left, black,
> gold, blue. Since the first color in the top row
> is neither black nor silver, this is the EIA
> code. The significant figures are 1, 0, 0 (100)
> and the decimal multiplier is 1 (black). The
> capacitance is therefore 100 μμf. The gold dot
> shows that the tolerance is ± 5% and the blue
> dot indicates 600-volt rating.

In the component specifications in this
Handbook, it is to be understood that when
no tolerance is specified the *largest* tolerance
available in that value will be satisfactory.

Values that do not fit into the preferred-
number system (such as 500, 25,000, etc.)
easily can be substituted. It is obvious, for

Ceramic Capacitors

Conventional markings for ceramic capacitors are shown in the lower drawing of Fig.
20-5. The colors have the meanings indicated
in Table 20-III. In practice, dots may be used
instead of the *narrow* bands indicated in Fig.
20-5.

> Example: A ceramic capacitor has the fol-
> lowing markings: Broad band, violet; narrow
> bands or dots, green, brown, black, green. The
> significant figures are 5, 1 (51) and the decimal
> multiplier is 1, so the capacitance is 51 μμf.
> The temperature coefficient is − 750 parts per
> million per degree C., as given by the broad
> band, and the capacitance tolerance is ±5%.

TABLE 20-III
Resistor-Capacitor Color Code

Color	Significant Figure	Decimal Multiplier	Tolerance (%)	Voltage Rating*
Black	0	1	–	—
Brown	1	10	1*	100
Red	2	100	2*	200
Orange	3	1,000	3*	300
Yellow	4	10,000	4*	400
Green	5	100,000	5*	500
Blue	6	1,000,000	6*	600
Violet	7	10,000,000	7*	700
Gray	8	100,000,000	8*	800
White	9	1,000,000,000	9*	900
Gold	–	0.1	5	1000
Silver	–	0.01	10	2000
No color	–	—	20	500

* Applies to capacitors only.

TABLE 20-IV
Color Code for Ceramic Capacitors

Color	Significant Figure	Decimal Multiplier	Capacitance Tolerance More than 10 μμf. (in %)	Capacitance Tolerance Less than 10 μμf. (in μμf.)	Temp. Coeff. p.p.m. /deg. C.
Black	0	1	± 20	2.0	0
Brown	1	10	± 1		−30
Red	2	100	± 2		−80
Orange	3	1000			−150
Yellow	4				−220
Green	5				−330
Blue	6		± 5	0.5	−470
Violet	7				−750
Gray	8	0.01		0.25	30
White	9	0.1	± 10	1.0	500

TABLE 20-V
Capacitor Characteristic Code

Color Sixth Dot	Temperature Coefficient p.p.m./deg. C.	Capacitance Drift
Black	± 1000	± 5% +1 μμf.
Brown	± 500	± 3% +1 μμf.
Red	+200	± 0.5%
Orange	+100	± 0.3%
Yellow	−20 to +100	± 0.1% +0.1 μμf.
Green	0 to +70	± 0.05% +0.1 μμf.

Fixed Composition Resistors

Composition resistors (including small wire-wound units molded in cases identical with the composition type) are color-coded as shown in Fig. 20-6. Colored bands are used on resistors having axial leads; on radial-lead resistors the colors are placed as shown in the drawing. When bands are used for color coding the body color has no significance.

Examples: A resistor of the type shown in the lower drawing of Fig. 20-6 has the following color bands: A, red; B, red; C, orange; D, no color. The significant figures are 2, 2 (22) and the decimal multiplier is 1000. The value of resistance is therefore 22,000 ohms and the tolerance is ± 20%.

A resistor of the type shown in the upper drawing has the following colors: body (A), blue; end (B), gray; dot, red; end (D), gold. The significant figures are 6, 8 (68) and the decimal multiplier is 100, so the resistance is 6800 ohms. The tolerance is ± 5%.

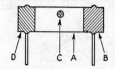

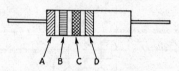

Fig. 20-6—Color coding of fixed composition resistors. The color code is given in Table 20-III. The colored areas have the following significance:
A—First significant figure of resistance in ohms.
B—Second significant figure.
C—Decimal multiplier.
D—Resistance tolerance in per cent. If no color is shown the tolerance is ±20%.

I.F. Transformers

Blue — plate lead.
Red — "B" + lead.
Green — grid (or diode) lead.
Black — grid (or diode) return.

NOTE: If the secondary of the i.f.t. is center-tapped, the second diode plate lead is green-and-black striped, and black is used for the center-tap lead.

A.F. Transformers

Blue — plate (finish) lead of primary.
Red — "B" + lead (this applies whether the primary is plain or center-tapped).
Brown — plate (start) lead on center-tapped primaries. (Blue may be used for this lead if polarity is not important.)
Green — grid (finish) lead to secondary.
Black — grid return (this applies whether the secondary is plain or center-tapped).
Yellow — grid (start) lead on center-tapped secondaries. (Green may be used for this lead if polarity is not important.)

NOTE: These markings apply also to line-to-grid and tube-to-line transformers.

Power Transformers

1) Primary Leads .... *Black*
     If tapped :
       Common .... *Black*
       Tap..................... *Black and Yellow Striped*
       Finish....................... *Black and Red Striped*
2) High-Voltage Plate Winding.................... *Red*
     Center-Tap.......... *Red and Yellow Striped*
3) Rectifier Filament Winding.................. *Yellow*
     Center-Tap........ *Yellow and Blue Striped*

4) Filament Winding No. 1..........................*Green*
    Center-Tap......*Green and Yellow Striped*
5) Filament Winding No. 2....................*Brown*
    Center-Tap....*Brown and Yellow Striped*
6) Filament Winding No. 3........................*Slate*
    Center-Tap........*Slate and Yellow Striped*

TABLE VI
Color Code for Hookup Wire

Wire Color	Type of Circuit
Black	Grounds, grounded elements, and returns.
Brown	Heaters or filaments, off ground.
Red	Power supply B plus.
Orange	Screen grids and Base 2 of transistors.
Yellow	Cathodes and transistor emitters.
Green	Control grids, diode plates, and Base 1 of transistors.
Blue	Plates and transistor collectors.
Violet	Power supply, minus leads.
Gray	A.c. power line leads.
White	Bias supply, B or C minus, a.g.c.

Wires with tracers are coded in the same manner as solid-color wires, allowing additional circuit identification over solid-color wiring. The body of the wire is white and the color band spirals around the wire lead. When more than one color band is used, the widest band represents the 1st color.

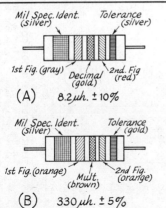

(A)   8.2 μh. ± 10%

(B)   330 μh. ± 5%

Fig. 20-7—Color coding for tubular encapsulated r.f. chokes. At A, an example of the coding for an 8.2-uh. choke is given. At B, the color bands for a 330-uh. inductor are illustrated.

Color	Figure	Multiplier	Tolerance
Black	0	1	
Brown	1	10	
Red	2	100	
Orange	3	1,000	
Yellow	4		
Green	5		
Blue	6		
Violet	7		
Gray	8		
White	9		
None			20%
Silver			10%
Gold			5%

Multiplier is the factor by which the two color figures are multiplied to obtain the inductance value of the choke coil.

TABLE 20-VII
Metric Multiplier Prefixes

Multiples and submultiples of fundamental units (e.g., ampere, farad, gram, meter, watt) may be indicated by the following prefixes.

prefix	abbreviation	multiplier
tera	T	10^{12}
giga	G	10^{9}
mega	M	10^{6}
kilo	k	10^{3}
hecto	h	10^{2}
deci	d	10^{-1}
centi	c	10^{-2}
milli	m	10^{-3}
micro	μ	10^{-6}
nano	n	10^{-9}
pico	p	10^{-12}

PILOT-LAMP DATA

Lamp No.	Bead Color	Base (Miniature)	Bulb Type	RATING Volts	RATING Amp.
40	Brown	Screw	T-3¼	6–8	0.15
40A[1]	Brown	Bayonet	T-3¼	6–8	0.15
41	White	Screw	T-3¼	2.5	0.5
42	Green	Screw	T-3¼	3.2	**
43	White	Bayonet	T-3¼	2.5	0.5
44	Blue	Bayonet	T-3¼	6–8	0.25
45	*	Bayonet	T-3¼	3.2	**
46[2]	Blue	Screw	T-3¼	6–8	0.25
47[1]	Brown	Bayonet	T-3¼	6–9	0.15
48	Pink	Screw	T-3¼	2.0	0.06
49[3]	Pink	Bayonet	T-3¼	2.0	0.06
49A[3]	White	Bayonet	T-3¼	2.1	0.12
50	White	Screw	G-3½	6–8	0.2
51[2]	White	Bayonet	G-3½	6–8	0.2
53	—	Bayonet	G-3½	14.4	0.12
55	White	Bayonet	G-4½	6–8	0.4
292[5]	White	Screw	T-3¼	2.9	0.17
292A[5]	White	Bayonet	T-3¼	2.9	0.17
1455	Brown	Screw	G-5	18.0	0.25
1455A	Brown	Bayonet	G-5	18.0	0.25
1487	—	Screw	T-3¼	12–16	0.20
1488	—	Bayonet	T-3¼	14	0.15
1813	—	Bayonet	T-3¼	14.4	0.10
1815	—	Bayonet	T-3¼	12–16	0.20

[1] 40A and 47 are interchangeable.
[2] Have frosted bulb.
[3] 49 and 49A are interchangeable.
[4] Replace with No. 48.
[5] Use in 2.5-volt sets where regular bulb burns out too frequently.
 * White in G.E. and Sylvania; green in National Union, Raytheon and Tung-Sol.
 ** 0.35 in G.E. and Sylvania; 0.5 in National Union, Raytheon and Tung-Sol.

COPPER-WIRE TABLE

Wire Size A.W.G. (B&S)	Diam. in Mils[1]	Circular Mil Area	Turns per Linear Inch[2] — Enamel	Turns — S.C.E.	Turns — D.C.C.	Cont.-duty current[3] single wire in open air	Cont.-duty current[3] wires or cables in conduits or bundles	Feet per Pound, Bare	Ohms per 1000 ft. 25° C.	Current Carrying Capacity[4] at 700 C.M. per Amp.	Diam. in mm.	Nearest British S.W.G. No.
1	289.3	83690	—	—	—	—	—	3.947	.1264	119.6	7.348	1
2	257.6	66370	—	—	—	—	—	4.977	.1593	94.8	6.544	3
3	229.4	52640	—	—	—	—	—	6.276	.2009	75.2	5.827	4
4	204.3	41740	—	—	—	—	—	7.914	.2533	59.6	5.189	5
5	181.9	33100	—	—	—	—	—	9.980	.3195	47.3	4.621	7
6	162.0	26250	—	—	—	—	—	12.58	.4028	37.5	4.115	8
7	144.3	20820	—	—	—	—	—	15.87	.5080	29.7	3.665	9
8	128.5	16510	7.6		7.1	73	46	20.01	.6405	23.6	3.264	10
9	114.4	13090	8.6		7.8			25.23	.8077	18.7	2.906	11
10	101.9	10380	9.6	9.1	8.9	55	33	31.82	1.018	14.8	2.588	12
11	90.7	8234	10.7		10.9			40.12	1.284	11.8	2.305	13
12	80.8	6530	12.0	11.3	12.8	41	23	50.59	1.619	9.33	2.053	14
13	72.0	5178	13.5		13.8			63.80	2.042	7.40	1.828	15
14	64.1	4107	15.0	14.0	14.7	32	17	80.44	2.575	5.87	1.628	16
15	57.1	3257	16.8		16.4			101.4	3.247	4.65	1.450	17
16	50.8	2583	18.9	17.3	18.1	22	13	127.9	4.094	3.69	1.291	18
17	45.3	2048	21.2		19.8			161.3	5.163	2.93	1.150	18
18	40.3	1624	23.6	21.2	21.8	16	10	203.4	6.510	2.32	1.024	19
19	35.9	1288	26.4		23.8			256.5	8.210	1.84	.912	20
20	32.0	1022	29.4	25.8	26.0	11	7.5	323.4	10.35	1.46	.812	21
21	28.5	810.1	33.1		30.0			407.8	13.05	1.16	.723	22
22	25.3	642	37.0	31.3	35.6		5	514.2	16.46	.918	.644	23
23	22.6	510	41.3		37.6			648.4	20.76	.728	.573	24
24	20.1	404	46.3	37.6	38.6			817.7	26.17	.577	.511	25
25	17.9	320	51.7		41.8			1031	33.00	.458	.455	26
26	15.9	254	58.0	46.1	45.0			1300	41.62	.363	.405	27
27	14.2	202	64.9		48.5			1639	52.48	.288	.361	29
28	12.6	160	72.7	54.6	51.8			2067	66.17	.228	.321	30
29	11.3	127	81.6		55.5			2607	83.44	.181	.286	31
30	10.0	101	90.5	64.1	59.2			3287	105.2	.144	.255	33
31	8.9	80	101		62.6			4145	132.7	.114	.227	34
32	8.0	63	113	74.1	66.3			5227	167.3	.090	.202	36
33	7.1	50	127		70.0			6591	211.0	.072	.180	37
34	6.3	40	143	86.2	73.5			8310	266.0	.057	.160	38-39
35	5.6	32	158		77.0			10480	335	.045	.143	39-40
36	5.0	25	175	103.1	80.3			13210	423	.036	.127	41
37	4.5	20	198		83.6			16660	533	.028	.113	42
38	4.0	16	224	116.3	86.6			21010	673	.022	.101	43
39	3.5	12	248		89.7			26500	848	.018	.090	44
40	3.1	10	282	131.6				33410	1070	.014	.080	

[1] A mil is 0.001 inch. [2] Figures given are approximate only; insulation thickness varies with manufacturer. [3] Max. wire temp. of 212° F and max. ambient temp. of 135° F. [4] 700 circular mils per ampere is a satisfactory design figure for small transformers, but values from 500 to 1000 c.m. are commonly used.

SEMICONDUCTOR DIODE COLOR CODE

The "IN" prefix is omitted. A double-width band, which also identifies the cathode terminal end of the diode, is usually used as the first band. (An alternative method uses equal band widths with the set not clearly grouped toward the cathode end.) The code is read starting at the cathode end.

Diodes having two-digit numbers are coded with a black band followed by second and third bands. A suffix letter is indicated by a fourth band.

Diodes with three-digit numbers are coded with the sequence numbers in the first, second and third bands. Any suffix letter is indicated by a fourth band.

Diodes with four-digit numbers are coded by four bands followed by a black band. A suffix letter is indicated by a fifth band replacing the black band.

The color code (numbers) is the same as the resistor-capacitor code. The suffix-letter code is A—brown, B—red, C—orange, D—yellow, E—green, and F—blue.

Chapter 21

Measurements

It is practically impossible to operate an amateur station without making measurements at one time or another. Although quite crude measurements often will suffice, more refined equipment and methods will yield more and better information. With adequate information at hand it becomes possible to adjust a piece of equipment for optimum performance quickly and surely, and to design circuits along established principles rather than depending on cut-and-try.

Measuring and test equipment is valuable during construction, for testing components before installation. It is practically indispensable in the initial adjustment of radio gear, not only for establishing operating values but also for tracing possible errors in wiring. It is likewise needed for locating breakdowns and defective components in existing equipment.

The basic measurements are those of current, voltage, and frequency. Determination of the values of circuit elements—resistance, inductance and capacitance — are almost equally important. The inspection of waveform in audio-frequency circuits is highly

useful. For these purposes there is available a wide assortment of instruments, both complete and in kit form; the latter, particularly, compare very favorably in cost with strictly home-built instruments and are frequently more satisfactory both in appearance and calibration. The home-built instruments described in this chapter are ones having features of particular usefulness in amateur applications, and not ordinarily available commercially.

In using any instrument it should always be kept in mind that the accuracy depends not only on the inherent accuracy of the instrument itself (which, in the case of commercially built units is usually within a few per cent, and in any event should be specified by the manufacturer) but also the conditions under which the measurement is made. Large errors can be introduced by failing to recognize the existence of conditions that affect the instrument readings. This is particularly true in certain types of r.f. measurements, where stray effects are hard to eliminate, and in the measurement of d.c. and a.c. voltages across extremely high-impedance circuits.

VOLTAGE, CURRENT, AND RESISTANCE

D.C. MEASUREMENTS

A direct-current instrument — voltmeter, ammeter, milliammeter or microammeter — is a device using electromagnetic means to deflect a pointer over a calibrated scale in proportion to the current flowing. In the **D'Arsonval** type a coil of wire, to which the pointer is attached, is pivoted between the poles of a permanent magnet, and when current flows through the coil it causes a magnetic field that interacts with that of the magnet to cause the coil to turn. The design of the instrument is usually such as to make the pointer deflection directly proportional to the current.

A less expensive type of instrument is the **moving-vane** type, in which a pivoted soft-iron vane is pulled into a coil of wire by the magnetic field set up when current flows through the coil. The farther the vane extends into the coil the greater the magnetic pull on it, for a given change in current, so this type of instrument does not have "linear" deflection—the intervals of equal current are crowded together at the low-current end and

spread out at the high-current end of the scale.

The same basic instrument is used for measuring either current or voltage. Good-quality instruments are made with fairly high **sensitivity** — that is, they give full-scale pointer deflection with very small currents — when intended to be used as voltmeters. The sensitivity of instruments intended for measuring large currents can be lower, but a highly sensitive instrument can be, and frequently is, used for measurement of currents much greater than needed for full-scale deflection.

Panel-mounting instruments of the D'Arsonval type will give a smaller deflection when mounted on iron or steel panels than when mounted on nonmagnetic material. Readings may be as much as ten per cent low. Specially calibrated meters should be obtained for mounting on such panels.

VOLTMETERS

Only a fraction of a volt is required for full-scale deflection of a sensitive instrument (1 milliampere or less full scale) so for meas-

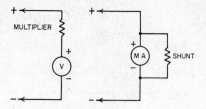

Fig. 21-1—How voltmeter multipliers and milliammeter shunts are connected to extend the range of a d.c. meter.

uring voltage a high resistance is connected in series with it, Fig. 21-1. Knowing the current and the resistance, the voltage can easily be calculated from Ohm's Law. The meter is calibrated in terms of the voltage drop across the series resistor or **multiplier**. Practically any desired full-scale voltage range can be obtained by proper choice of multiplier resistance, and voltmeters frequently have several ranges selected by a switch.

The sensitivity of the voltmeter is usually expressed in "ohms per volt." A sensitivity of 1000 ohms per volt means that the resistance

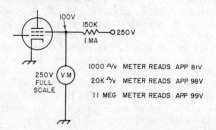

Fig. 21-2—Effect of voltmeter resistance on accuracy of readings. It is assumed that the d.c. resistance of the screen circuit is constant at 100 kilohms. The actual current and voltage without the voltmeter connected are 1 ma. and 100 volts. The voltmeter readings will differ because the different types of meters draw different amounts of current through the 150-kilohm resistor.

of the voltmeter is 1000 times the full-scale voltage, and by Ohm's Law the current required for full-scale deflection is 1 milliampere. A sensitivity of 20,000 ohms per volt, another commonly used value, means that the instrument is a 50-microampere meter. The higher the resistance of the voltmeter the more accurate the measurements in high-resistance circuits. This is because the current flowing through the voltmeter will cause a change in the voltage between the points across which the meter is connected, compared with the voltage with the meter absent, as shown in Fig. 21-2.

Multipliers

The required multiplier resistance is found by dividing the desired full-scale voltage by the current, in amperes, required for full-scale deflection of the meter alone. Strictly,

the internal resistance of the meter should be subtracted from the value so found, but this is seldom necessary (except perhaps for very low ranges) because the meter resistance will be negligibly small compared with the multiplier resistance. An exception is when the instrument is already provided with an internal multiplier, in which case the multiplier resistance required to extend the range is

$$R = R_\mathrm{m}(n - 1)$$

where R is the multiplier resistance, R_m is the total resistance of the instrument itself, and n is the factor by which the scale is to be multiplied. For example, if a 1000-ohms-per-volt voltmeter having a calibrated range of 0–10 volts is to be extended to 1000 volts, R_m is $1000 \times 10 = 10,000$ ohms, n is $1000/10 = 100$, and $R = 10,000(100 - 1) = 990,000$ ohms.

If a milliammeter is to be used as a voltmeter, the value of series resistance can be found by Ohm's Law:

$$R = \frac{1000E}{I}$$

where E is the desired full-scale voltage and I the full-scale reading of the instrument in milliamperes.

Accuracy

The accuracy of a voltmeter depends on the calibration accuracy of the instrument itself and the accuracy of the multiplier resistors. Good-quality instruments are generally rated for an accuracy within plus or minus 2 per cent. This is also the usual accuracy rating of the basic meter movement.

When extending the range of a voltmeter or converting a low-range milliammeter into a voltmeter the rated accuracy of the instrument is retained only when the multiplier resistance is precise. Precision wire-wound resistors are used in the multipliers of high-quality instruments. These are relatively expensive, but the home constructor can do quite well with 1% tolerance composition resistors. They should be "derated" when used for this purpose — that is, the actual power dissipated in the resistor should not be more than $\frac{1}{4}$ to $\frac{1}{2}$ the rated dissipation — and care should be used to avoid overheating the body of the resistor when soldering to the leads. These precautions will help prevent permanent change in the resistance of the unit.

Ordinary composition resistors are generally furnished in 10% or 5% tolerance ratings. If possible errors of this order can be accepted, resistors of this type may be used as multipliers. They should be operated below the rated power dissipation figure, in the interests of long-time stability.

MILLIAMMETERS AND AMMETERS

A microammeter or milliammeter can be used to measure currents larger than its full-scale reading by connecting a resistance shunt across its terminals as shown in Fig. 21-1. Part of the current flows through the shunt and part through the meter. Knowing the meter resistance and the shunt resistance, the relative currents can easily be calculated.

The value of shunt resistance required for a given full-scale current range is given by

$$R = \frac{R_m}{n-1}$$

where R is the shunt, R_m is the internal resistance of the meter, and n is the factor by which the original meter scale is to be multiplied. The internal resistance of a milliammeter is preferably determined from the manufacturer's catalog, but if this information is not available it can be measured by the method shown in Fig. 21-3. Do not attempt to use an ohmmeter to measure the internal

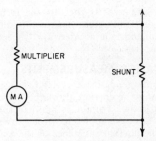

Fig. 21-4—Voltmeter method of measuring current. This method permits using relatively large values of resistance in the shunt, standard values of fixed resistors frequently being usable. If the multiplier resistance is 20 (or more) times the shunt resistance, the error in assuming that all the current flows through the shunt will not be of consequence in most practical applications.

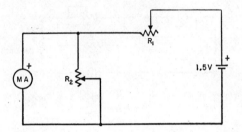

Fig. 21-3—Determining the internal resistance of a milliammeter or microammeter. R_1 is an adjustable resistor having a maximum value about twice that necessary for limiting the current to full scale with R_2 disconnected; adjust it for exactly full-scale reading. Then connect R_2 and adjust it for exactly half-scale reading. The resistance of R_2 is then equal to the internal resistance of the meter, and the resistor may be removed from the circuit and measured separately. Internal resistances vary from a few ohms to several hundred ohms, depending on the sensitivity of the instrument.

resistance of a milliammeter; the instrument may be ruined by doing so.

Homemade milliammeter shunts can be constructed from any of the various special kinds of resistance wire, or from ordinary copper wire if no resistance wire is available. The Copper Wire Table in this *Handbook* gives the resistance per 1000 feet for various sizes of copper wire. After computing the resistance required, determine the smallest wire size that will carry the full-scale current (250 circular mils per ampere is a satisfactory figure for this purpose). Measure off enough wire to provide the required resistance. Accuracy can be checked by causing enough current to flow through the meter to make it read full scale without the shunt; connecting the shunt should then give the correct reading on the new range.

Current Measurement with a Voltmeter

A current-measuring instrument should have very low resistance compared with the resistance of the circuit being measured;

otherwise, inserting the instrument will cause the current to differ from its value with the instrument out of the circuit. (This may not matter if the instrument is left permanently in the circuit.) However, the resistance of many circuits in radio equipment is quite high and the circuit operation is affected little, if at all, by adding as much as a few hundred ohms in series. In such cases the voltmeter method of measuring current, shown in Fig. 21-4, is frequently convenient. A voltmeter — or low-range milliammeter provided with a multiplier and operating as a voltmeter — having a full-scale voltage range of a few volts, is used to measure the voltage drop across a comparatively high resistance acting as a shunt. The formula previously given is used for finding the proper value of shunt resistance for a given scale-multiplying factor, R_m in this case being the multiplier resistance.

D.C. Power

Power in direct-current circuits is determined by measuring the current and voltage. When these are known, the power is equal to the voltage in volts multiplied by the cur-

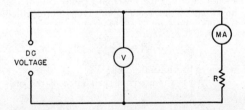

Fig. 21-5—Measuring resistance with a voltmeter and milliammeter. If the approximate resistance is known the voltage can be selected to cause the milliammeter, MA, to read about half scale. If not, additional resistance should be first connected in series with R to limit the current to a safe value for the milliammeter. The set-up then measures the total resistance, and the value of R can be found by subtracting the known additional resistance from the total.

rent in amperes. If the current is measured with a milliammeter, the reading of the instrument must be divided by 1000 to convert it to amperes.

RESISTANCE MEASUREMENTS

Measurement of d.c. resistance is based on measuring the current through the resistance when a known voltage is applied, then using Ohm's Law. A simple circuit is shown in Fig. 21-5. The internal resistance of the ammeter or milliammeter, MA, should be low compared with the resistance, R, being measured, since the voltage read by the voltmeter, V, is the voltage across MA and R in series. The instruments and the d.c. voltage should be chosen so that the readings are in the upper half of the scale, if possible, since the percentage error is less in this region.

An **ohmmeter** is an instrument consisting fundamentally of a voltmeter (or milliammeter, depending on the circuit used) and a small dry battery as a source of d.c. voltage, calibrated so the value of an unknown resistance can be read directly from the scale. Typical ohmmeter circuits are shown in Fig. 21-6. In the simplest type, shown in Fig. 21-6A, the meter and battery are connected in series with the unknown resistance. If a given deflection is obtained with terminals A-B shorted, inserting the resistance to be measured will cause the meter reading to decrease. When the resistance of the voltmeter is known, the following formula can be applied:

$$R = \frac{eR_m}{E} - R_m$$

where R is the resistance under measurement,
  e is the voltage applied (A-B shorted),
  E is the voltmeter reading with R connected, and
  R_m is the resistance of the voltmeter.

The circuit of Fig. 21-6A is not suited to measuring low values of resistance (below a hundred ohms or so) with a high-resistance voltmeter. For such measurements the circuit of Fig. 21-6B can be used. The milliammeter should be a 0–1 ma. instrument, and R_1 should be equal to the battery voltage, e, multiplied by 1000. The unknown resistance is

$$R = \frac{I_2 R_m}{I_1 - I_2}$$

where R is the unknown,
  R_m is the internal resistance of the milliammeter,
  I_1 is the current in ma. with R disconnected from terminals A-B, and
  I_2 is the current in ma. with R connected.

The formula is approximate, but the error will be negligible if e is at least 3 volts so that R_1 is at least 3000 ohms.

A third circuit for measuring resistance is shown in Fig. 21-6C. In this case a high-resistance voltmeter is used to measure the

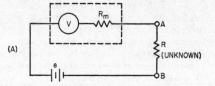

(A)

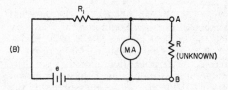

(B)

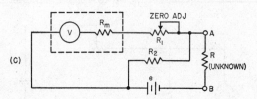

(C)

Fig. 21-6—Ohmmeter circuits. Values are discussed in the text.

voltage drop across a reference resistor, R_2, when the unknown resistor is connected so that current flows through it, R_2 and the battery in series. By suitable choice of R_2 (low values for low resistance, high values for high-resistance unknowns) this circuit will give equally good results on all resistance values in the range from one ohm to several megohms, provided that the voltmeter resistance, R_m, is always very high (50 times or more) compared with the resistance of R_2. A 20,000-ohms-per-volt instrument (50-μamp. movement) is generally used. Assuming that the current through the voltmeter is negligible compared with the current through R_2, the formula for the unknown is

$$R = \frac{eR_2}{E} - R_2$$

where R and R_2 are as shown in Fig. 21-6C,
  e is the voltmeter reading with A-B shorted, and
  E is the voltmeter reading with R connected.

The "zero adjuster," R_1, is used to set the voltmeter reading exactly to full scale when the meter is calibrated in ohms. A 10,000-ohm variable resistor is suitable with a 20,000-ohms-per-volt meter. The battery voltage is usually 3 volts for ranges up to 100,000 ohms or so and 6 volts for higher ranges.

A. C. Measurements

Several types of instruments are available for measurement of low-frequency alternating currents and voltages. The better-grade panel instruments for power-line frequencies are of the **dynamometer** type. This compares with the D'Arsonval movement used for d.c. measurements, but instead of a permanent magnet the dynamometer movement has a field coil which, together with the moving coil, is connected to the a.c. source. Thus the moving coil is urged to turn in the same direction on both halves of the a.c. cycle.

Moving-vane type instruments, described earlier, also are used for a.c. measurements. This is possible because the pull exerted on the vane is in the same direction regardless of the direction of current through the coil. The calibration of a moving-vane instrument on a.c. will, in general, differ from its d.c. calibration.

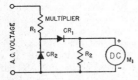

Fig. 21-7—Rectifier-type a.c. voltmeter circuit, with "linearizing" resistor and diode for back-current correction.

For measurements in the audio-frequency range, and in applications where high impedance is required, the **rectifier-type** a.c. instrument is generally used. This is essentially a sensitive d.c. meter, of the type previously described, provided with a rectifier for converting the a.c. to d.c. A typical rectifier-type voltmeter circuit is shown in Fig. 21-7. The half-wave meter rectifier, CR_1, is frequently of the copper-oxide type, but crystal diodes can be used. Such a rectifier is not "perfect"

— that is, the application of a voltage of reversed polarity will result in a small current flow — and so CR_2 is used for eliminating the effect of reverse current in the meter circuit. It does this by providing a low-resistance path across CR_1 and the meter during the a.c. alternations when CR_1 is not conducting.

Resistor R_2 shunted across M_1 is used for improving the linearity of the circuit. The effective resistance of the rectifier decreases with increasing current, leading to a calibration scale with nonuniform divisions. This is overcome to a considerable extent by "bleeding" several times as much current through R_2 as flows through M_1 so the rectifier is always carrying a fairly large current.

Because of these expedients and the fact that with half-wave rectification the average current is only 0.45 times the r.m.s. value of a sine wave producing it, the impedance of a rectifier-type voltmeter is rather low compared with the resistance of a d.c. voltmeter using the same meter. Values of 1000 ohms per volt are representative, when the d.c. instrument is a 0–200 microammeter.

The d.c. instrument responds to the average value of the rectified alternating current. This average current will vary with the shape of the a.c. wave applied to the rectifier, and so the meter reading will not be the same for different wave forms having the same maximum values or the same r.m.s. values. Hence a "wave-form error" is always present unless the a.c. wave is very closely sinusoidal. The actual calibration of the instrument usually is in terms of the r.m.s. value of a sine wave.

Modern rectifier-type a.c. voltmeters are capable of good accuracy, within the wave-form limitations mentioned above, throughout the audio-frequency range.

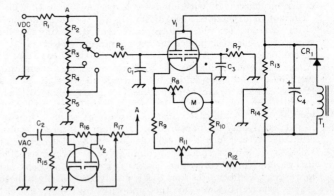

Fig. 21-8—Vacuum-tube voltmeter circuit.

C_1, C_3—0.002- to 0.005-μf. mica.
C_2—0.01 μf., 1000 to 2000 volts, paper or mica.
C_4—16 μf. electrolytic, 150 volts.
CR_1—400 p.i.v. rectifier.
R_1—1 megohm, ½ watt.
R_2 to R_5, inc.—To give desired voltage ranges, totaling 10 megohms.
R_6, R_7—2 to 3 megohms.
R_8—10,000-ohm variable.
R_9, R_{10}—2000 to 3000 ohms.
R_{11}—5000- to 10,000-ohm control.
R_{12}—10,000 to 50,000 ohms.
R_{13}, R_{14}—App. 25,000 ohms. A 50,000-ohm slider-type wire-wound can be used.

R_{15}—10 megohms.
R_{16}—3 megohms.
R_{17}—10-megohm variable.
T_1—130-volt 15-ma. transformer (only secondary shown).
M—0-200 μamp. to 0-1 ma. range.
V_1—Dual triode, 12AU7.
V_2—Dual diode, 6AL5.

COMBINATION INSTRUMENTS— THE V.O.M.

Since the same basic instrument is used for measuring current, voltage and resistance, the three functions can readily be combined in one unit using a single meter. Various models of the "v.o.m." (volt-ohm-milliammeter) are available commercially, both completely assembled and in kit form. The less expensive ones use a 0-1 milliammeter as the basic instrument, providing voltmeter ranges at 1000 ohms per volt. The more elaborate meters of this type use a microammeter—0-50 microamperes, frequently—with voltmeter resistances of 20,000 ohms per volt. With the more sensitive instruments it is possible to make resistance measurements in the megohms range. A.c. voltmeter scales also are frequently included.

The v.o.m., even a very simple one, is among the most useful instruments for the amateur. Besides current and voltage measurements, it can be used for checking continuity in circuits, for finding defective components before installation — shorted capacitors, open or otherwise defective resistors, etc. — shorts or opens in wiring, and many other checks that, if applied during the construction of a piece of equipment, save much time and trouble. It is equally useful for servicing, when a component fails during operation.

THE VACUUM-TUBE VOLTMETER

The usefulness of the **vacuum-tube voltmeter (v.t.v.m.)** is based on the fact that a vacuum tube can amplify without taking power from the source of voltage applied to its grid. It is therefore possible to have a voltmeter of extremely high resistance, and thus take negligible current from the circuit under measurement, without using a d.c. instrument of exceptional sensitivity.

The v.t.v.m. has the disadvantage that it requires a source of power for its operation, as compared with a regular d.c. instrument. Also, it is susceptible to r.f. pick-up when working around an operating transmitter, unless well shielded and filtered. The fact that one of its terminals is grounded is also disadvantageous in some cases, since a.c. readings in particular may be inaccurate if an attempt is made to measure a circuit having both sides "hot" with respect to ground. Nevertheless, the high resistance of the v.t.v.m. more than compensates for these disadvantages, especially since in the majority of measurements they do not apply.

While there are several possible circuits, the one commonly used is shown in Fig. 21-8. A dual triode, V_1, is arranged so that, with no voltage applied to the left-hand grid, equal currents flow through both sections. Under this condition the two cathodes are at the same potential and no current flows through M. The currents can be adjusted to balance by potentiometer R_{11}, which takes care of variations in the tube sections and in the values of cathode resistors R_9 and R_{10}. When a positive d.c. voltage is applied to the left-hand grid the current through that tube section increases, so the current balance is upset and the meter indicates. The sensitivity of the meter is regulated by R_8, which serves to adjust the calibration. R_{12}, common to the cathodes of both tube sections, is a feed back resistor that stabilizes the system and makes the readings linear. R_6 and C_1 form a filter for any a.c. component that may be present, and R_6 is balanced by R_7 connected to the grid of the second tube section.

To stay well within the linear range of operation the scale is limited to 3 volts or less in the average commercial instrument. Higher ranges are obtained by means of the voltage divider formed by R_1 to R_5, inclusive. As many ranges as desired can be used. Common practice is to use 1 megohm at R_1, and to make the sum of R_2 to R_5, inclusive, 10 megohms, thus giving a total resistance of 11 megohms, constant for all voltage ranges. R_1 should be at the probe end of the d.c. lead to minimize capacitive loading effects when measuring d.c. voltages in r.f. circuits.

Values to be used in the circuit depend considerably on the supply voltage and the sensitivity of the meter, M. R_{12}, and R_{13}–R_{14}, should be adjusted by trial so that the voltmeter circuit can be brought to balance, and to give full-scale deflection on M with about 3 volts applied to the left-hand grid. The meter connections can be reversed to read voltages that are negative with respect to ground.

A.C. Voltage

For measuring a.c. voltages up to 4 Mc., the rectifier circuit in the lower left of Fig. 21-8 is used. One diode of V_2 is a half-wave rectifier and the other acts as a balancing device, adjustable by R_{17}, against contact potential effects that would cause a residual d.c. voltage to appear at the v.t.v.m. grid.

The rectifier output voltage is proportional to the peak amplitude of the a.c. wave, rather than to the average or r.m.s. values. Since the positive and negative peaks of a complex wave may not have equal amplitudes, a different reading may be obtained on such wave forms when the voltmeter probe terminals are reversed. This "turnover" effect is inherent in any peak-indicating device, but is not necessarily a disadvantage. The fact that the readings are not the same when the voltmeter connections are reversed is an indication that the wave form under measurement is unsymmetrical. In some measurements, as in audio amplifiers, a peak measurement is more useful than an r.m.s. or average-value measurement because amplifier capabilities are based on the peak amplitudes.

The scale calibration usually is based on the r.m.s. value of a sine wave, R_8 being set so that the same scale can be used either for a.c. or d.c. The r.m.s. reading can easily be converted to a peak reading by multiplying by 1.41.

INSTRUMENT CALIBRATION

When extending the range of a d.c. instrument, calibration usually is necessary — although resistors for voltmeter multipliers often can be purchased to close-enough tolerances so that the new range will be accurately known. However, in calibrating an instrument such as a v.t.v.m. a known voltage must be available to provide a starting point. Fresh dry cells have an open-circuit terminal voltage of approximately 1.6 volts, and one or more of them may be connected in series to provide several calibration points on the low range. Gas regulator tubes in a power supply, such as the 0C3, 0D3, etc., also provide a stable source of voltage whose value is known within a few per cent. Once a few such points are determined the voltmeter ranges may be extended readily by adding multipliers or a voltage divider as appropriate.

Shunts for a milliammeter may be adjusted by first using the meter alone in series with a source of voltage and a resistor selected to limit the current to full scale. For example, a 0-1 milliammeter may be connected in series with a dry cell and a 2000-ohm variable resistor, the latter being adjusted to allow exactly 1 milliampere to flow. Then the shunt is added across the meter and its resistance adjusted to reduce the meter reading by exactly the scale factor, n. If n is 5, the shunt would be adjusted to make the meter read 0.2 milliampere, so the full-scale current will be 5 ma. Using the new scale, the second shunt is added to give the next range, the same procedure being followed. This can be carried on for several ranges, but it is advisable to check the meter on the highest range against a separate meter used as a standard, since the errors in this process tend to be cumulative.

MEASUREMENT OF FREQUENCY

ABSORPTION FREQUENCY METERS

The simplest possible frequency-measuring device is a resonant circuit, tunable over the desired frequency range and having its tuning dial calibrated in terms of frequency. It operates by extracting a small amount of energy from the oscillating circuit to be measured, the frequency being determined by the tuning setting at which the energy absorption is maximum (Fig. 21-9).

Such an instrument is not capable of very

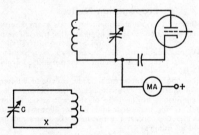

Fig. 21-9—Absorption frequency meter and a typical application. The meter consists simply of a calibrated resonant circuit LC. When coupled to an amplifier or oscillator the tube plate current will rise when the frequency meter is tuned to resonance. A flashlight lamp may be connected in series at X to give a visual indication, but it decreases the selectivity of the instrument and makes it necessary to use rather close coupling to the circuit being measured.

high accuracy, because the Q of the tuned circuit cannot be high enough to avoid uncertainty as to the exact dial setting and because any two coupled circuits interact to some extent and change each others' tuning. Nevertheless, the absorption frequency meter or "wavemeter" is a highly useful instrument. It is compact, inexpensive, and requires no power supply. There is no ambiguity in its indications, as is frequently the case with the heterodyne-type instruments.

When an absorption meter is used for checking a transmitter, the plate current of the tube connected to the circuit being checked can provide the necessary resonance indication. When the frequency meter is loosely coupled to the tank circuit the plate current will give a slight upward flicker as the meter is tuned through resonance. The accuracy is greatest when the loosest possible coupling is used.

A receiver oscillator may be checked by tuning in a steady signal and heterodyning it to give a beat note as in ordinary c.w. reception. When the frequency meter is coupled to the oscillator coil and tuned through resonance the beat note will change. Again, the coupling should be made loose enough so that a just-perceptible change in beat note is observed.

An approximate calibration for the meter, adequate for most purposes, may be obtained by comparison with a calibrated receiver. The usual receiver dial calibration is sufficiently accurate. A simple oscillator circuit covering the same range as the frequency meter will be useful in calibration. Set the receiver to a given frequency, tune the oscillator to zero beat at the same frequency, and adjust the frequency meter to resonance with the oscillator as described above. This gives one calibration point. When a sufficient number of such points has been obtained a graph may be

STANDARD FREQUENCIES AND TIME SIGNALS

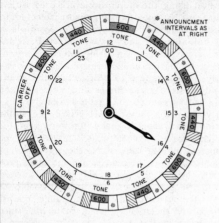

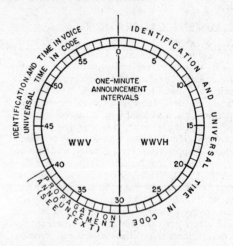

The National Bureau of Standards maintains two radio transmitting stations, WWV at Fort Collins, Colo., and WWVH at Puunene, Hawaii, for broadcasting standard radio frequencies of high accuracy. WWV broadcasts are on 2.5, 5, 10, 15, 20 and 25 Mc., and those from WWVH are on 5, 10, and 15 Mc. The r.f. signals are modulated by pulses at 1 c.p.s., and also by standard audio frequencies alternating between 440 and 600 c.p.s.

Transmissions are continuous, with the following exceptions: The WWV transmissions are interrupted for a 4-minute period beginning at approximately 45 minutes after the hour, as indicated above; the WWVH transmissions are interrupted for a 4-minute period beginning 15 minutes after the hour.

WWVB and WWVL at Fort Collins, Colorado, transmit standard frequency signals at 60 and 20 kc., respectively.

Transmitted frequencies from WWV are accurate to 5 parts in 10^{11}. Frequencies are based on an atomic standard, and daily corrections to the transmitted frequencies are subsequently published each month in the *Proceedings of the IEEE*.

Complete information on the services can be found in Miscellaneous Publication 236, "Standard Frequencies and Time Services", for sale for 15 cents by the Superintendent of Documents, U. S. Government Printing Office, Washington, D.C. 20402.

Geophysical Alerts

"GEOALERTS" are broadcast each day by WWV, starting at 0418 GMT, and at 0448 GMT by WWVH. The broadcasts are repeated at hourly intervals until a new alert is issued. Geoalerts tell of geophysical events affecting radio propagation, such as magnetic storms, proton flares, stratospheric warming, etc. Code signals indicate the type of disturbance in progress. Complete information on Geoalerts is given in the NBS Bulletin 236, U.S. Dep't. of Commerce.

Time Signals

The 1-c.p.s. modulation is a 5-millisecond pulse at intervals of precisely one second, and is heard as a tick. The pulse transmitted by WWV consists of 5 cycles of 1000-cycle tone; that transmitted by WWVH consists of 6 cycles of 1200-cycle tone. On the WWV transmissions, the 440- or 600-cycle tone is blanked out beginning 10 milliseconds before and ending 25 milliseconds after the pulse. On the WWVH transmissions, the pulse is superimposed on the tone. The pulse on the 59th second is omitted, and for additional identification the zero-second pulse is followed by another 100 milliseconds later. On WWV during the minutes identified by coarse cross-hatching (above) a high-speed pulse code is transmitted, giving the time of day and the accuracy of the time. It sounds like an erratic "buzz."

Propagation Notices

Following the announcement intervals every 5 minutes, propagation notices applying to transmission paths over the North Atlantic are transmitted from WWV on 2.5, 5, 10, 15, 20, and 25 Mc. Similar forecasts for the North Pacific are transmitted from WWVH.

These notices, in telegraphic code, consist of a letter and a number. The letter applies to the transmission-path conditions at the time of the broadcast: N for normal, U for unsettled, and W for disturbed. The number is the forcast for the next six hours and is defined as follows:

1—useless	5—fair	6—fair-to-good
2—very poor		7—good
3—poor		8—very good
4—poor-to-fair		9—excellent

If, for example, conditions are normal when the forecast is issued but are expected to become "poor-to-fair" during the next six hours, the forecast would be broadcast as N4.

CHU

CHU, the Canadian time-signal station, transmits on 3330.0, 7335.0 and 14,670.0 kc. Voice announcement of the minute is made each minute; the 29th second time tick is omitted. Voice announcements are made in English and French.

drawn to show frequency *vs.* dial settings on the frequency meter.

INDICATING FREQUENCY METERS

The plain absorption meter requires fairly close coupling to the oscillating circuit in order to affect the plate current of a tube sufficiently to give a visual indication. However, by adding a rectifier and d.c. microammeter or milliammeter, the sensitivity of the instrument can be increased to the point where very loose coupling will suffice for a good reading. A typical circuit for this purpose is given in Fig. 21-11.

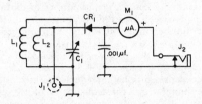

Fig. 21-11—Circuit of typical wavemeter with built-in indicator. The circuit responds to the frequency for which L_1C_1 is resonant; a small amount of energy is coupled to L_2, rectified by CR_1 and indicated by the meter. By plugging in a pair of headphones at J_1, any modulation on the signal will be heard.

L_2—1 to 2 turns or 10 percent of L_1, whichever is greater.

Wound adjacent to or over grounded end of L_1.

MA—Microammeter or 0-1 milliammeter.

The rectifier, a crystal diode, is coupled to the tuned circuit L_1C_1 through a coupling coil, L_2, having a relatively small number of turns. The step-down transformer action from L_1 to L_2 provides for efficient energy transfer from the high-impedance tuned circuit to the low-impedance rectifier circuit. The number of turns on L_2 can be adjusted for maximum reading on the d.c. milliammeter; when doing this, use a fixed value of coupling between L_1 and the source of energy. The proper number of turns for this purpose will depend on the sensitivity of M_1. Less than optimum coupling is preferable, in most cases, since heavy loading lowers the Q of the tuned circuit L_1C_1 and makes it less selective. The coupling is reduced by reducing the number of turns on L_2.

The meter can be used with a pick-up loop and coaxial line connected to J_1. Energy picked up by the loop is fed through the cable to L_2 and thence coupled to L_1C_1. This is a convenient method of coupling to circuits where it would be physically difficult to secure inductive coupling to L_1. The pick-up cable should not be self-resonant, as a transmission-line section, at any frequency within the range in which it is to be used. A 5-foot length of RG-58/U is useful up to about 30 Mc.; a one-foot length is good to about 200 Mc.

By plugging a headset into the output jack, J_2, (phones having 2000 ohms or greater resistance should be used for greatest sensitivity) the frequency meter can be used as a monitor for modulated transmissions. Detailed information on building a calibrated wavemeter was published in March 1967 *QST*, p. 25.

100-KC. FREQUENCY STANDARD

The frequency standard shown in Fig. 21-11A combines the features of compactness and battery-powered operation to provide the builder with a simple, yet stable calibrator. Using a 2N2925 "economy" type transistor, the solid-state oscillator provides useful calibration signals at 100-kc. intervals up to approximately 60 Mc.

The standard shown is built on an etched-circuit board and is mounted on a $3\frac{1}{4} \times 2\frac{1}{8} \times 1\frac{5}{8}$-inch Minibox. Conventional wiring techniques, using a logical parts placement, may be used if desired. S_1 is mounted on the Minibox front lip. It controls the power to the unit, which is supplied by a single 9-volt battery, mounted in the Minibox cover. A homemade U-type bracket holds the battery in place.

Connection between the calibrator and the receiver is made by joining J_1 and the receiver antenna terminal, using a short length of coaxial cable. The frequency of the standard should be set for zero beat with WWV by adjusting C_1. The station receiver can be used for this purpose.

Adjusting to Frequency

The frequency can be adjusted exactly to 100 kc. by making use of the WWV transmissions tabulated later in this chapter. Select the WWV frequency that gives a good signal at your location at the time of day most convenient. Tune it in with the receiver b.f.o. off and wait for the period during which the modulation is absent. Then switch on the 100-kc. oscillator and adjust its frequency, by means of C_1 until its harmonic is in zero beat with WWV. The exact setting is easily found by observing the slow pulsation in background noise as the harmonic comes close to zero beat, and adjusting to where the pulsation disappears or occurs at a very slow rate. The pulsation can be observed even more readily by switching on the receiver's b.f.o., after approximate zero beat has been secured, and observing the rise and fall in intensity (not frequency) of the beat tone. For best results the WWV signal and the signal from the 100-kc. oscillator should be about the same strength. It is advisable not to try to set the 100-kc. oscillator during the periods when the WWV signal is tone-modulated, since it is difficult to tell whether the harmonic is being adjusted to zero beat with the carrier or with a sideband.

Using the Standard

Basically, the 100-kc. standard provides a means for indicating the exact receiver dial

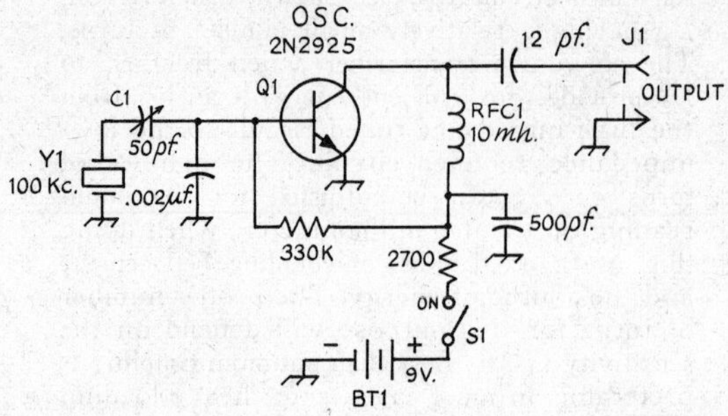

Fig. 21-11—Circuit of the 100-Kc. frequency standard. Resistances are in ohms. Resistors are ½ watt. K-1000.

BT₁—9-volt transistor radio battery.

C₁—50 pf. (Centralab type 827 or Elmenco type 404).

J₁—Phono jack.

Q₁—For text reference.

RFC₁—10-Mh. choke (Miller 6306).

S₁—S.p.s.t. slide switch.

Y₁—100-kc. crystal (International Type F-13).

settings at which frequencies that are multiples of 100 kc. are to be found. The harmonics of the standard can thus be used to check the dial calibration of a receiver, and many of the better-grade communications receivers either include a 100-kc. oscillator for this purpose or have provision for installing one as an accessory. The actual frequency of at least one 100-kc. point in a given amateur band must be known, of course, but this is generally an easy matter since the activity in amateur bands usually makes identification of the band-edge "marker signal" quite simple. After one frequency is known, the consecutive 100-kc. harmonic signals are simply counted off from it.

Although the 100-kc. standard does not make possible the exact measurement of a frequency, it is readily possible to determine whether or not the signal is in a particular 100-kc. segment. If the unknown signal tunes in between, say, 21,200 and 21,300 kc., as indicated by the marker signals in the receiver, its frequency obviously lies between those two figures. For purposes of complying with the amateur regulations it is usually sufficient to know that the signal is above, or below, some specified 100-kc. point, since the edges of the amateur bands or sub-bands usually are at such points. If a closer measurement is desired a fairly good estimate usually can be made by counting the number of dial divisions between two 100-kc. points and dividing the number into 100 to find how many kilocycles there are per dial division.

In using the receiver to check one's own transmitting frequency it is necessary to take special precautions to reduce the strength of the signal from the transmitter to the point where it does not overload the receiver nor create spurious responses that could be taken for the actual signal. This invariably means that the receiving antenna must be disconnected from the receiver, and it may be necessary, in addition, to short-circuit the receiver's antenna input terminals. Try to reduce stray pickup to such an extent that the transmitter's signal is no stronger than normal incoming signals at the regular gain-control settings. With some receivers this may require additional shielding around the signal-frequency circuits, and perhaps filtering of the a.c. and speaker leads where they leave the chassis, to prevent energy picked up on these leads from getting into the front end of the receiver.

BAND-EDGE MARKERS

Every amateur has the obligation to confine his transmissions within the band or sub-band limits for which the particular type of emission is authorized. There are no restrictions on the frequency that can be used *within* such limits; in other words, the transmitting frequency does not have to be known exactly, so long as it *is* known to be inside the designated limits.

The edges of all amateur bands and sub-bands are exact multiples of 25 kHz. This means that harmonics of a source of signal on exactly 25 kHz. can be used to mark all such band limits with high accuracy. While a 25-kHz. oscillator would be a usable signal source, an oscillator having the requisite stability without crystal control would be extremely difficult to build. Unfortunately, crystals for this frequency are not ordinarily available. However, crystals for 100 kHz. can be obtained at little cost, and it is relatively easy to build an oscillator for this frequency and follow it by a frequency divider to reduce the frequency to 25 kHz. Divider circuits usually also generate strong harmonics throughout a

large part of the frequency spectrum, so that marker signals at 25-kHz. intervals are available in the most-used amateur bands.

The frequency-marker generator shown in Figs. 21-12 through 21-14 uses a 100-kHz. crystal oscillator and an integrated-circuit dual flip-flop divider, giving a choice of harmonics at 100-, 50-, and 25-kHz. intervals. The 50- and 100-kHz. intervals are useful for identifying the frequency, as it might otherwise be difficult to distinguish between, say, 3850, 3875, and 3900 kHz. The marker generator has a self-contained battery power supply and so is completely portable, but provision also is made for using an external supply that will give longer operating life than the small dry batteries that fit inside the Minibox.

The oscillator, Fig. 21-12, is basically a grounded-base Colpitts arrangement with the 100-kHz. crystal used as a series resonator in the r.f. base lead. The frequency can be adjusted to exactly 100 kHz. by means of the series capacitance formed by C_6 and C_7 in parallel. The oscillator is followed by a direct-coupled two-stage

Band-edge marker-signal generator. Crystal controlled, it offers a choice of marker signals at 100-, 50- or 25-kHz. intervals in the h.f. and v.h.f. spectrum. It is housed in a 2¼ by 2¼ by 4-inch Minibox and contains a dry-battery power supply. The frequency can be adjusted through the hole in the right rear corner.

buffer amplifier/harmonic generator, Q_2Q_3, which produces a square-wave output suitable for driving the flip-flop, FF_1. There are two identical flip-flops in the Motorola MC790P package; one divides the 100-kHz. input by 2, giving 50-kHz. output which is then applied to the second flip-flop to divide the 50 kHz. signal by 2, giving 25-kHz. output. The desired interval is selected by S_{1A}, and is coupled by C_8 to the output con-

nector, J_1. S_{1A} controls the collector supply to the oscillator and buffer amplifier, while S_{1B} similarly controls the supply for the flip-flop. The latter is operative only in the 50- and 25-kHz. positions; this conserves battery drain when only the 100-kHz. output is needed.

Except for S_1, C_8 and J_1, which are mounted on the front of the Minibox, the marker generator is built on an etched circuit board measuring 3-¾ by 2 inches. The inside view shows the layout, except for Q_3 and FF_1, which are hidden by the switch. The board is mounted at its four corners by 4-40 screws through the bottom of the box, and is held away from the box by ¼-inch tubular spacers. The crystal, at the top in this view, plugs into a Millen type 33302 crystal socket. To the right of the crystal on the rear of the box is a 3-prong socket (Amphenol type 78-S3S) for the power connections. The section of the box at the left contains the batteries. One is a 9-volt transistor radio battery and the other consists of two penlite cells connected in series for 3 volts. These are held in place by a piece of aluminum, just wide enough to fit between the box walls and bent so that it holds the batteries securely. Wires from the batteries go to a plug (Amphenol type 71-3S) which mates with the power socket. This connection is made externally.

Although a pocket-size assembly such as this is convenient if portability is a consideration, it is readily possible to use other methods of construction. The principal problem is in handling the integrated circuit, which has 14 leads, 7 on a side, spaced only 1/10 inch apart. Care must be used to prevent adjacent leads from touching, whatever the mounting method.

For introducing the marker signal into the receiver the 3-foot length of audio cable shown in Fig. 21-11 can be used. It is fitted with a phono plug at one end and a pair of clips at the other. This cable will work satisfactorily at frequencies as high as 54 MHz., with receivers having low-impedance (50 ohms) antenna input. At 144 MHz. and higher the cable capacitance effectively short-circuits the marker output, and the connection to the receiver should be made with a single wire. When this is done the 25-kHz. harmonics can easily be heard on the 144-MHz. band. The 100-kHz. harmonics are usable in the 420-MHz. band with the same type of connection.

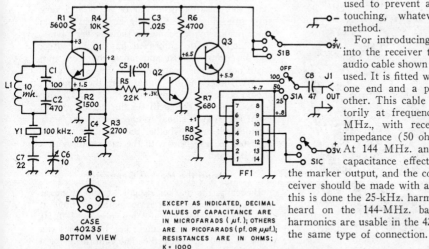

Fig. 21-12—Circuit of the band-edge marker. Voltages shown are typical, measured with vacuum-tube voltmeter with the circuit operating.

C_1, C_2, C_5—Dipped silver mica.

C_3, C_4—Disk ceramic, 50 volts.

C_6—10-pf. tubular trimmer (Centralab 829-10).

C_7—Dipped silver mica. Value must be selected to permit adjustment to exact frequency with C_6; 15 or 27 pf. may be required.

C_8—Disk ceramic.

FF_1—Dual type JK flip-flop integrated circuit (Motorola MC790P. Pin numbering is shown in bottom view; black dots indicate bosses on bottom of package).

J_1—Phono jack.

L_1—10-mh. r.f. choke (Miller 6306).

Q_1, Q_2, Q_3—RCA 40235, or similar v.h.f. silicon transistor.

R_1-R_8, inc.—Composition, ½ watt.

S_1—3-pole, 4-position rotary (Mallory 3134J).

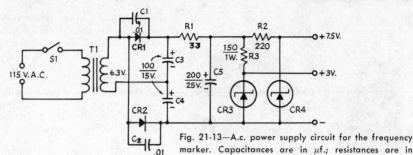

Fig. 21-13—A.c. power supply circuit for the frequency marker. Capacitances are in μf.; resistances are in ohms; resistors are ½ watt unless otherwise indicated.

C_1, C_2—Disk ceramic (for eliminating a.c. "hash"; may not be required).
C_3, C_4, C_5—Electrolytic.
CR_1, CR_2—Any silicon rectifier rated at 100 ma., 50 volts or more.

CR_3—Zener, app. 3 volts, 400 mw. (1N746A).
CR_4—Zener, app. 7.5 volts, 1 watt (GE Z4XL7.5 or equivalent).
S_1—S.p.s.t. toggle.
T_1—6.3-volt filament transformer, 0.5 or 1 amp.

Current drain of the oscillator and buffer at 9 volts is approximately 9 ma. The flip-flop will take 30 to 40 ma. at 3 volts, depending on the particular unit. These currents are comparable with those normally taken from batteries of this type, and for intermittent use satisfactory life can be obtained. For heavy-duty operation an a.c. supply is recommended, and a suitable circuit is shown in Fig. 21-13. The 7.5-volt output is adequate for operating the oscillator and buffer.

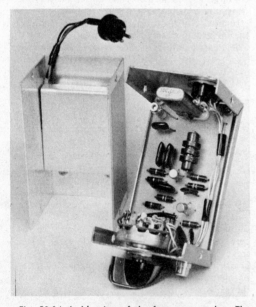

Fig. 21-14—Inside view of the frequency marker. The etched circuit board is mounted under the top of the case, allowing the adjustment screw on C_6 to be reached through a hole in the top. The bottom piece, left, has the battery supply mounted under a homemade aluminum clamp. Two penlite cells are wired in series for the 3-volt supply by soldering wires to the positive post and exposed negative container at the bottom. This wiring must be insulated from the case. The 9-volt supply is a transistor battery with clip-on connector.

Adjusting to Frequency

The frequency of the oscillator can be adjusted exactly to 100 kHz. by making use of the WWV transmissions tabulated later in this chapter. Select the WWV frequency that gives a good signal at your location at the time of day most convenient. Tune it in with the receiver b.f.o. off and wait for the period during which the modulation is absent. Then switch on the 100-kc. oscillator and adjust its frequency, by means of C_6, until its harmonic is in zero beat with WWV. The exact setting is easily found by observing the slow pulsation in background noise as the harmonic comes close to zero beat. Adjust C_6 to make the pulsation disappear or occur at a very slow rate. The pulsation can be observed even more readily by switching on the receiver's b.f.o., after approximate zero beat has been secured, and observing the rise and fall in intensity (not frequency) of the beat tone. For best results the WWV signal and the signal from the oscillator should be about the same strength. It is advisable not to try to set the oscillator during the periods when the WWV signal is tone-modulated, since it is difficult to tell whether the harmonic is being adjusted to zero beat with the carrier or with a tone sideband.

Using the Marker Generator

Basically, the marker signals provide a means for indicating the exact receiver dial settings at which frequencies that are multiples of 100, 50, or 25 kHz. are to be found. The harmonics can thus be used to check the dial calibration of a receiver. (Many of the better-grade communications receivers either include a 100-kHz. oscillator for this purpose or have provision for installing one as an accessory. These "crystal calibrators" do not give signals at 50- and 25-kHz. intervals, however.) The actual frequency of at least one point in a given amateur band must be known, of course, but this is generally easy since the activity in amateur bands usually makes identification of a band-edge marker signal quite simple. After one frequency is known, the consecutive harmonic signals are simply counted off from it.

Although the marker generator does not make possible the exact measurement of a frequency, it is readily possible to determine whether or not the signal is in a particular segment. If the unknown signal tunes in between, say, 21,200 and 21,225 kHz., as indicated by the marker signals in the receiver, its frequency obviously lies between those two figures. If a closer measurement is desired a fairly good estimate usually can be made by counting the number of dial divisions between two 25-kHz. points and dividing the number into 25 to find how many kHz. there are per dial division.

In using the receiver to check one's own transmitting frequency it is necessary to take special precautions to reduce the strength of the signal from the transmitter to the point where it does not overload the receiver nor create spurious responses that could be taken for the actual signal. This invariably means that the receiving antenna must be disconnected from the receiver, and it may be necessary, in addition, to short-circuit the receiver's antenna input terminals. Try to reduce stray pickup to such an extent that the transmitter's signal is no stronger than normal incoming signals at the regular gain-control settings. With some receivers this may require additional shielding around the signal-frequency circuits, and perhaps filtering of the a.c. and speaker leads where they leave the chassis, to prevent energy picked up on these leads from getting into the front end of the receiver.

TEST OSCILLATORS AND SIGNAL GENERATORS

THE GRID-DIP METER

The **grid-dip meter** is a simple vacuum-tube oscillator to which a microammeter or low-range milliammeter has been added for reading the oscillator grid current. A 0-1 milliammeter is sensitive enough in most cases. The grid-dip meter is so called because if the oscillator is coupled to a tuned circuit the grid current will show a decrease or "dip" when the oscillator is tuned through resonance with the unknown circuit. The reason for this is that the external circuit will absorb energy from the oscillator when both are tuned to the same frequency; the loss of energy from the oscillator circuit causes the feed-back to decrease and this in turn is accompanied by a decrease in grid current. The dip in grid current is quite sharp when the circuit to which the oscillator is coupled has reasonably high Q.

The grid-dip meter is most useful when it covers a wide frequency range and is compactly constructed so that it can be coupled to circuits in hard-to-reach places such as in a transmitter or receiver chassis. It can thus be used to check tuning ranges and to find unwanted resonances of the type described in the chapter on TVI. Since it is its own source of r.f. energy it does not require the circuit being checked to be energized. In addition to resonance checks, the grid-dip meter also can be used as a signal source for receiver alignment and, as described later in this chapter, is useful in measurement of inductance and capacitance in the range of values used in r.f. circuits.

The grid-dip meter shown in Fig. 21-15 is representative, although this particular unit has a higher frequency limit than similar inexpensive units. It uses the 6CW4 (Nuvistor) triode for the oscillator, and it can be used with the power supply and metering circuit shown in Fig. 21-18.

Referring to the circuit in Fig. 21-16, a resistor, R_2, is plugged in with each coil (the resistor is mounted in the coil form). It forms

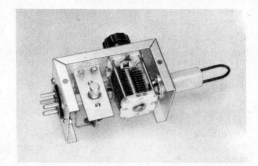

Fig. 21-15—Grid-dip meter covering the range 1.7 to 275 Mc., with the 90-165 Mc. coil in place. The power supply and transistor meter booster are a separate unit (see Fig. 21-17). The split-stator tuning capacitor is made from a single-stator variable. The Nuvistor tube socket is mounted on a small bracket, and a tie point under the bracket supports associated capacitors and resistors that aren't supported by socket and tuning-capacitor terminals.

a voltage divider with the normal grid leak, R_1, and brings the metering circuit into the best range for the transistor booster.

The construction of the meter is straightforward; a small aluminum bracket supports the Nuvistor socket within the $2\frac{1}{4} \times 2\frac{1}{4} \times 4$-inch Minibox that is used as a housing. A 5-pin socket (Amphenol 78-S5S) is mounted at one end of the Minibox, and the variable capacitor stator leads are soldered directly to two of the pins. Coils in the low-frequency ranges are wound with enameled wire on $\frac{3}{4}$-inch diameter forms. In the intermediate ranges coil stock (B&W Miniductor) is mounted inside the coil forms, with one end of the coil close to the open end of the form, for ease in coupling. The two highest-range coils are hairpin loops of No. 14 wire, covered with insulation as a safety precaution. In every case the associated R_2 is mounted in the coil form. The highest range requires that only the base of the coil form be used, since the loop is shorter than the form.

The power supply for the grid-dip meter may be included with the oscillator, but since this increases the bulk and weight a separate supply is often desirable. The power supply shown in Fig. 21-18 uses a miniature power transformer with a silicon rectifier and a simple filter to give approximately 120 volts for the oscillator plate. It also uses a transistor booster for the meter because it was designed for use with a u.h.f. grid-dip meter. A supply to be used with only the unit of Fig. 21-15 could eliminate the transistor by using a 0-1 milliammeter between lead 3 of P_1 and chassis ground. In this case R_2 could also be eliminated, and the B+ for pin 4 of P_1 should be derived from the arm of a 0.1-megohm potentiometer connected across the power supply. The adjustable plate voltage source is necessary to bring the grid current into the range of the meter.

The instrument may be calibrated by listening to its output with a calibrated receiver. The calibration should be as accurate as possible, although "frequency-meter accuracy" is not required in the applications for which a grid-dip meter is useful.

The grid-dip meter may be used as an indicating-type absorption wavemeter by removing the plate voltage and using the grid and cathode of the tube as a diode. However, this type of circuit is not as sensitive as the crystal-detector type shown earlier in this chapter, because of the high-resistance grid leak in series with the meter.

In using the grid-dip meter for checking the resonant frequency of a circuit the coupling should be set to the point where the dip in grid current is just perceptible. This reduces interaction between the two circuits to a minimum and gives the highest accuracy. With too-close coupling the oscillator frequency may be "pulled" by the circuit being checked, in which case different readings will be obtained when resonance is approached from the high-frequency side as compared with approaching from the low side.

U.H.F. Grid-Dip Oscillator

The range of the grid-dip meter shown in Fig. 21-17 is from 275 to 725 Mc., a higher range than any of the inexpensive meters now available. It is able to cover these high frequencies by virtue of the 6CW4 (Nuvistor) tube and the series-tuned circuit. Unfortunately the series-tuned circuit becomes impractical with this tube at lower frequencies, and to cover the lower frequencies the circuit of Fig. 21-16 must be used. The u.h.f. grid-dip oscillator uses a transistor amplifier to amplify the changes across the unusually-low value of grid resistor. The low value of grid resistor is required because higher values will cause the oscillator to "squegg."

The grid-dip meter is built in a $2\frac{1}{4} \times 2\frac{1}{4} \times$

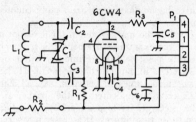

Fig. 21-16—Circuit diagram of the grid-dip meter.

C_1—50 $\mu\mu$f. per section (Johnson 167-11 with stator bars sawed between 6th and 7th plates).

C_2, C_3—100-$\mu\mu$f. ceramic.

C_4, C_5, C_6—0.001-μf. disk ceramic.

P_1—4-pin chassis plug (Amphenol 86-CP4).

R_1—47,000 ohms, ½ watt.

R_2—See table below.

R_3—10,000 ohms.

Range	L_1	R_2
1.7-3.2 Mc.	195 turns No. 34 enam.*	680
2.7-5.0	110 turns No. 30 enam.*	470
4.4-7.8	51½ turns No. 30 enam.*	470
7.5-13.2	24½ turns No. 30 enam.*	470
12-22	31 t. No. 24 (B&W 3004)**	1000
20-36	14 t. No. 24 (B&W 3004)**	680
33-60	8½ t. No. 20 (B&W 3003)***	680
54-99	3¾ t. No. 20 (B&W 3003)***	1000
90-165	3⅜-inch loop No. 14, ½-inch separation	1500
150-275	1¼-inch loop No. 14, ¼-inch separation	3300

*Wound on ¾-inch diameter polystyrene form (Allied Radio 47D6693).

**32 t.p.i.   ***16 t.p.i.

4-inch Minibox, and the power supply and meter circuit is built in a similar enclosure. In use the two Miniboxes are connected by a short length of four-conductor cable.

The "heart" of the meter is the oscillator section, which is built on a 1¾ × 1⅞-inch piece of ⅛-inch thick polystyrene. The Nuvistor socket is mounted in one corner and the tuning capacitor is mounted a little above center. The coil socket, a National CS-6, is mounted on the end of the Minibox. The polystyrene sheet is supported by four 1-inch 6-32 screws, and the sockets and variable capacitor are positioned so that direct connections can be made between plate pin and coil socket, capacitor rotor and coil socket, and capacitor stator and grid pin. The various resistors and r.f. chokes are supported at one end by a multiple-terminal tie strip mounted on the polystyrene sheet and at the other end by the socket pins and other terminals.

The coils are made from No. 10 tinned copper wire; as a safety precaution they are covered except at the tips by clear plastic insulation. Details are given in Fig. 21-19.

Frequency calibration of the meter can be started by reference to u.h.f. TV stations in the area, if any, or by reference to 420-Mc. amateur gear.

Fig. 21-17—Grid-dip meter for the 300- to 700-Mc. range. The oscillator section is at the left in its own case, and the power supply plus transistorized indicator is at the center and right. In the oscillator section, the 6CW4 (Nuvistor) socket is to the left of the tuning capacitor.

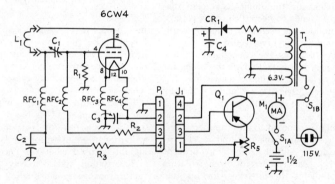

Fig. 21-18—Circuit diagram of the u.h.f. grid-dip meter.

C₁—8-$\mu\mu$f. midget variable (Hammarlund MAC-10 with one rotor plate removed).

C₂—150 pf. ceramic.

C₃—0.001-μf. ceramic.

C₄—20-μf., 250-volt electrolytic.

CR₁—400 p.i.v. rectifier (Sarkes Tarzian 2F4).

J₁—4-pin tube socket.

M₁—0-500 microammeter.

P₁—4-pin plug (Amphenol 86-CP4).

Q₁—2N2613 transistor.

R₁—330 ohms, 1 watt.

R₂—47,000 ohms, ½ watt.

R₃—10,000 ohms.

R₄—22 ohms, ½ watt.

R₅—10,000-ohm potentiometer.

RFC₁, RFC₂—22-μh. r.f. choke (Millen 34300-22).

RFC₃, RFC₄—0.82-μh. r.f. choke (Millen 34300-.82).

S₁ₐ, S₁ᵦ—D.p.s.t., part of R₅. Switches should be open when R₅ at maximum resistance.

T₁—6.3- and 125-v. transformer (Knight 61 G 410).

Range	Dimension "L"	"M"
271-324 Mc.	2¾	$^{11}/_{16}$
312-378	3⅛	—
372-463	2	—
413-519	1⅝	—
446-565	1¼	—
544-730	½*	—

*Shape closed end to be nearly square.

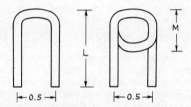

Fig. 21-19—Details of the coils used in the u.h.f. grid-dip meter. The material is No. 10 tinned-copper wire. One turn in end of low-frequency coil.

AN F.E.T. AUDIO GENERATOR

The generator described here uses one FET and four conventional transistors in a bridged-T circuit. Its three bands cover respectively 25 to 250, 250 to 2500 and 2500 to 25,000 cycles. Three variable output ranges are provided (0.01, 0.1 and 1 volt r.m.s.) for resistive loads of 600 ohms or more.

The oscillator circuit, shown in Fig. 21-21 consists of a Siliconix type U112 FET voltage amplifier, Q_1, and two 2N404's, Q_2 and Q_3, in a Darlington-configuration emitter-follower. Two feedback paths are provided. Lamp I_1 and capacitor C_3 form a positive feedback path between the source electrode of Q_1 (marked S) and the emitter of Q_3. The bridged-T network consisting of R_2, R_3, C_1 and C_2 completes a negative-feedback loop between the gate electrode of Q_1 (marked G) and the emitter of Q_3. Oscillations occur at the null frequency of the bridge, where degeneration is at a minimum (i.e., the degenerative feedback becomes slightly less than the regenerative feedback). R_1 adjusts the degree of positive feedback for minimum waveform distortion. Lamp I_1 tends to keep the output voltage constant throughout the oscillator range by regulating the amount of positive feedback.

Trimmer C_2 balances the capacitance of one side of the bridged-T with that of the other for proper tracking of the tuning capacitor, C_1. Switch S_1 selects the desired audio band by changing the resistive elements in the bridged-T network.

The oscillator is coupled to an amplifier stage, Q_4, through a coupling capacitor and R_4. R_4 attenuates the input signal enough to prevent overdriving Q_4. An emitter-follower isolation stage, Q_5, completes the all-transistor line up. A 10,000-ohm control, R_5, in the base lead of Q_5 varies the overall output level. Switch S_2 turns the unit on and off and selects (from a resistive attenuator network) one of three output levels (1, 0.1 or 0.01 volts).

Construction

The FET oscillator is constructed in a $5 \times 6 \times 9$-inch utility cabinet as shown in the photographs. Output connectors J_1 and J_2 are mounted on top of the box. Three double battery holders are on the right side, rear view. A Jackson Brothers type 4511DAF 6:1 planetary drive is mounted on the front panel along with both potentiometers and both switches. Switched resistors are mounted directly on S_1 and S_2. C_1 is insulated from the cabinet with ceramic pillers and from the planetary drive by a Millen type 39016 insulated shaft coupling. Trimmer C_2 is fastened to the rear of C_1 with two 4-40 machine screws and hex nuts. The 6-watt lamp holder is bolted to the left side of the cabinet below the tuning capacitor. All of the remaining components are mounted on a $6\frac{3}{4} \times 4\frac{13}{16}$-inch sheet of prepunched terminal board (Vector 85G24EP) with push-in terminals (Vector T-28). Six $\frac{1}{2}$-

Fig. 21-20—Front view of the FET audio oscillator. The generator is completely self-contained. Battery drain is only 16 ma. The large tuning dial is a modified Johnson type 116-262.

inch 6–32 threaded spacers support the terminal board above the base of the cabinet. For neatness and ease of wiring the parts arrangement on the board more or less resembles the circuit diagram; however, any reasonable layout should work without difficulty.

Care should be taken while soldering the various components, as too much heat can damage a transistor or permanently change the value of a composition resistor. A heat sink should be used wherever necessary.

The tuning dial as received from the manufacturer consists of a knob, a phenolic skirt and an etched satin aluminum calibrated dial scale. Disassemble the unit and discard the skirt. Bolt a small plate of aluminum to the vernier drive assembly. Attach the dial scale to this plate and the knob to the tuning shaft. Later, a calibrated paper scale can be pasted on the aluminum dial.

Testing

Once the unit has been constructed and the wiring checked, install the six flashlight batteries in their holders and the 22.5 volt battery BT_2 in its holder. Connect a length of shielded cable between either J_1 or J_2 and the vertical input terminals of an oscilloscope. Set C_1 at maximum capacitance and R_5 full on (arm of R_5 at maximum resistance to ground). With the band switch in the "C" position (see resistor table), set the range switch at maximum output (1 volt). Adjust R_1 for good output waveshape at an amplitude of about 1 volt r.m.s. Tune C_1 to the high end of the band and adjust C_2 for the same output level as on the low end. Output should now be constant within 1 db. across the band, with good waveshape. It might be necessary to readjust R_1 and C_2 a few times before

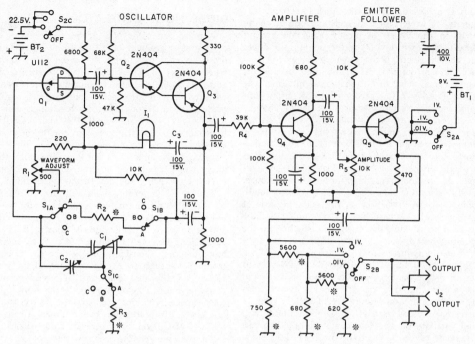

Fig. 21-21—Circuit diagram of the transistor audio oscillator. Unless specified otherwise, all capacitors are miniature electrolytics, all capacitances are in microfarads (μf.) Resistors marked with an asterisk are ½ watt $\pm$ 5 percent, others are $\pm$ 10 percent, resistances are in ohms.

BT_1—Six 1.5-volt flashlight batteries (size D) in series.

BT_2—Small 22.5-volt battery. (Eveready 505, RCA VS 705, or similar.)

C_1—Dual variable, 365-pf. per section, compression trimmers removed (Miller 2112).

C_2—8-50-pf. ceramic-disc trimmer (Erie 557-000U2PO-34R).

I_1—6-watt 120-volt lamp (GE 6S6).

J_1, J_2—Phono jacks.

R_1—500-ohm control, linear taper (Ohmite CLU5011).

R_2, R_3—See resistor table.

R_5—10,000-ohm control, linear taper (Ohmite CU1031).

S_1—Phenolic rotary, 1-section, 4-poles (3 used) 3-positions non-shorting type (Mallory 3243J).

S_2—Phenolic rotary, 1-section, 3-poles 4-positions shorting type (Mallory 3134J).

Field-effect transistor U112 is available from Siliconix Incorporated, 1140 West Evelyn Ave., Sunnyvale, Calif. 94086.

Fig. 21-22—Interior view of the audio generator. Three 1-inch ceramic stand-offs insulate the tuning capacitor from the side of the cabinet. The amplitude control is to the right of the large variable. From left to right, along the lower half of the front panel, are the waveform-adjust control, the band switch, and the attenuator switch. Parts are arranged on the terminal board in a manner similar to the schematic diagram. Oscillator components are on the left, amplifier parts in the center and emitter-follower circuitry is at the right. The two double side-to-side battery holders nearest the front of the cabinet are Keystone type 176. The holder for BT_2 is at the upper right, but is not visible. A Keystone type 186 double end-to-end holder is at the rear.

this is achieved. Check the other two bands for purity of waveform and constant output. Note that on the lowest-frequency band the output level drops off below 60 cycles, being 3 db. down at 30 cycles and 6 db. down at 25 cycles (0.5 volts r.m.s. output). Also note that because of the thermal delay in I_1 and the circuit time constant, it takes a few seconds for the output amplitude to settle down after a frequency change.

All transistors of any one type aren't necessarily uniform, and it may at first appear to be impossible to get a full 1 volt (r.m.s.) of undistorted output on any of the bands. In this case, a slight change of a bias or load resistance will put the circuit in working order. For instance, if the base-to-ground resistor of Q_4 is too small, there will be distortion on the negative half of the cycle. If Q_4's base-to-negative-supply resistor is too low in value, there will be distortion on the positive half cycle.

Any individual band of frequencies ("A," "B" or "C") might be distorted or not present at all if the correct R_2-to-R_3 ratio for that band is not maintained. If the output waveforms throughout any one range are distorted, slightly decrease R_2 or increase R_3. If the oscillator will not oscillate on any one band, slightly increase R_2 or decrease R_3. Once the correct relationships are established, R_1 should not have to be reset upon changing bands.

Resistor Table			
Band	Range (c.p.s.)	R_2	R_3
A	25–250	40 Meg. (22 Meg. & 18 Meg. in series)	8.2 Meg.
B	250–2500	3.9 Meg.	750 K
C	2.5K–25K	390 K	68 K

Calibration

Once the unit performs satisfactorily, the audio oscillator may be calibrated using Lissajous patterns. Connect the generator to the vertical input terminals of a scope and a source of 60 cycles to the horizontal input terminals. Several calibration points between 30 and 600 cycles in both bands "A" and "B" can easily be found using this method. Calibration frequencies between 300 and 6000 cycles in bands "B" and "C" can be located using the 440- and 600-cycle tones transmitted by WWV. Just connect the audio output of a receiver tuned to WWV to the horizontal input terminals of the scope. Above 6000 cycles (and also below) hi-fi and stereo test records will prove useful. Of course if you can borrow a calibrated oscillator, calibration will be relatively simple.

Once enough calibration points have been located, make a three-band paper scale as shown in the front view. Spray the paper with clear acrylic plastic (to protect it from finger marks) and cement it to the aluminum dial scale.

DIODE NOISE GENERATORS

A noise generator is a device for creating a controllable amount of r.f. noise ("hiss"-type noise) evenly distributed throughout the spectrum of interest. The simplest type of noise generator is a diode, either vacuum-tube or crystal, with d.c. flowing through it. The current is also made to flow through a load resistance which usually is chosen to equal the characteristic impedance of the transmission line to be connected to the receiver's input terminals. The resistance then substitutes for the line, and the amount of r.f. noise fed to receiver input is controlled by varying the d.c. through the diode.

The noise generator is useful for adjusting the "front-end" circuits of a receiver for best noise figure (see Chapter Five). A simple circuit using a crystal diode is shown in Fig. 21-26. The unit can be built into a small metal box; the main consideration is that the circuit from C_1 through to P_1 be as compact as possible. A calibrated knob on R_1 will permit resetting the generator to roughly the same spot each time, for making comparisons. If the leads are short, the generator can be used through the 144-Mc. band for receiver comparisons.

To use the generator, screw the coaxial fitting on the receiver's input fitting, open S_1, and measure the noise output of the receiver

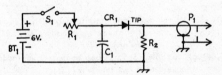

Fig. 21-26—Circuit of a simple crystal-diode noise generator.

BT₁—Dry-cell battery, any convenient type.

C₁—500-$\mu\mu$f. ceramic, disk or tubular.

CR₁—Silicon diode, 1N21 or 1N23. Diodes with "R" suffix have reversed polarity. (Do not use ordinary germanium diodes).

P₁—Coaxial fitting, cable type.

R₁—50,000-ohm control, c.c.w. logarithmic taper.

R₂—51 or 75 ohms, ½-watt composition.

S₁—S.p.s.t. toggle (may be mounted on R₁).

using an a.c. vacuum-tube voltmeter or similar a.f. voltage indicator. Make sure that the receiver's r.f. and audio gain controls are set well within the linear range, and do not use a.g.c. Then turn on the noise generator and set R_1 for an appreciable increase in output, say twice the original noise voltage, and note the dial setting. Receiver front-end adjustments may then be made with the object of attaining the same noise increase with the lowest possible d.c. through the diode—that is, with the largest resistance at R_1.

While the simple crystal-diode noise generator is a useful device within the shack for evaluating receiver performance, it does not permit good comparisons with other receivers measured

Fig. 21-27—Two diode noise generators and (left) their power supply. Useful generator range is (right) 7 to 90 Mc. and (center) 90 to 450 Mc.

with other noise generators. Diode noise generators that allow the noise figure to be measured are shown in Figs. 21-27 and 21-29. Referring to the circuit diagram in Fig. 21-28, a 5722 noise diode is used in place of the crystal diode. A power supply that can be used with either generator unit (which differ only in their filtering and plug connector) is shown in Fig. 21-30. The heart of the supply is a heavy-duty filament rheostat, R_3, that is used to control the diode filament temperature. With S_2 in the N.F. position, the 0-1 milliammeter reads the current through the diode by measuring the voltage across the 100-ohm resistor. Full-scale reading is 10 ma. or 50 ma., depending upon the position of S_3. The meter also serves as an output indicator for the receiver when S_2 is in the OUT position. Terminals are provided for connecting the meter mounted in the power supply to the receiver speaker terminals, so that the receiver output can be monitored.

An important part of the design of the noise-generator power supply is the resistor R_1. This tapped resistor serves as an output load for the receiver. With S_1 in the OFF position, and S_2 in the OUT position, the receiver output is rectified by the 1N34A and a suitable meter indication can be obtained by variation of the receiver volume control. When S_1 is switched to ON, only a fraction of the receiver noise output is rectified and, at the same time, the diode noise generator is turned on. If the meter now reads half the receiver output noise power, and the re-

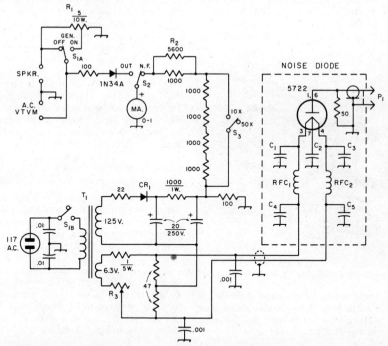

Fig. 21-28—Circuit diagram of the diode noise generators and power supply. Unless indicated otherwise, resistances are in ohms, resistors are ½-watt, capacitances are in μf.

C_1-C_3—0.001-μf. disk ceramic in 7-90 Mc.; button (Centralab ZA-102) in 90-450 Mc.
C_4, C_5—0.001-μf. disk ceramic
CR_1—400 p.i.v. silicon rectifier.
P_1—PL-259 in 7-90 Mc.; UG-260B/U in 90-450 Mc.
R_1—5-ohm 10-watt adjustable, tap set at about 3½ ohms to ground. See text.

R_2—Approximately 5600 ohms. See text.
R_3—4-ohm 50-watt rheostat (Ohmite 0311).
RFC_1, RFC_2—7-90 Mc.: Approximately 9 μh. 38 turns No. 22 Nylclad on ½-inch diameter form (Millen 69046), slug set for maximum inductance. 90-450 Mc.: 0.22 μh. (Miller RFC-420).
T_1—125 volts at 50 ma., 6.3 v. at 2 a. (Knight 61 G 411).

Fig. 21-29—Each diode noise generator is housed in a 4 × 2⅛ × 1⅝-inch "Minibox" (Bud CU-2102-A). Power connections are made through double-pin male receptacles (Amphenol 80 PC2M), and the r.f. connection is made to the receiver or converter by a suitable plug. The plug on the 7- to 90-Mc. generator (left) is a PL-259 held to the face of the "Minibox" by a small copper plate and a UG-176/U reducing adapter.

ceiver noise output has been doubled by the noise from the diode noise generator, the meter reading will remain the same for either position of S_2. Since the meter needle will "wiggle" back and forth about a mean reading, it is much easier to match readings that are made at the same point on the meter scale than it is to "read" the meter at two different points on the scale.

The tap on R_1 is set to 70.7 per cent of the full resistance. If the "5-ohm" resistor is exactly 5.00 ohms, the tap should be set to read 3.54 ohms $(0.707 \times 5.00 = 3.54)$ to ground.

The resistor R_2 may not have a value of exactly 5.6K, as shown in Fig. 21-28. It should be considered as an adjustment of the voltmeter multiplier for the meter in the N.F. position. By proper selection of R_2, opening S_3 will give a

Fig. 21-30—Power supply for the noise generators is housed in a 7-inch wide sloping-panel cabinet (Bud AC-1613). Switches, from left to right, are (referring to Fig. 21-25) S_3, S_1 and S_2.

meter reading of 1/5 the reading when S_3 is closed. Check this for several points on the meter, obtaining various values of current by changing the setting of R_3.

To measure the noise figure of a receiver, connect the applicable noise-diode unit to the input of the receiver to be checked. Connect the output of the receiver to the SPKR terminals. With S_1 in the OFF position, and S_2 in the OUT position, run the gain controls of the receiver up to get a suitable reading on the meter. A "suitable" reading is one that is somewhat less than the maximum that can be obtained; it is very important that the receiver be operated at all times well below any overload or limiting point. Note the reading of the meter and throw S_1 to ON. Slowly decrease the value at R_3 and watch the meter. When the meter reading matches the previous reading (when S_1 was at OFF), flip S_2 to read the diode current. It is good practice to do this the first time with S_3 at 50×, to avoid possible injury to the meter. When the process has been repeated several times, and a reasonably "firm" figure for the diode current has been obtained, the noise figure can be found from

$$\text{Noise figure} = 20IR$$

where I = diode current in amperes
         R = generator resistance in ohms

Thus if the diode current is 5 ma. and the resistance is 50 ohms, the noise figure is 5.0 (20 × 0.005 × 50 = 5.0). The noise figure is often expressed in db. above a perfect receiver; in the example it would be 7 db. (10 log 5 = 10 × 0.7 =7).

It should be appreciated that the current through the 100-ohm resistor must be measured with a reasonable degree of accuracy, and the accuracy of this circuit should be confirmed by comparison with another meter or by the use of low-tolerance components.

R.F. MEASUREMENTS

R.F. CURRENT

R.f. current-measuring devices use a **thermocouple** in conjunction with an ordinary d.c. instrument. The thermocouple is made of two dissimilar metals which, when heated, generate a small d.c. voltage. The thermocouple is

heated by a resistance wire through which the r.f. current flows, and since the d.c. voltage developed is proportional to the heating, which in turn is proportional to the power used by the heating element, the deflections of the d.c. instrument are proportional to power rather than to current. This causes the calibrated scale to be compressed at the low-current end and spread out at the high-current end. The useful range of such an instrument is about 3 or 4 to 1; that is, an r.f. ammeter having a full-scale reading of 1 ampere can be read with satisfactory accuracy down to about 0.3 ampere, one having a full scale of 5 amperes can be read down to about 1.5 amperes, and so on. No single instrument can be made to handle a wide range of currents. Neither can the r.f. ammeter be shunted satisfactorily, as can be done with d.c. instruments, because even a very small amount of reactance in the shunt will cause the readings to be highly dependent on frequency.

Fig. 21-31 shows a convenient way of using

Fig. 21-31—R.f. ammeter mounted in a Minibox, with u.h.f. style connectors for placing meter in series with a coaxial line. The meter can be used for r.f. power measurements ($P = I^2 R$) when connected between a transmitter and a nonreactive load of known resistance.

an r.f. ammeter for measuring current in a coaxial line. The instrument is simply mounted in a metal box with a short lead from each terminal to a coaxial fitting. The shunt capacitance of an ammeter mounted in this way has only a negligible effect on accuracy at frequencies as high as 30 Mc. if the instrument has a bakelite case. Metal-cased meters should be mounted on a bakelite panel which in turn can be mounted behind a cut-out that clears the meter case by $\frac{1}{4}$ inch or so.

R.F. VOLTAGE

An r.f. voltmeter is a rectifier-type instrument in which the r.f. is converted to d.c., which is then measured with a d.c. instrument. The best type of rectifier for most applications is a crystal diode, such as the 1N34 and similar types, because its capacitance is so low as to have little effect on the behavior of the r.f. circuit to which it is connected. The principal limitation of these rectifiers is their rather low value of safe inverse peak voltage. Vacuum-tube diodes are considerably better in this respect, but their size, shunt capacitance, and the fact that power is required for heating the cathode constitute serious disadvantages in many applications.

One of the principal uses for such voltmeters is as null indicators in r.f. bridges, as described later in this chapter. Another useful application is in measurement of the voltage between the conductors of a coaxial line, to show when a transmitter is adjusted for optimum output. In either case the voltmeter

impedance should be high compared with that of the circuit under measurement, to avoid taking appreciable power, and the relationship between r.f. voltage and the reading of the d.c. instrument should be as linear as possible —that is, the d.c. indication should be directly proportional to the r.f. voltage at all points of the scale.

All rectifiers show a variation in resistance with applied voltage, the resistance being highest when the applied voltage is small. These variations can be fairly well "swamped out" by using a high value of resistance in the d.c. circuit of the rectifier. A resistance of at least 10,000 ohms is necessary for reasonably good linearity with a 0–1 milliammeter. High resistance in the d.c. circuit also raises the impedance of the r.f. voltmeter and reduces its power consumption.

The basic voltmeter circuit is shown in Fig. 21-32. It is simply a half-wave rectifier with a meter and a resistor, R_1, for improving the linearity. The time constant of $C_1 R_1$ should be large compared with the period of the lowest radio frequency to be measured — a condition that can easily be met if R_1 is at least 10,000 ohms and C_1 is 0.001 μf. or more — so C_1 will stay charged near the peak value of the r.f. voltage. The radio-frequency choke may be omitted if there is a low-resistance d.c. path through the circuit being measured. C_2 provides additional r.f. filtering for the d.c. circuit.

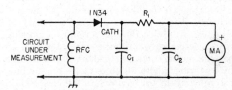

Fig. 21-32—R.f. voltmeter circuit using a crystal rectifier and d.c. microammeter or 0-1 milliammeter.

The simple circuit of Fig. 21-32 is useful for voltages up to about 20 volts, a limitation imposed by the inverse-peak voltage ratings of crystal diodes. A dual range voltmeter circuit, 0-20 and 0-100 volts, is shown in Fig. 21-33.

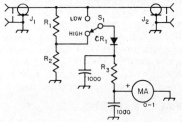

Fig. 21-33—Dual-range r.f. voltmeter circuit. Capacitances are in $\mu\mu$f.; capacitors are disk ceramic.

CR₁—1N34 or equivalent.
J₁, J₂—Coaxial connectors, chassis-mounting type.
R₁—3300 ohms, 2 watts.
R₂—1000 ohms, 1 watt.
R₃—App. 22,000 ohms (see text), $\frac{1}{2}$ watt.
S₁—S.p.d.t. rotary switch (Centralab 1460).

Fig. 21-34—Dual-range r.f. voltmeter for use in coaxial line, using a 0-1 d.c. milliammeter. The voltage-divider resistors, R_1 and R_2 (Fig. 21-30) are at the center in the lower compartment. The bypass capacitors and R_3 are mounted on a tie-point strip at the right. The unit is built in a 4 × 6 × 2 inch aluminum chassis, with an aluminum partition connecting the two sides of the box to form a shielded space. A bottom plate, not shown, is used to complete the shielding.

A voltage divider, R_1R_2, is used for the higher range. An instrument using this circuit is shown in Fig. 21-34. It is designed for connection into a coaxial line. The principal constructional precautions are to keep leads short, and to mount the components in such a way as to minimize stray coupling between them and to keep them fairly well separated from metal surfaces.

For accurate calibration (the power method described below may be used) R_3 should be adjusted, by selection of resistors or using two in series to obtain the desired value, so that the meter reads full scale, with S_1 set for the low range, with 20 volts r.m.s. on the line. A frequency in the vicinity of 14 Mc. should be used. Then, with S_1 set for the high range, various resistors should be tried at R_1 or R_2 until with the same voltage the meter reads 20 per cent of full scale. The resistance variations usually will be within the range of 10 per cent tolerance resistors of the values specified. The readings at various other voltages should be observed in order to check the linearity of the scale.

Calibration

Calibration is not necessary for purely comparative measurements. A calibration in actual voltage requires a known resistive load and an r.f. ammeter. The setup is the same as for r.f. power measurement as described later.

V.T.V.M. R.F. PROBE

R.f. up to about 30 volts peak and a frequency of 200 Mc. is most conveniently measured with a v.t.v.m. (Fig. 21-8) and an r.f. probe. An r.f. probe is merely a rectifier that is used in conjunction with a v.t.v.m. to read r.f. voltages.

The unit shown in Figs. 21-35 and 21-37 and schematically in Fig. 21-33 is similar in circuitry to most of the conventional peak-indicating, shunt-type commercial r.f. probes. However, it can be constructed for considerably less than the cost of a commercial unit. If all parts, including the shielded wire, alligator clip, tie point, resistor, phone plug, tube socket, tube shield, capacitor, and diode are purchased new, the total cost of the unit is approximately $2.25.

Fig. 21-35—The r.f. probe is used in conjunction with a vacuum-tube voltmeter. The case of the probe is constructed from a 7-pin ceramic tube socket and a 2¼-inch tube shield. A half-inch grommet at the top of the tube shield prevents the output lead of the probe from chafing. The flexible copper-braid grounding lead and alligator clip provide a low-inductance return path from the test circuit. The d.c. output of the probe goes to the phone plug, which plugs into the d.c. input jack of the v.t.v.m.

The isolation capacitor, crystal diode, and resistor are mounted on a bakelite 5-lug terminal strip, as shown in Fig. 21-38. One end lug should be rotated 90 degrees so that it extends off the end of the strip. All other lugs should be cut off flush with the edge of the strip. Where the inner conductor connects to the terminal lug, unravel the shield three-quarters of an inch, slip a piece of spaghetti over it, and then solder the braid to the ground lug on the terminal strip. Remove the spring from the tube shield, slide it over the cable, and crimp it to the remaining quarter inch of shield braid. Solder both the spring and a 12-inch length of flexible copper braid to the shield.

Next, cut off the pins on a seven-pin miniature ceramic or mica shield-base tube socket. Use a socket with a cylindrical center post, such as the Johnson 120-277. Crimp the terminal lug previously bent out at the end of

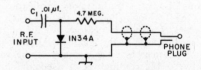

Fig. 21-36—The r.f. probe circuit.

Fig. 21-37—Close-up of the inside of the probe. The 1N34A crystal diode rectifier, calibrating resistor, and input capacitor are mounted tight to the terminal strip with shortest leads possible. Spaghetti tubing is placed on the diode leads to prevent accidental short circuits. The tube-shield spring and flexible-copper grounding lead are soldered to the cable braid (the cable is RG-58/U coax). The tip can be either a phone tip or a short pointed piece of heavy wire.

the strip and insert it into the center post of the tube socket from the top. Insert the end of a phone tip or a pointed piece of heavy wire into the bottom of the tube socket center post, and solder the lug and tip to the center post. Insert a half-inch grommet at the top of the tube shield, and slide the shield over the cable and flexible braid down onto the tube socket. The spring should make good contact with the tube shield to insure that the tube shield (probe case) is grounded. Solder an alligator clip to the other end of the flexible braid and mount a phone plug on the free end of the shielded wire.

Mount components close to the terminal strip, to keep lead lengths as short as possible and minimize stray capacitance. Use spaghetti over all wires to prevent accidental shorts. When soldering the crystal diode, hold the end to be soldered with a pair of long-nose pliers, to conduct damaging heat away from the diode.

The a.c. input voltage that the probe can handle safely is limited to about 21 volts r.m.s. or 30 volts peak, as a result of the 60-volt peak-inverse rating of the 1N34A crystal diode. The phone plug on the probe cable plugs into the d.c. input jack of the v.t.v.m., and r.m.s. voltages are read on the vacuum-tube voltmeter's negative d.c. scale. When using the probe be sure that any d.c. voltage on the circuit being checked does not exceed the d.c. voltage rating of C_1.

The accuracy of the probe is approximately ± 10 per cent from 50 kc. to 250 Mc. For

example, if the error of the v.t.v.m. used with the probe is ± 5 per cent, then the over-all error of the measuring system is ± 15 per cent. At low values of input voltage, below a volt or so, the accuracy of the probe is somewhat poorer because of the nonlinearity of the 1N34A crystal diode. At these lower input voltages the output of the probe more closely approaches a square-law relationship than a linear one.

The approximate input impedance of a probe of this type is 6000 ohms shunted by 1.75 µµf. (at 200 Mc.), and the amount of error introduced because of circuit loading by the probe is dependent on the impedance of the source of the a.c. voltage being measured.

The shunt rectifier delivers a d.c. voltage close to the r.f. peak voltage. When the probe is used with an 11-megohm input resistance v.t.v.m., the meter reading is close to 0.71 of the peak r.f. voltage. Thus for a sine waveform, the v.t.v.m. reads r.m.s. directly.

R.F. POWER

Measurement of r.f. power requires a resistive load of known value and either an r.f. ammeter or a calibrated r.f. voltmeter. The power is then either I^2R or E^2/R, where R is the load resistance in ohms.

The simplest method of obtaining a load of known resistance is to use an antenna system with coax-coupled matching circuit of the type described in the chapter on transmission lines. When the circuit is adjusted, by means of an s.w.r. bridge, to bring the s.w.r. down to 1 to 1 the load is resistive and of the value for which the bridge was designed (52 or 75 ohms).

The r.f. ammeter should be inserted in the line in place of the s.w.r. bridge after the matching has been completed, and the transmitter then adjusted — without touching the matching circuit — for maximum current. A 0–1 ammeter is useful for measuring the approximate range 5–50 watts in 52-ohm line, or 7.5–75 watts in 75-ohm line; a 0–3 instrument can be used for 13–450 watts in 52-ohm line and 20–675 watts in 75-ohm line. The accuracy is usually greatest in the upper half of the scale.

An r.f. voltmeter of the type described in the preceding section also can be used for power measurement in a similar setup. It has the advantage that, because its scale is substantially linear, a much wider range of powers can be measured with one instrument.

INDUCTANCE AND CAPACITANCE

The ability to measure inductance and capacitance saves time that might otherwise be spent in cut-and-try. A convenient instrument for this purpose is the grid-dip oscillator, described earlier in this chapter.

For measuring inductance, use is made of a capacitance of known value as shown at A in

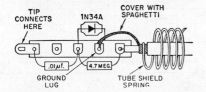

Fig. 21-38—Component mounting details.

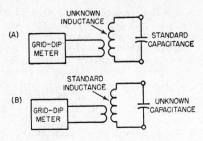

Fig. 21-39—Setups for measuring inductance and capacitance with the grid-dip meter.

Fig. 21-39. With the unknown coil connected to the standard capacitor, couple the grid-dip meter to the coil and adjust the oscillator frequency for the grid-current dip, using the loosest coupling that gives a detectable indication. The inductance is then given by the formula

$$L_{\mu h.} = \frac{25,330}{C_{\mu\mu f.} \cdot f^2_{Mc.}}$$

The reverse procedure is used for measuring capacitance — that is, a coil of known inductance is used as a standard as shown at B. The unknown capacitance is

$$C_{\mu\mu f.} = \frac{25,330}{L^{\mu h.} \cdot f^2_{Mc.}}$$

The accuracy of this method depends on the accuracy of the grid-dip meter calibration and the accuracy with which the standard values of L and C are known. Postage-stamp silver-mica capacitors make satisfactory ca-

pacitance standards, since their rated tolerance is ± 5 per cent. Equally good inductance standards can be made from commercial machine-wound coil material.

A single pair of standards will serve for measuring the L and C values commonly used in amateur equipment. A good choice is 100 $\mu\mu f.$ for the capacitor and 5 $\mu h.$ for the coil. Based on these values the chart of Fig. 21-41 will give the unknown directly in terms of the resonant frequency registered by the grid-dip meter. In measuring the frequency the coupling between the grid-dip meter and resonant circuit should be kept at the

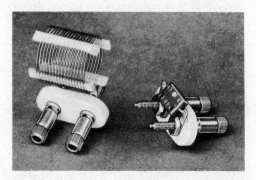

Fig. 21-40—A convenient mounting, using binding-post plates, for L and C standards made from commercially-available parts. The capacitor is a 100-$\mu\mu f.$ silver mica unit, mounted so the lead length is as nearly zero as possible. The inductance standard, 5 $\mu h.$, is 17 turns of No. 3015 B & W Miniductor, 1-inch diameter, 16 turns per inch.

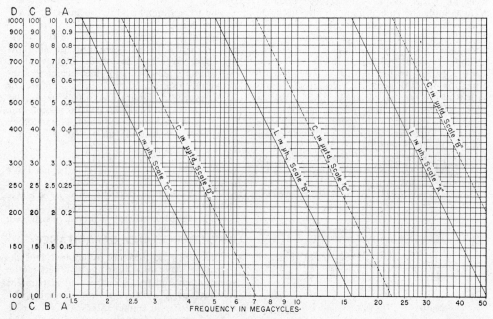

Fig. 21-41—Chart for determining unknown values of L and C in the range of 0.1 to 100 $\mu h.$ and 2 to 1000 $\mu\mu f.$, using standards of 100 $\mu\mu f.$ and 5 $\mu h.$

smallest value that gives a definite indication.

A correction should be applied to measurements of very small values of L and C to include the effects of the shunt capacitance of the mounting for the coil, and for the inductance of the leads to the capacitor. These amount to approximately 1 $\mu\mu$f. and 0.03 μh., respectively, with the method of mounting shown in Fig. 21-40.

Coefficient of Coupling

The same equipment can be used for measurement of the coefficient of coupling between two coils. This simply requires two measurements of inductance (of *one* of the coils) with the coupled coil first open-circuited and then short-circuited. Connect the 100-$\mu\mu$f. standard capacitor to one coil and measure the inductance with the terminals of the second coil open. Then short the terminals of the second coil and again measure the inductance of the first. The coefficient of coupling is given by

$$k = \sqrt{1 - \frac{L_2}{L_1}}$$

where $k =$ coefficient of coupling
$L_1 =$ inductance of first coil with terminals of second coil open
$L_2 =$ inductance of first coil with terminals of second coil shorted.

R.F. RESISTANCE

Aside from the bridge methods used in transmission-line work, described later, there is relatively little need for measurement of r.f. resistance in amateur practice. Also, measurement of resistance by fundamental methods is not practicable with simple equipment. Where such measurements are made, they are usually based on known characteristics of available resistors used as standards.

Most types of resistors have so much inherent reactance and skin effect that they do not act like "pure" resistance at radio frequencies, but instead their effective resistance and impedance vary with frequency. This is especially true of wire-wound resistors. Composition (carbon) resistors of 25 ohms or more as a rule have negligible inductance for frequencies up to 100 Mc. or so. The skin effect also is small, but the shunt capacitance cannot be neglected in the higher values of these resistors, since it reduces their impedance and makes it reactive. However, for most purposes the capacitive effects can be considered to be negligible in composition resistors of values up to 1000 ohms, for frequencies up to 50 to 100 Mc., and the r.f. resistance of such units is practically the same as their d.c. resistance. Hence they can be considered to be practically pure resistance in such applications as r.f. bridges, etc., provided they are mounted in such a way as to avoid magnetic coupling to other circuit components, and are not so close to grounded metal parts as to give an appreciable increase in shunt capacitance.

TESTING UNKNOWN RECTIFIERS

There are many "bargain" rectifiers advertised; many of these are indeed bargains if they live up to their claimed characteristics. Checking them is not too difficult; a few meters and a couple of voltage sources are required.

Two basic checks can be made on any unknown silicon rectifier; a p.i.v. (peak inverse voltage) test and a (forward) current rating test.

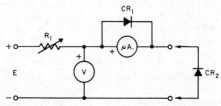

Fig. 21-41—Test circuit for determining p.i.v. rating of unknown rectifiers.
CR₁—400 p.i.v. silicon, to protect meter.
CR₂—Diode under test.
E—Voltage source, low current.
R₁—About 1000 ohms per inverse volt. See text.

Referring to Fig. 21-42, the p.i.v. test requires a source of adjustable high voltage, a high-sensitivity voltmeter and a microammeter. The maximum of the high-voltage source should be about 2½ times the expected p.i.v. Typical values for R_1, the limiting resistor, are 50,000 ohms for a 50 p.i.v. rectifier and 0.5 megohm for a 400 p.i.v. diode.

To test an unknown rectifier, the voltage E is increased slowly while the two meters are monitored. A good silicon diode will show very little reverse current until a value of about 10 μa. is reached; then the reverse current will increase rapidly as the voltage is increased. The diode should be given a p.i.v. rating of about 80 per cent of the voltage at which the current started to increase rapidly.

Example: A diode was tested and found to run 9 μa. reverse current at 500 volts, after which the current increased rapidly as the voltage was increased. The diode was rated at 400 p.i.v. (0.8 × 500 = 400)

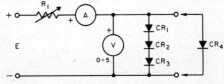

Fig. 21-42—Test circuit for checking semiconductor diode current rating.
A—Ammeter or milliammeter, 2 to 5 times expected current rating.
CR₁-CR₃—400 p.i.v. silicon diode
CR₄—Diode under test.
E—10 to 25 volts
R₁—Sufficient to limit current to maximum expected rating of CR₄.

The current rating of a diode is checked by using the test circuit of Fig. 21-42. It is essentially a measurement of the voltage drop across the rectifier; a v.t.v.m. can be used.

The test consists of setting R_1 for the rated current through the diode, as indicated by A. If the voltage drop across the diode is greater than 3 volts, throw away the diode. If the drop with 0.75 ampere through the diode is 1.4 volts, rate the diode at 400 ma. A diode goods for 3 amperes will show less than 1.5 volts drop at that current; a diode good for 2 amperes will show 2.5 volts or less drop at 2 amperes forward current. If an alleged 3-ampere diode shows 2 volts drop, reduce its rating to 2 amperes.

A Simple Transistor Tester

The transistor test circuit shown in Fig. 21-43 is useful to the experimenter or inveterate purchaser of "bargain" transistors. It can be built on a piece of Vectorboard; the two flashlight cells can be plugged into a battery holder. The contacts marked C, B and E can be a transistor socket or three leads terminated in miniature clips, or both.

Fig. 21-44—This simple transistor checker is assembled on a piece of perforated circuit board. Transistor under test is plugged into the socket under the meter. Short flexible leads with alligator clips can be wires in parallel with the base, emitter, and collector pins of the socket, permitting tests of large transistors which cannot be plugged in.

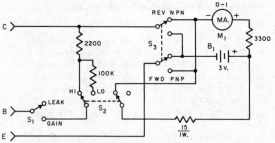

Fig. 21-43—Circuit diagrams of the transistor tester. Resistors are ½ watt.
B_1—Two C cells connected in series
M_1—O-1 milliameter (Lafayette 99 C 5052)
S_1, S_2, S_3—D.p.d.t. miniature slide switch

After connecting the transistor to be tested and with S_1 at LEAK, S_3 should be tried in both positions if the transistor type is unknown. In the correct position, only a small reading should appear on the meter. This is the collector-emitter leakage current.

With S_1 closed to GAIN, a current of $30\mu a$. (LO) or slightly more than 1 ma. (HI) is fed to the base. In the LO position the meter maximum is less than 1 ma.; in the HI position the maximum is about 200 ma.

ANTENNA AND TRANSMISSION-LINE MEASUREMENTS

Two principal types of measurements are made on antenna systems: (1) the standing-wave ratio on the transmission line, as a means for determining whether or not the antenna is properly matched to the line (alternatively, the input resistance of the line or antenna may be measured); (2) the comparative radiation field strength in the vicinity of the antenna, as a means for checking the directivity of a beam antenna and as an aid in adjustment of element tuning and phasing. Both types of measurements can be made with rather simple equipment.

FIELD-STRENGTH MEASUREMENTS

The radiation intensity from an antenna is measured with a device that is essentially a very simple receiver equipped with an indicator to give a visual representation of the comparative signal strength. Such a **field-strength meter** is used with a "pick-up antenna" which should always have the same polarization as the antenna being checked — e.g., the pick-up antenna should be horizontal if the transmitting antenna is. Care should be taken to prevent stray pickup by the field-strength meter or by any transmission line that may connect it to the pickup antenna.

Field-strength measurements preferably should be made at a distance of several wave-lengths from the transmitting antenna being tested. Measurements made within a wave-length of the antenna may be misleading, because of the possibility that the measuring equipment may be responding to the combined induction and radiation fields of the antenna, rather than to the radiation field alone. Also, if the pick-up antenna has dimensions comparable with those of the antenna under test it is likely that the coupling between the two antennas will be great enough to cause the pick-up antenna to tend to become part of the radiating system and thus result in misleading field-strength readings.

A desirable form of pick-up antenna is a dipole installed at the same height as the antenna being tested, with low-impedance line such as 75-ohm Twin-Lead connected at the center to transfer the r.f. signal to the field-strength meter. The length of the dipole need only be great enough to give adequate meter readings. A half-wave dipole will give high sensitivity, but such length will not be needed unless the distance is several wavelengths and a relatively insensitive meter is used.

Field-Strength Meters

The crystal-detector wavemeter described earlier in this chapter may be used as a field-strength meter. It may be coupled to the transmission line from the pick-up antenna through the coaxial-cable jack, J_1.

The indications with a crystal wavemeter connected as shown in Fig. 21-10 will tend to be "square law" — that is, the meter reading will be proportional to the square of the r.f.

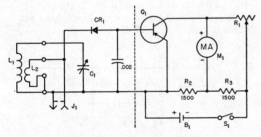

Fig. 21-45—Transistor d.c. amplifier applied to the wavemeter of Fig. 21-10 to increase sensitivity. Components not listed below are the same as in Fig. 21-10.

B_1—Small flashlight cell.

M_1—0-1 d.c. milliammeter (see text).

Q_1—2N705, 2N1638, etc.

R_1—10,000-ohm control.

voltage. This exaggerates the effect of relatively small adjustments to the antenna system and gives a false impression of the improvement secured. The meter reading can be made more linear by connecting a fairly large resistance in series with the milliammeter (or microammeter). About 10,000 ohms is required for good linearity. This considerably reduces the sensitivity of the meter, but the lower sensitivity can be compensated for by making the pick-up antenna sufficiently large.

Transistorized Wavemeter and Field-Strength Meter

A sensitive field-strength meter can be made by using a transistor as a d.c. amplifier following the crystal rectifier of a wavemeter. A circuit of this type is shown in Fig. 21-42. Depending on the characteristics of the particular transistor used, the amplification of current may be 10 or more times, so that a 0–1 milliampere d.c. instrument becomes the equivalent of a sensitive microammeter.

The circuit to the left of the dashed line in Fig. 21-42 is the same as the wavemeter circuit of Fig. 21-10, and the transistor amplifier can easily be accommodated in the case housing the wavemeter.

The transistor is connected in the common-emitter circuit with the rectified d.c. from the crystal diode flowing in the base-emitter circuit. Since there is a small residual current in the collector circuit with no current flowing in the base-emitter circuit, the d.c. meter is connected in a bridge arrangement so the residual current can be balanced out. This is accomplished, in the absence of any signal input to the transistor base, by adjusting R_1 so that the voltage drop across it is equal to the voltage drop from collector to emitter in the transistor. R_2 and R_3, being of the same resistance, have equal voltage drops across them and so there is no difference of potential across the meter terminals until the collector current increases because of current flow in the base-emitter circuit.

The collector current in a circuit of this type is not strictly proportional to the base current, particularly for low values of base current. The meter readings are not directly proportional to the field strength, therefore, but tend toward "square law" response just as in the case of a simple diode with little or no resistance in its d.c. circuit. For this reason the d.c. meter, M_1, should not have too-high sensitivity if reasonably linear response is desired. A 0-1 milliammeter will be satisfactory.

IMPEDANCE AND STANDING-WAVE RATIO

Adjustment of antenna matching systems requires some means either of measuring the input impedance of the antenna or transmission line, or measuring the standing-wave ratio. "Bridge" methods are suitable for either measurement.

There are many varieties of bridge circuits, the two shown in Fig. 21-49 being among the most popular for amateur purposes. The simple resistance bridge of Fig. 21-46A consists essentially of two voltage dividers in parallel across a source of voltage. When the voltage drop across R_1 equals that across R_S the drops across R_2 and R_L are likewise equal and there is no difference of potential between points A and B. Hence the voltmeter reading

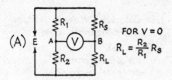

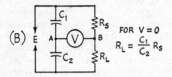

Fig. 21-46—Basic bridge circuits. (A) Resistance bridge; (B) resistance-capacitance bridge. The latter circuit is used in the "Micromatch," with R_s a very low resistance (1 ohm or less) and the ratio C_1/C_2 adjusted accordingly for a desired line impedance.

is zero and the bridge is said to be "balanced." If the drops across R_1 and R_s are not equal, points A and B are at different potentials and the voltmeter will read the difference. The operation of the circuit of Fig. 21-46B is similar, except that one of the voltage dividers is capacitive instead of resistive.

Because of the characteristics of practical components at radio frequencies, the circuit of Fig. 21-46A is best suited to applications where the ratio R_1/R_2 is fixed; this type of bridge is particularly well suited to measurement of standing-wave ratio. The circuit of Fig. 21-46B is well adapted to applications where a variable voltage divider is essential (since C_1 and C_2 may readily be made variable) as in measurement of unknown values of R_L.

S.W.R. Bridge

In the circuit of Fig. 21-46A, if R_1 and R_2 are made equal, the bridge will be balanced when $R_L = R_s$. This is true whether R_L is an actual resistor or the input resistance of a perfectly matched transmission line, provided R_s is chosen to equal the characteristic impedance of the line. Even if the line is not properly matched, the bridge will still be balanced for power traveling *outward* on the line, since outward-going power sees only the Z_0 of the line until it reaches the load. However, power reflected back from the load does not "see" a bridge circuit and the reflected voltage registers on the voltmeter. From the known relationship between the outgoing or "forward" voltage and the reflected voltage, the s.w.r. is easily calculated:

$$\text{S.W.R.} = \frac{V_o + V}{V_o - V}$$

where V_o is the forward voltage and V_r is the reflected voltage. The forward voltage is equal to $E/2$ since R_s and R_L (the Z_0 of the line) are equal. It may be measured either by disconnecting R_L or shorting it.

Measuring Voltages

For the s.w.r. formula above to apply with reasonable accuracy (particularly at high standing-wave ratios) the current taken by the voltmeter must be inappreciable compared with the currents through the bridge "arms." The voltmeter used in bridge circuits employs a crystal diode rectifier (see discussion earlier in this chapter) and in order to meet the above requirement — as well as to have linear response, which is equally necessary for calibration purposes — should use a resistance of at least 10,000 ohms in series with the milliammeter or microammeter.

Since the voltage applied to the line is measured by shorting or disconnecting R_L (that is, the line input terminals), while the reflected voltage is measured with R_L connected, the load on the source of voltage E is different in the two measurements. If the regulation of the voltage source is not perfect, the voltage E will not remain the same under these two conditions. This can lead to large errors. Such errors can be avoided by using a second voltmeter to maintain a check on the voltage applied to the bridge, readjusting the coupling to the voltage source to maintain constant applied voltage during the two measurements. Since the "input" voltmeter is simply used as a reference, its linearity is not important, nor does its reading have to bear any definite relationship to that of the "bridge" voltmeter, except that its range has to be at least twice that of the latter.

A practical circuit incorporating these features is given in Fig. 21-47.

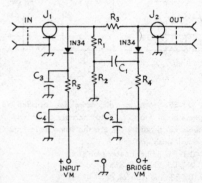

Fig. 21-47—Bridge circuit for s.w.r. measurements. This circuit is intended for use with a d.c. voltmeter, range 5 to 10 volts, having a resistance of 10,000 ohms per volt or greater.

C_1, C_2, C_3, C_4—0.005- or 0.01-μf. disk ceramic.

R_1, R_2—47-ohm composition, $\frac{1}{2}$ or 1 watt.

R_3—52- or 75-ohm (depending on line impedance) composition, $\frac{1}{2}$ or 1 watt; precision type preferred.

R_4, R_5—10,000 ohms, $\frac{1}{2}$ watt.

J_1, J_2—Coaxial connectors.

Meter connects to either "input" or "bridge" position as required.

AN S.W.R. BRIDGE FOR LOW-POWER TRANSMITTERS

One problem in using very low-powered transmitters is the difficulty in making antenna adjustments or checking output when tuning up. The regular garden variety of reflectometer, such as the Monimatch, isn't sensitive enough. The Millimatch, described here, provides adequate sensitivity—even for v.h.f. rigs with output levels as low as 10 milliwatts.

Millimatch Circuit

The Millimatch is similar to the Monimatch Mark II[1], except that a transistor current amplifier has been added. Fig. 21-49 is the circuit of the Millimatch.[2] Of all the reflectometers that have been described since the original Monimatch, the Mark II is one of the best designs for accuracy of readings at v.h.f., up to and including the 144-Mc. band.

Referring to Fig. 21-49, the J_1 end of the Millimatch is connected to the transmitter and the J_2 end to the antenna. When the transmitter is turned on, r.f. current flowing along the conductor between the fittings induces voltages in L_1 and L_2. The voltage induced in L_1 is proportional to the forward line voltage, and the voltage induced in L_2 is proportional to the reflected line voltage. The L_1 voltage is rectified by CR_1, and the d.c. is applied to the base of Q_1. Q_1 amplifies this d.c., which is then read on M_1. When S_1 is switched to read reflected voltage, the voltage in L_2 is rectified by CR_2 and fed through the amplifier.

The standing-wave ratio on the coaxial line is found by first switching S_1 to read forward voltage and adjusting sensitivity control, R_6, so that M_1 reads exactly full scale; then S_1 is switched to reflected voltage and the meter reading noted. Let's assume the meter is calibrated from 0 to 10 in even divisions. The formula for determining the s.w.r. is quite simple:

$$S.W.R. = \frac{V_o + V_r}{V_o - V_r}$$

where V_o is the forward voltage and V_r is the reflected voltage. For example, suppose that we set R_6 so that M_1 reads full scale, or 10, in the forward position, and when we switch to reflected we have a reading of 3. This would amount to

$$\frac{10 + 3}{10 - 3} = \frac{13}{7} = 1.8 \text{ to } 1.$$

However—and this is a point that some amateurs overlook—many reflectometers are not truly accurate instruments for measuring s.w.r. They are excellent for showing when a matched condition (an s.w.r. of 1 to 1) exists, but under any other condition the voltage readings are not dependable, because of poor linearity of the diode rectifiers used at CR_1 and CR_2. If the diodes were perfectly linear over the entire range of re-

[1] McCoy, "Monimatch Mark II," Feb. 1957, *QST*.
[2] Described in *QST*, Aug., 1967.

Fig. 21-48—This is the completed Millimatch. At the left is the sensitivity control, R_6. S_1 is in the center, and Q_1 at the right.

flected and forward voltages being measured, the formula above would give accurate s.w.r. checks. If sufficient resistance is used in series with the diodes, their output tends to become more linear, but the sensitivity is reduced. We used R4 and R5 to improve the accuracy, and the loss in sensitivity is more than made up for by the amplifier, Q_1. In the Millimatch, another factor that gets into the act to upset the accuracy of s.w.r. readings is the linearity of the transistor used as an amplifier. However, regardless of the accuracy of s.w.r. readings, the bridge is excellent for showing when a match is achieved.

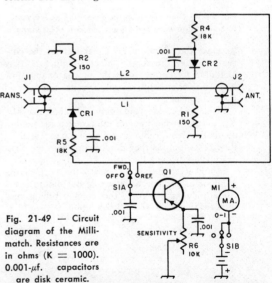

Fig. 21-49 — Circuit diagram of the Millimatch. Resistances are in ohms (K = 1000). 0.001-μf. capacitors are disk ceramic.
CR₁, CR₂—1N34A germanium diode.
J₁, J₂—Coax chassis receptacle, SO-239.
L₁, L₂—See text.
M₁—0–1 milliammeter. A more sensitive type can be used, but is not required.
R₁, R₂—150 ohms, ½ watt carbon or composition for 50-ohm bridge, 100 ohms for 75-ohm unit.
R₄, R₅—18,000 ohms, ½ watt.
R₆—25,000-ohm control, miniature type.
S₁—2-pole, 3 position switch (Mallory 3223J or similar.)

Additionally, by setting S_1 in the forward position, the relative r.f. output of the transmitter can be observed on M_1, this is a valuable tool when tuning up a transmitter.

Construction Information

The Millimatch is enclosed in a $2\frac{1}{4} \times 2\frac{1}{4} \times$ 5-inch Minibox. The transmission-line section consists of an inner conductor (a piece of $\frac{1}{4}$-inch o.d. copper tubing, $4\frac{5}{8}$ inches long) and two pieces of copper flashing for the outer conductor. These two pieces measure 1 inch wide and $4\frac{7}{8}$ inches long, plus a $\frac{1}{4}$-inch lip at each end for mounting under the screws that secure J_1 and J_2. Separation between the copper strips and inner conductor is maintained by two insulated spacers, Fig. 21-50. These spacers also serve

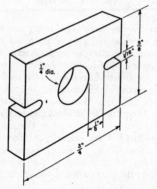

Fig. 21-50—Dimensions of the insulating spacers used to hold bridge wires and outer conductor strips in place.

to space the pickup wires L_1 and L_2 at the correct distance from the inner conductor. Any available insulating material of reasonably low loss, such as bakelite or polystyrene, can be used for the spacers.

Mounted on the front of the Minibox are M_1, S_1, and R_6. Almost any of miniature panel meters available from radio distributors can be used for M_1 as long as they don't protrude more than $1\frac{1}{4}$ inches behind the panel.

Mount J_1 and J_2 as close to the rear of the Minibox as possible, as shown in the photographs. Slide the spacers over the copper tubing and then tin the inside ends of the tubing with solder.

Also tin the inner-conductor terminals of J_1 and J_2. Slide the ends of the tubing over the conductor terminals and solder. You can then mount the copper strips in place.

The pickup wires, L_1 and L_2, are $3\frac{3}{8}$-inch lengths of No. 14 tinned wire. The wires are centered in the spacers as shown in the photograph and cemented in place with Duco cement. R_1 and R_2 are $\frac{1}{2}$-watt resistors and must be carbon or composition, *not wire-wound*. For a 50-ohm bridge use 150-ohm resistors and for a 75-ohm unit, use 100-ohm resistors. The ends of the resistors that are soldered to L_1 and L_2 are $\frac{1}{8}$ inch long. Tin the ends of the pickup wires and the ends of the resistors with solder and solder the resistors in place. Don't overheat the resistor as too much heat can change the value. The remaining ends of the resistors are soldered to lugs mounted under screws that hold J_1 and J_2, keeping the leads as short as possible.

When connecting CR_1 and CR_2 to the pickup wires, use a heat sink on the lead between the body of the diode and the lead being soldered. Too much heat can easily ruin the diode.

Although a transistor socket was used for mounting Q_1, it could be mounted by its own leads if desired. The battery was installed by soldering wires to both ends, no holder being used.

Almost any p-n-p type transistor will work for Q_1. Several were tried—2N114, 2N117, 2N705, and 4JD1A67—and they all had more than adequate gain.

Testing and Using The Millimatch

Connect the Millimatch to your transmitter, using 50- or 75-ohm coax as required. Leave the antenna end of the bridge unconnected. Turn on the rig, switch S1 to forward and set the sensitivity for about half-scale reading. Next, switch to reflected. The readings for forward and reflected should be about the same. Next, if you want to check the accuracy of the bridge, connect a 1-watt carbon resistor of the appropriate value, 50 or 75 ohms, between the inner hole and outer shell of J_2. Switch S_1 to forward and adjust the sensitivity to full scale. Then switch to reflected and the reading should drop to zero.

You may find that when you first turn on the Millimatch, you will get a slight reading on the meter without the transmitter being on. This is the "no-signal current" in the transistor. Whatever the no-signal current reading is, and it will be very small, assume this value as "zero" when the transmitter is turned on and worked into a matched load.

You can check the accuracy of the s.w.r. readings with the formula previously mentioned by using dummy—load resistances of various values. For example, a 150-ohm resistor will represent a 3-to-1 s.w.r. with a 50-ohm bridge.

Fig. 21-51—This photo shows the inside of the Millimatch. Pickup line L_1 is mounted in the grooves on the insulated spacers. CR_1 is at the left. At the right, just in front of the sensitivity control, is Q_1 in its socket.

A VARIMATCHER S.W.R. INDICATOR

The s.w.r. bridge of Fig. 21-52 is easy to build and has excellent sensitivity, even at 1.8 Mc.[1] It is for low-power use from 1.8 to 30 Mc. and can handle the power from a 300-watt (or less) 1-kw. transmitter. It is designed to be used with 50- or 75-ohm lines and can be set up for either impedance by a simple adjustment procedure, described later. Although precise measurements of s.w.r. cannot be made with this style of bridge, it is satisfactory for amateur radio use.

How It Works

R. f. from the transmitter is applied to the bridge at J_1, Fig. 21-53. The current flows along L_1 and out through J_2 to the load. The pickup line, L_2, is centered in L_1. Because L_2 is inside L_1, and because the line current does not flow on the inner wall of L_1, coupling between the two takes place only at the ends. This arrangement offers two benefits: The reflected- and forward-power portions of the pickup line, L_2, are divorced from one another physically, resulting in better isolation between the two halves of the pickup element. This contributes to better balance in the bridge. Also, with this construction it has been found that it is unnecessary to tinker with the value of terminating resistance, regardless of the element length or shape. The termination is approximately 51 ohms for 50-ohm lines and 33 ohms for 75-ohm lines.

The bridge has an outer conductor (Fig. 21-53), L_3, for the coaxial element (outer channel and L_1) which is necessary to prevent stray coupling between the forward- and reflected-power ends of L_2.

Some of the forward power is sampled by section A of L_2 and rectified by CR_1. Similarly, the reflected power is sampled by section B of L_2 and is rectified by CR_2. The meter switch, S_1, routes the direct current from CR_1 and CR_2 to the sensitivity control, R_2, and then to the 1-ma. meter. The meter is adjusted for full-scale deflection with S_1 in the FORWARD position by varying the resistance of R_2, and if the line is matched to the load, there will be no reading when the meter is switched to read reflected power. The higher the standing-wave ratio, the greater will be the meter deflection in the REFLECTED position.

Building the Bridge

Ordinary hand tools can be used for building the Varimatcher. The cabinet is home made and is $9\frac{1}{2}$ inches long, 3 inches high, and 3 inches deep.[2] The bridge channel, L_3, can be formed in a bench vise. The $\frac{1}{4}$-inch diameter copper tube, L_1, can be cut to length with a hacksaw or tubing cutter. The hole in the center of L_1 is made with the narrow side of a flat file. The important consideration when forming the parts of the bridge is to maintain symmetry. The

Fig. 21-52—Front view of the Varimatcher s.w.r. bridge. The unit is housed in a home-made cabinet. The sensitivity control is at the right. The forward-reflected power switch is at the center of the front panel. The bridge null control and the two coax fittings are on the rear wall of the box.

walls of L_3 should be $\frac{7}{8}$ inch apart across the entire length of the channel. The center hole in L_1 should be equidistant from the ends of the line. Pickup line L_2 is made from the inner conductor and polyethylene insulation of a piece of RG-59/U coax cable. The ends of L_2 should protrude equally from L_1 (Fig. 4). The connection to R_1 is made by a short length of bus wire (the shorter the better) from the center of L_2 to the center lug on R_1.

The tap on L_2 should be made before the pickup line is inserted into L_1. This can easily be done by cutting away approximately $\frac{1}{8}$ inch of the poly insulation at the dead center of L_2 and soldering a 2-inch length of No. 20 bus wire to the element. The bus wire should be folded back against the pickup line and pulled through L_1 until it is visible at the center hole of the copper tubing. It is a simple matter to pull it out through the hole for connection to R_1 after which a few drops of epoxy cement should be placed in the hole. This will insulate the center-tap wire and will anchor L_2 inside L_1, assuring long-term symmetry. (Do not insert L_2 into L_1 until after L_1 is soldered to J_1 and J_2).

The coax fittings, J_1 and J_2, are mounted on one wall of L_3, Fig. 21-55, and R_1 is at the center of the same wall. L_1 is centered in L_3 and soldered to J_1 and J_2. Fixed resistors can be used in place of control R_1 if only one transmission line impedance is to be used. The resistors should be $\frac{1}{2}$-watt composition units, preferably with 5-percent tolerance. Normally, the lead length between the fixed resistors and the center of L_2 should be kept as short as possible. The $\frac{1}{2}$-watt resistors showed no evidence of capacitive or inductive reactance that would cause bad effects in the 1.8- to 30-Mc. range.

The bridge shown in Fig. 21-52 uses an Allen-Bradley 100-ohm linear-taper control for R_1. Of the many brands tried, the Allen-Bradley (Ohmite) potentiometer was the least reactive. In practice, it compares favorably to the $\frac{1}{2}$-watt fixed resistors used. The bridge was nulled at 30 Mc. and held calibration over the entire range from 1.8 to 30 Mc.

[1] DeMaw, The Varimatcher, *QST*, May 1966.
[2] The Easy Box, *QST*, Sept. 1966, p. 17.

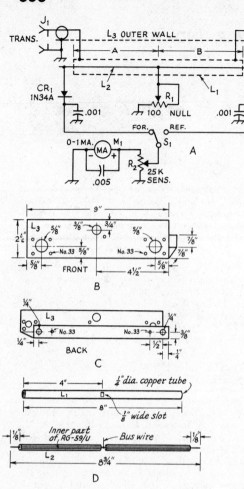

Fig. 21-53—Schematic diagram of the Varimatcher. Capacitors are 1000-volt disk ceramic and values are in pf. Layout dimensions for the bridge. At B, the outer channel (L_3). At C, the back side of L_3. Shown at D, the copper tubing dimensions (L_1) and the inner line L_2. L_2 fits into L_1 after the buss wire is soldered to the center of L_2.

CR$_1$, CR$_2$—Matched germanium diodes. 1N34A or equal.

J$_1$, J$_2$—SO-239 coax fitting.

L$_1$, L$_2$, L$_3$—See Fig. 4.

M$_1$—1-ma. meter.

R$_1$—100-ohm, linear-taper carbon control (Ohmite CLU-10011). See text for fixed resistor values.

R$_2$—25,000-ohm linear-taper control.

S$_1$—S.p.d.t. toggle or slide switch.

Fig. 21-54—Rear view of the Varimatcher. The screwdriver adjust control at the center of the panel is R_1, the bridge-null potentiometer. A two-tone paint job gives the cabinet a professional look. Light and dark gray spray-can paints were used.

Fig. 21-55—Bridge element of the Varimatcher. Style of construction permits mounting the bridge in transmitter cabinets, transmatch housings, or individual cabinets. The diode pigtails are routed through the holes in the outer channel and are soldered to the terminal lugs. The 0.001-pf. capacitors are also soldered to the terminal strips at the ends of the channel.

When soldering CR_1 and CR_2 into the circuit, be sure to grasp the pigtails of the diodes with a pair of long-nose pliers so as to conduct heat away from the bodies of the diodes. This will prevent damage to them. The wiring from the cathode ends of CR_1 and CR_2 is not critical and can be routed along the sides of the cabinet.

Adjusting the Varimatcher

The bridge should be checked out on the 10-meter band. A Heath Cantenna or equivalent 50-ohm dummy load can be connected to J_2. The more accurate the termination at J_2, the more accurate the bridge will be.

With a few watts of power applied at J_1, adjust R_2 for full-scale deflection of the meter while S_1 is in the FORWARD position. Then set S_1 to the REFLECTED position and adjust R_1 for a null in the meter reading. This should be zero deflection when the circuit is working properly. If the bridge is to be set up for use with 75-ohm loads, the procedure is the same but a 75-ohm dummy must be used. If fixed resistors are used

in place of the control at R_1, no tinkering should be required to secure a perfect null.

After nulling the bridge, check again and make sure that full-scale meter deflection occurs in the *forward* position of S_1. Next, reverse the cables at J_1 and J_2, set S_1 to the REFLECTED position, and see if a full-scale meter reading results. If CR_1 and CR_2 are reasonably well matched, the meter readings will match up. If you do not wish to purchase a set of matched diodes, and have a supply of IN34s on hand, you can select a pair that will work well in the circuit by measuring the front and back resistance of a few of them and picking a pair that are about the same value.

Using the Bridge

The Varimatcher will handle up to 300 watts without harming the diodes. With R_2 wired into the circuit as shown in Fig. 21-53, the resistance in series with CR_1 and CR_2, must be *decreased* to maintain a full-scale meter reading as the transmitter power is increased.

IMPEDANCE BRIDGE

The bridge shown in Figs. 21-48 to 21-50, inclusive, uses the basic circuit of Fig. 21-40B and incorporates a "differential" capacitor to obtain an adjustable ratio. When a resistive load of unknown value is connected in place of R_L, the C_1/C_2 ratio may be varied to attain a balance, as indicated by a null reading. The capacitor settings can be calibrated in terms of resistance at R_L, so the unknown value can be read off the calibration.

The differential capacitor consists of two identical capacitors on the same shaft, arranged so that when the shaft is rotated to increase the capacitance of one unit, the capacitance of the other decreases. The practical circuit of the bridge is given in Fig. 21-49. Satisfactory operation hinges on observing the same constructional precautions as in the case of the s.w.r. bridge. Although a high-impedance voltmeter is not essential, since the bridge is always adjusted for a null, the use of such a voltmeter is advisable because its better linearity makes the actual null settings more accurately observable.

With the circuit arrangement and capacitor shown, the useful range of the bridge is from about 5 ohms to 400 ohms. The calibration is such that the percentage accuracy of reading is approximately constant at all parts of the scale. The midscale value is in the range 50–75 ohms, to correspond to the Z_0 of coaxial cable. The reliable frequency range of the bridge includes all amateur bands from 3.5 to 54 Mc.

Checking and Calibration

A bridge constructed as shown in the photographs should show a complete null at all frequencies within the range mentioned above when a 50-ohm "dummy" load of the type

described earlier in connection with the s.w.r. bridge is connected to the load terminals. The bridge may be calibrated by using a number of ½-watt 5% tolerance composition resistors of different values in the 5–400 ohm range as loads, in each case balancing the bridge by adjusting C_1 for a null reading on the meter. The leads between the test resistor and J_2 should be as short as possible, and the calibration preferably should be done in the 3.5-Mc. band where stray inductance and capacitance will have the least effect.

Fig. 21-56—An *RC* bridge for measuring unknown values of impedance. The bridge operates at an r.f. input voltage level of about 5 volts. The aluminum box is 3 by 4 by 5 inches.

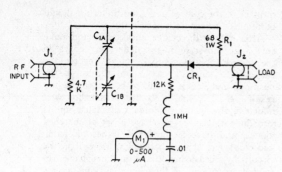

Fig. 21-57—Circuit of the impedance bridge. Resistors are composition, ½ watt except as noted. Fixed capacitors are ceramic.

C_1—Differential capacitor, 11-161 $\mu\mu f.$ per section (Millen 28801).

CR_1—Germanium diode (1N34, 1N48, etc.).

J_1, J_2—Coaxial connectors, chassis type.

M_1—0-500 microammeter.

Using the Bridge

Strictly speaking, a simple bridge can measure only purely resistive impedances. When the load is a pure resistance, the bridge can be balanced to a good null (meter reading

Fig. 21-58—All components except the meter are mounted on one of the removable sides of the box. The variable capacitor is mounted on an L-shaped piece of aluminum (with half-inch lips on the inner edge for bolting to the box side) 2 inches wide, 2¼ inches high and 2¾ inches deep, to shield the capacitor from the other components. The terminals project through holes as shown, with associated components mounted directly on them and the load connector, J_2. Since the rotor of C_1 must not be grounded, the capacitor is operated by an extension shaft and insulated coupling.

The lead from J_1 to C_{1A} should go directly from the input connector to the capacitor terminal (lower right) to which the 68-ohm resistor is attached. The 4700-ohm resistor is soldered across J_1.

zero). If the load has a reactance component the null will not be complete; the higher the ratio of reactance to resistance in the load the poorer the null reading. The operation of the bridge is such that when an exact null cannot be secured, the readings approximate the resistive component of the load for very low values of impedance, and approximate the total impedance at very high values of impedance. In the mid-range the approximation to either is poor, for loads having considerable reactance.

In using the bridge for adjustment of matching networks C_1 is set to the desired value (usually the Z_0 of the coaxial line) and the matching network is then adjusted for the best possible null.

PARALLEL-CONDUCTOR LINES

Bridge measurements made directly on parallel-conductor lines are frequently subject to considerable error because of "antenna" currents flowing on such lines. These currents, which are either induced on the line by the field around the antenna or coupled into the line from the transmitter by stray capacitance, are in the same phase in both line wires and hence do not balance out like the true transmission-line currents. They will nevertheless actuate the bridge voltmeter, causing an indication that has no relationship to the standing-wave ratio.

S.W.R. Measurements

The effect of "antenna" currents on s.w.r. measurements can be largely overcome by using a coaxial bridge and coupling it to the parallel-conductor line through a properly designed impedance-matching circuit. A suitable circuit is given in Fig. 21-51. An antenna coupler can be used for the purpose. In the balanced tank circuit the "antenna" or parallel components on the line tend to balance out and so are not passed on to the s.w.r. bridge. It is essential that L_1 be coupled to a "cold" point on L_2 to minimize capacitive coupling, and also desirable that the center of L_2 be grounded to the chassis on which the circuit is mounted. Values should be such that $L_2 C_2$ can be tuned to the operating frequency and that L_1 provides sufficient coupling, as described in the transmission-line chapter. The measurement procedure is as follows:

Connect a noninductive (½- or 1-watt carbon) resistor, having the same value as the characteristic impedance of the parallel-conductor line, to the "line" terminals. Apply r.f. to the bridge, adjust the taps on L_2 (keeping them equidistant from the center), while varying the capacitance of C_1 and C_2, until the bridge shows a null. After the null is obtained, do not touch any of the circuit adjustments. Next, short-circuit the "line" terminals and adjust the r.f. input until the bridge voltmeter reads full scale. Remove the short-circuit and test resistor, and connect the regu-

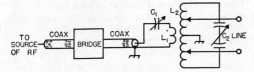

Fig. 21-59—Circuit for using coaxial s.w.r. bridge for measurements on parallel-conductor lines. Values of circuit components are identical with those used for the similar "antenna-coupler" circuit discussed in the chapter on transmission lines.

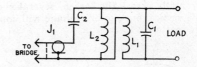

Fig. 21-60—Tuned balun for coupling between balanced and unbalanced lines. L_1 and L_2 should be built as a bifilar winding to get as tight coupling as possible between them. Typical constants are as follows:

Freq., Mc.	L_1, L_2	C_1	C_2
28	3 turns each on 2-inch form, equally spaced over $\frac{7}{16}$ inch, total.	4 $\mu\mu$f.	420 $\mu\mu$f.
14	Same as 28 Mc.	39 $\mu\mu$f.	0.0015 μf.
7	8 turns of 150-ohm Twin-Lead, no spacing between turns, on 2¾-inch dia. form.	None	0.001 μf.
3.5	Same as 7 Mc.	62 $\mu\mu$f.	0.0045 μf.

Capacitors in unit shown in Fig. 21-50 are NPO disk ceramic. Units may be paralleled to obtain proper capacitance.

lar transmission line. The bridge will then indicate the standing-wave ratio on the line.

The circuit requires rematching, with the test resistor, whenever the frequency is changed appreciably. It can, however, be used over a portion of an amateur band without readjustment, with negligible error.

Impedance Measurements

Measurements on parallel-conductor lines and other balanced loads can be made with the impedance bridge previously described by using a balun of the type shown schematically in Fig. 21-52. This is an autotransformer having a 2-to-1 turns ratio and thus provides a 4-to-1 step-down in impedance from a balanced load to the output circuit of the bridge, one side of which is grounded. L_1 and L_2 must be as tightly coupled as possible, and so should be constructed as a bifilar winding. The circuit is resonated to the operating frequency by C_1, and C_2 serves to tune out any residual reactance that may be present because the coupling between the two coils is not quite perfect.

THE OSCILLOSCOPE

The **cathode-ray oscilloscope** gives a visual representation of signals at both audio and radio frequencies and can therefore be used for many types of measurements that are not possible with instruments of the types discussed earlier in this chapter. In amateur work, one of the principal uses of the scope is for displaying an amplitude-modulated signal so a phone transmitter can be adjusted for proper modulation and continuously monitored to keep the modulation precentage within proper limits. For this purpose a very simple circuit will suffice, and a typical circuit is described later in this section.

The versatility of the scope can be greatly increased by adding amplifiers and linear deflection circuits, but the design and adjustment of such circuits tends to be complicated if optimum performance is to be secured, and is somewhat outside the field of this section. Special components are generally required. Oscilloscope kits for home assembly are available from a number of suppliers, and since their cost compares very favorably with that of a home-built instrument of comparable design, they are recommended for serious consideration by those who have need for or are interested in the wide range of measurements that is possible with a fully-equipped scope.

Types of Sweeps

A sawtooth sweep-voltage wave shape, such as is shown in Fig. 21-61, is called a **linear sweep**, because the deflection in the horizontal direction is directly proportional to time. If the sweep were perfect the **fly-back** time, or time taken for the spot to return from the end (H) to the beginning (I or A) of the horizontal trace, would be zero, so that the line HI would be perpendicular to the axis $Y-Y'$. Although the fly-back time cannot be made zero in practicable sweep-voltage generators it can be made quite small in comparison to the time of the desired trace AH, at least at most frequencies within the audio range. The line $H'I'$ is called the **return trace**; with a linear sweep it is less brilliant than the pattern, because the spot is moving much more rapidly during the fly-back time than during the time of the main trace.

The linear sweep shows the shape of the wave in the same way that it is usually represented graphically. If the period of the a.c. voltage applied to the vertical plates is considerably less than the time taken to sweep horizontally across the screen, several cycles of the vertical or "signal" voltage will appear in the pattern.

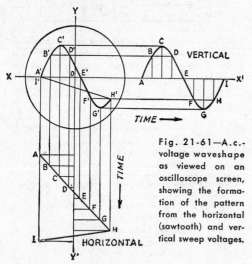

Fig. 21-61—A.c.-voltage waveshape as viewed on an oscilloscope screen, showing the formation of the pattern from the horizontal (sawtooth) and vertical sweep voltages.

For many amateur purposes a satisfactory horizontal sweep is simply a 60-cycle voltage of adjustable amplitude. In modulation monitoring (described in the chapter on amplitude modulation) audio-frequency voltage can be taken from the modulator to supply the horizontal sweep. For examination of audio-frequency wave forms, the linear sweep is essential. Its frequency should be adjustable over the entire range of audio frequencies to be inspected on the oscilloscope.

Lissajous Figures

When sinusoidal a.c. voltages are applied to the two sets of deflecting plates in the

PATTERNS	FREQ. RATIO
◯	1:1
∞	2:1
⧓	3:1
⧖	3:2
⧗	4:3

Fig. 21-62—Lissajous figures and corresponding frequency ratios for a 90-degree phase relationship between the voltages applied to the two sets of deflecting plates.

oscilloscope the resultant pattern depends on the relative amplitudes, frequencies and phase of the two voltages. If the ratio between the

two frequencies is constant and can be expressed in integers a stationary pattern will be produced. This makes it possible to use the oscilloscope for determining an unknown frequency, provided a variable frequency standard is available, or for determining calibration points for a variable-frequency oscillator if a few known frequencies are available for comparison.

The stationary patterns obtained in this way are called **Lissajous figures.** Examples of some of the simpler Lissajous figures are given in Fig. 21-62. The frequency ratio is found by counting the number of loops along two adjacent edges. Thus in the third figure from the top there are three loops along a horizontal edge and only one along the vertical, so the ratio of the vertical frequency to the horizontal frequency is 3 to 1. Similarly, in the fifth figure from the top there are four loops along the horizontal edge and three along the vertical edge, giving a ratio of 4 to 3. Assuming that the known frequency is applied to the horizontal plates, the unknown frequency is

$$f_2 = \frac{n_2}{n_1}\, f_1$$

where $f_1 =$ known frequency applied to horizontal plates,

$f_2 =$ unknown frequency applied to vertical plates,

$n_1 =$ number of loops along a vertical edge, and

$n_2 =$ number of loops along a horizontal edge.

An important application of Lissajous figures is in the calibration of audio-frequency signal generators. For very low frequencies the 60-cycle power-line frequency is held accurately enough to be used as a standard in most localities. The medium audio-frequency range can be covered by comparison with the 440- and 600-cycle modulation on the WWV transmissions. An oscilloscope having both horizontal and vertical amplifiers is desirable, since it is convenient to have a means for adjusting the voltages applied to the deflection plates to secure a suitable pattern size. It is possible to calibrate over a 10-to-1 range, both upwards and downwards, from each of the latter frequencies and thus cover the audio range useful for voice communication.

Basic Oscilloscope Circuit

The essential oscilloscope circuit is shown in Fig. 21-63. The minimum requirements are: supplying the various electrode potentials, plus controls for focusing and centering the spot on the face of the tube and adjusting the spot intensity. The circuit of Fig. 21-63 can be used with electrostatic-deflection tubes from two to five inches in face diameter, with voltages up to 2500. This includes practically all the types popular for small oscilloscopes. The circuit has provision for introducing

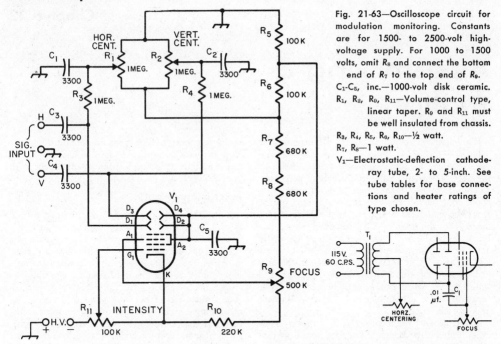

Fig. 21-63—Oscilloscope circuit for modulation monitoring. Constants are for 1500- to 2500-volt high-voltage supply. For 1000 to 1500 volts, omit R_8 and connect the bottom end of R_7 to the top end of R_9.

C_1-C_5, inc.—1000-volt disk ceramic.
R_1, R_2, R_9, R_{11}—Volume-control type, linear taper. R_9 and R_{11} must be well insulated from chassis.
R_3, R_4, R_5, R_6, R_{10}—½ watt.
R_7, R_8—1 watt.
V_1—Electrostatic-deflection cathode-ray tube, 2- to 5-inch. See tube tables for base connections and heater ratings of type chosen.

signal voltages to the two sets of deflecting plates. Either set of deflecting electrodes (D_1D_2, or D_3D_4) may be used for either horizontal or vertical deflection, depending on how the tube is mounted.

In the circuit of Fig. 21-63 the centering controls are not too high above electrical ground, so no special insulating of the controls is required. However, the focusing and intensity controls are at a high voltage above ground and therefore should be carefully insulated. Insulated couplings or extension shafts should be used.

The tube should be protected from stray magnetic fields, either by enclosing it in an iron or steel box or by using one of the special c.r. tube shields available. If the heater transformer (or other transformer) is mounted in the same cabinet, care must be used to place it so the stray field around it does not deflect the spot. The spot cannot be focussed to a fine point when influenced by a transformer field. The heater transformer must be well insulated, and one side of the heater should be connected to the cathode.

Modulation Monitoring

Methods for connecting the oscilloscope to a transmitter for checking or monitoring modulation are given in Chapter Eleven.

When one changes from a.m. to single sideband, he can no longer use the familiar trapezoid oscilloscope pattern for monitoring his transmissions. If the scope includes a sawtooth horizontal sweep oscillator there is no problem, of course, but there is an easy conversion for a scope with no oscillator.

A 60-cycle transformer with a center-tapped winding is required. An old 250- to 350-v.c.t. transformer will do. The exact value can't be

Fig. 21-64—A linear time base for an oscilloscope can be obtained from the "center" portion of a sine wave. Coupling the a.c. to the grid gives "intensity modulation" that blanks the retrace.

C_1—Ceramic capacitor of adequate voltage rating.
T_1—250-to 350-volt center-tapped secondary. If voltage is too high, use dropping resistor in primary side.

specified because the horizontal deflection sensitivity varies with different types of tubes. The voltage should merely be sufficient to deflect the spot well off the screen on either side. You now have a substantially linear sweep but it is as bright on retrace as on left to right. To blank it in one direction, it is only necessary to couple the a.c. to the No. 1 grid of the scope. The circuit is shown in Fig. 21-64.

It will be found that the spot cannot be focused as sharply as before, and you will have to settle for a wider trace. However, it is still quite adequate for monitoring a linear amplifier's output.

Frequency Limitations of Oscilloscopes

Most commercial or kitted oscilloscopes include vacuum-tube amplifiers between the input terminals and the deflection plates, to increase the sensitivity and usefulness of the instrument. Depending upon the construction of the amplifiers, their useful frequency range may be only as high as several hundred kc., although more expensive instruments will include amplifiers that work in the megacycle range. No such frequency limits apply when the connection is made directly to the deflection plates, and consequently r.f. at 20 to 30 Mc. can be applied by the methods described in Chapter Eleven.

Chapter 22

Assembling a Station

The actual location inside the house of the "shack"—the room where the transmitter and receiver are located—depends, of course, on the free space available for amateur activities. Fortunate indeed is the amateur with a separate room that he can reserve for his hobby, or the few who can have a special small building separate from the main house. However, most amateurs must share a room with other domestic activities, and amateur stations will be found tucked away in a corner of the living room, a bedroom, or even in a large closet! A spot in the cellar or the attic can almost be classed as a separate room, although it may lack the "finish" of a normal room.

Regardless of the location of the station, however, it should be designed for maximum operating convenience and safety. It is foolish to have the station arranged so that the throwing of several switches is required to go from "receive" to "transmit," just as it is silly to have the equipment arranged so that the operator is in an uncomfortable and cramped position during his

This modern-day satellite-communications station is used by the Sohio Moonobounce group. This photo, submitted by W8FKC, shows a pen recorder at the left, a tape deck at the right of the pen recorder. This rack-and-panel installation is neat and functional, placing all of the equipment within easy reach of the operator.

operating hours. The reason for building the station as safe as possible is obvious, if you are interested in spending a number of years with your hobby!

CONVENIENCE

The first consideration in any amateur station is the operating position, which includes the operator's table and chair and the pieces of equipment that are in constant use (the receiver, send-receive switch, and key or microphone). The table should be as large as possible, to allow sufficient room for the receiver or receivers, transmitter frequency control, frequency-measuring equipment, monitoring equipment, control switches, and keys and microphones, with enough space left over for the logbook, a pad and pencil, and perhaps a *large* ash tray. Suitable space should be included for radiogram blanks and a call book, if these accessories are in frequent use. If the table is small, or the number of pieces of equipment is large, it is often necessary to build a shelf or rack for the auxiliary equipment, or to mount it in some less convenient location in or under the table. If one has the facilities, a semicircular "console" can be built of wood, or a simpler solution is to use two small wooden cabinets to support a table top of wood or Masonite. A flush-type door will make an excellent table top. Home-built tables or consoles can be finished in any of the available oil stains, varnishes, paints or lacquers. Many operators use a large piece of plate glass over part of their table, since it furnishes a good writing surface and can cover miscellaneous charts and tables, prefix lists, operating aids, calendar, and similar accessories.

If the major interests never require frequent band changing, or frequency changing within a band, the transmitter can be located some distance from the operator, in a location where the meters can be observed from time to time. If frequent band or frequency changes are a part of the usual operating procedure, the transmitter should be mounted close to the operator, either along one side or above the receiver, so that the controls are easily accessible without the need for leaving the operating position.

A compromise arrangement would place the v.f.o. or exciter at the operating position and the transmitter proper in some convenient location not adjacent to the operator. Since it is usually possible to operate over a portion of a band without retuning the transmitter stages, an operating position of this type is an advantage over one in which the operator must leave his position to change frequency.

Controls

The operator has an excellent chance to exercise his ingenuity in the location of the operating controls. The most important controls in the station are the receiver tuning dial and the send-receive switch. The receiver tuning dial should be located four to eight inches above the operating table, and if this requires mounting the receiver off the table, a small shelf or bracket will do the trick. With the single exception of the amateur whose work is almost entirely in traffic or rag-chew nets, which require little or no attention to the receiver, it will be found that the operator's hand is on the receiver tuning dial most of the time. If the tuning knob is too high or too low, the hand gets cramped after an extended period of operating, hence the importance of a properly located receiver. The majority of c.w. operators tune with the left hand, preferring to leave the right hand free for copying messages and handling the key, and so the receiver should be mounted where the knob can be reached by the left hand. Phone operators aren't tied down this way, and tune the communications receiver with the hand that is more convenient.

The hand key should be fastened securely to the table, in a line just outside the right shoulder and far enough back from the front edge of the table so that the elbow can rest on the table. A good location for the semiautomatic or "bug" key is right next to the hand-key, although some operators prefer to mount the automatic key in front of them on the left, so that the right forearm rests on the table parallel to the front edge.

The best location for the microphone is directly in front of the operator, so that he doesn't have to shout across the table into it, or run up the speech-amplifier gain so high that all manner of external sounds are picked up. If the microphone is supported by a boom or by a flexible "goose neck," it can be placed in front of the operator without its base taking up valuable table space.

In any amateur station worthy of the name, it should be necessary to throw no more than one switch to go from the "receive" to the "transmit" condition. In phone stations, this switch should be located where it can be easily reached by the hand that isn't on the receiver. In the case of c.w. operation, this switch is most conveniently located to the right or left of the key, although some operators prefer to have it mounted on the left-hand side of the operating position and work it with the left hand while the right hand is on the key. Either location is satisfactory, of course, and the choice depends upon personal preference. Some operators use a foot- or knee-controlled switch, which is a convenience but doesn't allow too much freedom of position during long operating periods.

If the microphone is hand-held during phone operation, a "push-to-talk" switch on the microphone is convenient, but hand-held microphones tie up the use of one hand and are not too desirable, although they are widely used in mobile and portable work.

The location of other switches, such as those used to control power supplies, and phone/c.w. change-over, is of no particular importance, and they can be located on the unit with which they are associated. This is not strictly true in the case of the phone/c.w. DX man, who sometimes has need to change in a hurry from c.w. to phone. In this case, the change-over switch should be at the operating table, although the actual change-over may be done by a relay controlled by the switch.

If a rotary beam is used the control of the beam should be convenient to the operator. The direction indicator, however, can be located anywhere within sight of the operator, and does not have to be located on the operating table unless it is included with the control.

Frequency Spotting

The operator should be able to turn on only the oscillator of his transmitter, so that he can spot accurately his location in the band with respect to other stations. This allows him to see if he has anything like a clear channel, or to see what his frequency is with respect to another station. Such a provision can be part of the "send-receive" switch. Switches are available with a center "off" position, a "hold" position on one side, for turning on the oscillator only, and a "lock" position on the other side for turning on the transmitter and antenna relay. If oscillator keying is used, the key serves the same purpose, provided a "send-receive" switch is available to disable the rest of the transmitter and prevent a signal going out on the air during adjustment of the oscillator frequency.

For phone operation, the telegraph key or an auxiliary switch can control the transmitter oscillator, and the "send-receive" switch can then be wired into the control system so as to control the oscillator as well as the other circuits.

Comfort

Of prime importance is the comfort of the operator. If you find yourself getting tired after a short period of operating, examine your station to find what causes the fatigue. It may be that the chair is too soft or hasn't a straight back or is the wrong height for you. The key or receiver may be located so that you assume an uncomfortable position while using them. If you get sleepy fast, the ventilation may be at fault. (Or you may need sleep!)

POWER CONNECTIONS AND CONTROL

Following a few simple rules in wiring your power outlets and control circuits will make it an easy job to change units in the station. If the station is planned in this way from the start, or if the rules are recalled when you are rebuilding, you will find it a simple matter to revise your station from time to time without a major rewiring job.

It is neater and safer to run a single pair of wires from the outlet over to the operating table or some central point, rather than to use a number of adapters at the wall outlet.

Interconnections

The a.c. wiring of most stations will entail little more than finding sufficient wall outlets to accept the power-cable plugs from the several units. However, a more sophisticated station would provide the various outlets at some inconspicuous area at the operating table or console. If the transmitter power is in excess of 500 watts it is advisable to provide 230 volts for its power supply (if it will work from 230 volts) rather than the more common 115-volt source. The higher voltage source will provide better regulation, and the house lights are less likely to "blink" with keying or modulation. A single switch, either on the wall of the "shack" or at the operating position, should control all of the 115- and/or 230-volt outlets; this makes it a simple matter to turn on the station to the "standby" condition.

The nature of the send-receive control circuitry depends so much upon the equipment in use that it is impossible to give anything but the broadest principles to follow. With commercial equipment, the instruction books usually provide some suggestions. In some cases the antenna-transfer relay is provided also, so that the antenna is connected to the transmitter and a cable from the transmitter is connected to the receiver. Normally the receiver is connected to the antenna through this relay. When the transmitter is "on" the relay transfers the antenna to the transmitter output circuit.

Lacking a built-in antenna transfer relay, many amateurs make do with a short separate wire for the receiving antenna. While this is acceptable in many instances, it is seldom as effective (on receiving) as using the same antenna for transmitting and receiving. A separate antenna relay can be used; several models are available, for use with coaxial or open-wire line. Models are available for use with 115-volt a.c. or 12-volt d.c. Some have an auxiliary set of contacts that can be used to control the transmitter "on" function and/or the receiver "mute" circuit.

Break-In and Push-To-Talk

In c.w. operation, "break-in" is any system that allows the transmitting operator to hear the other station's signal during the "key-up" periods between characters and letters. This allows the sending station to be "broken" by the receiving station at any time, to shorten calls, ask for "fills" in messages, and speed up operation in general. With present techniques, it requires the use of a separate receiving antenna or an electronic "t.r." switch and, with high power, some means for protecting the receiver

from the transmitter when the key is "down." If the transmitter is low-powered (50 watts or so), no special equipment is required except the separate receiving antenna and a receiver that "recovers" fast. Where break-in operation is used, the output stage should be disabled when adjusting the oscillator to a new frequency, to avoid radiating an unnecessary signal.

"Push-to-talk" is an expression derived from the "PUSH" switch on some microphones, and it means a phone station with a single control for all change-over functions. Strictly speaking, it should apply only to a station where this single send-receive switch must be held in place during transmission periods, but any fast-acting switch will give practically the same effect. A control switch with a center "OFF" position, and one "HOLD" and one "LOCK" position, will give more flexibility than a straight "push" switch. The one switch must control the transmitter, the receiver "on-off" circuit and, if one is used, the antenna change-over relay. The receiver control is necessary to disable its output during transmit periods, to avoid acoustic feedback. A "foot switch" on the floor at the operating position is a convenient control.

A practical solution for the limited-space dweller is shown here. This neat home-built ham station is housed in a metal filing cabinet/desk combination. When not in use, the station can be closed up and locked, making it accessible to only the operator. (This station was designed and built by WB2FSV)

Many s.s.b. transmitters provide for "VOX" (voice-controlled operation), where the transmitter is turned on automatically at the first voice syllable and is held on for a half second or more after the voice stops. Operation with a VOX-operated s.s.b. transmitter is similar to c.w. break-in, in that a separate receiving antenna or an antenna transfer relay or an electronic t.r. switch is required. Several examples of electronic t.r. switches are given at the end of this chapter.

Switches and Relays

It is dangerous to use an overloaded switch in the power circuits. After it has been used for some time, it may fail, leaving the power on the circuit even after the switch is thrown to the "off" position. For this reason, large switches, or relays with adequate ratings, should be used to control the plate power. Relays are rated by coil voltages (for their control circuits) and by their contact current and voltage ratings. Any switch or relay for the power-control circuits of an amateur station should be conservatively rated; overloading a switch or relay is very poor economy. Switches rated at 20 amperes at 125 volts will handle the switching of circuits at the kilowatt level, but the small toggle switches rated 3 amperes at 125 volts should be used only in circuits up to about 150 watts.

When relays are used, the send-receive switch closes the circuits to their coils. The energized relays close the heavy-duty relay contacts. Since the relay contacts are in the power circuit being controlled, the switch handles only the relay-coil current. As a consequence, this switch can have a low current rating.

SAFETY

Of prime importance in the layout of the station is the personal safety of the operator and of visitors, invited or otherwise, during normal operating practice. If there are small children in the house, every step must be taken to prevent their accidental contact with power leads of any voltage. A locked room is a fine idea, if it is possible, otherwise housing the transmitter and power supplies in metal cabinets is an excellent, although expensive, solution. Lacking a metal cabinet, a wooden cabinet or a wooden framework covered with wire screen is the next-best solution. Many stations have the power supplies housed in metal cabinets in the operating room or in a closet or basement, and this cabinet or entry is kept locked — with the key out of reach of everyone but the operator. The power leads are run through conduit to the transmitter, using ignition cable for the high-voltage leads. If the power supplies and transmitter are in the same cabinet, a lock-type main switch for the incoming line power is a good precaution.

A simple substitute for a lock-type main switch is an ordinary line plug with a short connecting wire between the two pins. By wiring a female receptacle in series with the main power line in the transmitter, the shorting plug will act as the main safety lock. When the plug is removed and hidden, it will be impossible to energize the transmitter, and a stranger or child isn't likely to spot or suspect the open receptacle.

An essential adjunct to any station is a **shorting stick** for discharging any high voltage to ground before any work is done in the transmit-

This modern amateur radio station is equipped for use from the h.f. bands through the u.h.f. spectrum. The equipment is neatly arranged to provide the operator with easy access to the various pieces of gear. The foundation unit is a home-made console which is fashioned from plywood, stained to the desired color, and finished off with several coats of varnish. The relay racks at the right and left of the operating position are mounted on dollies so that they can be moved with ease. The row of books across the top shelf of the console are used to record, in alphabetical order, information which relates to radio amateurs worked, their equipment, and other pertinent data to be kept on record. This station belongs to W1FZJ/KP4 and W1HOY/KP4 in Arecibo, P.R.

ter. Even if interlocks and power-supply bleeders are used, the failure of one or more of these components may leave the transmitter in a dangerous condition. The shorting stick is made by mounting a small metal hook, of wire or rod, on one end of a dry stick or bakelite rod. A piece of ignition cable or other well-insulated wire is then run from the hook on the stick to the chassis or common ground of the transmitter, and the stick is hung alongside the transmitter. Whenever the power is turned off in the transmitter to permit work on the rig, the shorting stick is first used to touch the several high-voltage leads (plate r.f. choke, filter capacitor, tube plate connection, etc.) to insure that there is no high voltage at any of these points.

Fusing

A minor hazard in the amateur station is the possibility of fire through the failure of a component. If the failure is complete and the component is large, the house fuses will generally blow. However, it is unwise and inconvenient to depend upon the house fuses to protect the lines running to the radio equipment, and every power supply should have its primary circuit individually fused, at about 150 to 200 per cent of the maximum rating of the supply. Circuit breakers can be used instead of fuses if desired.

Wiring

Control-circuit wires running between the operating position and a transmitter in another part of the room should be hidden, if possible. This can be done by running the wires under the floor or behind the base molding, bringing the wires out to terminal boxes or regular wall fixtures. Such construction, however, is generally only possible in elaborate installations, and the average amateur must content himself with trying to make the wires as inconspicuous as possible. If several pairs of leads must be run from the operating table to the transmitter, as is generally the case, a single piece of rubber- or vinyl-covered multiconductor cable will always look neater than several pieces of rubber-covered

lamp cord, and it is much easier to sweep around or dust.

Solid or stranded wire connected to a screw terminal (a.c. plug, antenna binding posts, etc.) should either be "hooked" around a *clockwise* direction or, better yet, be terminated in a soldering lug. If the wire is hooked in a counter-clockwise position, it will tend to move out from under the screw head as the screw is tightened.

The antenna wires always present a problem, unless coaxial-line feed is used. Open-wire line from the point of entry of the antenna line should always be arranged neatly, and it is generally best to support it at several points. Many operators prefer to mount any antenna-tuning assemblies right at the point of entry of the feedline, together with an antenna changeover relay (if one is used), and then the link from the tuning assembly to the transmitter can be made of inconspicuous coaxial line. If the transmitter is mounted near the point of entry of the line, it simplifies the problem of "What to do with the feeders?"

Lightning and Fire Protection

The National Electrical Code (NFPA No. 70) adopted by the National Fire Protection Association, although purely advisory as far as the NFPA is concerned, is of interest because it is widely used in law and for legal regulatory purposes. Article 810 deals with radio and television equipment, and Section C treats specifically amateur transmitting and receiving stations. Pertinent paragraphs are reprinted below:

810-11. **Material.** Antenna and lead-in conductors shall be of hard-drawn copper, bronze, aluminum alloy, copper-clad steel or other high-strength, corrosion-resistant material. Soft-drawn or medium-drawn copper may be used for lead-in conductors where the maximum span between points of support is less than 35 feet.

810-12. **Supports.** Outdoor antenna and lead-in conductors shall be securely supported. They shall not be attached to poles or similar structures carrying electric light or power wires or trolley wires of more than 250 volts between conductors. Insulators supporting the antenna conductors shall have sufficient mechanical strength to safely support the conductors.

A convenient and inexpensive operation position can be made by purchasing an unfinished door panel, attaching wooden or wrought iron legs, and finishing the surface of the table with a coat of spar varnish or similar heavy-duty material. This station is owned by W1CKK and WN1HTY of Meriden, Conn.

Lead-in conductors shall be securely attached to the antenna.

810-13. Avoidance of Contacts with Conductors of Other Systems. Outdoor antenna and lead-in conductors from an antenna to a building shall not cross over electric light or power circuits and shall be kept well away from all such circuits so as to avoid the possibility of accidental contact. Where proximity to electric light and power service conductors of less than 250 volts between conductors cannot be avoided, the installation shall be such as to provide a clearance of at least two feet. It is recommended that antenna conductors be so installed as not to cross under electric light or power conductors.

810-14. Splices. Splices and joints in antenna span shall be made with approved splicing devices or by such other means as will not appreciably weaken the conductors.

Soldering may ordinarily be expected to weaken the conductor. Therefore, the joint should be mechanically secure before soldering.

810-15. Grounding. Masts and metal structures supporting antennas shall be permanently and effectively grounded, without intervening splice or connection.

810-21. Grounding Material. The grounding conductor shall, unless otherwise specified, be of copper, aluminum, copper-clad steel, bronze, or other corrosion-resistant material.

810-22. Insulation. The grounding conductors may be uninsulated.

810-23. Supports. The grounding conductors shall be securely fastened in place and may be directly attached to the surface wired over without the use of insulating supports. Where proper support cannot be provided the size of the grounding conductor shall be increased proportionately.

810-24. Mechanical Protection. The grounding conductor shall be protected where exposed to physical damage or the size of the grounding conductor shall be increased proportionately to compensate for the lack of protection.

810-25. Run in Straight Line. The grounding conductor shall be run in as straight a line as practicable from the antenna mast and/or lightning arrestor to the grounding electrode.

810-26. Grounding Electrode. The grounding conductor shall be connected to a metallic underground water piping system. Where the building is not supplied with a (suitable) water system (one buried deeper than ten feet) the connection shall be made to the metal frame of the building when effectively grounded or to a grounding electrode. At a penthouse or similar location the ground conductor may be connected to a water pipe or rigid conduit.

810-27. Grounding Conductor. The grounding conductor may be run either inside or outside the building.

810-52. Size of Antenna. Antennas for amateur transmitting and receiving stations shall be of a size not less than given in Table 810-52.

Table 810-52

Size of Amateur-Station Outdoor Antenna Conductors

Material	Minimum Size of Conductors	
	When Maximum Open Span Length Is	
	Less than 150 feet	Over 150 feet
Hard-drawn copper	14	10
Copper-clad steel, bronze or other high-strength material	14	12

810-53. Size of Lead-In Conductors. Lead-in conductors for transmitting stations shall, for various maximum span lengths, be of a size at least as great as that of conductors for antenna specified in 810-52.

810-54. Clearance on Building. Antenna conductors for transmitting stations, attached to buildings, shall be firmly mounted at least 3 inches clear of the surface of the building on nonabsorptive insulating supports, such as treated pins or brackets, equipped with insulators having not less than 3-inch creepage and airgap distances. Lead-in conductors attached to buildings shall also conform to these requirements, except when they are enclosed in a continuous metal shield which is permanently and effectively grounded. In this latter case the metallic shield may also be used as a conductor.

810-55. Entrance to Building. Except where protected with a continuous metal shield which is permenently and effectively grounded, lead-in conductors for transmitting stations shall enter building by one of the following methods:

(a) Through a rigid, noncombustible, nonabsorptive insulating tube or bushing.

(b) Through an opening provided for the purpose in which the entrance conductors are firmly secured so as to provide a clearance of at least 2 inches.

(c) Through a drilled window pane.

810-56. Protection Against Accidental Contact. Lead-in conductors to radio transmitters shall be so located or installed as to make accidental contact with them difficult.

810-57. Lightning Arrestors—Transmitting Stations. Each conductor of a lead-in for outdoor antenna shall be provided with a lightning arrestor or other suitable means which will drain static charges from the antenna system.

Exception No. 1. When protected by a continuous metallic shield which is permanently and effectively grounded.

Exception No. 2. Where the antenna is permanently and effectively grounded.

810-59. Size of Protective Ground. The protective ground conductor for transmitting stations shall be as large as the lead-in, but not smaller than No. 10 copper, bronze or copper-clad steel.

810-60. Size of Operating Grounding Conductor. The operating grounding conductor for transmitting stations shall be not less than No. 14 copper or its equivalent.

810-70. Clearance from Other Conductors. All conductors inside the building shall be separated at least 4 inches from the conductors of other light or signal circuit unless separated therefrom by conduit or some firmly fixed non-conductor such as porcelain tubes or flexible tubing.

810-71. General. Transmitters shall comply with the following:

(a) **Enclosing.** The transmitter shall be enclosed in a metal frame or grille, or separated from the operating space by a barrier or other equivalent means, all metallic parts of which are effectually connected to ground.

(b) **Grounding of Controls.** All external metallic handles and controls accessible to the operating personnel shall be effectually grounded.

No circuit in excess of 150 volts between conductors should have any parts exposed to direct contact. A complete dead-front type of switchboard is preferred.

(c) **Interlocks on Doors.** All access doors shall be provided with interlocks which will disconnect all voltages in excess of 350 volts between conductors when any access door is opened.

(d) **Audio Amplifiers.** Audio amplifiers which are located outside the transmitter housing shall be suitably housed and shall be so located as to be readily accessible and adequately ventilated.

If coaxial line is used and an antenna has a d.c. return throughout (gamma match, etc.), compliance with 810-57 above is readily achieved by grounding the shield of the coax at the point where it is nearest to the ground outside the house. Use a heavy wire—the aluminum wire sold for grounding TV antennas is good. If the cable can be run underground, one or more grounding stakes should be located at the point where the cable enters the ground, at the antenna end. A grounding stake, to be effective in soils of average conductivity, should be not less than 8 feet long.

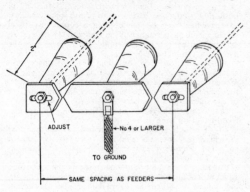

ADJUST

No 4 or LARGER

TO GROUND

SAME SPACING AS FEEDERS

Fig. 22-1—A simple lightning arrester made from three stand-off or feed-through insulators and sections of ⅛x½-inch brass or copper strap. It should be installed in the open-wire or Twin-Lead line at the point where it is nearest the ground outside the house. The heavy ground lead should be as short and direct as possible. Gap setting should be minimum for transmitter power.

Galvanized ¾-inch iron pipe is acceptable, as is ⅝-inch steel rod or ½-inch non-ferrous rod. Making connection to the outside of the outer conductor of the coaxial line will normally have no effect on the s.w.r. in the line, and consequently it can be done at any point or points. A commercial model of a lightning arrester for coaxial line is available.

In some areas the probability of lightning surges entering the home via the 120/240-volt line may be high. A portion of the lightning surges originating on an overhead primary feeder can pass through the distribution transformer by electrostatic and electromagnetic coupling to the secondary circuit, even though the primary is protected by distribution-class lightning arresters. Radio equipment can be protected from these surges by the use of a "secondary service lightning arrester." A typical unit is the G.E. Model 9L15CCB007, marketed as the Home Lightning Protector. It is mounted at the weatherhead or in the service entrance box.

Rotary beams using a T or gamma match and with each element connected to the boom will usually be grounded through the supporting metal tower. If the antenna is mounted on a wooden pole or on the top of the house, a No. 4 or larger wire should be connected from the beam to the ground by the shortest and most direct route possible, using insulators where the wire comes close to the building. From a lightning-protection standpoint, it is desirable to run the coaxial and control lines from a beam down a metal tower and underground to the shack. If the tower is well grounded and the antenna is higher than any surrounding objects, the combination will serve well as a lightning rod.

The sole purpose of lightning rods or grounded roofs is to protect a building in case a lightning stroke occurs; there is no accepted evidence that any form of protection can prevent a stroke.*

Experiments have indicated that a high vertical conductor will generally divert to itself direct hits that might otherwise fall within a cone-shaped space of which the apex is the top of the conductor and the base a circle of radius approximately two times the height of the conductor. Thus a radio mast may afford some protection to low adjacent structures, but only when low-impedance grounds are provided.

* See "Code for Protection Against Lightning," *National Bureau of Standards Handbook 46*, for sale by the Superintendent of Documents, Washington 25, D.C.

This homemade console, built of plywood and finished with light tan speckled spray paint, effectively conceals all power and antenna leads. The top of the console lifts off for access to the equipment.

Cherry-finished Formica is used for the desk top; there is a wooden top at the same height behind the console face, and the receiver and transmitters rest on wooden runners that elevate the equipment for greater convenience. A central control unit (behind the microphone) carries power switches, pilot lamps and beam-heading indicator. (K3NCN, Philadelphia, Pa.)

ELECTRONIC TRANSMIT-RECEIVE SWITCHES

Some antenna relays are not fast enough to switch an antenna from transmitter to receiver and back at normal keying speeds. As a consequence, when it is desired to use the same antenna for transmitting and receiving (a "must" when directional antennas are used) and to operate c.w. break-in or voice-controlled sideband, an electronic switch is used in the antenna. The word "switch" is a misnomer in this case; the transmitter is connected to the antenna at all times and the t.r. "switch" is a device for preventing burnout of the receiver by the transmitter.

One of the simplest approaches is the circuit shown in Fig. 22-2. The 6C4 cathode follower couples the incoming signal on the line to the receiver input with only a slight reduction in gain. When the transmitter is "on," the grid of the 6C4 is driven positive and the rectified current biases the 6C4 so that it can pass very little power on to the receiver. The factors that limit the r.f voltage the circuit can handle are the voltage break-down rating of the 47-$\mu\mu$f. capacitor and the voltage that may be safely applied between the grid and cathode of the tube.

To avoid stray pick-up on the lead between the cathode and the antenna terminal of the receiver, this lead should be well-shielded. Further, the entire unit should be shielded and mounted at the transmitter antenna terminals. In wiring the tube socket, input and output cir-

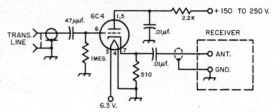

Fig. 22-2—Schematic diagram of cathode-follower t.r. switch. Resistors are ½-watt. The unit should be assembled in a small chassis or shield can and mounted on or very close to the transmitter antenna terminals. The transmitter transmission line can be connected at the coaxial jack with an M-358 Tee adapter.

The heater and plate power can be "borrowed" from the receiver in most cases. (Herzog, ex-W9LSK, K2AHB, QST, May, 1956)

cuit components should be separated to reduce feed-through by stray coupling.

The cable run to the receiver can be any convenient length, but if the t.r. switch is not located at or quite near to the transmitter there may be conditions where a loss of received signal will be noticed, caused by resonant conditions in the cable and the transmitter output circuit. This effect is more likely to be observed as one moves higher in frequency (to 21 and 28 Mc.).

SELF-CONTAINED ALL-BAND ELECTRONIC T.R. SWITCH

The t.r. switch shown in Fig. 22-3 differs in several ways from the preceding example. It contains its own power supply and consequently can be used with any transmitter/receiver combina-

Fig. 22-3—The knob at the left is used for peaking the tuned circuit. At the right is the bandswitch. Only four positions are shown and the 15-meter position also covers 10 meters, as mentioned in the text.

tion without "borrowing" power. It will add gain and front-end selectivity to the receiver. A homemade switch-coil-capacitor is shown in the unit, enabling the constructor to build his own.

Referring to the circuit diagram in Fig. 22-4, one triode of a 12AU7 is used as an amplifier stage, followed by the other triode as a cathode-follower stage to couple between the tuned circuit and the receiver. As in the simpler switch, the triodes are biased during transmission periods by rectified grid current, and insufficient power is fed to the receiver to injure its input circuit.

The t.r. switch is intended to mount behind the transmitter near its output terminal, so that the connecting cable is short. The lead from the t.r. switch to the receiver can be any reasonable length. Components are mounted above and below the chassis. In wiring the switch, a length of RG-58/U should be used between the cathode-follower load (resistor and r.f. choke) and the output jack J_2, to minimize "feedthrough" around the tube. A pair of 0.01 μf. capacitors across the a.c. line where it enters the chassis helps to hold down the r.f. that might otherwise ride in on the a.c. line.

In operation, it is only necessary to switch the unit to the band in use and peak capacitor C_4 for maximum signal or background noise. A significant increase in signal or background noise should be observed on any band within the range of the coil/capacitor combination.

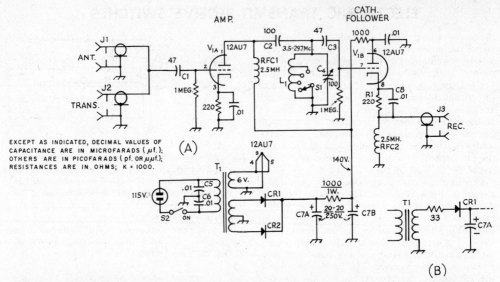

EXCEPT AS INDICATED, DECIMAL VALUES OF
CAPACITANCE ARE IN MICROFARADS (μf.);
OTHERS ARE IN PICOFARADS (pf. OR μμf.);
RESISTANCES ARE IN OHMS; K = 1000.

Fig. 22-4—Circuit diagram of the t.r. switch. Unless otherwise specified, resistors are ½ watt; decimal value fixed capacitors are disk ceramic, others are mica with the exception of C7, which is electrolytic. B—method of using a half-wave transformer for T_1. Circuit designations not listed below are for text reference.

C_4—100-pf. variable (Millen 20100 or similar).

C_{7A}, C_{7B}—20/20-μf., electrolytic 250 volts or more.

L_1—See Fig. 22-5.

J_1, J_2, J_3—Coax chassis receptacle, type SO-239.

S_1—Single-pole, four-position wafer switch (Mallory 3115J, 3215J, or similar).

S_2—S.p.s.t. toggle switch.

T_1—Power transformer, full-wave, 125-0-125 25 ma., 6.3 volts, 1 amp. (Stancor PS-8416, Knight 54A2008). B—half-wave, 125 v. 15 ma., 6 volts, 0.6 amp. (Stancor PS-8415, Knight 54A1410).

CR_1, CR_2—Silicon rectifier, 400 volts or more, any current rating over 40 ma.

TVI and T.R. Switches

The preceding t.r. switches generate harmonics when their grid circuits are driven positive, and these harmonics can cause TVI if steps are not taken to prevent it. Either switch should be well-shielded and used in the antenna transmission line between transmitter and low-pass filter.

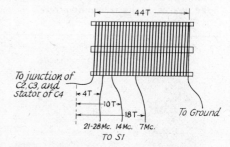

Fig. 22-5—Drawing of L_1 and associated taps. L_1 is 44 turns of No. 24, 32 turns per inch, 1 inch diameter (Miniductor 3016, Air Dux 832T). To solder the tap leads, indent each turn adjacent to the tap point. This will allow soldering room.

Fig. 22-6—The power transformer and filter components are mounted at the upper right. Just to the bottom of center is the socket for the 12AU7.

Chapter 23

INTERFERENCE WITH OTHER SERVICES

Every amateur has the obligation to make sure that the operation of his station does not, because of any shortcomings in equipment, cause interference with other radio and audio services. It is unfortunately true that much of the interference that amateurs cause to broadcast and television reception is directly the fault of b.c. and TV receiver construction. Nevertheless, the amateur can and should help to alleviate interference even though the responsibility for it does not lie with him.

Successful handling of interference cases requires winning the listener's cooperation. Here are a few pointers on how to go about it.

Clean House First

The first step obviously is to make sure that the transmitter has no radiations outside the bands assigned for amateur use. The best check on this is your own a.m. or TV receiver. It is always convincing if you can demonstrate that you do not interfere with reception in your own home.

Don't Hide Your Identity

Whenever you make equipment changes — or shift to a hitherto unused band or type of emission — that might be expected to change the interference situation, check with your neighbors. If no one is experiencing interference, so much the better; it does no harm to keep the neighborhood aware of the fact that you are operating without bothering anyone.

Should you change location, announce your presence and conduct occasional tests on the air, requesting anyone whose reception is being spoiled to let you know about it so steps may be taken to eliminate the trouble.

Act Promptly

The average person will tolerate a limited amount of interference, but the sooner you take steps to eliminate it, the more agreeable the listener will be; the longer he has to wait for you, the less willing he will be to cooperate.

Present Your Story Tactfully

When you interfere, it is natural for the complainant to assume that your transmitter is at fault. If you are certain that the trouble is not in your transmitter, explain to the listener that the reason lies in the receiver design, and that some modifications may have to be made in the receiver if he is to expect interference-free reception.

Arrange for Tests

Most listeners are not very competent observers of the various aspects of interference. If at all possible, enlist the help of another amateur and have him operate your transmitter while you see for yourself what happens at the affected receiver.

In General

In this "public relations" phase of the problem a great deal depends on your own attitude. Most people will be willing to meet you half way, particularly when the interference is not of long standing, if you as a person make a good impression. Your personal appearance is important. So is what you say about the receiver — no one takes kindly to hearing his possessions derided. If you discuss your interference problems on the air, do it in a constructive way — one calculated to increase listener cooperation, not destroy it.

INTERFERENCE WITH STANDARD BROADCASTING

Interference with a.m. broadcasting usually falls into one or more rather well-defined categories. An understanding of the general types of interference will avoid much cut-and-try in finding a cure.

Transmitter Defects

Out-of-band radiation is something that must be cured at the transmitter. Parasitic oscillations are a frequently unsuspected source of such radiations, and no transmitter can be considered satisfactory until it has been thoroughly checked for both low- and high-frequency parasitics. Very often parasitics show up only as transients, causing key clicks in c.w. transmitters and "splashes" or "burps" on modulation peaks in a.m. transmitters. Methods for detecting and eliminating parasitics are discussed in the transmitter chapter.

In c.w. transmitters the sharp make and break that occurs with unfiltered keying causes transients that, in theory, contain frequency components through the entire radio spectrum. Practically, they are often strong enough in the immediate vicinity of the transmitter to cause serious interference to broadcast reception. Key clicks can be eliminated by the methods detailed in the chapter on keying.

A distinction must be made between clicks generated in the transmitter itself and those set up by the mere opening and closing of the key contacts when current is flowing. The latter are of the same nature as the clicks heard in a receiver when a wall switch is thrown to turn a light on or off, and may be more troublesome nearby than the clicks that actually go out on the signal. A filter for eliminating them usually has to be installed as close as possible to the key contacts.

Overmodulation in a.m. phone transmitters generates transients similar to key clicks. It can be prevented either by using automatic systems for limiting the modulation to 100 per cent, or by continuously monitoring the modulation. Methods for both are described in the chapter on amplitude modulation.

BCI is frequently made worse by radiation from the power wiring or the r.f. transmission line. This is because the signal causing the interference, in such cases, is radiated from wiring that is nearer the broadcast receiver than the antenna itself. Much depends on the method used to couple the transmitter to the antenna, a subject that is discussed in the chapters on transmission lines and antennas. If it is at all possible the antenna itself should be placed so that it is not in close proximity to house wiring, telephone and power lines, and similar conductors.

Image and Oscillator-Harmonic Responses

Most present-day broadcast receivers use a built-in loop antenna as the grid circuit for the mixer stage. The selectivity is not especially high at the signal frequency. Furthermore, an appreciable amount of signal pick-up usually occurs on the a.c. line to which the receiver is connected, the signal so picked up being fed to the mixer grid by stray means.

As a result, strong signals from nearby transmitters, even though the transmitting frequency is far removed from the broadcast band, can force themselves to the mixer grid. They will normally be eliminated by the i.f. selectivity, except in cases where the transmitter frequency is the image of the broadcast signal to which the receiver is tuned, or when the transmitter frequency is so related to a harmonic of the broadcast receiver's local oscillator as to produce a beat at the intermediate frequency.

These image and oscillator-harmonic responses tune in and out on the broadcast receiver dial just like a broadcast signal, except that in the case of harmonic response the tuning rate is more rapid. Since most receivers use an intermediate frequency in the neighborhood of 455 kc., the interference is a true image only when the amateur transmitting frequency is in the 1800-kc. band. Oscillator-harmonic responses occur from 3.5- and 7-Mc. transmissions, and sometimes even from higher frequencies.

Since images and harmonic responses occur at definite frequencies on the receiver dial, it is possible to choose operating frequencies that will avoid putting such a response on top of the broadcast stations that are favored in the vicinity. While your signal may still be heard when the receiver is tuned off the local stations, it will at least not interfere with program reception.

There is little that can be done to most receivers to cure interference of this type except to reduce the amount of signal getting into the set through the a.c. line. A line filter such as is shown in Fig. 23-1 often will help accomplish this. The values used for the coils and capacitors are in general not critical. The effectiveness of the filter may depend considerably on the ground connection used, and it is advisable to use a short ground lead to a cold-water pipe if at all possible. The line cord from the set should be bunched up, to minimize the possibility of pick-up on the cord. It may be necessary to install the filter inside the receiver, so that the filter is connected between the line cord and the set wiring, in order to get satisfactory operation.

Cross-Modulation

With phone transmitters, there are occasionally cases where the voice is heard whenever the broadcast receiver is tuned to a b.c. station, but there is no interference when tuning between stations. This is cross-modulation, a result of rectification in one of the early stages of the receiver. Receivers that are susceptible to this trouble usually also get a similar type of interference from regular broadcasting if there is a strong local b.c. station and the receiver is tuned to some *other* station.

The remedy for cross-modulation in the receiver is the same as for images and oscillator-harmonic response — reduce the strength of the amateur signal at the receiver by means of a line filter.

The trouble is not always in the receiver, since cross modulation can occur in any nearby rectifying circuit — such as a poor contact in water or steam piping, gutter pipes, and other conductors in the strong field of the transmitting antenna — external to both receiver and transmitter. Locating the cause may be difficult, and is best attempted with a battery-operated portable broadcast receiver used as a "probe" to find the spot where the interference is most intense. When such a spot is located, inspection of the metal structures in the vicinity should indicate the cause. The remedy is to make a good electrical bond between the two conductors having the poor contact.

Audio-Circuit Rectification

The most frequent cause of interference from operation at 21 Mc. and higher frequencies is rectification of a signal that by some means gets into the audio system of the receiver. In the milder cases an amplitude-modulated signal will be heard with reasonably good quality, but is not tunable — that is, it is present no matter what the frequency to which the receiver dial is set. An unmodulated carrier may have no ob-servable effect in such cases beyond causing a little hum. However, if the signal is very strong there will be a reduction of the audio output level of the receiver whenever the carrier is thrown on. This causes an annoying "jumping" of the program when the interfering signal is keyed. With phone transmission the change in audio level is not so objectionable because it occurs at less frequent intervals. Rectification ordinarily gives no audio output from a fre-quency-modulated signal, so the interference can be made almost unnoticeable if f.m. or p.m. is used instead of a.m.

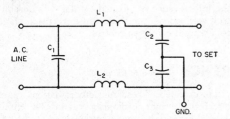

Fig. 23-1—"Brute-force" a.c. line filter for receivers. The values of C_1, C_2 and C_3 are not generally critical; capacitances from 0.001 to 0.01 μf. can be used. L_1 and L_2 can be a 2-inch winding of No. 18 enameled wire on a half-inch diameter form. In making up such a unit for use external to the receiver, make sure that there are no exposed conductors to offer a shock hazard.

Interference of this type usually results from a signal on the power line being coupled by some means into the audio circuits, although the pickup also may occur on the set wiring itself. A "brute-force" line filter as described above may or may not be completely effective, but in any event is the simplest thing to try. If it does not do the job, some modification of the receiver will be necessary. This usually takes the form of a simple filter connected in the grid circuit of the tube in which the rectification is occur-ring. Usually it will be the first audio amplifier, which is commonly a diode-triode type tube.

Filter circuits that have proved to be effective are shown in Fig. 23-2. In A, the value of the grid leak in the combined detector/first audio tube is reduced to 2 to 3 megohms and the grid is bypassed to chassis by a 250-$\mu\mu$f. mica or ceramic capacitor. A somewhat similar method that does not require changing the grid resistor is shown at B. In C, a 75,000-ohm (value not

critical) resistor is connected between the grid pin on the tube socket and all other grid con-nections. In combination with the input capac-itance of the tube this forms a low-pass filter to prevent r.f. from reaching the grid. In some cases, simply bypassing the heater of the de-tector/first audio tube to chassis with a 0.001-μf. or larger capacitor will suffice. In all cases, check to see that the a.c. line is bypassed to chassis; if it is not, install bypass capacitors (0.001 to 0.01 μf.).

Handling BCI Cases

Assuming that your transmitter has been checked and found to be free from spurious radiations, get another amateur to operate your station, if possible, while you make the actual check on the interference yourself. The follow-ing procedure should be used.

Tune the receiver through the broadcast band, to see whether the interference tunes like a regular b.c. station. If so, image or oscillator-harmonic response is the cause. If there is in-terference only when a b.c. station is tuned in, but not between stations, the cause is cross modulation. If the interference is heard at all settings of the tuning dial, the trouble is pickup in the audio circuits. In the latter case, the re-ceiver's volume control may or may not affect the strength of the interference, depending on the means by which your signal is being rectified.

Having identified the cause, explain it to the set owner. It is a good idea to have a line filter with you, equipped with enough cord to replace the set's line cord, so it can be tried then and there. If it does not eliminate the interference, explain to the set owner that there is nothing further that can be done without modifying the receiver. Recommend that the work be done by a competent service technician, and offer to ad-vise the service man on the cause and remedy. Don't offer to work on the set yourself, but if you are asked to do so use your own judgment about complying; set owners sometimes com-plain about the over-all performance of the receiver afterward, often without justification. If you work on it, take it to your station so the effect of changes you make can be seen. Return the receiver promptly when you have finished.

MISCELLANEOUS TYPES OF INTERFERENCE

The operation of amateur phone transmitters occasionally results in interference on telephone lines and in audio amplifiers used in public-ad-dress work and for home music reproduction.

Fig. 23-2—Methods of elimi-nating r.f. from the grid of a combined detector/first-audio stage. At A, the value of the grid leak is reduced to 2 or 3 megohms, and a bypass capacitor is added. At B, both grid and cathode are bypassed.

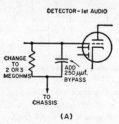

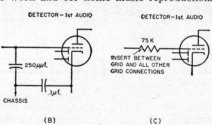

(A)   (B)   (C)

The cause is rectification of the signal in an audio circuit.

Telephone Interference

Telephone interference can be cured by connecting a bypass capacitor (about 0.001 μf.) across the microphone unit in the telephone handset. The telephone companies have capacitors for this purpose. When such a case occurs, get in touch with the repair department of the phone company, giving the particulars. Section 500-150-100 of the Bell System Practices *Plant Series* gives detailed instructions. Do not try to work on the telephone yourself.

Hi-Fi and P. A. Systems

In interference to public-address and "hi-fi" installations the principal sources of signal pickup are the a.c. line or a line from the power amplifier to a speaker. All amplifier units should be bonded together and connected to a good ground such as a cold-water pipe. Make sure that the a.c. line is bypassed to chassis in each unit with capacitors of about 0.01 μf. at the point where the line enters the chassis. The speaker line similarly should be bypassed to the amplifier chassis with about 0.01 μf.

If these measures do not suffice, the shielding on the amplifiers may be inadequate. A shield cover and bottom pan should be installed in such cases.

The spot in the system where the rectification is occurring often can be localized by seeing if the interference is affected by the volume control setting; if not, the cause is in a stage following the volume control.

TELEVISION INTERFERENCE   (See also Chap. 17)

Interference with the reception of television signals usually presents a more difficult problem than interference with a.m. broadcasting. In BCI cases the interference almost always can be attributed to deficient selectivity or spurious responses in the b.c. receiver. While similar deficiencies exist in many television receivers, it is also true that amateur transmitters generate harmonics that fall inside many or all television channels. These spurious radiations cause interference that ordinarily cannot be eliminated by anything that may be done at the receiver, so must be prevented at the transmitter itself.

The over-all situation is further complicated by the fact that television broadcasting is in three distinct bands, two in the v.h.f. region and one in the u.h.f.

V.H.F. TELEVISION

For the amateur who does most of his transmitting on frequencies below 30 Mc. the TV band of principal interest is the low v.h.f. band between 54 and 88 Mc. If harmonic radiation can be reduced to the point where no interference is caused to Channels 2 to 6, inclusive, it is almost certain that any harmonic troubles with channels above 174 Mc. will disappear also.

The relationship between the v.h.f. television channels and harmonics of amateur bands from 14 through 28 Mc. is shown in Fig. 23-3. Harmonics of the 7- and 3.5-Mc. bands are not shown because they fall in every television channel. However, the harmonics above 54 Mc. from these bands are of such high order that they are usually rather low in amplitude, although they may be strong enough to interfere if the television receiver is quite close to the amateur transmitter. Low-order harmonics — up to about the sixth — are usually the most difficult to eliminate.

Of the amateur v.h.f. bands, only 50 Mc. will have harmonics falling in a v.h.f. television channel (channels 11, 12 and 13). However, a transmitter for any amateur v.h.f. band may cause interference if it has multiplier stages either operating in or having harmonics in one or more of the v.h.f. TV channels. The r.f. energy on such

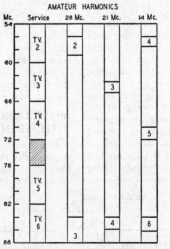
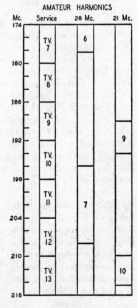

Fig. 23-3—Relationship of amateur-band harmonics to v.h.f. TV channels. Harmonic interference from transmitters operating below 30 Mc. is most likely to be serious in the low-channel group (54 to 88 Mc.).

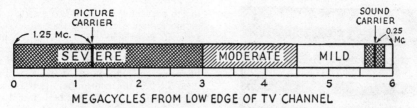

Fig. 23-4—Location of picture and sound carriers in a monochrome television channel, and relative intensity of interference as the location of the interfering signal within the channel is varied without changing its strength. The three regions are not actually sharply defined as shown in this drawing, but merge into one another gradually.

frequencies can be radiated directly from the transmitting circuits or coupled by stray means to the transmitting antenna.

Frequency Effects

The degree to which transmitter harmonics or other undesired radiation actually in the TV channel must be suppressed depends principally on two factors, the strength of the TV signal on the channel or channels affected, and the relationship between the frequency of the spurious radiation and the frequencies of the TV picture and sound carriers within the channel. If the TV signal is very strong, interference can be eliminated by comparatively simple methods. However, if the TV signal is very weak, as in "fringe" areas where the received picture is visibly degraded by the appearance of set noise or "snow" on the screen, it may be necessary to go to extreme measures.

In either case the intensity of the interference depends very greatly on the exact frequency of the interfering signal. Fig. 23-4 shows the placement of the picture and sound carriers in the standard TV channel. In Channel 2, for example, the picture carrier frequency is $54 + 1.25 = 55.25$ Mc. and the sound carrier frequency is $60 - 0.25 = 59.75$ Mc. The second harmonic of 28,010 kc. (56,020 kc. or 56.02 Mc.) falls $56.02 - 54 = 2.02$ Mc. above the low edge of the channel and is in the region marked "Severe" in Fig. 23-4. On the other hand, the second harmonic of 29,500 kc. (59,000 kc. or 59 Mc.) is $59 - 54 = 5$ Mc. from the low edge of the channel and falls in the region marked "Mild." Interference at

this frequency has to be about 100 times as strong as at 56,020 kc. to cause effects of equal intensity. Thus an operating frequency that puts a harmonic near the picture carrier requires about 40 db. more harmonic suppression, as compared with an operating frequency that puts the harmonic near the upper edge of the channel.

For a region of 100 kc. or so either side of the sound carrier there is another "Severe" region where a spurious radiation will interfere with reception of the sound program, and this region also should be avoided. In general, a signal of intensity equal to that of the picture carrier will not cause noticeable interference if its frequency is in the "Mild" region shown in Fig. 23-4, but the same intensity in the "Severe" region will utterly destroy the picture.

Interference Patterns

The visible effects of interference vary with the type and intensity of the interference. Complete "blackout," where the picture and sound disappear completely, leaving the screen dark, occurs only when the transmitter and receiver are quite close together. Strong interference ordinarily causes the picture to be broken up, leaving a jumble of light and dark lines, or turns the picture "negative" — the normally white parts of the picture turn black and the normally black parts turn white. "Cross-hatching" — diagonal bars or lines in the picture — accompanies the latter, usually, and also represents the most common type of less-severe interference. The bars are the result of the beat between the harmonic frequency and the picture carrier frequency. They are broad and relatively few in number if the beat frequency is comparatively low — near the picture carrier — and are numerous and very fine if the beat frequency is very high — toward the upper end of the channel. Typical cross-hatching is shown in Fig. 23-5. If the frequency falls in the "Mild" region in Fig. 23-4 the cross-hatching may be so fine as to be visible only on close inspection of the picture, in which case it may simply cause the apparent brightness of the screen to change when the transmitter carrier is thrown on and off.

Whether or not cross-hatching is visible, an amplitude-modulated transmitter may cause "sound bars" in the picture. These look about

Fig. 23-5—"Cross-hatching," caused by the beat between the picture carrier and an interfering signal inside the TV channel.

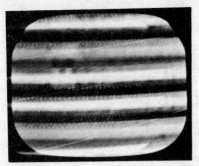

Fig. 23-6—"Sound bars" or "modulation bars" accompanying amplitude modulation of an interfering signal. In this case the interfering carrier is strong enough to destroy the picture, but in mild cases the picture is visible through the horizontal bars. Sound bars may accompany modulation even though the unmodulated carrier gives no visible cross-hatching.

as shown in Fig. 23-6. They result from the variations in the intensity of the interfering signal when modulated. Under most circumstances modulation bars will not occur if the amateur transmitter is frequency- or phase-modulated. With these types of modulation the cross-hatching will "wiggle" from side to side with the modulation.

Except in the more severe cases, there is seldom any effect on the sound reception when interference shows in the picture, unless the frequency is quite close to the sound carrier. In the latter event the sound may be interfered with even though the picture is clean.

Reference to Fig. 23-3 will show whether or not harmonics of the frequency in use will fall in any television channels that can be received in the locality. It should be kept in mind that not only harmonics of the final frequency may interfere, but also harmonics of any frequencies that may be present in buffer or frequency-multiplier stages. In the case of 144-Mc. transmitters, frequency-multiplying combinations that require a doubler or tripler stage to operate on a frequency actually in a low-band v.h.f. channel in use in the locality should be avoided.

Harmonic Suppression

Effective harmonic suppression has three separate phases:

1) Reducing the amplitude of harmonics generated in the transmitter. This is a matter of circuit design and operating conditions.

2) Preventing stray radiation from the transmitter and from associated wiring. This requires adequate shielding and filtering of all circuits and leads from which radiation can take place.

3) Preventing harmonics from being fed into the antenna.

It is impossible to build a transmitter that will not generate *some* harmonics, but it is obviously advantageous to reduce their strength, by circuit design and choice of operating conditions, by as large a factor as possible before attempting to prevent them from being radiated. Harmonic radiation from the transmitter itself or from its associated wiring obviously will cause interference just as readily as radiation from the antenna, so measures taken to prevent harmonics from reaching the antenna will not reduce TVI if the transmitter itself is radiating harmonics. But once it has been found that the transmitter itself is free from harmonic radiation, devices for preventing harmonics from reaching the antenna can be expected to produce results.

REDUCING HARMONIC GENERATION

Since reasonably efficient operation of r.f. power amplifiers always is accompanied by harmonic generation, good judgment calls for operating all frequency-multiplier stages at a very low power level — plate voltages not exceeding 250 or 300. When the final output frequency is reached, it is desirable to use as few stages as possible in building up to the final output power level, and to use tubes that require a minimum of driving power.

Circuit Design and Layout

Harmonic currents of considerable amplitude flow in both the grid and plate circuits of r.f. power amplifiers, but they will do relatively little harm if they can be effectively bypassed to the cathode of the tube. Fig. 23-7 shows the paths followed by harmonic currents in an amplifier circuit; because of the high reactance of the tank coil there is little harmonic current in it, so the harmonic currents simply flow through the tank capacitor, the plate (or grid) blocking capacitor, and the tube capacitances. The lengths of the leads forming these paths is of great importance, since the inductance in this circuit will resonate with the tube capacitance at some frequency in the v.h.f. range (the tank and blocking capacitances usually are so large compared with the tube capacitance that they have little effect on the resonant frequency). If such a resonance happens to occur at or near the same frequency as one of the transmitter harmonics, the effect is just the same as though a harmonic tank circuit had been deliberately introduced; the harmonic at that frequency will be tremendously increased in amplitude.

Such resonances are unavoidable, but by keeping the path from plate to cathode and from

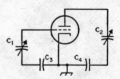

Fig. 23-7—A v.h.f. resonant circuit is formed by the tube capacitance and the leads through the tank and blocking capacitors. Regular tank coils are not shown, since they have little effect on such resonances. C_1 is the grid tuning capacitor and C_2 is the plate tuning capacitor. C_3 and C_4 are the grid and plate blocking or bypass capacitors, respectively.

grid to cathode as short as is physically possible, the resonant frequency usually can be raised above 100 Mc. in amplifiers of medium power. This puts it between the two groups of television channels.

It is easier to place grid-circuit v.h.f. resonances where they will do no harm when the amplifier is link-coupled to the driver stage, since this generally permits shorter leads and more favorable conditions for bypassing the harmonics than is the case with capacitive coupling. Link coupling also reduces the coupling between the driver and amplifier at harmonic frequencies, thus preventing driver harmonics from being amplified.

The inductance of leads from the tube to the tank capacitor can be reduced not only by shortening but by using flat strip instead of wire conductors. It is also better to use the chassis as the return from the blocking capacitor or tuned circuit to cathode, since a chassis path will have less inductance than almost any other form of connection.

The v.h.f. resonance points in amplifier tank circuits can be found by coupling a grid-dip meter covering the 50–250 Mc. range to the grid and plate leads. If a resonance is found in or near a TV channel, methods such as those described above should be used to move it well out of the TV range. The grid-dip meter also should be used to check for v.h.f. resonances in the tank coils, because coils made for 14 Mc. and below usually will show such resonances. In making the check, disconnect the coil entirely from the transmitter and move the grid-dip meter coil along it while exploring for a dip in the 54–88 Mc. band. If a resonance falls in a TV channel that is in use in the locality, changing the number of turns will move it to a less-troublesome frequency.

Operating Conditions

Grid bias and grid current have an important effect on the harmonic content of the r.f. currents in both the grid and plate circuits. In general, harmonic output increases as the grid bias and grid current are increased, but this is not necessarily true of a *particular* harmonic. The third and higher harmonics, especially, will go through fluctuations in amplitude as the grid current is increased, and sometimes a rather high value of grid current will minimize one harmonic as compared with a low value. This characteristic can be used to advantage where a particular harmonic is causing interference, remembering that the operating conditions that minimize one harmonic may greatly increase another.

For equal operating conditions, there is little or no difference between single-ended and push-pull amplifiers in respect to harmonic generation. Push-pull amplifiers are frequently trouble-makers on even harmonics because with such amplifiers the even-harmonic voltages are in phase at the ends of the tank circuit and hence appear with equal amplitude across the whole tank coil, if the center of the coil is not grounded. Under such circumstances the even harmonics can be coupled to the output circuit through stray capacitance between the tank and coupling coils. This does not occur in a single-ended amplifier having an inductively coupled tank, if the coupling coil is placed at the cold end, or with a pi-network tank.

Harmonic Traps

If a harmonic in only one TV channel is particularly bothersome — frequently the case when the transmitter operates on 28 Mc. — a trap tuned to the harmonic frequency may be installed in the plate lead as shown in Fig. 23-8. At the harmonic frequency the trap represents a very high impedance and hence reduces the amplitude of the harmonic current flowing through the tank circuit. In the push-pull circuit both traps have the same constants. The L/C ratio is not critical but a high-C circuit usually will have least effect on the performance of the plate circuit at the normal operating frequency.

Since there is a considerable harmonic voltage across the trap, radiation may occur from the trap unless the transmitter is well shielded. Traps should be placed so that there is no coupling between them and the amplifier tank circuit.

A trap is a highly selective device and so is useful only over a small range of frequencies.

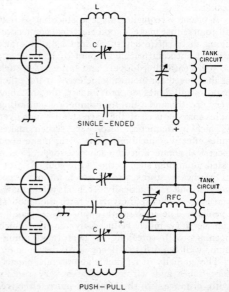

Fig. 23-8—Harmonic traps in an amplifier plate circuit. L and C should resonate at the frequency of the harmonic to be suppressed. C may be a 25- to 50-$\mu\mu$f. midget, and L usually consists of 3 to 6 turns about ½ inch in diameter for Channels 2 through 6. The inductance should be adjusted so that the trap resonates at about half capacitance of C before being installed in the transmitter. The frequency may be checked with a grid-dip meter. When in place, the trap should be adjusted for minimum interference to the TV picture.

A second- or third-harmonic trap on a 28-Mc. tank circuit usually will not be effective over more than 50 kc. or so at the fundamental frequency, depending on how serious the interference is without the trap. Because they are critical of adjustment, is is better to prevent TVI by other means, if possible, and use traps only as a last resort.

PREVENTING RADIATION FROM THE TRANSMITTER

The extent to which interference will be caused by direct radiation of spurious signals depends on the operating frequency, the transmitter power level, the strength of the television signal, and the distance between the transmitter and TV receiver. Transmitter radiation can be a very serious problem if the TV signal is weak, if the TV receiver and amateur transmitter are close together, and if the transmitter is operated with high power.

Shielding

Direct radiation from the transmitter circuits and components can be prevented by proper shielding. To be effective, a shield must completely enclose the circuits and parts and must have no openings that will permit r.f. energy to escape. Unfortunately, ordinary metal boxes and cabinets do not provide good shielding, since such openings as louvers, lids, and holes for running in connections allow far too much leakage.

A primary requisite for good shielding is that all joints must make a good electrical connection along their entire length. A small slit or crack will let out a surprising amount of r.f. energy; so will ventilating louvers and large holes such as those used for mounting meters. On the other hand, small holes do not impair the shielding very greatly, and a limited number of ventilating holes may be used if they are small — not over ¼ inch in diameter. Also, wire screen makes quite effective shielding if the wires make good electrical connection at each crossover. Perforated aluminum such as the "do-it-yourself" sold at hardware stores also is good, although not very strong mechanically. If perforated material is used, choose the variety with the smallest openings. The leakage through large openings can be very much reduced by covering such openings with screening or perforated aluminum, well bonded to all edges of the opening.

The intensity of r.f. fields about coils, capacitors, tubes and wiring decreases very rapidly with distance, so shielding is more effective, from a practical standpoint, if the components and wiring are not too close to it. It is advisable to have a separation of several inches, if possible, between "hot" points in the circuit and the nearest shielding.

For a given thickness of metal, the greater the conductivity the better the shielding. Copper is best, with aluminum, brass and steel following in that order. However, if the thickness is adequate for structural purposes (over 0.02

inch) and the shield and a "hot" point in the circuit are not in close proximity, any of these metals will be satisfactory. Greater separation should be used with steel shielding than with the other materials not only because it is considerably poorer as a shield but also because it will cause greater losses in near-by circuits than would copper or aluminum at the same distance. Wire screen or perforated metal used as a shield should also be kept at some distance from high-voltage or high-current r.f. points, since there is considerably more leakage through the mesh than through solid metal.

Where two pieces of metal join, as in forming a corner, they should overlap at least a half inch and be fastened together firmly with screws or bolts spaced at close-enough intervals to maintain firm contact all along the joint. The contact surfaces should be clean before joining, and should be checked occasionally — especially steel, which is almost certain to rust after a period of time.

The leakage through a given size of aperture in shielding increases with frequency, so such points as good continuous contact, screening of large holes, and so on, become even more important when the radiation to be suppressed is in the high band — 174-216 Mc. Hence 50- and 144-Mc. transmitters, which in general will have frequency-multiplier harmonics of relatively high intensity in this region, require special attention in this respect if the possibility of interfering with a channel received locally exists.

Lead Treatment

Even very good shielding can be made completely useless when connections are run to external power supplies and other equipment from the circuits inside the shield. Every such conductor leaving the shielding forms a path for the escape of r.f., which is then radiated by the connecting wires. Hence a step that is essential

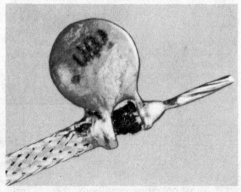

Fig. 23-9—Proper method of bypassing the end of a shielded lead using disk ceramic capacitor. The 0.001-μf. size should be used for 1600 volts or less; 500 μμf. at higher voltages. The leads are wrapped around the inner and outer conductors and soldered, so that the lead length is negligible. This photograph is about four times actual size.

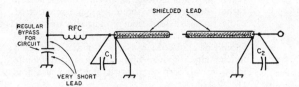

in every case is to prevent harmonic currents from flowing on the leads leaving the shielded enclosure.

Harmonic currents always flow on the d.c. or a.c. leads connecting to the tube circuits. A very effective means of preventing such currents from being coupled into other wiring, and one that provides desirable bypassing as well, is to use shielded wire for all such leads, maintaining the shielding from the point where the lead connects to the tube or r.f. circuit right through to the point where it leaves the chassis. The shield braid should be grounded to the chassis at both ends and at frequent intervals along the path.

Good bypassing of shielded leads also is essential. Bearing in mind that the shield braid about the conductor confines the harmonic currents to the *inside* of the shielded wire, the object of bypassing is to prevent their escape. Fig. 23-9 shows the proper way to bypass. The small 0.001-pf. ceramic disk capacitor, when mounted on the end of the shielded wire as shown in Fig. 23-9, actually forms a series-resonant circuit in the 54-88-Mc. range and thus represents practically a short circuit for low-band TV harmonics. The exposed wire to the connection terminal should be kept as short as is physically possible, to prevent any possible harmonic pickup exterior to the shielded wiring. Disk capacitors in the useful capacitance range of 500 to 1000 pf. are available in several voltage ratings up to 6000 volts.

These bypasses are essential at the connection-block terminals, and desirable at the tube ends of the leads also. Installed as shown with shielded wiring, they have been found to be so effective that there is usually no need for further harmonic filtering. However, if a test shows that additional filtering is required, the arrangement shown in Fig. 23-10 may be used. Such an r.f. filter should be installed at the tube end of the shielded lead, and if more than one circuit is filtered care should be taken to keep the r.f. chokes separated from each other and so oriented as to minimize coupling between them. This is necessary for preventing harmonics present in one circuit from being coupled into another.

In difficult cases involving Channels 7 to 13 — i.e., close proximity between the transmitter and receiver — and a weak TV signal — additional lead-filtering measures may be needed to prevent radiation of interfering signals by 50- and 144-Mc. transmitters. A recommended method is shown in Fig. 23-11. It uses a shielded lead by-

passed with a ceramic disk as described above, with the addition of a low-inductance feed-through type capacitor and a small r.f. choke, the capacitor being used as a terminal for the external connection. For voltages above 400, a capacitor of compact construction (as indicated in the caption) should be used, mounted so that there is a very minimum of exposed lead, inside the chassis, from the capacitor to the connection terminal.

As an alternative to the series-resonant bypassing described above, feed-through type capacitors such as the Sprague "Hypass" type may be used as terminals for external connections. The ideal method of installation is to mount them so they protrude through the chassis, with thorough bonding to the chassis all around the hole in which the capacitor is mounted. The principle is illustrated in Fig. 23-12.

Meters that are mounted in an r.f. unit should be enclosed in shielding covers, the connections being made with shielded wire with each lead bypassed as described above. The shield braid should be grounded to the panel or chassis immediately outside the meter shield, as indicated in Fig. 23-13. A bypass may also be connected across the meter terminals, principally to prevent any fundamental current that may be pres-

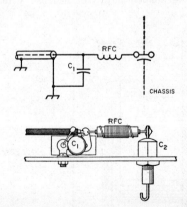

Fig. 23-11—Additional lead filtering for harmonics or other spurious frequencies in the high v.h.f. TV band (174-216 Mc.)

C_1—0.001-μf. disk ceramic.

C_2—500- or 1000-pf. feed-through bypass (Centralab FT-1000. Above 500 volts, substitute Centralab 858S-500.)

RFC—14 inches No. 26 enamel close-wound on ³⁄₁₆-inch diam. form or resistor.

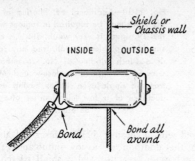

Fig. 23-12—The best method of using the "Hypass" type feed-through capacitor. Capacitances of 0.01 to 0.1 μf. are satisfactory. Capacitors of this type are useful for high-current circuits, such as filament and 115-volt leads, as a substitute for the r.f. choke shown in Fig. 23-10, in cases where additional lead filtering is needed.

ent from flowing through the meter itself. As an alternative to individual meter shielding the meters may be mounted entirely behind the panel, and the panel holes needed for observation may be covered with wire screen that is carefully bonded to the panel all around the hole.

Care should be used in the selection of shielded wire for transmitter use. Not only should the insulation be conservatively rated for the d.c. voltage in use, but the insulation should be of material that will not easily deteriorate in soldering. The r.f. characteristics of the wire are not especially important, except that the attenuation of harmonics in the wire itself will be greater if the insulating material has high losses at radio frequencies; in other words, wire intended for use at d.c. and low frequencies is preferable to cables designed expressly for carrying r.f. The attenuation also will increase with the length of the wire; in general, it is better to

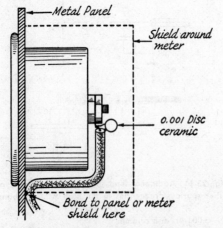

Fig. 23-13—Meter shielding and bypassing. It is essential to shield the meter mounting hole since the meter will carry r.f. through it to be radiated. Suitable shields can be made from 2½- or 3-inch diameter metal cans or small metal chassis boxes.

make the leads as long as circumstances permit rather than to follow the more usual practice of using no more lead than is actually necessary. Where wires cross or run parallel, the shields should be spot-soldered together and connected to the chassis. For high voltages, automobile ignition cable covered with shielding braid is recommended.

Proper shielding of the transmitter requires that the r.f. circuits be shielded entirely from the external connecting leads. A situation such as is shown in Fig. 23-15, where the leads in the r.f. chassis have been shielded and properly filtered but the chassis is mounted in a large shield, simply invites the harmonic currents to travel over the chassis and on out over the leads *outside* the chassis. The shielding about the r.f. circuits should make complete contact with the chassis on which the parts are mounted.

Checking Transmitter Radiation

A check for transmitter radiation always should be made before attempting to use low-pass filters or other devices for preventing harmonics from reaching the antenna system. The only really satisfactory indicating instrument is a television receiver. In regions where the TV signal is strong an indicating wavemeter such as one having a crystal or tube detector may be useful; if it is possible to get any indication at all from harmonics either on supply leads or around the transmitter itself, the harmonics are probably strong enough to cause interference. However, the absence of any such indication does not mean that harmonic interference will not be caused. If the techniques of shielding and lead filtering described in the preceding section are followed, the harmonic intensity on any external leads should be far below what any such instruments can detect.

Radiation checks should be made with the transmitter delivering full power into a dummy antenna, such as an incandescent lamp of suitable power rating, preferably installed inside the shielded enclosure. If the dummy must be external, it is desirable to connect it through a coax-matching circuit such as is shown in Fig. 23-16. Shielding the dummy antenna circuit is also desirable, although it is not always necessary.

Make the radiation test on all frequencies that are to be used in transmitting, and note whether or not interference patterns show in the received picture. (These tests must be made while a TV signal is being received, since the beat patterns will not be formed if the TV picture carrier is not present.) If interference exists, its source can be detected by grasping the various external leads (by the insulation, not the live wire!) or bringing the hand near meter faces, louvers, and other possible points where harmonic energy might escape from the transmitter. If any of these tests cause a *change* — not necessarily an *increase* — in the intensity of the interference, the presence of harmonics at that point is indicated. The location of such "hot" spots usually will point the way to the

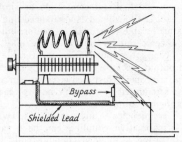

Fig. 23-15—A metal cabinet can be an adequate shield, but there will still be radiation if the leads inside can pick up r.f. from the transmitting circuits.

remedy. If the TV receiver and the transmitter can be operated side-by-side, a length of wire connected to one antenna terminal on the receiver can be used as a probe to go over the transmitter enclosure and external leads. This device will very quickly expose the spots from which serious leakage is taking place.

As a final test, connect the transmitting antenna or its transmission line terminals to the outside of the transmitter shielding. Interference created when this test is applied indicates that weak currents are on the outside of the shield and can be conducted to the antenna when the normal antenna connections are used. Currents of this nature represent interference that is conducted *over* low-pass filters, and hence cannot be eliminated by such filters.

TRANSMITTING ANTENNA CONSIDERATIONS

When a well-shielded transmitter is used in conjunction with an effective low-pass filter, and there is no incidental rectification in the area, it is impossible to have "harmonic-type" TVI, regardless of the type of transmitting antenna. However, the type of transmitting antenna in use can be responsible for "fundamental-overload" TVI.

To minimize the chances of TVI, the trans-

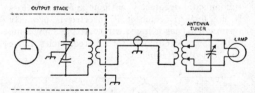

Fig. 23-16—Dummy-antenna circuit for checking harmonic radiation from the transmitter and leads. The matching circuit helps prevent harmonics in the output of the transmitter from flowing back over the transmitter itself, which may occur if the lamp load is simply connected to the output coil of the final amplifier. See transmission-line chapter for details of the matching circuit. Tuning must be adjusted by cut-and-try, as the bridge method described in the transmission-line chapter will not work with lamp loads because of the change in resistance when the lamps are hot.

mitting antenna should be located as far as possible from the receiving antenna. The chances of fundamental overload at the television receiver are reduced when a horizontal transmitting antenna or beam is mounted higher than the TV antenna. Other things being equal, fundamental overload is more likely to occur with a vertical transmitting antenna than with a horizontal one, because the vertical antenna has a stronger field at a low angle. If a ground-plane antenna can be located well above the height of the TV receiving antenna, there is less likelihood of fundamental overload than when it is at the same height or below the television antenna.

The s.w.r. on the line to the transmitting antenna has no effect on TVI. However, when the line to the antenna passes near the TV antenna, radiation from the line can be a source of TVI. Methods for minimizing radiation from the line are discussed in the chapter on transmission lines.

PREVENTING HARMONICS FROM REACHING THE ANTENNA

The third and last step in reducing harmonic TVI is to keep the spurious energy generated in or passed through the final stage from traveling over the transmission line to the antenna. It is seldom worthwhile even to attempt this until the radiation from the transmitter and its connecting leads has been reduced to the point where, with the transmitter delivering full power into a dummy antenna, it has been determined by actual testing with a television receiver that the radiation is below the level that can cause interference. If the dummy antenna test shows enough radiation to be seen in a TV picture, it is a practical certainty that harmonics will be coupled to the antenna system no matter what preventive measures are taken.

In inductively coupled output systems, some harmonic energy will be transferred from the final amplifier through the mutual inductance between the tank coil and the output coupling coil. Harmonics of the output frequency transferred in this way can be greatly reduced by providing sufficient selectivity between the final tank and the transmission line. A good deal of selectivity, amounting to 20 to 30 db. reduction of the second harmonic and much higher reduction of higher-order harmonics, is furnished by a matching circuit of the type shown in Fig. 23-16 and described in the chapter on transmission lines. An "antenna coupler" is therefore a worthwhile addition to the transmitter.

In 50- and 144-Mc. transmitters, particularly, harmonics not directly associated with the output frequency — such as those generated in low-frequency early stages of the transmitter — may get coupled to the antenna by stray means. For example, a 144-Mc. transmitter might have an oscillator or frequency multiplier at 48 Mc., followed by a tripler to 144 Mc. Some of the 48-Mc. energy will appear in the plate circuit of the tripler, and if passed on to the grid of the final amplifier will appear as a 48-Mc. modula-

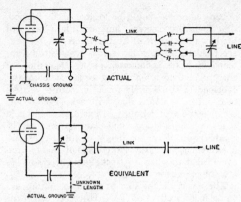

Fig. 23-17—The stray capacitive coupling between coils in the upper circuit leads to the equivalent circuit shown below, for v.h.f. harmonics.

tion on the 144-Mc. signal. This will cause a spurious signal at 192 Mc., which is in the high TV band, and the selectivity of the tank circuits may not be sufficient to prevent its being coupled to the antenna. Spurious signals of this type can be reduced by using link coupling between the driver stage and final amplifier (and between earlier stages as well) in addition to the suppression afforded by using an antenna coupler.

Capacitive Coupling

The upper drawing in Fig. 23-17 shows a parallel-conductor link as it might be used to couple into a parallel-conductor line through a matching circuit. Inasmuch as a coil is a sizable metallic object, there is capacitance between the final tank coil and its associated link coil, and between the matching-circuit coil and its link. Energy coupled through these capacitances travels over the link circuit and the transmission line as though these were merely single conductors. The tuned circuits simply act as masses of metal and offer no selectivity at all for capacitively-coupled energy. Although the actual capacitances are small, they offer a good coupling medium for frequencies in the v.h.f. range.

Capacitive coupling can be reduced by coupling to a "cold" point on the tank coil — the end connected to ground or cathode in a single-ended stage. In push-pull circuits having a split-stator capacitor with the rotor grounded for r.f., all parts of the tank coil are "hot" at even harmonics, but the center of the coil is "cold" at the fundamental and odd harmonics. If the center of the tank coil, rather than the rotor of the tank capacitor, is grounded through a bypass capacitor the center of the coil is "cold" at all frequencies, but this arrangement is not very desirable because it causes the harmonic currents to flow through the coil rather than the tank capacitor and this increases the harmonic transfer by pure inductive coupling.

With either single-ended or balanced tank circuits the coupling coil should be grounded to the chassis by a short, direct connection as shown in Fig. 23-18. If the coil feeds a balanced line or link, it is preferable to ground its center, but if it feeds a coax line or link one side may be grounded. Coaxial output is much preferable to balanced output, because the harmonics have to stay *inside* a properly installed coax system and tend to be attenuated by the cable before reaching the antenna coupler.

At high frequencies — and possibly as low as 14 Mc. — capacitive coupling can be greatly reduced by using a shielded coupling coil. The inner conductor of a length of coaxial cable is used to form a one-turn coupling coil. The outer conductor serves as an open-circuited shield around the turn, the shield being grounded to the chassis. The shielding has no effect on the inductive coupling. Because this construction is suitable only for one turn, the coil is not well adapted for use on the lower frequencies where many turns are required for good coupling.

A shielded coupling coil or coaxial output will not prevent stray capacitive coupling to the antenna if harmonic currents can flow over the *outside* of the coax line. In Fig. 23-19, the arrangement at either A or C will allow r.f. to flow over the outside of the cable to the antenna system. The proper way to use coaxial cable is to shield the transmitter completely, as shown at B, and make sure that the outer conductor of the cable is a continuation of the transmitter shielding. This prevents r.f. inside the transmitter from getting out by any path except the *inside* of the cable. Harmonics flowing *through* a coax line can be stopped by an antenna coupler or low-pass filter installed in the line.

Low-Pass Filters

A low-pass filter properly installed in a coaxial line, feeding either a matching circuit (antenna coupler) or feeding the antenna directly, will provide very great attenuation of harmonics. When the main transmission line is of the parallel-conductor type, the coax-coupled matching-circuit arrangement is highly recommended as a means for using a coax low-pass filter.

A low-pass filter will transmit power at the fundamental frequency without appreciable loss if the line in which it is inserted is properly terminated (has a low s.w.r.). At the same time it has large attenuation for all frequencies above the "cut-off" frequency.

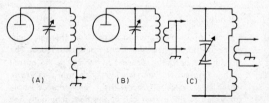

Fig. 23-18—Methods of coupling and grounding link circuits to reduce capacitive coupling between the tank and link coils. Where the link is wound over one end of the tank coil the side toward the hot end of the tank should be grounded, as shown at B.

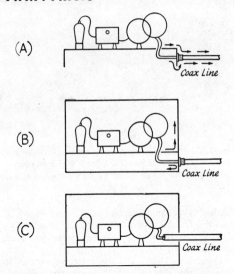

Fig. 23-19—Right (B) and wrong (A and C) ways to connect a coaxial line to the transmitter. In A or C, harmonic energy coupled by stray capacitance to the outside of the cable will flow without hindrance to the antenna system. In B the energy cannot leave the shield and can flow out only through, not over, the cable.

Low-pass filters of simple and inexpensive construction for use with transmitters operating below 30 Mc. are shown in Figs. 23-20 and 23-22. The former is designed to use mica capacitors of readily available capacitance values, for compactness and low cost. Both use the same circuit, Fig. 23-21, the only difference being in the L and C values. Technically, they are three-section filters having two full constant-k sections and two m-derived terminating half-sections, and their attenuation in the 54-88-Mc. range varies from over 50 to nearly 70 db., depending on the frequency and the particular set of values used. At high frequencies the ultimate attenuation will depend somewhat on internal resonant conditions associated with component lead lengths. These leads should be kept as short as possible.

The power that filters using mica capacitors can handle safely is determined by the voltage and current limitations of the capacitors. The power capacity is least at the highest frequency. The unit using postage-stamp silver mica capacitors is capable of handling approximately 50 watts in the 28-Mc. band, when working into a properly-matched line, but is good for about 150 watts at 21 Mc. and 300 watts at 14 Mc. and lower frequencies. A filter with larger mica capacitors (case type CM-45) will carry about 250 watts safely at 21 Mc., this rating increasing to 500 watts at 21 Mc. and a kilowatt at 14 Mc. and lower. If there is an appreciable mismatch between the filter and the line into which it works, these ratings will be considerably decreased, so in order to avoid capacitor failure

it is highly essential that the line on the output side of the filter be carefully matched.

The power capacity of these filters can be increased considerably by substituting r.f. type fixed capacitors (such as the Centralab 850 series) or variable air capacitors, in which event the power capability will be such as to handle the maximum amateur power on any band. The construction can be modified to accommodate variable air capacitors as shown in Fig. 23-22.

Using fixed capacitors of standard tolerances, there should be little difficulty in getting proper filter operation. A grid-dip meter with an accurate calibration should be used for adjustment of the coils. First, wire up the filter without L_2 and L_4. Short-circuit J_1 at its inside end with a screwdriver or similar conductor, couple the grid-dip meter to L_1 and adjust the inductance of L_1, by varying the turn spacing, until the circuit resonates at f_∞ as given in the table. Do the same thing at the other end of the filter with L_5. Then couple the meter to the circuit formed by L_3, C_2 and C_3, and adjust L_3 to resonate at the frequency f_1 as given by the table. Then remove L_3, install L_2 and L_4 and adjust L_2 to make the circuit formed by L_1, L_2, C_1 and C_2 (without the short across J_1) resonate at f_2 as given in the table. Do the same with L_4 for the circuit formed by L_4, L_5, C_3 and C_4. Then replace L_3 and check with the grid-dip meter at any coil in the filter; a distinct resonance should be found at or very close to the cut-off frequency, f_c.

FILTERS FOR V.H.F. TRANSMITTERS

High rejection of unwanted frequencies is possible with the tuned-line filters of Fig. 23-23.

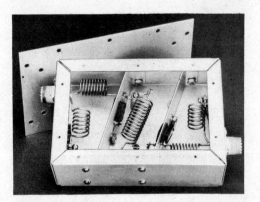

Fig. 23-20—An inexpensive low-pass filter using silver-mica postage-stamp capacitors. The box is a 2 by 4 by 6 aluminum chassis. Aluminum shields, bent and folded at the sides and bottom for fastening to the chassis, form shields between the filter sections. The diagonal arrangement of the shields provides extra room for the coils and makes it easier to fit the shields in the box, since bending to exact dimensions is not essential. The bottom plate, made from sheet aluminum, extends a half inch beyond the ends of the chassis and is provided with mounting holes in the extensions. It is held on the chassis with sheet-metal screws.

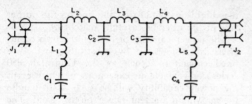

Fig. 23-21—Low-pass filter circuit. In the table below the letters refer to the following:

A—Using 100- and 70-pf. 500-volt silver mica capacitors in parallel for C_2 and C_3.

B—Using 70- and 50-pf. silver mica capacitors in parallel for C_2 and C_3.

C—Using 100- and 50-pf. mica capacitors, 1200-volt (case-style CM-45) in parallel for C_2 and C_3.

D and E—Using variable air capacitors, 500- to 1000-volt rating, adjusted to values given.

	A	B	C	D	E	
Z_0	52	75	52	52	75	ohms
f_0	36	35.5	41	40	40	Mc.
f_∞	44.4	47	54	50	50	Mc.
f_1	25.5	25.2	29	28.3	28.3	Mc.
f_2	32.5	31.8	37.5	36.1	36.1	Mc.
C_1, C_4	50	40	50	46	32	pf.
C_2, C_3	170	120	150	154	106	pf.
L_1, L_5	5½	6	4	5	6½	turns*
L_2, L_4	8	11	7	7	9½	turns*
L_3	9	13	8	8½	11½	turns*

*No. 12 or 14 wire, ½-inch inside diameter, 8 t.p.i.

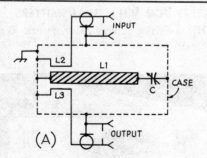

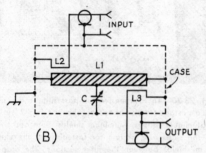

Fig. 23-23—Equivalent circuits for the strip-line filters. At A, the circuit for the 6- and 2-meter filters is shown. L_2 and L_3 are the input and output links. These filters are bilateral, permitting interchanging of the input and output terminals.

At B, the representative circuit for the 220- and 432-MHz. filters. These filters are also bilateral.

Fig. 23-22—Low-pass filter using variable capacitors. The unit is housed in two 2¼ x 2¼ x 5-inch Miniboxes, end to end. The cover should be secured to the box at several points.

Examples are shown for each band from 50 through 450 Mc. Construction is relatively simple, and the cost is low. Standard boxes are used, for ease of duplication.

The filter of Fig. 23-25 is selective enough to pass 50-Mc. energy and attenuate the 7th harmonic of an 8-Mc. oscillator, that falls in TV Channel 2. With an insertion loss at 50 Mc. of about 1 db., it can provide up to 40 db. of attenuation to energy at 57 Mc. in the same line. This should be more than enough attenuation to take care of the worst situations, provided that the radiation is by way of the transmitter output coax only. The filter will not eliminate intefering energy that gets out from power cables, the a.c. line, or from the transmitter circuits themselves. It also will do nothing for TVI that results from deficiencies in the TV receiver.

The 50-Mc. filter, Fig. 23-25, uses a folded line, in order to keep it within the confines of a standard chassis. The case is a 6 by 17 by 3-inch chassis (Bud AC-433) with a cover plate that fastens in place with self-tapping screws. An aluminum

Fig. 23-24—High-Q strip-line filters for 50 Mc. (top), 220, 144 and 420 Mc. Those for the two highest bands are half-wave line circuits. All use standard chassis.

Fig. 23-25—Interior of the 50-Mc. strip-line filter. Inner conductor of aluminum strip is bent into U shape, to fit inside a standard 17-inch chassis.

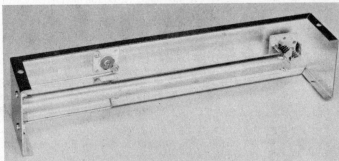

Fig. 23-26—The 144-Mc. filter has an inner conductor of ½-inch copper tubing 10 inches long, grounded to the left end of the case and supported at the right end by the tuning capacitor.

Fig. 23-27—A half-wave strip line is used in the 220-Mc. filter. It is grounded at both ends and turned at the center.

partition down the middle of the assembly is 14 inches long, and the full height of the chassis, 3 inches.

The inner conductor of the line is 32 inches long and $13/16$ inch wide, of $1/16$-inch brass, copper or aluminum. This was made from two pieces of aluminum spliced together to provide the 32-inch length. Splicing seemed to have no ill effect on the circuit Q. The side of the "U" are $2\frac{7}{8}$ inches apart, with the partition at the center. The line is supported on ceramic standoffs. These were shimmed up with sections of hard wood or bakelite rod, to give the required $1\frac{1}{2}$-inch height.

The tuning capacitor is a double-spaced variable (Hammarlund HF-30-X) mounted $1\frac{1}{2}$ inches from the right end of the chassis. Input and output coupling loops are of No. 10 or 12 wire, 10 inches long. Spacing away from the line is adjusted to about $\frac{1}{4}$ inch.

The 144-Mc. model, is housed in a $2\frac{1}{4}$ by $2\frac{1}{2}$ by 12-inch Minibox (Bud CU-2114-A).

One end of the tubing is slotted $\frac{1}{4}$ inch deep with a hacksaw. This slot takes a brass angle bracket $1\frac{1}{2}$ inches wide, $\frac{1}{4}$ inch high, with a

$\frac{1}{2}$-inch mounting lip. This $\frac{1}{4}$-inch lip is soldered into the tubing slot, and the bracket is then bolted to the end of the box, so as to be centered on the end plate.

The tuning capacitor (Hammarlund HF-15-X) is mounted $1\frac{1}{4}$ inches from the other end of the box, in such a position that the inner conductor can be soldered to the two stator bars.

The two coaxial fittings (SO-239) are $1\frac{1}{16}$ inch in from each side of the box, $3\frac{1}{2}$ inches from the left end. The coupling loops are No. 12 wire, bent so that each is parallel to the center line of the inner conductor, and about $\frac{1}{8}$ inch from its surface. Their cold ends are soldered to the brass mounting bracket.

The 220-Mc. filter uses the same size box as the 144-Ms. model. The inner conductor is $\frac{1}{16}$-inch brass or copper, $\frac{5}{8}$ inch wide, just long enough to fold over at each end for bolting to the box. It is positioned so that there will be $\frac{1}{8}$ inch clearance between it and the rotor plates of the tuning capacitor. The latter is a Hammarlund HF-15-X, mounted slightly off-center in the box, so that its stator plates connect to the exact midpoint of the line. The ⁵⁄₁₆-inch mounting hold in the case is 5½ inches from one end. The SO-239 coaxial fittings are 1 inch in from opposite sides of the box, 2 inches from the ends. Their coupling links are No. 14 wire, ⅛ inch from the inner conductor of the line.

The 420-Mc. filter is similar in design, using a 1⅝ by 2 by 10-inch Minibox (Bud CU-2113-A). A half-wave line is used, with disk tuning at the center. The disks are ¹⁄₁₆-inch brass, 1¼-inch diameter. The fixed one is centered on the inner conductor, the other mounted on a No. 6 brass lead-screw. This passes through a threaded bushing, which can be taken from the end of a discarded slug-tuned form. An advantage of these is that usually a tension device is included. If there is none, use a lock nut.

Type N coaxial connectors were used on the 420-Mc. model. They are ⅝ inch in from each side of the box, and 1⅜ inches in from the ends. Their coupling links of No. 14 wire are ¹⁄₁₆ inch from the inner conductor.

Adjustment and Use

If you want the filter to work on both transmitting and receiving, connect the filter between antenna line and s.w.r. indicator. With this arrangement you need merely adjust the filter for minimum reflected power reading on the s.w.r. bridge. This should be zero, or close to it, if the antenna is well-matched. The bridge should be used, as there is no way to adjust the filter properly without it. If you insist on trying, adjust for best reception of signals on frequencies close to the ones you expect to transmit on. This works only if the antenna is well matched.

When the filter is properly adjusted (with the s.w.r. bridge) you may find that reception can be improved by retuning the filter. Don't do it, if you want the filter to work best on the job it was intended to do; the rejection of unwanted energy, transmitting or receiving. If you want to improve reception with the filter in the circuit, work on the receiver input circuit. To get maximum power out of the transmitter and into the line, adjust the transmitter output coupling, not the filter. If the effect of the filter on reception bothers you, connect it in the line from the antenna relay to the transmitter only.

SUMMARY

The methods of harmonic elimination outlined in this chapter have been proved beyond doubt to be effective even under highly unfavorable conditions. It must be emphasized once more, however, that the problem must be solved one step at a time, and the procedure must be in logical order. It cannot be done properly without two items of simple equipment: a grid-dip meter and wavemeter covering the TV bands, and a dummy antenna.

To summarize:
1) Take a critical look at the transmitter on the basis of the design considerations outlined under "Reducing Harmonic Generation".

2) Check all circuits, particularly those connected with the final amplifier, with the grid-dip meter to determine whether there are any resonances in the TV bands. If so, rearrange the circuits so the resonances are moved out of the critical frequency region.

3) Connect the transmitter to the dummy antenna and check with the wavemeter for the presence of harmonics on leads and around the transmitter enclosure. Seal off the weak spots in the shielding and filter the leads until the wavemeter shows no indication at any harmonic frequency.

4) At this stage, check for interference with a TV receiver. If there is interference, determine the cause by the methods described previously and apply the recommended remedies until the interference disappears.

5) When the transmitter is completely clean on the dummy antenna, connect it to the regular antenna and check for interference on the TV receiver. If the interference is not bad, an antenna coupler or matching circuit installed as previously described should clear it up. Alternatively, a low-pass filter may be used. If neither the antenna coupler nor filter makes any difference in the interference, the evidence is strong that the interference, at least in part, is being caused by receiver overloading because of the strong fundamental-frequency field about the TV antenna and receiver. A coupler and/or filter, installed as described above, will invariably make a difference in the intensity of the interference if the interference is caused by transmitter harmonics alone.

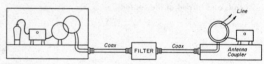

Fig. 23-28—The proper method of installing a low-pass filter between the transmitter and antenna coupler or matching circuit. If the antenna is fed through coax the antenna coupler may be omitted but the same construction should be used between the transmitter and filter. To be effective, the filter should be thoroughly shielded.

6) If there is still interference after installing the coupler and/or filter, and the evidence shows that it is probably caused by a harmonic, more attenuation is needed. A more elaborate filter may be necessary. However, it is well at this stage to assume that part of the interference may be caused by receiver overloading, and take steps to alleviate such a condition before trying highly-elaborate filters, traps, etc., on the transmitter.

HARMONICS BY RECTIFICATION

Even though the transmitter is completely free from harmonic output it is still possible for interference to occur because of harmonics generated outside the transmitter. These result from rectification of fundamental-frequency currents induced in conductors in the vicinity of the transmitting antenna. Rectification can take place at any point where two conductors are in poor electrical contact, a condition that frequently exists in plumbing, downspouting, BX cables crossing each other, and numerous other places in the ordinary residence. It also can occur in any exposed vacuum tubes in the station, in power supplies, speech equipment, etc., that may not be enclosed in the shielding about the r.f. circuits. Poor joints anywhere in the antenna system are especially bad, and rectification also may take place in the contacts of antenna changeover relays. Another common cause is overloading the front end of the communications receiver when it is used with a separate antenna (which will radiate the harmonics generated in the first tube) for break-in.

Rectification of this sort will not only cause harmonic interference but also is frequently responsible for cross-modulation effects. It can be detected in greater or less degree in most locations, but fortunately the harmonics thus generated are not usually of high amplitude. However, they can cause considerable interference in the immediate vicinity in fringe areas, especially when operation is in the 28-Mc. band. The amplitude decreases rapidly with the order of the harmonic, the second and third being the worst. It is ordinarily found that even in cases where destructive interference results from 28-Mc. operation the interference is comparatively mild from 14 Mc., and is negligible at still lower frequencies.

Nothing can be done at either the transmitter or receiver when rectification occurs. The remedy is to find the source and eliminate the poor contact either by separating the conductors or bonding them together. A crystal wavemeter (tuned to the fundamental frequency) is useful for hunting the source, by showing which conductors are carrying r.f. and, comparatively, how much.

Interference of this kind is frequently intermittent since the rectification efficiency will vary with vibration, the weather, and so on. The possibility of corroded contacts in the TV receiving antenna should not be overlooked, especially if it has been up a year or more.

TV RECEIVER DEFICIENCIES

Front-End Overloading

When a television receiver is quite close to the transmitter, the intense r.f. signal from the transmitter's fundamental may overload one or more of the receiver circuits to produce spurious responses that cause interference.

If the overload is moderate, the interference is of the same nature as harmonic interference; it is caused by harmonics generated in the early stages of the receiver and, since it occurs only on channels harmonically related to the transmitting frequency, is difficult to distinguish

from harmonics actually radiated by the transmitter. In such cases additional harmonic suppression at the transmitter will do no good, but any means taken at the receiver to reduce the strength of the amateur signal reaching the first tube will effect an improvement. With very severe overloading, interference also will occur on channels *not* harmonically related to the transmitting frequency, so such cases are easily identified.

Cross-Modulation

Upon some circumstances overloading will result in cross-modulation or mixing of the amateur signal with that from a local f.m. or TV station. For example, a 14-Mc. signal can mix with a 92-Mc. f.m. station to produce a beat at 78 Mc. and cause interference in Channel 5, or with a TV station on Channel 5 to cause interference in Channel 3. Neither of the channels interfered with is in harmonic relationship to 14 Mc. Both signals have to be on the air for the interference to occur, and eliminating either at the TV receiver will eliminate the interference.

There are many combinations of this type, depending on the band in use and the local frequency assignments to f.m. and TV stations. The interfering frequency is equal to the amateur fundamental frequency either added to or subtracted from the frequency of some local station, and when interference occurs in a TV channel that is not harmonically related to the amateur transmitting frequency the possibilities in such frequency combinations should be investigated.

I. F. Interference

Some TV receivers do not have sufficient selectivity to prevent strong signals in the intermediate-frequency range from forcing their way through the front end and getting into the i.f. amplifier. The once-standard intermediate frequency of, roughly, 21 to 27 Mc., is subject to interference from the fundamental-frequency output of transmitters operating in the 21-Mc. band. Transmitters on 28 Mc. sometimes will cause this type of interference as well.

A form of i.f. interference peculiar to 50-Mc. operation near the low edge of the band occurs with some receivers having the standard "41-Mc." i.f., which has the sound carrier at 41.25 Mc. and the picture carrier at 45.75 Mc. A 50-Mc. signal that forces its way into the i.f. system of the receiver will beat with the i.f. picture carrier to give a spurious signal on or near the i.f. sound carrier, even though the interfering signal is not actually in the nominal passband of the i.f. amplifier.

There is a type of i.f. interference unique to the 144-Mc. band in localities where certain u.h.f. TV channels are in operation, affecting only those TV receivers in which double-conversion type plug-in u.h.f. tuning strips are used. The design of these strips involves a first intermediate frequency that varies with the TV channel to be received and, depending on the particular strip design, this first i.f. may be in or close to the 144-Mc. amateur band. Since there is comparatively little selectivity in the TV signal-frequency circuits ahead of the first i.f., a signal from a 144-Mc. transmitter will "ride into" the i.f., even when the receiver is at a considerable distance from the transmitter. The channels that can be affected by this type of i.f. interference are:

Receivers with 21-Mc. second i.f.	Receivers with 41-Mc. second i.f.
Channels 14–18, inc.	Channels 20–25, inc.
Channels 41–48, inc.	Channels 51–58, inc.
Channels 69–77, inc.	Channels 82 and 83.

If the receiver is not close to the transmitter, a trap of the type shown in Fig. 23-31 will be effective. However, if the separation is small the 144-Mc. signal will be picked up directly on the receiver circuits and the best solution is to readjust the strip oscillator so that the first i.f. is moved to a frequency not in the vicinity of the 144-Mc. band. This has to be done by a competent technician.

I.f. interference is easily identified since it occurs on all channels—although sometimes the intensity varies from channel to channel—and the cross-hatch pattern it causes will rotate when the receiver's fine-tuning control is varied. When the interference is caused by a harmonic, overloading, or cross modulation, the structure of the interference pattern does not change (its intensity may change) as the fine-tuning control is varied.

High-Pass Filters

In all of the above cases the interference can be eliminated if the fundamental signal strength can be reduced to a level that the receiver can handle. To accomplish this with signals on bands below 30 Mc., the most satisfactory device is a high-pass filter having a cut-off frequency between 30 and 54 Mc., installed at the tuner input terminals of the receiver. Circuits

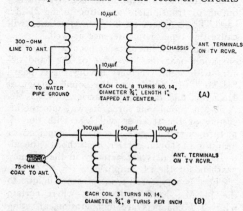

Fig. 23-29—High-pass filters for installation at the TV receiver antenna terminals. A—balanced filter for 300-ohm line, B—for 75-ohm coaxial line. Important: Do not use a direct ground on the chassis of a transformerless receiver. Ground through a 0.001-μf. mica capacitor.

that have proved effective are shown in Figs. 23–29 and 23–30. Fig. 23–30 has one more section than the filters of Fig. 23–29 and as a consequence has somewhat better cut-off characteristics. All the circuits given are designed to have little or no effect on the TV signals but will attenuate all signals lower in frequency than about 40 Mc. These filters preferably should be constructed in some sort of shielding container, although shielding is not always necessary. The dashed lines in Fig. 23–30 show how individual filter coils can be shielded from each other. The capacitors can be tubular ceramic units centered in holes in the partitions that separate the coils.

Simple high-pass filters cannot always be applied successfully in the case of 50-Mc. transmissions, because they do not have sufficiently-sharp cut-off characteristics to give both good attenuation at 50–54 Mc. and no attenuation above 54 Mc. A more elaborate design capable of giving the required sharp cut-off has been described (Ladd, "50-Mc. TVI—Its Causes and Cures," *QST*, June and July, 1954). This article

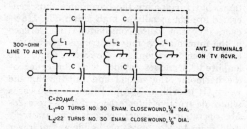

Fig. 23-30—Another type of high-pass filter for 300-ohm line. The coils may be wound on 1/8-inch diameter plastic knitting needles. Important: Do not use a direct ground on the chassis of a transformerless receiver. Ground through a 0.001-μf. mica capacitor.

also contains other information useful in coping with the TVI problems peculiar to 50-Mc. operation. As an alternative to such a filter, a high-Q wave trap tuned to the transmitting frequency may be used, suffering only the disadvantage that it is quite selective and therefore will protect a receiver from overloading over only a small range of transmitting frequencies in the 50-Mc. band. A trap of this type is shown in Fig. 23–31. These "suck-out" traps, while absorbing energy at the frequency to which they are tuned, do not affect the receiver operation otherwise. The assembly should be mounted near the input terminals of the TV tuner and its case should be grounded to the TV set chassis. The traps should be tuned for minimum TVI at the transmitter operating frequency. An insulated tuning tool should be used for adjustment of the trimmer capacitors, since they are at a "hot" point and will show considerable body-capacitance effect.

High-pass filters are available commercially at moderate prices. In this connection, it should be understood by all parties concerned that while an amateur is responsible for *harmonic* radia-

Parallel-tuned traps for installation in the 300-ohm line to the TV set. The traps should be mounted in an aluminum Minibox with a shield partition between them, as shown. For 50 Mc, the coils should have 9 turns of No. 16 enamel wire, close wound to a diameter of ½ inch. The 144-Mc traps should contain coils with a total of 6 turns of the same type wire, close-wound to a diameter of ¼ inch. Traps of this type can be used to combat fundamental-overload TVI on the lower-frequency bands as well.

tion from his transmitter, it is no part of his responsibility to pay for or install filters, wave traps, etc. that may be required at the receiver to prevent interference caused by his *fundamental* frequency. Proper installation usually requires that the filter be installed right at the input terminals of the r.f. tuner of the TV set and not merely at the external antenna terminals, which may be at a considerable distance from the tuner. The question of cost is one to be settled between the set owner and the organization with which he deals.

Some of the larger manufacturers of TV receivers have instituted arrangements for cooperating with the set dealer in installing high-pass filters at no cost to the receiver owner. FCC-sponsored TVI Committees, now operating in many cities, have all the information necessary for effectuating such arrangements. To find out whether such a committee is functioning in your community, write to the FCC field office having jurisdiction over your location. A list of the field offices is contained in *The Radio Amateur's License Manual*, published by ARRL.

If the fundamental signal is getting into the receiver by way of the line cord a line filter such as that shown in Fig. 23-1 may help. To be most effective it should be installed inside the receiver chassis at the point where the cord enters, making the ground connections directly to chassis at this point. It may not be so helpful if placed between the line plug and the wall socket unless the r.f. is actually picked up on the house wiring rather than on the line cord itself.

Antenna Installation

Usually, the transmission line between the TV receiver and the actual TV antenna will pick up a great deal more energy from a nearby transmitter than the television receiving antenna itself. The currents induced on the TV transmission line in this case are of the "parallel" type, where the phase of the current is the same in both conductors. The line simply acts like two wires connected together to operate as one. If the receiver's antenna input circuit were perfectly balanced it would reject these "parallel" or "unbalance" signals and respond only to the true transmission-line ("push-pull") currents; that is, only signals picked up on the actual

antenna would cause a receiver response. However, no receiver is perfect in this respect, and many TV receivers will respond strongly to such parallel currents. The result is that the signals from a nearby amateur transmitter are much more intense at the first stage in the TV receiver than they would be if the receiver response were confined entirely to energy picked up on the TV antenna alone. This situation can be improved by using shielded transmission line —coax or, in the balanced form, "twinax"— for the receiving installation. For best results the line should terminate in a coax fitting on the receiver chassis, but if this is not possible the shield should be grounded to the chassis right at the antenna terminals.

The use of shielded transmission line for the receiver also will be helpful in reducing response to harmonics actually being radiated from the transmitter or transmitting antenna. In most receiving installations the transmission line is very much longer than the antenna itself, and is consequently far more exposed to the harmonic fields from the transmitter. Much of the harmonic pickup, therefore, is on the receiving transmission line when the transmitter and receiver are quite close together. Shielded line, plus relocation of either the transmitting or receiving antenna to take advantage of directive effects, often will result in reducing overloading, as well as harmonic pickup, to a level that does not interfere with reception.

U.H.F. TELEVISION

Harmonic TVI in the u.h.f. TV band is far less troublesome than in the v.h.f. band. Harmonics from transmitters operating below 30 Mc. are of such high order that they would normally be expected to be quite weak; in addition, the components, circuit conditions and construction of low-frequency transmitters are such as to tend to prevent very strong harmonics from being generated in this region. However, this is not true of amateur v.h.f. transmitters, particularly those working in the 144-Mc. and higher bands. Here the problem is quite similar to that of the low v.h.f. TV band with respect to transmitters operating below 30 Mc.

There is one highly favorable factor in u.h.f.

TABLE 23-I

Harmonic Relationship—Amateur V.H.F. Bands and U.H.F. TV Channels

Amateur Band	Harmonic	Fundamental Freq. Range	Channel Affected
144 Mc.	4th	144.0–144.5	31
		144.5–146.0	32
		146.0–147.5	33
		147.5–148.0	34
	5th	144.0–144.4	55
		144.4–145.6	56
		145.6–146.8	57
		146.8–148	58
	6th	144–144.33	79
		144.33–145.33	80
		145.33–147.33	81
		147.33–148	82
220 Mc.	3rd	220–220.67	45
		220.67–222.67	46
		222.67–224.67	47
		224.67–225	48
	4th	220–221	82
		221–222.5	83
420 Mc.	2nd	420–421	75
		421–424	76
		424–427	77
		427–430	78
		430–433	79
		433–436	80

TV that does not exist in the most of the v.h.f. TV band: If harmonics are radiated, it is possible to move the transmitter frequency sufficiently (within the amateur band being used) to avoid interfering with a channel that may be in use in the locality. By restricting operation to a portion of the amateur band that will not result in harmonic interference, it is possible to avoid the necessity for taking extraordinary precautions to prevent harmonic radiation.

The frequency assignment for u.h.f. television consists of seventy 6-megacycle channels (Nos. 14 to 83, inclusive) beginning at 470 Mc. and ending at 890 Mc. The harmonics from amateur bands above 50 Mc. span the u.h.f. channels as shown in Table 23-I. Since the assignment plan calls for a minimum separation of six channels between any two stations in one locality, there is ample opportunity to choose a fundamental frequency that will move a harmonic out of range of a local TV frequency.

COLOR TELEVISION

The color TV signal includes a subcarrier spaced 3.58 megacycles from the regular picture carrier (or 4.83 Mc. from the low edge of the channel) for transmitting the color information. Harmonics which fall in the color subcarrier region can be expected to cause break-up of color in the received picture. This modifies the chart of Fig. 23-3 to introduce another "severe" region centering around 4.8 Mc. measured from the low-frequency edge of the channel. Hence with color television reception there is less oppor-

tunity to avoid harmonic interference by choice of operating frequency. In other respects the problem of eliminating interference is the same as with black-and-white television.

INTERFERENCE FROM TV RECEIVERS

The TV picture tube is swept horizontally by the electron beam 15,750 times per second, using a wave shape that has very high harmonic content. The harmonics are of appreciable amplitude even at frequencies as high as 30 Mc., and when radiated from the receiver can cause considerable interference to reception in the amateur bands. While measures to suppress radiation of this nature are required by FCC in current receivers, many older sets have had no such treatment. The interference takes the form of rather unstable, a.c.-modulated signals spaced at intervals of 15.75 kc.

Studies have shown that the radiation takes place principally in three ways, in order of their importance: (1) from the a.c. line, through stray coupling to the sweep circuits; (2) from the antenna system, through similar coupling; (3) directly from the picture tube and sweep-circuit wiring. Line radiation often can be reduced by bypassing the a.c. line cord to the chassis at the point of entry, although this is not completely effective in all cases since the coupling may take place outside the chassis beyond the point where the bypassing is done. Radiation from the antenna is usually suppressed by installing a high-pass filter on the receiver. The direct radiation requires shielding of high-potential leads and, in some receivers, additional bypassing in the sweep circuit; in severe cases, it may be necessary to line the cabinet with screening or similar shielding material.

Incidental radiation of this type from TV and broadcast receivers, when of sufficient intensity to cause serious interference to other radio services (such as amateur), is covered by Part 15 of the FCC rules. When such interference is caused, the user of the receiver is obligated to take steps to eliminate it. The owner of an offending receiver should be advised to contact the source from which the receiver was purchased for appropriate modification of the receiving installation. TV receiver dealers can obtain the necessary information from the set manufacturer.

It is usually possible to reduce interference very considerably, without modifying the TV receiver, simply by having a good amateur-band receiving installation. The principles are the same as those used in reducing "hash" and other noise — use a good antenna, such as the transmitting antenna, for reception; install it as far as possible from a.c. circuits; use a good feeder system such as a properly balanced two-wire line or coax with the outer conductor grounded; use coax input to the receiver, with a matching circuit if necessary; and check the receiver to make sure that it does not pick up signals or noise with the antenna disconnected.

Chapter 24

Operating a Station

The enjoyment of amateur radio comes mostly from the operation of our station once we have finished its construction. Upon the *station* and its *operation* depend the communication records that are made. The standing of individuals as amateurs and respect for the capabilities of the whole institution of amateur radio depend to a considerable extent on the practical communications established by amateurs, the aggregate of all our station efforts.

An operator with a slow, steady, clean-cut method of sending has a big advantage over the poor operator. The technique of speaking in connected thoughts and phrases is equally important for the voice operator. Good sending is partly a matter of practice but patience and judgment are just as important qualities of an operator as a good "fist."

Operating knowledge embracing standard procedures, development of skill in employing c.w. to expand the station range and operating effectiveness at minimum power levels and some net know-how are all essentials in achieving a triumphant amateur experience with top station records, personal results, and demonstrations of what our stations can do in practical communications.

OPERATING COURTESY AND TOLERANCE

Operating interests in amateur radio vary considerably. Public service is of course the most important activity (more about this later). Other interests include rag-chewing, working DX, contest operating, award-seeking, or experimenting on the air. Inevitably, amateurs in pursuit of their own favorite activity often get into each other's hair.

Interference is one of the things we amateurs have to live with. However, we can conduct our operating in a way designed to alleviate this as much as possible. *Before putting the transmitter on the air, listen on your own frequency.* If you hear stations engaged in communication on that frequency, stand by until you are sure no interference will be caused by your operations, or *shift to another frequency.* No amateur or any group of amateurs has any *exclusive* claim to any frequency in any band but we must work together, each respecting the rights of others. Remember, those other chaps can cause you as much interference as you cause them, sometimes more!

In this chapter we'll recount some fundamentals of operating success, cover major procedures for successful general work and include proper forms to use in message handling and other fields. Note also the sections on special activities, awards and organization. These permit us all to develop through our organization more success together than we could ever attain by separate uncoordinated efforts.

C.W. PROCEDURE

The best c.w. operators observe certain operating procedures regarded as "standard practice," as follows:

1) *Calls.* A short, snappy call is usually the most effective. Standard practice for years has been the "three by three," that is the station being called three times followed by the called station three times, thus: WØDX WØDX WØDX DE W1AW W1AW W1AW AR. But much depends on the circumstances. In a contest, a "one by one" may be more effective. The general principle is to *keep it short,* so as not to clutter up the air with unnecessary QRM.

CQ. One hears many stations calling CQ over and over without signing. Three CQ's followed by one or two identifications repeated not more than three times should be sufficient under any circumstances. Use a general CQ *only* when you are willing to work any station who answers you. Listen on the frequency first; don't plop on a QSO in progress.

The directional CQ: The best way to find some specific state, country or place is to *listen* and *call* when what you are looking for is heard. Directional or selective CQ's usually just cause unnecessary interference. However, occasionally they work, and it is preferable to call a selective CQ than to call a general one and not answer if the station replying is not what you want. *Example:* A station looking for Vermont might call: CQ VT CQ VT CQ VT DE W4IA W4IA W4IA K. Keep such calls short. Repeat frequently if no results. And remember, always *listen first* to avoid causing QRM.

LIKE A BRIDGE, A CALL SHOULD BE JUST LONG ENOUGH TO DO THE JOB

OPERATING ABBREVIATIONS AND PREFIXES

Q SIGNALS

Given below are a number of Q signals whose meanings most often need to be expressed with brevity and clearness in amateur work. (Q abbreviations take the form of questions only when each is sent followed by a question mark.)

QRG Will you tell me my exact frequency (or that of.......)? Your exact frequency (or that of......)is......kc.

QRH Does my frequency vary? Your frequency varies.

QRI How is the tone of my transmission? The tone of your transmission is.....(1. Good; 2. Variable; 3. Bad).

QRJ Are you receiving me badly? Are my signals weak? I cannot receive you. Your signals are too weak.

QRK What is the intelligibility of my signals (or those of...)? The intelligibility of your signals (or those of...) is..(1. bad; 2. poor; 3. fair; 4. good; 5. excellent).

QRL Are you busy? I am busy (or I am busy with ......). Please do not interfere.

QRM Are you being interfered with?. I am being interfered with..(1. nil; 2. slightly; 3. moderately; 4. severely; 5. extremely).

QRN Are you troubled by static? I am troubled by static..(1-5 as under QRM).

QRO Shall I increase power? Increase power.

QRP Shall I decrease power? Decrease power.

QRQ Shall I send faster? Send faster (.....w.p.m.).

QRS Shall I send more slowly? Send more slowly (.... w.p.m.).

QRT Shall I stop sending? Stop sending.

QRU Have you anything for me? I have nothing for you.

QRV Are you ready? I am ready.

QRW Shall I inform.....that you are calling him on .....kc.? Please inform.....that I am calling on.....kc.

QRX When will you call me again? I will call you again at......hours (on........kc.).

QRY What is my turn? Your turn is Number...

QRZ Who is calling me? You are being called by..... (on......kc.).

QSA What is the strength of my signals (or those of ......)? The strength of your signals (or those of.....) is.......(1. Scarcely perceptible; 2. Weak; 3. Fairly good; 4. Good; 5. Very good).

QSB Are my signals fading? Your signals are fading.

QSD Is my keying defective? Your keying is defective.

QSG Shall I send.....messages at a time? Send..... messages at a time.

QSK Can you hear me between your signals and if so can I break in on your transmission? I can hear you between my signals; break in on my transmission.

QSL Can you acknowledge receipt? I am acknowledging receipt.

QSM Shall I repeat the last message which I sent you, or some previous message? Repeat the last message which you sent me [or message(s) number(s).....].

QSN Did you hear me (or...) on..kc.? I did hear you (or...) on..kc.

QSO Can you communicate with....direct or by relay? I can communicate with.....direct (or by relay through.....).

QSP Will you relay to.....? I will relay to....

QSU Shall I send or reply on this frequency (or on ..k.c.)? Send or reply on this frequency (or on..k.c.)

QSV Shall I send a series of Vs on this frequency (or ....kc.)? Send a series of Vs on this frequency (or.....kc.).

QSW Will you send on this frequency (or on....kc.)? I am going to send on this frequency (or on .....kc.).

QSX Will you listen to.....on.....kc.? I am listening to.....on.....kc.

QSY Shall I change to transmission on another frequency? Change to transmission on another frequency (or on....kc.).

QSZ Shall I send each word or group more than once? Send each word or group twice (or....times).

QTA Shall I cancel message number....as if it had not been sent? Cancel message number..... as if it had not been sent.

QTB Do you agree with my counting of words? I do not agree with your counting of words; I will repeat the first letter or digit of each word or group.

QTC How many messages have you to send? I have ....messages for you (or for.....).

QTH What is your location? My location is.....

QTR What is the correct time? The time is......

Special abbreviations adopted by ARRL:

QST General call preceding a message addressed to all amateurs and ARRL members. This is in effect "CQ ARRL."

QRRR Official ARRL "land SOS." A distress call for emergency use only by a station in an emergency situation.

The R-S-T System

READABILITY

1 — Unreadable.
2 — Barely readable, some words distinguishable.
3 — Readable with considerable difficulty.
4 — Readable with practically no difficulty.
5 — Perfectly readable.

SIGNAL STRENGTH

1 — Faint signals, barely perceptible.
2 — Very weak signals.
3 — Weak signals.
4 — Fair signals.
5 — Fairly good signals.
6 — Good signals.
7 — Moderately strong signals.
8 — Strong signals.
9 — Extremely strong signals.

TONE

1 — Extremely rough hissing note.
2 — Very rough a.c. note, no trace of musicality.
3 — Rough low-pitched a.c. note, slightly musical.
4 — Rather rough a.c. note, moderately musical.
5 — Musically-modulated note.
6 — Modulated note, slight trace of whistle.
7 — Near d.c. note, smooth ripple.
8 — Good d.c. note, just a trace of ripple.
9 — Purest d.c. note.

If the signal has the characteristic stability of crystal control, add the letter X to the RST report. If there is a chirp, the letter C may be added to so indicate. Similarly for a click, add K.

This reporting system is used on both c.w. and voice, leaving out the "tone" report on voice.

Hams who do not raise stations readily may find that their sending is poor, their calls ill-timed or their judgment in error. When conditions are right to bring in signals from the desired locality, you can call them. Short calls, at about the same frequency, with breaks to listen, will raise stations with minimum time and trouble.

2) *Answering a Call:* Call three times (or less) ; send DE ; sign three times (or less) ; after contact is established decrease the use of the call signals of both stations to *once only.* When a station receives a call but does not receive the call letters of the station calling, QRZ? may be used. It means "By whom am I being called?" QRZ should not be used in place of CQ.

3) *Ending Signals and Sign-Off:* The proper use of $\overline{AR}$, K, $\overline{KN}$, $\overline{SK}$ and CL ending signals is as follows:

$\overline{AR}$—End of transmission. Recommended after call to a specific station before contact has been established.

> *Example:* W6ABC W6ABC W6ABC
> DE W9LMN W9LMN $\overline{AR}$. Also at the end of transmission of a radiogram, immediately following the signature, preceding identification.

K—Go ahead (any station). Recommended after CQ and at the end of each transmission during QSO when there is no objection to others breaking in.

> *Example:* CQ CQ CQ DE W1ABC W1ABC
> K or W9XYZ DE W1ABC K.

$\overline{KN}$—Go ahead (specific station), all others keep out. Recommended at the end of each transmission during a QSO, or after a call, when calls from other stations are not desired and will not be answered.

> *Example:* W4FGH DE EL4A $\overline{KN}$.

$\overline{SK}$—End of QSO or communication. Recommended before signing *last* transmission at end of a QSO.

> *Example:* .... $\overline{SK}$ W8LMN DE W5BCD.

CL—I am closing station. Recommended when a station is going off the air, to indicate that it will not listen for any further calls.

> *Example:* .... $\overline{SK}$ W7HIJ DE W2JKL
> CL.

4) *Testing.* When it is necessary to make test signals on the air they should continue for not more than ten seconds and must be identified by your call letters. Avoid excessive testing, but *always* listen before using any frequency for this purpose. Use a dummy load if possible.

5) *Receipting* for conversation or traffic: Never receipt for a transmission until it has been entirely received. "R" means *only* "transmission received as sent." Use R only when *all* is received correctly.

6) *Repeats.* When part of a transmission is lost, a call should be followed by correct abbreviations to ask for repeats. When a few words on the end of a transmission are lost, the *last word received correctly* is given after ?AA, meaning "all after." When a few words at the beginning of a transmission are lost, ?AB for "all before" a stated word should be used. The quickest way to ask for a fill in the middle of a transmission is to send the last word received correctly, a question mark, then the next word received correctly. Or send "?BN [word] and [word]."

Do not send words twice (QSZ) unless it is requested. Send single. Do not fall into the bad habit of sending double *without a request* from fellows you work. Don't say "QRM" or "QRN" when you mean "QRS."

General Practices

Here are a few recommended general practices to make your c.w. operating more proficient:

1) Use the "double dash" or "break" sign ($\overline{BT}$) to separate thoughts or sentences in a rag chew, instead of punctuation.

2) Make full use of c.w. abbreviations to shorten transmissions. (See list on p. 610.) *Avoid* such inanities as "over to you" and "how copy?" on c.w. They are unnecessarily long and HW? says the same thing.

3) Use the letter R in place of a decimal or a colon in time designations. (E.g., 3R5 MC, 2R30 PM.

4) "Break in" is helpful in all c.w. operation. Being able to hear the other station between the spaces in your sending enables him to "break" you if he is not receiving you, thus preventing "blind" transmission. It also enables you to hear a called station if he comes back to someone else, preventing unnecessary calling.

5) "Swing" in sending is *not* the mark of a good operator. Send evenly, *watch your spacing.* It is very easy to get into the habit of running your words together. Correct your errors ; the other guy is no mindreader.

6) A long dash can be used for a zero in casual ragchewing, but avoid it in call letters and formal messages.

7) It is good practice to repeat unusual words and things you want to make sure the other operator receives. A question mark after a word means that you intend repeating it.

8) Be sure you identify as required by FCC regs.

Good Sending

Assuming that an operator has learned sending properly, and comes up with a precision "fist" — not fast, but clean, steady, making well-formed rhythmical characters and spacing beautiful to listen to — he then becomes subject to outside pressures to his own possible detriment in everyday operating. He will want to "speed it up" because the operator at the other end is going faster, and so he begins, unconsciously, to run his words together or develops a "swing."

Perhaps one of the easiest ways to get into bad habits is to do too much playing around with special keys. Too many operators spend only enough time with a straight key to acquire "passable" sending, then subject their newly-developed "fists" to the entirely different movements of bugs, side-swipers, electronic keys, or what-have-you. All too often, this results in the ruination of what might have become a very good "fist."

Think about your sending a little. Are you satisfied with it? You should not be—ever. Nobody's sending is perfect, and therefore *every* operator should continually strive for improvement. Do you ever run letters together — like Q for MA, or P for AN — especially when you are in a hurry? Practically everybody does at one time or another. Do you have a "swing"? Any recognizable "swing" is a deviation from perfection. Strive to send like tape sending; copy a W1AW Bulletin and try to send it with the same spacing using a local oscillator on a subsequent transmission.

Check your spacing in characters, between characters and between words occasionally. A visual recording of your fist will show up your faults as nothing else will. Practice the correction of faults.

Using Break-in

The technical requirements for c.w. break-in are detailed elsewhere in this *Handbook* (see Ch. 7). Once this part of it is accomplished, the full advantages of break-in operation can be realized. Unnecessarily long calls are avoided, QRM is reduced, more communication per hour can be realized. Brief calls with frequent short pauses for reply can approach (but not equal) break-in efficiency.

With break-in, ideas and messages to be transmitted can often be pulled right through the holes in the QRM and QRN. "Fills" are unnecessary. Neither operator need send for any period of time without being copied. Once you get used to it, break-in is a "must."

In traffic-handling circles, the station without break-in is considered at best an indifferent traffic-handling station. But even in day-to-day QSOing, break-in can be a great advantage.

In calling, the transmitting operator sends the letters "BK" at intervals during his call so that stations hearing the call may know that break-in is in use and take advantage of the fact. *He pauses at intervals* during his call, to listen for a moment for a reply. If the station being called does not answer, the call can be continued.

With a tap of the key, the man on the receiving end can interrupt (if a word is missed). The other operator is constantly monitoring, awaiting just such directions. It is not necessary that *you* have perfect facilities to take advantage of break-in when the stations you work are break-in-equipped. After an invitation to *break* is given (and at each pause) press your key—and contact can start *immediately*.

VOICE OPERATING

The use of proper procedure to get best results is just as important as in using code. In telegraphy words must be spelled out letter by letter. It is therefore but natural that abbreviations and

---

Voice-Operating Hints

1) Listen before calling.

2) Make short calls with breaks to listen. Avoid long CQs; do not answer over-long CQs.

3) Use push-to-talk or voice control. Give essential data concisely in first transmission.

4) Make reports honest. Use definitions of strength and readability for reference. Make your reports informative and useful. Honest reports and *full* word description of signals save amateur operators from FCC trouble.

5) Limit transmission length. Two minutes or less will convey much information. When three or more stations converse in round tables, brevity is essential.

6) Display sportsmanship and courtesy. Bands are congested . . . make transmissions meaningful . . . give others a break.

7) Check transmitter adjustment . . . avoid a.m. overmodulation and splatter. On s.s.b. check carrier balance carefully. Do not radiate when moving v.f.o. frequency or checking n.f.m. swing. Use receiver b.f.o. to check stability of signal. Complete testing before busy hours!

---

shortcuts have come into use. In voice work, however, abbreviations are not necessary, and have less importance in our operating procedure.

The letter "K" is used in telegraphic practice so that the operator will not have to pound out the separate letters "go ahead." The voice operator can *say* the words "go ahead" or "over," or "come in please."

One laughs on c.w. by sending HI. On phone, *laugh* when one is called for.

The matter of reporting *readability* and *strength* is as important to phone operators as to those using code. With telegraph nomenclature, it is necessary to spell out words to describe signals or use abbreviated signal reports. But on voice, we have the ability to "say it with words." "Readability four, strength eight" is the best way to give a quantitative report, but reporting can be done so much more meaningfully with ordinary words: "You are weak but I can understand you, so go ahead," or "Your signal is strong but you are buried under local interference."

Voice Equivalents to Code Procedure

Voice	Code	Meaning
Go ahead; over	K	Self-explanatory
Wait; stand by	$\overline{AS}$	Self-explanatory
Received	R	Receipt for a correctly-transcribed message or for "solid" transmission with no missing portions
Clear	$\overline{SK}$	Self-explanatory
Clear and Leaving the air	CL	Self-explanatory

Phone-Operating Practice

Efficient voice communication, like good c.w. communication, demands good operating. Adherence to certain points "on getting results" will go a long way toward improving our phone-band operating conditions.

Use push-to-talk technique. Where possible arrange on-off switches, controls or voice-controlled break-in for fast back-and-forth exchanges. This will help reduce the length of transmissions and keep brother amateurs from calling you a "monologuist" — a guy who likes to hear himself talk!

Listen with care. Keep noise and "backgrounds" out of your operating room to facilitate good listening. It is natural to answer the strongest signal, but take time to listen and give some consideration to the *best* signals, regardless of strength. Every amateur cannot run a kilowatt transmitter, but there is no reason why every amateur cannot have a signal of good quality, and utilize uniform operating practices to aid in the understandability and ease of his own communications.

Interpose your call regularly and at frequent intervals. Three short calls are better than one long one. In calling CQ, one's call should certainly appear at least once for every five or six CQs. Calls with frequent breaks to listen will save time and be most productive of results. In identifying, always transmit your *own* call *last.* *Don't* say "This is W1ABC standing by for W2DEF"; say "W2DEF, this is W1ABC, over." FCC regulations show the call of the transmitting station sent *last.*

Monitor your own frequency. This helps in timing calls and transmissions. Transmit only when the frequency is clear and there is a chance of being copied successfully—not when you are merely "more QRM." Timing transmissions is an art to cultivate.

Keep modulation constant. By turning the gain "wide open" you are subjecting anyone listening to the diversion of whatever noises are present in or near your operating room, to say nothing of the possibility of feedback, echo due to poor acoustics, and modulation excesses due to sudden loud noises. Speak near the microphone, and don't let your gaze wander all over the station causing sharply-varying input to your speech amplifier; at the same time, keep far enough from the microphone so your signal is not modulated by your breathing. Change distance to the microphone or gain only as necessary to insure uniform transmitter performance without splatter or distortion.

Make connected thoughts and phrases. Don't mix disconnected ideas or subjects. Ask questions consistently. Pause for a moment and then get the answers.

Have a pad of paper handy. It is convenient and desirable to jot down questions as they come, in order not to miss any. It will help you to make intelligent to-the-point replies.

Steer clear of inanities and soap-opera stuff. Our amateur radio and personal reputation as serious communications workers depend on us.

Avoid repetition. Don't repeat back what the other fellow has just said. Too often we hear: "Okay on your new antenna there, okay on receiving me okay, okay on the trouble you're having with your receiver, okay on the company who just came in with some ice cream and cake, okay . . . [etc.]." Just *say* you received everything

O.K. Don't try to prove it.

Use phonetics only as required. When clarifying genuinely doubtful expessions and in getting your call identified positively we suggest use of the ARRL Phonetic List or the International Civil Aviation Organization list. The ARRL list was designed for amateur use (no confusion between phonetics and station location). Whichever you learn, don't overdo its use.

The speed of radiotelephone transmission (with perfect accuracy) depends almost entirely upon the skill of the two operators involved. One must learn to speak at a rate allowing perfect understanding as well as permitting the receiving operator to copy down the message text, if that is necessary. Because of the similarity of many English speech sounds, the use of word lists has been found necessary. All voice-operated stations should use a *standard* list as needed to identify call signals or unfamiliar expressions.

PHONETIC ALPHABETS

	ARRL	ICAO		ARRL	ICAO
A	—ADAM	ALFA	N	—NANCY	NOVEMBER
B	—BAKER	BRAVO	O	—OTTO	OSCAR
C	—CHARLIE	CHARLIE	P	—PETER	PAPA
D	—DAVID	DELTA	Q	—QUEEN	QUEBEC
E	—EDWARD	ECHO	R	—ROBERT	ROMEO
F	—FRANK	FOXTROT	S	—SUSAN	SIERRA
G	—GEORGE	GOLF	T	—THOMAS	TANGO
H	—HENRY	HOTEL	U	—UNION	UNIFORM
I	—IDA	INDIA	V	—VICTOR	VICTOR
J	—JOHN	JULIETT	W	—WILLIAM	WHISKEY
K	—KING	KILO	X	—X-RAY	X-RAY
L	—LEWIS	LIMA	Y	—YOUNG	YANKEE
M	—MARY	MIKE	Z	—ZEBRA	ZULU

Example: W1AW . . . W 1 ADAM WILLIAM . . . W1AW

Round Tables. The round table has many advantages if run properly. It clears frequencies of interference, especially if all stations involved are on the same frequency, while the enjoyment value remains the same, if not greater. By use of push-to-talk, the conversation can be kept lively and interesting, giving each station operator ample opportunity to participate without waiting overlong for his turn.

Round tables can become very unpopular if they are not conducted properly. The monologuist, off on a long spiel about nothing in particular, cannot be interrupted; *make your transmissions short and to the point.* "Butting in" is discourteous and unsportsmanlike; *don't enter a round table, or any contact between two other amateurs, unless you are invited.* It is bad enough trying to copy through prevailing interference without the added difficulty of poor voice quality; *check your transmitter adjustments frequently.* In general, follow the precepts as hereinbefore outlined for the most enjoyment in round tables as well as any other form of radiotelephone communication.

WORKING DX

Most amateurs at one time or another make "working DX" a major aim. As in every other phase of amateur work, there are right and wrong ways to go about getting best results in working foreign stations, and it is the intention of this section to outline a few of them.

The ham who has trouble raising DX stations readily may find that poor transmitter efficiency is not the reason. He may find that his sending is poor, or his calls ill-timed, or his judgment in error. When conditions are right to bring in the DX, and the receiver sensitive enough to bring in several stations from the desired locality, the way for U.S. and Canadian stations to work DX is to use the appropriate frequency and timing and *call these stations,* as against the common practice of calling "CQ DX."

The call CQ DX means slightly different things to amateurs in different bands:

a) On v.h.f., CQ DX is a general call ordinarily used only when the band is open, under favorable "skip" conditions. For v.h.f. work, such a call is used for looking for new states and countries, also for distances beyond the customary "line-of-sight" range on most v.h.f. bands.

b) CQ DX on our 7-, 14-, 21- and 28-MHz. bands may be taken to mean "General call to any foreign station." The term "foreign station" usually refers to any station in a foreign continent. (*Experienced* amateurs in the U. S. A. and Can-

ada do *not* use this call, but *answer* such calls made by foreign stations.)

c) CQ DX used on 3.5 MHz. under winter-night conditions may be used in this same manner. At other times, under average 3.5 MHz. propagation conditions, the call may be used in domestic work when looking for new states or countries in one's own continent, usually applying to stations located over 1000 miles distant from you.

The way to work DX is not to use a CQ call at *all* (in our continent). Instead, use your best tuning skill — and listen — and listen — and *listen. You have to hear them before you can work them.* Hear the desired stations first; time your calls well. Use your utmost skill. A sensitive receiver is often more important than the power input in working foreign stations. If you can hear stations in a particular country or area, chances are that you will be able to work someone there.

One of the most effective ways to work DX is to know the operating habits of the DX stations sought. Doing too much transmitting on the DX bands is not the way to do this. Again, *listening* is effective. Once you know the operating habits of the DX station you are after you will know when and where to call, and when to remain silent waiting your chance.

Some DX stations indicate where they will tune for replies by use of "10U" or "15D." (See point 4 of the DX Operating Code.) In voice work the overseas operator may say "listening on 14,225 kHz." or "tuning upward from 28,500 kHz." Many a DX station will not reply to a call on his exact frequency.

ARRL has recommended some operating procedures to DX stations aimed at controlling some of the thoughtless operating practices sometimes used by W/VE amateurs. A copy of these recommendations (Operating Aid No. 5) can be obtained free of charge from ARRL Headquarters.

In any band, particularly at line-of-sight frequencies, when directional antennas are used, the directional CQ such as CQ W5, CQ north, etc., is the preferable type of call. Mature amateurs agree that CQ DX is a wishful rather than a practical type of call for most stations in the North Americas looking for foreign contacts. Ordinarily, it is a cause of unnecessary QRM.

Conditions in the transmission medium often make it possible for the signals from low-powered transmitters to be received at great distances. In general, the higher the frequency band the less important power considerations become, for occasional DX work. This accounts in part

---

DX OPERATING CODE
(For W/VE Amateurs)

Some amateurs interested in DX work have caused considerable confusion and QRM in their efforts to work DX stations. The points below, if observed by all W/VE amateurs, will go a long way toward making DX more enjoyable for everybody.

1. Call DX only after he calls CQ, QRZ?, signs $\overline{SK}$, or phone equivalents thereof
2. Do *not* call a DX station:
   a. On the frequency of the station he is working until you are *sure* the QSO is over. This is indicated by the ending signal $\overline{SK}$ on c.w. and any indication that the operator is listening, on phone
   b. Because you hear someone else calling him
   c. When he signs $\overline{KN}$, $\overline{AR}$, CL, or phone equivalents
   d. Exactly on his frequency
   e. After he calls a directional CQ, unless of course you are in the right direction or area.
3. Keep within frequency-band limits. Some DX stations operate outside. Perhaps they can get away with it, but you cannot
4. Observe calling instructions of DX stations. "10U" means call ten kc. *up* from his frequency, "15D" means 15 kc. *down,* etc.
5. Give honest reports. Many foreign stations *depend* on W and VE reports for adjustment of station and equipment
6. Keep your signal clean. Key clicks, chirps, hum or splatter give you a bad reputation and may get you a citation from FCC.
7. *Listen* for and *call* the station you want. Calling CQ DX is not the best assurance that the *rare* DX will reply.
8. When there are several W or VE stations waiting to work a DX station, avoid asking him to "listen for a friend." Let your friend take his chances with the rest. Also avoid engaging DX stations in rag-chews against their wishes.

DATE TIME (GMT)	STATION CALLED	CALLED BY	HIS FREQ. OR DIAL	HIS SIGNAL RST	MY SIGNAL RST	FREQ. MHZ	EMISSION TYPE	POWER INPUT WATTS	TIME OF ENDING QSO	OTHER DATA	NAME	QSLs S	R
11-14-68													
2300	W3EML	X	3.65	589	57X	3.5	A1	250	2309	RCVD 3, SENT 3	Bill		
2315	CQ	X				7	"	"					
2319	CQ	W5NWJ	7.03	469	479	"	4	"	2329	CNDX FAIR	SOUPY	√	
2335	W2ZVW	X	3.84	59	59	3.8	A3A	150	2355	SKED			
11-15-68													
0005	IIA9OH	X	14.02	579	579	14	A1	250	0010	NOVOSIBIRSK	VLADIS	√	
0015	UW9PT	X	14.03	569	579	"	"	"	0022	" "	VIK	√	
0023	X	IIA9PO	"	569	589	"	"	"	0028	" "	ANNA	√	
1202	CQ	VK3NR	14.02	589	579	"	"	"	1215	MELBOURNE	NOEL	√	

KEEP AN ACCURATE AND COMPLETE STATION LOG AT ALL TIMES. FCC REQUIRES IT.

A page from the official ARRL log is shown above, answering every FCC requirement in respect to station records. Bound logs made up in accord with the above form can be obtained from Headquarters for a nominal sum or you can prepare your own, in which case we offer this form as a suggestion. The ARRL log has a special wire binding and lies perfectly flat on the table.

for the relative popularity of the 14-, 21- and 28-MHz. bands among amateurs who like to work DX.

KEEPING AN AMATEUR STATION LOG

The FCC requires every amateur to keep a complete station operating record (log) that shows (1) the date and time of each transmission, (2) all calls and transmissions made, whether contacts resulted or not, (3) the input power to the last stage of the transmitter, (4) the frequency band used, (5) the time of ending each contact (QSO), and (6) the signature of the licensed operator. Written messages handled in standard form must be included in the log or kept on file for a period of at least one year.

But a log can be more than just a legal record of station operation. It can be a "diary" of your amateur experience. Make it a habit to enter thought and comments, changes in equipment, operating experiences and reactions, anything that might make enjoyable reminiscences in years to come. Your log is a reflection of your personal experience in amateur radio. Make it both neat and complete.

ARRL headquarters stocks log books and message blanks for the convenience of amateurs. See the catalog section of this *Handbook*.

PUBLIC SERVICE OPERATING

Amateurs interested in rendering public service in operating have "closed ranks" in the Amateur Radio Public Service Corps, a new name for a very old concept. ARPSC links two time-honored ARRL operating entities, the Amateur Radio Emergency Corps (AREC) and the National Traffic System (NTS) along with the Radio Amateur Civil Emergency Service (RACES); these three entities are the "Emergency," "Traffic" and "Civil Defense" divisions of ARPSC respectively.

Practically speaking, little change has been made in any of them. All continue as before, AREC to provide communication for peacetime emergency, NTS to handle amateur traffic on a daily basis and RACES to provide emergency backup for civil defense. The big difference is that all three now conduct regular liaison with each other and NTS, in an emergency, conducts long haul traffic with efficiency and dispatch through the system's facilities in accordance with an emergency communications plan making provision for special extended operation of the system during time of emergency.

The detailed workings of the AREC, NTS and RACES are fully explained in separate ARRL publications available without charge to amateurs interested. In this *Handbook* we will confine ourselves mostly to basics.

MESSAGE HANDLING

Amateur operators in the United States and a few other countries enjoy a privilege not available to amateurs in most countries—that of handling third-party message traffic. In the early history of amateur radio in this country, some amateurs who were among the first to take advantage of this privilege formed an extensive relay organization which became the ARRL.

Thus, amateur message-handling has had a long and honorable history and, like most services, has gone through many periods of development and change. Those amateurs who handled traffic in 1914 would hardly recognize it the way some of us do it today, just as equipment in those days was far different from that in use now. Progress has been made and new methods have been developed in step with advancement in communication techniques of all kinds. Amateurs who handled a lot of traffic found that organized operating schedules were more effective than random relays, and as techniques advanced and messages increased in number, trunk lines were organized, spot frequencies began to be used, and there came into existence a number of traffic nets in which many stations operated on the same frequency to effect wider coverage in less time with fewer relays; but the old methods are still available to the amateur who handles only an occasional message.

Although message handling is as old an art as is amateur radio itself, there are many amateurs who do not know how to handle a message and have never done so. As each amateur grows older and gains experience in the amateur service, there is bound to come a time when he will be called upon to handle a written message, during a communications emergency, in casual contact with one of his many acquaintances on the air, or as a result of a request from a non-amateur friend. Regardless of the occasion, if it comes to you, you will want to rise to it! Considerable embarrassment is likely to be experienced by the amateur who finds he not only does not know the form in which the message should be prepared, but does not know how to go about putting it on the air.

Traffic work need not be a complicated or time-consuming activity for the casual or occasional message-handler. Amateurs may participate in traffic work to whatever extent they wish, from an occasional message now and then to becoming a part of organized traffic systems. This chapter explains some principles so the reader may know where to find out more about the subject and may exercise the message-handling privilege to best effect as the spirit and opportunity arise.

Responsibility

Amateurs who originate messages for transmission or who receive messages for relay or delivery should first consider that in doing so they are accepting the responsibility of clearing the message from their station on its way to its destination in the shortest possible time. Forty-eight hours after filing or receipt is the generally-accepted rule among traffic-handling amateurs, but it is obvious that if every amateur who relayed the message allowed it to remain in his station this long it might be a long time reaching its destination. Traffic should be relayed or delivered as quickly as possible.

Message Form

Once this responsibility is realized and accepted, handling the message becomes a matter of following generally-accepted standards of form and transmission. For this purpose, each message is divided into four parts: the preamble, the address, the text and the signature. Some of these parts themselves are subdivided. It is necessary in preparing the message for transmission and in actually transmitting it to know not only what each part is and what it is for, but to know in what *order* it should be transmitted, and to know the various procedure signals used with it when sent by c.w. If you are going to send a message, you may as well send it right.

Standardization is important! There is a great deal of room for expressing originality and individuality in amateur radio, but there are also times and places where such expression can only cause confusion and inefficiency. Recognizing the need for standardization in message form and message transmitting procedures, ARRL has long since recommended such standards, and most traffic-interested amateurs have followed them. In general, these recommendations, and the various changes they have undergone from

Here is an example of a plain-language message as it would be prepared for delivery. If the message were for relay instead of delivery, the information at the bottom would be filled in instead of that in the box.

year to year, have been at the request of amateurs participating in this activity, and they are completely outlined and explained in *Operating an Amateur Radio Station,* a copy of which is available upon request or by use of the coupon at the end of this chapter.

Clearing a Message

The best way to clear a message is to put it into one of the many organized traffic networks, or to give it to a station that can do so. There are many amateurs who make the handling of traffic their principal operating activity, and many more still who participate in this activity to a greater or lesser extent. The result is a system of traffic nets which spreads to all corners of the United States and covers most U. S. possessions and Canada. Once a message gets into one of these nets, regardless of the net's size or coverage, it is systematically routed toward its destination in the shortest possible time.

Amateurs not experienced in message handling should depend on the experienced message-handler to get a message through, if it is important; but the average amateur can enjoy operating with a message to be handled either through a local traffic net or by free-lancing. The latter may be accomplished by careful listening for an amateur station at desired points, directional CQs, use of recognized calling and net frequencies, or by making and keeping a schedule with another amateur for regular work between specified points. He may well aim at learning and enjoying through doing. The joy and accomplishment in thus developing one's operating skill to the peak of perfection has a reward all its own.

If you decide to "take the bull by the horns" and put the message into a traffic net yourself (and more power to you if you do!), you will need to know something about how traffic nets operate, and the special Q signals and procedure they use to dispatch all traffic with a maximum of efficiency. The frequency and operating time of the net in your section, or of other nets into which your message can go, is given in ARRL's Net Directory. This annually-revised publication is available on request. Listening for a few minutes at the time and frequency indicated should acquaint you with enough fundamentals to enable you to report into the net and indicate your traffic. From that time on you follow the instructions of the net control station, who will tell you when and to whom (and on what frequency, if different from the net frequency) to send your message. Since c.w. nets use the special "QN" signals, it is helpful to have a list of these before you (available from ARRL Hq., Operating Aid No. 9A).

Network Operation

About this time, you may find that you are enjoying this type of operating activity and want to know more about it and increase your proficiency. Many amateurs are happily "addicted" to traffic handling after only one or two brief exposures to it. Much traffic is at present being conducted by c.w., since this mode of communication seems to be popular for record purposes—but this does not mean that high code speed is a necessary prerequisite to working in traffic networks. There are many nets organized specifically for the slow-speed amateur, and most of the so-called "fast" nets are usually glad to slow down to accommodate slower operators.

It is a significant operating fact that code speed or word speed alone does *not* make for efficiency—sometimes the contrary! A high-speed operator who does not know procedure can "foul up" a net much more completely and more quickly than can a slow operator. It is a proven fact that a bunch of high-speed operators who are not "savvy" in net operation cannot accomplish as much during a specified period as an equal number of slow operators who *know* net procedure. Don't let low code speed deter you from getting into traffic work. Given a little time, your speed will reach the point where you can easily hold your own. Concentrate first on learning the net procedures.

Much traffic is also handled on phone. This mode is exceptionally well suited to short-range traffic work and requires knowledge of phonetics and procedure peculiar to voice operation. Procedure is of paramount importance on phone, since the public may be listening.

Teamwork is the theme of net operation. The net which functions most efficiently is the net in which all participants are thoroughly familiar with the procedure used, and in which operators refrain from transmitting except at the direction of the net control station, and do not occupy time with extraneous comments, even the exchange of pleasantries. There is a time and place for everything. When a net is in session it should concentrate on handling traffic until all traffic is cleared. Before or after the net is the time for rag-chewing and discussion. Some details of net operation are included in *Operating an Amateur Radio Station,* mentioned earlier, but there is no substitute for actual participation.

The National Traffic System

To facilitate and speed the movement of message traffic, there is in existence an integrated national system by means of which originated traffic can normally reach its destination area the same day the message is originated. This system uses the state or section net as a basis. Each section net sends a representative to a "region" net (normally covering a call area) and each "region" net sends a representative to an "area" net (normally covering a time zone). After the area net has cleared all its traffic, its members then go back to their respective region nets, where they clear traffic to the various section net representatives. By means of connecting schedules between the area nets, traffic can flow both ways so that traffic originated on the West Coast reaches the East Coast with a maximum of dispatch, and vice versa. In general section nets function at 1900, region nets at 1945, area nets at 2030 and the same or different regional personnel again at 2130. Some section nets conduct a late session at 2200 to effect traffic delivery the same night. Local standard time is referred to in each case.

The NTS plan somewhat spreads traffic opportunity so that casual traffic may be reported into nets for efficient handling one or two nights per week, early or late; or the ardent traffic man can operate in *both* early and late groups and in between to roll up impressive totals and speed traffic reliably to its destination. Old-time traffic men who prefer a high degree of organization and teamwork have returned to the traffic game as a result of the new system. Beginners have shown more interest in becoming part of a system nationwide in scope, in which *anyone* can participate. The National Traffic System has vast and intriguing possibilities as an amateur service. It is open to any amateur who wishes to participate.

The above is but the briefest résumé of what is of necessity a rather complicated arrangement of nets and schedules. Complete details of the System and its operation are included in the ARRL *Public Service Communications Manual.*

EMERGENCY COMMUNICATION

One of the most important ways in which the amateur serves the public, thus making his existence a national asset, is by his preparation for and his participation in communications emergencies. Every amateur, regardless of the extent of his normal operating activities, should give some thought to the possibility of his being the only means of communication should his community be cut off from the outside world. It has happened many times, often in the most unlikely places; it has happened without warning, finding some amateurs totally unprepared; it can happen to *you*. Are you ready?

There are two principal ways in which any amateur can prepare himself for such an eventuality. One is to provide himself with equipment capable of operating on any type of emergency power (i.e., either a.c. or d.c.), and equipment which can readily be transported to the scene of disaster. Mobile equipment is especially desirable in most emergency situations.

Such equipment, regardless of how elaborate or how modern, is of little use, however, if it is not used properly and at the right times; and so another way for an amateur to prepare himself for emergencies, by no means less important than the first, is to *learn to operate efficiently*. There are many amateurs who feel that they know how to operate efficiently but who find themselves considerably handicapped at the crucial time by not knowing proper procedure, by being unable, due to years of casual amateur operation, to adapt themselves to snappy, abbreviated transmissions, and by being unfamiliar with message form and procedures. It is dangerous to overrate your ability in this; it is better to assume you have things to learn.

In general it can be said that there is more emergency equipment available than there are operators who know properly how to operate during emergency conditions, for such conditions require clipped, terse procedure with complete break-in on c.w. and fast push-to-talk on phone. The casual rag-chewing aspect of amateur radio, however enjoyable and worth-while in its place, must be forgotten at such times in favor of the business at hand. There is only one way to gain experience in this type of operation, and that is by practice. During an emergency is no time for practice; it should be done beforehand, as often as possible, on a regular basis.

This leads up to the necessity for emergency organization and preparedness. ARRL has long recognized this necessity and has provided for it. The Section Communications Manager (whose address appears on page 6 of every issue of *QST*) is empowered to appoint certain qualified amateurs in his section for the purpose of coordinating emergency communication organization and preparedness in specified areas or communities. This appointee is known as an Emergency Coordinator for the city or town. One should be specified for each community. For coordination and promotion at section level a Section Emergency Coordinator arranges for and recommends the appointments of various Emergency Coordinators at activity points throughout the section. Emergency Coordinators organize amateurs in their communities according to local needs for emergency communication facilities.

The community amateurs taking part in the local organization are members of the Amateur Radio Emergency Corps (AREC). *All* amateurs are invited to register in the AREC, whether they are able to play an active part in their local organization or only a supporting role. Application blanks are available from your EC, SEC, SCM or direct from ARRL Headquarters. In the event that inquiry reveals no Emergency Coordinator appointed for your community, your SCM would welcome a recommendation either from yourself or from a radio club of which you are a member. By holding an amateur operator license, you have the respon-

---

Before Emergency

PREPARE yourself by providing emergency power for your station.

TEST your emergency equipment and operating ability in the annual Simulated Emergency Test and Field Day.

REGISTER with your ARRL Emergency Coordinator. If none, offer your services to local and civic relief agencies and explain what amateur radio can do during disasters.

In Emergency

LISTEN before you transmit, *always!*

REPORT to your Emergency Coordinator so he will have latest data on your facilities. Offer local civic and relief agencies your services directly in the absence of an EC.

RESTRICT all on-the-air work in accordance with FCC regulations, Sec. 97.107.

QRRR is the official ARRL c.w. "land SOS," a distress call for *emergency only*. The phone equivalent is "CQ Emergency."

RESPECT the fact that success in emergency depends on circuit discipline. The net control station is the supreme authority.

COOPERATE with those we serve. Be ready to help, but stay off the air unless there is a specific job to be done that you can handle more efficiently than any other station.

COPY bulletins from W1AW. During emergencies, special bulletins are transmitted.

After Emergency

REPORT to ARRL Headquarters promptly and fully so that the Amateur Service can receive full credit.

---

sibility to your community and to amateur radio to uphold the traditions of the service.

Among the League's publications is a booklet entitled *Public Service Communications*. This booklet, while small in size, contains a wealth of information on AREC organization and functions and is invaluable to any amateur participating in emergency or civil defense work. It is free to AREC members and should be in every amateur's shack. Drop a line to the ARRL Communications Department if you want a copy, or use the coupon at the end of this chapter.

The Radio Amateur Civil Emergency Service

Following World War II there was established within our government the Federal Civil Defense Administration (FCDA), which, at the behest of ARRL and other amateurs, considered the role of the amateur in civil defense communication should the U.S. become embroiled in another war. This resulted, in 1951, in the establishment of the Radio Amateur Civil Emergency Service (RACES) with rules promulgated by FCC as a part of the Amateur Radio Service. FCDA has evolved into the present Office of Civil Defense, part of the Department of the Army, and although the RACES rules have undergone several minor changes they are still essentially the same as originally put into effect. In 1966, by action of the ARRL Board of Directors, RACES was recognized as an essential part of the amateur's public service effort by including it nominally in the League's Amateur Radio Public Service Corps as a division thereof.

RACES is intended solely for civil defense communication through the medium of amateur radio and is designed to continue operation during any extreme national emergency such as war. It shares certain segments of frequencies with the regular (i.e., normal) Amateur Service on a nonexclusive basis. Its regulations are a subpart of the familiar amateur regulations (Part 97) and are included in full in the ARRL *License Manual*.

If *every* amateur participated, we would still be short of the total operating personnel required properly to implement RACES. As the service which bears the responsibility for the successful implementation of this important function, we face not only the task of installing (and in some cases building) the necessary equipment, but also of the training of thousands of additional people. This can and should be a function of the local unit of the Amateur Radio Emergency Corps under its EC and his assistants, working in close collaboration with the local civil defense organization.

The first step in organizing RACES locally is the appointment of a radio officer by the local civil defense director, possibly on the recommendation of his communications officer. A complete and detailed communications plan must be approved successively by local, state and OCD regional directors, by the OCD national office, and by FCC. Once this has been accomplished, applications for station authorizations under this plan can be submitted direct to FCC. *QST* carries further information from time to time, and ARRL will keep its field officials fully informed by bulletins as the situation requires. A complete bibliography of *QST* articles dealing with the subject of civil defense and RACES is available upon request from the ARRL Communications Department.

In the event of war, civil defense will place great reliance on RACES for back-up radio communication. Even in peacetime, RACES can be of great value in natural disaster communications. As a part of our Amateur Service and our Public Service Corps, it deserves our wholehearted and enthusiastic support and will permit us to continue to function in the public service, as amateurs, in RACES in wartime as we function in AREC and NTS during peacetime. If interested, inquire of your local civil defense agency and get signed up with your radio officer.

ARRL OPERATING ORGANIZATION

Amateur operation must have point and constructive purpose to win public respect. Each individual amateur is the ambassador of the entire fraternity in his public relations and attitude toward his hobby. ARRL field organization adds point and purpose to amateur operating.

The Communications Department of the League is concerned with the practical operation of stations in all branches of amateur activity. Appointments or awards are available for ragchewer, traffic enthusiast, phone operator, DX man and experimenter.

There are seventy-four ARRL Sections in the League's field organization, which embraces the United States, Canada and certain other territory. Operating affairs in each Section are supervised by a Section Communications Manager (SCM) elected by members in that section for a two-year term of office. Organization appointments are made by the SCMs, elected as provided in the Rules and Regulations of the Communications Department, which accompany the League's By-Laws and Articles of Association. SCM addresses for all sections are given in full in each issue of *QST*. SCMs welcome monthly activity reports from all amateurs in their sections, regardless of status.

Whether your activity embraces phone or telegraphy, or both, there is a place for you in the League organization.

LEADERSHIP POSTS

To advance each type of station work and group interest in amateur radio, and to develop practical communications plans with the greatest success, appointments of leaders and organizers in particular single-interest fields are made by SCMs. Each leadership post is important. Each provides activities and assistance for appointee groups and individual members along the lines of natural interest. Some posts further the general ability of amateurs to communicate efficiently at all times by pointing activity toward networks and round tables; others are aimed specifically at establishment of provisions for organizing the amateur service as a standby communications group to serve the public in disaster, civil defense need or emergency of any sort. The SCM appoints the following in accordance with section needs and individual qualifications:

PAM   Phone Activities Manager. Organizes activities for voice operators in his section. Promotes phone nets and recruits Official Phone Station appointees. The appointment of VHF-PAM is open to both general and technician licensees.

RM   Route Manager. Organizes and coordinates c.w. traffic activities. Supervises and promotes nets and recruits Official Relay Station appointees.

SEC   Section Emergency Coordinator. Promotes and administers section emergency radio organization.

EC   Emergency Coordinator. Organizes amateurs of a community or other local area for emergency radio service; maintains liasion with officials and agencies served, also with other local communication facilities. Sponsors tests, recruits for AREC and encourages alignment with RACES.

STATION APPOINTMENTS

ARRL's field organization has a place for every active amateur who has a station. The Communications Department organization exists to increase individual enjoyment and station effectiveness in amateur radio work, and we extend a cordial invitation to every amateur to participate fully in the activities, to report results monthly, and to apply to the SCM for one of the following station appointments. ARRL membership and the conditional class or higher license or VE equivalent is prerequisite to all appointments, except where otherwise indicated.

OPS   Official Phone Station. Sets high voice operating standards and procedures, furthers phone nets and traffic.

ORS   Official Relay Station. Traffic service, operates c.w. nets; noted for 15 w.p.m. and procedure ability. Open to RTTY traffickers.

OBS   Official Bulletin Station. Transmits ARRL and FCC bulletin information to amateurs. Open to Technician licensees.

OVS   Official V.H.F. Station. Collects and reports v.h.f.-u.h.f.-s.h.f. propagation data, may engage in facsimile, TT, TV, work on 50 Mc. and/or above. Takes part as feasible in v.h.f. traffic work, reports same, supports v.h.f. nets, observes procedure standards. Open to both Novice and Technician licensees.

OO   Official Observer. Sends cooperative notices to amateurs to assist in frequency observance, insures high-quality signals, and prevents FCC trouble.

Emblem Colors

Members wear the ARRL emblem with black-enamel background. A red background for an emblem will indicate that the wearer is SCM. SECs, ECs, RMs, and PAMs may wear the emblem with green background. Observers and all *station* appointees are entitled to wear blue emblems.

NETS

Amateurs gain experience and pleasure and add much accomplishment to the credit of all of amateur radio, when organized into effective nets interconnecting cities and towns.

The successful operation of a net depends a lot on the Net Control Station. This station should be chosen carefully and be one that will not hesitate to enforce each and every net rule and set the example in his own operation.

A progressive net grows, obtaining new members both directly and through other net members. Bulletins may be issued at intervals to keep in direct contact with the members regarding general net activity, to keep tab on net procedure, make suggestions for improvement, keep track of active members and weed out inactive ones.

A National Traffic System is sponsored by ARRL to facilitate the over-all expeditious relay and delivery of message traffic. The system recognizes the need for handling traffic beyond the section-level networks that have the popular support of both phone and c.w. groups (OPS and ORS) throughout the League's field organization. Area and regional provisions for NTS are furthered by Headquarters correspondence. The ARRL Net Directory, revised each fall, includes the frequencies and times of operation of the hundreds of different nets operating on amateur band frequencies.

RADIO CLUB AFFILIATION

ARRL is pleased to grant affiliation to any amateur society having (1) at least 51% of the voting club membership as full members of the League, and (2) at least 51% of members government-licensed radio amateurs. In high school radio clubs *bearing the school name,* the first above requirement is modified to require one full member of ARRL in the club. Where a society has common aims and wishes to add strength to that of other club groups and strengthen amateur radio by affiliation with the national amateur organization, a request addressed to the Communications Manager will bring the necessary forms and information to initiate the application for affiliation. Such clubs receive field-organization bulletins and special information at intervals for posting on club bulletin boards or for relay to their memberships. A travel plan providing communications, technical and secretarial contact from the Headquarters is worked out seasonally to give maximum benefits to as many as possible of the thirteen hundred active *affiliated* radio clubs. Papers on club work, suggestions for organizing, for constitutions, for radio courses of study, etc., are available on request.

Club Training Aids

One section of the ARRL Communications Department handles the Training Aids Program. This program is a service to ARRL affiliated clubs. Material is aimed at education, training and entertainment of club members. Interesting quiz material is available.

Training Aids include such items as motion-picture films, film strips, slides, audio tapes and lecture outlines. Bookings are limited to ARRL-affiliated clubs, since the visual aids listings are not sufficiently extensive to permit such services to other groups.

All Training Aids materials are loaned free (except for shipping charges) to ARRL affiliated clubs. Numerous groups use this ARRL service to good advantage. If your club is affiliated but has not yet taken advantage of this service, you are missing a good chance to add the available features to your meeting programs and general club activities. Watch club bulletins and *QST* or write the ARRL Communications Department for TA-21.

W1AW

The Maxim Memorial Station, W1AW, is dedicated to fraternity and service. Operated by the League headquarters, W1AW is located adjacent to the Headquarters offices on a seven-acre site. The station is on the air daily, except holidays, and available time is divided between the different bands and modes. Telegraph and phone transmitters are provided for all bands

from 1.8 to 144 Mc. Visiting hours and the station schedule are listed every month in *QST*.

Operation is roughly proportional to amateur interest in different bands and modes, with one kw. except on 160 and v.h.f. bands. W1AW's daily bulletins and code practice aim to give operational help to the largest number.

W1AW was established as a living memorial to Hiram Percy Maxim, to carry on the work and traditions of amateur radio. The station is on the air daily and is open to visitors at all times it is in operation. The W1AW schedule of operation and visiting hours is printed each month in the *Operating News* section of *QST*.

OPERATING ACTIVITIES

Within the ARRL field organization there are special activities. For all appointees and officials (phone and c.w.) quarterly CD (Communications Department) parties are scheduled to develop operating ability and a spirit of fraternalism.

In addition to those for appointees and officials, ARRL sponsors various other activities open to all amateurs. The DX-minded amateur may par-

ticipate in the Annual ARRL International DX Competition during February and March. This popular contest may bring you the thrill of working new countries and building up your DXCC totals; certificate awards are offered to top scorers in each country and ARRL section (see page 6 of any *QST*) and to club leaders. Then is the ever-popular Sweepstakes in November. Of domestic scope, the SS affords the opportunity to work new states for that WAS award. A Novice activity is planned annually. The interests of v.h.f. enthusiasts are also provided for in contests held in January, June and September of each year. Where enough logs (three) are received to constitute minimum "competition" a certificate in spot activities, such as the "SS" and v.h.f. party, is awarded the leading newcomer for his work considered only in competition with other newcomers.

As in all our operating, the idea of having a good time is combined in the Annual Field Day with the more serious thought of preparing ourselves to render public service in times of emergency. A premium is placed on the use of equipment without connection to commercial power sources. Clubs and individual groups always enjoy themselves in the "FD," and learn much about the requirements for operating under knockabout conditions afield.

ARRL contest activities are diversified to appeal to all operating interests, and will be found announced in detail in issues of *QST* preceding the different events.

AWARDS

The League-sponsored operating activities heretofore mentioned have useful objectives and provide much enjoyment for members of the fraternity. Achievement in amateur radio is recognized by various certificates offered through the League and detailed below.

WAS Award

WAS means "Worked All States." An amateur, anywhere in the world, who succeeds in getting confirmed contacts with all fifty U.S. states and sends them in for examination, may receive this award from the League. There is a nominal service charge to those amateurs located within the League's operating territory (U.S., possessions, Puerto Rico and Canada) who are not ARRL members. For others, there is no charge except postage, which is expected to accompany the cards.

You can make the contacts over any period of time and on any or all amateur bands. If you wish, you may have your WAS award issued for some special way in which you made it, such as all c.w., all phone, all on one band, all with low power, etc. — only providing all cards submitted plainly show that a contact took place under the special circumstances for which you wish the award issued.

Before you send in your cards, drop the ARRL Communications Department a line requesting a copy of the rules and an application blank.

DX Century Club Award

The DXCC is one of the most popular and sought-after awards in all of amateur radio, and among the most difficult to acquire. Its issuance is carefully supervised at ARRL headquarters by an Assistant Communications Manager who spends full time on this function alone.

To obtain DXCC, an amateur must make two-way contact with 100 "countries" listed on ARRL Operating Aid #7, which also contains the complete rules. Written confirmations are required for proof of contact. Such confirmations must be sent to ARRL headquarters, where each one is carefully scrutinized to make sure it actually confirms a contact with the applying amateur, that it was not altered or tampered with, and that the "country" claimed is actually on the ARRL list. Further safeguards are applied to maintain the high standards of this award. A handsome king-size certificate is sent to each amateur qualifying.

The term "country" is an arbitrary one not necessarily agreeing with the dictionary definition of such. For DXCC purposes, many bodies of land not having independent status politically are classified as countries. For example, Alaska and Hawaii, while states of the U.S., are considered separate "countries" because of their distance from the mainland. There are over 300 such designations on the ARRL list. Once a basic DXCC is issued, the certificate can be endorsed, by sticker, for additional countries by sending the additional cards in to headquarters for checking.

A separate DXCC award is also available for stations making all contacts by phone.

Because of the meticulous care in checking cards and handling this award, amateurs in the U.S., its possessions (including P.R.) and Canada who are not League members, are charged a nominal service fee both for basic DXCC and endorsements.

Before sending in your cards, be sure you are familiar with the rules (ARRL Operating Aid No. 7), which are quite detailed. In addition, get a copy of the DXCC application form (CD-164).

Five-Band DXCC

Entirely separate from DXCC, ARRL also offers a Five-Band DXCC (5BDXCC) Award for those amateurs who submit written proof of having made two-way contact with 100 or more countries on each of five amateur bands since Jan. 1, 1969. Only full ARRL members are eligible in the U.S., possessions and Canada; elsewhere, any amateur may apply.

A charge of $10 (U.S.) is made for application forms; this covers the cost of returning cards by first class registered mail and issuance of a personalized engraved plaque for those qualifying.

For a copy of the complete rules, drop a line to ARRL Headquarters, 225 Main St., Newington, Conn. 06085.

WAC Award

The WAC award, Worked All Continents, is issued by the International Amateur Radio Union (IARU) upon proof of contact with each of the six continents. Amateurs in the U.S.A., Possessions and Canada should apply for the award through ARRL, headquarters society of the IARU. Those elsewhere must submit direct to their own IARU member-society. Residents of countries not represented in the Union may apply directly to ARRL for the award. Two basic types of WAC certificates are issued. One contains no endorsements and is awarded for c.w, or a combination of c.w. and phone contacts; the other is awarded when all work is done on phone. There is a special endorsement to the phone WAC when all of the confirmations submitted clearly indicate that the work was done on two-way s.s.b. The *only* special band endorsements are for 3.5 and 50 MHz.

Code Proficiency Award

Many hams can follow the general idea of a contact "by ear" but when pressed to "write it down" they "muff" the copy. The Code Proficiency Award permits each amateur to prove himself as a proficient operator, and sets up a system of awards for step-by-step gains in copying proficiency. It enables every amateur to check his code proficiency, to better that proficiency, and to receive a certification of his receiving speed.

This program is a whale of a lot of fun. The League will give a certificate to any licensed radio amateur who demonstrates that he can copy perfectly, for at least one minute, plain-language Continental code at 10, 15, 20, 25, 30 or 35 words per minute, as transmitted monthly from W1AW and W6OWP.

As part of the ARRL Code Proficiency program W1AW transmits plain-language practice material each evening at speeds from 5 to 35 w.p.m., occasionally in reverse order. All amateurs are invited to use these transmissions to increase their code-copying ability. Non-amateurs are invited to utilize the lower speeds, 5, 7½ and 10 w.p.m., which are transmitted for the benefit of persons studying the code in preparation for the amateur license examination. Refer to any issue of *QST* for details.

Rag Chewers Club

The Rag Chewers Club is designed to encourage friendly contacts and discourage the "hello-good-by" type of QSO. It furthers fraternalism through amateur radio.

Membership certificates are awarded to amateurs who report a fraternal-type contact with another amateur lasting a half hour or longer. This does not mean a half hour spent trying to get a message through or in trying to work a rare DX station, but a solid half hour of pleasant "visiting" with another amateur discussing subjects of mutual interest and getting to know each other.

Members sign "RCC" after their calls to indicate that they are interested in a chat, not just a contact.

Operating Aids

The following Operating Aids are available free, upon request: 4) Emergency Operating. 5) DX Operating Code. 6) Contest Duplicate Contact Record. 7) DXCC Countries List. 8) W.A.S. Record. 9a) ARRL Message Form. 13) Ready Reference Information. 14) A composite aid; Ending Signals, Time Conversion, Phonetic Alphabets, RST System and Steps in an Emergency.

A-1 Operator Club

The A-1 Operator Club should include in its ranks every good operator. To become a member, one must be nominated by at least two operators who already belong. General keying or voice technique, procedure, copying ability, judgment and courtesy all count in rating candidates under the club rules detailed at length in *Operating an Amateur Radio Station*. Aim to make yourself a fine operator, and one of these days you may be pleasantly surprised by an invitation to belong to the A-1 Operator Club, which carries a worth-while certificate in its own right.

Brass Pounders League

Every individual reporting more than a specified minimum in official monthly traffic totals is given an honor place in the *QST* listing known as the Brass Pounders League and a certificate to recognize his performance is furnished by the SCM. In addition, a *BPL Traffic Award* (medallion) is given to individual amateurs working at their own stations after the third

time they "make BPL" provided it is duly reported to the SCM and recorded in *QST*.

The value to amateurs in operator training, and the utility of amateur message handling to the members of the fraternity itself as well as to the general public, make message-handling work of prime importance to the fraternity. Fun, enjoyment, and the feeling of having done something really worth while for one's fellows is accentuated by pride in message files, records, and letters from those served.

Old Timers Club

The Old Timers Club is open to anyone who holds an amateur call at the present time, and who held an amateur license (operator or station) 20-or-more years ago. Lapses in activity during the intervening years are permitted.

If you can qualify as an "Old Timer," send an outline of your ham career. Indicate the date of your first amateur license and your present call. If eligible for the OTC, you will be added to the roster and will receive a membership certificate.

YOUR COMMUNICATIONS DEPARTMENT

The material in this chapter, and in the tables which follow, represent services offered by the ARRL Communications Department, a part of your headquarters establishment and the League organization unique in amateur radio but as old as the League itself. Its functions represent a principal reason why ARRL is a membership organization and not just a "publishing house." The CD consists of branches devoted to administration, public service, awards, affiliated clubs, contests and the headquarters station—all of which are designed to serve the amateur fraternity and the ARRL member.

We invite you to participate in these organized programs. Amateur radio is capable of giving enjoyment, self-training, social and organizational benefits in proportion to what the individual amateur puts into it. All amateurs are invited to become ARRL members, to work toward awards, to accept the challenge and opportunities offered in field organization appointments. Your amateur radio life is only half complete otherwise.

Two free publications are offered which will assist immeasurably in all your amateur operating pursuits. See page 611 and send for them today.

COUNTRIES LIST • (Use A.R.R.L. Op. Aid 7 for DXCC purposes.)

AC3 ....Sikkim
AC4 ....Tibet
AC1, 2, 5-Ø ....Bhutan
AP ....Pakistan
BV ....Taiwan
BY ....China
CE ....Chile
CE9AA-AM, FB8Y, KC4, LU-Z, OR, UA1, VKØ, VP8, ZL5, 8J ....Antarctica
CEØA ....Easter Island
CEØZ ..Juan Fernandez Archipelago
CEØX ....San Felix
CM, CO ....Cuba
CN2, 8, 9 ....Morocco
CP ....Bolivia
CR3 ....Portuguese Guinea
CR4 ....Cape Verde Islands
CR5 ......Principe, Sao Thome
CR6 ....Angola
CR7 ....Mozambique
CR8 ....Portuguese Timor
CR9 ....Macao
CT1 ....Portugal
CT2 ....Azores
CT3 ....Madeira Islands
CX ....Uruguay
DJ, DK, DL, DM ....Germany
DU ....Philippine Islands
EA ....Spain
EA6 ....Balearic Islands
EA8 ....Canary Islands
EA9 ....Ifni
EA9 ....Rio de Oro
EA9 ....Spanish Morocco
EAØ ....Spanish Guinea
EI ....Republic of Ireland
EL ....Liberia
EP ....Iran
ET3, 9F ....Ethiopia
F ....France
FB8Z .Amsterdam & St. Paul Isls.
FB8Y ....(See CE9AA-AM)
FB8W ....Crozet Island
FB8X ...Kerguelen Islands
FC (unofficial) ....Corsica
FG7 ....Guadeloupe
FH8 ....Comoro Islands
FK8 ....New Caledonia
FL8 ....French Somaliland
FM7 ....Martinique
FO8 ....Clipperton Island
FO8 ....French Oceania
FO8M ....Maria Theresa
FP8 .St. Pierre & Miquelon Islands
FR7 ....Glorioso Islands
FR7 ....Juan de Nova
FR7 ....Reunion
FR7 ....Tromelin
FS7 ....Saint Martin
FU8, YJ ....New Hebrides
FW8 .....Wallis & Futuna Islands
FY7 ......French Guiana & Inini
G ....England
GC ......Guernsey & Dependencies
GC ....Jersey Island
GD ....Isle of Man
GI ....Northern Ireland
GM ....Scotland
GW ....Wales
HA, HG ....Hungary
HB ....Switzerland
HBØ ....Liechtenstein
HC ....Ecuador
HC8 ....Galapagos Islands
HH ....Haiti
HI ....Dominican Republic
HK ....Colombia
HKØ ....Bajo Nuevo
HKØ ....Malpelo Island
HKØ ..San Andres and Providencia
HKØ ....(See KS4B)
HL, HM ....Korea
HP ....Panama
HR ....Honduras
HS ....Thailand
HV ....Vatican
HZ, 7Z ....Saudi Arabia
I, IT ....Italy
IS ....Sardinia
JA, KA ....Japan
JT ....Mongolia
JW ....Svalbard
JX ....Jan Mayen

JY ....Jordan
K, W ....United States of America
KA1 ....(See KG6I)
KB6 ..Baker, Howland & American Phoenix Islands
KC4 ....Navassa Island
KC4 ....(See CE9AA-AM)
KC6 .....Eastern Caroline Islands
KC6 ....Western Caroline Islands
KG4 ....Guantanamo Bay
KG6 ....Guam
KG6I ....Marcus Island
KG6I, KA1 ....Bonin & Volcano Islands
KG6R, S, T ....Mariana Islands
KH6 ....Hawaiian Islands
KH6 ....Kure Island
KJ6 ....Johnston Island
KL7 ....Alaska
KM6 ....Midway Islands
KP4 ....Puerto Rico
KP6 .Palmyra Group, Jarvis Island
KR6, 8 ....Ryukyu Islands
KS4B, HKØ ....Serrana Bank & Roncador Cay
KS4 ....Swan Islands
KS6 ....American Samoa
KV4 ....Virgin Islands
KW6 ....Wake Island
KX6 ....Marshall Islands
KZ5 ....Canal Zone
LA, LG ....Norway
LA ....(See CE9AA-AM)
LU ....Argentina
LU ....(See CE9AA-AM)
LX ....Luxembourg
LZ ....Bulgaria
M1, 9A1 ....San Marino
MP4B ....Bahrein
MP4Q ....Qatar
MP4M, VS9O ......Sultanate of Muscat & Oman
MP4D, T ....Trucial Oman
OA ....Peru
OD5 ....Lebanon
OE ....Austria
OH, OF ....Finland
OHØ ....Aland Islands
OK, OL ....Czechoslovakia
ON ....Belgium
OR ....(See CE9AA-AM)
OX, XP ....Greenland
OY ....Faroe Islands
OZ ....Denmark
PA, PE, PI ....Netherlands
PJ ....Netherlands Antilles
PJ-M, S ....Sint Maarten
PX ....Andorra
PY ....Brazil
PYØ ....Fernando de Noronha
PYØ .St. Peter & St. Paul's Rocks
PYØ ....Trindade & Martim Vaz Islands
PZ1 ....Surinam
SL, SM ....Sweden
SP ....Poland
ST2 ....Sudan
SU ....Egypt
SV ....Crete
SV ....Dodecanese
SV ....Greece
TA ....Turkey
TF ....Iceland
TG ....Guatemala
TI ....Costa Rica
TI9 ....Cocos Island
TJ ....Cameroun
TL ....Central African Republic
TN ....Congo Republic
TR ....Gabon Republic
TT ....Chad Republic
TU ....Ivory Coast
TY ....Dahomey Republic
TZ ....Mali Republic
UA, UV, UW1-6, UN1..European Russian S.F.S.R.
UA1 ....(See CE9AA-AM)
UA1 ....Franz Josef Land
UA2 ....Kaliningradsk
UA, UV, UW9, Ø.. ....Asiatic Russian S.F.S.R.
UB5, UT5, UY5 ....Ukraine
UC2 ....White Russian S.S.R.
UD6 ....Azerbaijan

UF6 ....Georgia
UG6 ....Armenia
UH8 ....Turkoman
UI8 ....Uzbek
UJ8 ....Tadzhik
UL7 ....Kazakh
UM8 ....Kirghiz
UO5 ....Moldavia
UP2 ....Lithuania
UQ2 ....Latvia
UR2 ....Estonia
VE ....Canada
VK ....Australia
VK ....Lord Howe Island
VK ....Willis Islands
VK9 ....Christmas Island
VK9 ....Cocos Islands
VK9 ....Nauru Island
VK9 ....Norfolk Island
VK9 ....Papua Territory
VK9 ...Territory of New Guinea
VKØ ....Heard Island
VKØ ....Macquarie Island
VK4 ....(See CE9AA-AM)
VO .....Newfoundland, Labrador
VP1 ....British Honduras
VP2K ....Anguilla
VP2A ....Antigua, Barbuda
VP2V ..British Virgin Islands
VP2D ....Dominica
VP2G ..Granada & Dependencies
VP2M ....Montserrat
VP2K ....St. Kitts, Nevis
VP2L ....St. Lucia
VP2S ....St. Vincent & Dependencies
VP5 ......Turks & Caicos Islands
VP7 ....Bahama Islands
VP8 ....(See CE9AA-AM)
VP8 ....Falkland Islands
VP8, LU-Z..South Georgia Islands
VP8, LU-Z..South Orkney Islands
VP8, LU-Z.South Sandwich Islands
VP8, LU-Z, CE9..So. Shetland Is.
VP9 ....Bermuda Islands
VQ1 ....Zanzibar
VQ8 .....Agalega & St. Brandon
VQ8 ....Mauritius
VQ8 ....Rodriguez Island
VQ9 ....Aldabra Islands
VQ9 ....Chagos Islands
VQ9 ....Desroches
VQ9 ....Farquhar
VQ9 ....Seychelles
VR1 ....British Phoenix Islands
VR1 ....Gilbert & Ellice Islands & Ocean Island
VR2 ....Fiji Islands
VR3 .Fanning & Christmas Islands
VR4 ....Solomon Islands
VR5 ....Tonga Islands
VR6 ....Pitcairn Island
VS5 ....Brunei
VS6 ....Hong Kong
VS9 A, P, S ......Aden & Socotra
VS9K ....Kamaran Islands
VS9M, 8Q ......Maldive Islands
VS9O ....(See MP4M)
VU .Andaman and Nicobar Islands
VU ....India
VU ....Laccadive Islands
W ....(See K)
XE, XF ....Mexico
XF4 ....Revilla Gigedo
XP ....(See OX)
XT ....Voltaic Rep.
XU ....Cambodia
XV5 ....(See 3W8)
XW8 ....Laos
XZ2 ....Burma
YA ....Afghanistan
YI ....Iraq
YJ, FU ....New Hebrides
YK ....Syria
YN, YNØ ....Nicaragua
YO ....Rumania
YS ....Salvador
YU ....Yugoslavia
YV ....Venezuela
YVØ ....Aves Island
ZA ....Albania
ZB2 ....Gibraltar
ZC4 ....(See 5B4)
ZD3 ....Gambia

ZD5	Swaziland	3X	Rep. of Guinea	8F	Indonesia
ZD7	St. Helena	3Y	Bouvet	8P	Barbados
ZD8	Ascension Island	4S7	Ceylon	8J	(See CE9AA-AM)
ZD9	Tristan da Cunha &	4U	I.T.U. Geneva	8Q	(See VS9M)
	Gough Islands	4W	Yemen	8R	Guyana
ZE	Rhodesia	4X, 4Z	Israel	8Z4	Saudi Arabia/Iraq N.Z.
ZF1	Cayman Islands	5A	Libya	8Z5	(See 9K3)
ZK1	Cook Islands	5B4	Cyprus	9A1	(See M1)
ZK1	Manihiki Islands	5H3	Tanganyika	9F	(See ET3)
ZK2	Niue	5N2	Nigeria	9G1	Ghana
ZL	Auckland Isl. & Campbell Isl.	5R8	Malagasy Rep.	9H1	Malta
ZL	Chatham Islands	5T	Mauritania	9J2	Zambia
ZL	Kermadec Islands	5U7	Niger Rep.	9K2	Kuwait
ZL	New Zealand	5V	Togo	9K3, 8Z5	Kuwait/Saudia Arabia
ZL5	(See CE9AA-AM)	5W1	Western Samoa		Neutral Zone
ZM7	Tokelau (Union) Islands	5X5	Uganda	9L1	Sierra Leone
ZP	Paraguay	5Z4	Kenya	9M2	Malaya
ZS1, 2, 4, 5, 6	South Africa	6O1, 2, 6	Somali Rep.	9M6	Sabah
ZS2	Prince Edward &	6W8	Senegal Rep.	9M8	Sarawak
	Marion Islands	6Y	Jamaica	9N1	Nepal
ZS3	South-West Africa	7G1	(See 3X)	9Q5	Rep. of Congo
ZS9	Botswana	7P	Lesotho	9U5	Burundi
3A	Monaco	7Q	Nyasaland	9V1	Singapore
3V8	Tunisia	7X	Algeria	9X5	Rwanda
3W8, XV5	Vietnam	7Z	(See HZ)	9Y4	Trinidad & Tobago

INTERNATIONAL PREFIXES

AAA-ALZ	United States of America	OKA-OMZ	Czechoslovakia
AMA-AOZ	Spain	ONA-OTZ	Belgium
APA-ASZ	Pakistan	OUA-OZZ	Denmark
ATA-AWZ	India	PAA-PIZ	Netherlands
AXA-AXZ	Commonwealth of Australia	PJA-PJZ	Netherlands Antilles
AYA-AZZ	Argentine Republic	PKA-POZ	Republic of Indonesia
BAA-BZZ	China	PPA-PYZ	Brazil
CAA-CEZ	Chile	PZA-PZZ	Surinam
CFA-CKZ	Canada	QAA-QZZ	(Service abbreviations)
CLA-CMZ	Cuba	RAA-RZZ	Union of Soviet Socialist Republics
CNA-CNZ	Morocco	SAA-SMZ	Sweden
COA-COZ	Cuba	SNA-SRZ	People's Republic of Poland
CPA-CPZ	Bolivia	SSA-SSM	United Arab Republic
CQA-CRZ	Portuguese Overseas Provinces	SSN-STZ	Sudan
CSA-CUZ	Portugal	SUA-SUZ	United Arab Republic
CVA-CXZ	Uruguay	SVA-SZZ	Greece
CYA-CZZ	Canada	TAA-TCZ	Turkey
DAA-DTZ	Germany	TDA-TDZ	Guatemala
DUA-DZZ	Republic of the Philippines	TEA-TEZ	Costa Rica
EAA-EHZ	Spain	TFA-TFZ	Iceland
EIA-EJZ	Ireland	TGA-TGZ	Guatemala
EKA-EKZ	Union of Soviet Socialist Republics	THA-THZ	France and French Community
ELA-ELZ	Liberia	TIA-TIZ	Costa Rica
EMA-EOZ	Union of Soviet Socialist Republics	TJA-TJZ	Republic of Cameron
EPA-EQZ	Iran	TKA-TKZ	France, and French Community
ERA-ERZ	Union of Soviet Socialist Republics	TLA-TLZ	Central African Republic
ESA-ESZ	Estonia	TMA-TMZ	France, French Community
ETA-ETZ	Ethiopia	TNA-TNZ	Republic of Congo (Brazzaville)
EUA-EWZ	Bielorussian Soviet Socialist Republic	TOA-TQZ	France, French Community
EXA-EZZ	Union of Soviet Socialist Republics	TRA-TRZ	Republic of Gabon
FAA-FZZ	France and French Community	TSA-TSZ	Tunisia
GAA-GZZ	United Kingdom	TTA-TTZ	Republic of Chad
HAA-HAZ	Hungarian People's Republic	TUA-TUZ	Republic of the Ivory Coast
HBA-HBZ	Switzerland	TVA-TXZ	France, French Community
HCA-HDZ	Ecuador	TYA-TYZ	Republic of Dahomey
HEA-HEZ	Switzerland	TZA-TZZ	Republic of Mali
HFA-HFZ	People's Republic of Poland	UAA-UQZ	Union of Soviet Socialist Republics
HGA-HGZ	Hungarian People's Republic	URA-UTZ	Ukrainian Soviet Socialist Republic
HHA-HHZ	Republic of Haiti	UUA-UZZ	Union of Soviet Socialist Republics
HIA-HIZ	Dominican Republic	VAA-VGZ	Canada
HJA-HKZ	Republic of Colombia	VHA-VNZ	Commonwealth of Australia
HLA-HMZ	Korea	VOA-VOZ	Canada
HNA-HNZ	Iraq	VPA-VSZ	British Overseas Territories
HOA-HPZ	Republic of Panama	VTA-VWZ	India
HQA-HRZ	Republic of Honduras	VXA-VYZ	Canada
HSA-HSZ	Thailand	VZA-VZZ	Commonwealth of Australia
HTA-HTZ	Nicaragua	WAA-WZZ	United States of America
HUA-HUZ	Republic of El Salvador	XAA-XIZ	Mexico
HVA-HVZ	Vatican City State	XJA-XOZ	Canada
HWA-HYZ	France and French Community	XPA-XPZ	Denmark
HZA-HZZ	Saudi Arabia	XQA-XRZ	Chile
IAA-IZZ	Italy	XSA-XSZ	China
JAA-JSZ	Japan	XTA-XTZ	Republic of the Upper Volta
JTA-JVZ	Mongolian People's Republic	XUA-XUZ	Cambodia
JWA-JXZ	Norway	XVA-XVZ	Viet-Nam
JYA-JYZ	Jordan	XWA-XWZ	Laos
JZA-JZZ	Indonesia	XXA-XXZ	Portuguese Overseas Provinces
KAA-KZZ	United States of America	XYA-XZZ	Burma
LAA-LNZ	Norway	YAA-YAZ	Afghanistan
LOA-LWZ	Argentine Republic	YBA-YHZ	Republic of Indonesia
LXA-LXZ	Luxembourg	YIA-YIZ	Iraq
LYA-LYZ	Lithuania	YJA-YJZ	New Hebrides
LZA-LZZ	People's Republic of Bulgaria	YKA-YKZ	Syria
MAA-MZZ	United Kingdom	YLA-YLZ	Latvia
NAA-NZZ	United States of America	YMA-YMZ	Turkey
OAA-OCZ	Peru	YNA-YNZ	Nicaragua
ODA-ODZ	Lebanon	YOA-YRZ	Roumanian People's Republic
OEA-OEZ	Austria	YSA-YSZ	Republic of El Salvador
OFA-OJZ	Finland		

Prefix	Country	Prefix	Country
YTA-YUZ	Yugoslavia	5UA-5UZ	Republic of the Niger
YVA-YYZ	Venezuela	5VA-5VZ	Togolese Republic
YZA-YZZ	Yugoslavia	5WA-5WZ	Western Samoa
ZAA-ZAZ	Albania	5XA-5XZ	Uganda
ZBA-ZJZ	British Overseas Territories	5YA-5ZZ	Kenya
ZKA-ZMZ	New Zealand	6AA-6BZ	United Arab Republic
ZNA-ZOZ	British Overseas Territories	6CA-6CZ	Syria
ZPA-ZPZ	Paraguay	6DA-6JZ	Mexico
ZQA-ZQZ	British Overseas Territories	6KA-6NZ	Korea
ZRA-ZUZ	Republic of South Africa	6OA-6OZ	Somalia
ZVA-ZZZ	Brazil	6PA-6SZ	Pakistan
A2A-A2Z	Botswana	6TA-6UZ	Sudan
2AA-2ZZ	Great Britain	6VA-6WZ	Republic of the Senegal
3AA-3AZ	Monaco	6XA-6XZ	Malagasy Republic
3BA-3FZ	Canada	6YA-6YZ	Jamaica
3GA-3GZ	Chile	6ZA-6ZZ	Liberia
3HA-3UZ	China	7AA-7IZ	Indonesia
3VA-3VZ	Tunisia	7JA-7NZ	Japan
3WA-3WZ	Viet-Nam	7OA-7O2	South Yemen Popular Republic
3XA-3XZ	Guinea	7QA-7QZ	Malawi
3YA-3YZ	Norway	7RA-7RZ	Algeria
3ZA-3ZZ	People's Republic of Poland	7SA-7SZ	Sweden
4AA-4CZ	Mexico	7TA-7YZ	Algeria
4DA-4IZ	Republic of the Philippines	7ZA-7ZZ	Saudi Arabia
4JA-4LZ	Union of Soviet Socialist Republics	8AA-8IZ	Indonesia
4MA-4MZ	Venezuela	8JA-8NZ	Japan
4NA-4OZ	Yugoslavia	8OA-8OZ	Botswana
4PA-4SZ	Ceylon	8SA-8SZ	Sweden
4TA-4TZ	Peru	8TA-8YZ	India
4UA-4UZ	United Nations	8ZA-8ZZ	Saudi Arabia
4VA-4VZ	Republic of Haiti	9AA-9AZ	San Marino
4WA-4WZ	Yemen	9BA-9DZ	Iran
4XA-4XZ	State of Israel	9EA-9FZ	Ethiopia
4YA-4YZ	International Civil Aviation Organization	9GA-9GZ	Ghana
4ZA-4ZZ	State of Israel	9HA-9HZ	Malta
5AA-5AZ	Libya	9IA-9JZ	Zambia
5BA-5BZ	Republic of Cyprus	9KA-9KZ	Kuwait
5CA-5GZ	Morocco	9LA-9LZ	Sierra Leone
5HA-5IZ	Tanzania	9MA-9MZ	Malaysia
5JA-5KZ	Colombia	9NA-9NZ	Nepal
5LA-5MZ	Liberia	9OA-9TZ	Republic of the Congo (Leopoldville)
5NA-5OZ	Nigeria	9UA-9UZ	Burundi
5PA-5QZ	Denmark	9VA-9VZ	Singapore
5RA-5SZ	Malagasy Republic	9WA-9WZ	Malaysia
5TA-5TZ	Islamic Republic of Mauretania	9XA-9XZ	Rwanda
		9YA-9ZZ	Trinidad and Tobago

ABBREVIATIONS FOR C.W. WORK

Abbreviations help to cut down unnecessary transmission. However, make it a rule not to abbreviate unnecessarily when working an operator of unknown experience.

Abbr.	Meaning	Abbr.	Meaning
AA	All after	NW	Now; I resume transmission
AB	All before	OB	Old boy
ABT	About	OM	Old man
ADR	Address	OP-OPR	Operator
AGN	Again	OT	Old timer; old top
ANT	Antenna	PBL	Preamble
BCI	Broadcast interference	PSE	Please
BCL	Broadcast listener	PWR	Power
BK	Break; break me; break in	PX	Press
BN	All between; been	R	Received as transmitted; are
C	Yes	RCD	Received
CFM	Confirm; I confirm	RCVR (RX)	Receiver
CK	Check	REF	Refer to; referring to; reference
CL	I am closing my station; call	RIG	Station equipment
CLD-CLG	Called; calling	RPT	Repeat; I repeat
CUD	Could	SED	Said
CUL	See you later	SIG	Signature; signal
CUM	Come	SINE	Operator's personal initials or nickname
CW	Continuous wave	SKED	Schedule
DLD-DLVD	Delivered	SRI	Sorry
DX	Distance, foreign countries	SVC	Service; prefix to service message
ES	And, &	TFC	Traffic
FB	Fine business; excellent	TMW	Tomorrow
GA	Go ahead (or resume sending)	TNX-TKS	Thanks
GB	Good-by	TT	That
GBA	Give better address	TU	Thank you
GE	Good evening	TVI	Television interference
GG	Going	TXT	Text
GM	Good morning	UR-URS	Your; you're; yours
GN	Good night	VFO	Variable-frequency oscillator
GND	Ground	VY	Very
GUD	Good	WA	Word after
HI	The telegraphic laugh; high	WB	Word before
HR	Here; hear	WD-WDS	Word; words
HV	Have	WKD-WKG	Worked; working
HW	How	WL	Well; will
LID	A poor operator	WUD	Would
MA, MILS	Milliamperes	WX	Weather
MSG	Message; prefix to radiogram	XMTR (TX)	Transmitter
N	No	XTAL	Crystal
ND	Nothing doing	XYL (YF)	Wife
NIL	Nothing; I have nothing for you	YL	Young lady
NM	No more	73	Best regards
NR	Number	88	Love and kisses

▶ *Operating an Amateur Radio Station* covers the details of practical amateur operating. In it you will find information on Operating Practices, Emergency Communication, ARRL Operating Activities and Awards, the ARRL Field Organization, Handling Messages, Network Organization, "Q" Signals and Abbreviations used in amateur operating, important extracts from the FCC Regulations, and other helpful material. It's a handy reference that will serve to answer many of the questions concerning operating that arise during your activities on the air.

▶ *Public Service Communications* is the "bible" of the Amateur Radio Public Service Corps. Within its pages are contained the fundamentals of operation of the Amateur Radio Emergency Corps (AREC), the National Traffic System (NTS), and the Radio Amateur Civil Emergency Service (RACES), the three "divisions" of ARPSC, including diagrams of how each is organized and how it operates. The role of the American Red Cross and FCC's regulations concerning amateur operation in emergencies also come in for some special attention.

The two publications described above may be obtained without charge by any *Handbook* reader. Either or both will be sent upon request.

AMERICAN RADIO RELAY LEAGUE
225 Main Street
Newington, Conn. 06111

   Please send me, without charge, the following:
☐ **OPERATING AN AMATEUR RADIO STATION**
☐ **PUBLIC SERVICE COMMUNICATIONS**

Name . . . .
                                            (Please Print)

Address . . . .

. . . .

Chapter 25

Vacuum Tubes and Semiconductors

For the convenience of the designer, the receiving-type tubes listed in this chapter are grouped by filament voltages and construction types (glass, metal, miniature, etc.). For example, all miniature tubes are listed in Table I, all metal tubes are in Table II, and so on.

Transmitting tubes are divided into triodes and tetrodes-pentodes, then listed according to rated plate dissipation. This permits direct comparison of ratings of tubes in the same power classification.

For quick reference, all tubes are listed in numerical-alphabetical order in the index. Types having no table reference are either obsolete or of little use in amateur equipment. Base diagrams for these tubes are listed.

Tube Ratings

Vacuum tubes are designed to be operated within definite maximum (and minimum) ratings. These ratings are the maximum safe operating voltages and currents for the electrodes, based on inherent limiting factors such as permissible cathode temperature, emission, and power dissipation in electrodes.

In the transmitting-tube tables, maximum ratings for electrode voltage, current and dissipation are given separately from the typical operating conditions for the recommended classes of operation. In the receiving-tube tables, ratings and operating data are combined. Where only one set of operating conditions appears, the positive electrode voltages shown (plate, screen, etc.) are, in general, also the maximum rated voltages.

For certain air-cooled transmitting tubes, there are two sets of maximum values, one designated as CCS (Continuous Commercial Service) ratings, the other ICAS (Intermittent Commercial and Amateur Service) ratings. Continuous Commercial Service is defined as that type of service in which long tube life and reliability of performance under continuous operating conditions are the prime consideration. Intermittent Commercial and Amateur Service is defined to include the many applications where the transmitter design factors of minimum size, light weight, and maximum power output are more important than long tube life. ICAS ratings are considerably higher than CCS ratings. They permit the handling of greater power, and although such use involves some sacrifice in tube life, the period over which tubes give satisfactory performance in intermittent service can be extremely long.

The plate dissipation values given for transmitting tubes should not be exceeded during normal operation. In plate modulated amplifier applications, the maximum allowable carrier-condition plate dissipation is approximately 66 percent of the value listed and will rise to the maximum value under 100 percent sinusoidal modulation.

Typical Operating Conditions

The typical operating conditions given for transmitting tubes represent, in general, maximum ICAS ratings where such ratings have been given by the manufacturer. They do not represent the *only* possible method of operation of a particular tube type. Other values of plate voltage, plate current, etc., may be used so long as the maximum ratings for a particular voltage or current are not exceeded.

Detailed information and characteristic curves are available from tube and semiconductor manufacturers, in books sold through radio dealers or direct from the factory.

Semiconductors

The semiconductor tabulation in this chapter is restricted to some of the more common transistors. The units listed were selected to represent those types that are useful for most amateur radio experimental applications. These transistors were chosen for their low cost and availability. Most of them can be obtained from the large mail-order houses or from the local manufacturer's distributor. Because there are thousands of transistor types on today's market, this list is by no means complete.

INDEX TO VACUUM-TUBE TYPES

Base-diagram section pages V5-V15. Classified data pages V16-V34.

Type	Page	Base
6J6A	V19	7BF
6J6A	V25	7BF
6J7	V21	7R
6J8G	—	8H
6J11	V23	12BW
6JB6	V23	9QL
6JC6	V19	9PM
6JC8	V19	9PA
6JD6	—	9PM
6JE6	V23	9QL
6JE6A	V23	9QL
6JF6	V23	9QL
6JH6	—	7CM
6JH8	—	9DP
6JK8	V19	9AJ
6JN8	—	9FA
6JT8	—	9DX
6JV8	—	9DX
6K5GT	—	5U
6K6GT	V22	7S
6K7	V21	7R
6K8	V21	8K
6K11	V23	12BY
6KD6	V23	12GW
6KD8	V19	9AE
6KE8	V18	9DC
6KM6	V23	9QL
6KR8	V19	9DX
6KT6	V19	9PM
6KT8	V19	9QP
6KV8	—	9DX
6KY6	V19	9GK
6KZ8	19	9FZ
6L4	V23	7BR
6L5G	—	6Q
6L6GA	—	7S
6L6GB	V21	7S
6L6GX	—	7S
6L7	V21	7T
6LJ8	V19	9GF
6LQ6	V23	9QL
6LY8	V19	9DX
6M5	—	9N
6M6G	—	7S
6M7G	—	7R
6M8GT	—	8AU
6M11	V23	12CA
6N4	—	7CA
6N5	—	6R
6N6G	—	7AU
6N7GT	V21	8B
6N7GT	V26	8B
6N8	—	9T
6P5GT	—	6Q
6P7G	—	7U
6P8G	—	8K
6Q4	—	9S
6Q5G	—	6Q
6Q6G	—	6Y
6Q7	V21	7V
6Q11	V23	12BY
6R4	—	9R
6R6G	—	6AW
6R7	V21	7V
6R8	—	9E
6S4	—	9AC
6S4A	V19	9AC
6S6GT	—	5AK
6S7	—	7R
6S8GT	V22	8CB
6SA7GT	V21	8R
6SB7Y	V21	8R
6SC7	V21	8S
6SD7GT	V22	8N
6SE7GT	—	8N
6SF5	V21	6AB
6SF7	V21	7AZ
6SG7	V21	8BK
6SH7	V21	8BK
6SH7L	—	8BK
6SJ7	V21	8N
6SJ7Y	V21	8N
6SK7	V21	8N
6SL7GT	V22	8BD
6SN7GTA	—	8BD
6SN7GTB	V22	8BD
6SQ7GT	V21	8Q
6SR7	V21	8Q
6SS7	—	8N
6ST7	—	8Q
6SU7GTY	—	8BD
6SV7	—	7AZ
6SZ7	—	8Q
6T4	V19	7DK
6T5	—	6R
6T6GM	—	6Z
6T7	—	7V
6T8	—	9E
6T8A	V19	9E
6T9	V23	12FM
6U3	—	9BM
6U4GT	V25	4CG
6U5	—	6R
6U6GT	—	7S
6U7G	—	7R
6U8	—	9AE
6U8A	V19	9AE
6V3	—	9BD
6V3A	—	9BD
6V4	V25	9M
6V5GT	—	6AO
6V6GTA	V21	7S
6V7G	—	7V
6V8	—	9AH
6W4GT	—	4CG
6W5G	—	6S
6W6GT	V22	7S
6W7G	—	7R
6X4/6063	V25	7CF
6X5GT	V25	6S
6X6G	—	7AL
6X8	—	9AK
6X8A	V19	9AK
6Y3G	—	4AC
6Y5	—	6J
6Y6G	—	7S
6Y6GA	V22	7S
6Y6GT	—	7S
6Y7G	—	8B
6Z3	V25	4G
6Z4	—	5D
6Z5	—	6K
6Z7G	—	8B
6ZY5G	—	6S
7A4	—	5AC
7A5	—	6AA
7A6	—	7AJ
7A7	—	8V
7A8	V22	8U
7AB7	—	8BO
7AD7	—	8V
7AF7	—	8AC
7AG7	—	8V
7AH7	V22	8V
7AJ7	—	8V
7AK7	V22	8V
7B4	—	5AC
7B5	—	6AE
7B6	—	8W
7B7	V22	8V
7B8	—	8X
7C4	—	4AH
7C5	—	6AA
7C6	—	8W
7C7	V22	8V
7D7	—	8AR
7E5	V23	8BN
7E6	—	8W
7E7	V22	8AE
7EP4	—	11N
7EV6	—	7AC
7EY6	—	7AC
7F7	—	8AC
7F8	V22	8BW
7G7	—	8V
7G8	—	8BV
7GP4	—	14G
7H7	—	8V
7J7	—	8BL
7JP1-4-7	—	14R
7K7	V22	8BF
7L7	—	8V
7N7	—	8AC
7Q7	—	8AL
7R7	—	8AE
7S7	—	8BL
7T7	—	8V
7V7	—	8V
7VP1	—	14R
7W7	—	8BJ
7X6	—	7AJ
7X7	—	8BZ
7Y4	—	5AB
7Z4	—	5AB
8BP4	—	14G
9BM5	—	7BZ
9BW6	—	9AM
9NP1	—	6BN
10	—	4D
10EB8	—	9DX
10GP4	—	14G
10HP4	—	14G
10Y	—	4D
11/12	—	4F
12A4	—	9AG
12A5	—	7F
12A6	—	7S
12A7	—	7K
12A8GT	—	8A
12AB5	V19	9EU
12AB6	—	7CC
12AC6	V19	7BK
12AD6	V19	7CH
12AD7	—	9A
12AE6A	V19	7BT
12AE7	V19	9A
12AF6	V19	7BK
12AG6	—	7CH
12AH7GT	—	8BE
12AH8	—	9BP
12AJ6	V19	7BT
12AL5	—	6BT
12AL8	V19	9GS
12AQ5	V19	7BZ
12AT6	—	7BT
12AT7	V19	9A
12AU6	—	7BK
12AU7A	V27	9A
12AU7A	V19	9A
12AV5GA	—	6CK
12AV6	—	7BT
12AV7	V19	9A
12AW6	V19	7CM
12AW7	—	7CM
12AX4GT	—	4CG
12AX4GTA	—	4CG
12AX7A	V19	9A
12AY7	V19	9A
12AZ7A	V19	9A
12B4	—	9AG
12B4A	V19	9AG
12B6M	—	6Y
12B7	—	8V
12B7ML	—	8V
12B8GT	—	8T
12BA6	—	7BK
12BA7	—	8CT
12BD6	—	7BK
12BE6	—	7CH
12BF6	—	7BT
12BH7	—	9A
12BH7A	V19	9A
12BK5	—	9BQ
12BK6	—	7BT
12BL6	V19	7BK
12BN6	—	7DF
12BQ6GA	—	6AM
12BQ6GT	—	6AM
12BQ6GTB	—	6AM
12BR7A	V19	9CF
12BT6	—	7BT
12BU6	—	7BT
12BW4	—	9DJ
12BV7	V19	9BF
12BX6	V19	9AQ
12BY7	—	9BF
12BY7A	V19	9BF
12BZ6	—	7CM
12BZ7	V19	9A
12C5	—	7CV
12C8	—	8E
12CA5	—	7CV
12CM6	—	9CK
12CN5	V19	7CV
12CR6	—	7EA
12CS5	—	9CK
12CS6	—	7CH
12CT8	V19	9DA
12CU5	—	7CV
12CU6	—	6AM
12CX6	V19	7BK
12DB5	—	9GR
12DE8	V19	Fig. 81
12DF5	V25	9BS
12DF7	—	9A
12DK7	V19	9HZ
12DL8	V19	9HR
12DM7	V19	9A
12DQ6A	—	6AM
12DQ7	V19	9BF
12DS7	V20	9JU
12DT5	—	9HN
12DT6	V20	7EN
12DT7	V20	9A
12DT8	—	9DE
12DU7	V20	9JX
12DV7	V20	9JY
12DV8	V20	9HR
12DW5	—	9CK
12DW7	V20	9A
12DW8	V20	9JC
12DY8	V20	9JD
12DZ6	V20	7BK
12E5GT	—	6Q
12EA6	V20	7BK
12EC8	V20	9FA
12ED5	V20	7CV
12EF6	—	7S
12EG6	V20	7CH
12EK6	V20	7BK
12EL6	V20	7FB
12EM6	V20	9HV
12EN6	—	7S
12F5GT	—	5M
12F8	V20	9FH
12FK6	V20	7BT
12FM6	V20	7BT
12FP7	—	14E
12FQ8	V20	9KT
12FR8	V20	9KU
12FT6	V20	7BT
12FX5	V20	7CV
12FX8A	V20	9KV
12G4	—	6BG
12G7G	—	7V
12G8	—	9CZ
12GA6	V20	7CH
12GE5	—	12BJ
12GJ5	V23	9NM
12GW6	—	6AM
12GN7	—	9BF
12GP7	—	14S
12H4	V20	7DW
12H6	—	7Q
12HP7	—	11J
12J5GT	—	6Q
12J7GT	—	7R
12J8	V20	9GC
12K5	V20	7EK
12K7GT	—	7R
12K8	—	8K
12L6GT	—	7S
12L8GT	—	8BU
12Q7GT	—	7V
12R5	V20	7CV
12S8GT	—	8CB
12SA7	—	8R
12SC7	—	8S
12SF5	—	6AB
12SF7	—	7AZ
12SG7	—	8BK
12SH7	—	8BK
12SJ7	—	8N
12SK7	—	8N
12SL7GT	—	8BD
12SN7GT	—	8BD
12SN7GTA	—	8BD
12SQ7	—	8Q
12SR7	—	8Q
12SW7	—	8Q
12SX7	—	8BD
12SY7	—	8R
12U7	V20	9A
12V6GT	—	7S
12W6GT	—	7S
12X4	V25	5BS
12Z3	—	4G
12Z5	—	7L
14A4	—	5AC
14A5	—	6AA
14A7	—	8V
14AF7	—	8AC
14AP1-4	—	12A
14B6	—	8W
14B8	—	8X
14C5	—	6AA
14C7	—	8V
14E6	—	8W
14E7	—	8AE
14F7	—	8AC
14F8	—	8BW
14H7	—	8V
14J7	—	8BL
14N7	—	8AC
14Q7	—	8AL
14R7	—	8AE
14S7	—	8BL
14V7	—	8V
14W7	—	8BJ
14X7	—	8BZ
14Y4	—	5AB
14Z3	—	4G
15	—	5F
15A6	—	9AR
15E	V26	Fig. 51
16A5	—	9BL
17	—	3G
17Z3	—	9CB
18	—	6B
18FW6A	V20	7CC
18FX6A	V20	7CH
18FY6A	V20	7BT
19	—	6C
19CL8A	—	9FX
19X3	—	9BM
19Y3	—	9BM
20	—	4D
20AP1-4	—	12A
20J8GT	—	8H
21A6	—	9AS
21A7	—	8AR
21EX6	—	5BT
22	—	4K
24-A	—	5E
24-G	V26	2D
24XH	—	Fig. 1
25A6	—	7S
25A7GT	—	8F
25AC5GT	—	6Q
25AV5GA	—	6CK
25AV5GT	—	6CK
25AX4GT	—	4CG
25B5	—	6D
25B6G	—	7S
25B8GT	—	8T
25BK5	—	9BQ
25BQ6GA	—	6AM
25BQ6GT	—	6AM
25BQ6GTB	—	6AM
25C5	—	7CV
25C6G	—	7AC
25C6GA	—	7S
25CA5	—	7CV
25CD6G	—	5BT
25CD6GA	—	5BT
25CD6GB	—	5BT
25CU6	—	6AM
25D8GT	—	8AF
25DN6	—	5BT
25DQ6	—	6AM
25EC6	—	5BT
25EH5	—	7CV
25F5	V20	7CV
25L6GT	—	7S
25N6G	—	7W
25S	—	6M
25SA7GT	—	8AD
25T	V26	3G
25W4GT	—	4CG
25W6GT	—	7S
25X6GT	—	7Q
25Y4GT	—	5AA
25Y5	—	6E
25Z3	—	4G
25Z4	—	5AA
25Z5	V25	6E
25Z6	—	7Q
26	—	4D
26A6	—	7BK
26A7GT	—	8BU
26BK6	—	7BT
26C6	—	7BT
26CG6	—	7BK
26D6	—	7CH
26Z5W	—	9BS
27	—	5A
28Z5	—	5AB
30	—	4D
31	—	4D
32	—	4K
32ET5	V20	7CV
32L7GT	—	8Z
33	—	5K
34	—	4M
34GD5	V20	7CV
35/51	—	5E
35A5	—	6AA
35B5	V20	7BZ
35C5	—	7CV
35L6GT	—	7S
35T	V26	3G
35TG	V26	2D
35W4	V25	5BQ
35Y4	—	5AL
35Z3	—	4Z
35Z4GT	V25	5AA
35Z5G	V25	6AD
35Z6G	—	7Q
36	—	5E
36AM3	V25	5BQ
37	—	5A
38	—	5F
39/44	—	5F
40	—	4D
40Z5GT	—	6AD
41	—	6B
42	—	6B
43	—	6B
45	—	4D
45Z3	—	5AM
45Z5GT	—	6AD
46	—	5C
47	—	5B
48	—	6A
49	—	5C
50	—	4D
50A5	—	6AA
50AX6G	—	7Q
50B5	V20	7BZ
50BK5	—	9BQ
50C5	—	7CV
50C6G	—	7S
50C6GA	—	7S
50DC4	V25	5BQ
50FK5	V20	7CV
50L6GT	—	7S
50T	—	2D
50X6	—	7AJ
50Y6GT	V25	7Q
50Y7GT	—	8AN
50Z6G	—	7Q
50Z7G	—	8AN
51	—	5E
52	—	6C
53	—	7B
53A	—	Fig. 53
55	—	6G
56	—	5A
56AS	—	5A
57	—	6F
57AS	—	6F
58	—	6F
58AS	—	6F
59	—	7A
70A7GT	—	8AB
70L7GT	—	8AA
71-A	—	4D
72	—	4P
73	—	4Y
75	—	6G
75TH	V27	2D
75TL	V27	2D
76	—	5A
77	—	6F
78	—	6F
79	—	6H
80	V25	4C
81	—	4B
82	—	4C
83	V25	4C
83-V	V25	4AD
84/6Z4	—	5D
85	—	6G
85AS	—	6G
89	—	6F
90C1	V24	5BO
99	—	4D
100TH	V27	2D
100TL	V27	2D
111H	—	2D
112-A	—	4D
117L7GT	—	8AO
117M7GT	—	8AO
117N7GT	V25	8AV
117P7GT	—	8AV
117Z3	V25	4CB
117Z4GT	—	5AA
117Z6GT	—	7Q
128AS	—	5A
150T	—	2N
152TH	V27	4BC
152TL	V27	4BC
182-B	—	4D
183	—	4D
203-A	—	4E
203-H	—	3N
204-A	—	Fig. 39
205-D	—	4D
211	V27	4E
212-E	—	Fig. 43
217-A	—	4AT
217-C	—	4AT
227-A	—	Fig. 53
241-B	—	Fig. 44
242-A	—	4E
242-B	—	4E
242-C	—	4E
249-B	—	Fig. 29
250TH	V28	2N
250TL	V28	2N
254	V27	2N
254-A	—	Fig. 57
254-B	—	Fig. 57
261-A	—	4E
270-A	—	Fig. 39
276-A	—	4E
282-A	—	Fig. 57
284-B	—	3N
284-D	—	4E
295-A	—	4E
300T	—	2N
303-A	—	4E
304-A	—	Fig. 39
304-B	—	2D
304TH	V28	4BC
304TL	V28	4BC
305-A	—	Fig. 59
306-A	—	Fig. 63
307-A	—	Fig. 61
308-B	—	Fig. 43
310	—	4D
311	V27	4E
311CH	—	Fig. 32
312-A	—	Fig. 68
312-E	—	Fig. 44
316-A	V26	—
327-A	—	Fig. 50
327-B	—	Fig. 50
342-B	—	4E
356-A	—	Fig. 55
361-A	—	4E
376-A	—	4E
408A	—	7BD
417-A	V20	9V
482-B	—	4D
483	—	4D
485	—	5A
527	—	Fig. 53
559	—	Fig. 10
572	V27	3G
575-A	—	4AT
592	V28	Fig. 28
705-A	—	Fig. 45
717-A	—	8BK
756	—	4D
800	—	2D
801A/801	V26	4D
802	—	6BM
803	V30	5J
804	—	Fig. 61
805	V27	3N
806	V27	2N
807	V29	5AW
807W	V29	5AW
808	—	2D
809	V26	3G
810	V27	2N
811	—	3G
811A	V27	3G
812	—	3G
812A	V27	3G
812H	—	3G
813	V30	5BA
814	V30	Fig. 64
815	V29	8BY
816	V25	4P
822	—	3N
822S	—	2N
826	V27	7BO
828	V30	5J
829	—	7BP
829A	—	7BP
829B	V29	7BP
830	—	4D
830B	V27	3G
831	—	Fig. 40
832	—	7BP
832A	V29	7BP
833A	V28	Fig. 41
834	—	2D
835	—	4E
836	V25	4P
837	V29	6BM
838	—	4E
840	—	5J
841	—	4D
841A	—	3G
841SW	—	3G
843	—	5A
844	—	5AW

Type	Page	Base
849	—	Fig. 39
850	—	Fig. 47
852	—	2D
860	—	Fig. 58
861	—	Fig. 42
864	—	4D
865	—	Fig. 57
866	—	4P
866A-AX	V25	4P
866B	V25	4P
866jr.	V25	4B
871	—	4P
872A/872	V25	4AT
874	—	4S
878	—	4P
879	—	4AB
884	V24	6Q
885	—	5A
902A	—	8CD
906P1-11	—	7AN
908A	—	7CE
909	—	5BP
910	—	7AN
911	—	7AN
914A	—	6BF
930B	V27	3G
938	—	4E
950	—	5K
951	—	4M
954	V23	5BB
955	V23	5BC
955	V25	5BC
956	V23	5BB
957	—	5BD
958	—	5BD
958A	V23	5BD
958A	V25	5BD
959	V23	5BE
967	V24	3G
975A	—	4AT
1003	—	4R
1005	—	5AQ
1006	—	4C
1201	V23	8BN
1203	—	4AH
1204	—	8BO
1206	—	8BV
1218A	V20	7DK
1221	—	6F
1223	—	7BF
1229	—	4K
1230	—	4D
1231	—	8V
1232	—	8V
1265	V24	4AJ
1266	V24	4AJ
1267	V24	4V
1273	—	8V
1274	—	6S
1275	—	4C
1276	—	4D
1280	—	8V
1284	—	8V
1291	—	7BE
1293	—	4AA
1294	—	4AH
1299	—	6BB
1602	—	4D
1603	—	6F
1608	—	4D
1609	—	5B
1610	—	Fig. 62
1611	—	7S
1612	—	7T
1613	—	7S
1614	V29	7AC
1616	—	4P
1619	—	Fig. 74
1620	V21	7R
1621	—	7S
1622	—	7AC
1623	V26	3G
1624	V29	Fig. 66
1625	V29	5AZ
1626	—	6Q
1627	—	2N
1628	—	Fig. 54
1629	—	6RA
1631	—	7AC
1632	—	7S
1633	—	8BD
1634	—	8S
1635	V22	8B
1641	—	Fig. 52
1642	—	7BH
1644	—	Fig. 4
1654	—	2Z
1802P1-11	—	11A
1805P1-4	—	11A
1806P1	—	11N
1851	—	7R
1852	V21	8N
1853	—	8N
2002	—	Fig. 1
2005	—	Fig. 1
2050	V24	8BA
2051	—	8BA
2523N/128A	—	5A
4604	V29	7CL
5514	V27	4BO
5516	—	7CL
5517	—	5BU
5556	—	4D
5562	—	Fig. 30
5590	—	7BD
5591	—	7BD
5608	—	7BD
5608A	—	7B
5610	—	6CG
5618	—	7CU
5651	V24	5BO
5654	—	7BD
5656	—	9F
5662	V24	Fig. 79
5663	—	6CE
5670	—	8CJ
5675	V26	Fig. 21
5679	—	7CX
5686	V20	9G

Type	Page	Base
5687	V20	9H
5690	—	Fig. 38
5691	—	8BD
5692	—	8BD
5693	V21	8N
5694	—	8CS
5696	V24	7BN
5722	V20	5CB
5725	—	7CM
5726	—	6BT
5727	V24	7BN
5731	—	5BC
5749	—	7BK
5750	—	7CH
5751	—	9A
5755	—	9J
5763	V29	9K
5765	—	Fig. 21
5766	See 2C37	
5767	See 2C37	
5768	—	Fig. 21
5794	—	Fig. 21
5812	—	7CQ
5814	—	9A
5823	V24	4CK
5824	—	7S
5825	—	4P
5839	—	6S
5842	V20	9V
5844	—	7BF
5845	—	5CA
5847	—	9X
5852	—	6S
5857	—	9AB
5866	V27	Fig. 3
5867	V28	Fig. 3
5871	—	7AC
5876	—	Fig. 21
5879	V20	9AD
5881	—	7AC
5890	—	12J
5893	V26	Fig. 21
5894A	V29	Fig. 7
5910	—	6AR
5915	—	7CH
5920	—	7BF
5933	V29	5AW
5961	—	8R
5962	V24	2AG
5963	—	9A
5964	—	7BF
5965	—	9A
5993	—	Fig. 35
5998	V24	8BD
6005	—	7BZ
6023	—	9CD
6026	V26	Fig. 16
6028	—	7BD
6045	—	7BF
6046	—	7AC
6057	—	9A
6058	—	6BT
6059	—	9BC
6060	—	9A
6061	—	9AM
6062	—	9K
6063	V25	7CF
6064	—	7DB
6065	—	7DB
6066	—	7BT
6067	—	9A
6072	—	9A
6073	V24	5BO
6074	V24	5BO
6080	—	8BD
6082	—	8BD
6083	—	Fig. 5
6084	—	9BJ
6085	—	9A
6086	—	9BK
6087	—	5L
6101	—	7BF
6132	—	9BA
6135	—	6BG
6136	—	7BK
6137	—	8N
6140	—	9BY
6141	—	9BZ
6146	V29	7CK
6146A	V29	7CK
6146B	V29	7CK
6155	V30	5BK
6156	V30	5BK
6157	—	Fig. 36
6158	—	9A
6159	V29	7CK
6173	V23	Fig. 34
6186	—	7BD
6197	—	9BV
6201	—	9A
6211	—	9A
6216	—	Fig. 37
6218	—	9CG
6227	—	9BA
6252	V29	Fig. 7
6263	V26	—
6264	V26	—
6265	—	7CM
6287	—	9CT
6308	V24	8EX
6336A	V24	8BD
6350	—	9CZ
6354	V24	Fig. 12
6360	V29	Fig. 13
6374	—	9BW
6386	V20	8CJ
6417	V29	9K
6443	—	9BW
6485	V24	7BK
6524	V29	Fig. 76
6550	V22	7S
6627	—	5BO
6660	—	7CC
6661	—	7CM
6662	—	7CM
6663	—	6BT
6664	—	5CE
6669	—	7BZ
6676	—	7CM

Type	Page	Base
6677	—	9BV
6678	—	9AE
6679	—	9A
6680	—	9A
6681	—	9A
6816	V30	Fig. 77
6829	—	9A
6850	V29	Fig. 76
6883	V29	7CK
6884	V30	Fig. 77
6887	V20	6BT
6893	V29	7CK
6897	—	—
6907	—	Fig. 7
6939	V29	Fig. 13
6973	V20	9EU
7000	—	7R
7025	—	9A
7027A	V22	8HY
7034	V30	Fig. 75
7035	V30	Fig. 75
7054	—	9BF
7055	—	6BT
7056	—	6CM
7057	—	9AJ
7058	—	9A
7059	—	9AE
7060	—	9DX
7061	—	9EU
7077	V23	—
7094	V30	Fig. 82
7137	—	7BQ
7167	—	7EW
7189A	V20	9CV
7247	—	9A
7258	V20	9DA
7270	V30	Fig. 84
7271	V30	Fig. 84
7308	—	9DE
7360	V23	9KS
7408	—	7AC
7543	—	7BK
7551	V29	9LK
7558	V29	9LK
7581A	—	7AC
7586	V20	12AQ
7587	V20	12AS
7591	V22	8KQ
7695	V23	9PX
7700	—	6F
7701	—	9MS
7717	—	7EW
7854	V30	Fig. 7
7868	V23	9NZ
7895	V20	12AQ
7905	V29	9PB
7984	V29	12EU
8000	V28	2N
8001	V30	7BM
8003	—	3N
8005	V27	3G
8008	—	Fig. 8
8012	—	Fig. 54
8013-A	—	4P
8016	—	3C
8020	—	4P
8025	V26	4AQ
8032	V29	7CK
8056	V20	12AQ
8058	V20	12CT
8072	V30	Fig. 85
8117	V30	Fig. 7
8121	V30	Fig. 86
8122	V30	Fig. 85
8163	V28	Fig. 3
8166/ 4-1000A	V31	—
8203	V29	12AQ
8298A	V29	7CK
8334	—	7DK
8393	V20	12AQ
8458	V29	Fig. 13
8628	V20	12AQ
8646	V30	—
8677	V20	12CT
9001	V20	7BD
9002	V20	7BS
9002	V25	7BS
9003	V20	7BD
9004	V23	4BJ
9005	—	5BG
9006	—	6BH
AT-340	—	5BK
AX9900	V27	Fig. 3
AX9901	V28	Fig. 3
AX9903	V29	Fig. 7
AX9905	—	Fig. 2
AX9909	—	Fig. 5
AX9910	V29	Fig. 7
BA	—	4J
BH	—	4J
BR	—	4H
CE220	—	4P
CK1005	—	5AQ
CK1006	—	4C
CK1007	—	Fig. 73
DR3B27	—	4P
DR123C	—	Fig. 15
DR200	—	2N
ECC81	—	9A
ECC82	—	9A
ECC83	—	9A
EF50	—	9C
F123A	—	Fig. 15
F127A	—	Fig. 15
G84	V24	4B
GL2C39A	V27	—
GL2C39B	V27	—
GL2C44	—	Fig. 9
GL5C24	—	Fig. 15
GL146	V27	Fig. 56
GL152	V27	Fig. 56
GL159	—	Fig. 56
GL169	—	Fig. 56
GL446A	—	Fig. 11
GL446B	—	Fig. 11
GL464A	—	Fig. 9
GL559	—	Fig. 10
GL6442	V26	—

Type	Page	Base
GL6463	—	9CZ
GL8012A	—	Fig. 54
HD203A	—	3N
HF60	—	2D
HF75	—	2D
HF100	—	2D
HF120	—	4F
HF140	—	4F
HF175	—	Fig. 46
HF200	—	2N
HF201A	V27	Fig. 15
HF250	—	2N
HF300	V28	2N
HK24	V26	3G
HK54	V26	2D
HK57	—	Fig. 33
HK154	—	2D
HK158	—	2D
HK252L	—	4BC
HK253	—	4AT
HK254	—	2N
HK257	V30	7BM
HK257B	V30	7BM
HK304L	—	4BC
HK354	—	2N
HK354C	—	2N
HK354D	—	2N
HK354E	—	2N
HK354F	—	2N
HK454H	—	2N
HK454L	—	2N
HK654	—	2N
HV12	—	3N
HV18	—	2N
HV27	—	3N
HY6J5GTX	—	6Q
HY6L6GTX	—	7AC
HY24	—	4D
HY25	—	3G
HY30Z	—	4BO
HY31Z	V26	Fig. 60
HY40	—	3G
HY40Z	—	3G
HY51A	—	3G
HY51B	—	3G
HY51Z	—	4BO
HY57	—	3G
HY60	—	5AW
HY61	—	5AW
HY63	—	Fig. 72
HY65	—	Fig. 72
HY67	—	Fig. 65
HY69	—	Fig. 64
HY75	—	2T
HY75A	V26	2T
HY114B	V25	2T
HY615	V26	Fig. 71
HY801A	—	4D
HY866jr	—	4P
HY1231Z	V26	Fig. 60
HY1269	—	Fig. 65
HYE1148	V26	Fig. 71
TK66	—	7AC
KY21	V24	—
NU2C35	—	Fig. 23
PE340	—	5BK
PL172/8295	V31	—
PL175A	V30	Fig. 78
PL177A	V30	Fig. 14
PL6549	V30	Fig. 14
PL6569	V28	Fig. 3
PL6580	V28	5BK
PL8295/172	V31	—
RK10	—	4D
RK11	—	3G
RK12	—	3G
RK15	—	4D
RK16	—	5A
RK17	—	5F
RK18	—	3G
RK19	—	4AT
RK20	—	Fig. 61
RK20A	—	Fig. 61
RK21	—	4P
RK22	—	Fig. 52
RK23	—	6BM
RK24	—	4D
RK25	—	6BM
RK25B	—	6BM
RK28	—	5J
RK28A	—	5J
RK30	—	2D
RK31	—	3G
RK32	—	2D
RK33	—	Fig. 69
RK34	V26	Fig. 70
RK35	—	2D
RK36	—	2D
RK37	—	2D
RK38	—	2D
RK39	—	5AW
RK41	—	5AW
RK42	—	4D
RK43	—	6C
RK44	—	6BM
RK46	—	Fig. 61
RK47	—	Fig. 64
RK48	—	Fig. 64
RK48A	—	Fig. 64
RK49	—	6A
RK51	—	3G
RK52	—	3G
RK56	—	5AW
RK57	—	3N
RK58	—	3N
RK59	—	Fig. 60
RK61	V24	—
RK62	—	4D
RK63	—	2N
RK63A	—	2N
RK64	—	5AW
RK65	—	Fig. 48
RK66	—	Fig. 61
RK75	—	Fig. 61
RK100	—	Fig. 67
RK705A	—	Fig. 45
RK866	—	4P
T20	V26	3G
T21	—	6A

Type	Page	Base
T40	V27	3G
T55	V27	3G
T60	—	2D
T100	—	2D
T125	—	2N
T160L	V27	3G
T200	V28	2N
T300	V28	—
T814	—	3N
T822	—	3N
TB35	—	Fig. 30
TUF20	—	2T
TW75	—	2D
TW150	—	2N
TZ20	V26	3G
TZ40	V26	3G
UE100	—	2D
UE468	—	Fig. 32
UH35	—	3G
UH50	—	2D
UH51	—	2D
V70	—	3N
V70A	—	3N
V70B	—	3G
V70C	—	3G
V70D	V27	3G
VR75	V24	4AJ
VR90	V24	4AJ
VR105	V24	4AJ
VR150	V24	4AJ
VT52	—	4D
VT127A	V27	Fig. 53
VT191	V26	—
WE304A	—	2D
X6030	—	Fig. 2
XXB	—	Fig. 6
XXD	—	8AC
XXL	—	5AC
XXFM	—	8BZ
ZB60	—	2D
ZB120	—	4E

SEMICONDUCTORS

Type	Page
1N21B	V31
1N21E	V31
1N21F	V31
1N23C	V31
1N23E	V31
1N34A	V31
1N52A	V31
1N60	V31
1N64	V31
1N82A	V31
1N270	V31
1N416G	V31
1N634	V31
1N1612	V31
1N1613	V31
1N3193	V31
1N3195	V31
1N3256	V31
1N3563	V31
1N4822	V31
1N4885	V31
1N5054	V31
10B	V31
10C10	V31
MA-4060A	V31
MA-4062D	V31
MV1620	V31
MV1628	V31
MV1636	V31
MV1644	V31
MV1650	V31
Z4XL6.2	V31
Z4XL9.1	V31
Z4XL12	V31
Z4XL14	V31
Z4XL16	V31
Z4XL18	V31
Z4XL20	V31
Z4XL22	V31
2N251A	V32
2N457B	V32
2N706A	V32
2N1907	V32
2N2102	V32
2N2157	V32
2N2631	V32
2N2869	V32
2N2876	V32
2N2925	V32
2N3391A	V32
2N3512	V32
2N3553	V32
2N3583	V32
2N3663	V32
2N3866	V32
2N4124	V32
2N4126	V32
2N4296	V32
2N4396	V32
2N4401	V32
2N4410	V32
2N4416	V32
3N128	V32
3N140	V32
3N141	V32
MJ480	V32
MPF102	V32
MPF105	V32
MPF106	V32
TIP-14	V32
TIS48	V32
TIS54	V32
TIXM10	V32
40231	V32
40235	V32
40280	V32
40310	V32
40312	V32
40394	V32
40394V2	V32
40424	V32

E.I.A. VACUUM-TUBE BASE DIAGRAMS

Socket connections correspond to the base designations given in the column headed "Base" in the classified tube-data tables. Bottom views are shown throughout. Terminal designations are as follows:

A = Anode	D = Deflecting Plate	IS = Internal Shield	RC = Ray-Control Eelectrode
B = Beam	F = Filament	K = Cathode	Ref = Reflector
BP = Bayonet Pin	FE = Focus Elect.	NC = No Connection	S = Shell
BS = Base Sleeve	G = Grid	P = Plate (Anode)	TA = Target
C = Ext. Coating	H = Heater	P₁ = Starter-Anode	U = Unit
CL = Collector	IC = Internal Con.	P_BF = Beam Plates	• = Gas-Type Tube

Alphabetical subscripts D, P, T and HX indicate, respectively, diode unit, pentode unit, triode unit or hexode unit in multi-unit types. Subscript CT indicates filament or heater tap.

Generally when the No. 1 pin of a metal-type tube in Table II, with the exception of all triodes, is shown connected to the shell, the No. 1 pin in the glass (G or GT) equivalent is connected to an internal shield.

* On 12AQ, 12AS and 12CT: index = large lug; • = pin cut off

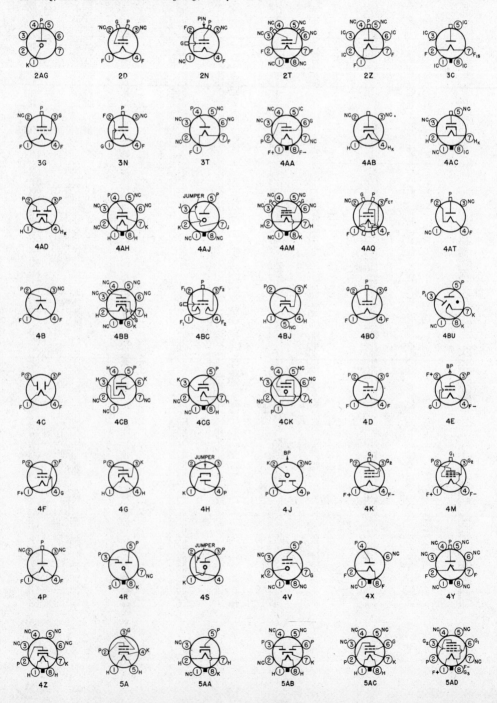

TUBE BASE DIAGRAMS

Bottom views are shown. Terminal designations on sockets are given on page V5.

TUBE BASE DIAGRAMS

Bottom views are shown. Terminal designations on sockets are given on page V5.

6AP 6AR 6AS 6AU 6AW 6AX

6B 6BA 6BB 6BF 6BG 6BH

6BM 6BN 6BQ 6BT 6BW 6BX

6C 6CA 6CB 6CC 6CE 6CG

6CH 6CK 6CN 6D 6E 6F

6G 6H 6J 6K 6L 6M

6Q 6R 6RA 6S 6T 6W

6X 6Y 6Z 7A 7AA 7AB

7AC 7AD 7AG 7AH 7AJ 7AK

TUBE BASE DIAGRAMS

Bottom views are shown. Terminal designations on sockets are given on page V5.

TUBE BASE DIAGRAMS

Bottom views are shown. Terminal designations on sockets are given on page V5.

TUBE BASE DIAGRAMS

Bottom views are shown. Terminal designations on sockets are given on page V5.

TUBE BASE DIAGRAMS

Bottom views are shown. Terminal designations on sockets are given on page V5.

TUBE BASE DIAGRAMS

Bottom views are shown. Terminal designations on sockets are given on page V5.

TUBE BASE DIAGRAMS

Bottom views are shown. Terminal designations on sockets and * meaning are given on page V5.

TUBE BASE DIAGRAMS

Bottom views are shown. Terminal designations on sockets are given on page V5.

TUBE BASE DIAGRAMS

Bottom views are shown. Terminal designations on sockets are given on page V5.

TABLE I—MINIATURE RECEIVING TUBES **V16**

Type	Name	Base	Fil. or Heater		Capacitances pf.			Plate Supply V.	Grid Bias	Screen Volts	Screen Ma.	Plate Ma.	Plate Res. Ohms.	Transconductance[11]	Amp. Factor[4]	Load Res. Ohms	Watts Output
			V.	Amp.	C_{in}	C_{out}	C_{gp}										
1A3	H.f. Diode	5AP	1.4	0.15	—	—	—	Max. a.c. voltage per plate —117. Max. output current —0.5 ma.									
1L4	Sharp Cut-off Pent.	6AR	1.4	0.05	3.6	7.5	0.008	90	0	90	2.0	4.5	350K	1025	—	—	—
1L6	Pentagrid Conv.	7DC	1.4	0.05	7.5	12.0	0.3	90	0	45	0.6	0.5	650K	300	—	—	—
1R5	Pentagrid Conv.	7AT	1.4	0.05	7.0	12.0	0.3	90	0	67.5	3.5	1.5	400K	280	Grid No. 1 100K		
1S4	Pentagrid Pwr. Amp.	7AV	1.4	0.1	—	—	—	90	—7.0	67.5	1.4	7.4	100K	1575	—	8K	0.270
1S5	Diode — Pentode A₁ Amp. R.f. Amp.	6AU	1.4	0.05	—	—	—	67.5	0	67.5	0.4	1.6	600K	625	—	—	—
								90		90			Screen Resistor 3 meg., grid 10 meg.		1 meg.		0.050
1T4	Variable-µ Pent.	6AR	1.4	0.05	3.6	7.5	0.01	90	0	67.5	1.4	3.5	500K	900	—	—	—
1U4	Sharp Cut-off Pent.	6AR	1.4	0.05	3.6	7.5	0.01	90	0	90	0.5	1.6	1 meg.	900	—	—	—
1U5	Diode Pentode	6BW	1.4	0.05	—	—	—	67.5	0	67.5	0.4	1.6	600K	625	—	—	—
2E30	Beam Pwr. Pent.	7CQ	6.0	0.65	9.5	6.6	0.2	250	450*	250	3.3/7.4	44²	63K	3700	40⁵	4.5K	4.5
	A₁ Amp.							250	225*	250	6.6/14.8	88²	—	—	80⁵	9K⁶	9
	A₁ Amp.³							250	—25	250	3/13.5	82²	—	—	48⁵	8K⁶	12.5
	AB₁ Amp.³ AB₂ Amp.³							250	—30	250	4/20	120²	—	—	40⁵	3.8⁶	17
2EA5‡	Sharp Cut-off Pent.	7EW	2.4	0.60	3.8	2.3	0.06	250	—1	150	—	10	150K	8000	—	—	—
2EN5‡	Dual Diode	7FL	2.1	0.45	—	—	—	Max. a.c. voltage per plate —200. Max. output current —5.0 ma.									
3A4	Pwr. Amp. Pent.	7BB	1.4	0.2	4.8	4.2	0.34	135	—7.5	90	2.6	14.9²	90K	1900	—	8K	0.6
			2.8	0.1				150	—8.4	90	2.2	14.1²	100K				0.7
3A5	H.f. Dual Triode[10]	7BC	1.4	0.22	0.9	1.0	3.2	90	—2.5	—	—	3.7	8.3K	1800	15	—	—
			2.8	0.11													
3DK6‡	Sharp Cut-off Pent.	7CM	3.15	0.6	6.3	1.9	0.02	300	—6.5	150	3.8	12	—	9800	—	—	—
3Q4	Pwr. Amp. Pent.	7BA	1.4	0.1	5.5	3.8	0.2	90	—4.5	90	2.1	9.5	100K	2150	—	10K	0.27
			2.8	0.05							1.7	7.7	120K	2000	—	10K	0.24
3S4	Pwr. Amp. Pent.	7BA	1.4	0.1	—	—	—	90	—7	67.5	1.4	7.4	100K	1575	—	8K	0.27
			2.8	0.05							1.1	6.1		1425			0.235
4EW6‡	Sharp Cut-off Pent.	7CM	4.2	0.6	10.0	2.4	0.04	300	—3.5	180	3.2	11	—	1400	—	—	—
6AB4	U.h.f. Triode	5CE	6.3	0.15	2.2	0.5	1.5	250	200*	—	—	10	10.9K	5500	60	—	—
6AF4A	U.h.f. — Triode A₁ Amp. Osc. 950 Mc.	7DK	6.3	0.225	2.2	0.45	1.9	80	150*	—	—	16	2.27K	6600	15	—	—
								100	10KΩ		0.4⁹	22					
6AG5	Sharp Cut-off Pent.	7BD	6.3	0.3	6.5	1.8	0.03	250	180*	150	2.0	6.5	800K	5000	—	—	—
								100	100*	100	1.4	4.5	500K	4500	—	—	—
6AH6	Sharp Cut-off Pent. Amp. Pent. Triode Amp.	7BK	6.3	0.45	10.0	2.0	0.03	300	160*	150	2.5	10	500K	9600	—	—	—
								150	160*	—	—	12.5	3.6K	11K	40	—	—
6AJ4	U.h.f. Triode	9BX	6.3	0.225	4.4	0.18	2.4	125	68*	—	—	16	4.2K	10K	42	—	—
								180	200*	120	2.4	7.7	690K	5100	—	—	—
6AK5	Sharp Cut-off Pent.	7BD	6.3	0.175	4.0	2.8	0.02	150	330*	140	2.2	7	420K	4300	—	—	—
								120	200*	120	2.5	7.5	340K	5000	—	—	—
6AK6	Pwr. Amp. Pent.	7BK	6.3	0.15	3.6	4.2	0.12	180	—9	180	2.5	15	200K	2300	—	10K	1.1
6AL5	Dual Diode[10]	6BT	6.3	0.3	—	—	—	Max. r.m.s. voltage —117. Max. d.c. output current —9 ma.[1]									
6AM4	U.h.f. Triode	9BX	6.3	0.225	4.4	0.16	2.4	150	100*	—	—	7.5	10K	9000	90	—	—
6AM8A‡	Diode — Sharp Cut-off Pent.	9CY	6.3	0.45	6.0	2.6	0.015	200	120*	150	2.7	11.5	600K	7000	—	—	—
6AN4	U.h.f. Triode	7DK	6.3	0.225	2.8	0.28	1.7	200	100*	—	—	13	—	10K	70	—	—
6AN5	Beam Pwr. Pent.	7BD	6.3	0.45	9.0	4.8	0.075	120	120*	120	12.0	35	12.5K	8000	—	2.5K	1.3
6AN8A‡	Medium-µ Triode	9DA	6.3	0.45	2.0	2.7	1.5	200	—6	—	—	13	5.75K	3300	—	—	—
	Sharp Cut-off Pent.				7.0	2.3	0.04	200	180*	150	2.8	9.5	30K	6200	—	—	—
6AQ5A‡	Beam Pwr. Pent.	7BZ	6.3	0.45	8.3	8.2	0.35	180	—8.5	180	3/4	30²	58K	3700	29⁵	5.5K	2.0
								250	—12.5	250	4.5/7	47²	52K	4100	45⁵	5K	4.5
6AQ6	Dual Diode — High-µ Triode	7BT	6.3	0.15	1.7	1.5	1.8	100	—1	—	—	0.8	61K	1150	70	—	—
								250	—3	—	—	1	58K	1200	70	—	—
6AQ8	High-µ Twin Triode	9AJ	6.3	0.435	0.3	1.2	1.5	250	—2	—	—	10	9.7K	6000	—	—	—
6AR5	Pwr. Amp. Pent.	6CC	6.3	0.4	—	—	—	250	—16.5	250	5.7/10	35²	65K	2400	34⁵	7K	3.2
								250	—18	250	5.5/10	33²	68K	2300	32⁵	7.6K	3.4
6AR8	Sheet Beam	9DP	6.3	0.3	—	—	—	TV Color Ckts. — Synchronous Detector — Burst Gate									
6AS5	Beam Pwr. Amp.	7CV	6.3	0.8	12	6.2	0.6	150	—8.5	110	2/6.5	36²	—	5600	35⁵	4.5K	2.2
6AS6	Sharp Cut-off Pent.	7CM	6.3	0.175	4	3	0.2	120	—2	120	3.5	5.2	110K	3200	—	—	—
6AS8	Diode — Sharp Cut-off Pent.	9DS	6.3	0.45	7	2.2	0.04	200	180*	150	3	9.5	300K	6200	—	—	—
6AT6	Duplex Diode — High-µ Triode	7BT	6.3	0.3	2.3	1.1	2.1	250	—3	—	—	1	58K	1200	70	—	—
6AT8A‡	Medium-µ Triode	9DW	6.3	0.45	2	0.5	1.5	100	100*	—	—	8.5	6.9K	5800	40	—	—
	Sharp Cut-off Pent.				4.5	0.9	0.025	250	200*	150	1.6	7.7	750K	4600	—	—	▪
6AU6A‡	Sharp Cut-off Pent.	7BK	6.3	0.3	5.5	5	0.0035	250	68*	150	4.3	10.6	1 meg.	5200	—	—	—
6AU8A‡	Medium-µ Triode	9DX	6.3	0.6	2.6	0.34	2.2	150	150*	—	—	9	8.2K	4900	40	—	—
	Sharp Cut-off Pent.				7.5	3.4	0.06	200	82*	125	3.4	15	150K	7000	—	—	—
6AV6	Dual Diode — High-µ Triode	7BT	6.3	0.3	2.2	0.8	2.0	250	—2	—	—	1.2	62.5K	1600	100	—	—
6AW8A‡	High-µ Triode	9DX	6.3	0.6	3.2	0.32	2.2	200	—2	—	—	4	17.5K	4000	70	—	—
	Sharp Cut-off Pent.				11	2.8	0.036	200	180*	150	3.5	13	400K	9000	—	—	—
6AX8	Medium-µ Triode	9AE	6.3	0.45	2.5	1	1.8	150	56*	—	—	18	5K	8500	40	—	—
	Sharp Cut-off Pent.				5	3.5	0.006	250	120*	110	3.4	10	400K	6000	—	—	—
6AZ8	Medium-µ Triode	9ED	6.3	0.45	2	1.7	1.7	200	—6	—	—	13	5.75K	3300	19	—	—
	Semiremote Cut-off Pent.				6.5	2.2	0.02	200	180*	150	3	9.5	300K	6000	—	—	—
6BA6	Remote Cut-off Pent.	7BK	6.3	0.3	5.5	5	0.0035	250	68*	100	4.2	11	1 meg.	4400	—	—	—
6BA7	Pentagrid Conv.	8CT	6.3	0.3	Osc. 20KΩ			250	—1	100	10	3.8	1 meg.	950	—	—	—
6BA8A‡	Medium-µ Triode	9DX	6.3	0.6	2.5	0.7	2.2	200	—8	—	—	8	6.7K	2700	18	—	—
	Sharp Cut-off Pent.				11	2.8	0.036	200	180*	150	3.5	13	400K	9000	—	—	...
6BC4	U.h.f. Medium-µ Triode	9DR	6.3	0.225	2.9	0.26	1.6	150	100*	—	—	14.5	4.8K	10K	48	—	—
6BC5	Sharp Cut-off Pent.	7BD	6.3	0.3	6.5	1.8	0.03	250	180*	150	2.1	7.5	800K	5700	—	—	—
6BC7	Triple Diode	9AX	6.3	0.45				Max. diode current per plate = 12 Ma. Max. htr.-cath. volts = 200									
6BC8	Medium-µ Dual Triode[10]	9AJ	6.3	0.4	2.5	1.3	1.4	150	220*	—	—	10	—	6200	35	—	—
6BD6	Remote Cut-off Pent.	7BK	6.3	0.3	4.3	5.0	0.005	100	—1	100	5	13	150K	2500	—	—	—
								250	—3	100	3	9	800K	2000	—	—	—

Type	Name	Base	V.	Amp.	Cin	Cout	Cgp	Plate Supply V.	Grid Bias	Screen Volts	Screen Ma.	Plate Ma.	Plate Res. Ohms	Transconductance[11]	Amp. Factor[1]	Load Res. Ohms	Watts Output
6BE6	Pentagrid Conv.	7CH	6.3	0.3	Osc. 20KΩ			250	−1.5	100	6.8	2.9	1 meg.	475	—	—	—
6BE8A‡	Medium-μ Triode	9EG	6.3	0.45	2.8	1.5	1.8	150	56*	—	—	18	5K	8500	40	—	—
	Sharp Cut-off Pent.				4.4	2.6	0.04	250	68*	110	3.5	10	400K	5200	—	—	—
6BF5	Beam Pwr. Amp.	7BZ	6.3	1.2	14	6	0.65	110	−7.5	110	4/10.5	39²	12K	7500	36⁵	2.5K	1.9
6BF6	Dual Diode — Medium-μ Triode	7BT	6.3	0.3	1.8	0.8	2	250	−9	—	—	9.5	8.5K	1900	16	10K	0.3
6BH6	Sharp Cut-off Pent.	7CM	6.3	0.15	5.4	4.4	0.0035	250	−1	150	2.9	7.4	1.4 meg.	4600	—	—	—
6BH8‡	Medium-μ Triode	9DX	6.3	0.6	2.6	0.38	2.4	150	−5	—	—	9.5	5.15K	3300	17	—	—
	Sharp Cut-off Pent.				7	2.4	0.046	200	82*	125	3.4	15	150K	7000	—	—	—
6BJ6A	Remote Cut-off Pent.	7CM	6.3	0.15	4.5	5.5	0.0035	250	−1	100	3.3	9.2	1.3 meg.	3800	—	—	—
6BJ7	Triple Diode	9AX	6.3	0.45	Max. peak inverse plate voltage = 330 V. Max. d.c. plate current each diode = 1.0 Ma.												
6BJ8‡	Dual Diode — Medium-μ Triode	9ER	6.3	0.6	2.8	0.38	2.6	250	−9	—	—	8	7.15K	2800	20	—	—
6BK5	Beam Pwr. Pent.	9BQ	6.3	1.2	13	5	0.6	250	−5	250	3.5/10	37²	100K	8500	35⁵	6.5K	3.5
6BK6	Dual Diode — High-μ Triode	7BT	6.3	0.3	—	—	—	250	−2	—	—	1.2	62.5K	1600	100	—	—
6BK7B	Medium-μ Dual Triode[10]	9AJ	6.3	0.4	3	1	1.8	150	56*	—	—	18	4.6K	9300	43	—	—
6BL8	Triode	9DC	6.3	0.43	2.5	1.8	1.5	250	−1.3	—	—	14	—	5000	20	—	—
	Pentode				5.2	3.4	0.025	250	−1.3	175	2.8	10	400K	6200	47	—	—
6BN4A	Medium-μ Triode	7EG	6.3	0.2	3.2	1.4	1.2	150	220*	—	—	9	6.3K	6800	43	—	—
6BN6	Gated-Beam Pent.	7DF	6.3	0.3	4.2	3.3	0.004	80	−1.3	60	5	0.23	—	—	—	68K	—
6BN8‡	Dual Diode — High-μ Triode	9ER	6.3	0.6	3.6	0.25	2.5	250	−3	—	—	1.6	28K	2500	70	—	—
6BQ5	Pwr. Amp. Pent.	9CV	6.3	0.76	10.8	6.5	0.5	300	−7.3	200	10.8	49.5²	38K	—	—	5.2K	17³
6BQ7A	Medium-μ Dual Triode[10]	9AJ	6.3	0.4	2.85	1.35	1.15	150	220*	—	—	9	6.1K	6400	39	—	—
6BR8A‡	Medium-μ Triode	9FA	6.3	0.45	2.5	0.4	1.8	150	56*	—	—	18	5K	8500	40	—	—
	Sharp Cut-off Pent.				5	2.6	0.015	250	68*	110	3.5	10	400K	5200	—	—	—
6BS8	Low-Noise Dual Triode[10]	9AJ	6.3	0.4	2.6	1.35	1.15	150	220*	—	—	10	5K	7200	36	—	—
6BT6	Dual Diode — High-μ Triode	7BT	6.3	0.3	—	—	—	250	−3	—	—	1	58K	1200	70	—	—
6BT8	Dual Diode — Pent.	9FE	6.3	0.45	7	2.3	0.04	200	180*	150	2.8	9.5	300K	6200	—	—	—
6BU6	Dual Diode — Low-μ Triode	7BT	6.3	0.3	—	—	—	250	−9	—	—	9.5	8.5K	1900	16	10K	0.3
6BU8	Dual Pent.[10]	9FG	6.3	0.3	6	3¹	—	100¹	—	67.5	3.3	2.2	—	—	—	—	—
6BV8‡	Dual Diode — Medium-μ Triode	9FJ	6.3	0.6	3.6	0.4	2	200	330*	—	—	11	5.9K	5600	33	—	—
6BW8	Dual Diode — Pent.	9HK	6.3	0.45	4.8	2.6	0.02	250	68*	110	3.5	10	250K	5200	—	—	—
6BX8	Dual Triode[10]	9AJ	6.3	0.4	—	—	1.4	65	−1	—	—	9	—	6700	25	—	—
6BY6	Pentagrid Amp.	7CH	6.3	0.3	5.4	7.6	0.08	250	−2.5	100	9	6.5	Ec₃ = −2.5 V.	1900	—	—	—
6BY8‡	Diode — Sharp Cut-off Pent.	9FN	6.3	0.3	5.5	5	0.0035	250	68*	150	4.3	10.6	1 meg.	5200	—	—	—
6BZ6	Semiremote Cut-off Pent.	7CM	6.3	0.3	7.5	1.8	0.02	200	180*	150	2.6	11	600K	6100	—	—	—
6BZ7	Medium-μ Dual Triode[10]	9AJ	6.3	0.4	2.5	1.35	1.15	150	220*	—	—	10	5.6K	6800	38	—	—
6BZ8	Dual Triode[10]	9AJ	6.3	0.4	—	—	—	125	100*	—	—	10¹	5.6K	8000	45	—	—
6C4	Medium-μ Triode	6BG	6.3	0.15	1.8	1.3	1.6	250	−8.5	—	—	10.5	7.7K	2200	17	—	—
6CA5	Beam Pent.	7CV	6.3	1.2	15	9	0.5	125	−4.5	125	4/11	36²	15K	9200	37⁵	4.5K	1.5
6CB6A‡	Sharp Cut-off Pent.	7CM	6.3	0.3	6.5	1.9	0.02	200	180*	150	2.8	9.5	600K	6200	—	—	—
6CE5‡	R.f. Pent.	7BD	6.3	0.3	6.5	1.9	0.03	200	180*	150	2.8	9.5	600K	6200	—	—	—
6CF6	Sharp Cut-off Pent.	7CM	6.3	0.3	6.3	1.9	0.02	200	180*	150	2.8	9.5	600K	6200	—	—	—
6CG6	Semiremote Cut-off Pent.	7BK	6.3	0.3	5	5	0.008	250	−8	150	2.3	9	720K	2000	—	—	—
6CG7‡	Medium-μ Dual Triode[10]	9AJ	6.3	0.6	2.3	2.2	4	250	−8	—	—	9	7.7K	2600	20	—	—
6CG8A‡	Medium-μ Triode	9GF	6.3	0.45	2.6	0.05	1.5	100	100*	—	—	8.5	6.9K	5800	40	—	—
	Sharp Cut-off Pent.				4.8	0.9	0.03	250	200*	150	1.6	7.7	750K	4600	—	—	—
6CH8	Medium-μ Triode	9FT	6.3	0.45	1.9	1.6	1.6	200	−6	—	—	13	5.75K	3300	19	—	—
	Sharp Cut-off Pent.				7	2.25	0.025	200	180*	150	2.8	9.5	300K	6200	—	—	—
6CL6	Pwr. Amp. Pent.	9BV	6.3	0.65	11	5.5	0.12	250	−3	150	7/7.2	31²	150K	11K	30⁵	7500	2.8
6CL8A‡	Medium-μ Triode	9FX	6.3	0.45	2.7	0.4	1.8	300	—	—	—	15	5K	8000	40	—	—
	Sharp Cut-off Tetrode				5	0.02	0.02	300	−1	300	4	12	100K	6400	—	—	—
6CM6	Beam Pwr. Amp.	9CK	6.3	0.45	8	8.5	0.7	315	−13	225	2.2/6	35²	80K	3750	34⁵	8.5K	5.5
6CM7‡	Medium-μ Triode No. 1	9ES	6.3	0.6	2	0.5	3.8	200	−7	—	—	5	11K	2000	20	—	—
	Dual Triode Triode No. 2				3.5	0.4	3	250	−8	—	—	10	4.1K	4400	18	—	—
6CM8‡	High-μ Triode	9FZ	6.3	0.45	1.6	0.22	1.9	250	−2	—	—	1.8	50K	2000	100	—	—
	Sharp Cut-off Pent.				6	2.6	0.02	200	180*	150	2.8	9.5	300K	6200	—	—	—
6CN7‡	Dual Diode — High-μ Triode	9EN	6.3	0.3	1.5	0.5	1.8	100	−1	—	—	0.8	54K	1300	70	—	—
			3.15	0.6				250	−3	—	—	1	58K	1200	70	—	—
6CQ8‡	Medium-μ Triode	9GE	6.3	0.45	2.7	0.4	1.8	125	56*	—	—	15	5K	8000	40	—	—
	Sharp Cut-off Tetrode				5	2.5	0.019	125	−1	125	4.2	12	140K	5800	—	—	—
6CR6	Diode — Remote Cut-off Pent.	7EA	6.3	0.3	—	—	—	250	−2	100	3	9.5	200K	1950	—	—	—
6CS5	Beam Pwr. Pent.	9CK	6.3	1.2	15	9	0.5	200	180*	125	2.2	47²	28K	8000	—	4K	3.8
6CS6	Pentagrid Amp.	7CH	6.3	0.3	5.5	7.5	0.05	100	—	30	1.1	0.75	1 meg.	950	Ec₃ = 0 V.	—	—
6CS7‡	Medium-μ Triode No. 1	9EF	6.3	0.6	1.8	0.5	2.6	250	−8.5	—	—	10.5	7.7K	2200	17	—	—
	Dual Triode Triode No. 2				3.0	0.5	2.6	250	−10.5	—	—	19	3.45K	4500	15.5	—	—
6CU5	Beam Pwr. Pent.	7CV	6.3	1.2	13.2	8.6	0.7	120	−8	110	4/8.5	50²	10K	7500	—	2.5K	2.3
6CW4	Triode	12AQ	6.3	0.13	4.1	1.7	0.92	70	0	—	—	8	5.44K	12.5K	68	—	—
6CW5	Pentode	9CV	6.3	0.76	12	6	0.6	170	−12.5	170	5	70	—	—	—	2.4K	5.6
6CX8	Medium-μ Triode	9DX	6.3	0.75	2.2	0.38	4.4	150	150*	—	—	9.2	8.7K	4600	40	—	—
	Sharp Cut-off Pent.				9	4.4	0.06	200	68*	125	5.2	24	70K	10K	—	—	—
6CY5	Sharp Cut-off Tetrode	7EW	6.3	0.3	4.5	3	0.03	125	−7	80	1.5	10	100K	8000	—	—	—
6CY7	Dissimilar — Dual Triode	9EF	6.3	0.75	1.5⁷	0.37⁷	1.8⁷	250⁷	−3⁷	—	—	1.2⁷	52K⁷	1300⁷	68⁷	—	—
					5⁸	1⁸	4.4⁸	150⁸	620*⁸	—	—	30⁸	920⁸	5400⁸	5⁸	—	—
6CZ5‡	Beam Pwr. Amp. A₁ Amp.	9HN	6.3	0.45	8	8.5	0.7	250	−14	250	4.6/8	48²	73K	4800	46⁵	5K	5.4
	AB₁ Amp³							350	−23.5	280	3/13	103²	—	—	46⁵	7.5K⁶	1.5
6DB5	Beam Pwr. Amp.	9GR	6.3	1.2	15	9	0.5	200	180*	125	2.2/8.5	46/47	28K	8000	—	4K	3.8
6DB6	Sharp Cut-off Pent.	7CM	6.3	0.3	6	5	0.0035	150	−1	150	6.6	5.8	50K	2050	Ec₃ = −3 V.	—	—
6DC6	Semiremote Cut-off Pent.	7CM	6.3	0.3	6.5	2	0.02	200	180*	150	9	9	500K	5500	—	—	—

TABLE I—MINIATURE RECEIVING TUBES—Continued   **V18**

Type	Name	Base	Fil. or Heater V.	Amp.	Cin	Cout	Cgp	Plate Supply V.	Grid Bias	Screen Volts	Screen Ma.	Plate Ma.	Plate Res. Ohms	Transconductance[11]	Amp. Factor[4]	Load Res. Ohms	Watts Output
6DE6	Sharp Cut-off Pent.	7CM	6.3	0.3	6.3	1.9	0.02	200	180*	150	2.8	9.5	600K	6200	—	—	—
6DE7	Dissimilar— Dual Triode	9HF	6.3	0.9	2.2[7]	0.52[7]	4[7]	250[7]	-11[7]	—	—	5.5[7]	8.75K[7]	2000[7]	17.5[7]		
					5.5[8]	1[8]	8.5[8]	150[8]	-17.5[8]	—	—	35[8]	925[8]	6500[8]	6[8]		
6DJ8	Twin Triode	9AJ	6.3	0.365	3.3	1.8	1.4	90	-1.3	—	—	15	—	12.5K	33		
6DK6	Sharp Cut-off Pent.	7CM	6.3	0.3	6.3	1.9	0.02	300	-6.5	150	3.8	12	—	9800			
6DR7	Dissimilar— Dual Triode	9HF	6.3	0.9	2.2	0.34	4.5	330	-3	—	—	1.4	—	1600	68[7]		
					5.5	1.0	8.5	275	-17.5	—	—	35	—	6500	6[8]		
6DS4	High-μ Triode	12AQ	6.3	0.135	4.1	1.7	.92	70	0	—	—	8	5.44K	12.5K	68		
6DS5	Beam Pwr. Amp.	7BZ	6.3	0.8	9.5	6.3	0.19	250	-8.5	200	3/10	32[2]	28K	5800	32[5]	8K	3.8
								250	270*	200	3/9	25[2]	28K	5800	27[5]	8K	3.6
6DT5	Pwr. Amp. Pent.	9HN	6.3	0.76	10.8	6.5	0.5	300	-7.3	200	10.8	49.5[2]	38K	—	—	5.2K	17
6DT6	Sharp Cut-off Pent.	7EN	6.3	0.3	5.8	—	0.02	150	560*	100	2.1	1.1	150K	615	—	—	—
6DT8	High-μ Dual Triode[10]	9DE	6.3	0.3	2.7	1.6	1.6	250	200*	—	—	10	10.9K	5500	60		
6DV4	Triode	12EA	6.3	0.135	3.7	0.25	1.8	75	100*	—	—	10.5	3.1K	11.5K	35		
6DW5	Beam Pwr. Amp.	9CK	6.3	1.2	14	9	0.5	200	-22.5	150	2	55	15K	5500			
6DX8	High-μ Triode	9HX	6.3	0.720	4.0	2.3	2.7	200	-1.7	—	—	3	—	4000			
	Sharp Cut-off Pent.				9.0	4.5	0.1	200	-2.9	200	3	18	130K	10.4K			
6DZ4	Medium-μ Triode	7DK	6.3	0.225	2.2	1.3	1.8	80	-11	—	—	15	2.0K	6700	14		
6EA5	Sharp Cut-off Tet.	7EW	6.3	0.2	3.8	2.3	.06	250	-1	140	0.95	10	150K	8000			
6EA8‡	Triode	9AE	6.3	0.45	3	0.3	1.7	330	-12	—	—	18	5K	8500	40		
	Sharp Cut-off Pent.				5	2.6	0.02	330	-9	330	4	12	6400				
6EB5	Dual Diode	6BT	6.3	0.3	Max. P.I.V. 550, Max. D.C. output current 5.5 ma.												
6EB8	High-μ Triode	9DX	6.3	0.75	2.4	.36	4.4	330	-5	—	—	2	37K	2700	100		
	Sharp Cut-off Pent.				11	4.2	0.1	330	-9	—	7	25	75K	12.5K			
6EH5	Power Pentode	7CV	6.3	1.2	17	9	0.65	135	0	117	14.5	42	11K	14.6K	—	3K	1.4
6EH7	Remote Cut-off Pent.	9AQ	6.3	0.3	9	3	.005	200	-2	90	4.5	12	500K	12.5K			
6EH8	Triode	9JG	6.3	0.45	2.8	1.7	1.8	125	-1	—	—	13.5	—	7500	40		
	Pentagrid Conv.				4.8	2.4	0.02	125	-1	125	4	12	170K	6000			
6EJ7	Sharp Cut-off Pent.	9AQ	6.3	0.3	10	3	.005	200	-2.5	200	4.7	10	350K	15K			
6ER5	Tetrode	7FN	6.3	0.18	4.4	3.0	0.38	200	-1.2	0	0	10	8K	10.5K	80		
6ES5	Triode	7FP	6.3	0.20	3.2	3.2	0.5	200	-1	—	—	10	8K	9000	75		
6ES8	Dual Triode	9DE	6.3	0.365	3.4	1.7	1.9	130	-1.2	—	—	15	—	12.5K	34		
6EU7	Twin Triode	9LS	6.3	0.3	1.6	0.2	1.5	100	-1	—	—	0.5	80K	1250	100		
6EU8	Triode	9JF	6.3	0.45	5.0	2.6	0.02	150	-1	—	—	18	5K	8500	40		
	Pentode				3.0	1.6	1.7	125	-1	125	4	12	80K	6400			
6EV5	Sharp Cut-off Tet.	7EW	6.3	0.2	4.5	2.9	0.035	250	-1	80	0.9	11.5	150K	8800			
6EZ8	Triple Triode No. 1 / Triodes No. 2 & 3	9KA	6.3	0.45	2.6	1.4 / 1.2	1.5	330	-4	—	—	4.2	13.6K	4200	57		
6FG5	Pentode	7GA	6.3	0.2	4.2	2.8	0.02	250	-0.2	250	.42	9	250K	9500			
6FG7	Triode	9GF	6.3	0.45	3.0	1.3	1.8	125	-1	—	—	13	5700	7500	43		
	Pentode				5.0	2.4	0.2	125	-1	125	4	11	180K	6000			
6FH5	Triode	7FP	6.3	0.2	3.2	3.2	0.6	135	-1	—	—	11	5600	9000	50		
6FM8	Duplex Diode	9KR	6.3	0.45	2.4 / 2.2	—	—	Max. a.c. voltage = 200. Max. d.c. output current = 5 ma.									
	Triode				1.5	0.16	1.8	300	-3	—	—	1	58K	1200	70		
6FQ5A‡	Triode	7FP	6.3	0.18	4.8	4.0	0.4	135	-1.2	—	—	11.5	5500	11K	60		
6FS5	V.h.f. Pent.	7GA	6.3	0.2	4.8	2.0	.03	275	-0.2	135	0.17	9	240K	10K			
6FV6	Sharp Cut-off Tetrode	7FQ	6.3	0.2	4.5	3	0.03	125	-1	80	1.5	10	100K	8000			
6FV8A‡	Triode	9FA	6.3	0.45	2.8	1.5	1.8	330	-1	—	—	14	5K	8000	40		
	Pentode				5	2	0.02	330	-1	125	4	12	200K	6500			
6FW8	Medium-μ Twin Triode	9AJ	6.3	0.4	3.4	2.4	1.9	100	-1.2	—	—	15	2500	13K	33		
6FY5	Tetrode	7FN	6.3	0.2	4.75	3.3	0.50	135	-1	—	—	11	—	13K	70		
6GC5	Pwr. Pent.	9EU	6.3	1.2	18.0	7.0	0.9	110	-7.5	110	4	50	13K	8000	—	2K	2.1
6GJ8	Triode	9AE	6.3	0.6	3.4	1.6	2.6	125	-1	—	—	13.5	5K	8500	40		
	Pentode				8	2.4	0.36	125	-1	125	4.5	12	150K	7500			
6GK5	High-μ Triode	7FP	6.3	0.18	5	3.5	0.52	135	-1	—	—	11.5	5400	15K	78		
6GK6	Power Pentode	9GK	6.3	0.76	10	7.0	0.14	250	-7.3	250	5.5	48	38K	11.3K	—	5.2K	5.7
6GM6	Pentode	7CM	6.3	0.3	10	2.4	0.036	125	—	125	3.4	14	200K	13K			
6GN8	High-μ Triode	9DX	6.3	0.75	2.4	0.36	4.4	250	-2	—	—	2	37K	2700	100		
	Sharp Cut-off Pent.				11	4.2	0.1	200	—	150	5.5	25	60K	11.5K			
6GS8	Twin Pentode	9LW	6.3	0.30	6.0	3.2	—	100	-10	125	3.6	2.0					
6GU5	Beam Pent.	7GA	6.3	0.22	7	3.2	0.018	135	-0.4	135	0.25	9.0	670K	1500			
6GV8	High-μ Triode	9LY	6.3	0.9	—	—	—	100	-0.8	—	—	5	7.6K	6500	50		
					—	—	—	170	-15	170	2.7	41	25K	7500			
6GY8	Triple Triode	9MB	6.3	0.45	—	—	—	125	-1	—	—	4.5	14K	4500	63		
6GW5	V.h.f. Triode	7GK	6.3	0.19	5.5	4.0	0.6	135	-1	—	—	12.5	5.8K	15K	70		
6GZ5	Pwr. Amp. Pent.	7CV	6.3	0.38	8.5	3.8	0.24	250	270*	250	2.7	16	150K	8400	—	15K	1.1
6HB6	Power Pentode	9PU	6.3	0.76	13	8.0	0.18	250	100*	250	6.2	40	24K	20K			
6HB7	Sharp Cut-off Pent.	9QA	6.3	0.45	5.0	3.4	0.010	125	-1	125	4	12	200K	6400			
	Medium-μ Triode				3.0	1.9	1.9	150	56*	—	—	18	5K	8500	40		
6HF8	High-μ Triode	9DX	6.3	0.78	2.8	2.6	3.5	200	-2	—	—	4	17.5K	4000	70		
	Sharp Cut-off Pent.				10	4.2	0.1	200	68*	125	7	25	75K	12.5K			
6HG5	Pwr. Amp. Pent.	7BZ	6.3	0.45	8.0	8.5	0.4	250	-12.5	250	4.5	47	52K	4100	—	5K	4.5
6HK5	Triode	7GM	6.3	0.19	4.4	2.6	0.29	135	-1.0	—	—	12.5	5K	15K	75		
6HM5/ 6HA5	High-μ Triode	7GM	6.3	0.18	4.3	2.9	0.36	135	—	—	—	19	4K	20K	80		
6HQ5	Sharp Cut-off Triode	7GM	6.3	0.2	5.0	3.5	0.52	135	-1	—	—	11.5	5.4K	15K	78		
6HS6	Sharp Cut-off Pent.	7BK	6.3	0.45	8.8	5.2	.006	150	0	75	2.8	8.8	500K	9500			
6HZ8	High-μ Triode	9DX	6.3	1.125	3.8	0.4	5.0	200	-2	—	—	3.5	—	4K	70		
	Sharp Cut-off Pent.				12	5	0.1	250	100*	170	6	29	140K	12.6K			

Type	Name	Base	Fil. or Heater		Capacitances pf.			Plate Supply V.	Grid Bias	Screen Volts	Screen Ma.	Plate Ma.	Plate Res. Ohms	Transconductance[11]	Amp. Factor[4]	Load Res. Ohms	Watts Output
			V.	Amp.	Cin	Cout	Cgp										
6J4	Grounded-Grid Triode	7BQ	6.3	0.4	7.5	3.9	0.12	150	100*	—	—	15	4.5K	12K	55	—	—
6J6A‡	Medium-µ A₁ Amp.[10] Dual Triode Mixer	7BF	6.3	0.45	2.2	0.4	1.6	100	50*	—	—	8.5	7.1K	5300	38	—	—
								150	810*	—	—	4.8	10.2K	1900	Osc. peak voltage = 3 V		
6JC6A	Sharp Cut-off Pent.	9PM	6.3	0.3	8.5	3	0.19	125	56*	125	3.4	14	180K	16K	—	—	—
6JC8	Med.-µ Triode	9PA	6.3	0.45	2.8	.44	1.3	125	−1	—	—	12	6K	6500	40	—	—
	Sharp Cut-off Pent.				4.8	0.9	0.038	125	−1	125	2.2	9	300K	5500	—	—	—
6JK8	Dual V.h.f. Triode	9AJ	6.3	0.4	3.0	1.0	1.4	100	−1	—	—	5.3	8K	6800	55	—	—
					5.0	4.0	0.6	135	−1.2	—	—	10	5.4K	13K	70	—	—
6KD8	Sharp Cut-off Pent.	9AE	6.3	0.4	5.0	2.6	0.015	125	−1	110	3.5	9.5	200K	5000	—	—	—
	Medium-µ Triode				1.5	2.8	1.8	125	−1	—	—	13.5	—	7500	40	—	—
6KE8	Medium-µ Triode	9DC	6.3	0.4	2.4	2.0	1.3	125	68*	—	—	13	5.0K	8000	40	—	—
	Sharp Cut-off Pent.				5.0	3.4	.015	125	33*	125	2.8	10	125K	12K	—	—	—
6KR8	Sharp Cut-off Pent.	9DX	6.3	0.75	13	4.4	0.075	200	82*	100	3.0	19.5	60K	20K	—	—	—
	Medium-µ Triode				4.2	3.0	2.6	125	68*	—	—	15	4400	10.4K	46	—	—
6KT6	Remote Cut-off Pent.	9PM	6.3	0.3	9.5	3	0.19	125	56*	125	.4.2	17	—	18K	—	—	—
6KT8	High-µ Triode	9QP	6.3	0.6	32	1.6	3.0	250	−2	—	—	1.8	31.5K	3200	100	—	—
	Sharp Cut-off Pent.				7.5	2.2	0.046	125	−1	125	4.5	12	150K	10K	—	—	—
6KY6	Sharp Cut-off Pent.	9GK	6.3	0.52	14	6.0	0.16	125	0	135	5.2	30	40K	30K	—	—	—
6KZ8	Sharp Cut-off Pent.	9FZ	6.3	0.45	5.5	3.4	0.01	125	−1	125	4	12	200K	7500	—	—	—
	Medium-µ Triode				3.2	1.8	1.6	125	−1	—	—	13.5	5400	8500	46	—	—
6LJ8	Sharp Cut-off Pent.	9GF	6.3	0.4	5.5	3.4	0.015	125	33*	125	3.5	12	125K	13K	—	—	—
	Medium-µ Triode				2.4	2.0	1.4	125	68*	—	—	13	5K	8000	40	—	—
6LY8	High-µ Triode	9DX	6.3	0.75	2.6	2.8	3.8	200	−2.0	—	—	1.0	59K	1700	53	—	—
	Sharp Cut-off Pent.				13.0	4.4	0.75	200	—	100	3	19.5	60K	20K	—	—	—
6S4A	Medium-µ Triode	9AC	6.3	0.6	4.2	0.9	2.6	250	−8	—	—	26	3.6K	4500	16	—	—
6T4	U.h.f. Triode	7DK	6.3	0.225	2.6	0.25	1.7	80	150*	—	—	18	1.86K	7000	13	—	—
6T8A‡	Triple Diode-High-µ Triode	9E	6.3	0.45	1.6	1	2.2	100	−1	—	—	0.8	54K	1300	70	—	—
								250	−3	—	—	1	58K	1200	70	—	—
6U8A‡	Medium-µ Triode	9AE	6.3	0.45	2.5	0.4	1.8	150	56*	—	—	18	5K	8500	40	—	—
	Sharp Cut-off Pent.				5	2.6	0.01	250	68*	110	3.5	10	400K	5200	—	—	—
6X8A‡	Medium-µ Triode	9AK	6.3	0.45	2.0	0.5	1.4	100	100*	—	—	8.5	6.9K	—	40	—	—
	Sharp Cut-off Pent.				4.3	0.7	0.09	250	200*	150	1.6	7.7	750K	—	—	—	—
12AB5	Beam Pwr. Amp. A₁ Amp. AB₁ Amp.[3]	9EU	12.6	0.2	8	8.5	0.7	250	−12.5	250	4.5/7	47[2]	50K	4100	45[5]	5K	4.5
								250	−15	250	5/13	79[2]	60K[1]	3750	70[5]	10K[6]	10
12AC6	Remote Cut-off Pent.	7BK	12.6	0.15	4.3	5	0.005	12.6	0	12.6	0.2	0.55	500K	730	—	—	—
12AD6	Pentagrid Conv.	7CH	12.6	0.15	8	8	0.3	12.6	0	12.6	1.5	0.45	1 meg.	260	Grid No. 1 Res. 33K		
12AE6A	Dual Diode — Medium-µ Triode	7BT	12.6	0.15	1.8	1.1	2	12.6	0	—	—	0.75	15K	1000	15	—	—
12AE7	Low-µ Dissimilar Double Triode	9A	12.6	0.45	4.7	0.75	3.9	16	—	—	—	1.9	31.5K	4000	13	—	—
					4.2	0.85	3.4	16	—	—	—	7.5	985	6500	6.4	—	—
12AF6	R.f. Pent.	7BK	12.6	0.15	5.5	4.8	0.006	12.6	0	12.6	0.35	0.75	300K	1150	—	—	—
12AJ6	Dual Diode — High-µ Triode	7BT	12.6	0.15	2.2	0.8	2	12.6	0	—	—	0.75	45K	1200	55	—	—
12AL8	Medium-µ Triode	9GS	12.6	0.45	1.5	0.3	12	12.6	−0.9	—	—	0.25	27K	550	15	—	—
	Tetrode				8	1.1	—	12.6	−0.8	12.6**	50**	25	1K	8000	—	—	—
12AQ5	Beam Pwr. Amp. A₁ Amp. AB₁ Amp.[3]	7BZ	12.6	0.225	8.3	8.2	0.35	250	−12.5	250	4.5/7	47[2]	52K	4100	45[5]	5K	4.5
								250	−15	250	5/13	79[2]	60K[1]	3750[1]	70[5]	10K[6]	10
12AT7	High-µ Dual Triode[10]	9A	12.6	0.15	2.2[7]	0.5[7]	1.5[7]	100	270*	—	—	3.7	15K	4000	60	—	—
			6.3	0.3	2.2[8]	0.4[8]	1.5[8]	250	200*	—	—	10	10.9K	5500	60	—	—
12AU7A	Medium-µ Dual Triode[10]	9A	12.6	0.15	1.6[7]	0.5[7]	1.5[7]	100	0	—	—	11.8	6.25K	3100	19.5	—	—
			6.3	0.3	1.6[8]	0.35[8]	1.5[8]	250	−8.5	—	—	10.5	7.7K	2200	17	—	—
12AV7	Medium-µ Dual Triode[10]	9A	12.6	0.225	3.1[7]	0.5[7]	1.9[7]	100	120*	—	—	9	6.1K	6100	37	—	—
			6.3	0.45	3.1[8]	0.4[8]	1.9[8]	150	56*	—	—	18	4.8K	8500	41	—	—
12AW6	Sharp Cut-off Pent.	7CM	12.6	0.15	6.5	1.5	0.025	250	200*	150	2	7	800K	5000	42	—	—
12AX7A	High-µ A₁ Amp.[10] Dual Triode Class B	9A	12.6	0.15	1.6[7]	0.46[7]	1.7[7]	250	−2	—	—	1.2	62.5K	1600	100	—	—
			6.3	0.3	1.6[8]	0.34[8]	1.7[8]	300	0	—	—	40[2]	—	—	14[5]	16K[6]	7.5
12AY7	Medium-µ A₁ Amp. Dual Triode[10] Low-Level Amp.	9A	12.6	0.15	1.3	0.6	1.3	250	−4	—	—	3	—	1750	40	—	—
			6.3	0.3				150	2700*	Plate resistor = 20K. Grid resistor = 0.1 meg. V. G. = 12.5								
12AZ7A‡	High-µ Dual Triode[10]	9A	12.6	0.225	3.1[7]	0.5[7]	1.9[7]	100	270*	—	—	3.7	15K	4000	60	—	—
			6.3	0.45	3.1[8]	0.4[8]	1.9[8]	250	200*	—	—	10	10.9K	5500	60	—	—
12B4A‡	Low-µ Triode	9AG	12.6	0.3	5	1.5	4.8	150	−17.5	—	—	34	1.03K	6300	6.5	—	—
			6.3	0.6													
12BH7A‡	Medium-µ Dual Triode[10]	9A	12.6	0.3	3.2[7]	0.5[7]	2.6[7]	250	−10.5	—	—	11.5	5.3K	3100	16.5	—	—
			6.3	0.6	3.2[8]	0.4[8]	2.6[8]										
12BL6	Sharp Cut-off Pent.	7BK	12.6	0.15	5.5	4.8	0.006	12.6	−0.65	12.6	0.0005	1.35	500K	1350	—	—	—
12BR7A‡	Dual Diode — Medium-µ Triode	9CF	12.6	0.225	2.8	1	1.9	100	270*	—	—	3.7	15K	4000	60	—	—
			6.3	0.45				250	200*	—	—	10	10.9K	5500	60	—	—
12BV7	Sharp Cut-off Pent.	9BF	12.6	0.3	11	3	0.055	250	68*	150	6	25	90K	12K	1100	—	—
			6.3	0.6													
12BX6	Pentode	9AQ	12.6	0.15	7.5	3.3	0.007	200	−2.5	200	2.6	10	550K	7100	—	—	—
12BY7A‡	Sharp Cut-off Pent.	9BF	12.6	0.3	11.1	3	0.055	250	68*	150	6	25	90K	12K	1200	—	—
			6.3	0.6													
12BZ7	High-µ Dual Triode[10]	9A	12.6	0.3	6.5[7]	0.7[7]	2.5[7]	250	−2	—	—	2.5	31.8K	3200	100	—	—
			6.3	0.6	6.5[8]	0.55[8]	2.5[8]										
12CN5	Pentode	7CV	12.6	0.45	—	—	0.25	12.6	0	12.6	0.35	4.5	40K	3800	—	—	—
12CT8	Medium-µ Triode	9DA	12.6	0.3	2.4	0.19	2.2	150	−6.5	—	—	9	8.2K	4400	40	—	—
	Sharp Cut-off Pent.				7.5	2.4	0.044	200	−8	125	3.4	15	150K	7000	—	—	—
12CX6	Sharp Cut-off Pent.	7BK	12.6	0.15	7.6	6.2	0.05	12.6	0	12.6	1.4	3	40K	3100	—	—	—
12DE8	Diode — Remote Cut-off Pent.	Fig. 81	12.6	0.2	5.5	5.7	0.006	12.6	−0.8	12.6	0.5	1.3	300K	1500	—	—	—
12DK7	Dual Diode — Tetrode	9HZ	12.6	0.5	—	—	—	12.6	0	12.6	1	6	4K	5000	—	3.5K	0.01
12DL8	Dual Diode — Tetrode	9HR	12.6	0.55	12	1.3	—	12.6	−0.5	12.6**	75**	40	480	15K	7.2	—	—
12DM7	Twin Triode	9A	6.3	0.26	1.6	0.39	1.7	100	−1.0	—	—	0.5	80K	1250	100	—	—
			12.6	0.13													
12DQ7	Beam Pwr. Pent.	9BF	12.6	0.3	10	3.8	0.1	330	—	180	5.6	26	53K	10.5K	—	—	—
			6.3	0.6													

TABLE I—MINIATURE RECEIVING TUBES—*Continued* **V20**

Type	Name	Base	Fil. or Heater		Capacitances pf.			Plate Supply V.	Grid Bias	Screen Volts	Screen Ma.	Plate Ma.	Plate Res. Ohms	Transconductance[11]	Amp. Factor[4]	Load Res. Ohms	Watts Output
			V.	Amp.	Cin	Cout	Cgp										
12DS7	Dual Diode	9JU	12.6	0.4	Max. a.c. voltage = 16. Max. d.c. output current = 5 ma.												
	Pwr. Tetrode				—	—	—	16	—	16	75	40	480	15K	7.2	800	.04
12DT6	Pentode	7EN	12.6	0.15	—	—	—	150	−4.5	100	2.1	1	150K				
12DT7	High-μ	9A	12.6	0.15	1.6	0.46	1.7	300	−2	—	—	1.2	62.5K	1600	100	—	
	Dual Triode		6.3	0.3	1.6	0.34	1.7										
12DU7	Dual Diode	9JX	12.6	0.275				Max. average diode current = 10 ma.									
	Tetrode				11	3.6	0.6	16	—	16	1.5	12	6K	6200	—	2.7K	.025
12DV7	Dual Diode	9JY	12.6					Max. average diode current = 10 ma.									
	Triode				1.3	0.38	1.6	16	—	—	—	0.4	19K	750	14	—	
12DV8	Dual Diode — Tetrode	9HR	12.6	0.375	9.0	1.0	12	12.6	18*	—	—	6.8²	—	—	7.6	1250	.005
12DW7	Double Triode	9A	12.6	0.15	1.6	0.44	1.7	250	−2	—	—	1.2	62.5K	1600	100	—	
			6.3	0.30	1.7	0.4	1.5	250	−8.5	—	—	10.5	7.7K	2200	17	—	
12DW8	Diode	9JC	12.6	0.45	1.6⁷	0.7	1.8	16	0	—	—	1.9⁷	—	2700	9.5	—	
	Dissimilar Dual Triode				4.4⁸	0.7⁸	3.2					7.5⁸	—	6500	6.4	—	
12DY8	Sharp Cut-off Triode	9JD	12.6	0.35	2	2	1.5	16	0	—	—	1.2	10K	2000	20	—	
	Tetrode				11	3	0.74	16	—	12.6	2	14	5K	6000	—	—	
12DZ6	Pwr. Amp. Pent.	7BK	12.6	0.175	12.5	8.5	0.25	12.6	—	12.6	2.2	4.5²	25K	3800	—	—	
12EA6	R.F. Pent.	7BK	12.6	0.175	11	4	0.04	12.6	−3.4	12.6	1.4	3.2²	32K	3800	—	—	
12EC8	Medium-μ Triode	9FA	12.6	0.225	2.6	0.4	1.7	16	−2.2	—	—	2.4	6K	4700	25	—	
	Pent.				4.6	2.6	0.02	16	−1.6	12.6	—	0.66	750K	2000	—	—	
12ED5‡	Pwr. Amp. Pent.	7CV	12.6	0.45	14	8.5	0.26	150	−4.5	150	11	36²	14K	8500	—	—	1.5
12EG6	Dual Control Heptode	7CH	12.6	0.15	—	—	—	30	—	12.6	2.4	0.4	150K	800	—	—	
12EK6	R.f. Pent.	7BK	12.6	0.2	10	5.5	0.032	12.6	−4.0	12.6	2	4.4	40K	4200	—	—	
12EL6	Dual Diode — High-μ Triode	7FB	12.6	0.15	2.2	1	1.8	12.6	0	—	—	0.75	45K	1200	55	—	
12EM6	Diode — Tetrode	9HV	12.6	0.5	—	—	—	12.6	—	12.6	1	6	4K	5000	—	—	
12F8	Dual Diode — Remote Cut-off Pent.	9FH	12.6	0.15	4.5	3	0.06	12.6	0	12.6	0.38	1	333K	1000	—	—	
12FK6	Dual Diode — Low-μ Triode	7BT	12.6	0.15	1.8	0.7	1.6	16	0	—	—	1.3	6.2K	1200	7.4	—	
12FM6	Dual Diode — Med.-μ Triode	7BT	12.6	0.15	2.7	1.7	1.7	30	0	—	—	1.8	5.6K	2400	13.5	—	
12FQ8	Twin Double Plate Triode	9KT	12.6	0.15	1.7	0.27	0.9	250	−1.5	—	—	1.5	76K	1250	95	—	
12FR8	Pentode	9KU	12.6	0.32	8.5	5.5	0.15	12.6	−0.8	12.6	0.7	1.9	400K	2700	—	—	
	Triode — Diode				2.6	2.0	1.7	12.6	−0.6	—	—	1.0	—	1200	10	—	
12FT6	Dual Diode — Triode	7BT	12.6	0.15	1.8	1.1	2.0	30	0	—	—	2	7.6K	1900	15	—	
12FX5	Beam Pwr. Pent.	7CV	12.6	0.45	17	9	0.6	110	62*	115	12	35	—	—	—	3.0K	1.3
12FX8A	Triode	9KV	12.6	0.27	2.2	0.25	1.3	12.6	—	—	—	0.29	—	1400	10	—	
	Heptode				—	—	—	12.6	1.6	—	—	1.3	500K	—	—	—	
12GA6	Heptode	7CH	12.6	0.15	5.0	13	0.05	12.6	0	12.6	0.80	0.30	1 meg.	140	—	—	
12H4	General Purpose Triode	7DW	12.6	0.15	2.4	0.9	3.4	90	0	—	—	10	—	3000	20	—	
			6.3	0.3				250	−8	—	—	9	—	2600	20	—	
12J8	Dual Diode — Tetrode	9GC	12.6	0.325	10.5	4.4	0.7	12.6	0	12.6	1.5	12⁵	6K	5500	—	2.7K	0.02
12K5	Tetrode (Pwr. Amp. Driver)	7EK	12.6	0.45	—	—	—	12.6	−2	12.6**	85**	8	800	7000	5.6	800	0.035
12R5‡	Beam Pwr. Pent.	7CV	12.6	0.6	13	9	0.55	110	−8.5	110	3.3	40	13K	7000	—	—	
12U7	Dual Medium-μ Triode[10]	9A	12.6	0.15	1.6⁷'⁸	0.4⁷	1.5⁷'⁸	12.6	0	—	—	1	12.5K	1600	20	—	
18FW6A‡	Remote Cut-off Pent.	7CC	18	0.1	5.5	5	0.0035	150	—	100	4.4	11	250K	4400	—	—	
18FX6A‡	Dual Control Heptode	7CH	18	0.1	—	—	—	150	—	—	—	2.3	400K	—	—	—	
18FY6A‡	High-μ Triode — Diode	7BT	18	0.1	2.4	0.22	1.8	150	−1	—	—	0.6	77K	1300	100	—	
25F5	Beam Pwr. Pent.	7CV	25	0.15	12	6	0.57	110	−7.5	110	3/7	36/37	16K	5800	—	2.5K	1.2
32ET5	Beam Pwr. Pent.	7CV	32	0.1	12	6	0.6	150	−7.5	130	—	21.5K	5500	—	2.8K	1.2	
34GD5	Beam Pwr. Pent.	7CV	34	0.1	12	6	0.6	110	−7.5	110	3	35	13K	5700	—	2.5K	1.4
35B5	Beam Pwr. Amp.	7BZ	35	0.15	11	6.5	0.4	110	−7.5	110	3/7	41²	—	5800	40⁵	2.5K	1.5
50B5	Beam Pwr. Amp.	7BZ	50	0.15	13	6.5	0.5	110	−7.5	110	4/8.5	50²	14K	7500	49⁵	2.5K	1.9
50FK5	Pwr. Pent.	7CV	50	0.15	17	9	0.65	110	62*	115	12	32	14K	12.8K	—	3K	1.2
1218A	U.h.f. Triode	7DK	6.3	0.225	2.9	0.25	1.7	200	100*	—	—	18	—	10.75K	55	—	
5686	Beam Pwr. Pent.	9G	6.3	0.35	6.4	8.5	0.11	250	−12.5	250	3⁵	27⁵	45K	3100	—	9K	2.7
5687	Medium-μ Dual Triode[10]	9H	12.6	0.45	4⁷	0.6⁷	4⁷	120	−2	—	—	36	1.7K	11K	18.5	—	
			6.3	0.9	4⁸	0.5⁸	4⁸	250	−12.5	—	—	12.5	3K	5500	16.5	—	
5722	Noise Generating Diode	5CB	6.3	1.5	—	2.2	—	200	—	—	—	35	—	—	—	—	
5842/417A	High-μ Triode	9V	6.3	0.3	9.0	1.8	0.55	150	62*	—	—	26	1.8K	24K	43	—	
5879	Sharp Cut-off Pent.	9AD	6.3	0.15	2.7	2.4	0.15	250	−3	100	0.4	1.8	2 meg.	1000	—	—	
6386	Medium-μ Dual Triode[10]	8CJ	6.3	0.35	2	1.1	1.2	100	200*	—	—	9.6	4.25K	1400	17	—	
6887	Dual Diode	6BT	6.3	0.2	Max. peak inverse plate voltage = 360 V. Max. d.c. plate current each diode = 10 ma.												
6973	Pwr. Pentode	9EU	6.3	0.45	6	6	0.4	440	−15	300	—	—	73K	4800	—	—	
7189A	High-μ Triode	9CV	6.3	0.76	10.8	6.5	0.5	250	−7.3	250	5.5	48	40K	11.3K	—	—	
7258	Sharp Cut-off	9DA	12.6	0.195	7	2.4	0.4	330	—	125	3.8	12	170K	7800	—	—	
	Medium-μ Triode				2	0.26	1.5	330	−3	—	—	15	4.7K	4500	21	—	
7586	Medium-μ Triode	12AQ	6.3	0.135	4.2	1.6	2.2	75	100*	—	—	10	3000	11.5K	35	—	
7587	Sharp Cut-off Tet.	12AS	6.3	0.15	6.5	1.4	0.01	125	68*	50	2.7	10	200K	10.5K	—	—	
7895	High-μ Triode	12AQ	6.3	0.135	4.2	1.7	0.9	110	0	—	—	7	6800	9400	64	—	
8056	Medium-μ Triode	12AQ	6.3	0.135	4.0	1.7	2.1	12	0	—	—	5.8	1.6K	8000	12.5	—	
8058	High-μ Triode	12CT	6.3	0.135	6.0	0.046	1.3	110	47*	—	—	10	—	10K	—	—	
8393	High-μ Triode	12AQ	13.5	0.060	4.4	1.7	2.4	75	100*	—	—	10.5	3000	11.5K	35	—	
8628	High-μ Triode	12AQ	6.3	0.10	10	3.4	1.7	150	3.3K*	—	—	0.3	41K	3100	127	7K	
8677	Power Triode	12CT	6.3	0.15	6.0	1.2	—	180	1.2K*	—	—	20	3K	5400	70	—	1.4
9001	Sharp Cut-off Pent.	7BD	6.3	0.15	3.6	3	0.01	250	−3	100	0.7	2	1 meg.	1400	—	—	
9002	U.h.f. Triode	7BS	6.3	0.15	1.2	1.1	1.4	250	−7	—	—	6.3	11.4K	2200	25	—	
9003	Remote Cut-off Pent.	7BD	6.3	0.15	3.4	3	0.1	250	−3	100	2.7	6.7	700K	1800	—	—	
9006	U.h.f. Diode	6BH	6.3	0.15	Max. a.c. voltage = 270. Max. d.c. output current = 5 ma.												

‡ Controlled heater warm-up characteristic.
Ω Oscillator gridleak or screen-dropping resistor ohms.
* Cathode resistor ohms.
** Space-charge grid.

[1] Per Plate.
[2] Maximum-signal current for full-power output.
[3] Values are for two tubes in push-pull.
[4] Unless otherwise noted.
[5] No signal plate ma.
[6] Effective plate-to-plate.
[7] Triode No. 1.
[8] Triode No. 2.
[9] Oscillator grid current ma.
[10] Values for each section.
[11] Micromhos.
[12] Through 33K.

TABLE II—METAL RECEIVING TUBES

Characteristics given in this table apply to all type numbers shown, including
metal tubes, glass tubes with "G" suffix, and bantam tubes with "GT" suffix.
For "G" and "GT"-tubes not listed (not having metal counterparts), see Tables III, V, VI and VIII.

Type	Name	Base	Fil. or Heater V.	Amp.	Cap. C_{in}	C_{out}	C_{gp}	Plate Supply V.	Grid Bias	Screen Volts	Screen Ma.	Plate Ma.	Plate Res. Ohms	Transconductance[12]	Amp. Factor[13]	Load Res. Ohms	Watts Output
6A8	Pentagrid Conv.	8A	6.3	0.3	—	—	—	250	-3	100	2.7	3.5	360K	550	—	—	—
								E_{bb} (Osc.) 250 V. through 20K. Grid resistor (Osc.) 50K. I_b = 4 ma. I_{g1} = 0.4 ma.									
6AC7 1852	Sharp Cut-off Pent.	8N	6.3	0.45	11	5	0.15	300	160*	150	2.5	10	1 meg.	9000	—	—	—
								300	160*	60K[8]	2.5	10	1 meg.	9000	—	—	—
6AG7	Pwr. Amp. Pent.	8Y	6.3	0.65	13	7.5	0.06	300	-3	150	7/9	30/31	130K	11K	—	10K	3
6B8	Dual-Diode — Pent.	8E	6.3	0.3	6	9	0.005	250	-3	125	2.3	10	600K	1325	—	—	—
6F6	Pwr. Amp. Pent. — A_1 Amp.[1,5]	7S	6.3	0.7	6.5	13	0.2	250	-20	20[10]	—	31/34	2.6K	2600	6.8	4K	0.85
	AB_2 Amp.[1,6]							350	730*	132[11]	—	50/60	—	—	—	10K[7]	9
								350	-38	123[11]	—	48/92	—	—	—	6K[7]	13
	A_1 Amp.[5]							250	-16.5	250	6/11	34/36	80K	2500	—	7K	3.2
								285	-20	285	7/13	38/40	78K	2500	—	7K	4.8
	AB_2 Amp.[6]							375	-26	250	5/20	34/82	—	—	82[11]	10K[7]	18.5
								375	340*	250	8/18	54/77	—	—	94[11]	10K[7]	19
6J5	Medium-μ Triode	6Q	6.3	0.3	3.4	3.6	3.4	250	-8	—	—	9	7.7K	2600	20	—	—
6J7	Sharp Cut-off Pent. A_1 Amp.	7R	6.3	0.3	7	12	0.005	250	-3	100	0.5	2	1 meg.	1225	—	—	—
	Biased Detector							250	10K*	100	Zero signal cathode current = 0.43 ma.				0.5 meg.		
6K7	Variable-μ Pent. R.f. Amp.	7R	6.3	0.3	7	12	0.005	250	-3	125	2.6	10.5	600K	1650	—	—	—
	Mixer							250	-10	100	Osc. peak volts = 7						
6K8	Triode — Hexode Conv. Hexode	8K	6.3	0.3	—	—	—	250	-3	100	6	2.5	600K	350	—	—	—
	Triode							100	50K[8]	—	—	3.8	I_{g1} (Osc.) = 0.15 ma.				
6L6-GB[2]	Beam Pwr. Amp. A_1 Amp.[1,5]	7AC	6.3	0.9	11.5	9.5	0.9	250	-20	20[10]	—	40/44	1.7K	4700	8	5K	1.4
	A_1 Amp.[5] Self Bias							250	167*	250	5.4/7.2	75/78	—	—	14[10]	2.5K	6.5
								300	218*	200	3/4.6	51/55	—	—	12.7[10]	4.5K	6.5
	A_1 Amp.[5] Fixed Bias							250	-14	250	5/7.3	72/79	22.5K	6000	14[10]	2.5K	6.5
								350	-18	250	2.5/7	54/66	33K	5200	18[10]	4.2K	10.8
	A_1 Amp.[6] Self Bias							250	125*	250	10/15	120/130	—	—	35.6[11]	5K[7]	13.8
								270	125*	270	11/17	134/145	—	—	28.2[11]	5K[7]	18.5
	A_1 Amp.[6] Fixed Bias							250	-16	250	10/16	120/140	24.5K	5500[5]	32[11]	5K[7]	14.5
								270	-17.5	270	11/17	134/155	23.5K	5700[5]	35[11]	5K[7]	17.5
	AB_1 Amp.[6] Self Bias							360	270*	270	5/17	88/100	—	—	40.6[11]	9K[7]	24.5
	AB_1 Amp.[6] Fixed Bias							360	-22.5	270	5/11	88/140	—	—	45[11]	3.8K[7]	18
								360	-22.5	270	5/15	88/132	—	—	45[11]	6.6K[7]	26.5
	AB_2 Amp.[6] Fixed Bias							360	-18	225	3.5/11	78/142	—	—	52[11]	6K[7]	31
								360	-22.5	270	5/16	88/205	—	—	72[11]	3.8K[7]	47
6L7	Pentagrid — Mixer Amp. A_1 Amp.	7T	6.3	0.3	—	—	—	250	-3	100	6.5	5.3	600K	1100	-3[14]	—	—
	Mixer							250	-6	150	9.2	3.3	1 meg.	350	-15[14]	—	—
6N7GT	Class-B Twin Triode B Amp.[9]	8B	6.3	0.8	—	—	—	300	0	—	—	35/70	—	—	82[11]	8K[7]	10
	A_1 Amp.[15]							250	-5	—	—	6	11.3K	3100	—	—	—
6Q7	Dual Diode — High-μ Triode	7V[2]	6.3	0.3	5	3.8	1.4	250	-3	—	—	1	58K	1200	70	—	—
6R7	Dual Diode — Triode	7V[2]	6.3	0.3	4.8	3.8	2.4	250	-9	—	—	9.5	8.5K	1900	16	10K	0.28
6SA7GT	Pentagrid Conv.	8R[2]	6.3	0.3	9.5	12	0.13	250	0[3]	100	8	3.4	800K	Grid No. 1 resistor 20K.			
6SB7Y	Pentagrid Conv.	8R	6.3	0.3	9.6	9.2	0.13	100	-1	100	10.2	3.6	50K	900	—	—	—
								250	-1	100		3.8	1 meg.	950	—	—	—
								250	22K[8]	12K[8]	12/13	6.8/6.5	Osc. Section in 88—108 Mc. Service.				
6SC7	High-μ Dual Triode[5]	8S	6.3	0.3	2	3	2	250	-2	—	—	2	53K	1325	70	—	—
6SF5	High-μ Triode	6AB[2]	6.3	0.3	4	3.6	2.4	250	-2	—	—	0.9	66K	1500	100	—	—
6SF7	Diode — Variable-μ Pent.	7AZ	6.3	0.3	5.5	6	0.004	250	-1	100	3.3	12.4	700K	2050	—	—	—
6SG7	H.f. Amp. Pent.	8BK	6.3	0.3	8.5	7	0.003	250	-2.5	150	3.4	9.2	1 meg.	4000	—	—	—
6SH7	H.f. Amp. Pent.	8BK	6.3	0.3	8.5	7	0.003	250	-1	150	4.1	10.8	900K	4900	—	—	—
6SJ7[4]	Sharp Cut-off Pent.	8N	6.3	0.3	6	7	0.005	250	-3	100	0.8	3	1 meg.	1650	—	—	—
6SK7	Variable-μ Pent.	8N	6.3	0.3	6	7	0.003	250	-3	100	2.6	9.2	800K	2000	—	—	—
6SQ7GT	Dual Diode — High-μ Triode	8Q	6.3	0.3	3.2	3	1.6	250	-2	—	—	0.9	91K	1100	100	—	—
6SR7	Dual Diode — Triode	8Q	6.3	0.3	3.6	2.8	2.4	250	-9	—	—	9.5	8.5K	1900	16	—	—
6V6GTA	Beam Pwr. Amp. A_1 Amp.[5]	7AC	6.3	0.45	10	11	0.3	180	-8.5	180	3/4	29/30	50K	3700	8.5[10]	5.5K	2
								250	-12.5	250	4.5/7	45/47	50K	4100	12.5[10]	5K	4.5
								315	-13	225	2.2/6	34/35	80K	3750	13[10]	8.5K	5.5
	AB_1 Amp.[6]							250	-15	250	5/13	70/79	60K	3750	30[11]	10K[7]	10
								285	-19	285	4/13.5	70/92	70K	3600	38[11]	8K[7]	14
1620	Sharp Cut-off Pent.	7R	6.3	0.3	7	12	0.005	250	-3	100	0.5	2	1 meg.	1225	—	—	—
5693	Sharp Cut-off Pent.	8N	6.3	0.3	5.3	4.2	0.005	250	-3	100	0.85	3	1 meg.	1650	—	—	—

* Cathode resistor-ohms.
[1] Screen tied to plate.
[2] No connection to Pin No. 1 for 6L6G, 6Q7G, 6RGT/G, 6S7G, 6SA7GT/G and 6SF5-GT.
[3] Grid bias = 2 volts if separate oscillator excitation is used.
[4] Also type 6SJ7Y.
[5] Values are for single tube or section.
[6] Values are for two tubes in push-pull.
[7] Plate-to-plate value.
[8] Osc. grid leak — Scrn. res.
[9] Values for two units.
[10] Peak a.f. grid voltage.
[11] Peak a.f. G-G voltage.
[12] Micromhos.
[13] Unless otherwise noted.
[14] G_3 voltage.
[15] Units connected in parallel.

TABLE III — 6.3-VOLT GLASS TUBES WITH OCTAL BASES
(For "G" and "GT"-type tubes not listed here, see equivalent type in Tables II and VIII; characteristics and connections will be similar)

Type	Name	Plate Dissipation Watts	Base	Fil. or Heater		Capacitances pf.			Plate Supply V.	Grid Bias	Screen Volts	Screen Ma.	Plate Ma.	Plate Res. Ohms	Transconductance[4]	Amp. Factor	Load Res. Ohms	Watts Output
				V.	Amp.	C_{in}	C_{out}	C_{gp}										
6AL7GT	Electron-Ray Indicator	—	8CH	6.3	0.15	—	—	—	Outer edge of any of the three illuminated areas displaced $\frac{1}{16}$ in. min. outward with +5 volts to its electrode. Similar inward disp. with −5 volts. No pattern with −6 volts grid.								
6AQ7GT	Dual Diode — High-μ Triode	—	8CK	6.3	0.3	2.8	3.2	3	250	−2	—	—	2.3	44K	1600	70	—	—
6AR6	Beam Pent.	—	6BQ	6.3	1.2	11	7	0.55	250	−22.5	250	5	77	21K	5400	—	—	—
6AR7GT	Dual Diode — Remote Pent.	—	7DE	6.3	0.3	5.5	7.5	0.003	250	−2	100	1.8	7	1.2 meg.	2500	—	—	—
6AS7GA	Low-μ Twin Triode — D.C. Amp.[1]	—	8BD	6.3	2.5	6.5	2.2	7.5	135	250*	—	—	125	0.28K	7000	2	—	—
6AU5GT	Beam Pwr. Amp.[3]	10	6CK	6.3	1.25	11.3	7	0.5	115	−20	175	6.8	60	6K	5600	—	—	—
6AV5GA	Beam Pwr. Amp.[3]	11	6CK	6.3	1.2	14	7	0.5	250	−22.5	150	2.1	55	20K	5500	—	—	—
6BG6GA	Beam Pwr. Amp.[3]	20	5BT	6.3	0.9	11	6	0.8	250	−15	250	4	75	25K	6000	—	—	—
6BL7GTA	Medium-μ Dual Triode[1]	—	8BD	6.3	1.5	4.4	0.9	6	250	−9	—	—	40	2.15K	7000	15	—	—
6BQ6GTB 6CU6	Beam Pwr. Amp.[3]	11	6AM	6.3	1.2	15	7	0.6	250	−22.5	150	2.1	57	14.5K	5900	—	—	—
6BX7GT	Dual Triode[1]	—	8BD	6.3	1.5	5	3.4	4.2	250	390*	—	—	42	1.3K	7600	10	—	—
6CB5A	Beam Pwr. Amp.[3]	26	8GD	6.3	2.5	22	10	0.4	175	−30	175	6	90	5K	8800	—	—	—
6CD6GA	Beam Pwr. Amp.[3]	20	5BT	6.3	2.5	24	9.5	0.8	175	−30	175	5.5	75	7.2K	7700	—	—	—
6CK4	Low-μ Triode	—	8JB	6.3	1.25	8	1.8	6.5	550	−26	—	—	55	1.0K	6500	6.7	—	—
6CL5	Beam Pwr. Amp.[3]	25	8GD	6.3	2.5	20	11.5	0.7	175	−40	175	7	90	6K	6500	—	—	—
6CU6	Beam Pwr. Amp.[3]	11	6AM	6.3	1.2	15	7	0.55	250	−22.5	150	2.1	55	20K	5500	—	—	—
6DG6GT	Beam Pwr. Amp.	—	7S	6.3	1.2	—	—	—	200	180*	125	8.5	47	28K	8000	—	4K	3.8
6DN6	Beam Pwr. Pent.[3]	15	5BT	6.3	2.5	22	11.5	0.8	125	−18	125	6.3	70	4K	9000	—	—	—
6DN7	Dissimilar Dual Triode	—	8BD	6.3	0.9	2.2	0.7	4	350	−8	—	—	8	9K	2500	22	—	—
						4.6	1	5.5	550	−9.5	—	—	68	2K	7700	15	—	—
6DQ5	Beam Pwr. Amp.[3]	24	8JC	6.3	2.5	23	11	0.5	175	−25	125	5	110	5.5K	10.5K	—	—	—
6DQ6B	Beam Pwr. Amp.[3]	18	6AM	6.3	1.2	15	7	0.55	250	−22.5	150	2.4	75	20K	6600	—	—	—
6DZ7	Twin Pwr. Pent.[1]	13.2	8JP	6.3	1.52	11	5	0.6	300	120*	250	15	80	—	—	—	9K[2]	12
6E5	Electron Ray — Triode	—	6R	6.3	0.3	—	—	—	250	—	—	—	—	—	—	—	—	—
6EA7	Dissimilar — Dual Triode	—	8BD	6.3	1.05	2.2	0.6	4	350	−3	—	—	1.5	34K	1900	65	—	—
							1.3	8	550	−25	—	—	95	770	6500	5	—	—
6EF6	Beam Pwr. Amp.[5]	—	7S	6.3	0.9	11.5	9	0.8	250	−18	250	2	50	—	—	—	—	—
6EX6	Beam Pwr. Amp.[3]	22	5BT	6.3	2.25	22	8.5	1.1	175	−30	175	3.3	67	8.5K	7700	—	—	—
6EY6	Beam Pwr. Pent.	—	7AC	6.3	0.68	8.5	7	0.7	350	−17.5	300	3	44	60K	4400	—	—	—
6EZ5	Beam Pwr. Pent.	—	7AC	6.3	0.8	9	7	0.6	350	−20	300	3.5	43	50K	4100	—	—	—
6FH6	Beam Pwr. Pent.	—	6AM	6.3	1.2	33	8	0.4	770	−22.5	220	1.7	75	12K	6000	—	—	—
6GW6	Beam Power Amp.[3]	17.5	6AM	6.3	1.2	17	7	0.5	250	−22.5	150	2.1	70	15K	7100	—	—	—
6K6GT	Pwr. Amp. Pent.	—	7S	6.3	0.4	5.5	6	0.5	315	−21	250	4/9	25/28	110K	2100	—	9K	4.5
6S8GT	Triple-Diode — Triode	—	8CB	6.3	0.3	1.2	5	2	250	−2	—	—	—	91K	1100	100	—	—
6SD7GT	Semi-Remote Pent.	—	8N	6.3	0.3	9	7.5	0.0035	250	−2	125	3	9.5	700K	4250	—	—	—
6SL7GT	High-μ Dual Triode[1]	—	8BD	6.3	0.3	3.4	3.8	2.8	250	−2	—	—	2.3	44K	1600	70	—	—
6SN7GTB	Medium-μ Dual Triode[1]	—	8BD	6.3	0.6	3	1.2	4	250	−8	—	—	9	7.7K	2600	20	—	—
6W6GT	Beam Pwr. Amp.	—	7S	6.3	1.2	15	9	0.5	200	180*	125	2/8.5	46/47	28K	8000	—	4K	3.8
6Y6GA	Beam Pwr. Amp.	—	7S	6.3	1.25	15	1	0.7	200	−14	135	2.2/9	61/66	18.3K	7100	—	2.6K	6
1635	High-μ Dual Triode	—	8B	6.3	0.6	—	—	—	300	0	—	—	6.6/54	—	—	—	12K[2]	10.4
6550	Power Pentode	35	7S	6.3	1.6	14	12	0.85	400	−16.5	225	18	105	27K	9000	—	3K	20
7027A	Beam Pwr. Amp.	—	8HY	6.3	0.9	10	7.5	1.5	450	−30	350	19.2	194	—	6000	—	6K[2]	50
7591	Beam Pwr. Amp.	19	8KQ	6.3	0.8	10	5	0.25	450	200*	400	22	94	—	—	—	9K[2]	28

* Cathode resistor-ohms.   2 Plate-to-plate value.   3 Horz. Deflection Amp.   4 Micromhos.
1 Per section.   5 Vert. Deflection Amp.

TABLE IV — 6.3-VOLT LOCK-IN-BASE TUBES
For other lock-in-base types see Tables V, VI, and VII

Type	Name	Base	Fil. or Heater		Capacitances pf.			Plate Supply V.	Grid Bias	Screen Volts	Screen Ma.	Plate Ma.	Plate Res. Ohms	Transconductance[3]	Amp. Factor	Load Res. Ohms	Watts Output
			V.	Amp.	C_{in}	C_{out}	C_{gp}										
7A8	Octode Conv.	8U	6.3	0.15	7.5	9	0.15	250	−3	100	3.2	3	50K	Anode grid 250 Volts max.[1]			
7AH7	Remote Cut-off Pent.	8V	6.3	0.15	7	6.5	0.005	250	250*	250	1.9	6.8	1 meg.	3300	—	—	—
7AK7	Sharp Cut-off Pent.	8V	6.3	0.8	12	9.5	0.7	150	0	90	21	41	11.5K	5500	—	—	—
7B7	Remote Cut-off Pent.	8V	6.3	0.15	5	6	0.007	250	−3	100	1.7	8.5	750K	1750	—	—	—
7C7	Sharp Cut-off Pent.	8V	6.3	0.15	5.5	6.5	0.007	250	−3	100	0.5	2	2 meg.	1300	—	—	—
7E7	Dual Diode — Pent.	8AE	6.3	0.3	4.6	5.5	0.005	250	330*	100	1.6	7.5	700K	1300	—	—	—
7F8	Medium-μ Dual Triode[2]	8BW	6.3	0.3	2.8	1.4	1.2	250	500*	—	—	6	14.5K	3300	48	—	—
7K7	Dual Diode — High-μ Triode	8BF	6.3	0.3	2.4	2	1.7	250	−2	—	—	2.3	44K	1600	70	—	—

* Cathode resistor-ohms.   1 Through 20K resistor.   2 Each section.   3 Micromhos.

TABLE V — 1.5-VOLT FILAMENT BATTERY TUBES

Type	Name	Base	Fil. or Heater V.	Amp.	Capacitances pf. C_{in}	C_{out}	C_{gp}	Plate Supply V.	Grid Bias	Screen Volts	Screen Ma.	Plate Ma.	Plate Res. Ohms	Transconductance[2]	Amp. Factor	Load Res. Ohms	Watts Output
1A7GT	Pentagrid Conv.	7Z	1.4	0.05	7	10	0.5	90	0	45	0.7	0.6	600K	E_{bb} Anode-grid = 90 Volts.			
1H5GT	Diode High-μ Triode	5Z	1.4	0.05	1.1	4.6	1	90	0	—	—	0.15	240K	275	65	—	—
1LN5	Sharp Cut-off Pent.	7AO	1.4	0.05	3	8	0.007	90	0	90	0.35	1.6	1.1 meg.	800	—	—	—
1N5GT	R.f. Pentode	5Y	1.4	0.05	3	10	0.007	90	0	90	0.3	1.2	1.5 meg.	750	—	—	—
3E6	Sharp Cut-off Pent.	7CJ	2.8[1]	0.05	5.5	8	0.007	90	0	90	1.2	2.9	325K	1700	—	—	—

[1] Center-tap filament permits 1.4 volt operation. [2] Micromhos.

TABLE VI — SPECIAL RECEIVING TUBES

Type	Name	Plate Dissipation Watts	Base	Fil. or Heater V.	Amp.	Capacitances pf. C_{in}	C_{out}	C_{gp}	Plate Supply V.	Grid Bias	Screen Volts	Screen Ma.	Plate Ma.	Plate Res. Ohms	Transconductance[1]	Amp. Factor	Load Res. Ohms	Watts Output
6AV11	Triple Triode	—	12BY	6.3	0.6	1.9	1.5	1.2	250	−8.5	—	—	10.5	7.7K	2200	17	—	—
6B10	Dual Triode / Dual Diode	—	12BF	6.3	0.6	—	—	—	250	−8	—	—	10	7.2K	2500	18	—	—
									Diode current for continuous operation = 5 ma.									
6BW11	Dual Pent. Pent. 1 / Pent. 2	4.0 / 3.1	12HD	6.3	0.8	7.5 / 12	2.8 / 2.8	0.03 / 0.03	125 / 125	56* / 56*	125 / 125	4.8 / 3.8	22 / 11	120K / 200K	8500 / 13K	—	—	—
6C10	Triple Triode	—	12BQ	6.3	0.6	1.6	0.3	1.7	250	−2	—	—	1.2	62.5K	1600	100	—	—
6D10	Triple Triode	—	12BQ	6.3	0.45	2.2	0.5	1.5	125	−1	—	—	4.2	13.6K	4200	57	—	—
6EW7	Dissimilar Dual Triode	—	9HF	6.3	0.9	2.2 / 7.0	0.4 / 1.2	4.2 / 9.0	250 / 150	−11 / −17.5	—	—	5.5 / 45	8.75K / 800	2000 / 7500	17.5 / 6	—	—
6F4	Acorn Triode	—	7BR	6.3	0.225	2	0.6	1.9	80	150*	—	—	13	2.9K	5800	17	—	—
6FJ7	Dissimilar Dual Triode	—	12BM	6.3	0.9	2.2 / 4.0	0.48 / 0.54	3.8 / 5.0	250 / 250	−8 / −9.5	—	—	8 / 41	9K / 2K	2500 / 7700	22.5 / 15.4	—	—
6GE5	Beam Pwr. Pent.	17.5	12BJ	6.3	1.2	16	7	0.34	250	−22.5	150	1.8	65	18K	7300	—	—	—
6GJ5	Beam Pwr. Pent.	17.5	9NM	6.3	1.2	15	6.5	0.26	250	−22.5	150	2.1	70	15K	7100	—	—	—
6GT5	Beam Pwr. Pent.	17.5	9NZ	6.3	1.2	15	6.5	0.26	250	−22.5	150	2.1	70	15K	7100	—	—	—
6HB5	Beam Pwr. Pent.	18	12BJ	6.3	1.5	22	9.0	0.4	130	−20	130	1.75	50	11K	9100	—	—	—
6HF5	Beam Pwr. Pent.	28	12FB	6.3	2.25	24	10	0.56	175	−25	125	4.5	125	5.6K	11.3K	—	—	—
6J11	Twin Pentode	—	12BW	6.3	0.8	11	2.8	0.04	125	56*	125	3.8	11	200K	13K	—	—	—
6JB6	Beam Pwr. Pent.	17.5	9QL	6.3	1.2	15	6.0	0.2	250	−22.5	150	2.1	70	15K	7100	—	—	—
6JE6	Pentode	24	9QL	6.3	2.5	21	11	0.44	175	−25	125	5	115	5.5K	10.5K	—	—	—
6JE6A	Beam Power Amp.	30	9QL	6.3	2.5	22	11	0.56	175	−35	145	2.4	95	7K	7500	—	—	—
6K11	Triple Triode	—	12BY	6.3	0.6	1.9 / 1.8 / 1.8	1.8 / 0.7 / 1.8	1.3 / 1.3 / 1.3	250 / 250 / 250	−8.5 / −2.0 / −2.0	—	—	10.5 / 1.2 / 1.2	7.7K / 62.5K / 62.5K	2200 / 1600 / 1600	17 / 100 / 100	—	—
6KD6	Beam Pwr. Pent.	33	12GW	6.3	2.85	—	—	—	150	−22.5	110	1.8	120	6K	14K	—	—	—
6JF6	Beam Pwr. Pent.	17	9QL	6.3	1.6	22	9	1.2	130	−20	125	2.5	80	12K	10K	—	—	—
6KM6	Beam Power Amp.	20	9QL	6.3	1.6	22	9.0	1.2	140	−24.5	140	2.4	80	6K	9500	—	—	—
6L4	Acorn Triode	—	7BR	6.3	0.225	1.8	0.5	1.6	80	150*	—	—	9.5	4.4K	6400	28	—	—
6LQ6	Beam Pwr. Pent.	30	9QL	6.3	2.5	22	11	0.56	175	−35	145	2.4	95	7K	7500	—	—	—
6M11	Twin Triode / Pentode	—	12CA	6.3	0.77	3.4 / 12	0.8 / 2.8	1.8 / 0.03	125 / 125	120* / 56*	— / 125	— / 3.4	8 / 11	10K / 200K	8K / 13K	58 / —	—	—
6Q11	Triple Triode	—	12BY	6.3	0.6	1.9 / 1.8 / 1.8	1.7 / 0.6 / 1.7	1.8 / 2.0 / 2.0	150 / 250 / 250	0 / −2 / −2	—	—	22 / 1.2 / 1.2	7K / 62.5K / 62.5K	2500 / 1600 / 1600	18 / 100 / 100	—	—
6T9	Triode / Pentode	1.5 / 12	12FM	6.3	0.93	3.4 / 11	1.1 / 11	2.6 / 0.2	250 / 250	−2.0 / −8.0	— / 250	— / 7	45K / 39	2100 / 100K	95 / 6500	— / —	— / 5K	— / 4.2
7E5/1201	H.f. Triode	—	8BN	6.3	0.15	3.6	2.8	1.5	180	−3	—	—	5.5	12K	3000	36	—	—
12GJ5	Beam Pwr. Pent.	17.5	9NM	12.6	0.6	15	6.5	0.26	250	−22.5	150	2.1	70	15K	7100	—	—	—
954	Detector Amp. — Pentode (Acorn) A_1 Amp. / Detector	—	5BB	6.3	0.15	3.4	3	0.007	250 / 250	−3 / −6	100 / 100	0.7	2	1 meg.	1400	—	—	—
									I_b adjusted to 0.1 ma. with no signal.								250K	
955	Medium-μ Triode (Acorn)	—	5BC	6.3	0.15	1	0.6	1.4	250 / 90	−7 / −2.5	—	—	6.3 / 2.5	11.4K / 14.7K	2200 / 1700	25 / 25	—	—
956	Remote Cut-off Pent. (Acorn) A_1 Amp. / Mixer	—	5BB	6.3	0.15	3.4	3	0.007	250 / 250	−3 / −10	100 / 100	2.7	6.7	700K	1800	—	—	—
									Oscillator peak volts −7 min.									
958A	Medium-μ Triode (Acorn)	—	5BD	1.25	0.1	0.6	0.8	2.6	135	−7.5	—	—	3	10K	1200	12	—	—
959	Sharp Cut-off Pent. (Acorn)	—	5BE	1.25	0.05	1.8	2.5	0.015	135	−3	67.5	0.4	1.7	800K	600	—	—	—
6173	U.h.f. "Pencil" Diode	—	Fig. 34	6.3	0.135	Plate to K = 1.1			Peak inverse −375 Volts. Peak I_p −50 Ma. Max. d.c. output −5.5 ma.									
7077	Ceramic U.h.f. Triode	—	—	6.3	0.24	1.9	0.01	1.0	250	−5	—	—	6.4	8.9K	9000	—	—	—
7360	Beam Deflection	—	9KS	6.3	0.35	—	—	—	For Practical Circuits See Chap. 11									
7695	Beam Pwr. Pent.	16	9PX	50	0.15	14	9	0.75	140	100*	140	14	100	—	—	—	1100	4.5
7868	Pwr. Pent.	19	9NZ	6.3	0.8	11	4.4	0.15	300	−10	300	15	75	29K	10.2K	—	3K	11

* Cathode resistor-ohms   [1] Micromhos.

TABLE VII—CONTROL AND REGULATOR TUBES   **V24**

Type	Name	Base	Cathode	Fil. or Heater Volts	Fil. or Heater Amp.	Peak Anode Voltage	Max. Anode Ma.	Minimum Supply Voltage	Operating Voltage	Operating Ma.	Grid Resistor	Tube Voltage Drop
0A2 6073	Voltage Regulator	5BO	Cold	—	—	—	—	185	150	5–30	—	—
0A3A/VR75	Voltage Regulator	4AJ	Cold	—	—	—	—	105	75	5–40	—	—
0A4G 1267	Gas Triode Starter-Anode Type	4V 4V	Cold	—	—	With 105–120-volt a.c. anode supply, peak starter-anode a.c. voltage is 70 peak r.f. voltage 55. Peak d.c. ma = 100. Average d.c. ma = 25.						
0A5	Gas Pentode	Fig. 19	Cold	—	—	Plate −750 V., Screen −90 V., Grid +3 V., Pulse −85 V.						
0B2 6074	Voltage Regulator	5BO	Cold	—	—	—	—	133	108	5–30	—	—
0B3/VR90	Voltage Regulator	4AJ	Cold	—	—	—	—	125	90	5–40	—	—
0C2	Voltage Regulator	5BO	Cold	—	—	—	—	105	75	5–30	—	—
0C3A/VR105	Voltage Regulator	4AJ	Cold	—	—	—	—	135	105	5–40	—	—
0D3A/VR150	Voltage Regulator	4AJ	Cold	—	—	—	—	185	150	5–40	—	—
2D21	Grid-Controlled Rectifier Relay Tube	7BN	Htr.	6.3	0.6	650 / 400	500 / —	—	650 / —	100 / —	0.1–10[4] / 1.0[4]	8 / —
6D4	Control Tube	5AY	Htr.	6.3	0.25	Ep = 350; Grid volts = −50; Peak Ma. = 100; Voltage drop = 16.						
90C1	Voltage Regulator	5BO	Cold	—	—	—	—	125	90	1–40	—	—
884	Gas Triode Grid Type	6Q	Htr.	6.3	0.6	300 / 350	300 / 300	—	—	2 / 75	25000 / 25000	—
967	Grid-Controlled Rectifier	3G	Fil.	2.5	5.0	2500	500	−5[2]	—	—	—	10–24
1265	Voltage Regulator	4AJ	Cold	—	—	—	—	130	90	5–30	—	—
1266	Voltage Regulator	4AJ	Cold	—	—	—	—	—	70	5–40	—	—
1267	Relay Tube	4V	Cold	—	—	Characteristics same as 0A4G						
2050	Grid-Controlled Rectifier	8BA	Htr.	6.3	0.6	650	500	—	—	100	0.1–10[4]	8
5651	Voltage Regulator	5BO	Cold	—	—	115	—	115	87	1.5–3.5	—	—
5662	Thyratron — Fuse	Fig. 79	Htr.	6.3	1.5	200[3]	I_k to fuse — 150 Amp., 60 cycle, half-wave					50 V.
5696	Relay Service	7BN	Htr.	6.3	0.15	500[3]	100 ma. peak current; 25-ma. average.					
5727	Gas Thyratron	7BN	Htr.	6.3	0.6	650	—	—	—	—	—	—
5823	Relay or Trigger	4CK	Cold	—	—	Max. peak inv. volts = 200; Peak Ma. = 100; Avg. Ma. = 25.						
5962	Voltage Regulator	2AG	Cold	—	—	—	—	730	700	5/55[5]	—	—
5998	Series Regulator	8BD	Htr.	6.3	2.4	250	125	—	110	100	350[6]	—
6308	Voltage Regulator	8EX	Cold	—	—	—	3.5	115	87	—	—	—
6336A	Twin Triode Series-Regulator	8BD	Htr.	6.3	5.0	Ep = 400; Ip 400 ma.; Grid volts = − 300						
6354	Voltage Regulator	Fig. 12	Cold	—	—	—	—	180	150	5–15	—	—
KY21	Grid-Controlled Rectifier	—	Fil.	2.5	10.0	—	—	—	3000	500	—	—
RK61	Radio-Controlled Relay	—[1]	Fil.	1.4	0.05	45	1.5	30	—	0.5–1.5	3[4]	30

1 No base. Tinned wire leads.
2 At 1000 anode volts.
3 Peak inverse voltage.
4 Megohms.
5 Values in microamperes.
6 Cathode resistor-ohms.

TABLE VIII—RECTIFIERS—RECEIVING AND TRANSMITTING
See Also Table VII—Controls and Regulator Tubes

Type	Name	Base	Cathode	Fil. or Heater Volts	Fil. or Heater Amp.	Max. A.C. Voltage Per Plate	D.C. Output Current Ma.	Max. Inverse Peak Voltage	Peak Plate Current Ma.	Type
0Z4-G	Full-Wave Rectifier	4R	Cold	—	—	300	75	1000	200	GAS
1G3-GT/ 1B3-GT	Half-Wave Rectifier	3C	Fil.	1.25	0.2	—	1.0	33000	30	HV
1K3/1J3	Half-Wave Rectifier	3C	Fil.	1.25	0.2	—	0.5	26000	50	HV
1V2	Half-Wave Rectifier	9U	Fil.	0.625	0.3	—	0.5	7500	10	HV
2B25	Half-Wave Rectifier	3T	Fil.	1.4	0.11	1000	1.5	—	9	HV
2X2-A	Half-Wave Rectifier	4AB	Htr.	2.5	1.75	4500	7.5	—	—	HV
2Y2	Half-Wave Rectifier	4AB	Fil.	2.5	1.75	4400	5.0	—	—	HV
2Z2/G84	Half-Wave Rectifier	4B	Fil.	2.5	1.5	350	50	—	—	HV
3B24	Half-Wave Rectifier	Fig. 49	Fil.	5.0 / 2.5[5]	3.0 / 3.0	—	60 / 30	20000 / 20000	300 / 150	HV
3B28	Half-Wave Rectifier	4P	Fil.	2.5	5.0	—	250	10000	1000	GAS
5AT4	Full-Wave Rectifier	5L	Htr.	5.0	2.25	550	800	1550	—	HV
5AU4	Full-Wave Rectifier	5T	Fil.	5.0	4.5	300[3] / 400[3] / 500[4]	350[3] / 325[3] / 325[4]	1400	1075	HV
5AW4	Full-Wave Rectifier	5T	Fil.	5.0	4.0	450[3] / 550[4]	250[3] / 250[4]	1550	750	HV
5BC3	Full-Wave Rectifier	9NT	Fil.	5.0	3.0	500	150	1700	1000	HV

TABLE VIII — RECTIFIERS — RECEIVING AND TRANSMITTING — *Continued*
See Also Table VII — Controls and Regulator Tubes

Type	Name	Base	Cathode	Fil. or Heater Volts	Amp.	Max. A.C. Voltage Per Plate	D.C. Output Current Ma.	Max. Inverse Peak Voltage	Peak Plate Current Ma.	Type
5R4GY 5R4GYA	Full-Wave Rectifier	5T	Fil.	5.0	2.0	900³ 950⁴	150³ 175⁴	2800	650	HV
5U4G	Full-Wave Rectifier	5T	Fil.	5.0	3.0	Same as Type 5Z3				HV
5U4GA	Full-Wave Rectifier	5T	Fil.	5.0	3.0	300³ 450³ 550⁴	275³ 250³ 250⁴	1550	900	HV
5U4GB 5AS4A	Full-Wave Rectifier	5T	Fil.	5.0	3.0	300³ 450³ 550⁴	300³ 275³ 275⁴	1550	1000	HV
5V3	Full-Wave Rectifier	5T	Htr.	5.0	3.8	425³ 500⁴	350	1400	1200	HV
5V4GA	Full-Wave Rectifier	5L	Htr.	5.0	2.0	375³	175	1400	525	HV
5X4G	Full-Wave Rectifier	5Q	Fil.	5.0	3.0	Same as Type 5Z3				HV
5Y3-G-GT	Full-Wave Rectifier	5T	Fil.	5.0	2.0	Same as Type 80				HV
5Y4-G-GT	Full-Wave Rectifier	5Q	Fil.	5.0	2.0	Same as Type 80				HV
5Z3	Full-Wave Rectifier	4C	Fil.	5.0	3.0	500	250	1400	—	HV
5Z4	Full-Wave Rectifier	5L	Htr.	5.0	2.0	400	125	1100	—	HV
6AF3	Half-Wave Rectifier	9CB	Htr.	6.3	1.2	—	185	4500	750	HV
6AL3	Half-Wave Rectifier	9CB	Htr.	6.3	1.55	—	220	7500	550	HV
6AV4	Full-Wave Rectifier	5BS	Htr.	6.3	0.95	—	90	1250	250	HV
6AX5GT	Full-Wave Rectifier	6S	Htr.	6.3	1.2	450	125	1250	375	HV
6BW4	Full-Wave Rectifier	9DJ	Htr.	6.3	0.9	450	100	1275	350	HV
6BX4	Full-Wave Rectifier	5BS	Htr.	6.3	0.6	—	90	1350	270	HV
6BY5G	Full-Wave Rectifier	6CN	Htr.	6.3	1.6	375³	175	1400	525	HV
6CA4	Full-Wave Rectifier	9M	Htr.	6.3	1.0	350³	150	1000	450	HV
6DA4A	Half-Wave Diode	4CG	Htr.	6.3	1.2	—	155	4400	900	HV
6DE4	Half-Wave Rectifier	4CG	Fil.	6.3	1.6	—	175	5000	1100	HV
6U4GT	Half-Wave Rectifier	4CG	Htr.	6.3	1.2	—	138	1375	660	HV
6V4	Full-Wave Rectifier	9M	Htr.	6.3	0.6	350	90	—	—	HV
6X4/6063 6X5GT	Full-Wave Rectifier	7CF 6S	Htr.	6.3	0.3	325³ 450⁴	70	1250	210	HV
6Z3	Half-Wave Rectifier	4G	Fil.	6.3	0.3	350	50	—	—	HV
12DF5	Full-Wave Rectifier	9BS	Htr.	6.3 12.6	0.9 0.45	450	100	1275	350	HV
12X4	Full-Wave Rectifier	5BS	Htr.	12.6	0.3	650³ 900⁴	70 70	1250 1250	210 210	HV
25Z5	Rectifier-Doubler	6E	Htr.	25	0.3	125	100	—	500	HV
35W4	Half-Wave Rectifier	5BQ	Htr.	35¹	0.15	125	60	330	600	HV
35Z4GT	Half-Wave Rectifier	5AA	Htr.	35	0.15	250	100	700	600	HV
35Z5G	Half-Wave Rectifier	6AD	Htr.	35¹	0.15	125	60	—	—	HV
36AM3	Half-Wave Rectifier	5BQ	Htr.	36	0.1	117	75	365	530	HV
50DC4	Half-Wave Rectifier	5BQ	Htr.	50	0.15	117	100	330	720	HV
50Y6GT	Full-Wave Rectifier	7Q	Htr.	50	0.15	125	85	—	—	HV
80	Full-Wave Rectifier	4C	Fil.	5.0	2.0	350³ 500⁴	125 125	1400	375	HV
83	Full-Wave Rectifier	4C	Fil.	5.0	3.0	500	250	1400	800	MV
83-V	Full-Wave Rectifier	4AD	Htr.	5.0	2.0	400	200	1100	—	HV
117N7GT	Rectifier-Tetrode	8AV	Htr.	117	0.09	117	75	350	450	HV
117Z3	Half-Wave Rectifier	4CB	Htr.	117	0.04	117	90	300	—	HV
816	Half-Wave Rectifier	4P	Fil.	2.5	2.0	2200	125	7500	500	MV
836	Half-Wave Rectifier	4P	Htr.	2.5	5.0	—	—	5000	1000	HV
866-A-AX	Half-Wave Rectifier	4P	Fil.	2.5	5.0	3500	250	10000	1000	MV
866B	Half-Wave Rectifier	4P	Fil.	5.0	5.0	—	—	8500	1000	MV
866 Jr.	Half-Wave Rectifier	4B	Fil.	2.5	2.5	1250	250²	—	—	MV
872A/872	Half-Wave Rectifier	4AT	Fil.	5.0	7.5	1250	—	10000	5000	MV

¹ Tapped for pilot lamps.
² Per pair with choke input.
³ Capacitor input.
⁴ Choke input.
⁵ Using only one-half of filament.

TABLE IX — TRIODE TRANSMITTING TUBES

Type	Maximum Ratings Plate Dissipation Watts	Plate Voltage	Plate Current Ma.	D.C. Grid Current Ma.	Freq. Mc. Full Ratings	Amplification Factor	Cathode Volts	Amperes	Capacitances Cin pf.	Cgp pf.	Cout pf.	Base	Typical Operation Class of Service¹	Plate Voltage	Grid Voltage	Plate Current Ma.	D.C. Grid Current Ma.	Approx. Driving Power Watts	P-to-P Load Ohms	Approx. Output Power Watts
958-A	0.6	135	7	1.0	500	12	1.25	0.1	0.6	2.6	0.8	5BD	C-T-O	135	−20	7	1.0	0.035	—	0.6
6J6A↑²	1.5	300	30	16	250	32	6.3	0.45	2.2	1.6	0.4	7BF	C-T	150	−10	30	1.6	0.035	—	3.5
9002	1.6	250	8	2.0	250	25	6.3	0.15	1.2	1.4	1.1	7BS	C-T-O	180	−35	7	1.5	—	—	0.5
955	1.6	180	8	2.0	250	25	6.3	0.15	1.0	1.4	0.6	5BC	C-T-O	180	−35	7	1.5	—	—	0 5
HY114B	1.8	180	12	3.0	300	13	1.4	0.155	1.0	1.3	1.0	2T	C-T-O	180	−30	12	2.0	0.2	—	1.4³
													C-P	180	−35	12	2.5	0.3	—	1.4³
6F4	2.0	150	20	8.0	500	17	6.3	0.225	2.0	1.9	-0.6	7BR	C-T-O	150	−15 550* 2000⁴	20	7.5	0.2	—	1.8

TABLE IX — TRIODE TRANSMITTING TUBES — Continued

V26

Type	Plate Dissipation Watts	Plate Voltage	Plate Current Ma.	D.C. Grid Current Ma.	Freq. Mc. Full Ratings	Amplification Factor	Volts	Amperes	Cin pf.	Cgp pf.	Cout pf.	Base	Class of Service[1]	Plate Voltage	Grid Voltage	Plate Current Ma.	D.C. Grid Current Ma.	Approx. Driving Power Watts	P-to-P Load Ohms	Approx. Output Power Watts
12AU7A[2]	2.76[6]	350	12[6]	3.5[6]	54	18	6.3	0.3	1.5	1.5	0.5	9A	C-T-O	350	−100	24	7	—	—	6.0
6026	3.0	150	30	10	400	24	6.3	0.2	2.2	1.3	0.38	Fig. 16	C-T-O	135	1300[4]	20	9.5	—	—	1.25
HY615 HY-E1148	3.5	300	20	4.0	300	20	6.3	0.175	1.4	1.6	1.2	Fig. 71	C-T-O	300	−35	20	2.0	0.4	—	4.0[3]
													C-P	300	−35	20	3.0	0.8	—	3.5[3]
6C4	5.0	350	25	8.0	54	18	6.3	0.15	1.8	1.6	1.3	6BG	C-T-O	300	−27	25	7.0	0.35	—	5.5
2C36	5	1500[5]	—	—	1200	25	6.3	0.4	1.4	2.4	0.36	Fig. 21	C-T-O[10]	1000[5]	0	900[5]	—	—	—	200[5]
2C37	5	350	—	—	3300	25	6.3	0.4	1.4	1.85	0.02	Fig. 21	C-T-O[12]	150	3000[4]	15	3.6	—	—	0.5
5764	5	1500[5]	11.5	—	3300	25	6.3	0.4	1.4	1.85	0.02	Fig. 21	C-T-O[16]	1000[5]	0	1300[5]	—	—	—	200[5]
5675	5	165	30	8	3000	20	6.3	0.135	2.3	1.3	0.09	Fig. 21	G-G-O	120	−8	25	4	—	—	0.05
6N7GT[2]	5.5[6]	350	30[6]	5.0[6]	10	35	6.3	0.8	—	—	—	8B	C-T-O	350	−100	60	10	—	—	14.5
2C40	6.5	500	25	—	500	36	6.3	0.75	2.1	1.3	0.05	Fig. 11	C-I-O	250	−5	20	0.3	—	—	0.075
5893	8.0	400	40	13	1000	27	6.0	0.33	2.5	1.75	0.07	Fig. 21	C-T	350	−33	35	13	2.4	—	6.5
													C-P	300	−45	30	12	2.0	—	6.5
GL-6442	8.0	350	35	15	2500	47	6.3	0.9	5.0	2.3	0.03	—	C-T	350	−50	35	15	—	—	—
													C-P	275	−50	35	15	—	—	—
2C34/ RK34[2]	10	300	80	20	250	13	6.3	0.8	3.4	2.4	0.5	Fig. 70	C-T-O	300	−36	80	20	1.8	—	16
2C43	12	500	40	—	1250	48	6.3	0.9	2.9	1.7	0.05	Fig. 11	C-T-O	470	—	38[7]	—	—	—	9[7]
6263	13	400	55	25	500	27	6.3	0.28	2.9	1.7	0.08	—	C-T	350	−58	40	15	3	—	10
													C-P	320	−52	35	12	2.4	—	8
6264	13	400	50	25	500	40	6.3	0.28	2.95	1.75	0.07	—	C-T	350	−45	40	15	3	—	8
HY75A	15	450	90	25	175	9.6	6.3	2.6	1.8	2.6	1.0	2T	C-T	450	−140	90	20	5.2	—	26
													C-P	400	−140	90	20	5.2	—	21
801-A/801	20	600	70	15	60	8.0	7.5	1.25	4.5	6.0	1.5	4D	C-T	600	−150	65	15	4.0	—	25
													C-P	500	−190	55	15	4.5	—	18
													B[7]	600	−75	130	320[9]	3.0[8]	10K	45
T20	20	750	85	25	60	20	7.5	1.75	4.9	5.1	0.7	3G	C-T	750	−85	85	18	3.6	—	44
													C-P	750	−140	70	15	3.6	—	38
TZ20	20	750	85	30	60	62	7.5	1.75	5.3	5.0	0.6	3G	C-T	750	−40	85	28	3.75	—	44
													C-P	750	−100	70	23	4.8	—	38
													B[7]	800	0	40/136	160[9]	1.8[8]	12K	70
15E[18]	20	—	—	—	600	25	5.5	4.2	1.4	1.15		Fig. 51	C-T-O	2000	−130	63	18	4.0	—	100
25T 3-25A3	25	2000	75	25	60	24	6.3	3.0	2.7	1.5	0.3	3G		1500	−95	67	13	2.2	—	75
														1000	−70	72	9	1.3	—	47
													B[7]	2000	−80	16/80	270[9]	0.7[8]	55.5K	110
3C28[18] 3C34[18] 3-25D3 24G	25	2000	75	25	100 60 150	23	6.3	3.0	2.1 2.5 2.0 1.7	1.8 1.7 1.6 1.5	0.1 0.4 0.2 0.3	Fig. 31 3G 2D	C-T-O	2000	−170	63	17	4.5	—	100
														1500	−110	67	15	3.1	—	75
														1000	−80	72	15	2.6	—	47
														2000	−85	16/80	290[9]	1.1[8]	55.5K	110
3C24	25 / 17 / 25	2000 / 1600 / 2000	75 / 60 / 75	7[13]	60	24	6.3	3.0	1.7	1.6	0.2	2D	C-T	2000	−130	63	18	4	—	100
													C-P	1600	−170	53	11	3.1	—	68
													AB2[7]	1250	−42	24/130	270[9]	3.4[8]	21.4K	112
HK24	25	2000	75	30	60	25	6.3	3.0	2.5	1.7	0.4	3G	C-T	2000	−140	56	18	4.0	—	90
													C-P	1500	−145	50	25	5.5	—	60
8025	30 / 20 / 30	1000	65 / 65 / 80	— / 20 / 20	500	18	6.3	1.92	2.7	2.8	0.35	4AQ	G-M-A	1000	−135	50	4	3.5	—	20
													C-P	800	−105	40	10.5	1.4	—	22
													C-T	1000	−90	50	14	1.6	—	35
HY31Z[2] HY1231Z[2]	30	500	150	30	60	45	6.3 12.6	3.5 1.7	5.0	5.5	1.9	Fig. 60	C-T	500	−45	150	25	2.5	—	56
													C-P	400	−100	150	30	3.5	—	45
316A VT-191	30	450	80	12	500	6.5	2.0	3.65	1.2	1.6	0.8	—	C-T	450	—	80	12	—	—	7.5
													C-P	400	—	80	12	—	—	6.5
809	30	1000	125	—	60	50	6.3	2.5	5.7	6.7	0.9	3G	C-T	1000	−75	100	25	3.8	—	75
													C-P	750	−60	100	32	4.3	—	55
													B[7]	1000	−9	40/200	155[9]	2.7[8]	11.6K	145
1623	30	1000	100	25	60	20	6.3	2.5	5.7	6.7	0.9	3G	C-T-O	1000	−90	100	20	3.1	—	75
													C-P	750	−125	100	20	4.0	—	55
													B[7]	1000	−40	30/200	230[9]	4.2[8]	12K	145
T40	40	1500	150	40	60	25	7.5	2.5	4.5	4.8	0.8	3G	C-T-O	1500	−140	150	28	9.0	—	158
													C-P	1250	−115	115	20	5.25	—	104
TZ40	40	1500	150	45	60	62	7.5	2.5	4.8	5.0	0.8	3G	C-T-O	1500	−90	150	38	10	—	165
													C-P	1250	−100	125	30	7.5	—	116
													B[7]	1500	−9	250[8]	285[9]	6.0[8]	12K	250
3-50A4 35T 3-50D4 35TG	50	2000	150	50	100	39	5.0	4.0	4.1 2.5	1.8	0.3 0.4	3G 2D	C-T	2000	−135	125	45	13	—	200
													C-P	1500	−150	90	40	11	—	105
													B[7]	2000	−40	4/167	255[9]	4.0[8]	27.5K	235
HK54	50	3000	150	30	100	27	5.0	5.0	1.9	1.9	0.2	2D	C-T	3000	−290	100	25	10	—	250
													C-P	2500	−250	100	20	8.0	—	210
													B[7]	2500	−85	20/150	360[9]	5.0	40K	275

[1] See page V28 for Key to Class-of-Service abbreviations.

TABLE IX — TRIODE TRANSMITTING TUBES — *Continued*

Type	Plate Dissipation Watts	Plate Voltage	Plate Current Ma.	D.C. Grid Current Ma.	Freq. Mc. Full Ratings	Amplification Factor	Volts	Amperes	Cin pf.	Cgp pf.	Cout pf.	Base	Class of Service[1]	Plate Voltage	Grid Voltage	Plate Current Ma.	D.C. Grid Current Ma.	Approx. Driving Power Watts	P-to-P Load Ohms	Approx. Output Power Watts
T55	55	1500	150	40	60	20	7.5	3.0	5.0	3.9	1.2	3G	C-T	1500	−170	150	18	6.0	—	170
													C-P	1500	−195	125	15	5.0	—	145
826	55	1000	140	40	250	31	7.5	4.0	3.0	2.9	1.1	7BO	C-T-O	1000	−70	130	35	5.8	—	90
													C-P	1000	−160	95	40	11.5	—	70
													G-M-A	1000	−125	65	9.5	8.2	—	25
830B 930B	60	1000	150	30	15	25	10	2.0	5.0	11	1.8	3G	C-T-O	1000	−110	140	30	7.0	—	90
													C-P	800	−150	95	20	5.0	—	50
													B[7]	1000	−35	20/280	270[9]	6.0[8]	7.6K	175
811-A	65	1500	175	50	60	160	6.3	4.0	5.9	5.6	0.7	3G	C-T	1500	−70	173	40	7.1	—	200
													C-P	1250	−120	140	45	10.0	—	135
													G-G-B	1250	0	27/175	28	12	—	165
													AB₁ AB[1]	1250	0	27/175	13	3.0	—	155
812-A	65	1500	175	35	60	29	6.3	4.0	5.4	5.5	0.77	3G	C-T	1500	−120	173	30	6.5	—	190
													C-P	1250	−115	140	35	7.6	—	130
													B[7]	1500	−48	28/310	270[9]	5.0	13.2K	340
5514	65	1500	175	60	60	145	7.5	3.0	7.8	7.9	1.0	4BO	C-T	1500	−106	175	60	12	—	200
													C-P	1250	−84	142	60	10	—	135
													B[7]	1500	−4.5	350[8]	88[8]	6.5[8]	10.5K	400
3-75A3 75TH	75	3000	225	40	40	20	5.0	6.25	2.7	2.3	0.3	2D	C-T	2000	−200	150	32	10	—	225
													C-P	2000	−300	110	15	6	—	170
													B[7]	2000	−90	50/225	350[9]	3[8]	19.3K	300
3-75A2 75TL	75	3000	225	35	40	12	5.0	6.25	2.6	2.4	0.4	2D	C-T	2000	−300	150	21	8	—	225
													C-P	2000	−500	130	20	14	—	210
													AB₂[7] AB[2,7]	2000	−190	50/250	600[9]	5[8]	18K	350
8005	85	1500	200	45	60	20	10	3.25	6.4	5.0	1.0	3G	C-T	1500	−130	200	32	7.5	—	220
													C-P	1250	−195	190	28	9.0	—	170
													B[7]	1500	−70	40/310	310[9]	4.0	10K	300
V-70-D	85	1750	200	45	30	—	7.5	3.25	4.5	4.5	1.7	3G	C-T	1750	−100	170	19	3.9	—	225
														1500	−90	165	19	3.9	—	195
													C-P	1500	−90	165	19	3.7	—	185
														1250	−72	127	16	2.6	—	122
3-100A4 100TH	100	3000	225	60	40	40	5.0	6.3	2.9	2.0	0.4	2D	C-T C-P	3000	−200	165	51	18	—	400
													B[7]	3000	−65	40/215	335[9]	5.0[8]	31K	650
3-100A2 100TL	100	3000	225	50	40	14	5.0	6.3	2.3	2.0	0.4	2D	C-T C-P	3000	−400	165	30	20	—	400
													G-M-A	3000	−560	60	2.0	7.0	—	90
													B[7]	3000	−185	40/215	640[9]	6.0[8]	30K	450
VT127A	100	3000	—	—	150	15.5	5.0	10.4	2.7	2.3	0.35	Fig. 53	C-T	2000	−340	210	67	25	—	315
													B[7]	1500	−125	242	44	7.3	3K	200
211 311	100	1250	175	50	15	12	10	3.25	6.0	14.5	5.5	4E	C-T	1250	−225	150	18	7.0	—	130
									6.0	9.25	5.0		C-P	1000	−260	150	35	14	—	100
													B[7]	1250	−100	20/320	410[9]	8.0[8]	9K	260
254	100	4000	225	60	—	25	5.0	7.5	2.5	2.7	0.4	2N	C-T	3000	−245	165	40	18	—	400
													C-P	2500	−360	168	40	23	—	335
													B[7]	2500	−80	40/240	460[9]	25	25.2K	420
3CX100A5[15]	100 70	1000 600	125[14] 100[14]	50	2500	100	6.0	1.05	7.0	2.15	0.035	—	G-G-A	800	−20	30	30	6	—	27
													C-P	600	−15	75	40	6	—	18
3X100A11 2C39	100	1000	60	40	500	100	6.3	1.1	6.5	1.95	0.03	—	G-I-C	600	−35	60	40	5.0	—	20
GL2C39A[15] GL2C39B[15]	100 70	1000	125[14]	50	500	100	6.5 7.0	1.9 1.9	0.035 0.035			—	C-T-O	900	−40	90	30	—	—	40
													C-P	600	−150	100[14]	50	—	—	—
GL146	125	1500	200	60	15	75	10	3.25	7.2	9.2	3.9	Fig. 56	C-T-O	1250	−150	180	30	—	—	150
													C-P	1000	−200	160	40	—	—	100
													B[7]	1250	0	34/320			8.4K	250
GL152	125	1500	200	60	15	25	10	3.25	7.0	8.8	4.0	Fig. 56	C-T-O	1250	−150	180	30	—	—	150
													C-P	1000	−200	160	30	—	—	100
													B[7]	1250	−40	16/320			8.4K	250
805	125	1500	210	70	30	40/60	10	3.25	8.5	6.5	10.5	3N	C-T	1500	−105	200	40	8.5	—	215
													C-P	1250	−160	160	60	16	—	140
													B[7]	1500	−16	84/400	280[9]	7.0[8]	8.2K	370
AX9900/ 5866[15]	135	2500	200	40	150	25	6.3	5.4	5.8	5.5	0.1	Fig. 3	C-T	2500	−200	200	40	16	—	390
													C-P	2000	−225	127	40	16	—	204
													B[7]	2500	−90	80/330	350[9]	14[8]	15.68K	560
3-150A3 152TH	150	3000	450	85	40	20	5.0 10	12.5 6.25	5.7	4.8	0.4	4BC	C-T	3000	−300	250	70	27	—	600
													C-P	2500	−350	200	30	15	—	400
													B[7]	2500	−125	40/340	390[9]	16[8]	17K	600
3-150A2 152TL	150	3000	450	75	40	12	5 10	12.5 6.25	4.5	4.4	0.7	4BC	C-T	3000	−400	250	40	20	—	600
													B[7]	3000	−260	65/335	675[9]	3[8]	20.4K	700
HF201A	150	2500	200	50	30	18	10-11	4.0	8.8	7.0	1.2	Fig. 15	C-T	2500	−300	200	18	8	—	380
													C-P	2000	350	160	20	9	—	250
													B[7]	2500	−130	60/360	460[9]	8[8]	16K	600
572B/T160L	160	2750	275	—	—	170	6.3	4.0				3G	C-T	1650	−70	165	32	6	—	205
													G-G-B	2400	−2.0	90/500	—	100	—	600
810	175	2500	300	75	30	36	10	4.5	8.7	4.8	12	2N	C-T	2500	−180	300	60	19	—	575
													C-P	2000	−350	250	70	35	—	380
													G-M-A	2250	−140	100	2.0	4	—	75
													B[7]	2250	−60	70/450	380[9]	13[8]	11.6K	725

[1] See page V28 for Key to Class-of-Service abbreviations.

TABLE IX — TRIODE TRANSMITTING TUBES — Continued V28

Type	Plate Dissipation Watts	Plate Voltage	Plate Current Ma.	D.C. Grid Current Ma.	Freq. Mc. Full Ratings	Amplification Factor	Volts	Amperes	Cin pf.	Cgp pf.	Cout pf.	Base	Class of Service[1]	Plate Voltage	Grid Voltage	Plate Current Ma.	D.C. Grid Current Ma.	Approx. Driving Power Watts	P-to-P Load Ohms	Approx. Output Power Watts
8000	175	2500	300	45	30	16.5	10	4.5	5.0	6.4	3.3	2N	C-T-O	2500	-240	300	40	18	—	575
													C-P	2000	-370	250	37	20	—	380
													G-M-A	2250	-265	100	0	2.5	—	75
													B[7]	2250	-130	65/450	560[9]	7.9[8]	12K	725
T200	200	2500	350	80	30	16	10	5.75	9.5	7.9	1.6	2N	C-T	2500	-280	350	54	25	—	685
													C-P	2000	-260	300	54	23	—	460
592/[15] 3-200A3	200	3500	250	25[13]	150	25	10	5.0	3.6	3.3	0.29	Fig. 28	C-T	3500	-270	228	30	15	—	600
	130	2600	200	25[13]									C-P	2500	-300	200	35	19	—	375
	200	3500	250	25[13]									B[7]	2000	-50	120/500	520[9]	20[8]	8.5K	600
4C34 HF300	200	3000	275	60	60/20	23	11-12	4.0	6.0	6.5	1.4	2N	C-T	3000	-400	250	28	16	—	600
													C-P	2000	-300	250	36	17	—	385
													B[7]	3000	-115	60/360	450[9]	13[8]	20K	780
T-300	200	3000	300	—	—	23	11	6.0	6.0	7.0	1.4	—	C-T	3000	-400	250	28	20	—	600
													C-P	2000	-300	250	36	17	—	385
													B[7]	2500	-100	60/450		7.5[8]	—	750
806	225	3300	300	50	30	12.6	5.0	10	6.1	4.2	1.1	2N	C-T	3300	-600	300	40	34	—	780
													C-P	3000	-670	195	27	24	—	460
													B[7]	3300	-240	80/475	930[9]	35[8]	16K	1120
3-250A4 250TH	250	4000	350	40[13]	40	37	5.0	10.5	4.6	2.9	0.5	2N	C-T-O	2000	-100	357	94	29	—	464
													C-T-O	3000	-150	333	90	32	—	750
													C-P	2000	-160	250	60	22	—	335
													C-P	2500	-180	225	45	17	—	400
													C-P	3000	-200	200	38	14	—	435
													AB2[7]	1500	0	220/700	460[9]	46[8]	4.2K	630
3-250A2 250TL	250	4000	350	35[13]	40	14	5.0	10.5	3.7	3.0	0.7	2N	C-T-O	2000	-200	350	45	22	—	455
													C-T-O	3000	-350	335	45	29	—	750
													C-P	2000	-520	250	29	24	—	335
													C-P	2500	-520	225	20	16	—	400
													C-P	3000	-520	200	14	11	—	435
													AB2[7]	1500	-40	200/700	780[9]	38[8]	3.8K	580
5867 AX-9901	250	3000	400	80	100	25	5.0	14.1	7.7	5.9	0.18	Fig. 3	C-T	3000	-250	363	69	27	—	840
													C-P	2500	-300	250	70	28	—	482
													B[7]	3000	-110	570[8]	465[9]	32	14.2K	1280
PL-6569	250	4000	300	120	30	45	5.0	14.5	7.6	3.7	0.1	Fig. 3	G-G-A	2500	-70	300	85	75[11]	—	555
													G-G-A	3000	-95	300	110	85[11]	—	710
													G-G-A	3500	-110	285	90	85[11]	—	805
													G-G-A	4000	-120	250	50	70[11]	—	820
3-300A3 304TH	300	3000	900	60[13]	40	20	5.0 / 10	25 / 12.5	13.5	10.2	0.7	4BC	C-T-O	1500	-125	665	115	25	—	700
													C-T-O	2000	-200	600	125	39	—	900
													C-P	1500	-200	420	55	18	—	500
													C-P	2000	-300	440	60	26	—	680
													C-P	2500	-350	400	60	29	—	800
													AB2[7]	1500	-65	1065[8]	330[9]	25[8]	2.84K	1000
3-300A2 304TL	300	3000	900	50[13]	40	12	5.0 / 10	25 / 12.5	12.1	8.6	0.8	4BC	C-T-O	1500	-250	665	90	33	—	700
													C-T-O	2000	-300	600	85	36	—	900
													C-P	2000	-500	250	30	18	—	410
													C-P	2000	-500	500	75	52	—	810
													C-P	2500	-525	200	18	11	—	425
													C-P	2500	-550	400	50	36	—	830
													AB1[7]	1500	-118	270/572	236[9]	0	2.54K	256
													AB2[7]	2500	-230	160/483	460[9]	0	8.5K	610
													AB2[7]	1500	-118	1140[8]	490[9]	39[8]	2.75K	1100
833A	350 / 450[15]	3300 / 4000[15]	500	100	30 / 20[15]	35	10	10	12.3	6.3	8.5	Fig. 41	C-T-O	2250	-125	445	85	23	—	780
													C-T-O	3000	-160	335	70	20	—	800
													C-P	2500	-300	335	75	30	—	635
													C-P	3000	-240	335	70	26	—	800
													B[7]	3000	-70	100/750	400[9]	20[8]	9.5K	1650
3-400Z	400	3000	400	—	110	200	5	14.5	7.4	4.1	0.07	Fig. 3	G-G-B	3000	0	100/333	120	32	—	655
PL-6580	400	4000[15]	350	120	—	45	5.0	14.5	7.6	3.9	0.1	5BK	G-G-A	4000	-110	350	92	105[11]	—	1080
														2500	-70	350	95	85	—	660
8163	400	3000	400	20[13]	30	350	5.0	14.1	8.0	5.0	0.3	Fig. 3	G-G-B	2500	0	72/400	140	35	—	640
3-500Z	500	4000	400	—	110	160	5	14.5	7.4	4.1	0.07	Fig. 3	G-G-B	3000		370	115	30	5K	750
													C-T	3500	-75	300	115	22	—	850
3-1000Z	1000	3000	800	—	110	200	7.5	21.3	17	6.9	0.12	Fig. 3	G-G-B	3000	0	180/670	300	65	—	1360

* Cathode resistor in ohms.

[1] KEY TO CLASS-OF-SERVICE ABBREVIATIONS
A1 = Class-A1 a.f. modulator.
AB1 = Class-AB1 push-pull a.f. modulator.
AB2 = Class-AB2 push-pull a.f. modulator.
B = Class-B push-pull a.f. modulator.
C-M = Frequency multiplier.
C-P = Class-C plate-modulated telephone.
C-T = Class-C telegraph.
C-T-O = Class-C amplifier-osc.
G-G-A = Grounded-grid class-C amp.
G-G-B = Grounded-grid class-B amp. (Single Tone).

G-G-O = Grounded-grid osc.
G-I-C = Grid-isolation circuit.
G-M-A = Grid-modulated amp.
[2] Twin triode. Values, except interelectrode capacitances, are for both sections in push-pull.
[3] Output at 112 Mc.
[4] Grid leak resistor in ohms.
[5] Peak values.
[6] Per section.
[7] Values are for two tubes in push-pull.
[8] Max. signal value.

[9] Peak a.f. grid-to-grid volts.
[10] Plate-pulsed 1000-Mc. osc.
[11] Includes bias loss, grid dissipation, and feed-through power.
[12] 1000-Mc. c.w. osc.
[13] Max. grid dissipation in watts.
[14] Max. cathode current in ma.
[15] Forced-air cooling required.
[16] Plate-pulsed 3300-Mc. osc.
[17] 1900-Mc. c.w. osc.
[18] No Class-B data available.

TABLE X — TETRODE AND PENTODE TRANSMITTING TUBES

Type	Plate Dissipation Watts	Plate Voltage	Screen Dissipation Watts	Screen Voltage	Freq. Mc. Full Ratings	Volts	Amperes	Cin pf.	Cgp pf.	Cout pf.	Base	Class of Service[14]	Plate Voltage	Screen Voltage	Suppressor Voltage	Grid Voltage	Plate Current Ma.	Screen Current Ma.	Grid Current Ma.	Approx. Driving Power Watts	P-to-P Load Ohms	Approx. Output Power Watts
8203	1.8	400	—	—	250	6.3	0.16	4.2	2.2	1.6	12AQ	C-P/C-T	155	—	—	14/2700[1]	21	—	5	0.4		1.55
6939[3]	7.5	275	3	200	500	6.3 / 12.6	0.75 / 0.375	6.6	0.15	1.55	Fig. 13	C-T	200	200	—	-20	60	13	2	1.0		7.5
												C-P	180	180	—	-20	55	11.5	1.7	1.0		6
												C-M	200	190	—	68K[1]	46	10	2.2	0.9		—
2E30	10	250	2.5	250	160	6	0.65	10	0.5	4.5	7CQ	C-T	250	200	—	-50	50	10	2.5	0.2		—
												AB2[6]	250	250	—	-30	40/120	4/20	2.3[7]	0.2	3.8K	17
7905	10	300	1.5	300	175	6.3	0.65	8.5	5.5	0.14	9PB	C-T	300	185	—	-39	60	4	2.2	1.0		7
												C-P	250	250	—	-70	60	2.5	2.1	1.0		6.5
												C-M	300	215	—	-80	50	3.4	1.5	0.5		3.5
837	12	500	8	300	20	12.6	0.7	16	0.2	10	6BM	C-T	500	200	40	-70	80	15	4	0.4		28
												C-P	400	140	40	-40	45	20	5	0.3		11
7551 7558	12	300	2	250	175	12.6 / 6.3	0.38 / 0.8	10	0.15	5.5	9LK	C-T	300	250	—	-55	80	5.1	1.6	1.5		10
												C-P	250	250	—	-75	70	3.0	2.3	1.0		7.5
5763 6417	13.5	350	2	250	50	6.3 / 12.6	0.75 / 0.375	9.5	0.3	4.5	9K	C-T	350	250	—	-28.5	48.5	6.2	1.6	0.1		12
												C-P	300	250	—	-42.5	50	6	2.4	0.15		10
												C-M[2]	300	250	—	-75	40	4	1	0.6		2.1
												C-M[4]	300	235	—	-100	35	5	1	0.6		1.3
2E24	13.5	600	2.5	200	125	6.3[5]	0.65	8.5	0.11	6.5	7CL	C-P	500	180	—	-45	54	8	2.5	0.16		18
												C-T	600	195	—	-50	66	10	3	0.21		27
2E26 6893	13.5	600	2.5	200	125	6.3 / 12.6	0.8 / 0.4	12.5	0.2	7	7CK	C-T	600	185	—	-45	66	10	3	0.17		27
												C-P	500	180	—	-50	54	9	2.5	0.15		18
												AB1	500	200	—	-25	9/45	10[7]	0	0		15
6360[3]	14	300	2	200	200	6.3 / 12.6	0.82 / 0.41	6.2	0.1	2.6	Fig. 13	C-T	300	200	—	-45	100	3	3	0.2		18.5
												C-P	300	100	—	15K[1]	86	3.1	3.3	0.2		9.8
												C-M[11]	300	150	—	-100	65	3.5	3.8	0.45		4.8
												AB2	300	200	—	-21.5	30/100	1/11.4	64[8]	0.04	6.5K	17.5
2E25	15	450	4	250	125	6	0.8	8.5	0.15	6.7	5BJ	C-T-O	450	250	—	-45	75	15	3	0.4		24
												C-P	400	200	—	-45	60	12	3	0.4		16
												AB2[6]	450	250	—	-30	44/150	10/40	3	0.97	6K	40
832A[3]	15	750	5	250	200	6.3 / 12.6	1.6 / 0.8	8	0.07	3.8	7BP	C-T	750	200	—	-65	48	15	2.8	0.19		26
												C-P	600	200	—	-65	36	16	2.6	0.16		17
8458	16	600	1	200		6.75 / 13.5	0.8 / 0.4	6.2	0.1	2.7	Fig. 13	C-T	400	190	—	-50	110	5	1.8	1.1		26.5
6252/ AX9910[3]	20	750	4	300	300	6.3 / 12.6	1.3 / 0.65	6.5	—	2.5	Fig. 7	C-T	600	250	—	-60	140	14	4	2.0		—
												C-P	500	250	—	-80	100	12	3	4.0		—
												B	500	250	—	-26	25/73	0.7/16	52[8]		20K	23.5
1614	25	450	3.5	300	80	6.3	0.9	10	0.4	12.5	7AC	C-T	450	250	—	-45	100	8	2	0.15		31
												C-P	375	250	—	-50	93	7	2	0.15		24.5
												AB1[6]	530	340	—	-36	60/160	20[7]	—	—	7.2K	50
815[3]	25	500	4	200	125	6.3 / 12.6	1.6 / 0.8	13.3	0.2	8.5	8BY	C-T-O	500	200	—	-45	150	17	2.5	0.13		56
												AB2	500	125	—	-15	22/150	32[7]	—	0.36[7]	8K	54
1624	25	600	3.5	300	60	2.5	2	11	0.25	7.5	Fig. 66	C-T	600	300	—	-60	90	10	5	0.43		35
												C-P	500	275	—	-50	75	9	3.3	0.25		24
												AB2[6]	600	300	—	-25	42/180	5/15	106[8]	1.2[7]	7.5K	72
4604	25	750	3	250	60	6.3	0.65	11	0.24	8.5	7CL	C-T	400	190	—	-60	150	11	2	4.5		30
6146 6146A	25	750	3	250	60	6.3	1.25	13	0.24	8.5	7CK	C-T	500	170	—	-66	135	9	2.5	0.2		48
												C-T	750	160	—	-62	120	11	3.1	0.2		70
8032 6883						12.6	0.585					C-T[12]	400	190	—	-54	150	10.4	2.2	3.0		35
												C-P	400	150	—	-87	112	7.8	3.4	0.4		32
												C-P	600	150	—	-87	112	7.8	3.4	0.4		52
6159B						26.5	0.3					AB2[6]	600	190	—	-48	28/270	1.2/20	2[7]	0.3	5K	113
												AB2[6]	750	165	—	-46	22/240	0.3/20	2.6[7]	0.4	7.4K	131
												AB1[6]	750	195	—	-50	23/220	1/26	100[8]	0	8K	120
6524[3] 6850	25	600	—	300	100	6.3 / 12.6	1.25 / 0.625	7	0.11	3.4	Fig. 76	C-T	600	200	—	-44	120	8	3.7	0.2		56
												C-P	500	200	—	-61	100	7	2.5	0.2		40
												AB2	500	200	—	-26	20/116	0.1/10	2.6	0.1	11.1K	40
7984	25	750	3	250	175	13.5[13]	0.58	16	0.16	6.0	12EU	C-P/C-T	375	160	—	-80	150	8.5	4	2		32
807 807W 5933	30	750	3.5	300	60	6.3	0.9	12	0.2	7	5AW	C-T	750	250	—	-45	100	6	3.5	0.22		50
												C-P	600	275	—	-90	100	6.5	4	0.4		42.5
												AB1	750	300	—	-35	15/70	3/8	75[8]	0		72
1625						12.6	0.45				5AZ	B[10]	750	—	—	0	15/240	—	555[8]	5.3[7]	6.65K	120
2E22	30	750	10	250	—	6.3	1.5	13	0.2	8	5J	C-T-O	750	250	22.5	-60	100	16	6	0.55		53
6146B/ 8298A	35	750	3	250	60	6.3	1.125	13	0.22	8.5	7CK	C-T	750	200	—	-77	160	10	2.7	0.3		85
												C-P	600	175	—	-92	140	9.5	3.4	0.5		62
												AB1	750	200	—	-48	25/125	6.3	—	—	3.6K	61
AX- 9903[3] 5894A	40	600	7	250	250	6.3 / 12.6	1.8 / 0.9	6.7	0.08	2.1	Fig. 7	C-T	600	250	—	-80	200	16	2	0.2		80
829B[3] 3E29[3]	40	750	7	240	200	6.3 / 12.6	2.25 / 1.125	14.5	0.12	7	7BP	C-T	500	200	—	-45	240	32	12	0.7		83
												C-P	425	200	—	-60	212	35	11	0.8		63
												B	500	200	—	-18	27/230	—	56[8]	0.39	4.8K	76
3D24	45	2000	10	400	125	6.3	3	6.5	0.2	2.4	Fig. 75	C-T-O	2000	375	—	-300	90	20	10	4.0		140
												C-T-O	1500	375	—	-300	90	22	10	4.0		105
4D22	50	750	14	350	60	12.6 / 25.2	1.6 / 0.8	28	0.27	13	Fig. 26	C-T	750	300	—	-100	240	26	12	1.5		135
												C-T	600	300	—	-100	215	30	10	1.25		100
4D32						6.3	3.75				Fig. 27	C-P	600	—	—	-100	220	28	10	1.25		100
												C-P	550	—	—	-100	175	17	6	0.6		70
												AB2[6]	600	250	—	-25	100/365	26[7]	70[8]	0.45[7]	3K	125

[14] See page V31 for Key to Class-of-Service abbreviations.

TABLE X — TETRODE AND PENTODE TRANSMITTING TUBES — *Continued* V30

Type	Plate Dissipation Watts	Plate Voltage	Screen Dissipation Watts	Screen Voltage	Freq. Mc. Full Ratings	Volts	Amperes	Cin pf.	Cgp pf.	Cout pf.	Base	Class of Service[14]	Plate Voltage	Screen Voltage	Suppressor Voltage	Grid Voltage	Plate Current Ma.	Screen Current Ma.	Grid Current Ma.	Approx. Driving Power Watts	P-to-P Load Ohms	Approx. Output Power Watts
8117[3]	60	750	7	300	175	6.3 / 12.6	1.8 / 0.9	11.8	3.7	0.09	Fig. 7	AB1	600	250	—	-32.5	60/212	1.9/25	—	—	1410	76
814	65	1500	10	300	30	10	3.25	13.5	0.1	13.5	Fig. 64	C-T	1500	300	—	-90	150	24	10	1.5	—	160
												C-P	1250	300	—	-150	145	20	10	3.2	—	130
4-65A	65	3000	10	600	150	6	3.5	8	0.08	2.1	Fig. 25	C-T-O	1500	250	—	-85	150	40	18	3.2	—	165
												C-T-O	3000	250	—	-100	115	22	10	1.7	—	280
												C-P	1500	250	—	-125	120	40	16	3.5	—	140
												C-P	2500	250	—	-135	110	25	12	2.6	—	230
												AB1	2500	400	—	-85	15/66	3[7]	—	—	—	100
7854[3]	68	1000	8	300	175	6.3 / 12.6	1.8 / 0.9	6.7	2.1	0.09	Fig. 7	C-T	750	260	—	-75	240	12.7	5.5	3.5	—	123
												C-P	600	225	—	-75	200	7.8	5.5	3.5	—	85
4E27/ 8001	75	4000	30	750	75	5	7.5	12	0.06	6.5	7BM	C-T	2000	500	60	-200	150	11	6	1.4	—	230
												C-P	1800	400	60	-130	135	11	8	1.7	—	178
HK257 HK257B	75	4000	25	750	75[16]	5	7.5	13.8	0.04	6.7	7BM	C-T	2000	500	60	-200	150	11	6	1.4	—	230
												C-P	1800	400	60	-130	135	11	8	1.7	—	178
PL-177A	75	2000	10	600	175	6	3.2	7.5	0.06	4.2	Fig. 14	C-T-C-P	2000	400	0	-125	150	12	5	0.8	—	220
												C-T-C-P	1000	400	0	-105	150	16	5	0.7	—	100
												AB1	2000	600	—	-115	25/175	0/7	0	0	—	210
PL-6549	75	2000	10	600	175	6	3.2	7.5	0.09	3.4	Fig. 14	C-T	2000	400	70	-125	150	12	5	0.8	—	270
												C-P	2000	400	70	-140	125	15	4	0.7	—	200
												AB2[6]	2000	400	70	-85	30/225	0.1/10	180[8]	0.05[7]	19K	325
828	80	2000	23	750	30	10	3.25	13.5	0.05	14.5	5J	C-T	1500	400	75	-100	180	28	12	2.2	—	200
												C-P	1250	400	75	-140	160	28	12	2.7	—	150
												AB1[6]	2000	750	60	-120	50/210	2/60	240	0	18.5K	385
7270 7271	80	1350	—	425	175	6.3 / 13.5	3.1 / 1.25	8	0.4	0.14	Fig. 84	C-T	850	—	—	-100	275	15	8	10	—	135
												AB1	665	400	—	-119	220	15	6	10	—	85
8072	100	2200	8	400	500	13.5	1.3	16	0.13	0.011	Fig. 85	C-T-O	700	200	—	-30	300	10	20	5	—	85
6816[9] 6884	115	1000	4.5	300	400	6.3 / 26.5	2.1 / 0.52	14	0.085	0.015	Fig. 77	C-T-O	900	300	—	-30	170	1	10	3	—	80
												C-P	700	250	—	-50	130	10	10	3	—	45
												AB1[6]	850	300	—	-15	80/200	0/20	30[8]	0	7K	80
												AB2[6]	850	300	—	-15	80/335	0/25	46[8]	0.3	3.96K	140
813[13]	125	2500	20	800	30	10	5	16.3	0.25	14	5BA	C-T-O	1250	300	0	-75	180	35	12	1.7	—	170
												C-T-O	2250	300	0	-155	220	40	15	4	—	375
												AB1	2500	750	0	-95	25/145	27[7]	0	0	—	245
												AB2[6]	2000	750	0	-90	40/315	1.5/58	230[8]	0.17	16K	455
												AB2[6]	2500	750	0	-95	35/360	1.2/55	235[8]	0.35[7]	17K	650
4-125A 4D21 6155	125	3000	20	600	120	5	6.5	10.8	0.07	3.1	5BK	C-T-O	2000	350	—	-100	200	50	12	2.8	—	275
												C-T-O	3000	350	—	-150	167	30	9	2.5	—	375
												AB2[6]	2500	350	—	-43	93/260	0/6	178[8]	1.0[7]	22K	400
												AB1[6]	2500	600	—	-96	50/232	0.3/8.5	192[8]	0	20.3K	330
												GG	2000	0	—	0	10/105[17]	30[17]	55[17]	16[17]	10.5K	145
4E27A/ 5-125B	125	4000	20	750	75	5	7.5	10.5	0.08	4.7	7BM	C-T	3000	350	60	-200	167	5	6	1.6	—	375
												C-T	1000	750	0	-170	160	21	3	0.6	—	115
803	125	2000	30	600	20	10	5	17.5	0.15	29	5J	C-T	2000	500	40	-90	160	45	12	2	—	210
												C-P	1600	400	100	-80	150	45	25	5	—	155
7094	125	2000	20	400	60	6.3	3.2	9.0	0.5	1.8	Fig. 82	C-T	1500	400	—	-100	330	20	5	4	—	340
												C-P	1200	400	—	-130	275	20	5	5	—	240
												AB1	2000	400	—	-65	30/200	3[7]	60[8]	0	12K	250
4X150A 4X150G[15]	150[9]	2000	12	400	500	6 / 2.5	2.6 / 6.25	15.5 / 27	0.03 / 0.035	4.5 / 4.5	Fig. 75 / —	C-T-O	1250	250	—	-90	200	20	10	0.8	—	195
												C-P	1000	250	—	-105	200	20	15	2	—	140
												AB2[6]	1250	300	—	-44	475[7]	0/65	100[8]	0.15[7]	5.6K	425
8121	150	2200	8	400	500	13.5	1.3	16	0.13	0.011	Fig. 85	C-T-O	1000	200	—	-30	300	10	30	5	—	165
8646	150	2200	8	400	500	26.5	0.64	16	0.13	0.011	—	C-T	1500	200	—	-30	300	5	30	8	—	235
4-250A 5D22 6156	250[9]	4000	35	600	110	5	14.5	12.7	0.12	4.5	5BK	C-T-O	2500	500	—	-150	300	60	9	1.7	—	575
												C-T-O	3000	500	—	-180	345	60	10	2.6	—	800
												C-P	2500	400	—	-200	200	30	9	2.2	—	375
												C-P	3000	400	—	-310	225	30	9	3.2	—	510
												AB2[6]	2000	300	—	-48	510[7]	0/26	198[8]	5.5[7]	8K	650
												AB1[6]	2500	600	—	-110	430[7]	0.3/13	100[8]	0	11.4K	625
4X250B	250[9]	2000	12	400	175	6	2.1	18.5	0.04	4.7	Fig. 75	C-T-O	2000	250	—	-90	250	25	27	2.8	—	410
												C-P	1500	250	—	-100	200	25	17	2.1	—	250
												AB1[6]	2000	350	—	-50	500[7]	30[7]	100[8]	0	8.26K	650
7034/ 4X150A 7035/ 4X150D	250 250	2000 2000	12 12	300 300	150	6 / 26.5	2.6 / 0.58	16	0.03	4.4	Fig. 75	C-T-O	2000	250	—	-88	250	24	8	2.5	—	370
												C-P	1600	250	—	-118	200	23	5	3	—	230
												AB2[6]	2000	300	—	-50	100/500	0/36	106[8]	0.2	8.1K	630
												AB1[6]	2000	300	—	-50	100/470	0/36	100[8]	0	8.76K	580
4CX-300A	300[9]	2000	12	400	500	6	2.75	29.5	0.04	4.8	—	C-T	2000	250	—	-90	250	25	27	2.8	—	410
												C-P	1500	250	—	-100	200	25	17	2.1	—	250
												AB1[6]	2000	350	—	-50	500[7]	30[7]	100[8]	0	8.26K	650
PL-175A	400	4000	25	600	—	5	14.5	15.1	0.06	9.8	Fig. 86	C-T-C-P	4000	600	0	-200	350	29	6	1.4	—	960
												C-T-C-P	2500	600	0	-180	350	40	7	1.6	—	600
												AB1	2500	750	—	-143	100/350	1/35	0	0	—	570
4-400A	400[9]	4000	35	600	110	5	14.5	12.5	0.12	4.7	5BK	C-T-C-P	4000	300	—	-170	270	22.5	10	10	—	720
												GG	2500	0	—	0	80/270[17]	55[17]	100[17]	38[17]	4.0K	325
												AB1	2500	750	—	-130	95/317	0/14	0	0	—	425
8122	400	2200	8	400	500	13.5	1.3	16	0.13	0.011	Fig. 86	C-T-O	2000	200	—	-30	300	5	30	5	—	300

[14] See page V31 for Key to Class-of-Service abbreviations.

TABLE X — TETRODE AND PENTODE TRANSMITTING TUBES — *Continued*

Type	Maximum Ratings					Cathode		Capacitances			Base	Typical Operation										
	Plate Dissipation Watts	Plate Voltage	Screen Dissipation Watts	Screen Voltage	Freq. Mc. Full Ratings	Volts	Amperes	C_{in} pf.	C_{gp} pf.	C_{out} pf.		Class of Service[14]	Plate Voltage	Screen Voltage	Suppressor Voltage	Grid Voltage	Plate Current Ma.	Screen Current Ma.	Grid Current Ma.	Approx. Driving Power Watts	P-to-P Load Ohms	Approx. Output Power Watts
5-500A	500	4000	35	600	30	10	10.2	19	0.10	12	—	C-T	3000	500	0	−220	432	65	35	12	—	805
												C-T	3100	470	0	−310	260	50	15	6	—	580
												AB₁	3000	750	0	−112	320	26	—	—	—	612
8166/ 4-1000A	1000	6000	75	1000	—	7.5	21	27.2	.24	7.6	—	C-T	3000	500	—	−150	700	146	38	11	—	1430
												C-P	3000	500	—	−200	600	145	36	12	—	1390
												AB₂	4000	500	—	−60	300/1200	0/95	—	11	7K	3000
												GG	3000	0	—	0	100/700[17]	105[17]	170[17]	130[17]	2.5K	1475
4CX1000A	1000	3000	12	400	400	6	12.5	35	.005	12	—	AB₁	2000	325	—	−55	500/2000	−4/60	—	—	2.8K	2160
													2500	325	—	−55	500/2000	−4/60	—	—	3.1K	2920
													3000	325	—	−55	500/1800	−4/60	—	—	3.85K	3360
PL-8295/ 172	1000	3000	30	600	—	6	8.2	38	.09	18	—	C-T	2000	500	35	−175	850	42	10	1.9	—	1155
													2500	500	35	−200	840	40	10	2.1	—	1440
													3000	500	35	−200	820	42	10	2.1	—	1770
												AB₁	2000	500	35	−110	200/800	12/43	110[8]	—	2.65K	1040
													2500	500	35	−110	200/800	11/40	115[8]	—	3.5K	1260
													3000	500	35	−115	220/800	11/39	115[8]	—	4.6K	1590

[1] Grid-resistor.
[2] Doubler to 175 Mc.
[3] Dual tube. Values for both sections, in push-pull. Interelectrode capacitances, however, are for each section.
[4] Tripler to 175 Mc.
[5] Filament limited to intermittent operation.
[6] Values are for two tubes
[7] Max.-signal value.
[8] Peak grid-to-grid volts.
[9] Forced-air cooling required.
[10] Two tubes triode connected, G₂ to G₁ through 20K Ω. Input to G₂.
[11] Tripler to 200 Mc.
[12] Typical Operation at 175 Mc.
[13] ± 1.5 volts.

[14] KEY TO CLASS-OF-SERVICE ABBREVIATIONS
AB₁ = Class-AB₁.
AB₂ = Class-AB₂.
B = Class-B push-pull a.f. modulator.
C-M = Frequency multiplier.
C-P = Class-C plate-modulated telephone.
C-T = Class-C telegraph.
C-T-O = Class-C amplifier-osc.
GG = Grounded-grid (grid and screen connected together).
[15] No Class B data available.
[16] HK257B 120 Mc. full rating.
[17] Single tone.

TABLE XI — SEMICONDUCTOR DIODES[1]

This list contains but a small percentage of the available diode types. A complete listing would be impractical.

Small-Signal General-Purpose Diodes

Type	Use	Max. Inverse Volts	Max. Average Ma.	Min. Forward Ma.[2]	Max. Reverse μ-amp
1N34A	General Purpose	75	50	5.0	500@ −50 V.
1N52A	General Purpose	85	50	5.0	100@ −50 V.
1N60	Vid. Detector	25	50	5.0	40@ −20 V.
1N64	Vid. Detector	20	50	0.1	25@ −1.3 V.
1N270	General Purpose	100	90	—	100@ −50 V.
1N634	60-Volt Very Low Z	120	—	50.0	115@ −100 V

Microwave Mixer and U.H.F. Diodes

Type	Use			
1N21B[3]	Mixer	Average Freq.—3060 Mc.	10db. Overall Noise Figure.	
1N21E[3]	Mixer	Average Freq.—3060 Mc.	7db. Overall Noise Figure.	
1N21F[3]	Mixer	Average Freq.—3060 Mc.	6db. Overall Noise Figure.	
1N23C[3]	Mixer	Average Freq.—9375 Mc.	9.8db. Overall Noise Figure.	
1N23E[3]	Mixer	Average Freq.—9375 Mc.	7.5db. Overall Noise Figure.	
1N82A	Mixer	Average Freq.—1000 Mc.	14db. Overall Noise Figure.	
1N4166[3]	Mixer	Average Freq.—3060 Mc.	5.5db. Overall Noise Figure.	

Voltage-Variable-Capacitance and Varactor Diodes

Type	Total Nominal C (at 4 V.)	Q (at 50 Mc.)	Tuning Ratio	Max. Power Diss. (Mw.)
MV1620	6.8	300	2.0/3.2	400
MV1628	15	250	2.0/3.2	400
MV1636	27	200	2.0/2.5	400
MV1644	56	150	2.0/2.5	400
MV1650	100	150	2.0/2.5	400
MA-4062D	P_{in} 10 watts, f_{in} 400-700 Mc., Junction C 10 pf. at 0 V.			
1N4885	P_{in} 25 watts, P_{out} 17 watts, f_{out} 450 Mc., Junction C 16 pf. at 40 V, 35 pf. at 6 V.			

Silicon Power Diodes

Type	Max. Reverse Voltage (peak)	Max. Forward Current (amps.)	Average Forward Current (amps.)	Max. Reverse Current (amps.)
1N1612	50	15	5	1
1N1613	100	15	5	1
1N3193	200	6	0.5	0.2
1N3195	600	6	0.5	0.2
1N3256	800	5	0.4	0.2
1N3563	1000	4	0.3	0.2
10B1	100	—	1.3	—
10C10	1000	—	1.3	—
1N4822	600	—	1.5	—
1N5054	1000	—	1.5	—

[1] A bar, plus sign, or color dot usually denotes the cathode end of crystal diodes. Diode color code rings are grouped toward the cathode end.
[2] at + 1 volt.
[3] Polarity is such that the base is the anode and the tip is the cathode, R-types have opposite polarity.

TABLE XII — SEMICONDUCTORS **V32**

SMALL-SIGNAL TYPES

No.	Type	Diss. (Watts)	V_CEO (Volts)	I_C (D.C.)	h_FE (Min.)	f_T (Typ.)	Noise Fig. (db.)	Use (Typ.)	Case Style	Base Conn.	Application
		Maximum Ratings			Characteristics			Other Data			
2N3391A	NPN	0.2*	25	100 ma.	250	160 Mc.	1.9	Audio	—	1	Low-noise Preamps.
40231	NPN	0.5*	18	100 ma.	55	60 Mc.	2.8	Audio	—	7	Preamps. and Drivers
2N2925	NPN	0.2*	25	100 ma.	170	160 Mc.	2.8	Gen. Purpose	—	1	Osc., R.F., I.F., A.F.
2N4124	NPN	0.3	25	200 ma.	120	250 Mc.	5	Audio-R.F.	—	2	
2N4126	PNP	0.3	25	200 ma.	120	250 Mc.	4	Audio-R.F.	—	2	
2N706A	NPN	0.3*	20	50 ma.	20	400 Mc.	—	R.F.	TO-18	8	R.F., Switching
2N4401	NPN	0.31*	40	600 ma.	20	250 Mc.	—	Gen. Purpose	TO-92	2	Osc., R.F., I.F., A.F.
2N4410	NPN	0.31*	80	250 ma.	60	250 Mc.	—	Gen. Purpose	TO-92	2	Osc., R.F., I.F., A.F.
2N3663	NPN	0.12*	12	25 ma.	20	900 Mc.	4	R.F.	—	1	V.H.F./U.H.F. Osc., Amp., Mix.
TIS48	NPN	1.2*	40	500 ma.	40	500 Mc.	—	R.F.	TO-92	3	R.F., Switching
TIS54	PNP	0.25*	−12	−80 ma.	30	300 Mc.	—	R.F.	TO-92	3	R.F., Switching
TIXM10	PNP	0.075*	−20	−30 ma.	20	630 Mc.	4	R.F.	TO-72	4	R.F., Preamp., V.H.F./U.H.F.
40235	NPN	0.18*	35	50 ma.	40	1200 Mc.	3.3	R.F.	—	9	V.H.F./U.H.F. R.F. Amp., Osc., Mix.

MEDIUM-SIGNAL TYPES

No.	Type	Diss. (Watts)	V_CEO (Volts)	I_C (D.C.)	h_FE (Min.)	f_T (Typ.)	Noise Fig. (db.)	Use (Typ.)	Case Style	Base Conn.	Application
2N2102	NPN	5†	65	1 A.	20	100 Mc.	6	Gen. Purpose	TO-5	8	A.F., R.F. Amps. (Linear)
2N3512	NPN	4	35	500 ma.	10	250 Mc.	—	Audio-R.F.	—	7	
40424	NPN	8†	300	150 ma.	30	25 Mc.	—	H.V. Gen. Purp.	TO-66	10	A.F./R.F. Osc., Amp.
2N3553	NPN	7†	40	1 A.	10	500 Mc.	—	R.F.	TO-39	8	Class A, B, C R.F. Mult., Amp., Osc.
40280	NPN	7†	36	0.5 A.	—	550 Mc.	—	R.F.	TO-39	8	Class C R.F. Mult., Amp., Osc.
2N3866	NPN	5†	30	0.4 A.	—	800 Mc.	—	R.F.	TO-39	8	Class A, B, C R.F. Mult., Amp., Osc.
2N2631	NPN	8.75†	60	1.5 A.	—	200 Mc.	—	R.F.	TO-39	8	Class C R.F. Amp., Osc.
TIP-14	NPN	10†	60	4 A.	30	40 Mc.	—	R.F.	—	5	R.F./A.F. Osc., Amp.
40394	PNP	7†	−40	−1 A.	−50	60 Mc.	—	Gen. Purpose	—	8	A.F., R.F. Amps., Osc.

LARGE-SIGNAL TYPES

No.	Type	Diss. (Watts)	V_CEO (Volts)	I_C (D.C.)	h_FE (Min.)	f_T (Typ.)	Noise Fig. (db.)	Use (Typ.)	Case Style	Base Conn.	Application
40349V2	NPN	11.7†	140	1.5 A.	25	1 Mc.	—	H.V. Gen. Purp.	—	8	A.F., D.C. Amps. Switch., Osc.
2N4296	NPN	20†	250	1 A.	50	20 Mc.	—	H.V. Gen. Purp.	TO-66	11	A.F., R.F. Osc., Switch. A.F., R.F., D.C. Amps. Relay Driver.
40310	NPN	29†	35	4 A.	20	1 Mc.	—	Gen. Purpose	TO-66	11	Audio, D.C. Amp. A.F., R.F. Osc.
40312	NPN	29†	60	4 A.	20	1 Mc.	—	Gen. Purpose	TO-66	11	Audio, D.C. Amp. A.F., R.F. Osc.
2N3583	NPN	35†	175	2 A.	10	15 Mc.	—	H.V. Gen. Purp.	TO-66	11	R.F., A.F. Osc., Amp. D.C. Amp.
2N4396	NPN	62†	60	5 A.	60	4 Mc.	—	Gen. Purpose	TO-3	11	R.F., A.F. Osc., Amp. D.C. Amp.
2N2869	PNP	30†	−50	−10 A.	50	200 kc.	—	Gen. Purpose	TO-3	11	A.F., Osc., Amp., Switch.
MJ480	NPN	87†	40	4 A.	30	4 Mc.	—	Gen. Purpose	TO-3	11	A.F., R.F. Amp., Osc.
2N251A	PNP	90†	−60	−7 A.	25	—	—	Gen. Purpose	TO-3	11	A.F. Amp., Osc., Switch.
2N457B	PNP	150†	−60	−7 A.	30	430 kc.	—	Gen. Purpose	TO-3	11	A.F. Amp., Osc., Switch.
2N1907	PNP	150†	−100	−20 A.	20	10 Mc.	—	R.F.	TO-3	11	Class-C R.F. Osc., Amp.
40282	NPN	23†	18	2 A.	—	350 Mc.	—	R.F.	TO-60	12	V.H.F. Class-C Amp.
2N2876	NPN	17.5†	60	1.5 A.	—	200 Mc.	—	R.F.	TO-60	12	V.H.F. Class-C Amp.
2N2157	PNP	170†	−60	−30 A.	40	—	—	A.F., D.C. Amp., Switch.	TO-36	13	

FIELD-EFFECT TRANSISTORS

No.	Type	Diss.	V_DS	V_GS	MIN. μ MHOS	C_ISS	MAX. I DSS	Top Freq.	Style	Base Conn.	Application
MPF102	N	200 Mw.	25	−2.5	2000	4.5 Pf.	20 ma.	200 Mc.	JFET	6	A.F., R.F. Amp., Mix., Osc.
MPF105	N	200 Mw.	25	−4.5	2000	4.5 Pf.	16 ma.	100 Mc.	JFET	6	A.F., R.F. Amp., Mix., Osc.
MPF106	N	200 Mw.	25	−25	2500	5 Pf.	30 ma.	432 Mc.	JFET	6	A.F., R.F. Amp., Mix., Osc.
3N140	N	400 Mw.	20	—	6000	5.5 Pf.	50 ma.	300 Mc.	Dual-Gate MOS FET	16	R.F. Amp.
3N128	N	100 Mw.	20	—	5000	5.8 Pf.	—	200 Mc.	IGFET	14	A.F., R.F., Amp., Mix., Osc.
3N141	N	400 Mw.	20	—	6000	5.5 Pf.	50 ma.	300 Mc.	Dual-Gate MOS FET	16	Mix.
2N4416	N	175 Mw.	30	−6.0	4000	4 Pf.	15 ma.	450 Mc.	JFET	15	V.H.F./U.H.F. R.F. Amp., Mix., Osc.

* = Ambient Temp. of 25°C (No heat sink).
† = Case Temp. of 25°C (with heat sink).

The semiconductors listed in this table were selected to represent those types that are useful for most amateur radio experimental applications. These transistors were chosen for their low cost and availability. Most of them can be obtained from the large mail-order houses or from the local manufacturer's distributor. Because there are thousands of transistor types on today's market, this list is by no means complete. It should, however, serve as a useful guide in selecting a specific semiconductor for a given application.

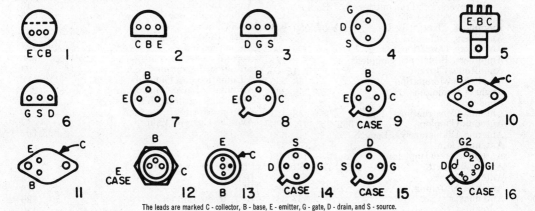

The leads are marked C - collector, B - base, E - emitter, G - gate, D - drain, and S - source.

Index

CATALOG SECTION

The Radio Amateur's Handbook

46th EDITION 1969

All companies whose advertising has been accepted for this section have met The American Radio Relay League's rigid standards for established integrity; their products and engineering methods have received the League's approval.

INDEX OF ADVERTISERS

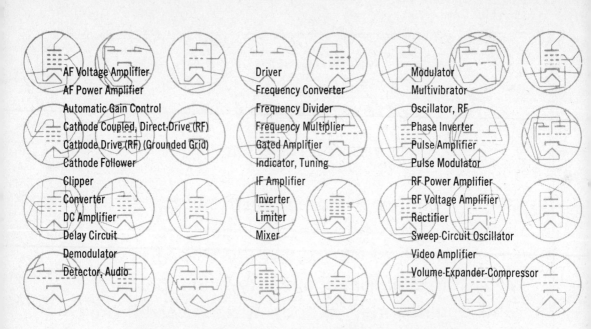

AF Voltage Amplifier	Driver	Modulator
AF Power Amplifier	Frequency Converter	Multivibrator
Automatic Gain Control	Frequency Divider	Oscillator, RF
Cathode Coupled, Direct-Drive (RF)	Frequency Multiplier	Phase Inverter
Cathode Drive (RF) (Grounded Grid)	Gated Amplifier	Pulse Amplifier
Cathode Follower	Indicator, Tuning	Pulse Modulator
Clipper	IF Amplifier	RF Power Amplifier
Converter	Inverter	RF Voltage Amplifier
DC Amplifier	Limiter	Rectifier
Delay Circuit	Mixer	Sweep-Circuit Oscillator
Demodulator		Video Amplifier
Detector, Audio		Volume-Expander-Compressor

34 places to use receiving-type tubes
and RCA has tubes for all of them!

Anywhere you look in your shack, you'll find places for RCA receiving-type tubes. In your equipment, socket by socket, they give you the top performance and long-lasting reliability you've come to expect from RCA.

That's because RCA tubes are the result of RCA's many, many years of technical experience and practical knowledge as a broad line, high-volume manufacturer of tubes for every application.

See your RCA Tube Distributor for all your tube needs. While you're at it, ask about the RCA Receiving Tube Manual, RC-26.

RCA Electronic Components, Harrison, N.J.

3

The World's Largest

THE FAMOUS HEATH DELUXE SB-SERIES

SB-101 80 Through 10 Meter SSB Transceiver . . . 180 watts PEP SSB, 170 watts CW. Front panel control for SSB or CW selectivity. Provisions for external LMO. Features USB/LSB & CW. PTT & VOX. Fixed or mobile optional power supplies. Unmatched engineering & design.
Kit SB-101, 23 lbs............................ **$370.00**

SB-110A 6-Meter SSB Transceiver . . . puts the famous Heath SB-Series on "6". 180 watts PEP input SSB . . . 150 watts CW — with single-knob linear tuning, 1 kHz dial calibration, and the ultimate in stability.
Kit SB-110A, 23 lbs............................ **$299.00**

SB-301 Amateur Band Receiver . . . SSB, AM, CW, and RTTY reception on 80 through 10 meters +15 MHz WWV reception. Tunes 6 & 2 meters with SBA-300-3 and SBA-300-4 plug-in converters.
Kit SB-301, 25 lbs. (less speaker) **$260.00**

SB-401 Amateur Band SSB Transmitter . . . 180 watts PEP SSB, 170 watts CW on 80 through 10 meters. Operates "Transceive" with SB-301 — requires SBA-401-1 crystal pack for independent operation.
Kit SB-401, 36 lbs............................ **$285.00**
SBA-401-1 crystal pack, 1 lb................... **$29.95**

SB-200 KW SSB Linear Amplifier . . . 1200 watts PEP input SSB, 1000 watts CW on 80 through 10 meters. Built-in antenna relay, SWR meter, and power supply. Can be driven by most popular SSB transmitters (100 watts nominal output).
Kit SB-200, 41 lbs............................ **$220.00**

SB-620 Amateur Radio Spectrum Monitor . . . displays all received signals up to 250 kHz either side of receiver tuned frequency. New narrow sweep function shows 10 kHz for single signal analysis.
Kit SB-620, 15 lbs............................ **$119.95**

SB-610 Signal Monitor Scope . . . operates with transmitters on 160 through 6 meters at power levels from 15 watts through 1 kw. Shows transmitted envelope. Operates with receiver IF's up to 6 MHz, showing received signal waveforms. Spots over modulation, etc.
Kit SB-610, 14 lbs............................ **$74.95**

SB-630 Amateur Station Console . . . including 24-hour clock, SWR meter, 10 minute timer with audio-visual signaling, and more. Styled to match your SB-Series station.
Kit SB-630, 10 lbs............................ **$74.95**

4

Selection Of Amateur Radio Equipment
LOW-COST GEAR FOR THE NOVICE AND BUDGET-MINDED

HW-16 Novice CW Transceiver . . . a high-performance 3-band CW transceiver . . . covers the lower 250 kHz of 80, 40, & 15 meters. 75 watts input for novice class — 90 watts for general class. Provisions for VFO transmitter control with Heathkit HG-10B.
Kit HW-16, 25 lbs **$109.95**

New HW-100 5-Band SSB-CW Transceiver . . . second only to the famous SB-101 in performance & value. 80-10 M coverage . . . 180 watts PEP SSB input, 170 watts CW. Solid-State (FET) VFO . . . patented Harmonic DriveTM dial mechanism . . . crystal filter . . . built-in 100 kHz calibrator.
Kit HW-100, 22 lbs **$240.00**

New HW-17 Solid-State 2-Meter AM Transceiver . . . the easy way to move up to 2-meter phone. 25-30 watts AM input . . . solid-state dual-conversion superhet receiver . . . four crystal sockets plus provision for external VFO . . . ANL . . . Squelch . . . comes with PTT mike & mobile gimbal mount.
Kit HW-17, 17 lbs **$129.95**

HW-18 Series CAP, MARS & 160 M SSB Transceivers . . . 200 Watts PEP SSB input . . . 25 watts with carrier for AM compatibility . . . 2 switch-selected crystal controlled channels . . . crystal filter IF for 2.1 kHz selectivity . . . 1 uV sensitivity . . . mobile mount & PTT mike included.
Kit HW-18-1, CAP xcvr., 16 lbs **$119.95**
Wired HWW-18-1, wired CAP xcvr., 16 lbs **$179.95**
Kit HW-18-2, MARS xcvr., 16 lbs **$109.95**
Kit HW-18-3, 160 M xcvr., 16 lbs **$109.95**

HR-10B Amateur Band Receiver . . . with extra-durable two-tone wrinkle finish to match the "Single-Banders" and novice transceiver. Tune AM, CW, and SSB with 80 through 10 meter coverage. Provisions for plug-in 100 kHz crystal calibrator.
Kit HR-10B, 20 lbs **$79.95**
Kit HRA-10-1, 100 kHz crystal calibrator, 1 lb **$8.95**

DX-60B Phone & CW Transmitter . . . with wrinkle finish matching HR-10B and the "Single-Banders". Here's 90 watts on 80 through 10 meters . . . operates at reduced power for novice class.
Kit DX-60B, 24 lbs **$79.95**

COLLINS / the most
talked-about performance

Collins' S/Line is respected universally for the quality of its SSB and CW communications. Plug in patch cords and you are ready to transceive. Flip a switch and you can operate the transmitter and receiver on separate frequencies.

The popular Collins KWM-2 Transceiver serves as a mobile rig, and as a full-power fixed station when teamed with a Collins linear amplifier.

Ask your Collins representative for details. He will show you how to get best performance and value for your station.

32S-3 Transmitter

The 32S-3 is an SSB or CW transmitter with nominal output of 100 watts from 3.4 to 5.0 MHz and from 6.5 to 30.0 MHz. Supplied crystals cover the 80-, 40-, 20-, and 15-meter bands, and 200 kHz of the 10-meter amateur band. Provisions are made for two additional crystals.

The 32S-3 features mechanical filter side-band generation, permeability-tuned VFO, crystal-controlled HF oscillator, RF inverse feedback, and automatic load control. The unit has blocked-grid keying, spotting control, keying hardness control and sidetone level adjust.

The 32S-3 can operate transceive by using oscillator injection voltages supplied by the 75S-3B or any of the 75S series receivers.

75S-3B, -3C Receivers

With Collins' 75S-3B or 75S-3C, you can be assured of the finest amateur receiver available for reception in the CW, SSB or RTTY modes. The 75S-3B provides SSB, CW and AM reception from 3.4 to 5.0 and from 6.5 to 30.0 MHz by selection of the appropriate HF heterodyning crystals. Crystals furnished with the 75S-3B cover the 80-, 40-, 20-, and 15-meter amateur bands and 200 kHz of the 10-meter band. The 75S-3C has provisions for 14 additional crystals which can be switch-selected from the front panel.

Features incorporated in the 75S-3B and 75S-3C include dual conversion with a crystal-controlled first heterodyning oscillator; band-pass first IF; stable permeability-tuned VFO; improved cross modulation and strong signal characteristics; 2.1-kHz mechanical filter; excellent AGC characteristics; both product and diode detectors; rejection notch filter; manual and crystal-controlled BFO's; and AGC time constant control. The 75S-3B and 75S-3C provide a choice of two degrees of selectivity with optional plug-in filters. Provision is made for obtaining power from a DC power supply.

312B-4 Speaker Console

The 312B-4 provides a unitized control for the S/Line or the KWM-2. It houses a speaker, RF directional wattmeter with 200- and 2000-watt scales, and switches for station control functions.

30S-1 Linear Amplifiers

Collins' linear amplifiers can be driven by the KWM-1, KWM-2, 32S-3 or equivalent equipment.

The 30S-1 is a completely self-contained, single tube, grounded grid linear amplifier that provides the full legal power input for SSB, CW or RTTY. The tube used is the Eimac 4CX-1000A.

The 30S-1 may be used on any frequency between 3.4 and 30.0 MHz. A special comparator tuning circuit allows tune-up at low power to avoid exceeding the legal DC input of 1 kw. The 30S-1 offers push-button selection of linear amplifier or exciter output from the front panel. Antenna relay is included. The unit is conservatively rated.

30L-1 Linear Amplifiers

The compact 30L-1 (same size as the KWM-2) provides for 1 kw PEP input on SSB (500 watts average DC) and 1000 watts average on CW. It has a self-contained power supply. The unit also features instant warm-up time, RF inverse feedback, automatic load control and silicon rectifiers. Automatic antenna switching from exciter to amplifier is included.

KWM-2, -2A SSB Transceivers

The versatile KWM-2 transceiver serves both fixed-station and mobile needs on any fourteen 200-kHz bands from 3.4 to 5.0 MHz, and from 6.5 to 30.0 MHz. Supplied crystals cover the 80-, 40-, 20-, and 15-meter bands, and 200 kHz of the 10-meter amateur band. Provision is made for two additional crystals. The KWM-2A has provisions for 14 additional crystals which can be switch-selected from the front panel.

The transceiver operates 80 through 10 meters with 175 watts PEP input on SSB or 160 watts on CW.

Top features of the KWM-2 are filter-type SSB generation, Collins permeability-tuned oscillator, crystal-controlled HF double conversion oscillator, VOX and anti-trip circuits, automatic load control and RF inverse feedback.

COLLINS

Where accuracy counts.

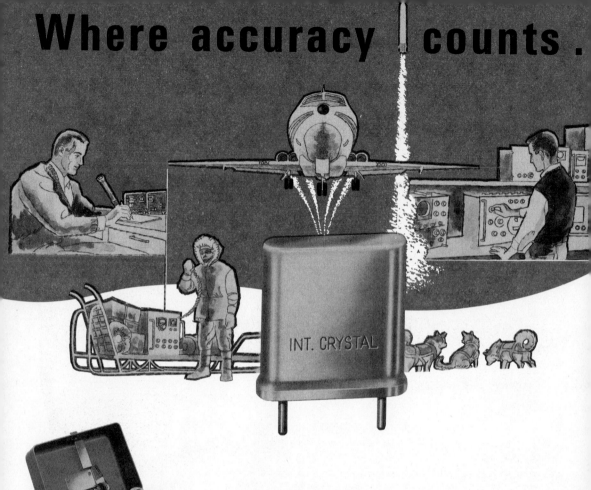

MODEL 6000 FREQUENCY METER

The Model 6000 Modular Frequency Meter will measure frequencies 10 KHz to 600 MHz with .000125% accuracy.

The wide variety of plug-in oscillator accessories and range modules makes the Model 6000 adaptable to a number of jobs in the field and in the laboratory. Portable, battery operated with rechargeable batteries.

Model 6000 with 601A charger, less plug-in modules	$195.00
Range Modules (Mixers)	$25.00 to $45.00 each
Oscillator Modules (Crystal Controlled for Frequency Measurement)	$30.00 to $90.00 each

FM-2400C FREQUENCY METER

The FM-2400C provides an accurate standard frequency signal for testing and adjustment of mobile transmitters and receivers at predetermined frequencies between 25 and 500 MHz. Up to 24 crystals may be inserted into the meter. The frequencies can be those of the radio frequency channels of operation, and/or of the intermediate frequencies of the receivers between 5 MHz and 40 MHz. Frequency stability (standard) ±.001% from 32° to 122°F. Frequency stability with built-in thermometer, calibrated crystals and temperature corrected charts, .00025% from +25° to +125°F. (.000125% special 450 MHz crystals available). Unit has solid state circuitry and rechargeable batteries.

FM 2400C (Meter Only)	$445.00
RF Crystals	
Hi-Band	$ 24.00 ea.
Lo-Band	15.00 ea.
IF Crystals	8.00 ea.

International Crystals & Frequency Meters

International offers a complete line of precision radio crystals from 70 KHz to 160 MHz. We can supply all types for the commercial user, experimenter and amateur. Crystals for use in military equipment can be supplied to conform to specifications of MIL-C-3098E.

These are important facts! • International Crystals are the product of a continuing research and development program. • International Crystals are designed and manufactured to operate under all types of field conditions... fixed or mobile. • International Crystals are used in all major makes of commercial two-way radio equipment. • All International Crystals are guaranteed against defective materials and workmanship for an unlimited time when used in equipment for which they were specifically made.

MODEL 1120 SECONDARY FREQUENCY STANDARD
All Transistor Circuits • Solid State Integrated Dividers

Using any general coverage communications receiver the International Model 1120 provides the necessary standard signals for measuring frequencies. Easily calibrated against WWV to provide an accuracy of 1×10^6 for measuring the frequency of harmonics of FM subcarrier frequencies. The Model 1120 is designed for field or bench use with its own self contained rechargeable battery and charger. Long term stability of ±10 cycles over range 40°F to 100°F. Short term stability of better than 1×10^7 can be obtained. Zero adjustment for oscillator on front panel. All transistor circuits provide outputs at 1 MHz, 100 KHz and 10 KHz. Level of signal can be set with gain control.

Cat. No. 620-106................................**$175 Complete**

INTERNATIONAL EX KITS

OX Oscillator (less crystal)..............$2.95
Crystal controlled transistor type.
Lo Kit 3,000 to 19,999 KHz
Hi Kit 20,000 to 60,000 KHz
(Specify when ordering)
EX Crystal for above..........................$3.95

MXX-1 Transistor RF Mixer..............$3.50
A single tuned circuit intended for signal conversion in the 3 to 170 MHz range. Harmonics of the OX oscillator are used for injection in the 60 to 170 MHz range.
Lo Kit 3 to 20 MHz
Hi Kit 20 to 170 MHz
(Specify when ordering)

SAX-1 Transistor RF Amplifier........$3.50
A small signal amplifier to drive MXX-1 mixer. Single tuned input and link output.
Lo Kit 3 to 20 MHz
Hi Kit 20 to 170 MHz
(Specify when ordering)

**PAX-1 Transistor RF
Power Amplifier**..............................$3.75
A single tuned output amplifier designed to follow the OX oscillator. Outputs up to 200 mw can be obtained depending on the frequency and voltage. Amplifier can be amplitude modulated for low power communication.
Frequency range 3,000 to 30,000 KHz.

BAX-1 Broadband Amplifier............$3.75
General purpose unit which may be used as a tuned or untuned amplifier in RF and audio applications 20 Hz to 150 MHz. Provides 6 to 30 db gain.

INTERNATIONAL
CRYSTAL MFG. CO., INC.
10 NO. LEE • OKLA. CITY, OKLA. 73102

KEEPING YOU ON FREQUENCY IS OUR BUSINESS! • **Write for Catalog**

Great things

are happening at NRCI

NCX-1000

Meet the authoritative 5-band 1000-Watt leader from NRCI. The rugged competence of this equipment is unmatched elsewhere. You can pay as much, or more, for only half the features.

☐ 1000-Watt PEP input on SSB, 900-Watt CW, 500-Watt AM, with equal power on all bands, selectable sideband (LSB or USB) on all bands, and identical calibration rate on all bands. Grid-block keying on CW. ☐ All solid-state, except transmitter driver and PA. ☐ Built-in R.F. speech clipper (use optional) doubles average SSB output power; amplified automatic level control (AALC); crystal oscillator for fixed frequency operation. ☐ Built-in VSWR detector reads relative power output and antenna VSWR. ☐ Built-in AC power supply and speaker, with provisions for head phones and external speaker. ☐ Double conversion in receiver and transmitter, receive vernier (±5 kHz), 100 kHz crystal calibrator, fast-attack/slow-decay AGC in all modes, separate AM and product detectors, built-in sidetone oscillator. Receiver sensitivity better than ½ microvolt for 10 dB S+N/N ratio. ☐ Complete safety and overload protection. Forced air cooled final stage.

NCX-500

Here's the potent 5-bander with a 500-Watt punch. Check the terrific features on this low-priced performer:

☐ 500-Watt PEP input on SSB, grid-block keying on CW and compatible AM operation. ☐ Sidetone monitor, plus built-in code practice oscillator. ☐ Receive vernier, with tuning range greater than ±3 kHz. ☐ Separate AM and product detection ☐ Fast-attack/slow release AGC in all modes. ☐ Crystal-controlled pre-mixing with single VFO for effective frequency stability, plus identical calibration rate on all bands. ☐ Crystal lattice filter for high sideband suppression on transmit, and rejection of adjacent-channel QRM on receive . . . plus solid-state balanced modulator for "Set-and-forget" carrier suppression.

AC-500 Power Supply . . . operates from 115/230 VAC and provides all operating voltages for the NCX-500.

the Great Transceivers

the Rockcrushing Linear
NCL-2000

Here's the full legal power, completely self-contained desk-top 2000-Watt SSB PEP linear amplifier for the 80 through 100 meter bands. Minimum peak output is 1300 Watts. The NCL-2000 may also be operated for CW, AM, or RTTY at 1000 Watts DC input.

☐ Built-in power supply, built-in cooling fan. ☐ Equal power output on all bands 80 through 100 meters. ☐ Most complete safety and overload protection, including 1 minute time delay relay, overload relay, lid interlock, and automatic shorting bar.

the Ambidextrous Power Meter
NCP-2000

NRCI introduces a versatile power meter that simultaneously measures both actual forward and reverse power. Now you can know what power is being radiated from your antenna. Check these features:

☐ Scale calibration in three ranges: 0-2000 Watts for maximum power, 0-200 Watts for general usage, and 0-10 Watts for accurate low-power measurement. Accuracy: Within 0.5 dB from 2-30 MHz; ± 1.0 dB from 1-2 MHz and from 30-60 MHz. ☐ Three modes of operation: Power, Tune, and VSWR. ☐ Two large 2½" meters for simultaneous forward and reverse readings. ☐ Designed for continuous, in-line use up to 2000 Watts.

the Classic Receiver HRO-500

No other receiver for the value can come close to the performance of the HRO-500, with the widest frequency range and greatest performance of any general coverage receiver ever built:

☐ 5 kHz through 30 MHz frequency range, in five main bands (60 500 kHz sub-bands) with one kHz calibration accuracy on ¼ inch per kiloHertz dial. ☐ All solid-state for high reliability, portability, low power requirements, and absolutely cool operation. ☐ Phase-locked frequency synthesizer for superior stability and overall calibration. ☐ AGC threshold control to knock out background QRM.

For complete details and specifications, write:

NATIONAL RADIO COMPANY, INC.
NRCI
37 Washington St., Melrose, Mass. 02176
Telephone: (617) 662-7700 TWX: 617-665-5032

Portrait of a most reliable family

More accurately, the portrait shows only *part* of a most reliable family. The E. F. Johnson Company makes hundreds of fine quality electronic components, including:

CAPACITORS—A dozen basic series of air variable capacitors, each in a wide choice of capacity values. They range from sub-miniature machined plate capacitors with maximums of 4.2 to 24.5 pf., to larger, heavy-duty types with capacity values to 1700 pf. and voltage ratings to 9000 volts peak.

There is a reliable Johnson capacitor to fit your application. Whatever the size, it offers excellent stability, high Q, low temperature coefficient, uniform capacitance, and excellent overall performance at competitive prices.

CONNECTORS—The Johnson line of jacks, plugs and terminals meets the needs of both military and commercial designers effectively and economically. For printed circuit applications, there are sub-miniature insulated tip plugs and jacks, plus the unique Test Point Strip / Handle for fast, efficient circuit testing.

Johnson's line of standard insulated connectors includes tip, banana and dual banana plugs, tip and banana jacks, military tip jacks, and binding posts.

RIB-LOC™ components consist of new miniature, one-piece, insulated terminals and jacks that press-mount with excellent retention characteristics.

TUBE SOCKETS, INSULATORS, PILOT LIGHTS, RF COMPONENTS AND HARDWARE—Dependable Johnson tube sockets include HF, VHF and UHF types for tubes of various power levels.

Low-loss, high-voltage-breakdown insulators are available in either steatite or porcelain.

Johnson offers 47 pilot light assemblies in neon and incandescent types. Standard and wide angle lens caps are available in glass and acrylic.

Other hardware includes panel bearings, shaft couplings, crystal sockets and RF chokes, plus a number of heavy-duty RF components for broadcast transmitting, RF heating, antenna phasing and other commercial applications.

FREE CATALOG gives complete details and specifications, including net prices, of E. F. Johnson quality electronic components. Write for your copy today, or ask us about your specific application requirements. Special components, to your exact requirements, may be available in production quantities.

E. F. JOHNSON COMPANY
1848 Tenth Ave. S. W., Waseca, Minnesota 56093
Providing nearly a half-century of communications leadership

13

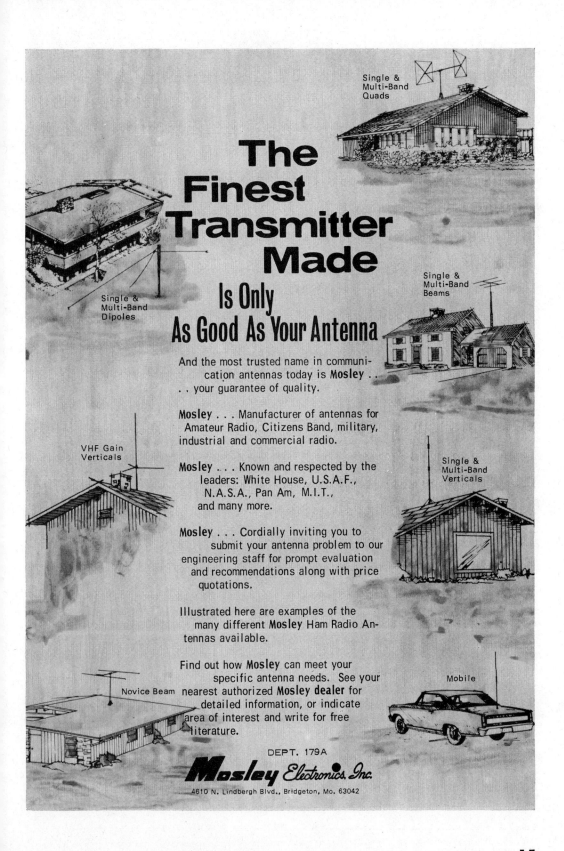

Single &
Multi-Band
Quads

The
Finest
Transmitter
Made

Is Only
As Good As Your Antenna

Single &
Multi-Band
Dipoles

Single &
Multi-Band
Beams

And the most trusted name in communication antennas today is **Mosley** . .
. . your guarantee of quality.

Mosley . . . Manufacturer of antennas for
Amateur Radio, Citizens Band, military,
industrial and commercial radio.

VHF Gain
Verticals

Mosley . . . Known and respected by the
leaders: White House, U.S.A.F.,
N.A.S.A., Pan Am, M.I.T.,
and many more.

Single &
Multi-Band
Verticals

Mosley . . . Cordially inviting you to
submit your antenna problem to our
engineering staff for prompt evaluation
and recommendations along with price
quotations.

Illustrated here are examples of the
many different **Mosley** Ham Radio Antennas available.

Find out how **Mosley** can meet your
specific antenna needs. See your
Novice Beam nearest authorized **Mosley dealer** for
detailed information, or indicate
area of interest and write for free
literature.

Mobile

DEPT. 179A

Mosley *Electronics, Inc.*

4610 N. Lindbergh Blvd., Bridgeton, Mo. 63042

HENRY RADIO SELLS LOTS OF SWAN.
BUT THEN, SWAN TRANSCEIVERS SELL THEMSELVES.
COME ON IN...TEST YOUR SALES RESISTANCE.

MODEL 500C   A complete SSB-AM-CW transceiver. Five bands, 520 watts . . . for home station, mobile and portable operation. Voice quality, performance and reliability are in the Swan tradition of being second to none.   *$520.00*

MODEL 350C   An improved version of the classic Model 350. An SSB-CW-AM transceiver, featuring 5 bands, 520 watts SSB P.E.P. input. Ideal for home station, mobile or portable operation. Dependable and loaded with worthwhile features.   *$420.00*

MODEL 250C   The newest member of the Swan family. A full 6 meter SSB-AM-CW transceiver. 240 watts P.E.P. input, selectable sideband, built-in 250 kc calibrator . . . plus many more worth-while features.   *$420.00*

MODEL TV-2   2 meter single sideband, 144-148 mc 240 watts P.E.P. input. The new Swan TV-2 transverter is a superb receiving and transmitting converter for the 2 meter band, designed to operate with most Swan transceivers.   *$295.00*

Henry Radio and Swan, long a great team and old time friends of Hams the world over, presents a choice of transceivers to fill the heart of any amateur with joy. There is no better time to buy than now and, of course, the very best place to shop is Henry Radio. At Henry Radio you can compare makes and models from exceptionally large stocks. You can trade in your old equipment and take advantage of our generous terms.

Exports! Of course, Henry Radio makes it simple for amateurs around the world to own the finest American radio equipment. Write for details.

Henry Radio Stores

CALL DIRECT . . . USE AREA CODE

Butler, Missouri, 64730	816 679-3127
11240 W. Olympic, Los Angeles, Calif., 90064	213 477-6701
931 N. Euclid, Anaheim, Calif., 92801	714 772-9200

"World's Largest Distributor of Amateur Radio Equipment"

When QRM Gets Tough
Choose
The Only
Microphone
With
Backbone!

**ELECTRO-VOICE
MODEL 676
DYNAMIC CARDIOID**

The backbone of the Electro-Voice Model 676 is no mere decoration. It's visible proof of the most exciting idea in directional microphones—Continuously Variable-D (CV-D)™.

Here's how it works. We attach a very special tapered tube to the back of the microphone element. This tube automatically varies in effective length with frequency. It's a long tube for lows—a short tube for highs. All this with no moving parts! The tube is always optimum length to most effectively cancel sound arriving from the back of the microphone, regardless of frequency.

This ingenious solution* is years ahead of the common fixed-path design found in most cardioid microphones. It means you pick up less noise and room reverberation, ensuring a crisp signal and optimum vox performance. It also is less sensitive to wind and shock—ideal for field days! There is almost no "proximity effect"... no boosted bass when you must operate extra close.

Long life and peak-free response are guaranteed by the exclusive E-V Acoustalloy® diaphragm. And the 676

has unusually high output for a microphone so small. Of course you get both 150-ohm and Hi-Z outputs, plus high efficiency dust, pop, and magnetic filters—indeed, all of the hallmarks of Electro-Voice design that have made E-V a leader for years.

But that's not all. The 676 has an exclusive bass control switch built in. Choose flat response (from 40 to 15,000 cps) or tilt off bass 5 or 10 db at 100 cps to eliminate power-robbing lows that reduce efficiency and lower intelligibility. You'll be amazed at the reports of improved audio you'll get when you switch to the E-V676.

Visit your E-V distributor to see this remarkable new microphone today. And when difficult QRM must be faced squarely, stand up and fight back with the microphone with a backbone (and CV-D)—the new Electro-Voice Model 676 dynamic cardioid!

Model 676 Satin Chrome or TV grey, $89.00 list; in Gold, $94.50 list. Shown on Model 420 Desk Stand, $21.00 list. Model 674 identical except stud-mounted with On-Off switch, $89.00 list. (Less normal trade discounts.)

ELECTRO-VOICE, INC.
Dept. 192LM, 631 Cecil Street
Buchanan, Michigan 49107

*Pat. No. 3,115,207

CPC Antenna Ratings are in Accordance with

EIA Standard RS 329

Test Procedures!

The Standard — adopted by the Electronic Industries Assn. for specific methods of gain, pattern and VSWR determination — provides uniform test procedure for all manufacturers of base station antennas.

Each CPC antenna, rated per EIA Standards, is catalogued "RS 329"—your assurance of performance to specifications!

RS 329

"There's no question about the specifications when you see RS 329!"

DUPLEXERS (144-174 MC)*

100 db Isolation for 3 Mc or Greater Separation

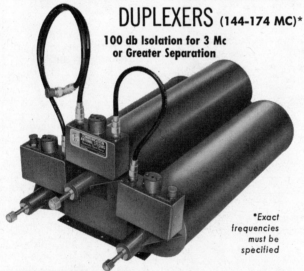

*Exact frequencies must be specified

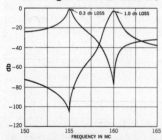

Cat. No. 499-509 Duplexer for use in the 144-174 Mc range consists of three Cat. No. 500-509 Cavities each with a special CPC developed notching circuit attached. Two cavities and notching circuit assemblies are used on the receiver side of the Duplexer, and a single cavity and notching circuit is used in the transmitter side. The Duplexer is supplied with mounting brackets which allow the unit to be mounted on either a vertical or horizontal surface. It weighs 33 lbs. and is 12⅞" deep by 16⅞" wide by 33" long. Response curves for a typical Cat. No. 499-509 Duplexer are shown at left.

5.25 dbd GAIN!

Super Stationmaster Base Station Antenna

Cat. No. 220-509 is a broadband, lightweight antenna with a measured omnidirectional gain of 5.25 db across its specified bandwidth. Only three antennas are required to cover the 150-174 Mc band, however, the Super Stationmaster is available in various overlapping ranges — 150-159 Mc, 155-164 Mc, 157-166 Mc, 160-169 Mc and 165-174 Mc. A wide-band heavy-duty unit, it provides much greater lightning protection than heretofore available in an antenna of this type.

Specifications

Nominal Input Impedance	**50 Ohms**
VSWR	**1.5:1**
Bandwidth	**9.0 Mc**
Maximum Power Input	**500 Watts**
Omnidirectional Gain	**5.25 db**
Vertical Beam Width	**18°**
Lightning Protection	**Direct Ground**
Rated Wind Velocity	**100 MPH**
Lateral Thrust at Rated Wind	**79 lbs.**
Bending Moment 1" below Ground Plane at Rated Wind	**251 ft. lbs.**
Radiating Element Material	**Copper**
Element Housing Material	**Fiberglas**
Weight	**30 lbs.**

Communication Products Company

P D ELECTRONICS

DIVISION OF **PHELPS DODGE** ELECTRONIC PRODUCTS CORPORATION

MARLBORO, NEW JERSEY 07746 — Telephone: (201) 462-1880
LOS ANGELES, CALIFORNIA 90065 — Telephone: (213) 245-1143

18

RCA has all-new FCC commercial license training

Get your license — or your money back!

Now RCA Institutes Home Study Training has the FCC License preparation material you've been looking for—all-new, both the training you need, and the up-to-date methods you use at home—at your own speed—to train for the license you want!

2 Convenient Payment Plans—You can pay for lessons as you order them, or take advantage of easy monthly payment plan. Choose the FCC License you're interested in—third, second or first phone. Take the course for the license you choose. If you need basic material first, apply for the complete License Training Program.

SPECIAL TO AMATEURS. This course—while designed for Commercial license qualification—contains much of the new material called for by FCC Docket 15928—advanced and extra class you'll want to qualify for before November of 1969. QRX until you get the information.

Mail coupon today for full details and a 64-page booklet telling you how RCA Institutes Home Training can show you the way to a new career—higher income—and your FCC License.

19

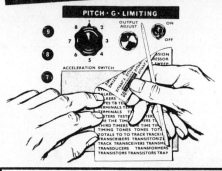

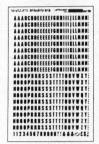

~REALISTIC~ DX-150 HAM/SWL SSB/CW RECEIVER

Get more receiver than you pay for: 11 front panel controls, 12¼″ slide-rule dial in five colors, continuous coverage from 535 KHz to 30 MHz including illuminated electrical bandspread for 160-10 meters (ham and CB), separate logging scale, sensitivity good to 0.5μV at 30 MHz. Standard AM reception, a product detector for SSB/CW, fast and slow AVC, variable pitch BFO, cascade RF stage, noise limiting in both the IF and audio stages, Zener stabilized so usual warm-up drift is virtually absent, OTL audio, illuminated "S" meter, built-in monitor speaker plus front panel jack for external (optional) matching speaker. Uses *over 30 semiconductors* — no tubes, no nuvistors — it's 100% solid state! Obsoletes tube receivers and their warm-up delay, banishes dependence on house current to stay in operation. If current fails or isn't available, the DX-150 runs up to 100 hours on 8 "D" cells. It will operate from a car's cigarette lighter or any 12 VDC negative ground mobile or base source. A 117 VAC power supply is built in, of course. The DX-150 is a husky brute: 14¼ x 9¼ x 6½″ with a massive brushed aluminum extruded front panel, solid metal knobs, grey metal cabinet, 14 pounds of quality. **119⁹⁵**

...it's the one with the

GUTS!

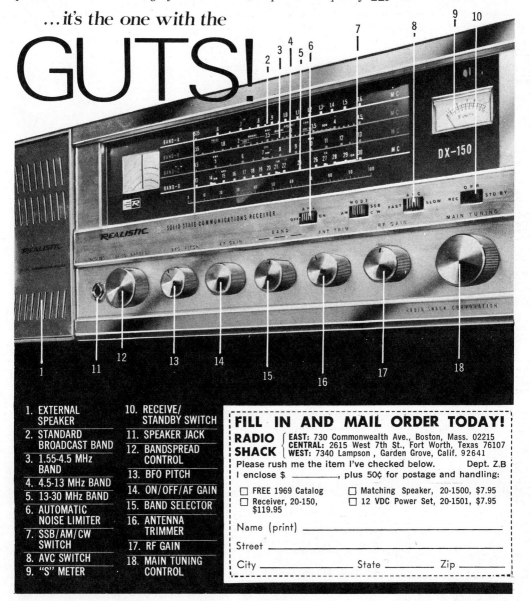

1. EXTERNAL SPEAKER
2. STANDARD BROADCAST BAND
3. 1.55-4.5 MHz BAND
4. 4.5-13 MHz BAND
5. 13-30 MHz BAND
6. AUTOMATIC NOISE LIMITER
7. SSB/AM/CW SWITCH
8. AVC SWITCH
9. "S" METER
10. RECEIVE/ STANDBY SWITCH
11. SPEAKER JACK
12. BANDSPREAD CONTROL
13. BFO PITCH
14. ON/OFF/AF GAIN
15. BAND SELECTOR
16. ANTENNA TRIMMER
17. RF GAIN
18. MAIN TUNING CONTROL

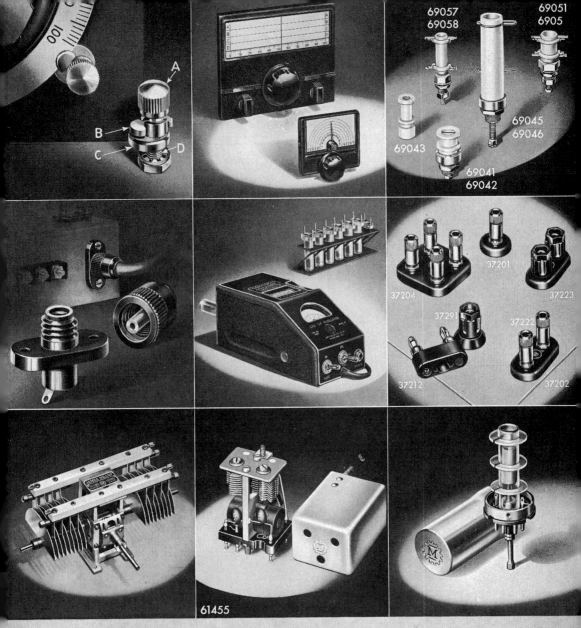

Herewith are illustrated just a few of the many exclusive Millen "Designed for Application" line of MODERN PARTS for MODERN CIRCUITS, which are fully listed and described in our general component parts catalog. A copy is available either through your distributor or direct from any of our district offices, or the factory.

JAMES MILLEN MFG. CO., INC.
150 EXCHANGE ST.   MALDEN, MASSACHUSETTS

You can earn more money if you get a Government FCC License

...and here's our famous CIE Warranty that you <u>will</u> get your License if you study with us at home

NOT SATISFIED with your present income? The most practical thing you can do about it is add to your Electronics know-how, pass the FCC exam and get your Government License.

The demand for licensed men is enormous. Today there are over a million licensed broadcast installations and mobile transmitters on the air, and the number is growing constantly. And according to Federal Law, no one is permitted to operate or service such equipment without a Government FCC License or without being under the direct supervision of a licensed operator.

This has resulted in a gold mine of new business for licensed service technicians. A typical mobile radio service contract pays an average of about $100 a month. It's possible for one trained technician to maintain eight to ten such mobile systems. Some men cover as many as fifteen systems, each with perhaps a dozen units.

Opportunities in Plants

And there are other exciting opportunities in the aerospace industry, electronics manufacturing, telephone companies, and plants operated by electronic automation. Inside industrial plants like these, it's the licensed technician who is always considered first for promotion and in-plant training programs. The reason is simple. Passing the Federal Government's FCC exam and getting your License is widely accepted proof that you know the fundamentals of Electronics.

So why doesn't everybody who "tinkers" with electronic components get an FCC License and start cleaning up?

The answer: it's not that simple. The Government's licensing exam is tough. In fact, an average of two out of every three men who take the FCC exam fail.

There is one way, however, of being pretty certain that you will pass the FCC exam. That's to take one of the FCC home study courses offered by the Cleveland Institute of Electronics.

CIE courses are so effective that better than 9 out of every 10 CIE graduates who take the exam pass it. That's why we can afford to back our courses with the iron-clad Warranty shown above: you get your FCC License or your money back.

Mail Coupon for Two Free Books

Want to know more? Send the coupon below for free copies of our school catalog, "How To Succeed In Electronics," describing opportunities in Electronics, together with our special booklet, "How To Get A Commercial FCC License." If coupon has been removed, just send your name and address to us.

> **ENROLL UNDER NEW G.I. BILL**
> All CIE courses are available under the new G.I. Bill. If you served on active duty since January 31, 1955, or are in service now, check box in coupon for G.I. Bill information.

CIE **Cleveland Institute of Electronics**
1776 East 17th Street, Cleveland, Ohio 44114

Matt Stuczynski, Senior Transmitter Operator, Radio Station WBOE: "I give CIE credit for my First Class Commercial FCC License. Even though I had only six weeks of high school algebra, CIE's lessons made Electronics easy. I now have a good job in studio operation, transmitting, proof of performance, equipment servicing...and am on my way up."

Thomas E. Miller, Jr., Engineer, Indiana Bell Telephone Company: "I completed my CIE course and passed my FCC exam while in the Navy. On my discharge, I was swamped with job offers from all over the country. My only problem was to pick the best one, and I did—engineer with Indiana Bell Telephone. CIE made the difference between just a job and a management position."

something different

A state-of-the-art magazine written so **you** can understand it.

For your sample copy and full details write

HAM RADIO · Greenville, N. H. 03048

also the exclusive North American distributor for
RADIO SOCIETY OF GREAT BRITAIN PUBLICATIONS

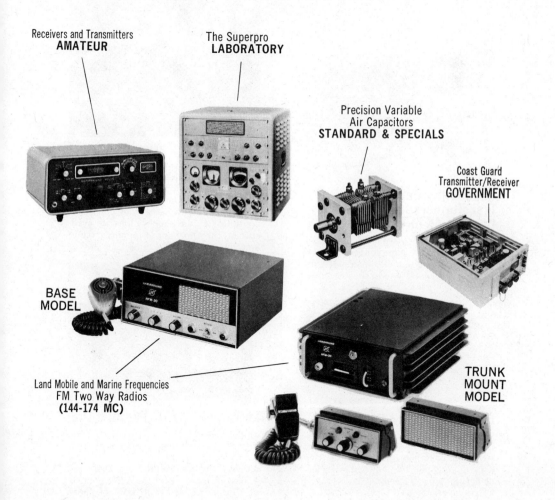

Look for this RF coil rack at your local distributor

... If he doesn't have one, ask him to call his friendly Miller man right away. (Nobody likes to feel left out.)

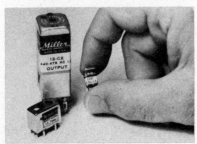

Communications IF Transformers from 50 kHz through 45 mHz

Get top performance when you build your receiver. Select the most appropriate tube or transistor type IF transformers for your set from the widest line in the electronic industry.

Prè-tuned solid state IF strip

Two-stage 455 kHz IF strip gives 8 kHz selectivity at 6 db when used with model 8901-B input IF transformer; can be used without input transformer when less selectivity is acceptable; gain 45-50 db.
8902-B IF Strip @ $4.75.
8901-B Input Transformer @ $2.10.
Both units $5.75 when ordered as kit 8903-B.

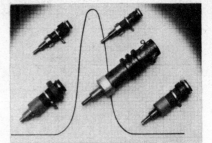

Resinite Adjustable RF Coils

Moderately priced resinite coils are used frequently for construction projects in amateur and experimenter publications.

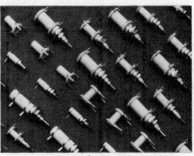

Ceramic Coil Forms

Ceramic coil forms in .205", .260", .375" and .500" diameters are now stocked in depth for applications in frequency ranges between 50 kHz and 300 mHz. Bushing mounted forms with fiberglass collars for high "Q"/low loss applications are available in 2-terminal and 4-terminal configurations.

Low Cost 6:1/36:1 Vernier Dial

Model MD-4 vernier dial permits fast tuning at 6 to 1 ratio over entire dial range with fine tuning at 36 to 1 ratio over any 6-division portion of the scale. Dial has 4 scales; measures $4^7/_8$"Wx$3^3/_4$"H; escutcheon extends only $1/_8$" in front of panel; net price $7.50.

Write for full line catalog.

J.W. MILLER COMPANY
5917 SOUTH MAIN STREET ▪ LOS ANGELES, CALIFORNIA 90003

AVAILABLE NATIONWIDE FROM DISTRIBUTORS AND MAIL ORDER HOUSES

Take the 5894 out of the Amperex line of twin tetrodes and what have you got...

what have you got?

You've got the best developed, best manufactured, best proven line of indirectly-heated push-pull tetrodes in the world!

You've got the kind of tube quality, uniformity and applications assistance that only the oldest and biggest producer of vehicular communications types can offer!

You've even got new tetrodes on the way that'll revolutionize your design thinking as completely as the 5894 already has.

So you've got everything except the 5894. Isn't it lucky you can get that from Amperex, too.

But come to think of it you always could. We developed the 5894 in the first place, you know.

To get the word on Amperex Indirectly-Heated Twin-Tetrodes for your special vehicular communications application, wire or write:

Amperex Electronic Corporation, Tube Division, Hicksville, L. I., N. Y. 11802.

TYPICAL OPERATING CONDITION

Tube Type	Freq. (Mc.)	Approx. Drive Power (Watts)	Approx. Load Power Output (Watts)
5894	250	6	96
	470	3	33
6252	200	2	67
6360	175	1.0	16
6907	470	3.0	24
6939	470	1.2	6.0
7377	470	1.4	12.5
	960	1.5	5.0
7854	175	3.5	163
8458	175	1.2	30

Amperex®

TOMORROW'S THINKING IN TODAY'S PRODUCTS

27

better sent...
better received
with Belden wire and cable
...easy to use packaged lengths.

Antenna Rotor Cables
Sturdy, flexible, plastic insulated cable for rotor applications. Color coded. Chrome, vinyl plastic jacket resists sun and aging.

Shielded Hook-Up and Grid Wire
Provide most effective TVI suppression. Vinyl insulated with tinned copper braid shield. Available from 24 AWG to 12 AWG.

Ham Transmission Lines—Parallel Type
Uniform quality control provides uniform impedance. Brown polyethylene for best weather resistance and lowest losses.

Power Supply Cables
Excellent mechanical and electrical characteristics for long service life. Special jacket offers maximum resistance to abrasion and ozone. Use as power supply cords and interconnecting cables. Ideal for remote control circuits, special press-to-talk microphone circuits, and other applications.

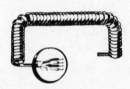

Coiled Microphone Cable
Provides low impedance for mobile microphone applications. Neoprene jacket remains flexible at low temperatures. Available with or without shielded conductors.

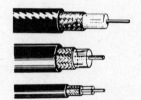

Ham Transmission Lines—RG/U Type
Designed for lowest losses, longer service life, and maximum dependability. Cables are essentially flat with no peaks in attenuation to reduce signal on either high or low frequencies.

FOR FULL INFORMATION CONTACT YOUR BELDEN ELECTRONIC DISTRIBUTOR
The Belden line gives you maximum efficiency with lowest losses under all conditions of operation. There's a Belden wire or cable to meet every ham transmitting and receiving need. Shown here is only a small portion of this complete line.

8-7-6A

BELDEN

BELDEN CORPORATION • P. O. BOX 5070-A, CHICAGO, ILLINOIS 60680

STILL
WE ∧ DON'T MAKE
AMATEUR RADIO EQUIPMENT
(But our basic interest
hasn't changed)

Like you, we of Communication Products Department of General Electric are vitally interested in the field of communications.

General Electric started the two-way radio business. And, as the world's largest electronics and electrical equipment manufacturer, we have left no stone unturned to maintain our leadership in the development of communications equipment and systems.

We make communications equipment for the government, industry and individuals. Microwave systems, power line carrier, and two-way radios. GE has a full line of professional communications equipment for almost any situation.

Where's it used? Just about everywhere. You'll find it in Viet Nam, in the oil fields of Iran, or in your home town. And to back it up, General Electric offers fast, efficient service around the world.

So, even though we still don't make amateur radio equipment, keep us in mind. Maybe you buy communication equipment in your business. Or, perhaps you would like to join the many other radio amateurs on the General Electric team now working for General Electric in Lynchburg, Va. and around the world. In either case, direct your inquiry to General Electric Co., Communication Products Dept., Section 317, Lynchburg, Virginia.

GENERAL GE **ELECTRIC**

472-06

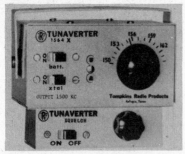

EARN BIG MONEY

IN MOBILE-RADIO MAINTENANCE

Get into this rapidly growing field with 2nd Class Ticket and

LAMPKIN MOBILE-SERVICE METERS

LAMPKIN 105-B MICROMETER FREQUENCY METER

FREQUENCY RANGE on local transmitters 0.1 to 175 MHz. ACCURACY guaranteed better than 0.001%. Dial calibrations for virtually EVERY mobile-radio channel available at less than 3c each — printed by computer. DIAL 4" diameter, 40 turns, totals 8000 divisions spread over 42 feet — resettable better than 3 parts per million. CRYSTAL thermometer on panel automatically indicates dial checkpoint. SIGNAL GENERATOR—a pinpoint CW source for mobile-receiver final alignment.

LAMPKIN 205-A FM MODULATION METER

FREQUENCY RANGE — continuous 25 MHz. to 500 MHz. No coils to change. PEAK FM swing shows directly on indicating meter — ranges to 1.25, 2.5, 12.5 and 25 KHz., positive or negative — for selective-calling systems as well as for voice modulation. VISUAL picture of transmitter modulation — connect your shop 'scope to the output jack. PORTABLE — just a two-finger load. No charts or tables.

LAMPKIN EQUIPMENT IS RELIABLE — INSTRUMENTS 5, 10, 20 YEARS OLD ARE MAINSTAYS FOR THOUSANDS OF SHOPS. PROMPT, REASONABLE, DIRECT FACTORY SERVICE.

THE LAMPKIN FREQUENCY METER IS CORRECTABLE VERSUS WWV. ALL QUARTZ CRYSTALS WILL AGE IN FREQUENCY. THE FCC SAYS WWV IS THE FINAL AUTHORITY FOR FREQUENCY MEASUREMENTS.

FOR 0.0001% ACCURACY USE ACCESSORY PPM METER WITH THE 105-B

FREE BOOKLET—with facts and figures—send for "HOW TO MAKE MONEY IN MOBILE-RADIO MAINTENANCE".

MAIL COUPON TODAY!

LAMPKIN LABORATORIES, INC.
BRADENTON, FLORIDA

Measurements Section
Lampkin Laboratories, Inc.
Bradenton, Florida 33505

11

At no obligation to me, please send

☐ "How To Make Money in Mobile-Radio Maintenance!"

☐ Technical data and prices on Lampkin Meters

Name _____

Address _____

City _____ State _____ Zip _____

HOWARD W. SAMS BOOKS FOR THE AMATEUR

Advanced & Extra-Class Amateur License Handbook
by Howard S. Pyle, W7OE. Provides all the information you need to obtain your advanced—or extra-class license. Makes preparation for these top licenses far easier for present holders of lower licenses. Includes sample questions for each exam. 192 pages.
20649, *only*.................................$3.95

General-Class Amateur License Handbook
by Howard S. Pyle, W7OE. A complete guide, including typical FCC test questions and answers, to help you prepare for the Technician, Conditional, or General-Class radio exam. 144 pages. 20639, *only*......$3.25

Building Your Amateur Radio Novice Station
by Howard S. Pyle, W7OE. Provides complete, easy-to-follow construction details for building an inexpensive transmitter and receiver, plus several valuable accessory items, for Novice or General Class operation. 128 pages. 20050, *only*.................................$3.75

International Code Training System
by International Teaching Systems, Inc. Special programmed charts and 33⅓-rpm recordings help you receive at 2-3 wpm in just a few minutes. You'll be receiving and sending up to 22 wpm with less than an hour of recorded instruction. 96 pages; 6 record sides.
20138, *only*.................................$7.50

Amateur Radio Construction Projects
by Charles Caringella, W6NJV. Shows how to build novice transmitters, converters, all-band phone-cw transmitter, and others. Provides detailed, easy-to-follow building and operating instructions. 136 pages.
20045, *only*.................................$3.25

Ham Antenna Construction Projects (2nd Ed.)
by J. A. Stanley. Practical guide to custom-building your own antennas; describes all types of arrays, installation, tuning up and testing; shows you how to make the best use of antenna power. 160 pages.
20654, *only*.................................$3.95

101 Easy Ham Radio Projects
by Robert M. Brown & Tom Kneitel. A selection of easy-to-build, inexpensive circuits for a variety of worthwhile ham devices. Provides brief descriptions, construction hints, diagrams, and parts lists; includes substitution guide appendix. 160 pages. 20674, *only*.........$3.95

Transistor Transmitters for the Amateur
by Donald L. Stoner, W6TNS. Shows how to build solid-state crystal checker/calibrator, low-power cw xmitter and eight other transistorized projects. 128 pages.
20450, *only*.................................$3.25

So You Want to Be a Ham (4th Ed.)
by Robert Hertzberg, W2DJJ. Completely revised to include information on the incentive licensing. This is the book to have to learn about amateur radio, ham equipment, operating procedures, and how to pass the FCC exam. 192 pages. 20607, *only*.................$4.50

ABC's of Ham Radio (3rd Ed.)
by Howard S. Pyle, W7OE. Enlarged and updated to include all the study material required to obtain the novice-class license. Covers latest FCC regulations, including new incentive licensing provisions. 144 pages. 20638, *only*.................................$2.95

Amateur Radio Mobile Handbook
by Charles Caringella, W6NJV. Provides complete information for going mobile. Explains circuitry and construction of commercially built mobile amateur equipment. Shows how to build mobile converters, transmitters, transceivers, and modulators, etc. 176 pages.
20035, *only*.................................$3.50

Amateur Radio Station Manual
The ideal log book designed the way hams want it. Provides sheets for entering all transmissions, frequently worked stations, complete operating records; includes special schedules, network data, prefix listings for all countries. 128 pages; comb-bound.
20049, *only*.................................$3.95

Amateur Radio Antennas (2nd Ed.)
by Harry D. Hooton, W6TYH. Provides full details on theory, design, construction, and application of antennas. Tells how to select the best antenna system for optimum performance. 176 pages. 20611, *only*....$3.95

Practical Ham Radio Projects
by Charles Caringella, W6NJV. Includes circuit diagrams, parts lists, and detailed instructions for building 12 unique and useful ham shack devices at the lowest possible cost (no item exceeds $50). 128 pages.
20042, *only*.................................$2.95

Transistorized Amateur Radio Projects
by Charles Caringella, W6NJV. Presents a complete selection of transistorized ham radio construction projects for the beginner as well as advanced amateur. Includes several printed-circuit board projects and the negatives for etching them. 140 pages.
20570, *only*.................................$3.50

**SAMS and E & E books are available
from your Electronics Parts Distributor**

Outstanding EDITOR & ENGINEERS books from SAMS

17TH EDITION OF THE FAMOUS
Radio Handbook
Tells how to design, build, and operate latest types of amateur transmitters, receivers, transceivers, and amplifiers. Provides extensive, simplified theory on practically every phase of radio. All original data, up-to-date, complete, 848 pages.
EE-167, *only*.................................$12.95

The VHF Amateur
by Robert M. Brown, K2ZSQ/W9HBF. Completely updated handbook incorporating the finest material on vital vhf subjects from the rare back issues of the famous *VHF Magazine*, plus new data of great interest to both old and new vhf men. 160 pages.
EE-65060, *only*.................................$4.50

**Commercial Radiotelephone License
Q&A Study Guide**
by Woodrow Smith & Robert Welborn. Invaluable preparation for the exams. Questions cover first four elements of the radiotelephone license exam. Answers are detailed and comprehensive. 272 pages.
EE-031, *only*.................................$6.95

Single Sideband: Theory and Practice
by Harry D. Hooton, W6TYH. The one-source guide to ssb, covering origin and principles, derivation of ssb signals, carrier-suppression techniques, sideband selection, and a complete analysis of ssb equipment. 388 pages. EE-350, *only*.................................$6.95

Transistor Radio Handbook
by Donald L. Stoner, W6TNS & Lester A. Earnshaw, ZL1AAX. Covers the use of transistorized communications equipment for amateur and commercial applications. Provides simplified theory, plus practical construction projects for solid-state equipment. 180 pages.
EE-044, *only*.................................$5.00

World-Wide Electronic Tube Data
Radio Tubes Vade-Mecum. 20th Ed. (1965-67). Characteristics and base connections of all existing tubes made in all countries. 534 pages. EE-504.......$11.00

Equivalent Radio Tubes Vade-Mecum. 19th Ed. (1963-65). Shows tube substitutions; over 43,900 comparisons; also military tubes of 7 nations. 300 pages.
EE-493 ....$9.00

TV & Special Tubes Vade-Mecum. 18th Ed. (1962-64). Characteristics and base connections of picture, CR, and other special-purpose tubes used in all countries. 292 pages. EE-482.................................$9.00

 HOWARD W. SAMS & CO., INC.
4300 W. 62nd St., Indianapolis, Ind. 46268

32

Shurite® ..STILL THE HAMS' *NO. 1 CHOICE*

Model 850 Series

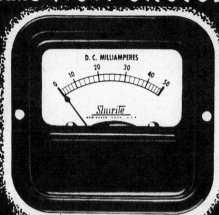

Model 950 Series

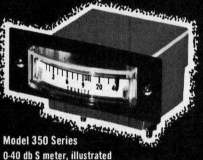

Model 350 Series
0-40 db S meter, illustrated

Select the right meter from 260 catalog types. For instance, 0-1 DC Milliammeter at left, above, has 1000 ohms internal resistance with bridge type design to minimize effects of external magnetic forces. Also available with zero adjuster.

All meters shown less than actual size

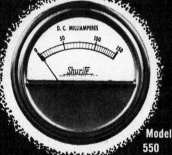

Model 550 Series

HAMS . . . have found these meters a wonderful buy, and year after year have made Shurite their No. 1 choice in its class of panel instrument. . . . For the same reasons these meters are preferred by many Original Equipment Manufacturers:

(1) AMERICAN MADE AND GUARANTEED: Every meter is manufactured in Shurite's spotless new plant by experienced Connecticut workers. Users are protected by a policy of continuing catalogued designs, so that additional meters, now or in the future will match in panel appearance, mechanical details, and electrical values. Backed by Shurite's one year guarantee against defective workmanship and material, a meter in warranty will be promptly repaired or replaced if sent postpaid to the factory with 50¢ handling charge.

(2) ATTRACTIVE CLEAR-PLASTIC OR METAL CASES: Hams are pleased to find a modern, expensive-looking Model 850 as illustrated costs only 10¢ more than an equivalent metal cased meter. Equally good news is the longer, more visible scale arc . . . the removable front . . . the high temperature case material . . . and the availability of zero adjusters on all Model 850 AC and DC ranges. (Mounting hole may be standard 2-5/32" down to 2-1/32".) Metal-cased models 550 and 950 (2-5/32" mounting hole) continue to be popular, especially where matching style, glass front, or severe usage are factors in the application. Zero adjusters are available on all DC ranges of these models.

(3) CHOICE OF MANY TYPES: AC and DC Ammeters, AC and DC Milliammeters, AC and DC Volt-

meters, new 0-500 DC Microammeters, DC Resistance Meters, VU, S, and new Field Strength Meters. AC meters are double-vane repulsion type with jeweled bearing. DC are polarized-vane solenoid type, moving magnet construction, or bridge-type design. Accuracy is well within ±5%; repeatability, 1% or less. Ask for Catalog 47A covering all types, and Bulletin VUS-67 with application notes on VU, S, and Field Strength Meters.

(4) EDGEWISE METERS: Model 350, made with new high-temperature plastic material, provides an ideal way to save panel space and dress up appearance. The clear jewel-like front gathers light for easy reading of the dial. Rectangular mounting hole of the meter itself is 1-31/32" x 17/32" and a metal escutcheon plate 2-3/8" x 7/8" is supplied to insure an easy, neat installation.

(5) WIDELY AVAILABLE: These American made meters are stocked by many leading electronic parts distributors for prompt deliveries. If by any chance, you do not find the meter you need, get in touch with the factory.

(6) REASONABLE PRICES:* Typical of the exceptional values are the meters illustrated, 0-50 DC Ma, $2.75 in the 550 or 950 Series, $2.85 in the 850 Series; 0-40 db S Meter in the 350 Series, $3.90; 0-1 DC Ma above without zero adjuster, $4.25; with zero adjuster, $4.60. 0-150 AC Volts, $4.55 in the 550 or 950 Series. Savings made possible by large quantity production are reflected in the reasonable prices.

*NOTE — Prices subject to change . . .

ACCEPT NO SUBSTITUTES—YOU'LL DO BETTER WITH SHURITE

SHURITE METERS

P.O. Box 1818, New Haven, Conn. 06508.

ARRL
PUBLICATIONS

Storehouses

of

Information

for:

- **Novices**

- **Old Timers**

- **Students**

- **Engineers**

**Supplies
for the
Active Amateur**

QST Since 1915 QST has been the bible of Amateur Radio. It faithfully reports each month the rapid developments which make Amateur Radio so intriguing. QST treats equipment, practices, construction and design. It is essential to the well-being of any radio amateur. QST goes to every member of the American Radio Relay League. Membership: $6.50 per year in the U.S.A., Possessions or Canada, $7.00 Elsewhere, U.S. funds. (See page 22 for application blank.)

THE RADIO AMATEUR'S V.H.F. MANUAL A thorough treatment of v.h.f. Covers receiving and transmitting principles, techniques and construction. Antenna and feed system design, construction and adjustment. Microwaves. Test equipment, construction and use. Interference, causes and cures. V.h.f. hints and kinks. Emphasis throughout is on tried and tested equipment and practice. A book about things that work and the ideas behind them. $2.50 U.S.A., $3.00 Elsewhere.

A COURSE IN RADIO FUNDAMENTALS This is a study guide and laboratory manual based on The Radio Amateur's Handbook. It describes in detail 40 experiments with simple apparatus giving a complete practical knowledge of radio theory and design. $1.00 U.S.A., $1.25 Elsewhere.

UNDERSTANDING AMATEUR RADIO Written for the beginner, it explains in simple language the elementary principles of electronic and radio circuits, tells how transmitters, receivers and antennas work, and includes complete how-to-build-it information on low-cost gear—receivers, phone and code transmitters up to 150 watts, v.h.f., measurements, and easy to build antenna systems. A "must" guide for the newcomer in setting up and operating his station. $2.50 U.S.A., $3.00 Elsewhere.

HOW TO BECOME A RADIO AMATEUR The standard elementary guide for the prospective amateur. Tells what amateur radio is, and how to get started. Special attention is given the needs of the Novice class licensee. It features equipment which is simple in construction, yet with a high degree of flexibility; this permits the various units to fit into the more elaborate station layouts, which inevitably result as the amateur progresses. $1.00.

THE RADIO AMATEUR'S LICENSE MANUAL Tells how to get your amateur radio license. In addition to a large amount of general information, it contains typical questions and answers such as are asked in the government examinations. If you know the answers to the questions in this book, you can pass the examinations without trouble. $1.00.

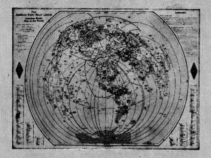

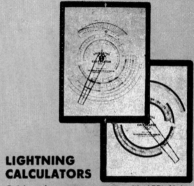

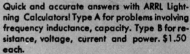

ARRL WORLD MAP

Printed in eight colors on heavy map paper with countries clearly outlined. Continental boundaries, time zones, amateur prefixes, plainly marked. Size: 30 x 40 inches. $2.00.

LIGHTNING CALCULATORS

Quick and accurate answers with ARRL Lightning Calculators! Type A for problems involving frequency inductance, capacity. Type B for resistance, voltage, current and power. $1.50 each.

LEARNING THE RADIO TELEGRAPH CODE Designed to train students to handle code skillfully and with precision, both in sending and receiving. Practice material is included for classwork as well as for home study. Excellent for the student who does not have the help of an experienced operator or access to a code machine. 50¢.

THE ARRL ANTENNA BOOK A comprehensive manual of antenna design and construction. Both the theory and the practice of all types of antennas used by the amateur, from simple doublets to multi-element rotaries, long wires, rhomboids, vees, mobile whips, v.h.f. systems, etc. Feed systems and their adjustment. The most comprehensive and reliable information ever published on the subject. $2.50 U.S.A., $3.00 Elsewhere.

SINGLE SIDEBAND FOR THE RADIO AMATEUR A digest of the best s.s.b. articles from QST. The newcomer to Single Sideband as well as the experienced s.s.b. user will find it indispensable. Includes discussions of theory and practical how-to-build-it descriptions of equipment. Covers both reception and transmission. $2.50 U.S.A., $3.00 Elsewhere.

THE MOBILE MANUAL FOR RADIO AMATEURS A collection of informative articles for the mobile amateur. Describes receivers, transmitters, antennas and power supplies, gives particular attention to the special problems encountered in the installation and operation of mobile stations. $2.50 U.S.A., $3.00 Elsewhere.

HINTS AND KINKS An amateur must be resourceful and also a good thinker. He must be able to make a small amount of money do a great deal for him. This book is a compilation of hundreds of good ideas which amateurs have found helpful. $1 U.S.A., $1.25 Elsewhere.

THE RADIO AMATEUR'S OPERATING MANUAL A ready reference source and guide for the amateur who wishes to brush-up on his operating procedures. Includes chapters on every operating aspect of amateur radio; NTS, RACES, ARPSC, AREC, ARRL etc. A must for the amateur who prides himself on good operating procedures. $1.50 U.S.A., $1.75 Elsewhere.

SUPPLIES FOR THE ACTIVE AMATEUR

ARRL offers many supplies for the active amateur. They are "must" items for the amateur who wishes a neat and organized operating position. ARRL supplies include: Type A and Type B calculators, World Map, Log Books, Message Blanks, and membership stationery.

QST BINDERS

No need to let your copies of QST rest in a disordered pile. A QST binder will keep them neat and orderly. Each holds a one-year file. $3.00 (available in U.S. and Possessions only).

SUPPLIES

Active amateurs need these supplies: ARRL Logbook, 50¢ U.S.A., 60¢ elsewhere. Minilog, 30¢ U.S.A., 35¢ elsewhere. Radiogram blanks, 35¢ per pad postpaid. Message delivery cards, 7¢ each stamped. 3¢ each unstamped. Members' stationery, 100 sheets $1.50; 250 sheets $3.00; 500 sheets $4.50

AMERICAN RADIO RELAY LEAGUE

Administrative Headquarters: Newington, Connecticut, U. S. A.

........................19....

AMERICAN RADIO RELAY LEAGUE,
Newington, Conn., U. S. A. 06111

Being genuinely interested in Amateur Radio, I hereby apply for membership* in the American Radio Relay League. I enclose remittance ($6.50 per year in the U. S. or Canada, $7.00 per year elsewhere, U. S. funds) in payment of dues for ....year(s), including subscription to *QST* for the same period. Please begin *QST* with the .... issue. Amount enclosed: $................................

The call of my station is................................

The class of my operator's license is ....

I belong to the following radio societies...................

....

Send Membership Certificate ☐   or Membership Card ☐

....
Name

....
Address

....
City, State, Zip Code

A bona fide interest in amateur radio is the only essential requirement, but full voting membership is granted only to licensed radio amateurs of the United States and Canada. Therefore, if you have a license, please be sure to indicate it above.

*Membership is available only to individuals. Life Membership is granted to Full Members for $130. Write the Secretary for details.

The subscription rate of *QST* to libraries, companies, laboratories and other organizations is $7.50 per year in the United States, Possessions and Canada, $8.00 elsewhere.

LET DOW-KEY HELP SOLVE YOUR ANTENNA SWITCHING PROBLEMS . . .

SP6T MANUAL 78-0604

SPDT REMOTE 115V ac 60-262842

SP6T REMOTE 115V ac 71-260401

SERIES 78 The series 78 coaxial switches are manually operated with true coaxial switching members (not wafer switches). They are offered in 2, 3, 4 & 6 position (illustrated) types, plus a transfer or crossover and DPDT. The useful frequency range is 0-1 Ghz except 500 Mhz using UHF connectors. The unused positions are open circuited or non-shorting. Also available with other type connectors such as N, BNC, TNC or C.

SERIES 60 The series 60 are remote operated, of rugged construction and designed for low-level to 1 KW use. The unit illustrated is equipped with a special high isolation connector ("G" type) at the normally closed or receive position. This "G" connector increases the isolation to greater than -100db at frequencies up to 500 Mhz, although it reduces the power rating through this connector to 20 watts. This is also available with other type connectors such as BNC, N, TNC,, C or solder terminals.

SERIES 71 High power 6 position switches commonly used for switching antennas, transmitters or receivers at frequencies up to 500 Mhz. The unit is weatherproof and can be mast mounted. The illustrated unit has the unused input shorted to ground. It is also available with a wide range of connectors, different coil voltages and non-shorting contacts or resistor terminations. Each of the six inputs has its own actuating coil for alternate or simultaneous switching.

DOW - KEY COMPANY

ORDERING INFORMATION: Contact your local electronics distributor or Dow-Key sales representative, or write direct to the factory.

2260 INDUSTRIAL LANE • BROOMFIELD, COLORADO 80020
TELEPHONE AREA CODE 303/466-7303 • P. O. BOX 348

LAFAYETTE RADIO ELECTRONICS

400 SERIES 6 AND 10 METER AMATEUR TRANSCEIVERS

SALE! As Low As **109⁹⁵**

COMPLETELY WIRED

Featuring Built-in VFO

99-2579WX HA-460 for 50 to 52 MHz **124.95**
99-2575WX HA-410 for 28.0 to 29.7 MHz **109.95**

• 2E26 Final—20 Watts DC
• Nuvistor RF Amplifier
• Built in 117 VAC and 12 VDC Power Supplies

Consult Our 1969 Catalog #690

FREE! 1969 CATALOG 690

OVER 500 PAGES

Write: Lafayette Radio Electronics Corp., Dept. 58019
P.O. Box 10, Syosset, L.I., N.Y. 11791

40

Learn Code the EASY Way

Beginners, Amateurs and Experts alike recommend the **INSTRUCTOGRAPH,** *to learn code and increase speed.*

Learning the INSTRUCTOGRAPH way will give you a decided advantage in qualifying for Amateur or Commercial examinations, and to increase your words per minute to the standard of an expert. The Government uses a machine in giving examinations.

Motor with adjustable speed and spacing of characters on tapes permit a speed range of from 3 to 40 words per minute. A large variety of tapes are available — elementary, words, messages, plain language and coded groups. Also an "Airways" series for those interested in Aviation.

MAY BE PURCHASED OR RENTED

The INSTRUCTOGRAPH is made in several models to suit your purse and all may be purchased on convenient monthly payments if desired. These machines may also be rented on very reasonable terms and if when renting you should decide to buy the equipment the first three months rental may be applied in full on the purchase price.

ACQUIRING THE CODE

It is a well-known fact that practice and practice alone constitutes ninety per cent of the entire effort necessary to "Acquire the Code," or, in other words, learn telegraphy either wire or wireless. The Instructograph supplies this ninety per cent. It takes the place of an expert operator in teaching the student. It will send slowly at first, and gradually faster and faster, until one is just naturally copying the fastest sending without conscious effort.

BOOK OF INSTRUCTIONS

Other than the practice afforded by the Instructograph, all that is required is well directed practice instruction, and that is just what the Instructograph's "Book of Instructions" does. It supplies the remaining ten per cent necessary to acquire the code. It directs one how to practice to the best advantage, and how to take advantage of the few "short cuts" known to experienced operators, that so materially assists in acquiring the code in the quickest possible time. Therefore, the Instructograph, the tapes, and the book of instructions is everything needed to acquire the code as well as it is possible to acquire it.

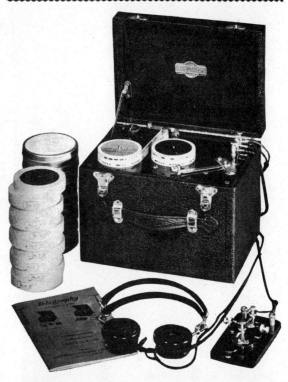

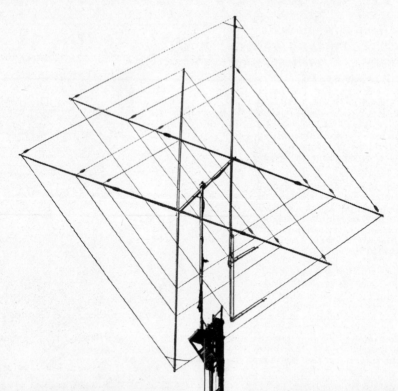

The Quad that made

Hy-Gain's all new Hy-Quad will outdo all other quads because it's engineered to do just that. The Hy-Quad is new, it's superior, it's complete. It's the first quad to have everything.

● The Hy-Quad has all parts including those not supplied by others, like a boom, wire and all hardware.
● The Hy-Quad is constructed of aluminum. Spreaders are broken up at strategic electrical points with cycolac insulators.
● Tri-band 2 element construction with individually resonated elements with no inter-action.
● Hy-Quad requires only one feed line for all three bands.
● Individually tuned gamma matches on each band with Hy-Gain exclusive vertex feed.
● DC grounded elements to drain off precipitation static. Provides low-noise operation.
● Full wave element loops require no tuning stubs, traps, loading coils, or baluns.
● Heavy duty mechanical construction of strong swaged aluminum tubing and die formed spreader-to-boom clamps.

all others obsolete!

● Extra heavy duty universal boom-to-mast bracket that tilts and mounts on any mast 1¼" to 2½" in diameter. So get in Hy-Gear to get a Hy-Quad from the best distributors under the sun—he's the one that stocks Hy-Gain!

Specifications

Overall length of spreaders . . .	305"
Turning radius	13'6"
Weight	42 lbs.
Boom diameter	2"
Boom length	8'
Mast diameter	1¼" to 2½"
Wind survival	100 mph
Input impedance	52 ohms
VSWR	1.2:1 or better at resonance on all bands.
Power	Maximum legal

The Hy-Quad from Hy-Gain

HY-GAIN ELECTRONICS CORPORATION
Highway 6 at Stevens Creek,
Lincoln, Nebraska 65501

 FOR THE STRONGEST SIGNAL UNDER THE SUN!

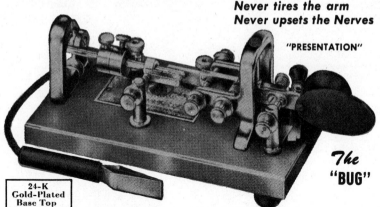
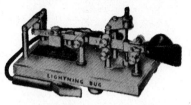

Earn Your
DEGREE IN ELECTRONICS
mostly by correspondence

The Grantham Electronics Degree Program is divided into two main courses — (1) *Electronics Engineering Technology,* which leads to the Associate Degree, and (2) Electronics Engineering, which leads to the Bachelor Degree. The second course is an extension of (or addition to) the first course, both courses together making up the entire degree curriculum.

The Associate Degree Course

The course in Electronics Engineering Technology, leading to the Associate Degree, consists of *six semesters* (or sections) *and* a final two-week class of review and examination. All sections of this curriculum except for #3 are offered *by correspondence.* Section #3 may be taken in residence, or credit for it may be given for at least one year of fulltime experience as an electronics technician. Thus, if you are an electronics technician, you may earn your Associate Degree in Electronics without any resident attendance except for a final two-week period of review and examination.

The Bachelor Degree Course

The curriculum in Electronics Engineering (leading to the Bachelor in Science Degree) includes all of the Associate Degree course and, in addition to that, includes one semester in resident classes at Grantham in Hollywood, and transfer credits in English, History, etc., to be earned at other colleges and transferred to Grantham.

The Grantham educational program in electronics places heavy stress on fundamental concepts of logic and mathematics rather than on superficial manipulative skills. Since these fundamental ideas are largely unfamiliar to many electronics technicians, it is necessary to develop them in a systematic manner, before real advancement is possible.

Grantham's strong-foundation educational program in electronics leads to non-obsolescent skills — to skills based more on reasoning than on merely doing — and leads first to the Associate and then to the Bachelor of Science Degree.

Accreditation and G.I. Bill Approval

Grantham School of Electronics is *accredited* by the Accrediting Commission of the National Home Study Council, is *approved* under the G.I. Bill, and is *authorized* under the laws of the State of California to grant academic degrees.

———

Mail the coupon below for our free Bulletin.

DX-ARRAY
NEW 20 ELEMENT ANTENNAS

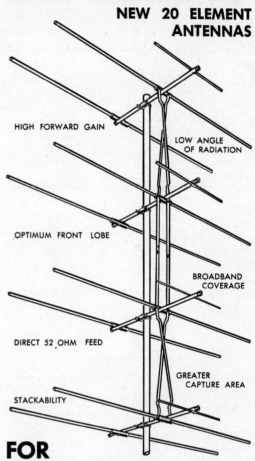

HIGH FORWARD GAIN

LOW ANGLE OF RADIATION

OPTIMUM FRONT LOBE

BROADBAND COVERAGE

DIRECT 52 OHM FEED

GREATER CAPTURE AREA

STACKABILITY

FOR
144 mhz   220 mhz   432 mhz

A breakthrough in VHF/UHF Amateur antennas! The new Cush Craft DX-Arrays combine the best yagi and colinear features into the World's most advanced amateur communication antennas.

Realizing that the antenna is the most important part of your station, Cush Craft engineers have devoted two years of intensive development and testing to perfect DX-Array. DX-Arrays have already established new records in Dx-ing and moonbounce programs.

Whatever your interest may be, ragchewing, contests, DX, or moonbounce, get in on the excitement of VHF hamming today with DX-Array.

DX-120 — 144 mhz $29.50
DX-220 — 220 mhz   22.50
DX-420 — 432 mhz   17.50

See your local distributor or write for complete specifications on these exciting new antennas from the world's leading manufacturer of UHF/VHF Amateur and Commercial Communication Antennas.

Cush Craft   621 HAYWARD STREET
MANCHESTER, N.H. 03103

THE LEAGUE IS YOU!

*W*orking together, the members of ARRL have for fifty years provided the base of support from which our great public-service hobby has grown and maintained the precious privileges that many amateurs now take for granted.

*T*hrough membership in the League and affiliated clubs, many people pool their knowledge, their skills, their energy, and a small part of their material resources to help one another. The result is top-notch training programs and publications, top-efficiency traffic nets, community communications programs—and an amateur radio service which is useful to our country and deserving of its privileges.

*N*ewcomers gain from the experience of the old timers, and old timers gain from the enthusiasm of the beginners. The more we work together in the League, the greater will be our collective achievements—and our security.

*E*ach and every radio amateur is vital to the League, and the League is vital to each and every radio amateur. Join now with almost 100,000 League members so that we can all share more fully in these mutual benefits. League membership; including QST each month, is only $6.50 in the U.S. and Canada, $7.00 elsewhere.

*I*f you are already a member, help strengthen your League by spreading this word to others!

THE AMERICAN RADIO RELAY LEAGUE INC.
Newington, Conn. 06111

45

MAC-KEY

PRO. MODEL
HAND KEY

MC9681R
INK RECORDER

MC958PT
KEYER

McELROY STANDARDS
NOW HAVE THE
FOLLOWING FEATURES:

- SOLID STATE DESIGN
- GLASS EPOXY PRINTED CIRCUIT BOARDS
- PLUG IN MAINTENANCE
- MODULAR CONSTRUCTION
- COMPUTERIZED "DIAL-A-SPEED" CONTROL WITH BETTER THAN 1% ACCURACY
- PROVEN 10 MILLION OPERATION KEYING HEAD
- POSITIVE SPROCKET CENTER HOLE DRIVE
- NEW PATENTED SOLID STATE RELAY
- 60% WEIGHT REDUCTION READY FOR DELIVERY 1 JANUARY, 1969

MC950PT
PERFORATOR

MP1
MORSE PACKAGE

McElroy ELECTRONICS CORPORATION

SHIRLEY, MASSACHUSETTS

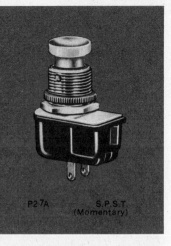

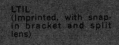

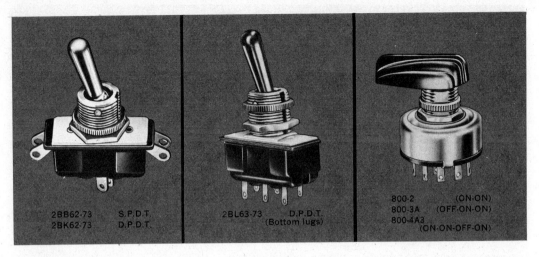
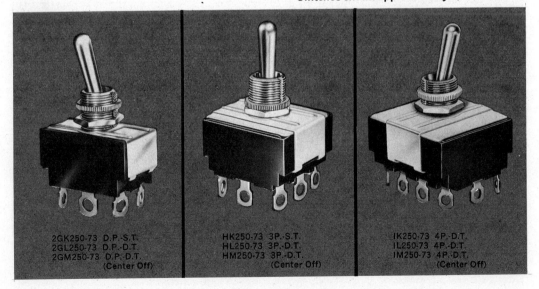

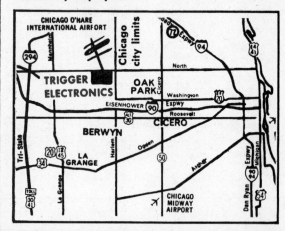